W9-CEW-919

Calculus Consultants

Laura Lenhardt   279-9593
Laura Miller   279-8409
Cathy Pezely   539-3554
Tony Lanutti   539-4278

Elements of Calculus
and Analytic Geometry

Elements of Calculus
and Analytic Geometry

George B. Thomas, Jr.
Department of Mathematics,
Massachusetts Institute of Technology

▲ **Addison-Wesley Publishing Company**

Menlo Park, California • Reading, Massachusetts • London • Amsterdam • Don Mills, Ontario • Sydney

BOOKS IN THE
Addison-Wesley
Secondary Mathematics Series

Algebra
R. Johnson, L. Lendsey, W. Slesnick
Annotated Teachers' Edition, Solution Manual

Geometry
E. Moise, F. Downs
Annotated Teachers' Edition with Solutions

Algebra and Trigonometry
R. Johnson, L. Lendsey, W. Slesnick, G. Bates
Annotated Teachers' Edition, Solution Manual

Pre-Calculus Mathematics
M. Shanks, C. Brumfiel, C. Fleenor, R. Eicholz
Teachers' Commentary, Solution Manual

Elements of Calculus and Analytic Geometry
G. Thomas
Teachers' Commentary, Solution Manual

CONSULTING EDITOR Richard S. Pieters

Cover photo by Nikolay Zurek for Addison-Wesley Publishing Company

Copyright © 1976, 1972 *by Addison-Wesley Publishing Company,*
Inc. Philippines Copyright 1976, 1972
All rights reserved. No part of this publication may be
reproduced, stored in a retrieval system, or transmitted,
in any form or by any means, electronic, mechanical,
photocopying, recording, or otherwise, without the prior
written permission of the publisher. Printed in the
United States of America. Published simultaneously in
Canada.

ISBN 0-201-07549-0
ABCDEFGHIJKL-VH-8079876

PREFACE

Calculus is a subject in which much can be learned by doing problems. In this text special attention has been given to selecting an unusually ample supply. These problems are arranged in three different fashions to give the student as wide a variety of experiences as possible. First, the exercise sets at the end of each section contain not only problems which require straightforward application of the material, but also problems which involve subtle use of new ideas in conjunction with concepts already developed. Further, at the end of each chapter there are two additional problem sets: review questions and exercises, and miscellaneous problems. Numerical answers are given for selected problems to provide a check for the student's own solutions. In cases where answers in different forms are correct, only one answer is given.

This book closely follows the recommendations of the Committee on Mathematics of the Advanced Placement Program. It contains the material on analytic geometry and essentially all of the material on functions of one variable from the author's *Calculus and Analytic Geometry*, Fourth Edition. In addition, there is a more leisurely introduction to such topics as inequalities, absolute value, intervals and neighborhoods, functions, and limits, and there is material on infinite series and differential equations. This selection of topics meets the requirements set forth in the syllabus of the College Entrance Examination Board for both the AB and BC examinations.

Some significant features of the book are worth noting. In order to motivate the idea of limit of a function, the concepts of slope of a curve and derivative of a function are introduced in Chapter 2, prior to the theory of limits in Chapter 3. Here the Greek letter ϵ (epsilon) is used in the usual way to restrict variation in the range of the function. But the introduction of the Greek letter δ (delta), which is ordinarily used to restrict variation in the domain, is deferred until the student is accustomed to thinking in terms of neighborhoods. A teacher may, in some classes, wish to skip the theory of limits in Chapter 3 and go directly on to Chapter 4. If so, a brief, intuitive discussion of the key theorems about limits of sums, differences, products, and quotients—without proofs—could be substituted in place of Chapter 3.

The theorems about limits of sums, products, and quotients that are proved in Chapter 3 are applied in Chapter 4 and later chapters to establish the standard differentiation formulas. In Chapter 5, applications of derivatives to problems in maxima and minima give the student some experience of the power of the calculus.

A knowledge of algebra, geometry, and some trigonometry is necessary for the study of calculus. Some of the key formulas in trigonometry are derived in the text in Chapter 6, Article 4. Using those formulas, we quickly derive the differentiation and integration laws for the sine and cosine. The derivatives of the other trigonometric functions, the inverse trigonometric functions, the natural logarithm, and the exponential function are studied in Chapter 8. The systematic study of methods of integration in Chapter 9, plus Chapter 12 on hyperbolic functions and Chapter 14 on infinite series, complete the calculus of functions of one real variable. (The student might note that a brief table of integrals has been included in an appendix at the end of the book. This table will be fully useful to him after he has learned the techniques of integration presented in Chapter 9.)

Chapters 10 and 11 deal with topics in analytic geometry in Cartesian and polar coordinates. These chapters could be studied before Chapter 2, Article 5, if one omits all applications of calculus to analytic geometry. Alternatively, they could be taken up following Chapter 8. The order in this book, however, has been found to be quite satisfactory in many schools.

The many analogies between hyperbolic functions and trigonometric functions, and some of the contrasts, are brought out in Chapter 12. The derivation, and solution, of the equation that describes equilibrium of a hanging cable is also included in this chapter as a mathematical model of a physical situation. The study of velocity and acceleration in terms of vectors in Chapter 13 provides another such model, closely related to planetary and earth-satellite orbital mechanics.

The treatment of differential equations in Chapter 15 is not exhaustive, but may serve as an introduction to a more systematic study of the important *linear* equations.

The basic formulas from the prerequisite subjects—algebra, geometry, and trigonometry—are collected for reference in an appendix at the end of the book. In general, however, the more difficult formulas are reviewed in the text at the time they are needed. The author's experience, both as a student and as a teacher, indicates that one by-product of a good calculus course is likely to be a much firmer grasp of the fundamental skills of high-school mathematics. This is particularly true when the student supplies the missing steps in illustrative exercises and elsewhere.

Many of the miscellaneous problems were provided by Professors T. M. Apostol of the California Institute of Technology and A. W. Tucker of Princeton. Most of the answers to these problems were provided by Richard T. Bumby, Robert R. D. Kemp, and C. Peter Wolk. The author is grateful for this friendly and valuable help.

It is a pleasure to acknowledge the expert assistance from the editorial and production staffs of the Addison-Wesley Publishing Company in producing this book. The author also acknowledges the many helpful suggestions from users of the first edition of *Elements of Calculus and Analytic Geometry* and related books. My daughters Jean (Mrs. Harry M. Nordberg) and Fay (Mrs. Ashok Bakhru) also studied from earlier versions of this book. It is a special pleasure to acknowledge Jean's assistance in preparing the manuscript for this new edition.

Any errors, in the text or in the answers to problems, are the responsibility of the author. He will very much appreciate having them brought to his attention.

G. B. T., Jr.

CONTENTS

ANALYTIC PREPARATION

CHAPTER 1

1.1 INTRODUCTION

Calculus is the mathematics of change and motion. Where there is motion or growth, where forces are at work producing acceleration, calculus is the right mathematical tool. This was true in the beginnings of the subject, and it is true today. Calculus is used to predict the orbits of earth satellites; in the design of inertial navigation systems, cyclotrons, and radar systems; to explore problems of space travel; and to test scientific theories about such things as the dynamics of the atmosphere, ocean currents, and even theories about economic, sociological, and psychological behavior. Of course the scientist needs a great deal more than mathematical competence, and he needs more mathematics than calculus. But calculus is a tool of great importance and usefulness and an understanding of its nature is prerequisite for further study in nearly all branches of higher mathematics.

One of the great mathematicians of the twentieth century, John von Neumann (1903–1957), has written:* "The calculus was the first achievement of modern mathematics, and it is difficult to overestimate its importance. I think it defines more unequivocally than anything else the inception of modern mathematics, and the system of mathematical analysis, which is its logical development, still constitutes the greatest technical advance in exact thinking."

The calculus is a branch of mathematics which provides methods for solving two large classes of problems. The first of these involves finding the rate at which a variable quantity is changing. For example, when a body, say a stone dropped from a tower, travels in a straight line, its distance from its starting point changes with time, and we may ask *how fast* it is moving at any given instant. *Differential calculus* is the branch of calculus which treats such problems.

The second type of problem the calculus deals with is that of finding a function when its rate of change is given. Thus, for example, if we are given the

---

* John von Neumann, "The Mathematician," in *The World of Mathematics*, Vol. 4, pp. 2053–2063.

velocity of a moving body at every instant of time, we may seek to find the distance it has moved as a function of time. This problem belongs to the domain of *integral calculus*. Modern science and engineering use both branches of the calculus as a language for expressing physical laws in precise mathematical terms, and as a tool for studying the consequences of those laws.

A large part of the subject matter of this branch of mathematics was developed by Sir Isaac Newton (1642–1727) as a tool to help him solve problems which arose in connection with his investigations in physics and astronomy. Credit for the invention of the calculus must also be shared, however, with a German mathematician and philosopher, Gottfried Wilhelm Leibniz (1646–1716), who independently and approximately concurrently also developed a large part of the subject, and whose notation has been almost universally adopted in preference to that used by Newton.

Analytic geometry, which forms a third division of the subject matter of this book, was the creation of several mathematicians.* Two French mathematicians, Pierre de Fermat (1601–1665) and René Descartes (1596–1650), are the chief claimants to the title of inventor of analytic geometry as we now know it. Descartes is credited with the important idea of locating a point in the plane by means of its distances from two perpendicular axes, and his name is commemorated in the terminology "Cartesian coordinates." We shall see that most of the theory in calculus can be presented in geometrical terms, so that calculus and analytic geometry may profitably be united and studied as a whole.

The basic idea in analytic geometry is the establishment of a one-to-one correspondence between the points of a plane on the one hand and pairs of numbers (x, y) on the other hand. We assume that

---

the basic ideas of analytic geometry and trigonometry are familiar, but some topics are reviewed from time to time.

In this book, if coordinates of points are given as pure numbers (i.e., without any physical units attached), it is to be assumed that the scales on the two axes are the same. In particular, this assumption is made wherever angles between lines or lengths of skew line segments are involved.

EXERCISES

In Exercises 1 through 15, plot the given point P and such of the following points as may apply.

(a) The point Q such that QP is perpendicular to the x-axis and is bisected by it. Give the coordinates of Q.

(b) The point R such that PR is perpendicular to and is bisected by the y-axis. Give the coordinates of R.

(c) The point S such that PS is bisected by the origin. Give the coordinates of S.

(d) The point T such that PT is perpendicular to and is bisected by the 45° line L through the origin bisecting the first and third quadrants. Give the coordinates of T, assuming equal units on the axes.

[*Note.* Q and P are symmetric with respect to the x-axis, R and P with respect to the y-axis, S and P with respect to the origin, and T and P with respect to L.] State rules for finding coordinates of Q, R, S, T in terms of the coordinates of P.

1. $(1, -2)$ 2. $(2, -1)$
3. $(-2, 2)$ 4. $(-2, 1)$
5. $(2, 2)$ 6. $(-2, -2)$
7. $(0, 1)$ 8. $(1, 0)$
9. $(-2, 0)$ 10. $(0, -3)$
11. $(-1, -3)$ 12. $(\sqrt{2}, -\sqrt{2})$
13. $(-\pi, -\pi)$ 14. $(-1.5, 2.3)$
15. $(\sqrt{2}, 0)$

In Exercises 16 through 20, take the units of length on the two axes to be equal.

16. A straight line is drawn through the point $(0, 0)$ and the point $(1, 1)$. What acute angle does it make with the positive x-axis? Sketch.

---

* See, for example, "Commentary on Descartes and Analytic Geometry," in *The World of Mathematics*, Vol. 1, pp. 235–237. Also Carl B. Boyer, "The Invention of Analytic Geometry," *Scientific American*, January, 1949.

17. A straight line is drawn through the point $A(1, 2)$ and the point $B(2, 4)$. Find $\tan \alpha$, where α is the acute angle that this line makes with the horizontal line through A. Sketch.

18. Show that the line through the pair of points $(1, 1)$ and $(2, 0)$ is parallel to the line through the pair of points $(-1, -1)$ and $(0, -2)$. Sketch.

19. The line through the pair of points $(2, 3)$ and $(1, 1)$ cuts the y-axis at the point $(0, b)$. Find b by using similar triangles. Sketch.

20. Does the line through the pair of points $(-1, -1)$ and $(1, 2)$ pass through the origin? Sketch. Give a reason, other than the evidence of your sketch, for your answer.

1.2 INCREMENTS

If, in a coordinate plane, a particle starts at a point $P_1(x_1, y_1)$ and goes to a new position $P_2(x_2, y_2)$, we say that its coordinates have received increments Δx (called *delta x*) and Δy (called *delta y*). For example, if a particle moves from $A(1, -2)$ to $B(6, 7)$, as in Fig. 1.1, then the increments received by its coordinates are

$$\Delta x = 5, \quad \Delta y = 9.$$

Observe that the increment in a coordinate is the net change given by

$$\Delta x = (x \text{ of terminal point}) - (x \text{ of initial point})$$

and

$$\Delta y = (y \text{ of terminal point}) - (y \text{ of initial point}).$$

So far as these increments are concerned, it doesn't matter at all what the positions of the particle may have been between its initial and terminal locations.

Definition. *If the initial position of a particle is* $P_1(x_1, y_1)$ *and its terminal position is* $P_2(x_2, y_2)$, *then the increments* Δx *and* Δy *are given by*

$$\Delta x = x_2 - x_1, \quad \Delta y = y_2 - y_1.$$

Note that either increment Δx or Δy can be any real number: positive, negative, or zero.

If the same unit of measurement is used on both axes, then we may also express all distances in the plane in terms of this fundamental unit. In particular, by applying the theorem of Pythagoras to the right triangle P_1RP_2 in Fig. 1.2, we readily find that the distance d between the two points $P_1(x_1, y_1)$ and $P_2(x_2, y_2)$ is simply

$$d = \sqrt{(\Delta x)^2 + (\Delta y)^2} \qquad (1)$$
$$= \sqrt{(x_2 - x_1)^2 + (y_2 - y_1)^2}.$$

1.1

1.2

Example. If a particle starts from $P_1(-1, 2)$ and travels in a straight line to the point $P_2(2, -2)$, then its abscissa (the x-coordinate) undergoes a change

$$\Delta x = x_2 - x_1 = 2 - (-1) = 3$$

and its ordinate (the y-coordinate) changes by an amount

$$\Delta y = y_2 - y_1 = -2 - 2 = -4.$$

The distance the particle travels from P_1 to P_2 is

$$d = \sqrt{(\Delta x)^2 + (\Delta y)^2} = \sqrt{9 + 16} = 5.$$

EXERCISES

In Exercises 1 through 10, points A and B are given and point C is to be found at the intersection of the horizontal line through A and the vertical line through B. Sketch, and find

(a) the coordinates of C, (b) Δx, (c) Δy,

(d) the length of AB under the assumption that the unit of length on the y-axis is the same as the unit of length on the x-axis.

1. $A(1, 1)$, $B(3, 4)$ 2. $A(3, 4)$, $B(1, 1)$
3. $A(-1, 2)$, $B(2, -1)$ 4. $A(2, -1)$, $B(-1, 2)$
5. $A(-1, -1)$, $B(1, 2)$ 6. $A(1, 2)$, $B(-1, -1)$
7. $A(-3, 2)$, $B(-1, -2)$ 8. $A(-1, -2)$, $B(-3, 2)$
9. $A(-3, -2)$, $B(-1, -1)$
10. $A(-1, -1)$, $B(-3, -2)$

11. What equation must be satisfied by the coordinates of a point $P(x, y)$ if P is on the circle of radius 5 with center at $C(h, k)$ if
    (a) $(h, k) = (0, 0)$,   (b) $(h, k) = (5, 0)$,
    (c) $(h, k) = (3, 4)$,   (d) $(h, k) = (h, k)$?

12. If a particle starts at $A(-2, 3)$ and its coordinates receive increments $\Delta x = 5$, $\Delta y = -6$, what will its new position be?

13. Find the starting position of a particle whose terminal position is $B(u, v)$ after its coordinates have received increments $\Delta x = h$, and $\Delta y = k$.

14. If a particle moves from the point $A(-2, 5)$ to the y-axis in such a way that $\Delta y = 3\,\Delta x$, what are its new coordinates?

15. A particle moves along the parabola $y = x^2$ from the point $A(1, 1)$ to the point $B(x, y)$. Show that

$$\frac{\Delta y}{\Delta x} = x + 1 \quad \text{if} \quad \Delta x \neq 0.$$

1.3 SLOPE OF A STRAIGHT LINE

Let L be a straight line which is not parallel to the y-axis. Let $P_1(x_1, y_1)$ and $P_2(x_2, y_2)$ be any two distinct points on L (Fig. 1.3). If we denote the slope of L by m, we have the definition:

$$m = \frac{\Delta y}{\Delta x} = \frac{y_2 - y_1}{x_2 - x_1}. \tag{1}$$

Remark 1. Suppose that instead of using the pair of points P_1 and P_2 to calculate the slope, we were to choose a different pair of points $P_1'(x_1', y_1')$, $P_2'(x_2', y_2')$ on L and calculate

$$m' = \frac{y_2' - y_1'}{x_2' - x_1'} = \frac{\Delta y'}{\Delta x'}.$$

Would we get the same slope? In other words, does

$$m' = m?$$

The answer is "yes." For in Fig. 1.3, the triangles P_1QP_2 and $P_1'Q'P_2'$ are similar, hence

$$m' = \frac{\Delta y'}{\Delta x'} = \frac{\Delta y}{\Delta x} = m.$$

In other words, Eq. (1) relates the change in x and the change in y between *any* pair of points (x, y) and $(x + \Delta x, y + \Delta y)$ on L.

Remark 2. If we multiply the first two terms of Eq. (1) by Δx, we obtain

$$\Delta y = m\,\Delta x. \tag{2}$$

This means, in the light of the comment above, that as a particle moves along L, the change in y is proportional to the change in x, and the slope m is the proportionality factor.

For example, suppose L is the line determined by the points $P_1(1, 2)$ and $P_2(3, 8)$, Fig. 1.4. Then the slope of L is

$$m = \frac{8 - 2}{3 - 1} = 3.$$

And, if $P(x, y)$, $Q(x + \Delta x, y + \Delta y)$ are any two points on L, then

$$\Delta y = 3\,\Delta x.$$

That is, for every unit of run, there are three units of rise. Thus, starting from $P_1(1, 2)$, if we increase x by 1 unit we should increase y by 3 units, which would bring us to the point $P_3(2, 5)$. Or, we could decrease x by 1 unit and y by 3 units and obtain the point $P_4(0, -1)$. [*Question:* At what point does L cross the x-axis?]

1.3

1.4

a |

b |

1.5

Remark 3. If we take equal scales on the x- and y-axes, we may interpret the slope of the line L as the tangent of the angle of inclination that L makes with the positive x-axis. That is,

$$m = \tan \phi.$$

Here ϕ is the angle, $0 \leq \phi < 180°$, that the line makes with the positively directed portion of the x-axis (Fig. 1.5).

For a line that slopes upward to the right (Fig. 1.5a), Δy is positive when Δx is. Also,

$$0 < \phi < 90°,$$

and $\tan \phi = \Delta y / \Delta x$ is positive.

For a line that slopes downward to the right (Fig. 1.5b), Δy is negative when Δx is positive. Also, $90° < \phi < 180°$, and $\tan \phi = \Delta y / \Delta x$ is negative.

For a horizontal line, Δy is zero for any Δx. Also $\phi = 0°$ and $\tan \phi = \Delta y / \Delta x$ is zero.

For a vertical line, Δx is zero for any Δy. Then $\Delta y / \Delta x$ is meaningless, since we cannot divide by zero. Also $\phi = 90°$, and $\tan 90°$ does not exist.

Example. Let us examine the slopes of lines whose inclination angles are near 90°, such as

$$\phi_1 = 89°59', \quad m_1 = \tan \phi_1 \approx 3437.7$$

and

$$\phi_2 = 90°01', \quad m_2 = \tan \phi_2 \approx -3437.7.$$

We see that such lines have slopes which are numerically very large. And by taking the angle still closer to 90°, we can make the slope numerically larger than any pre-assigned positive number N, no matter how large N may be. It is this fact which is sometimes summarized by the statements that "a vertical line has infinite slope," or "the slope of the line becomes infinite as its inclination angle approaches 90°."

The symbol ∞ is used to represent infinity, but we should not use this symbol in computations involving addition, subtraction, multiplication, or division in the way we use ordinary real numbers.

Two *parallel* lines have equal angles of inclination and hence have equal slopes $m_1 = m_2$. Conversely, two lines having equal slopes

$$m_1 = \tan \phi_1, \quad m_2 = \tan \phi_2$$

also have equal inclinations since

$$\tan \phi_1 = \tan \phi_2,$$

together with

$$0 \leq \phi_1 < 180°, \quad 0 \leq \phi_2 < 180°,$$

implies that ϕ_1 and ϕ_2 are equal.

1.6

Next, consider two *perpendicular* lines (Fig. 1.6). Their inclinations differ by 90°. Suppose, for example, that

$$\phi_2 = 90° + \phi_1.$$

Case 1. If one line is vertical, then the other must be horizontal.

Case 2. If neither line is vertical, then neither ϕ_1 nor ϕ_2 is 90° and

$$m_2 = \tan \phi_2 = \tan (90° + \phi_1)$$
$$= -\cot \phi_1 = -\frac{1}{\tan \phi_1}$$
$$= -1/m_1.$$

Thus the condition for *perpendicularity* in this case is

$$m_2 = -\frac{1}{m_1}. \tag{3}$$

Conversely, suppose that condition (3) is satisfied. Then one of the slopes is positive and the other is negative. With no loss of generality we may thus assume that m_1 is positive and m_2 is negative. (If not, renumber the lines.) Then

$$0 < \phi_1 < 90° < \phi_2 < 180°, \tag{4a}$$

and

$$\tan \phi_2 = -\cot \phi_1. \tag{4b}$$

Therefore

$$0 < (180° - \phi_2) < 90°, \tag{5a}$$

and

$$\tan (180° - \phi_2) = -\tan \phi_2 = \cot \phi_1. \tag{5b}$$

Equation (5b) and the inequalities (4a) and (5a) imply that ϕ_1 and $180° - \phi_2$ are complementary acute angles, as in Fig. 1.6. Therefore, the two lines are perpendicular.

EXERCISES

In Exercises 1 through 15, plot the given points A and B and find the slope of the straight line determined by them and of a perpendicular line.

1. $A(1, 2)$, $B(2, -1)$ 2. $A(-1, 2)$, $B(-2, -1)$
3. $A(-2, -1)$, $B(1, -2)$ 4. $A(2, -1)$, $B(-2, 1)$
5. $A(1, 0)$, $B(0, 1)$ 6. $A(-1, 0)$, $B(1, 0)$
7. $A(2, 3)$, $B(-1, 3)$ 8. $A(0, 3)$, $B(2, -3)$
9. $A(0, -2)$, $B(-2, 0)$ 10. $A(1, 2)$, $B(1, -3)$
11. $A(\frac{1}{2}, 0)$, $B(0, -\frac{1}{3})$
12. $A(0, 0)$, $B(x, y)$ $(x \neq 0,\ y \neq 0)$
13. $A(0, 0)$, $B(x, 0)$ $(x \neq 0)$
14. $A(0, 0)$, $B(0, y)$ $(y \neq 0)$
15. $A(a, 0)$, $B(0, b)$ $(a \neq 0,\ b \neq 0)$

In Exercises 16 through 20, plot the given points A, B, C, and D. Determine in each case whether or not $ABCD$ is a parallelogram. Also indicate those parallelograms that are rectangles.

16. $A(0, 1)$, $B(1, 2)$, $C(2, 1)$, $D(1, 0)$
17. $A(3, 1)$, $B(2, 2)$, $C(0, 1)$, $D(1, 0)$
18. $A(-2, 2)$, $B(1, 3)$, $C(2, 0)$, $D(-1, -1)$
19. $A(1, -2)$, $B(2, -1)$, $C(2, 1)$, $D(1, 0)$
20. $A(-1, 0)$, $B(0, -1)$, $C(2, 0)$, $D(0, 2)$

21. Find the coordinates of a point $P(x, y)$ which is so located that the line L_1 through the origin and P has slope equal to $+2$, and the line L_2 through the point $A(-1, 0)$ and P has slope equal to $+1$.

22. A line L goes through the origin and has slope equal to $+3$. If $P(x, y)$ is a point other than the origin and on the line L, show that $y = 3x$. Sketch the line.

In Exercises 23 through 27, plot the given points and determine analytically whether or not they all lie on a straight line. Give reasons for your answers.

23. $A(1, 0)$, $B(0, 1)$, $C(2, -1)$
24. $A(-2, 1)$, $B(0, 5)$, $C(-1, 2)$
25. $A(-2, -1)$, $B(-1, 1)$, $C(1, 5)$, $D(2, 7)$
26. $A(-2, 3)$, $B(0, 2)$, $C(2, 0)$
27. $A(-3, -2)$, $B(-2, 0)$, $C(-1, 2)$, $D(1, 6)$
28. Let $P_1(x_1, y_1)$ and $P_2(x_2, y_2)$ be two points. Find the midpoint of the segment $P_1 P_2$.
29. Given $A(0, -1)$, $B(4, 0)$, and $C(3, 4)$, show that ABC is a right triangle and find the center and radius of the circumscribed circle. Sketch.
30. Answer the question in Remark 2.

1.4 EQUATIONS OF A STRAIGHT LINE

In this article we shall discuss algebraic equations that represent straight lines. Let L be the line through the two points $P_1(x_1, y_1)$ and $P_2(x_2, y_2)$.

If $x_2 = x_1$, then the line L is vertical and all points on it have the same x-coordinate. Then $P(x, y)$ is on the line if and only if

$$x = x_1. \qquad (1)$$

If $x_2 \neq x_1$ (Fig. 1.7), we know the slope of the line is

$$m = \frac{y_2 - y_1}{x_2 - x_1}. \qquad (2)$$

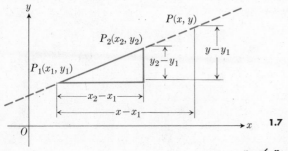

1.7

$$x_2 \neq x_1.$$

Then the point $P(x, y)$ is also on the line if and only if $P = P_1$ or $P \neq P_1$ and the slope of P_1P is the

same as the slope of P_1P_2. If $P \neq P_1$, x and y must satisfy the equation

$$\frac{y - y_1}{x - x_1} = m,$$

or

POINT SLOPE

$$y - y_1 = m(x - x_1), \qquad (3)$$

if P is on the line. Conversely, if x and y satisfy Eq. (3), then $P(x, y)$ is on the line. If P coincides with P_1, Eq. (3) is still satisfied, even though the slope of P_1P is then undefined.

Equation (3) is called the *point-slope* form of the equation of the line, since it gives the equation in terms of one point $P_1(x_1, y_1)$ on the line and the slope m.

We may also write Eq. (3) in the equivalent form

$$y = mx + b, \qquad (4)$$

where m is the slope of the line and

$$b = y_1 - mx_1$$

is a constant. In fact, $(0, b)$ is the point where the line crosses the y-axis. Equation (4) is expressed in terms of the slope m and the y-intercept b, and is therefore called the *slope-intercept* equation of the line.

More generally, an equation

$$m = \frac{-A}{B}$$

$$Ax + By + C = 0, \qquad (5)$$

where A, B, and C are constants with at least one of A and B different from zero, represents a *straight line*. For

if $B = 0$, then $Ax + C = 0$, $x = -\dfrac{C}{A}$,

and the line is a vertical line as in Eq. (1). On the other hand,

if $B \neq 0$, then $y = -\dfrac{A}{B}x - \dfrac{C}{B}$,

and this represents a straight line of the form of Eq. (4), with

$$m = -\frac{A}{B}, \quad b = -\frac{C}{B}.$$

An equation like (5) that contains only first powers of x and y is said to be "linear in x and in y." Thus we may summarize our discussion by saying that every straight line in the plane is represented by a linear equation and, conversely, every linear equation represents a straight line.

Problem 1. Find the slope of the line $2x + 3y = 5$.

Solution. Solving for y, we have

$$y = -\tfrac{2}{3}x + \tfrac{5}{3},$$

which compares with $y = mx + b$, see Equation (4), with $m = -\tfrac{2}{3}$ and $b = \tfrac{5}{3}$. Hence the slope is $-\tfrac{2}{3}$.

Problem 2. Let L be a line with equation

$$Ax + By + C = 0.$$

Let $P_1(x_1, y_1)$ be a point not on L. Find a formula for the distance from P_1 to L.

Solution. The line L' through P_1 and perpendicular to L has equation $Bx - Ay + C' = 0$, with

$$C' = Ay_1 - Bx_1. \tag{6}$$

The point $P_2(x_2, y_2)$ at which L and L' intersect has coordinates that satisfy the simultaneous equations

$$Ax_2 + By_2 + C = 0, \quad Bx_2 - Ay_2 + C' = 0.$$

If we multiply the first of these by A, the second by B, and add, we get

$$(A^2 + B^2)x_2 + AC + BC' = 0.$$

Therefore

$$x_2 = -\frac{AC + BC'}{A^2 + B^2}. \tag{7a}$$

Similarly, if the first equation (for L) is multiplied by B and the second by $-A$ and the results added, we get

$$(B^2 + A^2)y_2 + BC - AC' = 0.$$

Hence

$$y_2 = \frac{AC' - BC}{A^2 + B^2}. \tag{7b}$$

From Eqs. (6) and (7a), we get

$$x_2 = -\frac{AC + B(Ay_1 - Bx_1)}{A^2 + B^2}, \tag{8}$$

so that

$$
\begin{aligned}
x_1 - x_2 &= \frac{(A^2 + B^2)x_1 + AC + ABy_1 - B^2 x_1}{A^2 + B^2} \\
&= \frac{A}{A^2 + B^2}(Ax_1 + By_1 + C).
\end{aligned} \tag{9a}
$$

Similarly, Eqs. (6) and (7b) lead to

$$y_2 = \frac{A(Ay_1 - Bx_1) - BC}{A^2 + B^2}$$

and

$$
\begin{aligned}
y_1 - y_2 &= \frac{(A^2 + B^2)y_1 - A^2 y_1 + ABx_1 + BC}{A^2 + B^2} \\
&= \frac{B}{A^2 + B^2}(Ax_1 + By_1 + C).
\end{aligned} \tag{9b}
$$

Note the common factor

$$h = \frac{Ax_1 + By_1 + C}{A^2 + B^2}$$

in Eqs. (9a) and (9b). From the distance formula, we get

$$
\begin{aligned}
d &= \sqrt{(x_1 - x_2)^2 + (y_1 - y_2)^2} \\
&= \sqrt{(Ah)^2 + (Bh)^2} \\
&= |h|\sqrt{A^2 + B^2}.
\end{aligned}
$$

The desired formula for the distance is therefore

$$d = \frac{|Ax_1 + By_1 + C|}{\sqrt{A^2 + B^2}}. \tag{10}$$

$d = (x_1, y_1)$ to $Ax_1 + By_1 + C = 0$

We apply this formula to find the distances from the points $P_1(-1, 0)$, $P_2(1, 1)$, and $P_3(-3, 5)$ to the line L: $2x + 3y - 5 = 0$ (see Fig. 1.8). The distances are

$$d_1 = \frac{|2(-1) + 3(0) - 5|}{\sqrt{4 + 9}} = \frac{|-7|}{\sqrt{13}} = \frac{7}{\sqrt{13}},$$

$$d_2 = \frac{|2(1) + 3(1) - 5|}{\sqrt{13}} = 0,$$

$$d_3 = \frac{|2(-3) + 3(5) - 5|}{\sqrt{13}} = \frac{4}{\sqrt{13}}.$$

When the coordinates are substituted into the expression $2x + 3y - 5$, the results are $-7, 0$, and $+4$. These results indicate that point A is below L, B is on L, and C is above L. (See Exercise 28.) As Fig. 1.8 shows, the

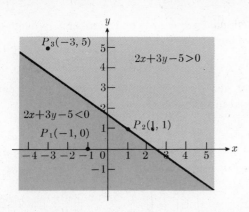

1.8 The line $2x + 3y - 5 = 0$ separates the plane into half-planes. Above L, $2x + 3y - 5$ is positive; below L, it is negative.

line $2x + 3y - 5 = 0$ separates the plane into half-planes. Above L, $2x + 3y - 5$ is positive; below L, it is negative.

EXERCISES

In Exercises 1 through 10, plot the given pair of points and find an equation for the line determined by them.

1. $(0, 0)$, $(2, 3)$ 2. $(1, 1)$, $(2, 1)$

3. $(1, 1)$, $(1, 2)$ 4. $(-2, 1)$, $(2, -2)$

5. $(-2, 0)$, $(-2, -2)$ 6. $(1, 3)$, $(3, 1)$

7. $(a, 0)$, $(0, b)$ 8. $(0, 0)$, $(1, 0)$
    $(a \neq 0, b \neq 0)$

9. $(0, 0)$, $(0, 1)$ 10. $(2, -1)$, $(-2, 3)$

In Exercises 11 through 20, find the slope of the given line.

11. $y = 3x + 5$ 12. $2y = 3x + 5$

13. $x + y = 2$ 14. $2x - y = 4$

15. $x - 2y = 4$ 16. $3x + 4y = 12$

17. $4x - 3y = 12$ 18. $x = 2y - 5$

19. $\dfrac{x}{a} + \dfrac{y}{b} = 1$ $(a, b$ constants $\neq 0)$

20. $x_1 x + y_1 y = 1$ $(x_1, y_1$ constants $\neq 0)$

21. Find the line that passes through the point $(1, 2)$ and is parallel to the line $x + 2y = 3$.

22. (a) Find the line L through $A(-2, 2)$ and perpendicular to the line $L': 2x + y = 4$.
(b) Find the point B where the lines L and L' of part (a) intersect.
(c) Using the result of part (b), find the distance from the point A to the line L' of part (a).

23. Find the line through $(1, 4)$ and having inclination angle $\phi = 60°$.

24. What is the inclination of the line $2x + y = 4$?

25. If A, B, C, C' are constants, show that
(a) the lines $Ax + By + C = 0$,   SAME m
    $Ax + By + C' = 0$ $C \neq C'$
are parallel, and
(b) the lines $Ax + By + C = 0$,
    $Bx - Ay + C' = 0$
are perpendicular.

26. (a) Let C and F denote, respectively, corresponding centigrade and Fahrenheit temperature readings. Given that the F vs. C graph is a straight line, find its equation from the following data: $(C = 0, F = 32)$ and $(C = 100, F = 212)$ are coordinates of two points on the graph.
(b) Is there a temperature at which $C = F$? If so, what is it?

27. The perpendicular distance ON from the origin to line L is p, and ON makes an angle α with the positive x-axis. Show that L has equation

$\alpha = $ alpha $x \cos \alpha + y \sin \alpha = p$.

28. In connection with Problem 2 and Eq. (10), explain the rule: If $Ax_1 + By_1 + C$ agrees in sign with B, then the point $P_1(x_1, y_1)$ is above L; if the sign is opposite to the sign of B, then the point is below L. (Assume that $B \neq 0$. If $B = 0$, the line is parallel to, or coincides with, the y-axis. How should the rule be modified if $B = 0$?)

29. Use Eq. (10) to find the distances from each of the following points to the line $3y = 4x + 5$.
(a) $(0, 0)$ (b) $(0, 4)$
(c) $(-2, 2)$ (d) $(1, 3)$

Sketch the line and show that the given points follow the rule stated in Exercise 28.

1.5 INEQUALITIES AND ABSOLUTE VALUE

If a and b are real numbers, we say that a is *less than b* and write

$$a < b, \qquad (1)$$

provided

$$b - a > 0. \qquad (2)$$

Using the properties of addition and multiplication over the reals, we can easily prove the following theorems.

Theorem 1. *If $a < b$ and c is any real number, then*

$$a + c < b + c.$$

Theorem 2. *If $a < b$ and c is positive, then $ca < cb$.*

Remark 1. If a is *less than b*, we also say that b is *greater than a*, and write

$$b > a.$$

Thus,

$a < b$ if and only if $b > a$.

In Exercises 1 through 5 you are asked to prove the following theorems.

Theorem 3. *If $a < b$ and $c < 0$, then $ac > bc$.*

Theorem 4. *If $a > b > 0$, then*

$$\frac{1}{a} < \frac{1}{b}.$$

Theorem 5. *If $a > 0 > b$, then*

$$\frac{1}{a} > 0 > \frac{1}{b}.$$

Theorem 6. *If $a < b < 0$, then*

$$\frac{1}{a} > \frac{1}{b}.$$

Theorem 7. *If $a < b$ and $b < c$, then $a < c$.*

Remark 2. Theorem 7 is known as the transitive property of inequalities.

The *absolute value* of a real number x is denoted by $|x|$. Thus,

$$|3| = 3, \qquad |-3| = 3, \qquad |0| = 0.$$

There are three equivalent ways that $|x|$ can be defined in terms of x.

Definition. (a) *Let x be a real number. The absolute value of x is x itself when x is positive or zero, and is $-x$ when x is negative:*

$$|x| = \begin{cases} x & \text{if } x \geq 0 \\ -x & \text{if } x < 0. \end{cases} \qquad (1)$$

Example 1. Sketch a graph of the equation $y = |x|$ and use it to describe the set of points in the xy-plane for which $y > |x|$.

Solution. The graph of $y = |x|$ coincides with the ray $y = x$, $x \geq 0$ in the first quadrant, and with $y = -x$ when $x \leq 0$, in the second quadrant. This follows from the definition given in Eq. (1) and the resulting graph is the V-shaped union of these two rays as shown in Figure 1.9. The vertex of the V is at the origin which is the point where the two rays join. Every point in the xy-plane that is not on this graph is either above it or below it. Those that are above it have coordinates (x, y) that satisfy the inequality $y > |x|$. This region is shown shaded in Figure 1.9.

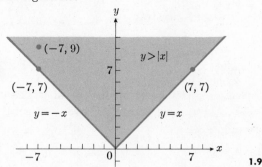

1.9

Notice that

$$(-x)^2 = x^2 = |x|^2.$$

Thus by taking $|x|$ as the nonnegative square root of x^2, we have a second (but equivalent) definition for absolute value.

Definition. (b) $\quad |x| = \sqrt{x^2}.$ $\qquad$ (2)

Example 1. $\quad |-7| = \sqrt{(-7)^2} = \sqrt{49} = 7.$

Finally, given the real number x, we can examine both x and $-x$. If $x \neq 0$, one of these is positive and the other is negative. The positive number is greater than the negative, so we can also say that $|x|$ is the maximum of the two numbers x and $-x$.

Definition. (c) $\quad |x| = \max \{x, -x\}.$ $\qquad$ (3)

Example 2. $\quad \begin{aligned} |5| &= \max \{5, -5\} = 5, \\ |-5| &= \max \{-5, 5\} = 5, \end{aligned}$

and

$$|0| = \max \{0, 0\} = 0.$$

Geometric interpretations of |x|

By applying Eq. (1) of Article 1.2, the distance between the point $P(x, 0)$ and the origin $O(0, 0)$ is

$$d = \sqrt{(x - 0)^2 + (0 - 0)^2} = \sqrt{x^2} = |x|. \qquad (4)$$

Thus we can say that

$|x|$ is the distance, in x-units, between the origin and the point $P(x, 0)$.

Figure 1.10(a) illustrates

$$|x_2| = P_2 O, \qquad |x_1| = OP_1$$

for points $P_2(x_2, 0)$ and $P_1(x_1, 0)$, with x_2 negative and x_1 positive.

If we want to describe the set of points on the x-axis that are not more than two units away from the origin, we simply require that

$$|x| \le 2. \qquad (5a)$$

Figure 1.10(b) shows these points; they are those for which

$$-2 \le x \le 2. \qquad (5b)$$

Note that we can apply the distance formula to the points $P(x, y)$ and $Q(0, y)$ to get

$$d = \sqrt{(x - 0)^2 + (y - y)^2} = \sqrt{x^2} = |x|,$$

1.10

because P and Q have the same y-coordinates. Thus, another interpretation for $|x|$ is the distance from a point $Q(0, y)$ on the y-axis to a point $P(x, y)$.

Sometimes we want to interpret an inequality like

$$|x - a| < 3 \qquad (6)$$

geometrically. Now

$$|x - a| = \sqrt{(x - a)^2} \qquad (7)$$

is just the distance between the points $P(x, 0)$ and $A(a, 0)$ on the x-axis. Hence the given inequality describes those points P that are on the x-axis and less than three units away from A. Such points have x-coordinates between $a - 3$ and $a + 3$. (See Fig. 1.10c.)

An inequality like

$$|x - a| > 3 \qquad (8)$$

can be interpreted geometrically also. Since

$$|x - a| = \sqrt{|x - a|^2} \qquad (9)$$

is the distance between the points $P(x, 0)$ and $A(a, 0)$ on the x-axis, the given inequality describes those points P that are on the x-axis and more than three units away from A. Such points have x-coordinates which are either greater than $a + 3$ or less than $a - 3$ (see Fig. 1.10d.)

$$\frac{\text{rise from } P \text{ to } Q}{\text{run from } P \text{ to } Q} = \frac{y_Q - y_P}{x_Q - x_P} = \frac{t^2 - 9}{t - 3}. \qquad (4a)$$

Because Q is not the same point as P, $t \neq 3$. Therefore, $t - 3$ is not zero, and the slope of PQ is

$$m_{PQ} = t + 3, \qquad t \neq 3. \qquad (4b)$$

Figure 1.16 shows the graph of this slope function $m = t + 3$ for t near, but not at, 3. The open circle indicates that the point $(3, 6)$ is not on the graph. But when t is near 3, $t + 3$ is near 6.

Remark 1. In Fig. 1.15, we show Q above and to the right of P, indicating $t > 3$. This means that the slope of PQ is greater than (but near) 6 when t is greater than (but near) 3. Had we chosen Q to the left of, and below, P on the curve, we would still have found $t + 3$ for the slope of PQ, and this would be slightly less than 6, when t is slightly less than 3. So secant lines PQ through P have slopes very close to 6 when Q is near P, and in Chapter 2 we will define the tangent to the graph of $y = x^2$ at $P(3, 9)$ as the line through P with slope 6.

Remark 2. In the example discussed above, the slope function of PQ is given by $m = t + 3$, $t \neq 3$. The number $t = 3$ is not in the *domain* of this function.* But we could choose a small positive number h, and every point of the neighborhood from $3 - h$ to $3 + h$, *except 3 itself*, would be in the domain. Such a neighborhood of 3, from which the single point $t = 3$ has been deleted, is an example of a deleted neighborhood of 3 (Fig. 1.17).

Remark 3. Ordinarily, we find that *symmetric* deleted neighborhoods (like the one shown in Fig. 1.17) work as well as nonsymmetric ones. An example of a nonsymmetric deleted neighborhood of 3 would be the union of the intervals

$$(3 - h, 3) \qquad \text{and} \qquad (3, 3 + 2h)$$

as shown in Fig. 1.18.

---

* Chapter 2 is an extensive treatment of functions. Domain is defined in Article 2.2.

1.16

1.17

1.18

One advantage of a symmetric deleted neighborhood is that it can always be characterized briefly by using absolute values. For example, the deleted neighborhood of $t = 3$ in Fig. 1.17 is the set of all values of t such that

$$0 < |t - 3| < h, \qquad (5)$$

because the left inequality in (5) requires that $t \neq 3$ and the right inequality specifies that the distance between 3 and t be less than h; that is, t is within h units of 3.

EXERCISES

1. Describe the set of t values that satisfies

$$0 < |t - 2| < 5,$$

and sketch the corresponding deleted neighborhood. What number is deleted? How far is it from one end to the other of this deleted neighborhood?

2. Suppose that Inequality (5) is changed to $|t - 3| < h$. How do you describe the set of t values that satisfies this new inequality? Sketch. How does it differ from Fig. 1.17?

3. For the curve $y = x^2$ shown in Fig. 1.15, suppose that $A(2, 4)$ and $B(t, t^2)$ are two points on the graph, with B near A, but different from A. Find an equation for the slope m of the secant line AB. If B is very near A, what number is m very nearly equal to?

4. If $C(x, x^2)$ and $D(t, t^2)$ are two points $(C \neq D)$ on the graph of the curve $y = x^2$, what is the slope m of the secant line CD? If t is very nearly equal to x (that is, t is in a deleted neighborhood $0 < |t - x| < h$, for h a small positive number) what is m very nearly equal to?

5. If $A(x, 1/x)$ and $B(t, 1/t)$ are two points $(A \neq B)$ on the graph of $y = 1/x$, what is the slope of the secant line AB? What is m approximately equal to when t is close to x?

6. If $A(x, \sqrt{x})$ and $B(t, \sqrt{t})$ are two points $(A \neq B)$ on the graph of $y = \sqrt{x}$, what is the slope m of the secant line AB? What number is m approximately equal to if $x = 4$ and t is close to 4?

REVIEW QUESTIONS AND EXERCISES

1. Define what is meant by the *slope* of a straight line. How would you find the slope of a straight line from its graph? From its equation?

2. In Fig. 1.19, the lines L_1, L_2, and L_3 have slopes m_1, m_2, m_3, respectively. Which slope is algebraically least? Greatest? Write the three slopes in order of increasing size with the symbols for "less than" or "greater than" correctly inserted between them.

1.19

3. Describe the family of lines $y - y_1 = m(x - x_1)$:

(a) If (x_1, y_1) is fixed and different lines are drawn for different values of m.

(b) If m and x_1 are fixed and different lines are drawn for different values of y_1.

4. Give three equivalent definitions of absolute value. What is the geometric interpretation of $|x|$ on the x-axis? of $|x - a|$?

5. Which points on the x-axis satisfy the inequality $|x - a| < h$? Which points $P(x, y)$ in the plane satisfy the inequality $|x - a| < h$?

6. What is the triangle inequality? How did it get its name? Using absolute values, write equivalent expressions for $|ab|$ and $|a/b|$. Complete the following inequality using $|a|$ and $|b|$: ____ $\leq |a - b| \leq$ ____.

7. Use inequalities to describe four kinds of intervals. Use square brackets and parentheses to represent these intervals in another way. What is the geometric interpretation of each of these intervals?

( )
[ ]
[ )
( ]

8. Define what is meant by a neighborhood of r, a real number. What are two special features of such a neighborhood? Give an example of a neighborhood of r and represent it in three different ways. What is the difference between a neighborhood of r and the corresponding deleted neighborhood?

$\frac{RISE}{RUN}$ or $\frac{y - y_1}{x - x_1}$ or $TAN\,\theta$

MISCELLANEOUS EXERCISES

1. (a) Plot the points $A(8, 1)$, $B(2, 10)$, $C(-4, 6)$, $D(2, -3)$, $E(4\frac{2}{3}, 6)$.

(b) Find the slopes of the lines AB, BC, CD, DA, CE, BD.

(c) Do four of the five points A, B, C, D, E form a parallelogram? (Why?)

(d) Do three of the five points lie on a common straight line? (Why?)

(e) Does the origin $(0, 0)$ lie on a straight line through two of the five points? (Why?)

(f) Find equations of the lines AB, CD, AD, CE, BD.

(g) Find the coordinates of the points in which the lines AB, CD, AD, CE, BD intersect the x- and y-axes.

2. Given the straight line $2y - 3x = 4$ and the point $(1, -3)$:

(a) Find the equation of the straight line through the given point and perpendicular to the given line.

(b) Find the shortest distance from the given point to the given line.

3. Plot the three points $A(6, 4)$, $B(4, -3)$, and $C(-2, 3)$.

(a) Is triangle ABC a right triangle? Why?

(b) Is it isosceles? Why?

(c) Does the origin lie inside, outside, or on the boundary of the triangle? Why?

(d) If C is replaced by a point $C'(-2, y)$ such that angle $C'BA$ is a right angle, find y, the ordinate of C'.

4. Find the equations of the straight lines passing through the origin which are tangent to the circle of center $(2, 1)$ and radius 2.

5. Let $P_1(x_1, y_1)$ and $P_2(x_2, y_2)$ be any two points. Find the coordinates of the midpoint of P_1P_2.

6. The x- and y-intercepts of a line L are respectively a and b. Show that an equation of L is $(x/a) + (y/b) = 1$.

7. Given the line L: $ax + by + c = 0$. Find (a) its slope, (b) its y-intercept, (c) its x-intercept, (d) the line through the origin perpendicular to L.

8. Show that the distance from a point $P(x_1, y_1)$ to a line $ax + by + c = 0$ is equal to

$$\frac{|ax_1 + by_1 + c|}{\sqrt{a^2 + b^2}}.$$

(There are neat solutions of this problem in Vol. 59, 1952, of the *American Mathematical Monthly*, pp. 242 and 248.)

9. How many circles can you find that are tangent to the three lines

L_1: $x + y = 1$; L_2: $y = x + 1$; L_3: $x - 3y = 1$?

Give the center and radius of at least one such circle. You may use the result of Exercise 8 that the distance from a point $P(x_1, y_1)$ to a line $ax + by + c = 0$ is

$$\frac{|ax_1 + by_1 + c|}{\sqrt{a^2 + b^2}}.$$

10. Find, in terms of b, b', and m, the perpendicular distance between the parallel lines $y = mx + b$ and $y = mx + b'$.

11. Given the two lines

$$L_1: a_1x + b_1y + c_1 = 0;$$
$$L_2: a_2x + b_2y + c_2 = 0.$$

If k is a constant, what is the locus whose equation is

$$(a_1x + b_1y + c_1) + k(a_2x + b_2y + c_2) = 0?$$

12. Determine the coordinates of the point on the straight line $y = 3x + 1$ that is equidistant from $(0, 0)$ and $(-3, 4)$.

13. Find the equation of a straight line which is perpendicular to $5x - y = 1$ and is such that the area of the triangle formed by the x-axis, the y-axis, and the straight line is equal to 5.

The following inequalities describe sets of points $P(x, y)$ in the plane. Sketch each set.

14. $1 < x \le 3$ and $2 \le y < 3$

15. $-4 < x < 7$ and $-9 < y < 5$

16. $|x - 3| \le 2$ and $|y + 2| < 3$

Use absolute values and inequalities to express the following facts.

17. The point t is closer to -3 than it is to the point b.

18. The point t is closer to the point b than it is to the origin.

19. The point t is farther from 2 than from the point b.

For each of the following inequalities give the interval or intervals on which the inequality is true.

20. $x^2 - x - 2 > 0$ 21. $x^2 - 1 \ge 0$

22. $x^2 - 6x + 9 < 0$ 23. $x^2 + 7x + 12 \le 0$

FUNCTIONS

CHAPTER 2

Calculus is used to study the behavior of functions. Conversely, specific functions and their graphs are often used to illustrate facts in calculus, to suggest theorems, or to provide counterexamples that disprove conjectures. In this chapter we are concerned with some properties of functions that do not depend upon our knowing any calculus.

For example, we know from algebra that the graph of the function

$$f(x) = 2x - 1, \qquad -3 \le x \le 3 \qquad (1)$$

is a line segment joining the points $(-3, -7)$ and $(3, 5)$, as shown in Fig. 2.1. Looking at the graph, we can say that the function given by (1) is strictly increasing, is bounded below by -7, is bounded above by 5, has exactly one value $f(a)$ for any number a in $[-3, 3]$, has the value 0 for just one number x between 0 and 1, has range $[-7, 5]$, and maps the interval $[-3, 3]$ onto the interval $[-7, 5]$.

2.1

The words *range, increasing, bounded above,* and some others in the preceding sentence are technical terms that we shall define later. In the next section, we start with a definition of *function* and show how functions can be interpreted in a variety of ways. The following problems should be handled intuitively, using graphs to answer the questions in the way Fig. 2.1 was used above.

EXERCISES

Graph each of the following exercises (1 through 5) and then answer these questions:

(a) Is the function increasing or decreasing?

(b) Is it bounded above? bounded below? If so, by what numbers?

(c) How many zeros (solutions of $f(x) = 0$) does the function have? Where are they located?

(d) What is the range of the function?

1. $f(x) = 2x + 3, \quad -2 \leq x \leq 3$
2. $f(x) = 3 - 2x, \quad -2 \leq x \leq 3$
3. $f(x) = x, \quad 0 < x < 1$
4. $f(x) = |x|, \quad -1 \leq x \leq 1$
5. $f(x) = \sin x, \quad -\pi \leq x \leq \pi$

2.2 WHAT IS A FUNCTION?

There are three equivalent definitions for a function, and they all involve a variety of ideas. We refer to these as

(a) mapping,

(b) domain-and-rule,

(c) set of ordered pairs.

Definitions

(a) *A function f is a mapping that associates with each element a, in some set D (called the domain of f), a unique element b, in a set R, called the range of f. We also say that b is the value of function f at a, and write $b = f(a)$.*

(b) *A function f consists of a domain D and a rule for assigning to any element a in D a unique element $f(a)$. The collection of all elements $f(a)$, for a in D, is called the range of f.*

(c) *A function f is a set of ordered pairs of elements $(a, f(a))$ such that no two ordered pairs have the same first members and different second members.*

If we look at a function as a set of ordered pairs of the form (a, b), we call the variable a which yields the first of the two numbers in the ordered pair the *independent variable*. The second variable b is called

the *dependent variable*. So the *domain* of the function is the set of all values taken on by the *independent* variable, and the *range* is the set of all values taken on by the *dependent* variable.

Remark 1. We can show that the three definitions of function are equivalent. To get one of the ordered pairs referred to in the third definition, from the mapping referred to in the first definition, one would select any element a from D, find the image $b = f(a)$ in R, and form the pair $(a, f(a)) = (a, b)$. If this is done for *all* elements a in D, the collection of all resulting ordered pairs (a, b) has the property that no two pairs (a_1, b_1) and (a_2, b_2) have $a_1 = a_2$ and $b_1 \neq b_2$, because the image of $a_1 = a_2$ under the mapping f is *unique*. Conversely, given a collection of ordered pairs as described in (c), if a is the first member of an ordered pair $(a, f(a))$, then there is only one such pair; thus the second member $f(a)$ is uniquely determined, and we call it the *image* of a under f. Thus the mapping for every a in D is indicated by

$$a \to f(a) = b,$$

and the first definition of function is equivalent to the third.

Finally, let us see whether the second definition of function (domain and rule) is equivalent to the third definition (set of ordered pairs). Starting with the domain-and-rule definition, if a is in D and the rule assigns $f(a)$ as the unique associated value for a, we form the pair $(a, f(a))$, and this is one of the ordered pairs called for in the third definition. Conversely, given all the ordered pairs $\{(a, f(a)) \mid a \in D\}$, the rule can be stated as follows:

Given any $a \in D$, find the unique ordered pair (a, b) in the set of ordered pairs and let $b = f(a)$.

So the second and third definitions of function are equivalent.

We have shown that the first and third as well as the third and second definitions of function are equivalent. Therefore, the three definitions are equivalent.

Notations. If we want to emphasize the *mapping* action of f, we might write

$$f: x \rightarrow x^2, \qquad -\infty < x < \infty, \qquad \text{(1a)}$$

read "f maps x into x^2."

The rule is implicit in the formula

$$f(x) = x^2. \qquad \text{(1b)}$$

Finally we may use ordered pairs to write the same function:

$$f = \{(x, x^2) \mid x \text{ is any real number}\}, \qquad \text{(1c)}$$

which is read: "f is the set of all ordered pairs of the form (x, x^2) such that x is any real number."

In (1a), the inequalities,

$$-\infty < x < \infty,$$

and in (1c), the words "x is any real number" say that the *domain* is the set of all real numbers. As written, Eq. (1b) does not say what the domain is. It is customary among mathematicians to rely on a general understanding that,

> when a rule (or formula) is given for $f(x)$ and the domain is not stated explicitly, the *natural domain* of f is the set of all values of x for which the formula makes sense when these values are substituted for x in that formula.

Two restrictions should always be kept in mind. First, we must **never divide by zero**. Thus if we see $y = x/(x - 2)$, we must always think "$x \neq 2$," even if this restriction is not stated explicitly. Second, we are dealing exclusively with real-valued functions. This means that the domain must be suitably restricted when we have square roots, or fourth roots, or other even roots. For example, if $y = \sqrt{4 - x^2}$, we should also think "x^2 must not be greater than 4; that is, the domain must not extend beyond the interval $-2 \leq x \leq +2$, or $|x| \leq 2$."

Remark 2. Since a function is determined by the domain and a rule, we shall often resort to such shorthand expressions as "consider the function

$f(x) = x/(x - 2)$" in place of the more precise expression "let f be a function whose domain is the set of all real numbers $x \neq 2$ and which associates with x the number $f(x) = x/(x - 2)$."

EXERCISES

1. Suppose f is a function whose domain is the interval $[-3, 2]$ with values given by the rule

$$f(x) = \begin{cases} 2 & \text{when} & -3 \leq x < 0 \\ x & \text{when} & 0 \leq x < 1 \\ 2 - x & \text{when} & 1 \leq x \leq 2. \end{cases}$$

Sketch a graph of f. What is the range? How many solutions are there of the equation $f(x) = 0$? of $f(x) = 1$? of $f(x) = 2$?

2. A function g has the following rule: "Choose any number x, add 3, multiply the result by x, add 4, multiply that result by x, subtract 7." Give a formula for $g(x)$, in two forms: (a) follow the steps given verbally, and (b) state as a polynomial in x.

In each exercise (3 through 10) state an equivalent rule for computing $f(x)$, not using absolute values or square roots. The rule may take different forms on different parts of the domain. Sketch the graph of $y = f(x)$.

3. $f(x) = |2x|, \qquad -3 \leq x \leq 3$
4. $f(x) = x + |x|, \qquad -2 \leq x \leq 2$
5. $f(x) = |\sin x|, \qquad -\pi \leq x \leq \pi$
6. $f(x) = \sin x + |\sin x|, \qquad -\pi \leq x \leq \pi$
7. $f(x) = |x - 2|, \qquad 0 \leq x \leq 5$
8. $f(x) = |2x - 1|, \qquad 0 \leq x \leq 3$
9. $f(x) = \sqrt{x^2 - 2x + 1}, \qquad -1 \leq x \leq 3$
10. $f(x) = x + \sqrt{4x^2 - 4x + 1}, \qquad 0 \leq x \leq 2$

In each exercise (11 through 21) what is the *natural domain* of the given function?

11. $f(x) = \dfrac{x}{\sqrt{x - 1}}$

12. $f(x) = \dfrac{\sqrt{x - 1}}{x}$

13. $f(x) = \dfrac{\sqrt{1 - x}}{x}$

14. $f(x) = x\sqrt{2 + x}$

15. $f(x) = \sqrt{(2 + 2x)(3 - x)}$

16. $f(x) = \sqrt{x^2 - 1}$

17. $f(x) = \sqrt{x^3 - x}$

18. $f(x) = \sqrt[4]{-x^2}$

19. $y = \dfrac{x^2}{x^2 + 1}$ 20. $y = \sqrt{\dfrac{x}{x + 1}}$ 21. $y = x - \dfrac{1}{x}$

22. Describe the domain of the variable x without the use of the "absolute value" symbol in each of the following cases: (a) $|x| < 2$, (b) $|x| \geq 2$, (c) $|x - 1| \leq 3$, (d) $|x - 2| < 2$ and simultaneously x must satisfy the additional restriction $|x - 3| \geq 1$.

23. When does $|1 - x|$ equal $1 - x$ and when does it equal $x - 1$?

2.3 EQUAL FUNCTIONS.   FUNCTIONS OF MORE THAN ONE VARIABLE

When a familiar formula is used along with a domain that is stated explicitly, the resulting function need not be the same as it would be if the same formula were applied to its natural domain.   Thus, for example, the functions f_1, f_2, and f_3, given by

$$f_1(x) = \frac{1}{x}, \quad x \neq 0 \text{ (the natural domain)}, \quad (4a)$$

$$f_2(x) = \frac{1}{x}, \quad x > 0 \text{ (domain, the positive}$$
$$\text{real numbers)}, \quad (4b)$$

$$f_3(x) = \frac{1}{x}, \quad 0 < x < 1 \text{ (domain, the}$$
$$\text{interval } (0, 1)), \quad (4c)$$

are not the same.   The graphs of f_1, f_2, f_3 are indicated in Fig. 2.2.   In Fig. 2.2(c), note the different scales on the x- and y-axes.   (The point $(1, 1)$ is not on the curve.)

Definition. *Two functions, f and g, are equal if and only if they have the same domain, $\underline{D_f = D_g}$, and the values of $f(x)$ and $g(x)$ are equal for each x in their domain.*

Example 1. Since $|x|$ and $\sqrt{x^2}$ are both defined for all real numbers x, and the values are the same for every x, the two functions

$$f(x) = |x|$$

and

$$g(x) = \sqrt{x^2}$$

are equal.   But the functions

2.2

2.3

$$h(x) = x$$

and

$$\phi(x) = \frac{x(x-1)}{x-1}$$

are not equal, because the domain of h contains the number $x = 1$ and the domain of ϕ does not.

Remark. The "function-is-a-machine" idea can be applied to functions defined by rules that are not simple formulas.

Example 2. Suppose f is a function whose domain is the interval $[-2, 2]$ with values given by the rule

$$f(x) = \begin{cases} x & \text{when} & -2 \le x < 0, & (5a) \\ 1 & \text{when} & x = 0, & (5b) \\ 2 - x & \text{when} & 0 < x \le 2. & (5c) \end{cases}$$

A computer could be programmed to compute the values of $f(x)$, according to the flow diagram of Fig. 2.3. Start at the base and follow the arrows upward. The three dark blocks containing question marks are decision makers. They tell whether x is in the domain, and if so, whether $x < 0$ or $x = 0$ or $x > 0$. (If x is neither less than zero nor greater than zero, we conclude that $x = 0$.)

There are at least four different ways of representing the functional relationship between the variables x and y, and all four of these methods are probably familiar to the reader. They are:

1. *By tables of values.* For example, the functions $y = \log_{10} x$, $y = \sin (x°)$, $y = \sqrt{x}$, $y = 1/x$, and many others are given in most numerical tables.

2. *By corresponding scales.* For example, the scales of a slide rule may be lined up so that opposite any number x on one scale, we may read $\sqrt{x}$, or x^2, or $\log_{10} x$, and so on, on other scales.

3. *By means of graphs.* Here we usually plot points (x, y) with x in the domain of the function and with $y = f(x)$, and draw a smooth curve through the plotted points. It is also customary to make a *table of values* of corresponding numbers x and y before we plot the curve.

4. *By means of equations*, from which we can calculate the value of y that corresponds to any given x.

Of these four methods, the ones most often used in this book will be the third and fourth, namely graphs and equations. However, any rule, whether expressed algebraically or verbally, that produces a unique value for y when x is given satisfies the requirements of expressing y as a function of x. There need not be a simple equation which gives y in terms of x. An example of an interesting function not given by a simple equation is the *greatest integer function*. This function is defined on the domain of all real numbers. With any x in the domain, the function associates the algebraically greatest integer which is less than or equal to x, and denotes this value as $[x]$.

$$[2.5] = 2$$
$$[.5] = 0$$
$$[-.5] = -1$$
$$y : x \to [x]$$

2.4

Example 3. If

$$x = 3.4, \text{ then } [x] = 3.$$

If

$$x = -4.7, \text{ then } [-4.7] = -5.$$

The graph of the function $y = [x]$ is shown in Fig. 2.4. It is clear from the graph why such a function is called a "step function." There are many examples of step functions in everyday life.

Such functions exhibit points of *discontinuity* where the function suddenly jumps from one value to another without taking on any of the intermediate values.

Functions of more than one independent variable

Occasionally we have functions which depend upon several independent variables. For example, if r is the base radius and h is the altitude of a right circular cone (Fig. 2.5), then the volume

$$v = \tfrac{1}{3}\pi r^2 h$$

is uniquely determined when r and h are given definite values. The physical meaning requires that r, h, and v be positive. The set of all ordered triples (r, h, v) with $v = \tfrac{1}{3}\pi r^2 h$, $r > 0$, $h > 0$ is an example of a function of two independent variables (r and h). Its *domain* is the set of all pairs (r, h) with $r > 0$, $h > 0$. Its *range* is the set of positive numbers $v > 0$. The variables r and h are *independent* in the sense that the value assigned to either of them need not depend upon the other. But the value of v is fixed by the other two variables, so we call v the *dependent* variable. It is also customary to be briefer, and somewhat less precise, and to say that "the volume of a right circular cone is a function of the radius and altitude," or, still more briefly, "v is a function of r and h." This means two things:

(a) r and h can be assigned values independently, and

(b) when r and h are given, v is uniquely determined.

2.5

EXERCISES

1. Sketch the graphs of the following functions to show that they are not the same:

$f_1(x) = x^2$,   the natural domain

$f_2(x) = x^2$, $x \geq 0$

$f_3(x) = x^2$, $-2 \leq x \leq 2$

$f_4(x) = x^2$, $-2 \leq x \leq 2$, where x is an integer.

2. State which of the following functions are equal to the function

$$f(x) = \frac{x^2 - 2x}{x}.$$

Give reasons for your answers.

$$g(x) = x - 2$$

$$h(x) = \frac{4x - 8}{4}$$

$$k(x) = \frac{x^3 - 2x^2}{x^2}$$

$$m(x) = \frac{2x^2 - 4x}{2x}$$

$$n(x) = \frac{x^2 - 3x + 2}{x - 1}$$

3. State which of the following functions are equal to the function

$$r(x) = |x - 2|.$$

Give reasons for your answers.

$$s(x) = \sqrt{x^2 - 4x + 4}$$

$$t(x) = \sqrt{\frac{(x - 2)^3}{x - 2}}$$

$$u(x) = \frac{|x - 2|^2}{|x - 2|}$$

$$v(x) = \frac{|6x - 12|}{6}$$

$$w(x) = \left| \frac{x^2 + x - 6}{x + 3} \right|$$

4. State which of the following functions are equal to the function

$$\phi(x) = \frac{\sin^2 x + 1}{x}.$$

Give reasons for your answers.

$$f(x) = \frac{\sin^2 x}{x} + \frac{1}{x}$$

$$g(x) = \frac{\sin^2 x}{x} + \frac{x - 1}{x^2 - x}$$

$$h(x) = \frac{2\sin^2 x + \cos^2 x}{x}$$

$$j(x) = \frac{2x - x\cos^2 x}{x^2}$$

5. Given the function

$$f(x) = x^2 + \left(\frac{1}{x}\right)$$

find $f(2)$, $f(-1)$, $f\left(\frac{1}{x}\right)$, $f(x + \Delta x)$.

6. Make a table corresponding to $x = 0, \frac{1}{2}, 1, \frac{3}{2}, 2$ and sketch a graph to represent the function

$$y = \begin{cases} x, & \text{when} & 0 \le x \le 1 \\ 2 - x, & \text{when} & 1 < x \le 2. \end{cases}$$

7. Given the function

$$y = |4 - x^2|, \qquad -3 \le x \le 3,$$

compute the values of y corresponding to each whole number in the domain and make a table of these values. Use this table to sketch a graph of the function.

8. Sketch graphs of the following functions for

$$-3 \le x \le 3.$$

(a) $f(x) = x - [x]$

(b) $g(x) = [x] + [-x]$

(c) $h(x) = \dfrac{[x]}{x}, \qquad x \ne 0$

9. Sketch a graph of the function defined by

$$f(x) = \begin{cases} \dfrac{x}{|x|} & \text{for } x \ne 0 \\ 0 & \text{for } x = 0. \end{cases}$$

This is known as the *signum function*, sgn (x).

10. Separate the equation

$$x^2 + xy + y^2 = 3$$

into two equations, each of which determines y as a function of x.

11. Let us define Δf as a function of two variables, x and h such that

$$\Delta f(x, h) = f(x + h) - f(x).$$

(a) Name a sufficient condition for $\Delta f(x, h) = 0$.

(b) If $f(x) = x^2$, find $\Delta f(0, 0)$, $\Delta f(-2, 4)$, $\Delta f(0.0001, -0.0001)$.

2.4 WAYS OF COMBINING FUNCTIONS

If f and g are two functions with domains D_f and D_g, then $f(x)$ and $g(x)$ exist for any x that is in both domains, and we can compute

$$f(x) + g(x),$$
$$f(x) - g(x),$$

and

$$f(x) \cdot g(x).$$

We can also find $f(x)/g(x)$, provided that $g(x) \ne 0$. The new functions so constructed are called the

$$\text{sum} \quad f + g : x \to f(x) + g(x), \qquad \text{(1a)}$$
$$\text{product} \quad f \cdot g : x \to f(x) \cdot g(x), \qquad \text{(1b)}$$
$$\text{difference} \quad f - g : x \to f(x) - g(x), \qquad \text{(1c)}$$
$$\text{quotient} \quad \frac{f}{g} : x \to \frac{f(x)}{g(x)}. \qquad \text{(1d)}$$

The domain of $f + g$, $f - g$, and $f \cdot g$ is the intersection of the domains of f and of g. The points at which $g(x) = 0$ must be excluded, however, to obtain the domain of f/g.

Example 1

$$f(x) = \sqrt{x}, \quad g(x) = \sqrt{1 - x}. \qquad \text{(2a)}$$

The natural domains of f and g are

$$D_f = \{x : x \ge 0\}, \quad D_g = \{x : x \le 1\}. \qquad \text{(2b)}$$

The intersection of D_f and D_g is

$$D_f \cap D_g = \{x : 0 \le x \le 1\} = [0, 1]. \qquad \text{(3)}$$
$$\text{sum} \quad f + g : x \to \sqrt{x} + \sqrt{1 - x},$$
$$\text{difference} \quad f - g : x \to \sqrt{x} - \sqrt{1 - x},$$
$$\text{product} \quad f \cdot g : x \to \sqrt{x(1 - x)},$$
$$\text{quotients} \quad \frac{f}{g} : x \to \sqrt{\frac{x}{1 - x}},$$
$$\frac{g}{f} : x \to \sqrt{\frac{1 - x}{x}}.$$

The domains of $f + g$, $f - g$, and $f \cdot g$ are all the same, $[0, 1]$. Since $g(x) = 0$ when $x = 1$, the domain of f/g is $[0, 1)$. Similarly, the domain of g/f is $(0, 1]$.

We can construct graphs of $f + g$, $f - g$, fg, f/g, or g/f from the separate graphs of f and g in the obvious way. For example, Fig. 2.6 shows a sketch of graphs of f, g, $f + g$, and $f \cdot g$.

Example 2. If $f(x) = x$ and $g(x) = 1/x$, then

$$D_f = (-\infty, \infty), \qquad D_g = \{x : x \neq 0\}.$$

The domain of $f \cdot g$ is the set of all nonzero real numbers. Hence, although $f(x) \cdot g(x) = 1$ when $x \neq 0$, we cannot say that $f \cdot g$ is the constant function 1, because the domain of that function is $(-\infty, \infty)$, and this is different from the domain of $f \cdot g$.

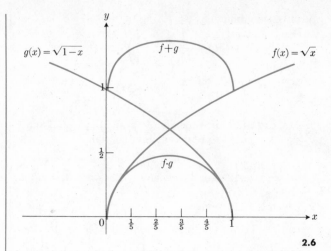

2.6

Translation and change of scale

It is well known that the graphs of

$$f(x) = x^2, \quad g(x) = (x - c)^2 \tag{4}$$

are very much alike, for any number c. Figure 2.7 shows the parabolas for the two functions f and g, with $c = 2$.

The formulas in Eq. (4) are related:

$$g(x) = f(x - c) = (x - c)^2. \tag{5}$$

If we look at the graphs in Fig. 2.7, we see that the graph of g is that of f *translated* or shifted two units to the right.

What can we say in general about the graphs of functions f and g that satisfy

$$g(x) = f(x - c) \tag{6}$$

for some number c? Assume that the domain of f is $[a, b]$. Then $f(x - c)$ is only defined when

$$a \leq x - c \leq b; \tag{7a}$$

or, adding c throughout, when

$$a + c \leq x \leq b + c. \tag{7b}$$

2.7

Thus

$$g(x) = f(x - c)$$

is defined on the domain

$$D_g = [a + c, b + c], \tag{8a}$$

while f itself has domain

$$D_f = [a, b]. \tag{8b}$$

2.8

Equations (8) show that the domain of g is the interval we get by shifting $[a, b]$ to the right c units, or to the left $|c|$ units if $c < 0$. Now take any x in the new interval $[a + c, b + c]$. Equation (6) shows that the value of g at that x is equal to the value of f at $x - c$. In other words, take the ordinate of f at $x - c$ and shift it to the right c units to get the ordinate of g at x. Figure 2.8 illustrates this situation for a positive value of c.

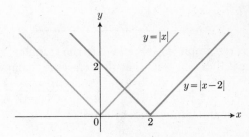

2.9

Problem. How is the graph of $y = |x|$ related to the graph of $y = |x - 2|$?

Solution. Figure 2.9 shows the two graphs. We just shift the graph of $|x|$ two units to the right to get the graph of $|x - 2|$.

A function can also be altered by a *change of scale* in the domain. This is illustrated by the example

$$f(x) = \sin x,$$
$$g(x) = \sin (\pi x). \qquad (9)$$

The natural domain is $(-\infty, \infty)$ for both functions f and g. But as x varies from 0 to 1, πx varies from 0 to π. Graphs of f, for $-\pi \le x \le \pi$, and of g, for $-1 \le x \le 1$, are shown in Fig. 2.10. The situation in Eq. (9) and Fig. 2.10(a) is that

$$g(x) = f(\pi x). \qquad (10)$$

If we want the argument πx of f in Eq. (10) to cover the interval $[-\pi, \pi]$, which corresponds to one complete sine wave, then

$$-\pi \le \pi x \le \pi$$

corresponds to

$$-1 \le x \le 1.$$

We get the g curve in Fig. 2.10(a) by compressing the f curve horizontally in the ratio π to 1.

We can also alter a function by changing the scale in the range. Let us take, for example,

$$f(x) = \sin x,$$
$$q(x) = 2 \sin x. \qquad (11)$$

The graph of f and q for $-\pi \le x \le \pi$ is shown in Fig. 2.10(b). The range of f in Fig. 2.10(b) is $[-1, 1]$,

a | b

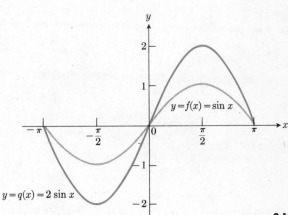

2.10

but the range of q is $[-2, 2]$. We get the q curve by stretching the f curve vertically in the ratio of 2 to 1.

More generally, suppose k is any positive constant and that

$$g(x) = f(kx). \tag{12}$$

How is the graph of $g(x)$ related to the graph of $f(x)$? Figure 2.10(a) suggests that the answer is "compress or stretch the x-axis by shrinking (if $k > 1$) or stretching (if $k < 1$) every interval of length k on the x-axis into an interval of length 1."

Note. For example, if D_f, the domain of f, is

$$D_f = [a, b],$$

and if

$$g(x) = f(kx), \tag{13}$$

then g is defined by (13) if and only if

$$a \le kx \le b,$$

or, assuming $k > 0$,

$$\frac{a}{k} \le x \le \frac{b}{k}.$$

That is, D_g, the domain of g, is

$$D_g = \left[\frac{a}{k}, \frac{b}{k}\right], \tag{14}$$

and for any x in D_g, we find kx in D_f, and take

$$g(x) = f(kx).$$

Figure 2.10 illustrates

$$f(x) = \sin x \quad \text{and} \quad g(x) = \sin(\pi x) = f(\pi x)$$

for $k = \pi$.

Another example is illustrated by Fig. 2.11 which shows the effect for

$$f(x) = \sqrt{1 - x^2} \quad \text{and} \quad g(x) = f(2x) = \sqrt{1 - 4x^2}$$

for $k = 2$.

We can also look at the situation in Fig. 2.10(b) more broadly. Suppose k is a positive constant and that

$$g(x) = kf(x).$$

The figure suggests that we can obtain the graph of q from the graph of f in either of the following two equivalent ways:

1. Stretch the f curve vertically (if $k > 1$), or compress it (if $k < 1$).

2. Change the scale on the y-axis so that points labeled 1, 2, 3, ... for the graph of f are relabeled k, $2k$, $3k$, ... for the graph of q.

EXERCISES

For each of the following pairs of functions f and g in Exercises 1 through 3, specify the natural domains of f and g and the corresponding domains of $f + g$, $f \cdot g$, f/g, and g/f.

1. $f(x) = x$, $g(x) = \sqrt{x - 1}$

2. $f(x) = \dfrac{1}{x - 2}$, $g(x) = \dfrac{1}{\sqrt{x - 1}}$

3. $f(x) = \sqrt{x}$, $g(x) = \sqrt[4]{x + 1}$

4. Suppose $f(x) = |x|$ and $g(x) = f(x - 3)$. Graph f and g. Compare the graphs of f and g.

5. Suppose c is positive and $g(x) = f(x + c)$. If $D_f = [a, b]$, what is D_g? How can you get the graph of g from the graph of f? Illustrate with

$$f(x) = \sin x, \quad -\pi \le x \le \pi,$$

$$g(x) = f(x + \pi/2).$$

6. If $\phi(x) = \sin x$, $-\pi \le x \le \pi$, sketch the graph of each of the following and state the domain and range of each.

(a) $p(x) = \phi\left(\dfrac{x}{2}\right)$ (b) $r(x) = \phi(3x)$

(c) $q(x) = \phi(-x)$

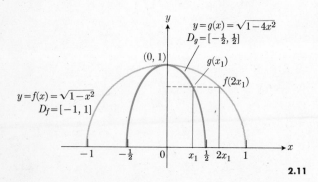

2.11

7. If $f(x) = 2x^2 - 2[|x|]^2$, $-2 < x < 2$, sketch the graph of f and of each of the following and state the domain and range of each.

   (a) $g(x) = f\left(\dfrac{x}{4}\right)$

   (b) $h(x) = f(\tfrac{3}{2}x)$

   (c) $k(x) = f(-2x)$

8. If $F(x) = 1 + 3\cos 2x$, $-\pi \le x \le \pi$, sketch the graph of F and of each of the following and state the domain and range of each.

   (a) $f(x) = \tfrac{1}{2}F(x)$ (b) $g(x) = F\left(\dfrac{x}{4}\right)$

   (c) $h(x) = F\left(x + \dfrac{\pi}{2}\right)$ (d) $H(x) = -F(x)$

9. Sketch the graph of

$$f(x) = \frac{1 + \operatorname{sgn}(x^2 - 4)}{3}, \quad -4 \le x \le 4,$$

and state its range.

10. Sketch the graph of each of the following and state the domain and range of each, where $f(x) = \sqrt{1 - x^2}$ for $|x| \le 1$.

   (a) $g(x) = \tfrac{3}{2}f(x)$

   (b) $h(x) = f(\tfrac{2}{3}x)$

   (c) $F(x) = 3f(2x)$

   (d) $H(x) = -f(-x)$

11. Sketch the graphs of

   (a) $f(x) = |x|$,

   (b) $g(x) = |2x|$,

   (c) $h(x) = |x^2 - 2x - 3|$,

   (d) $f(x) = |1 - x^2| - 2$,

   (e) $g(x) = \dfrac{2 + \operatorname{sgn}(-x)}{2}$,

   (f) $h(x) = 3 - [3x]$,

   (g) $f(x) = (\operatorname{sgn} x)(x - 1)^2 + x^2[\operatorname{sgn}(x - 1)]$.

12. For $|x| \le 3$, $f(x) = \max\{x, x^2\}$. Sketch its graph.

13. For $1 \le x \le 10$, let $g(x)$ be the number of positive integers n such that $n^2 \le x$. Sketch its graph.

14. For any positive real number x, let $\pi(x)$ be the number of primes that are not greater than x. (The first five primes are 2, 3, 5, 7, 11, so $\pi(7) = \pi(8) = 4$ and $\pi(12.7) = 5$.) Sketch the graph of this step function for $1 \le x \le 20$.

2.5 BEHAVIOR OF FUNCTIONS

We know that the linear function

$$f(x) = 3x \qquad (1)$$

has as its graph a straight line, through the origin, of slope $+3$. As x increases, the function values increase at a rate three times as fast, because a one-unit change in x produces a three-unit change in $f(x)$.

Example. If x_1 is an initial value of x, and $x_2 = x_1 + h$ is a new value obtained by increasing x by h units, then the corresponding increase in the value of the function is

$$f(x_1 + h) - f(x_1) = 3(x_1 + h) - 3x_1 = 3h, \qquad (2)$$

which is exactly three times the increase in x. See Fig. 2.12.

2.12

Remark 1. In Article 1.3, the notation Δx was introduced to represent the difference $x_2 - x_1$ between two values of x; that is,

$$\Delta x = x_2 - x_1. \qquad (3)$$

In the preceding illustration, we located x_2, the new value of x, by increasing the initial value x_1 by h units:

$$x_2 = x_1 + h. \qquad (4)$$

Note from (4) that

$$\Delta x = h = x_2 - x_1. \qquad (5)$$

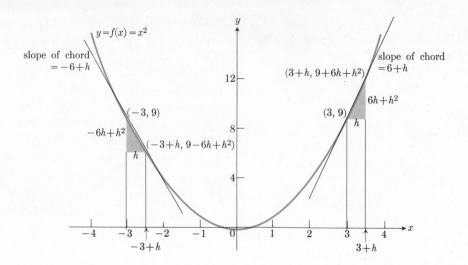

2.13

In other words Δx and h are different representations of the same thing, a change in the value of x. We shall use these two notations interchangeably.

Not all functions are as simple as the one just discussed. The function

$$f(x) = x^2 \qquad (6)$$

increases over some intervals of x-values and decreases over others. Its rate of change, per unit change in x, is not constant. Substituting $x_1 + h$ and x_1 on both sides of Eq. (6) and subtracting, we get

$$f(x_1 + h) - f(x_1) = (x_1 + h)^2 - x_1^2$$
$$= 2x_1 h + h^2. \qquad (7)$$

The increase in $f(x) = x^2$ depends upon x_1, the initial value of x, and also upon h, the amount of increase in x. We want to compare the increase in $f(x)$ with the increase in x. For the linear function $3x$ we saw that the increase in $f(x) = 3x$ was three times the increase in x. For the function $f(x) = x^2$, we see from Eq. (7) that we can write

$$f(x_1 + h) - f(x_1) = (2x_1 + h)h. \qquad (8)$$

Here, h represents the increase in x from x_1 to $x_1 + h$. Therefore we can say, "the increase in x^2, as x increases from x_1 to $x_1 + h$, is $2x_1 + h$ times the

increase in x." Alternatively we can divide the increase in $f(x)$ by the increase in x. This ratio,

$$\frac{f(x_1 + h) - f(x_1)}{(x_1 + h) - x_1} = \frac{f(x_1 + h) - f(x_1)}{h}$$
$$= \frac{\text{change in } f(x)}{\text{change in } x}, \qquad (9)$$

is called the *average rate of increase of $f(x)$, per unit of increase in x*, from x_1 to $x_1 + h$.

For the example $f(x) = x^2$, Eqs. (8) and (9) lead to the result

$$\frac{f(x_1 + h) - f(x_1)}{h} = 2x_1 + h \qquad (10)$$

for the average rate of increase of x^2 per unit of increase in x. Thus, if $x_1 = 2$ and $h = 1$, the right side of Eq. (10) gives $2x_1 + h = 5$, so that x^2 increases five times as much as x does in going from $x_1 = 2$ to $x_1 + h = 3$. The table on page 31 shows how the average rate of increase of x^2, per unit of increase in x, varies for four different starting values, x_1, and several different values of $h > 0$.

Two things are evident from the table below or from Eq. (10).

(a) If we fix x_1 and take smaller and smaller values of h, the average rate of change of x^2 per unit change in x tends to become almost equal to $2x_1$.

(b) When x_1 is negative, a small *increase* in x, from x_1 to $x_1 + h$, corresponds to a *negative increase* (that is, a *decrease*) in x^2.

h \ x_1	2	3	-2	-3
		$2x_1 + h$		
1	5	7	-3	-5
0.5	4.5	6.5	-3.5	-5.5
0.25	4.25	6.25	-3.75	-5.75
0.1	4.1	6.1	-3.9	-5.9
0.01	4.01	6.01	-3.99	-5.99
0.001	4.001	6.001	-3.999	-5.999

Figure 2.13 illustrates some of these ideas. There, we can see that the slope of the secant line through the points (x_1, x_1^2) and $((x_1 + h), (x_1 + h)^2)$ is $2x_1 + h$, for $x_1 = 3$ or -3.

For a *constant function*, such as

$$f(x) = 5,$$

of course, there is no change in the value of $f(x)$ when x increases from x_1 to $x_1 + h$, because

$$f(x_1 + h) = f(x_1) = 5.$$

For any such constant function, Eq. (9) leads to the result

$$\frac{f(x_1 + h) - f(x_1)}{h} = \frac{0}{h} = 0,$$

for any $h \neq 0$. We interpret this to say that "the average rate of increase of a constant function is zero," which is just what we would expect (see Fig. 2.14).

Remark 2. In the next chapters we shall develop systematic rules for calculating the rate of increase of a function $f(x)$ per unit change in x. *Differential calculus* (one of the two main branches of calculus—the other being integral calculus) is concerned with the *instantaneous* rate of increase, rather than with the average rate. For constant functions $f(x) = c$, and for linear functions $f(x) = mx + b$, the average rate of increase is constant and we need not distinguish between average rate and instantaneous rate.

2.14

2.15

(By analogy, if an automobile is traveling at a steady rate of 45 miles per hour, its average speed and its instantaneous speed are the same.) But we saw that the square function does not have the same average rate of increase everywhere, because if $f(x) = x^2$, and $h \neq 0$, then

$$\frac{f(x_1 + h) - f(x_1)}{h} = 2x_1 + h. \qquad (11)$$

Note the restriction $h \neq 0$: We cannot divide by 0 in Eq. (11). But we can consider h's in a deleted neighborhood of zero. Figure 2.15 shows a graph of the *slope function*

$$m(h) = 2x_1 + h \qquad (12)$$

for a typical positive value of x_1 and h in a deleted neighborhood of zero (in other words, for h "near zero"). The point $(0, 2x_1)$, which would be on the graph if we allowed h to be equal to zero on the right side of Eq. (12), is *not included*, because h must be different from zero if we want to identify $m(h)$ from

Eq. (12) with the difference quotient on the left-hand side of Eq. (11):

$$m(h) = \frac{f(x_1 + h) - f(x_1)}{h}. \qquad (13)$$

But $m(h)$ is bounded between $2x_1 + 0.01$ and $2x_1 - 0.01$ when $|h|$ is, say, less than 0.01. In fact, if ϵ (Greek letter read "epsilon") is any positive number, and we choose $|h| < \epsilon$, then from Eq. (12) we see that $m(h)$ is between $2x_1 - \epsilon$ and $2x_1 + \epsilon$ because

$$-\epsilon < h < \epsilon \Rightarrow 2x_1 - \epsilon < 2x_1 + h < 2x_1 + \epsilon$$

(double arrow, $\Rightarrow$, read "implies"). We also say that $m(h)$ is *approximated by* $2x_1$ *to within* ϵ when $0 < |h| < \epsilon$. Figure 2.16 illustrates the idea. The number $2x_1$ is called "the *limit* of $2x_1 + h$, as h approaches zero." This limit is also called the *instantaneous* rate of increase of $f(x) = x^2$, at $x = x_1$, and is indicated by the notation $f'(x_1)$, read "f prime at x_1." Formally, we make the following definition.

Definition. *We say* $m(h)$ *is approximated by* L *to within* ϵ *on an interval* (a, b), *provided*

$$L - \epsilon < m(h) < L + \epsilon$$

when

$$a < h < b.$$

Problem 1. Show $m(h) = 2h + 1$ is approximated by $L = 1$ to within $\epsilon = 0.5$ on the interval $(-\frac{1}{4}, \frac{1}{4})$.

Solution. We have

$$-\frac{1}{4} < h < \frac{1}{4}.$$

By using the properties of inequalities we get

$$2(-\tfrac{1}{4}) + 1 < 2h + 1 < 2(\tfrac{1}{4}) + 1.$$

Rewritten, we have

$$1 - 0.5 < m(h) < 1 + 0.5,$$

which demonstrates that the preceding definition applies with $L = 1$ and $\epsilon = 0.5$.

Problem 2. Find values of L and ϵ so that $m(h) = 3h + 2$ is approximated by L to within ϵ on the interval $(-0.5, 0.5)$.

2.16

Solution. A very large ϵ would always meet our conditions. We shall try to find a small ϵ. We know that

$$-0.5 < h < 0.5. \qquad (14)$$

We want to find L and ϵ, so that

$$L - \epsilon < m(h) < L + \epsilon.$$

From (14) we have

$$3(-0.5) + 2 < 3h + 2 < 3(0.5) + 2,$$

or

$$2 - 1.5 < 3h + 2 < 2 + 1.5.$$

So we can conclude that if we take $\epsilon = 1.5$ and $L = 2$, all possible values of $m(h)$ over the given interval will be between $2 + 1.5$ and $2 - 1.5$.

EXERCISES

For the functions 1 through 6, write the expression for the slope function $m(h)$ as defined for f by Eq. (13). Compute $m(h)$ for the given values of x_1 and h.

1. $f(x) = 2x - 1$, $x_1 = -1$, $h = 4$

2. $g(x) = x^2 + x$, $x_1 = 4$, $h = 2$

3. $F(x) = \dfrac{1}{x}$, $x_1 = 1$, $h = \dfrac{1}{4}$

4. $f(x) = \dfrac{x}{x - 3}$, $x_1 = 0$, $h = \dfrac{1}{10}$

5. $g(x) = |x|$, $x_1 = -1$, $h = \tfrac{1}{2}$

6. $F(x) = \sin x$, $x_1 = \dfrac{\pi}{3}$, $h = \dfrac{\pi}{6}$

In Exercises 7 through 11, demonstrate the truth or falsity of "$m(h)$ is approximated by L to within ϵ" on the given interval (a, b) for the given values of L and ϵ. Sketch appropriate graphs, showing $m(h)$, L, $L - \epsilon$, $L + \epsilon$, and (a, b).

7. $m(h) = h^2 + 4$, $L = 4$, $\epsilon = 0.01$, $(a, b) = (-0.1, 0.1)$
8. $m(h) = 2h + 3$, $L = 3$, $\epsilon = 0.5$, $(a, b) = (-\frac{1}{4}, \frac{1}{4})$
9. $m(h) = 2h + 3$, $L = 4$, $\epsilon = 0.5$, $(a, b) = (-\frac{1}{4}, \frac{1}{4})$
10. $m(h) = 2h + 3$, $L = 3$, $\epsilon = 0.5$, $(a, b) = (-\frac{1}{2}, \frac{1}{2})$
11. $m(h) = 3 + (2/h)$, $L = 3$, $\epsilon = 1$, $(a, b) = (10, 20)$

In Exercises 12 through 16, find values of L and of ϵ so that it is true that $m(h)$ is approximated by L to within ϵ on (a, b). (Answers are not unique: One could always take ϵ very large and use many different values of L. Try to answer with small values of ϵ.)

12. $m(h) = 5 + 6h$, $(a, b) = (-0.1, 0.1)$
13. $m(h) = 4 - 6h$, $(a, b) = (-0.1, 0.1)$
14. $m(h) = \dfrac{3 + h}{2 - h}$, $(a, b) = (-\frac{1}{2}, \frac{1}{2})$
15. $m(h) = (2 + h)(3 - h)$, $(a, b) = (-\frac{1}{2}, \frac{1}{2})$
16. $m(h) = (2 + h) + (5 - h^2)$, $(a, b) = (-0.1, 0.1)$

2.6 SLOPE OF A CURVE

In Article 1.3, we discussed the slope of the straight line. In this article we shall define what we mean by the *slope of a curve* at a point $P(x, y)$ on the curve. This is the way in which Leibniz approached the "differential calculus."

In Fig. 2.17, $P(x_1, y_1)$ is any point on the curve $y = f(x)$, and $Q(x_2, y_2)$ is another point on the same curve. Then the slope of the secant line joining the points P and Q is

$$m_{\text{sec}} = \frac{y_2 - y_1}{x_2 - x_1} = \frac{\Delta y}{\Delta x}. \tag{1}$$

Suppose now we hold P fixed and move Q along the curve toward P. As we do so, the slope of the secant line PQ will probably vary. But it may happen (and does for most curves encountered in practice) that as Q moves closer and closer to P, the slope of the secant line varies by smaller and smaller amounts and, in fact, approaches a constant limiting value. When this happens, as it does in the following example, we call this limiting value *the slope of the tangent to the curve at P* or, more briefly, *the slope of the curve at P*.

Remark. A geometric definition of tangent line can be given without reference to slope. One such definition is the following:

Let C be a curve and P a point on C. If there exists a line L through P such that the measure of one of the angles between L and the secant line PQ approaches zero as Q approaches P along C, then L is said to be tangent to C at P.

One advantage of such a definition is that it clearly does not depend upon the particular choice of coordinate axes. It also permits the tangent line to be a vertical line (to which no real number can be assigned as slope). However, in most instances we start with a given equation, implying a choice of axes, and it is easiest to use the methods of calculus to find the slope and then write down an equation for the line tangent to the curve, using the point-slope formula

$$y - y_1 = m(x - x_1).$$

Example. Consider the curve

$$y = x^3 - 3x + 3. \tag{2}$$

If $P(x_1, y_1)$ is a point on this curve, then its coordinates must satisfy the equation

$$y_1 = x_1^3 - 3x_1 + 3. \tag{3a}$$

Figure 2.17 shows the curve $y = f(x)$ with points $P(x_1, y_1)$, $Q(x_2, y_2)$, $R(x_2, y_1)$, $\Delta y = y_2 - y_1$, and $\Delta x = x_2 - x_1$. 2.17

If $Q(x_2, y_2)$ is a second point on the curve, and if

$$\Delta x = x_2 - x_1, \quad \Delta y = y_2 - y_1,$$

then

$$x_2 = x_1 + \Delta x, \quad y_2 = y_1 + \Delta y$$

must also satisfy Eq. (2). That is,

$$\begin{aligned} y_1 + \Delta y &= (x_1 + \Delta x)^3 - 3(x_1 + \Delta x) + 3 \\ &= x_1^3 + 3x_1^2 \Delta x + 3x_1 (\Delta x)^2 \\ &\quad + (\Delta x)^3 - 3x_1 - 3\,\Delta x + 3. \quad (3b) \end{aligned}$$

When we subtract the members of Eq. (3a) from Eq. (3b) we obtain

$$\Delta y = 3x_1^2 \Delta x + 3x_1 (\Delta x)^2 + (\Delta x)^3 - 3\,\Delta x. \quad (4)$$

From this we readily find the slope of the secant line PQ to be

$$m_{\text{sec}} = \frac{\Delta y}{\Delta x} = 3x_1^2 + 3x_1\,\Delta x + (\Delta x)^2 - 3. \quad (5)$$

Now comes the most important step! When Q approaches P along the curve, Δx and Δy both approach zero. Thus the slope of PQ will be the ratio of two small numbers. This information is not helpful, since the ratio of two small numbers may be practically anything. But we have further information here, since we also know from Eq. (5) that

$$m_{\text{sec}} = (3x_1^2 - 3) + (3x_1 + \Delta x)\,\Delta x.$$

The right-hand side of this equation is the sum of two terms, one of which,

$$3x_1^2 - 3,$$

remains constant as Δx approaches zero, while the other,

$$(3x_1 + \Delta x)\,\Delta x,$$

becomes smaller and, in fact, itself approaches zero when Δx does. We summarize this by saying that

the limit of m_{sec} as Δx approaches zero is $3x_1^2 - 3$,

and by definition, this limit is the slope of the tangent to the curve, or the slope of the curve, at the point (x_1, y_1). Since (x_1, y_1) might have been *any* point on the curve of Eq. (2), we may delete the subscript 1 and say that

$$m = 3x^2 - 3 \quad (6)$$

gives the slope of the curve at any point $P(x, y)$ on it.

We can make use of the slope as well as the equation of the curve itself to learn more about the shape of the curve than we would be likely to discover if we did not have this additional information. For example, we see that the tangent to the curve is horizontal, that is, $m = 0$, when $x = \pm 1$. We also see that the slope is negative for x between -1 and $+1$, and that elsewhere it is positive. If we substitute values of x between -2 and $+2$, say, into Eq. (2) to find y and into Eq. (6) to find m, we obtain the following table of values.

x	y	m
-2	1	9
-1	5	0
0	3	-3
1	1	0
2	5	9

When these points are plotted and the tangent line at each point is drawn, we get a very good picture of the shape of the curve. Of course the curve itself is smooth and does not follow the tangent lines, but these lines do afford considerable assistance in sketching the curve (see Fig. 2.18).

2.18

EXERCISES

Use the method illustrated in this article to find the slope of each of the following curves at a point (x, y) on the curve. Use the equation of the curve and the equation you get for its slope to make a table of values. Include in your table all points where the curve has a horizontal tangent. Sketch the curve, making use of all the information in your table of values.

1. $y = x^2 - 2x - 3$ 2. $y = 2x^2 - x - 1$
3. $y = 4 - x^2$ 4. $y = x^2 - 4x$
5. $y = x^2 - 4x + 4$ 6. $y = x^2 + 4x + 4$
7. $y = 6 + x - x^2$ 8. $y = 6 + 5x - x^2$
9. $y = x^2 + 3x + 2$ 10. $y = 2 - x - x^2$
11. $y = 2x^3 + 3x^2 - 12x + 7$
12. $y = x^3 - 3x$
13. $y = x^3 - 12x$ 14. $y = x^2(4x + 3) + 1$
15. $y = x^3 - 3x^2 + 4$

2.7 DERIVATIVE OF A FUNCTION

We now formulate the method for finding the slope of a curve representing the more general functional equation $y = f(x)$. Let $P(x_1, y_1)$ be a fixed point on the curve. The subscript 1 is used to emphasize that x_1 and y_1 are to be held constant throughout the following discussion. If $Q(x_1 + \Delta x, y_1 + \Delta y)$ is another point on the curve, then

$$y_1 + \Delta y = f(x_1 + \Delta x),$$

and from this we subtract

$$y_1 = f(x_1)$$

to obtain (Fig. 2.19)

$$\Delta y = f(x_1 + \Delta x) - f(x_1).$$

Then the slope of the secant line PQ is

$$m_{\text{sec}} = \frac{\Delta y}{\Delta x} = \frac{f(x_1 + \Delta x) - f(x_1)}{\Delta x}. \qquad (1)$$

2.19. $\Delta y = f(x_1 + \Delta x) - f(x_1).$

Let us note that the division in Eq. (1) can only be *indicated* when we are talking about a general function $f(x)$, but for any specific equation such as $f(x) = x^3 - 3x + 3$ in Eq. (2) of Article 2.6, this division of Δy by Δx is actually to be carried out [as we did in going from Eq. (4) to Eq. (5)] *before* we do the next operation.

Having performed the division indicated in Eq. (1), we now investigate what happens if we hold x_1 fixed and take Δx to be smaller and smaller, approaching zero. If m_{sec} approaches a constant value, we call this value its *limit* and define this to be the slope m_{tan} of the tangent to the curve at P. The mathematical symbols which summarize this discussion are

$$m_{\text{tan}} = \lim_{Q \to P} m_{\text{sec}} = \lim_{\Delta x \to 0} \frac{\Delta y}{\Delta x}$$
$$= \lim_{\Delta x \to 0} \frac{f(x_1 + \Delta x) - f(x_1)}{\Delta x}. \qquad (2)$$

The symbol "lim" with "$\Delta x \to 0$" written beneath it is read "the limit, as Δx approaches zero, of . . ."

Chapter 3 will treat the theory of limits in greater depth. For the remainder of this chapter, the reader is encouraged to use the following intuitive idea: "L is the limit of $m(h)$ as h approaches zero" means that when h is very close to zero, but not equal to zero, then $m(h)$ is very close to L, and possibly equal to L.

The result of carrying out the operations represented by the last term in Eq. (2) produces a number which we have called m_{tan}, or the slope of the tangent to the curve $y = f(x)$ at the point $P(x_1, y_1)$. It is also customary to indicate that this number is related to the original function f by writing it as $f'(x_1)$ (read "f-prime at x_1"). Thus $f'(x_1)$ is *defined* by

$$f'(x_1) = \lim_{\Delta x \to 0} \frac{f(x_1 + \Delta x) - f(x_1)}{\Delta x}. \qquad (3)$$

As mentioned above, the subscript 1 is used to emphasize the fact that x_1 is held constant while the various operations indicated on the right side of Eq. (3) are performed. The indicated limit may exist for some values of x_1 and fail to exist for other values. (We shall discuss this situation in more detail below.) At each point x_1 where the limit does exist, the function f is said to have a *derivative* (or to be *differentiable*) and the number $f'(x_1)$ is said to be the derivative of f at x_1.

The process of *finding the derivative of a function* is the fundamental operation of differential calculus. In fact we may now define *differential calculus* to be that branch of mathematics which is concerned with studying the following two general problems.

Problem 1. Given a function f, determine those values of x (in the domain of f) at which the function possesses a derivative.

Problem 2. Given a function f and an x at which the derivative exists, find $f'(x)$.

Example 1. In studying Eq. (2) of Article 2.6,

$$f(x) = x^3 - 3x + 3, \tag{4}$$

we found that for any x_1 whatever, the result of applying the operations on the right side of Eq. (3) gave us $3x_1^2 - 3$. That is, the function f in Eq. (4) possesses a derivative whose value at *any* x_1 is

$$f'(x_1) = 3x_1^2 - 3. \tag{5}$$

Thus the answer to Problem 1 above is: "The function f, Eq. (4), possesses a derivative at any x in the domain $-\infty < x < +\infty$," and the answer to Problem 2 is given by Eq. (5).

Now for most of the functions considered in this book, it will turn out that the answer to Problem 1 is that the derivative exists at all but a few values of x; that is, the places where the derivative fails to exist will be exceptional. Then the x_1 in Eq. (3) may be *any* of the nonexceptional values of x. Therefore, we might as well write x instead of x_1 in Eq. (3) if we remember that

x is to be held constant, while

Δx varies and approaches zero

in the calculation of the derivative

$$f'(x) = \lim_{\Delta x \to 0} \frac{f(x + \Delta x) - f(x)}{\Delta x}. \tag{6}$$

With this understanding, we shall henceforth omit the subscript 1 in talking about the derivative and shall use Eq. (6) to define the derivative of f, with respect to x, at any x in its domain for which the limit exists.

The derived function

Let x be a number in the domain of the function f. If the limit indicated in Eq. (6) exists, then it provides a rule for associating a number $f'(x)$ with the number x. The set of all pairs of numbers $(x, f'(x))$ that can be formed by this process is called the *derived function* f'. The *domain* of f' is a subset of the domain of f. It contains all numbers x in the domain of f such that the limit in (6) exists, but does not contain those exceptional values where the derivative fails to exist. The derived function f' is also called the *derivative* of f.

Example 2. Consider the absolute value function

$$f(x) = |x|, \quad -\infty < x < +\infty.$$

From the graph in Fig. 1.9 it is clear that the slope is $+1$ when x is positive and -1 when x is negative. But at $x_1 = 0$, the derivative fails to exist [the graph has no tangent at $(0,0)$]. Hence the *domain* of the derived function does not include 0. It consists of all real numbers $x \neq 0$. The values of the derived function are given by the rule

$$f'(x) = \begin{cases} -1 & \text{if } x < 0, \\ +1 & \text{if } x > 0. \end{cases}$$

See Exercise 21.

Notations. In addition to $f'(x)$, various notations are used to denote the derivative of $y = f(x)$ with respect to x. The ones most commonly used are

$$y', \quad \frac{dy}{dx}, \quad D_x y.$$

The last two of these may be interpreted as

$$\frac{dy}{dx} = \frac{d}{dx}(y),$$

where $d/dx\,(\ldots)$ stands for the operation *derivative with respect to x of* (the expression following), and where

$$D_x y = D_x(y),$$

*Good
EXAMPLE*

with $D_x \ldots$ meaning the same thing as $d/dx\ (\ldots)$, namely, *derivative with respect to x of* (the expression which follows it).

Problem 1. Find $f'(x)$ for the function

$$f(x) = x^2 + \frac{1}{x}, \quad x \neq 0.$$

Solution. We carry out the operations indicated on the right side of Eq. (6) in the following order.

treat this as ↗

1. $f(x + \Delta x) = (x + \Delta x)^2 + \dfrac{1}{x + \Delta x}$

$= x^2 + 2x\,\Delta x + (\Delta x)^2 + \dfrac{1}{x + \Delta x}.$

x² + 2xΔx + Δx²

2. $f(x) = x^2 + \dfrac{1}{x}.$

Subtract (2) from (1):

3. $f(x + \Delta x) - f(x) = 2x\,\Delta x + (\Delta x)^2 + \dfrac{1}{x + \Delta x} - \dfrac{1}{x}$

$= 2x\,\Delta x + (\Delta x)^2 + \dfrac{x - (x + \Delta x)}{x(x + \Delta x)}$

$= \Delta x \left(2x + \Delta x - \dfrac{1}{x(x + \Delta x)} \right).$

Divide by Δx:

4. $\dfrac{f(x + \Delta x) - f(x)}{\Delta x} = 2x + \Delta x - \dfrac{1}{x(x + \Delta x)}.$

5. $f'(x) = \lim\limits_{\Delta x \to 0} \dfrac{f(x + \Delta x) - f(x)}{\Delta x}$

$= \lim\limits_{\Delta x \to 0} \left(2x + \Delta x - \dfrac{1}{x(x + \Delta x)} \right)$ (a)

$= 2x + 0 - \dfrac{1}{x(x + 0)}$ (b)

$= 2x - \dfrac{1}{x^2}.$

In a later article we shall discuss the validity of the various limit operations involved in going from (a) to (b) above. If we anticipate these results, we may say that *after* the division by Δx has been carried out and the expression has been reduced to a form [as in (a) above]

which "make sense" (that is, does not involve division by zero) when Δx is taken equal to zero, then the limit as Δx *approaches* zero does exist and may be found by simply replacing Δx by zero in this reduced form.

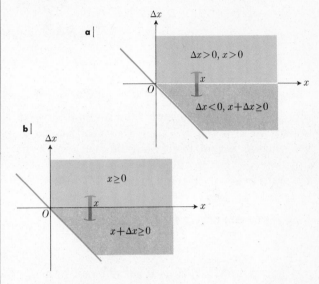

2.20 a| Domain of $g(x, \Delta x)$. Points on the x-axis are not included.

b| Domain of $h(x, \Delta x)$. The domain includes the positive x-axis.

Remark. In Problem 2 below, we arrive at the following functions of two variables x and Δx:

$$g(x, \Delta x) = \frac{\sqrt{x + \Delta x} - \sqrt{x}}{\Delta x},$$

$$h(x, \Delta x) = \frac{1}{\sqrt{x + \Delta x} + \sqrt{x}}.$$

These algebraic expressions are equal on the intersection of their domains, but the two domains are not identical. For g, the domain is the set of points $(x, \Delta x)$ for which

$$x \geq 0, \quad \Delta x \neq 0, \quad x + \Delta x \geq 0.$$

This domain is shown in Fig. 2.20(a). The domain for h consists of the points $(x, \Delta x)$ for which

$$x \geq 0, \quad x + \Delta x \geq 0, \quad \sqrt{x} + \sqrt{x + \Delta x} \neq 0.$$

This domain is shown in the shaded portion of Fig. 2.20(b). Are there any points in D_g that are not in D_h? No. Are there any points in D_h that are not in D_g? Yes: all the points where $x > 0$ and $\Delta x = 0$. (Note that the origin $x = 0$, $\Delta x = 0$ is in neither D_g nor D_h.) Therefore

$$D_g \subset D_h, \quad D_g \cap D_h = D_g.$$

We now argue as follows: For any $x > 0$, we can put $\Delta x = 0$ in h and get

$$h(x, 0) = \frac{1}{\sqrt{x + 0} + \sqrt{x}} = \frac{1}{2\sqrt{x}}.$$

Moreover it seems reasonable (and we shall prove it in Chapter 2) that $\sqrt{x + \Delta x}$ is very nearly equal to $\sqrt{x}$ when Δx is close to zero but different from zero. But when $\Delta x \neq 0$, the functions $g(x, \Delta x)$ and $h(x, \Delta x)$ are equal. Therefore we find it reasonable to expect that

$$g(x, \Delta x) \text{ is very nearly equal to } \frac{1}{2\sqrt{x}}$$

when $\qquad x > 0 \quad$ and

Δx is very nearly equal to 0 but different from 0,

because the corresponding statement for $h(x, \Delta x)$ seems reasonable. Thus, if the length of the colored segment in Fig. 2.20(a, b) is small, and the point $(x, \Delta x)$ is on that segment, and $\Delta x \neq 0$, then both g and h have values close to $1/(2\sqrt{x})$.

Problem 2. Find dy/dx if $y = \sqrt{x}$ and $x > 0$.

Solution. Let $y = \sqrt{x}$, $y + \Delta y = \sqrt{x + \Delta x}$, so that

$$\frac{\Delta y}{\Delta x} = \frac{\sqrt{x + \Delta x} - \sqrt{x}}{\Delta x}$$

$$= \frac{(\sqrt{x + \Delta x} - \sqrt{x})(\sqrt{x + \Delta x} + \sqrt{x})}{\Delta x(\sqrt{x + \Delta x} + \sqrt{x})} \qquad \text{(a)}$$

$$= \frac{(x + \Delta x) - x}{\Delta x(\sqrt{x + \Delta x} + \sqrt{x})} = \frac{1}{\sqrt{x + \Delta x} + \sqrt{x}}.$$

In step (a) we multiplied by a fraction equal to 1 and having a form such that it enabled us to get rid of the square roots in the numerator. Then in the next step we were able to carry out the division by Δx. Now we let Δx approach zero in the final form and have

$$\frac{dy}{dx} = \lim_{\Delta x \to 0} \frac{\Delta y}{\Delta x} = \lim_{\Delta x \to 0} \frac{1}{\sqrt{x + \Delta x} + \sqrt{x}} = \frac{1}{2\sqrt{x}}.$$

EXERCISES

For each of the following functions f, find the derivative $f'(x)$ by means of the definition in Eq. (6).

1. $f(x) = x^2$
2. $f(x) = x^3$
3. $f(x) = 2x + 3$
4. $f(x) = x^2 - x + 1$
5. $f(x) = \dfrac{1}{x}$
6. $f(x) = \dfrac{1}{x^2}$
7. $f(x) = \dfrac{1}{2x + 1}$
8. $f(x) = \dfrac{x}{x + 1}$
9. $f(x) = 2x^2 - x + 5$
10. $f(x) = x^3 - 12x + 11$
11. $f(x) = x^4$
12. $f(x) = ax^2 + bx + c \quad (a, b, c$ constants$)$
13. $f(x) = x - \dfrac{1}{x}$
14. $f(x) = ax + \dfrac{b}{x} \quad (a, b$ constants$)$
15. $f(x) = \sqrt{2x}$
16. $f(x) = \sqrt{x + 1}$
17. $f(x) = \sqrt{2x + 3}$
18. $f(x) = \dfrac{1}{\sqrt{x}}$
19. $f(x) = \dfrac{1}{\sqrt{2x + 3}}$
20. $f(x) = \sqrt{x^2 + 1}$

21. In Example 2, $f(x) = |x|$. What is the *range* of the derived function f'? What is its graph? Compare the graphs of

$$y = f'(x) \quad \text{and} \quad y = |x|/x, \ x \neq 0.$$

22. The signum function of x, sgn (x), has the value $+1$ if x is positive, -1 if x is negative, and zero if x is zero. Without making any hard calculations, discuss the domain and the range of its derived function, sgn$'\ (x)$.

2.8 VELOCITY AND RATES

When a body moves in a straight line, it is customary to represent the line of motion by a coordinate axis, select a reference point O on the line as origin, adopt a positive direction and a unit of distance on the line, and then describe the motion by means of an equation which gives the coordinate of the body as a function of the time t that has elapsed since the start of the motion.

Example 1. Thus for a freely falling body, the equation of motion is

$$s = \tfrac{1}{2}gt^2, \tag{1}$$

where g is the acceleration due to gravity and is approximately 32 (ft/sec^2), and s is the distance in feet that the body has fallen in t seconds from the start.

More generally, suppose the law of motion is given by a function f,

$$s = f(t), \tag{2}$$

and that we are required to find the *velocity* of the body at some instant of time t. First of all, how shall we *define* the instantaneous velocity of a moving body?

If we assume that *distance* and *time* are the fundamental physical quantities which we can measure, we may be led to reason as follows. At time t, the body is in the position

$$s = f(t), \tag{3}$$

and at time $t + \Delta t$ the body is in the position

$$s + \Delta s = f(t + \Delta t). \tag{4}$$

Hence, during the interval of time from t to $t + \Delta t$, it has undergone a displacement

$$\Delta s = f(t + \Delta t) - f(t). \tag{5}$$

The quantities in Eqs. (3), (4), and (5) are all physical quantities which can be measured (by clocks and tapelines, say).

We now define the *average velocity* to be Δs divided by Δt:

$$\frac{\Delta x}{\Delta y} \qquad v_{\mathrm{av}} = \frac{\Delta s}{\Delta t} = \frac{f(t + \Delta t) - f(t)}{\Delta t}. \tag{6}$$

Example 2. We are all familiar with applications of Eq. (6) in everyday life. For example, a sprinter runs 100 yards in 10 seconds. His average velocity is therefore

$$v_{\mathrm{av}} = \frac{\Delta s}{\Delta t} = \frac{100\ (\mathrm{yd})}{10\ (\mathrm{sec})} = 10\ (\mathrm{yd/sec}).$$

To obtain the *instantaneous* velocity at time t, we take the average velocity over shorter and shorter

intervals of time Δt. We are thereby led to the definition of instantaneous velocity, or what we call the velocity at time t, as the *limit* of v_{av} as Δt approaches zero; that is,

$$\lim \frac{\Delta \alpha}{\Delta y} \qquad v = \lim_{\Delta t \to 0} \frac{\Delta s}{\Delta t} = \lim_{\Delta t \to 0} \frac{f(t + \Delta t) - f(t)}{\Delta t}. \tag{7}$$

We recognize that Eq. (7) is the same as the definition of the derivative

$$v = \frac{ds}{dt} = f'(t). \tag{8}$$

Example 3. For the motion governed by Eq. (1),

$$s = \tfrac{1}{2}gt^2,$$

we find, by the methods of the previous article, that the velocity at time t is

$$v = \frac{ds}{dt} = gt.$$

2.21

When we refer to Fig. 2.21, we see that

$$v_{\mathrm{av}} = \frac{\Delta s}{\Delta t}$$

is the slope of the secant line PQ in the sense of measuring its rate of rise in units of s per unit of t. Here there is no reason to suppose that the unit of length used on the t-axis to represent one second is the same as the unit of length used on the s-axis to represent one foot. And certainly the geometrical inclination ϕ of the secant line PQ depends upon the scales used to represent the units of time and distance on the two axes. We can still say, however, that the average velocity equals the ratio of the opposite side to the adjacent side in the triangle PRQ, each with its proper units (and proper sign). Then the instantaneous velocity can also be interpreted geometrically as the rate of rise of the tangent line in units of s per unit of t.

Example 4. This geometrical interpretation is sometimes used to estimate the velocity when the motion is given by means of a graph instead of by an equation $s = f(t)$. For example, in the graph of Fig. 2.22, s represents the coordinate of some point of a bicycle which a girl is riding along a straight road. At $t = 8$, the tangent line appears to be rising at the rate of 40 s-units in an interval of 2 t-units; that is, the velocity at time $t = 8$ is apparently

$$\frac{40 \text{ (ft)}}{2 \text{ (sec)}} = 20 \text{ (ft/sec)}.$$

We say the velocity is "apparently" 20 ft/sec because we cannot be sure that we have accurately constructed the tangent to the curve. Indeed, an accurate construction would require that we know the derivative $f'(t)$, exactly, at $t = 8$ and this is the very thing we are trying to estimate. On the other hand, we can make a fair approximation to the tangent line by inspection and this is what we have done in the graph.

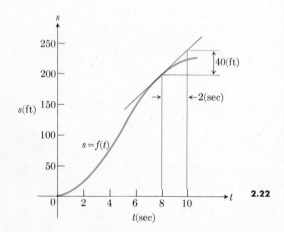

2.22

There are many other applications of the notion of average rate and instantaneous rate. For example, the quantity of water Q (gal) in a reservoir at time t (min) is a function of t. Water may flow into or out

of the reservoir. As it does so, suppose that Q changes by an amount ΔQ from time t to time $t + \Delta t$. Then the average rate of change of Q with respect to t is

$$\frac{\Delta Q}{\Delta t} \text{ (gal/min)}$$

and the instantaneous rate of change of Q with respect to t is

$$\frac{dQ}{dt} = \lim_{\Delta t \to 0} \frac{\Delta Q}{\Delta t} \text{ (gal/min)}.$$

Derivatives are important in economic theory, where they are usually indicated by the adjective "*marginal*." Suppose, for example, that a manufacturer produces x tons of steel per week at a total cost of $y = f(x)$ dollars. This total cost includes such items as a proportionate part of the cost of building and maintaining the company's steel mills, salaries of executives, taxes, office maintenance, cost of raw materials, labor, etc. Suppose that in order to produce $x + \Delta x$ tons of steel weekly, it would cost $y + \Delta y$ dollars. The increase in cost per unit increase in output would be $\Delta y/\Delta x$. The limit of this ratio, as Δx tends to zero, is called the *marginal cost*. In other words, if total cost is y for weekly output x, then the *marginal* cost is just the derivative of y with respect to x. It gives the rate of increase of cost per unit increase of output from the level x.

The manufacturer is also interested in revenue and in profits. To sell his output of x tons per week he finds that he may charge a price $P = F(x)$ per ton. (Usually, at a higher price he would sell less; at a lower price he could sell more.) His *revenue* is then the product

$$xP = xF(x).$$

The *marginal* revenue is the *derivative* of xP with respect to x. It gives the rate of increase of revenue per unit increase in output. The manufacturer's profit T is the difference between revenue and cost:

$$T = xP - y.$$

In Chapter 5 we shall see how the manufacturer should adjust his production to achieve maximum profit. The adjustment involves his *marginal* profit

dT/dx, which is the rate of increase of profit per unit increase of production.*

Any derivative may be interpreted as the instantaneous rate of change of one variable per unit change in the other. Thus, if the function defined by $y = f(x)$ has a derivative

$$f'(x) = \lim_{\Delta x \to 0} \frac{\Delta y}{\Delta x} = \lim_{\Delta x \to 0} \frac{f(x + \Delta x) - f(x)}{\Delta x},$$

we may interpret $\Delta y/\Delta x$ as *average* rate of change and

$$f'(x) = \lim_{\Delta x \to 0} \frac{\Delta y}{\Delta x}$$

as *instantaneous* rate of change of y with respect to x. Such a rate tells us the amount of change that would be produced in y a change of one unit in x, provided the rate of change remained constant.

The *average* rate of change of y per unit change in x, $\Delta y/\Delta x$, when multiplied by the number of units change in x, Δx, gives the actual change in y:

$$\Delta y = \frac{\Delta y}{\Delta x} \Delta x.$$

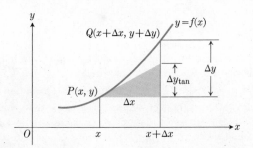

2.23 $\Delta y_{\text{tan}} = f'(x)\,\Delta x.$

The *instantaneous* rate of change of y per unit change in x, $f'(x)$, multiplied by the number of units

change in x, Δx, gives the change that would be produced in y if the point (x, y) were to move along the *tangent line* instead of moving along the curve; that is (Fig. 2.23)

$$\Delta y_{\text{tan}} = f'(x)\,\Delta x. \tag{9}$$

One reason calculus is important is that it enables us to find quantitatively how a change in one of two related variables affects the second variable.

EXERCISES

1. If a, b, c are constants and

$$f(t) = at^2 + bt + c,$$

   show that

$$f'(t) = \lim_{\Delta t \to 0} \frac{f(t + \Delta t) - f(t)}{\Delta t} = 2at + b.$$

In Exercises 2 through 10, the law of motion is used to express s as a function of t. Apply the *result* found in Exercise 1 above to write the velocity $v = ds/dt$ by inspection.

2. $s = 2t^2 + 5t - 3$ 3. $s = \frac{1}{2}gt^2 + v_0 t + s_0$
                                      (g, v_0, s_0 constants)

4. $s = 4t + 3$ 5. $s = t^2 - 3t + 2$

6. $s = 4 - 2t - t^2$ 7. $s = (2t + 3)^2$

8. $s = (2 - t)^2$ 9. $s = 3 - 2t^2$

10. $s = 64t - 16t^2$

11. The following data give the coordinate s of a moving body for various values of t. Plot s vs. t on coordinate paper and sketch a smooth curve through the given points. Assuming that this smooth curve represents the motion of the body, estimate the velocity (a) at $t = 1.0$, (b) at $t = 2.5$, (c) at $t = 2.0$.

s (ft)	10	38	58	70	74	70	58	38	10
t (sec)	0	0.5	1.0	1.5	2.0	2.5	3.0	3.5	4.0

12. A swimming pool is to be drained for cleaning. If Q represents the number of gallons of water in the pool t minutes after the pool has started to drain, and $Q = 200 (30 - t)^2$, how fast is the water running out at the end of 10 minutes? What is the *average* rate at which the water flows out during the first 10 minutes?

---

* For a further discussion of applications to economics, see R. G. D. Allen, *Mathematical Analysis for Economists*, Macmillan Co., New York, 1939. In particular, marginal cost and marginal revenue are discussed on pp. 152 ff.

13. (a) If the radius of a circle changes from r to $r + \Delta r$, what is the average rate of change of the area of the circle with respect to the radius?

   (b) Find the instantaneous rate of change of the area with respect to the radius.

14. The volume V (ft^3) of a sphere of radius r (ft) is $V = \frac{4}{3}\pi r^3$. Find the rate of change of V with respect to r.

15. The radius r and altitude h of a certain cone are equal at all times. Find the rate of change of the volume $V = \frac{1}{3}\pi r^2 h$ with respect to h.

REVIEW QUESTIONS AND EXERCISES

1. Define *function* in three ways. What is the *domain* of a function? What is its *range*?

2. The domain of a certain function is the set $0 \leq x \leq 2$. The range of the function is the single number $y = 1$.

   (a) Sketch and describe the graph of the function.

   (b) Write an expression for the function.

   (c) If we interchange the axes in part (a), does the new graph so obtained represent a function? Explain.

3. If $f(x) = 1/x$ and $g(x) = 1/\sqrt{x}$, what are the natural domains of f and g and the corresponding domains of $f - g$, $f \cdot g$, f/g, and g/f?

4. If f is a function with domain $[a, b]$ and $g(x) = f(x - c)$ for some positive number c, how can the graph of g be obtained from the graph of f? What is the name given to this process? What is the domain of g?

5. If $g(x) = f(kx)$, $k > 0$, what process is used to obtain the graph of g from the graph of f?

6. Give an example, different from those mentioned in the text, of a step-function.

7. Give an example, different from those in the text, of a function whose domain could be the set of all real numbers, $-\infty < x < +\infty$.

8. Is it appropriate to define a *tangent line* to a curve C at a point P on C as a line that has just the one point P in common with C? Illustrate your discussion with graphs.

9. Define, carefully, the concept of slope of a tangent to a curve at a point on the curve.

10. Define the concept of *average velocity*, of *instantaneous velocity*.

11. What more general concept includes both the concept of slope of the tangent to a curve and the concept of instantaneous velocity?

12. Define the derivative of a function at a point in its domain. Illustrate your definition by applying it to the function f defined by $f(x) = x^2$, at the point $x = 2$.

13. Suppose that a particle is moving along the curve $y = x^3$. (a) What is its distance above the x-axis when $x = 2$? (b) What is the slope of the tangent line at $x = 2$? (c) If the particle leaves the curve at $x = 2$ and follows the tangent line instead, how far above the x-axis will it be when $x = 2.2$?

MISCELLANEOUS EXERCISES

1. Given the equation $y = (x^2 + 2)/(x^2 - 1)$. Express x in terms of y and determine the range of values of y for which x is real.

2. Express the area A and the circumference C of a circle as functions of the radius r. Express A as a function of C.

3. In each of the following functions, what is the largest domain of x and the corresponding range of y?

   (a) $y = \dfrac{1}{1 + x}$;   (b) $y = \dfrac{1}{1 + x^2}$;

   (c) $y = \dfrac{1}{1 + \sqrt{x}}$.

4. Without the use of the absolute value symbol, describe the domain of x for which $|x + 1| < 4$.

5. If $y = 2x + |2 - x|$, determine x as a function of y.

6. For what range of values of y does the equation $y = x + |2 - x|$ determine x as a single-valued function of y? Solve for x in terms of y on this range of values.

7. If $y = x + (1/x)$, express x as the union of two functions of y and determine the domain of y for which x is real.

8. **Definition.** *A rational number is one that can be expressed in the form p/q, where p and q are integers with no common divisor greater than one, and $q > 0$. A real number that is not rational is called irrational.*
   With these definitions in mind, plot a few points on the graph of the function that maps the rational number p/q (reduced to lowest terms as above) into $1/q$, and maps each irrational number into zero. This function has been described as the "ruler function" because of the resemblance of its graph to the

markings on an ordinary ruler showing inches, half-inches, quarters, eighths, and sixteenths by lines of different lengths. The edge of the ruler corresponds to the x-axis. Do you see why this terminology is rather appropriate?

9. (a) If $f(x) = x^2 + 2x - 3$, find $f(-2)$; $f(-1)$; $f(x_1)$; $f(x_1 + \Delta x)$.

(b) If $f(x) = x - (1/x)$, show that $f(1/x) = -f(x) = f(-x)$.

10. Sketch the graph of each of the following equations:

(a) $y = |x - 2| + 2$; (b) $y = x^2 - 1$.

(c) Find the point on the curve in part (b) where the tangent to the curve makes an angle of $45°$ with the positive x-axis.

11. Sketch a graph of the function $y = |x + 2| + x$ for the domain $-5 \le x \le 2$. What is the range?

12. Show that the expression $M(a, b) = (a + b)/2 + |a - b|/2$ is equal to a when $a \ge b$ and is equal to b when $b \ge a$. In other words, $M(a, b)$ gives the larger of the two numbers a and b. Find a similar expression, $m(a, b)$, which gives the smaller of the two numbers.

For each of the following expressions for $f(x)$ in Exercises 13–16, sketch first the graph of $y = f(x)$, then the graph of $y = |f(x)|$ and finally the graph of $y = f(x)/2 + |f(x)|/2$.

13. $f(x) = (x - 2)(x + 1)$ 14. $f(x) = x^2$

15. $f(x) = -x^2$ 16. $f(x) = 4 - x^2$

17. *Lagrange interpolation formula.* Let (x_1, y_1), (x_2, y_2), $\ldots$, (x_n, y_n) be n points in the plane, no two of them having the same abscissas. Find a polynomial, $f(x)$, of degree $(n - 1)$ which takes the value y_1 at x_1, y_2 at x_2, $\ldots$, y_n at x_n; that is, $f(x_i) = y_i$ ($i = 1, 2, \ldots, n$). [*Hint:* $f(x) = y_1\phi_1(x) + y_2\phi_2(x) + \cdots + y_n\phi_n(x)$, where $\phi_k(x)$ is a polynomial which is zero at x_i ($i \ne k$) and $\phi_k(x_k) = 1$.]

18. If $f(x) = x/(x - 1)$, find (a) $f(1/x)$, (b) $f(-x)$.

Find $f'(x)$ using the definition of the derivative for each of the following expressions for $f(x)$.

19. $(x - 1)/(x + 1)$ 20. $x^{3/2}$ 21. $x^{1/3}$

Use the definition of the derivative in Problems 22 to 24.

22. Find $f'(x)$ if $f(x) = x^2 - 3x - 4$

23. Find $\dfrac{dy}{dx}$ if $y = \dfrac{1}{3x} + 2x$

24. Find $f'(t)$ if $f(t) = \sqrt{t - 4}$

25. (a) By means of the Δ-method, find the slope of the curve $y = 2x^3 + 2$ at the point $(1, 4)$. (b) At which point of the curve in (a) is the tangent to the curve parallel to the x-axis? Sketch the curve.

26. If $f(x) = 2x/(x - 1)$, find (a) $f(0)$, $f(-1)$, $f(1/x)$; (b) $\Delta f(x)/\Delta x$; (c) $f'(x)$, using the result of part (b).

27. Given $y = 180x - 16x^2$. Using the method of Article 2–6, find the slope of the curve at the point (x_1, y_1). Sketch the curve. At what point does the curve have a horizontal tangent?

28. Find the velocity $v = ds/dt$ if the distance a particle moves in time t is given by $s = 180t - 16t^2$. When does the velocity vanish?

29. If the pressure P and volume V of a certain gas are related by the formula $P = 1/V$, find (a) the average rate of change of P with respect to V, (b) the rate of change of P with respect to V at the instant when $V = 2$.

30. The volume V (in³) of water remaining in a leaking pail after t sec is $V = 2000 - 40t + 0.2t^2$. How fast is the volume decreasing when $t = 30$?

31. Let f be a function defined on an interval, and x_1 and x_2 a pair of numbers on the interval with $x_1 < x_2$. (a) If $f(x_1) < f(x_2)$, then f is an *increasing function*. (b) If $f(x_1) > f(x_2)$, then f is a *decreasing function*. (c) If $f(x_1) \le f(x_2)$, then f is a *weakly increasing function*. (d) If $f(x_1) \ge f(x_2)$, then f is a *weakly decreasing function*.

Definition. *A monotone function is one which is either weakly increasing or weakly decreasing. A strongly monotone function is one which is either increasing or decreasing.*

For each of the following functions state whether it is monotone increasing, monotone decreasing, or not monotone. If it is not monotone, divide its domain into parts such that the restriction of f to any of these parts gives a monotone or strongly monotone function.

(a) $f(x) = c$ (b) $f(x) = |x|$

(c) $f(x) = [x]$ (d) $f(x) = -x^2$

(e) $f(x) = x|x|$ (f) $f(x) = |x^2 - 4|$

(g) $f(x) = \dfrac{1}{x}$ (h) $f(x) = x^3$

LIMITS

CHAPTER 3

The purpose of this chapter is to introduce the formal definition of *limit* as an operation applied to a function at a point, and to prove theorems about limits of sums, products, and quotients of functions. We have already seen in Article 2.8 that the average rate of increase of a function $f(x)$, when x goes from x_1 to $x_1 + h$, is

$$\frac{f(x_1 + h) - f(x_1)}{h}, \quad h \neq 0.$$

The *instantaneous* rate of increase of f at x_1 is the limit (if there is one) of this expression as h tends to zero. We cannot just put $h = 0$ in the quotient because $0/0$ is meaningless. Thus, it is desirable to study the theory of limits before proceeding. We shall apply the various limit theorems in Chapter 4 when we resume the study of the rate of change of a function.

Definition. *Suppose f is a function defined for values of x near a. (The domain of f need not include a, although it may.) We say that*

L *is the limit of $f(x)$ as x approaches a,*

and write

$$L = \lim_{x \to a} f(x), \tag{1}$$

provided that, for any $\epsilon > 0$ there corresponds a deleted neighborhood N of a such that

$$L - \epsilon < f(x) < L + \epsilon \tag{2}$$

whenever x is in N and in D_f.

Notation. When L is the limit of $f(x)$ as x approaches a, we may indicate this fact by writing

$$f(x) \to L \quad \text{as} \quad x \to a,$$

which we read "$f(x)$ approaches L as x approaches a." However, the verb "approaches" has a connotation of motion which is not always justified. For example, a constant function that has the value $f(x) = L$ for all values of x certainly fulfills the conditions of the definition. Note that the verb "is" conveys the message when we say that

$f(x)$ is in $(L - \epsilon, L + \epsilon)$ when x is in $N \cap D_f$.

There is no connotation of x moving toward a or $f(x)$ moving toward L in that statement. Nevertheless the idea of motion (for example, "point Q moves along a curve toward the point P") was, and is, also important in the development of the calculus.

Intuitively, what we are looking for is some L so that we can make "$f(x)$ as close to L as we please" by taking x in a "small enough" deleted neighborhood of a. The definition gives a precise mathematical formulation of the phrases enclosed in quotes in the previous sentence.

Problem. Find $\lim_{x \to 1} (5x - 3)$, and prove that your answer is correct.

Solution. Let

$$f(x) = 5x - 3 \quad \text{and} \quad a = 1. \qquad (3)$$

We first guess an appropriate value of L by asking, what number is $f(x) = 5x - 3$ close to when x is close to 1? The obvious answer is

$$L = 2.$$

We try to satisfy the conditions in (2), assuming that $L = 2$ and ϵ is a given positive number. Thus we require that

$$2 - \epsilon < 5x - 3 < 2 + \epsilon. \qquad (4a)$$

After adding 3 throughout, we see that (4a) is equivalent to

$$5 - \epsilon < 5x < 5 + \epsilon, \qquad (4b)$$

or, after division by 5, to

$$1 - \frac{\epsilon}{5} < x < 1 + \frac{\epsilon}{5}. \qquad (4c)$$

The inequalities in (4c) describe the open interval $(1 - \epsilon/5, 1 + \epsilon/5)$, which is a neighborhood of $a = 1$. If we delete 1 from that neighborhood, the resulting *deleted* neighborhood is described by

$$0 < |x - 1| < \frac{\epsilon}{5}. \qquad (4d)$$

Figure 3.1 shows that if N_0 is this deleted neighborhood of 1, the inequalities in (4a) are satisfied whenever x is in N_0. Therefore, $\lim_{x \to 1} (5x - 3) = 2$.

3.1 The deleted neighborhood N_0 extends from the line $x = 1 - \epsilon/5$ to the line $x = 1 + \epsilon/5$, but does not include the point $x = 1$.

Remark 1. Note that the half-width of the deleted neighborhood in (4d) is $\epsilon/5$. Thus the neighborhood gets smaller if ϵ is decreased.

Remark 2. The half-width $\epsilon/5$ is the largest that will work for the above example. But the deleted neighborhood N_0 is not unique: We could, for example, use a smaller neighborhood N_1 such as $0 < |x - 1| < \epsilon/10$ or use a nonsymmetric deleted neighborhood N_2 like the union of the intervals

$$(1 - \epsilon/6, 1) \quad \text{and} \quad (1, 1 + \epsilon/8).$$

Since $\epsilon/10$, $\epsilon/6$, and $\epsilon/8$ are all less than $\epsilon/5$, these other deleted neighborhoods lie inside N_0. Thus if x_1 is in N_2 it is also in N_0 and the value of f at x_1 is between $2 - \epsilon$ and $2 + \epsilon$.

Example 1. We can show that the function F (Fig. 3.2) defined by

$$F(t) = [t] = (\text{greatest integer in } t)$$

has no limit as t approaches 3. Our first guess might be that there is a limit, $L = 3$, since certainly the functional values of $F(t) = [t]$ are close to 3 when t is equal to or

$$F(t) = [t]$$

3.2

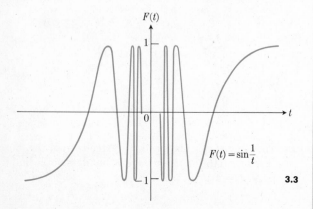

$$F(t) = \sin\frac{1}{t}$$

3.3

slightly *greater* than 3. But when t is slightly *less* than 3, say $t = 2.9999$, then $[t] = 2$. That is, if h is any positive number less than unity, $0 < h < 1$,

then $[t] = 2$ if $3 - h < t < 3$,

while $[t] = 3$ if $3 < t < 3 + h$.

Hence if we are challenged with a small positive ϵ, for example $\epsilon = 0.01$, we cannot find a deleted neighborhood N of 3 such that

$$|[t] - 3| < \epsilon \quad \text{when} \quad t \in N.$$

In fact, there is no number L that will work as the limit in this case, since when t is near 3 *some* of the functional values of $[t]$ are 2 while others are 3, and hence they are not all close to any one number L. That is,

$$\lim_{t \to 3} [t] \text{ does not exist.}$$

The so-called "right- and left-hand limits" do, however, exist. As the names imply, the right-hand limit $L+$ is a number such that the functional values of $F(t)$ are close to $L+$ when t is slightly greater than 3 (that is, to the right of 3), and the left-hand limit $L-$ is a number such that $F(t)$ is close to $L-$ when t is slightly less than 3.

In our example,

$$L+ = \lim_{t \to 3+} [t] = 3, \quad L- = \lim_{t \to 3-} [t] = 2.$$

The notation $t \to 3+$ may be read "t approaches 3 from above" (or "from the right," or "through values larger than 3") with an analogous meaning for $t \to 3-$.

Example 2. The function F, $F(t) = \sin(1/t)$, $t \neq 0$, possesses no limit as $t \to 0$. This is a consequence of the fact that in every neighborhood of $t = 0$ the function F takes all values between -1 and $+1$. Hence there is no single number L such that the functional values $F(t)$ are *all* close to L when t is close to zero. These remarks apply even when we restrict t to positive values or to negative values. In other words, this function does not even have a right-hand limit or a left-hand limit as t approaches zero (Fig. 3.3).

EXERCISES

Find an appropriate number L, and a deleted neighborhood N of a, such that given $\epsilon > 0$,

$$L - \epsilon < f(x) < L + \epsilon \quad \text{when } x \text{ is in } N.$$

Illustrate each of Exercises 1 through 7 with a graph similar to Fig. 3.1.

1. $f(x) = 5 - 3x$, $a = 2$ 2. $f(x) = 7$, $a = -1$

3. $f(x) = 4/x$, $a = 2$ 4. $f(x) = \dfrac{x^2 - 4}{x - 2}$, $a = 2$

5. $f(x) = \dfrac{x^2 + 6x + 5}{x + 5}$, $a = 5$

6. $f(x) = \dfrac{3x^2 + 8x - 3}{2x + 6}$, $a = -3$

7. $f(x) = \dfrac{(1/x) - (1/3)}{x - 3}$, $a = 3$

8. In the next article we use the fact that if N_1 and N_2 are deleted neighborhoods of a, then so is their intersection $N_1 \cap N_2$. Prove this fact by telling what the intersection is if

$$N_1 = \{x \mid h_1 < x < a \quad \text{or} \quad a < x < k_1\},$$

$$N_2 = \{x \mid h_2 < x < a \quad \text{or} \quad a < x < k_2\}.$$

Illustrate with a sketch. [*Hint.* First set up conditions for h_3 and k_3 in terms of h_1 and h_2 and k_1 and k_2 respectively, such that for N_3, the intersection of N_1 and N_2, we have

$$N_3 = \{x \mid h_3 < x < a \text{ or } a < x < k_3\}.$$

9. Find some deleted neighborhood of $t = 3$, that is, a domain $0 < |t - 3| < \delta$, such that when t is restricted to this domain, the difference between $t^2 + t$ and 12 will be numerically smaller than
   (a) $\frac{1}{10}$, (b) $\frac{1}{100}$,
   (c) ϵ, where ϵ may be any positive number.

10. Does the function $f(x) = x \sin(1/x)$, with domain all $x \neq 0$, have a limit as $x \to 0$? Prove your answer.

11. Does the function $g(x) = \text{sgn } x$ have a limit as $x \to 0$? Explain.

3.2 THEOREMS ABOUT LIMITS

In Chapter 2 we saw how to combine functions by adding, multiplying, subtracting, and dividing. In this and the following article we shall prove some useful theorems about limits of such combinations of functions. Our first theorem, however, is suggested by the example of Article 3.1.

Theorem 1. *If m, b, and a are any real numbers,*

and $\qquad f(x) = mx + b,$ $\qquad$ (1)

then $\qquad \lim_{x \to a} f(x) = ma + b.$ $\qquad$ (2)

Proof. Let $\epsilon > 0$ be given, and let $L = ma + b$. We need to prove that there exists a deleted neighborhood N, of a, such that

$$(ma + b) - \epsilon < mx + b < (ma + b) + \epsilon \quad (3)$$

when x is in N. Subtract $(ma + b)$ from the three expressions in (3) and get

$$-\epsilon < mx - ma < \epsilon \qquad (4a)$$

which is the same as

$$|m(x - a)| < \epsilon. \qquad (4b)$$

In the statement of the theorem, m is an arbitrary real number, so it may be positive, negative, or zero.

Case 1. If m is positive, divide both sides of (4b) by m and get the equivalent inequality

$$|x - a| < \frac{\epsilon}{m}. \qquad (5a)$$

Case 2. If m is negative, use the fact that

$$|m(x - a)| = |m|\,|x - a|$$

and divide both sides of (4b) by $|m|$ and get

$$|x - a| < \frac{\epsilon}{|m|}. \qquad (5b)$$

Case 3. If $m = 0$, inequality (4b) is satisfied for all values of x because

$$|0(x - a)| = 0 < \epsilon.$$

For either Case 1 or Case 2 we can take, for the deleted neighborhood N, the set of all x's that satisfy

$$0 < |x - a| < \frac{\epsilon}{|m|}, \qquad (6a)$$

and when $m = 0$ [$f(x) = b = $ constant], we can take N to be any deleted neighborhood, for example those x such that

$$0 < |x - a| < 1. \qquad (6b)$$

Therefore, given m, b, a, and $\epsilon > 0$, we can always find a deleted neighborhood N of a such that the inequalities in (3) hold for all x in N. Therefore, $L = ma + b$ satisfies condition (2) in the definition of a limit, Article 3.1, and we conclude that

$$\lim_{x \to a} (mx + b) = ma + b. \;\square^*$$

Example 1.

$$\lim_{x \to 5} (3x - 7) = 15 - 7 = 8, \quad (m = 3, b = -7).$$

Example 2. $\lim_{x \to a} x = a, \quad (m = 1, b = 0).$

Example 3. $\lim_{x \to a} b = b, \quad (m = 0).$

---

* This symbol indicates that the proof has been completed.

Uniqueness of limit

Is it possible for a function to approach two different limits as x approaches a? The answer is "No," as the following theorem shows.

Theorem 2. *If $f(x)$ has a limit as x approaches a, that limit is unique.*

Proof (Indirect proof: by contradiction). Suppose L_1 and L_2 are two different numbers, and

$$\lim_{x\to a} f(x) = L_1, \quad \lim_{x\to a} f(x) = L_2. \tag{7}$$

Then $L_1 \neq L_2$ means that $|L_1 - L_2|$ is positive, and we let

$$\epsilon = \tfrac{1}{2}|L_1 - L_2|. \tag{8}$$

You will see why this choice is made later in the proof.

By definition of limit, applied to L_1, we know there is a deleted neighborhood N_1 of a (see Fig. 3.4) such that

$$|f(x) - L_1| < \epsilon \tag{9a}$$

when x is in N_1.* Likewise there is a deleted neighborhood N_2 of a such that

$$|f(x) - L_2| < \epsilon \tag{9b}$$

when x is in N_2. If

$$N_1 = \{x \mid h_1 < x < a \quad \text{or} \quad a < x < k_1\}, \tag{10a}$$

$$N_2 = \{x \mid h_2 < x < a \quad \text{or} \quad a < x < k_2\}, \tag{10b}$$

then the intersection of N_1 and N_2 is a deleted neighborhood N_3 such that

$$N_3 = \{x \mid h_3 < x < a \quad \text{or} \quad a < x < k_3\} \tag{10c}$$

where

$$h_3 = \max\{h_1, h_2\},$$

$$k_3 = \min\{k_1, k_2\}.$$

Figure 3.4 illustrates these ideas. N_1 goes from h_1 to k_1, N_2 from h_2 to k_2. Here points $\neq a$ between h_1 and k_2 are in both N_1 and N_2, and hence are in

---

* It is also to be understood that $x \in D_f$ whenever we refer to $f(x)$. Thus (9a) holds for $x \in N_1 \cap D_f$, and (9b) holds for $x \in N_2 \cap D_f$.

3.4

$N_3 = N_1 \cap N_2$, where $h_3 = h_1$ and $k_3 = k_2$. For any x in N_3, both (9a) and (9b) hold simultaneously, and lead to the false conclusion

$$|L_1 - L_2| = |L_1 - f(x) + f(x) - L_2|$$
$$\leq |L_1 - f(x)| + |f(x) - L_2| < \epsilon + \epsilon$$
$$= 2\epsilon = |L_1 - L_2|.$$

Since the assumption

$$L_1 \neq L_2$$

leads to the contradiction

$$|L_1 - L_2| < |L_1 - L_2|,$$

that assumption must be false. Therefore $L_1 = L_2$, so the limit is unique. $\square$

Remark 1. The idea behind the foregoing result is quite simple and should not get lost in the fog: If we can make $f(x)$ very nearly equal to L_1 and also very nearly equal to L_2 by taking x close to a, then L_1 and L_2 must be close to each other. More precisely, if both

$$|f(x) - L_1| < \epsilon \quad \text{and} \quad |f(x) - L_2| < \epsilon,$$

then

$$|L_1 - L_2| < 2\epsilon.$$

However, L_1 and L_2 are fixed, and if they aren't equal, then we can't meet the ϵ-challenge for both L_1 and L_2 if ϵ *is not greater than* one-half the distance between them. In particular, we cannot meet the ϵ-challenge if $\epsilon = \tfrac{1}{2}|L_1 - L_2|$, as in the proof. Smaller starting values of ϵ, such as

$$\epsilon = \tfrac{1}{3}|L_1 - L_2|,$$

would obviously work. Hence we have shown that if $L_1 \neq L_2$, then there are *some* positive choices for ϵ such that condition (2) in the definition of limit cannot be satisfied for both. So $f(x)$ can't have two different limits as x approaches a.

Remark 2. Theorem 2 shows that if we can guess an answer to the question of finding a limit L for a function $f(x)$ as x approaches a, and then prove that this number L satisfies the conditions in the definition of a limit, then it is *the* answer—there is no other.

Problem. Prove that $\lim\limits_{x \to 3} (x^3 - 27)/(x - 3) = 27$.

Solution. Since

$$x^3 - 27 = (x - 3)(x^2 + 3x + 9),$$

we have

$$f(x) = \frac{x^3 - 27}{x - 3} = x^2 + 3x + 9 \quad \text{if } x \neq 3.$$

When x is *close* to (but not equal to) 3, $x^2 + 3x + 9$ is *close* to 27, and we guess that $L = 27$ is the answer. Now we can see if we can prove it. Suppose ϵ is a given positive number. Can we find a deleted neighborhood N of 3 such that

$$|f(x) - L| = |(x^2 + 3x + 9) - 27| < \epsilon \quad (11a)$$

when x is in N? We observe that

$$x^2 + 3x + 9 - 27 = x^2 + 3x - 18$$
$$= (x - 3)(x + 6),$$

so inequality (11a) is the same as

$$|x - 3|\,|x + 6| < \epsilon. \quad (11b)$$

When x is near 3, the factor $x - 3$ is near zero and $x + 6$ is near 9. Consider now the deleted neighborhood N_0,

$$0 < |x - 3| < 1. \quad (12)$$

If x is in N_0, then $-1 < x - 3 < 1$, or (by adding 9) $8 < x + 6 < 10$. Therefore $|x + 6| < 10$, and it follows that

$$|x - 3|\,|x + 6| < 10|x - 3|.$$

We now make

$$0 < 10|x - 3| < \epsilon$$

by keeping x in the deleted neighborhood N_1,

$$0 < |x - 3| < \frac{\epsilon}{10}. \quad (13)$$

To satisfy both inequalities (12) and (13), we take for N the smaller of the two neighborhoods N_0 and N_1. If

x is in N it follows that

$$|f(x) - 27| = |(x^2 + 3x + 9) - 27|$$
$$= |x^2 + 3x - 18|$$
$$= |x + 6|\,|x - 3|$$
$$< 10|x - 3| \quad \text{since } x \,\epsilon\, N \subseteq N_0{}^*$$
$$< 10\,\frac{\epsilon}{10} = \epsilon \quad \text{since } x \,\epsilon\, N \subseteq N_1$$
$$< \epsilon.$$

Therefore

$$\lim\limits_{x \to 3} f(x) = 27.$$

Remark 3. The foregoing example reduced to showing that

$$\lim\limits_{x \to 3} (x^2 + 3x + 9) = 27.$$

If we could have said

$$\lim (x^2 + 3x + 9) = \lim (x^2) + \lim (3x + 9)$$

and

$$\lim (x^2) = (\lim x)(\lim x),$$

the problem would have been much simpler. These are, in fact, correct statements, as the next two theorems will show. (See Theorem 4, Article 3.3.)

Theorem 3. **Limit of Sums.**

If $\quad \lim f(x) = L_1 \quad$ and $\quad \lim g(x) = L_2,$

then $\quad \lim (f(x) + g(x)) = \lim f(x) + \lim g(x)$
$$= L_1 + L_2,$$

where all limits are taken as $x \to a$.

Proof. Suppose $\epsilon > 0$ is given. We want to find a deleted neighborhood N of a, such that

$$|f(x) + g(x) - (L_1 + L_2)| < \epsilon \quad (14)$$

when x is in N. We use the fact that

$$|(f(x) + g(x)) - (L_1 + L_2)|$$
$$= |(f(x) - L_1) + (g(x) - L_2)|$$
$$\leq |(f(x) - L_1| + |g(x) - L_2|. \quad (15)$$

---

* We write $A \subseteq B$ to mean A is a subset of B which may be equal to B.

Because $\epsilon/2$ is positive and $f(x) \to L_1$, there is a deleted neighborhood N_1 of a such that

$$|f(x) - L_1| < \tfrac{1}{2}\epsilon \qquad (16a)$$

when x is in N_1. Likewise there is a deleted neighborhood N_2 of a such that

$$|g(x) - L_2| < \tfrac{1}{2}\epsilon \qquad (16b)$$

when x is in N_2. Let N be the intersection of N_1 and N_2:

$$N = N_1 \cap N_2.$$

Then the inequalities (16a) and (16b) both hold when x is in N, and so (14) also holds, since

$$|(f(x) + g(x)) - (L_1 + L_2)|$$
$$\leq |f(x) - L_1| + |g(x) - L_2|$$
$$< \tfrac{1}{2}\epsilon + \tfrac{1}{2}\epsilon = \epsilon. \ \square$$

EXERCISES

Evaluate the limits indicated in Exercises 1 through 8.

1. $\lim\limits_{x \to 2} 2x$

2. $\lim\limits_{x \to 0} 2x$

3. $\lim\limits_{x \to 4} 4$

4. $\lim\limits_{x \to -2} 4$

5. $\lim\limits_{x \to 1} (3x - 1)$

6. $\lim\limits_{x \to 1/3} (3x - 1)$

7. $\lim\limits_{y \to 2} \dfrac{y^2 + 5y + 6}{y + 2}$

8. $\lim\limits_{y \to 2} \dfrac{y^2 - 5y + 6}{y - 2}$

9. Suppose $\lim\limits_{x \to b} f(x) = 7$ and $\lim\limits_{x \to b} g(x) = -3$. What is $\lim\limits_{x \to b} [f(x) + g(x)]$?

10. Prove that
$$\lim_{x \to a} [p(x) + r(x) + s(x)]$$
$$= \lim_{x \to a} p(x) + \lim_{x \to a} r(x) + \lim_{x \to a} s(x),$$
provided that the last three limits exist.

11. Suppose
$$\lim_{x \to -2} p(x) = 4, \quad \lim_{x \to -2} r(x) = 0, \quad \lim_{x \to -2} s(x) = -3.$$
What is $\lim\limits_{x \to -2} [p(x) + r(x) + s(x)]$?

12. Prove that

   (a) $\lim\limits_{x \to 3} \dfrac{1}{x} = \dfrac{1}{3}$,

   (b) if $c \neq 0$, then $\lim\limits_{x \to c} \dfrac{1}{x} = \dfrac{1}{c}$.

In Exercises 13 through 18, guess the limit, then prove that your guess is correct.

13. $\lim\limits_{x \to 5} x^2$

14. $\lim\limits_{x \to 2} x(2 - x)$

15. $\lim\limits_{x \to 0} (x^2 - 2x + 1)$

16. $\lim\limits_{x \to 5} (x^2 - 3x - 18)$

17. $\lim\limits_{x \to 2} (x^3 - 4x + 1)$

18. $\lim\limits_{x \to 4} \sqrt{x}$

19. Give an example of functions f and g such that $f(x) + g(x)$ approaches a limit as x approaches zero, even though $f(x)$ and $g(x)$, separately, do not approach limits as $x \to 0$.

20. Repeat Exercise 19 for $f(x) \cdot g(x)$ in place of $f(x) + g(x)$.

3.3 MORE THEOREMS ABOUT LIMITS

In Article 3.2, we proved a very useful theorem involving the limit of a sum. In this article we shall prove two theorems involving the limit of a product and the limit of a quotient.

Theorem 4. **Limit of Products.**

If $\qquad \lim f(x) = L_1$ *and* $\lim g(x) = L_2,$

then $\lim f(x)g(x) = (\lim f(x))(\lim g(x)) = L_1 L_2,$

where all limits are taken as $x \to a.$

Proof. Let $\epsilon > 0$ be given. We need to show that there is a deleted neighborhood N of a such that

$$|f(x)g(x) - L_1 L_2| < \epsilon \qquad (1)$$

when x is in N.
  We write
$$f(x) = L_1 + (f(x) - L_1),$$
$$g(x) = L_2 + (g(x) - L_2)$$
so that
$$f(x)g(x) - L_1 L_2 = L_1(g(x) - L_2) + L_2(f(x) - L_1)$$
$$+ (f(x) - L_1)(g(x) - L_2).$$

Therefore

$$|f(x)g(x) - L_1L_2|$$
$$\leq |L_1(g(x) - L_2)| + |L_2(f(x) - L_1)|$$
$$+ |(f(x) - L_1)(g(x) - L_2)|$$

and

$$|f(x)g(x) - L_1L_2|$$
$$\leq |L_1| \cdot |g(x) - L_2| + |L_2| \cdot |f(x) - L_1|$$
$$+ |f(x) - L_1| \cdot |g(x) - L_2|. \qquad (2)$$

By hypothesis, there is a deleted neighborhood N_1 of a such that

$$|g(x) - L_2| < \frac{\epsilon}{3(1 + |L_1|)}$$

when x is in N_1, because $\lim g(x) = L_2$ and

$$\frac{\epsilon}{3(1 + |L_1|)}$$

is a positive number. Likewise there are deleted neighborhoods N_2, N_3, and N_4 such that

$$|f(x) - L_1| < \frac{\epsilon}{3(1 + |L_2|)} \quad \text{when } x \text{ is in } N_2,$$

$$|f(x) - L_1| < \sqrt{\epsilon/3} \qquad \text{when } x \text{ is in } N_3,$$

$$|g(x) - L_2| < \sqrt{\epsilon/3} \qquad \text{when } x \text{ is in } N_4.$$

[It will be apparent later why the particular positive numbers $\epsilon/3(1 + |L_1|)$, $\epsilon/3(1 + |L_2|)$, and $\sqrt{\epsilon/3}$ are chosen.] If N is the intersection of N_1, N_2, N_3, and N_4, the above inequalities all hold when x is in N, so that the right side of inequality (2) is less than

$$\frac{|L_1|\epsilon}{3(1 + |L_1|)} + \frac{|L_2|\epsilon}{3(1 + |L_2|)} + \sqrt{\frac{\epsilon}{3}} \cdot \sqrt{\frac{\epsilon}{3}}. \qquad (3)$$

Since

$$\frac{|L_1|}{1 + |L_1|} < 1 \quad \text{and} \quad \frac{|L_2|}{1 + |L_2|} < 1,$$

we have

$$\frac{|L_1|\epsilon}{3(1 + |L_1|)} < \frac{\epsilon}{3} \quad \text{and} \quad \frac{|L_2|\epsilon}{3(1 + |L_2|)} < \frac{\epsilon}{3}.$$

Therefore (3) is less than

$$\frac{\epsilon}{3} + \frac{\epsilon}{3} + \frac{\epsilon}{3} = \epsilon.$$

Remark 3. There is a reason for using $1 + |L_1|$ and $1 + |L_2|$ in the denominators in (3) instead of $|L_1|$ and $|L_2|$. If $L_1 = 0$, we do not want $|L_1|$ in the denominator. But $1 + |L_1|$ cannot be zero, and, as noted, $|L|/(1 + |L|)$ is always less than 1 because the denominator is greater than the numerator.

Corollary 4.1. *If* $\lim f(x) = L$ *and* k *is a constant, then* $\lim kf(x) = kL$, *where both limits are taken as* $x \to a$.

Proof. Apply Theorem 4 with $g(x) = k$, so that

$$L_2 = \lim g(x) = k.$$

Corollary 4.2. *The* $\lim\limits_{x \to a} x^n = a^n$ *for any positive integer* n.

Proof (By induction on n). If $n = 1$, then

$$\lim_{x \to a} x = a,$$

by Theorem 1, with $m = 1$, $b = 0$.

If $n - 1$ is a positive integer such that

$$\lim_{x \to a} x^{n-1} = a^{n-1},$$

then

$$\lim_{x \to a} x^n = \lim_{x \to a} (x \cdot x^{n-1}) = a \cdot a^{n-1} = a^n,$$

by Theorem 4 with $f(x) = x$, $g(x) = x^{n-1}$, $L_1 = a$, and $L_2 = a^{n-1}$.

Corollary 4.3.

If
$$f(x) = c_0 x^n + c_1 x^{n-1} + \cdots + c_n$$

is a polynomial in x, *then*

$$\lim_{x \to a} f(x) = c_0 a^n + c_1 a^{n-1} + \cdots + c_n = f(a).$$

Proof (Again by induction on n). Since we have already proved it for $n = 1$ in Theorem 1, assume that the result holds for the polynomial

$$g(x) = c_1 x^{n-1} + \cdots + c_n.$$

Then

$$\lim_{x \to a} (c_0 x^n + g(x)) = \lim_{x \to a} (c_0 x^n) + \lim_{x \to a} g(x)$$
$$= c_0 a^n + g(a)$$
$$= f(a),$$

from Corollaries 4.1 and 4.2 with $k = c_0$. □

Example 1.

$$\lim_{x \to 2} (5x^2 + 4x - 10) = 20 + 8 - 10 = 18.$$

Quotients

Is it true that

$$\lim \frac{1}{g(x)} = \frac{1}{\lim g(x)} \ ?$$

Since division by zero is not valid, we must assume that

$$\lim g(x) \neq 0.$$

With this proviso, the answer is "yes."

Theorem 5. Limit of Quotients.

Let $$\lim_{x \to a} g(x) = L \neq 0.$$

Then $$\lim_{x \to a} \left(\frac{1}{g(x)} \right) = \frac{1}{L}. \qquad (4)$$

Proof. Let $\epsilon > 0$ be given. We want a deleted neighborhood N of a such that

$$\left| \frac{1}{g(x)} - \frac{1}{L} \right| < \epsilon \qquad (5)$$

when x is in N. Inequality (5) is the same as

$$\left| \frac{L - g(x)}{L \cdot g(x)} \right| < \epsilon. \qquad (6)$$

The numerator on the left can be made as small as we like by taking x sufficiently near a, since $\lim_{x \to a} g(x) = L$. We apply Corollary 4.1 to the denominator:

$$\lim_{x \to a} L \cdot g(x) = L \lim_{x \to a} g(x) = L^2.$$

By definition of limit, with $\epsilon = L^2/2$, there is a deleted neighborhood N_1 of a such that, whenever x is in N_1,

$$L^2 - \epsilon < L \cdot g(x) < L^2 + \epsilon,$$

or, since $\epsilon = L^2/2$,

$$\frac{L^2}{2} < L \cdot g(x) < \frac{3L^2}{2}.$$

Hence $L \cdot g(x)$ is positive, and on taking reciprocals we get

$$\frac{2}{L^2} > \frac{1}{L \cdot g(x)}$$

when x is in N_1. Therefore

$$\left| \frac{L - g(x)}{L \cdot g(x)} \right| = \frac{|L - g(x)|}{L \cdot g(x)} < \frac{2}{L^2} |L - g(x)| \qquad (7)$$

when x is in N_1. Finally, to satisfy (6), there is a deleted neighborhood N_2 such that

$$|L - g(x)| < \frac{\epsilon L^2}{2} \qquad (8)$$

when x is in N_2. Now let N be the intersection of N_1 and N_2. When x is in N, inequalities (7) and (8) both hold, so that

$$\left| \frac{L - g(x)}{L \cdot g(x)} \right| < \frac{2}{L^2} |L - g(x)| < \frac{2}{L^2} \left(\frac{\epsilon L^2}{2} \right) = \epsilon. \ □$$

Corollary 5.1.

If $\lim_{x \to a} f(x) = L_1$ *and* $\lim_{x \to a} g(x) = L_2, \ L_2 \neq 0,$

then $$\lim_{x \to a} \frac{f(x)}{g(x)} = \frac{L_1}{L_2} = \frac{\lim f(x)}{\lim g(x)}.$$

Proof. Combine Theorems 4 and 5.

$$\lim \frac{f(x)}{g(x)} = \lim \left[f(x) \cdot \frac{1}{g(x)} \right]$$

$$= \lim f(x) \cdot \lim \left(\frac{1}{g(x)} \right)$$

$$= L_1 \cdot \frac{1}{L_2}. \ □$$

Corollary 5.2.

If
$$f(x) = b_0 x^m + b_1 x^{m-1} + \cdots + b_m$$

and
$$g(x) = c_0 x^n + c_1 x^{n-1} + \cdots + c_n$$

are polynomials and $g(a) \neq 0$, then

$$\lim_{x \to a} \frac{f(x)}{g(x)} = \frac{f(a)}{g(a)}.$$

Proof. Combine Corollaries 5.1 and 4.3 to get

$$\lim \frac{f(x)}{g(x)} = \frac{\lim f(x)}{\lim g(x)} = \frac{f(a)}{g(a)}. \quad \square$$

Remark 4. In effect, Corollary 5.2 says that to find the limit of the quotient of two polynomials as x *approaches* a, substitute $x = a$ and compute $f(a)/g(a)$, provided the denominator turns out to be *different from zero*. But you cannot find

$$\lim_{x \to 3} \frac{x^2 - 9}{x - 3} = \lim_{x \to 3} (x + 3) = 6$$

by dividing $3^2 - 9 = 0$ by $3 - 3 = 0$.

Example 2. $\lim_{x \to 1} \dfrac{x^2 - x + 2}{x^2 + x + 2} = \dfrac{1 - 1 + 2}{1 + 1 + 2} = \dfrac{1}{2}.$

We conclude this article with a theorem which is used repeatedly in our later work.

Theorem 6. *Suppose*

$$f(x) \leq g(x) \leq h(x),$$

for all values of x in some deleted neighborhood N_1 of c. Furthermore, suppose that the function values $f(x)$ and $h(x)$ approach a common limit L as x approaches c. Then $g(x)$ also approaches L as limit when x approaches c.

Proof. By hypothesis, to any positive number ϵ there corresponds a deleted neighborhood N_2 of c such that both $f(x)$ and $h(x)$ lie between $L - \epsilon$ and $L + \epsilon$ when x is in N_2; that is

$$L - \epsilon < f(x) < L + \epsilon,$$
$$L - \epsilon < h(x) < L + \epsilon.$$

But, for x in the intersection $N = N_1 \cap N_2$, this also implies that

$$L - \epsilon < f(x) \leq g(x) \leq h(x) < L + \epsilon,$$

or

$$L - \epsilon < g(x) < L + \epsilon.$$

In other words, $|g(x) - L| < \epsilon$ when x is in N. This establishes the conclusion

$$\lim_{x \to c} g(x) = L. \quad \square$$

Example 3. As an application of Theorem 6, we prove that

$$\lim_{\theta \to 0} \sin \theta = 0, \tag{9a}$$

$$\lim_{\theta \to 0} \cos \theta = 1, \tag{9b}$$

$$\lim_{\theta \to 0} \frac{\sin \theta}{\theta} = 1, \tag{9c}$$

provided that θ is measured in radians. [Recall that the radian measure of an angle can be defined by

$$\theta = s/r, \tag{10}$$

where s is the length of arc the angle intercepts on a circle of radius r when the center of the circle is the vertex of the angle. Figure 3.5(a) illustrates this definition.]

In Fig. 3.5(b), O is the center of a unit circle and θ is the radian measure of an acute angle AOP. Note that $s = \theta$ under these conditions. Now $\triangle APQ$ is a right triangle with legs of length

$$QP = \sin \theta, \quad AQ = 1 - \cos \theta.$$

From the theorem of Pythagoras, and the fact that $AP < \theta$, we get

$$\sin^2 \theta + (1 - \cos \theta)^2 = (AP)^2 < \theta^2. \tag{11}$$

Both terms on the left side of inequality (11) are positive, so each is smaller than their sum, and hence is less than θ^2:

$$\sin^2 \theta < \theta^2, \tag{12a}$$

$$(1 - \cos \theta)^2 < \theta^2. \tag{12b}$$

The inequalities (12a) and (12b) also imply

$$|\sin \theta| < |\theta|, \tag{13a}$$

$$|1 - \cos \theta| < |\theta|. \tag{13b}$$

a|b

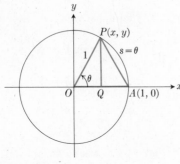

3.5 a| Radian measure.

b| Radian measure on a unit circle: $r = 1$, $s = \theta$.

3.6 Area $\triangle AOP <$ area sector $AOP <$ area $\triangle AOT$.

If ϵ is any positive number we can take $h = \epsilon$ and conclude that

$$|\sin \theta - 0| < \epsilon$$

and

$$|1 - \cos \theta| < \epsilon$$

whenever $0 < |\theta| < h$. Therefore

$$\lim_{\theta \to 0} \sin \theta = 0 \quad \text{and} \quad \lim_{\theta \to 0} \cos \theta = 1.$$

To establish Eq. (9c), let us assume that θ is positive and less than $\pi/2$ in Fig. 3.6. We compare the areas of $\triangle AOP$, sector AOP, and $\triangle AOT$, and note that

$$\text{area } \triangle AOP < \text{area sector } AOP < \text{area } \triangle AOT.$$

The area of sector AOP is the same fraction of the area of a circle of radius 1 that its arc is of the total circumference*:

$$\frac{\text{area sector } AOP}{\text{area circle}} = \frac{\text{arc } AP}{\text{circumference}}.$$

Thus

$$\frac{\text{area sector } AOP}{\pi r^2} = \frac{r\theta}{2\pi r} = \frac{\theta}{2\pi},$$

and therefore

$$\text{area sector } AOP = \tfrac{1}{2}r^2\theta \tag{14a}$$

$$= \tfrac{1}{2}\theta, \quad \text{when } r = 1. \tag{14b}$$

The altitude of $\triangle AOP$, with base $OA = 1$, is

$$y = QP = \sin \theta.$$

Hence

$$\text{area } \triangle AOP = \tfrac{1}{2}\sin \theta. \tag{15a}$$

The altitude of $\triangle AOT$, with base $OA = 1$, is

$$AT := \tan \theta,$$

and therefore

$$\text{area } \triangle AOT = \tfrac{1}{2}\tan \theta. \tag{15b}$$

But

$$\text{area } \triangle AOP < \text{area sector } AOP < \text{area } \triangle AOT,$$

and therefore

$$\tfrac{1}{2}\sin \theta < \tfrac{1}{2}\theta < \tfrac{1}{2}\tan \theta, \quad \text{if } 0 < \theta < \frac{\pi}{2}. \tag{16}$$

Dividing the three terms of inequality (16) by $\tfrac{1}{2}\sin \theta$, we get

$$1 < \frac{\theta}{\sin \theta} < \frac{1}{\cos \theta}, \quad \text{if } 0 < \theta < \frac{\pi}{2}. \tag{17a}$$

---

* We assume the results $A = \pi r^2$ and $C = 2\pi r$, for the area and circumference of a circle of radius r. These do, in fact, depend on limits but not on the trigonometric functions.

Recall that $\sin(-\theta) = -\sin\theta$, and $\cos(-\theta) = \cos\theta$, so (17a) also implies that

$$1 < \frac{-\theta}{\sin(-\theta)} < \frac{1}{\cos(-\theta)}, \quad \text{if } 0 < -\theta < \frac{\pi}{2},$$

or

$$1 < \frac{\theta}{\sin\theta} < \frac{1}{\cos\theta}, \quad \text{if } 0 > \theta > -\frac{\pi}{2}. \qquad (17b)$$

We can combine (17a) and (17b) to say

$$1 < \frac{\theta}{\sin\theta} < \frac{1}{\cos\theta}, \quad \text{if } 0 < |\theta| < \frac{\pi}{2}. \qquad (18)$$

Inequality (18) tells us about $\theta/(\sin\theta)$. We convert this to information about $(\sin\theta)/\theta$ by taking reciprocals and reversing the inequality signs, because

if $\qquad a$ and b are positive and $\quad a > b$;

then $\qquad\qquad (1/a) < (1/b)$.

Therefore $\qquad\quad 1 > \dfrac{\sin\theta}{\theta} > \cos\theta$

whenever $\qquad\quad 0 < |\theta| < \dfrac{\pi}{2}$.

Now apply Theorem 6. In this example, the two functions that are analogous to the functions $f(x)$ and $h(x)$ defined in Theorem 6 both approach 1 as common limit:

$$\lim_{\theta\to 0} 1 = 1, \quad \lim_{\theta\to 0} \cos\theta = 1.$$

Therefore we conclude that

$$\lim_{\theta\to 0} \frac{\sin\theta}{\theta} = 1.$$

Example 4

$$\lim_{x\to 0} \frac{\sin 3x}{x} = \lim_{3x\to 0} \frac{3\sin 3x}{3x}$$

$$= 3\lim_{\theta\to 0}\left(\frac{\sin\theta}{\theta}\right) = 3.$$

Example 5

$$\lim_{x\to 0} \frac{\tan x}{x} = \lim_{x\to 0}\left(\frac{\sin x}{x}\cdot\frac{1}{\cos x}\right)$$

$$= \left[\lim_{x\to 0}\left(\frac{\sin x}{x}\right)\right]\left[\lim_{x\to 0}\left(\frac{1}{\cos x}\right)\right]$$

$$= (1)(1) = 1.$$

EXERCISES

1. Suppose $\lim\limits_{x\to c} f(x) = 5$ and $\lim\limits_{x\to c} g(x) = -2$.

   (a) What is $\lim\limits_{x\to c} f(x)g(x)$?

   (b) What is $\lim\limits_{x\to c} 2f(x)g(x)$?

Evaluate the limits indicated in Exercises 2 through 20.

2. $\lim\limits_{x\to 1} [(2x-1)(x)]$ 　　3. $\lim\limits_{x\to 2} [3(2x-1)(x)]$

4. $\lim\limits_{x\to 2} [3(2x-1)(x+1)]$ 　5. $\lim\limits_{x\to 2} [3(2x-1)(x^2)]$

6. $\lim\limits_{x\to 2} [3(2x-1)(x+1)^2]$ 7. $\lim\limits_{x\to -1} (x+3)$

8. $\lim\limits_{x\to -1} (x+3)^2$ 　　　　9. $\lim\limits_{x\to -1} (x^2+6x+9)$

10. $\lim\limits_{x\to -2} (x+3)^{171}$ 　　11. $\lim\limits_{x\to -4} (x+3)^{1967}$

12. $\lim\limits_{x\to 1} (x^3+3x^2-2x-17)$

13. Suppose $\lim\limits_{x\to c} f(x) = 2$ and $\lim\limits_{x\to c} g(x) = 5$.

   (a) What is $\lim\limits_{x\to c} \dfrac{f(x)}{g(x)}$?   　(b) What is $\lim\limits_{x\to c} \dfrac{f(x)}{3g(x)}$?

14. $\lim\limits_{t\to 2} \dfrac{t+3}{t+2}$ 　　　　15. $\lim\limits_{x\to 5} \dfrac{x^2-25}{x-5}$

16. $\lim\limits_{x\to 5} \dfrac{x^2-25}{x+5}$

17. $\lim\limits_{x\to 5} \dfrac{x-5}{x^2-25}$, if it exists.

18. $\lim\limits_{x\to 5} \dfrac{x+5}{x^2-25}$, if it exists.

19. $\lim\limits_{x\to 1} \dfrac{x^2-x-2}{x^2-1}$ 　20. $\lim\limits_{x\to 0} \dfrac{5x^3+8x^2}{3x^4-16x^2}$

21. Give an example of functions f and g such that

$$\lim_{x\to 0} f(x)/g(x)$$

exists, but at least one of the functions f and g fails to have a limit as $x \to 0$.

22. As $x \to 0+$, the functions $1/x$, $1/x^2$, $1/\sqrt{x}$ all become very large. Which one increases most rapidly and which one least rapidly? [*Note.* $x \to 0+$ means

that x approaches 0 through positive values, that is, from the right.]

23. Suppose F is a function whose values are all less than or equal to some constant M: $F(t) \leq M$. Prove:

If
$$\lim_{t \to c} F(t) = L,$$

then
$$L \leq M.$$

Suggestion. An indirect proof may be used to show that $L > M$ is false. For if $L > M$, we may take $\frac{1}{2}(L - M)$ as a positive number ϵ, apply the definition of limit, and arrive at a contradiction.

24. Expand and simplify the left side of Eq. (11) and prove that $(1 - \cos \theta) < \theta^2/2$ for $0 < \theta < \pi/2$. Is $(1 - \cos \theta) < \theta^2/2$ true for $\theta = 0$? For $\theta = \pi/2$? For $0 < |\theta| < \pi/2$? For all $\theta \neq 0$?

Evaluate the following limits, or show that they do not exist.

25. (a) $\lim\limits_{x \to 0} \dfrac{x}{\sin 2x}$ (b) $\lim\limits_{x \to 0} \dfrac{\sin 7x}{4x}$

26. (a) $\lim\limits_{\theta \to 0} \dfrac{\sec 2\theta \tan 3\theta}{5\theta}$ (b) $\lim\limits_{t \to 0} \dfrac{15t}{\tan 6t}$

27. (a) $\lim\limits_{x \to 0} \dfrac{\tan 2x}{\sin 7x}$ (b) $\lim\limits_{x \to 0} \dfrac{\cot 4x}{\cot 3x}$

28. $\lim\limits_{y \to \pi/2} \dfrac{\cos y}{\pi/2 - y}$ (Let $x = \pi/2 - y$.)

29. $\lim\limits_{x \to 0} \dfrac{x \sin x}{1 - \cos x}$ (Multiply and divide by $1 + \cos x$.)

30. Use the trigonometric identity
$$\sin A - \sin B = 2 \sin \frac{A - B}{2} \cos \frac{A + B}{2}$$

to evaluate
$$\lim_{h \to 0} \frac{\sin (x + h) - \sin x}{h},$$

assuming that
$$\lim_{\theta \to 0} \cos (x + \theta) = \cos x.$$

31. Use the identity
$$\cos (A + B) = \cos A \cos B - \sin A \sin B$$

and appropriate theorems to prove that
$$\lim_{\theta \to 0} \cos (x + \theta) = \cos x.$$

3.4 INFINITY

The function
$$f(x) = \frac{1}{x}, \quad x \neq 0, \tag{1}$$

has as its domain the set of all real nonzero numbers. The graph is the curve shown in Fig. 3.7.

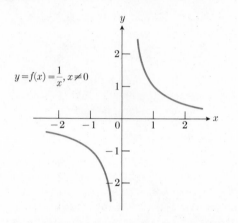

$$y = f(x) = \frac{1}{x}, \ x \neq 0$$

3.7

There are some facts about $1/x$ that are evident:

(a) When x is a small positive number, $1/x$ is a large positive number. For example,
$$1/0.001 = 1000.$$

(b) When x is a large number, $1/x$ is small. For example,
$$1/10{,}000 = 0.0001.$$

(c) When x is negative, $1/x$ is negative. For example,
$$1/(-0.001) = -1000$$
$$1/(-10{,}000) = -0.0001.$$

These facts are sometimes abbreviated by saying that

(a) $1/x$ approaches 0 as x tends to either $+\infty$ or $-\infty$,

(b) $1/x$ tends to $+\infty$ as x approaches 0 through positive values,

(c) $1/x$ tends to $-\infty$ as x approaches 0 through negative values.

The symbol ∞, is read *infinity*, but it does not represent any real number.

Note. In more advanced mathematics, a new system consisting of the real numbers and two additional elements, called $+\infty$ and $-\infty$, is sometimes used. It is called the *extended* real number system. However, special rules have to be set up, such as

$$a + (+\infty) = +\infty,$$
$$a - (+\infty) = -\infty,$$
$$a \cdot (+\infty) = +\infty \quad \text{if} \quad a > 0,$$
$$a \cdot (+\infty) = -\infty \quad \text{if} \quad a < 0,$$

for any real number a, and

$$(+\infty) \cdot (+\infty) = +\infty,$$
$$(+\infty) + (+\infty) = +\infty.$$

But such operations as $(+\infty) + (-\infty)$ and $0 \cdot (+\infty)$, or $(+\infty)/(+\infty)$ are not permitted because no consistent (unique) values can be assigned to such operations.

Mainly we shall avoid using the extended real number system in this book. And even in that system, division by zero has to be excluded if we hope to retain the usual laws of arithmetic and algebra.

Definition. *If $f(x)$ is defined for large values of x, we say that $f(x)$ approaches the real number L as limit as x tends to infinity, and write*

$$\lim_{x \to \infty} f(x) = L,$$

provided that to each positive number ϵ there corresponds a number M such that

$$L - \epsilon < f(x) < L + \epsilon \quad \text{when } x > M. \quad (2)$$

Remark 1. Graphically, the inequalities in (2) mean that the curve $y = f(x)$ stays between the lines $y = L - \epsilon$ and $y = L + \epsilon$ for x sufficiently large. The part of the statement that reads

$$\text{when } x > M$$

can also be written

$$\text{for } M < x < \infty,$$

or

$$\text{for } x \text{ in the open interval } (M, \infty).$$

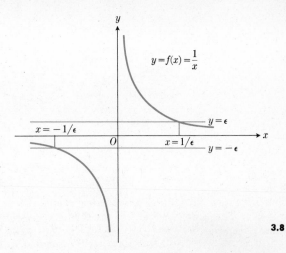

3.8

Such an open interval, consisting of all numbers greater than some fixed number M, is also called a *neighborhood of* ∞. Thus we could say that $f(x)$ stays inside the neighborhood $(L - \epsilon, L + \epsilon)$ when x is in the neighborhood (M, ∞) and in the domain of f.

Example 1. $\qquad\qquad \lim_{x \to \infty} \dfrac{1}{x} = 0.$

Example 2. $\qquad \lim_{x \to \infty} \dfrac{x}{x + 1} = \lim_{x \to \infty} \dfrac{1}{1 + (1/x)} = 1.$

Example 3.

$$\lim_{x \to \infty} \frac{2x^2 - x + 3}{3x^2 + 5} = \lim_{x \to \infty} \frac{2 - (1/x) + (3/x^2)}{3 + (5/x^2)} = \frac{2}{3}.$$

For Example 1, $f(x) = 1/x$, we have

$$-\epsilon < \frac{1}{x} < \epsilon \qquad (3a)$$

for any $\epsilon > 0$, provided that

$$|x| > \frac{1}{\epsilon}. \qquad (3b)$$

Thus, $f(x)$ is in the neighborhood $(-\epsilon, \epsilon)$ of zero, when x is in the neighborhood $(1/\epsilon, \infty)$ of ∞; see Fig. 3.8.

See Fig. 3.9 for the example

$$f(x) = 2 + \frac{\sin x}{x}.$$

$y = f(x) = 2 + \dfrac{\sin x}{x}$

3.9

The graph of this function oscillates about the line $y = 2$. The amplitude of the oscillations decreases toward zero as $x \to \infty$, and the curve lies between $y = 2 + \epsilon$ and $y = 2 - \epsilon$ when $x > 1/\epsilon$. When x is large, $\sin x / x \to 0$ and $f(x) \to L = 2$.

The following theorems about limits of sums, differences, products, and quotients are analogous to the corresponding theorems for limits when $x \to a$.

Theorem 7.

If $\lim\limits_{x \to \infty} f(x) = L_1$ *and* $\lim\limits_{x \to \infty} g(x) = L_2,$

where L_1 and L_2 are (finite) real numbers, then:

$$\lim_{x \to \infty} [f(x) + g(x)] = L_1 + L_2, \qquad (4a)$$

$$\lim_{x \to \infty} f(x)g(x) = L_1 L_2, \qquad (4b)$$

$$\lim_{x \to \infty} [f(x) - g(x)] = L_1 - L_2, \qquad (4c)$$

$$\lim_{x \to \infty} \frac{f(x)}{g(x)} = \frac{L_1}{L_2}, \quad \text{if} \quad L_2 \neq 0. \qquad (4d)$$

To prove these theorems, one only needs to repeat the proofs for the corresponding theorems for limits as $x \to a$ with only minor changes (mainly, replacing neighborhoods of a by neighborhoods of ∞).

Example 4. $\lim\limits_{x \to \infty} x \sin \dfrac{1}{x} = \lim\limits_{y \to 0} \dfrac{\sin y}{y} \quad \left(y = \dfrac{1}{x} \right)$

$$= 1.$$

Finally, we sometimes want to say such things as

$$\lim_{x \to a} f(x) = \infty, \qquad (5a)$$

$$\lim_{x \to a^+} f(x) = \infty, \qquad (5b)$$

$$\lim_{x \to a^-} f(x) = \infty, \qquad (5c)$$

$$\lim_{x \to \infty} f(x) = \infty. \qquad (5d)$$

In every instance, the symbol ∞ means the same as

$$f(x) \to +\infty$$

or that for any real number M that is given, no matter how large M may be, the condition

$$f(x) > M$$

is satisfied for all values of x in some restricted set, usually depending upon M. The appropriate set in (5a) is

in some deleted neighborhood of a.

In (5b), $x \to a^+$ means that we consider numbers close to a but greater than a; that is, an interval of the form $(a, a + h)$ for some $h > 0$. In (5c), $x \to a^-$ means we restrict attention to values of x that are near a and less than a; an interval of the form $(a - h, a)$ with $h > 0$. In (5d), the neighborhood is of the form (c, ∞); that is, for x large, or for $x > c$ for some c.

The following theorems are stated without proof. The exercises ask for proofs of some of them. They involve various ideas about *bounded* functions. We shall first give some definitions and an example.

Definitions. *If there is a real number b such that for all x in the domain of g*

$$g(x) \geq b,$$

then g(x) is bounded below.

If there is a real number b and a real number c such that for all x in the domain of g

$$g(x) \geq b \quad for \quad x > c,$$

then g(x) is bounded below for x large.

If there is a real number a such that for all x in the domain of g

$$g(x) \leq a,$$

then g(x) is bounded above.

If there are real numbers a, b, and c such that

$$a < g(x) < b \quad when \quad x > c,$$

then g(x) is bounded for x large.

Example 5.
$$g(x) = \frac{2x}{x+1} + \frac{1}{x}$$

is bounded for x large because

$$0 < g(x) < 2 \quad when \quad x > 1.$$

Theorem 8. *If*
$$\lim_{x \to \infty} f(x) = \infty$$

and g(x) is bounded below, for x large,

then
$$\lim_{x \to \infty} [f(x) + g(x)] = \infty.$$

Example 6.
$$\lim_{x \to \infty} x = \infty \quad and \quad \sin x \geq -1.$$

Hence
$$\lim_{x \to \infty} (x + \sin x) = \infty,$$

even though sin x does *not* have a limit as $x \to \infty$.

Theorem 9. *If*
$$\lim_{x \to \infty} f(x) = 0$$

and g(x) is bounded for x large,

then
$$\lim_{x \to \infty} f(x)g(x) = 0.$$

Example 7. $\lim_{x \to \infty} (1/x) = 0$ and $-1 \leq \cos x \leq 1$,

that is, cos x is bounded. Hence

$$\lim_{x \to \infty} \frac{\cos x}{x} = 0.$$

EXERCISES

Use Theorems 7, 8, and 9 to find the following limits.

1. $\lim\limits_{x \to \infty} \dfrac{2x + 3}{5x + 7}$

2. $\lim\limits_{x \to \infty} \dfrac{3x^3 + 5x^2 - 7}{10x^3 - 11x^2 + 5x}$

3. $\lim\limits_{x \to \infty} \dfrac{3x^2 - 6x}{4x - 8}$

4. $\lim\limits_{x \to \infty} \dfrac{7x - 28}{x^3}$

5. $\lim\limits_{x \to \infty} \dfrac{2x^2 + 3}{x^3 + x - 5} \operatorname{sgn} x$

6. $\lim\limits_{x \to \infty} \left(\dfrac{1}{x} + 1 \right) \left(\dfrac{5x^2 - 1}{x^2} \right)$

7. $\lim\limits_{x \to \infty} \left(\sqrt{x} + \dfrac{1}{[x]} \right)$

8. $\lim\limits_{x \to \infty} [\tan x + \sec x(5 \cos x - \sin x)]$

9. $\lim\limits_{x \to \infty} \dfrac{\sqrt{x+1}}{\sqrt{4x - 1}}$

10. What is
$$\lim_{x \to \infty} \frac{f(x)}{g(x)}$$

if f(x) is a polynomial of degree less than the degree of the polynomial g(x)?

11. What does $f(x)/g(x)$ tend to, as $x \to \infty$, if the degree of the polynomial g(x) is less than the degree of the polynomial f(x)?

12. Prove Eq. (4a) of Theorem 7.

13. Use Eq. (4b) of Theorem 7 to prove the following corollary: If $\lim\limits_{x \to \infty} f(x) = L$ where L is finite,

then
$$\lim_{x \to \infty} [-f(x)] = -L.$$

14. Use the result of Exercise 13 to prove Eq. (4c) of Theorem 7.

15. Prove Theorem 8.   16. Prove Theorem 9.

17. (a) Is the polynomial $g(x) = x^2 - 3x + 4$ bounded below for x large?

    (b) Is it bounded below for all values of x?

    (c) Is it bounded for x large?

18. State and prove a theorem like Theorem 6 as x approaches ∞.

19. If $(2x - 3)/x < f(x) < (2x^2 + 5x)/x^2$, find $\lim\limits_{x \to \infty} f(x)$.

20. Suppose that $f(x)$ and $g(x)$ are two polynomials, and that $g(x)$ is bounded below for x large. If the degree of $f(x)$ is less than the degree of $g(x)$, prove that $f(x) + g(x)$ is bounded below for x large.

REVIEW QUESTIONS AND EXERCISES

1. Define what it means to say that:

   (a) $\lim\limits_{x \to 2} f(x) = 5$ (b) $\lim\limits_{x \to c} g(x) = k$

2. Give two examples of deleted neighborhoods of the point $x = 2$, of which one is symmetric about 2 and the other is not.

3. Describe the intersection of the deleted neighborhoods $0 < |x - a| < 2$ and $(a - 1, a) \cup (a, a + 3)$.

4. What is wrong with the following "proof" of Theorem 5? Let

$$f_1(x) = g(x), \quad f_2(x) = 1/g(x),$$

$$L_1 = \lim_{x \to a} f_1(x), \quad L_2 = \lim_{x \to a} f_2(x).$$

Then, by Theorem 4,

$$\lim_{x \to a} f_1(x)f_2(x) = L_1 L_2.$$

But $f_1(x)f_2(x) = 1$, so we have, by Theorem 1 with $m = 0$, $b = 1$,

$$1 = \lim_{x \to a} f_1(x)f_2(x) = L_1 L_2.$$

Therefore, $L_2 = 1/L_1$.

5. Corollary 4.2, with $n = 2$, asserts that $\lim\limits_{x \to a} x^2 = a^2$, but it does not say that $\lim\limits_{x \to a} \sqrt{x} = \sqrt{a}$. Try to prove this result, for $a > 0$. (Do not assume the existence of the limit of $\sqrt{x}$. Work directly from the definition of limit.)

6. A function f, whose domain is the set of all real numbers, has the property that $f(x + h) = f(x) \cdot f(h)$ for all x and h; and $f(x) \neq 0$.

   (a) Show that $f(0) = 1$. [*Hint:* Let $h = x = 0$.]

   (b) If f has a derivative at 0, show that f has a derivative at every real number x, and that

$$f'(x) = f(x) \cdot f'(0).$$

7. Give an example of a function, defined for all real x, that fails to have a derivative (a) at some point, (b) at several points, (c) at infinitely many points.

MISCELLANEOUS EXERCISES

Evaluate the following limits, or show that the limit does not exist.

1. $\lim\limits_{x \to \infty} \dfrac{x + \sin x}{2x + 5}$ 2. $\lim\limits_{x \to \infty} \dfrac{1 + \sin x}{x}$

3. $\lim\limits_{x \to 1} \dfrac{x^2 - 4}{x^3 - 8}$ 4. $\lim\limits_{x \to 2} \dfrac{x^2 - 4}{x^3 - 8}$

5. $\lim\limits_{x \to \infty} \dfrac{x \sin x}{x + \sin x}$ 6. $\lim\limits_{x \to a} \dfrac{x^2 - a^2}{x - a}$

7. $\lim\limits_{x \to a} \dfrac{x^2 - a^2}{x + a}$ 8. $\lim\limits_{h \to 0} \dfrac{(x + h)^2 - x^2}{h}$

9. $\lim\limits_{h \to 0} \dfrac{\sqrt{x + h} - \sqrt{x}}{h}$ 10. $\lim\limits_{\Delta x \to 0} \dfrac{1/(x + \Delta x) - 1/x}{\Delta x}$

11. $\lim\limits_{x \to 0^+} \dfrac{1}{x}$ 12. $\lim\limits_{x \to 1} \dfrac{1 - \sqrt{x}}{1 - x}$

13. $\lim\limits_{x \to 1} \dfrac{(2x - 3)(\sqrt{x} - 1)}{2x^2 + x - 3}$ 14. $\lim\limits_{x \to \infty} (1 - \cos x)$

The following problems deal with limits of sequences. A function whose domain is the set of positive integers $1, 2, \ldots$ is said to be a *sequence*. Instead of writing the value of the function at n as $f(n)$, it is customary to write the nth term of the sequence as a_n, or S_n, or something similar. A sequence a_n is said to converge to the limit L as $n \to \infty$ if and only if to each positive number ϵ there corresponds an integer N such that

$$|a_n - L| < \epsilon \text{ for all values of } n \text{ greater than } N.$$

The following theorems about limits of sequences are analogous to theorems in this chapter about limits of other functions. Prove them.

15. If
$$\lim_{n\to\infty} a_n = A \text{ and } \lim_{n\to\infty} b_n = B,$$
then
$$\lim_{n\to\infty} (a_n + b_n) = A + B.$$

16. If $\lim_{n\to\infty} a_n = A$ and k is a number, then $\lim_{n\to\infty} (ka_n) = kA$.

17. If $\lim a_n$ exists (is a finite real number), then the sequence a_n is bounded.

18. If $\lim_{n\to\infty} a_n = A$ and $\lim_{n\to\infty} b_n = B$, then $\lim_{n\to\infty} (a_n b_n) = AB$.

19. If $\lim_{n\to\infty} b_n = B \neq 0$, then $\lim_{n\to\infty} 1/b_n = 1/B$.

Evaluate the following limits:

20. $\lim_{n\to\infty} \dfrac{3n^2 - 5n + \sin n}{4n^2 + 7n + 6}$

[*Hint:* divide the numerator and denominator by n^2.]

21. $\lim_{n\to\infty} \dfrac{2n^2 + 5n - 3}{n^3 + 2n}$

22. $\lim_{n\to\infty} (\sqrt{n^2 + n} - \sqrt{n^2 + 10})$

23. Suppose that $h_n = \sqrt[n]{n} - 1$. Then
$$n = (1 + h_n)^n = 1 + nh_n + \frac{n(n-1)}{2} h_n^2 + \cdots$$
$$> \frac{n(n-1)}{2} h_n^2$$
when $n > 2$. From the above inequality, and the definition of h_n, deduce that
$$0 < h_n < \sqrt{\frac{2}{n-1}} \quad \text{when} \quad n > 2.$$

Find: (a) $\lim_{n\to\infty} h_n$ (b) $\lim_{n\to\infty} \sqrt[n]{n}$

The *right-hand limit b* of a function f at a point a is the limit of the function at a for a right-hand domain $(a, a + \delta)$, $\delta > 0$. We write
$$\lim_{x\to a^+} f(x) = b.$$

Similarly, the *left-hand limit c* of a function f at a point a is the limit of the function at a for a left-hand domain

$(a - \delta, a)$, $\delta > 0$. We write
$$\lim_{x\to a^-} f(x) = c.$$

For example, $\lim_{x\to 5^+} [x] = 5$, but $\lim_{x\to 5^-} [x] = 4$.

Find each of the following limits:

24. $\lim_{x\to 0^+} \dfrac{|x|}{x}$

25. $\lim_{x\to 0^-} \dfrac{|x|}{x}$

26. $\lim_{x\to 4^-} [x] - x$

27. $\lim_{x\to 4^+} [x] - x$

28. $\lim_{x\to 3^+} \dfrac{[x]^2 - 9}{x^2 - 9}$

29. $\lim_{x\to 3^-} \dfrac{[x^2] - 9}{x^2 - 9}$

30. $\lim_{x\to 4^+} [[x]]$

31. $\lim_{x\to 0^+} \dfrac{\sqrt{x}}{\sqrt{4 + \sqrt{x}} - 2}$

32. Given $(x - 1)/(2x^2 - 7x + 5) = f(x)$. Find
(a) the limit of $f(x)$ as $x \to \infty$,
(b) the limit of $f(x)$ as $x \to 1$,
(c) $f(-1/x)$, $f(0)$, $1/f(x)$.

33. Compute the coordinates of the point of intersection of the straight lines
$$3x + 5y = 1, \quad (2 + c)x + 5c^2 y = 1,$$
and determine the limiting position of this point as c tends to 1.

34. Find
(a) $\lim_{n\to\infty} (\sqrt{n^2 + 1} - n)$,   (b) $\lim_{n\to\infty} (\sqrt{n^2 + n} - n)$.

35. Given $\epsilon > 0$, find $\delta > 0$ such that $\sqrt{t^2 - 1} < \epsilon$ when $0 < (t - 1) < \delta$.

36. Given $\epsilon > 0$, find M such that
$$\left| \frac{t^2 + t}{t^2 - 1} - 1 \right| < \epsilon \quad \text{when } t > M.$$

37. Show that $\lim_{t\to 0} t \sin (1/t)$ exists and is zero, even though $\sin (1/t)$ has no limit as t approaches zero.

38. Prove that if $f(t)$ is bounded [that is, $|f(t)| < M$ for some constant M] and $g(t)$ approaches zero as t approaches a, then $\lim_{t\to a} f(t)g(t) = 0$.

39. Prove that if $f(t)$ has a finite limit as t approaches a, then there exist numbers m, M, and $h > 0$ such that
$$m < f(t) < M \quad \text{if} \quad 0 < |t - a| < h.$$

DERIVATIVES OF ALGEBRAIC FUNCTIONS

CHAPTER 4

A single term of the form cx^n, where c is a constant and n is zero or a positive integer, is called a *monomial* in x. A function which is the sum of a finite number of monomial terms is called a *polynomial* in x. For example,

$$f(x) = x^3 - 5x + 7, \quad g(x) = (x^2 + 3)^3,$$

$$h(x) = 4x, \quad \phi(x) = 5$$

are special cases of polynomials in x, and

$$s = \tfrac{1}{2}gt^2, \quad v = v_0 + gt$$

are polynomials in t.

We shall now deduce some formulas which will enable us to find the derivatives of polynomial functions very easily. In every case we derive the formula by means of this basic definition:

Definition. *Let $y = f(x)$ define a function f. If the limit*

$$\frac{dy}{dx} = \lim_{\Delta x \to 0} \frac{\Delta y}{\Delta x}, \tag{1a}$$

meaning

$$f'(x) = \lim_{\Delta x \to 0} \frac{f(x + \Delta x) - f(x)}{\Delta x}, \tag{1b}$$

exists and is finite, we call this limit the derivative of y with respect to x and say that f is differentiable at x.

Theorem 1. *The derivative of a constant is zero.*

Proof. Let

$$y = c,$$

where c is a constant. Then when $x = x_1$ and again when $x = x_1 + \Delta x$, y has the same value c,

hence
$$y = c$$

and
$$y + \Delta y = c,$$

so that
$$\Delta y = 0.$$

Then, dividing by Δx, we have

$$\frac{\Delta y}{\Delta x} = 0.$$

The limit of 0, as $\Delta x \to 0$, certainly exists, and

$$\frac{dy}{dx} = \lim_{\Delta x \to 0} \frac{\Delta y}{\Delta x} = 0. \;\square$$

Remark 1. The slope of the line $y = c$ (Fig. 4.1) is zero at every point on it, so Theorem 1 is not telling us anything new. The formal proof is given here for completeness, and because it gives us an easy start.

4.1

Theorem 2. *The derivative with respect to x of x^n is nx^{n-1} when n is any positive integer.*

Proof. Let $y = x^n$, where n may be any positive integer. Then, by the binomial theorem, we may express the sum $y + \Delta y$ as a polynomial. We have

$$y + \Delta y = (x + \Delta x)^n = \begin{cases} x + \Delta x & \text{if } n = 1, \\ x^2 + 2x\,\Delta x + (\Delta x)^2 & \text{if } n = 2, \\ x^3 + 3x^2\,\Delta x + 3x\,(\Delta x)^2 + (\Delta x)^3 & \text{if } n = 3, \\ x^n + nx^{n-1}\,\Delta x + (\text{terms in } x \text{ and } \Delta x) \cdot (\Delta x)^2 & \text{if } n > 3. \end{cases}$$

From this we subtract $y = x^n$ and obtain

$$\Delta y = \begin{cases} \Delta x & \text{if } n = 1, \\ 2x\,\Delta x + (\Delta x)^2 & \text{if } n = 2, \\ 3x^2\,\Delta x + (3x + \Delta x) \cdot (\Delta x)^2 & \text{if } n = 3, \\ nx^{n-1}\,\Delta x + (\text{terms in } x \text{ and } \Delta x) \cdot (\Delta x)^2 & \text{if } n > 3. \end{cases}$$

Dividing by Δx, we find next that

$$\frac{\Delta y}{\Delta x} = \begin{cases} 1 & \text{if } n = 1, \\ 2x + \Delta x & \text{if } n = 2, \\ 3x^2 + (3x + \Delta x) \cdot \Delta x & \text{if } n = 3, \\ nx^{n-1} + (\text{terms in } x \text{ and } \Delta x) \cdot \Delta x & \text{if } n > 3. \end{cases}$$

Finally, we let Δx approach zero and find

$$\frac{dy}{dx} = \lim_{\Delta x \to 0} \frac{\Delta y}{\Delta x} = \begin{cases} 1 & \text{if } n = 1, \\ 2x & \text{if } n = 2, \\ 3x^2 & \text{if } n = 3, \\ nx^{n-1} & \text{if } n > 3. \end{cases}$$

In particular, the case $n = 1$ tells us that

$$\frac{dx}{dx} = 1.$$

This fits the general formula nx^{n-1} provided we take x^0 to be 1. This is the standard definition of x^0 when $x \neq 0$, and for convenience, here and in the chapter on infinite series, we adopt a suggestion* of Professor Herbert E. Vaughan to define 0^0 to be 1. Then the derivative with respect to x of x^n, for any positive integer n, is given by

$$\frac{dy}{dx} = nx^{n-1} \quad \text{if} \quad y = x^n \qquad (2)$$

and $n = $ any positive integer. □

Theorem 3. *If $u = f(x)$ is a differentiable function of x and c is a constant, then*

$$\frac{d(cu)}{dx} = c\frac{du}{dx}. \qquad (3)$$

Proof. Let

$$y = cu, \qquad (4a)$$

where $u = f(x)$. Then if x is replaced by $x + \Delta x$, we have

$$y + \Delta y = c(u + \Delta u), \qquad (4b)$$

where $u + \Delta u = f(x + \Delta x)$. Subtracting (4a) from (4b), we obtain

$$\Delta y = c\,\Delta u$$

and dividing this by Δx, we have

$$\frac{\Delta y}{\Delta x} = c\frac{\Delta u}{\Delta x}. \qquad (4c)$$

Since u has a derivative, the limit, when Δx approaches zero, of the right-hand side of Eq. (4c) exists:

$$\lim_{\Delta x \to 0} c\frac{\Delta u}{\Delta x} = c\frac{du}{dx}.$$

---

* Herbert E. Vaughan, "The Expression 0^0," *The Mathematics Teacher*, Vol. LXIII, Number 2, (Feb. 1970) pages 111–112.

Since both sides of (4c) are equal, its left-hand side must have the same limit. Because this limit exists, it is also equal to dy/dx, from the definition of the derivative. All of this is summarized in the following equation, which follows by taking limits in Eq. (4c):

$$\frac{dy}{dx} = \lim_{\Delta x \to 0} \frac{\Delta y}{\Delta x} = \lim_{\Delta x \to 0} c\frac{\Delta u}{\Delta x} = c\frac{du}{dx}.$$

Since $y = cu$, this is the same as

$$\frac{d(cu)}{dx} = c\frac{du}{dx}. \quad \square$$

Corollary. *If n is a positive integer and c is a number, then the function cx^n is differentiable for all x, and*

$$\frac{d}{dx}(cx^n) = cnx^{n-1}. \qquad (5)$$

Proof. Let $u = x^n$, and apply Theorems 2 and 3. □

Example 1. If $\qquad y = 7x^5,$

then $\qquad\qquad \dfrac{dy}{dx} = 35x^4.$

Theorem 4. *The derivative of the sum of a finite number of differentiable functions is equal to the sum of their derivatives.*

Proof. We first consider the sum of two terms,

$$y = u + v,$$

where we suppose that u and v are differentiable functions of x whose derivatives are

$$\frac{du}{dx} = \lim_{\Delta x \to 0} \frac{\Delta u}{\Delta x}, \qquad \frac{dv}{dx} = \lim_{\Delta x \to 0} \frac{\Delta v}{\Delta x}.$$

When x is replaced by $x + \Delta x$, the new values of the variables will satisfy the equation

$$y + \Delta y = (u + \Delta u) + (v + \Delta v).$$

We subtract

$$y = u + v$$

from this and obtain

$$\Delta y = \Delta u + \Delta v,$$

and hence

$$\frac{\Delta y}{\Delta x} = \frac{\Delta u}{\Delta x} + \frac{\Delta v}{\Delta x}.$$

By hypothesis, u and v are differentiable, so both $\Delta u/\Delta x$ and $\Delta v/\Delta x$ have limits as Δx approaches zero. Therefore their sum has a limit which is the sum of their limits. Hence

$$\frac{dy}{dx} = \lim_{\Delta x \to 0} \frac{\Delta y}{\Delta x} = \lim_{\Delta x \to 0} \left(\frac{\Delta u}{\Delta x} + \frac{\Delta v}{\Delta x}\right)$$

$$= \lim_{\Delta x \to 0} \frac{\Delta u}{\Delta x} + \lim_{\Delta x \to 0} \frac{\Delta v}{\Delta x},$$

and thus

$$\frac{d(u + v)}{dx} = \frac{du}{dx} + \frac{dv}{dx}.$$

This equation expresses the result that the derivative of the sum of two differentiable functions is the sum of their derivatives. □

Remark. We may proceed by induction to establish the result for the sum of any finite number of terms. For example, if

$$y = u_1 + u_2 + u_3,$$

where u_1, u_2, and u_3 are differentiable functions of x, then we may take

$$u = u_1 + u_2, \quad v = u_3,$$

and apply the result already established for the sum of two terms, namely,

$$\frac{dy}{dx} = \frac{d(u_1 + u_2)}{dx} + \frac{du_3}{dx}.$$

Since the first term is again a sum of two terms, we have

$$\frac{d(u_1 + u_2)}{dx} = \frac{du_1}{dx} + \frac{du_2}{dx},$$

so that

$$\frac{d(u_1 + u_2 + u_3)}{dx} = \frac{du_1}{dx} + \frac{du_2}{dx} + \frac{du_3}{dx}.$$

Finally, if it has been established for some integer n that

$$\frac{d(u_1 + u_2 + \cdots + u_n)}{dx} = \frac{du_1}{dx} + \frac{du_2}{dx} + \cdots + \frac{du_n}{dx},$$

and we let $y = u + v$, with

$$u = u_1 + u_2 + \cdots + u_n,$$

$$v = u_{n+1},$$

we find in the same way as above that

$$\frac{d(u_1 + u_2 + \cdots + u_{n+1})}{dx} = \frac{du_1}{dx} + \frac{du_2}{dx} + \cdots + \frac{du_{n+1}}{dx}.$$

This enables us to conclude that if the theorem is true for a sum of n terms it is also true for a sum of $(n + 1)$ terms, and since it is already established for the sum of two terms, we conclude that it is true for the sum of any finite number of terms.

Corollary. *Let f be a polynomial function*

$$f(x) = c_0 x^n + c_1 x^{n-1} + \cdots c_{n-1} x + c_n,$$

where n is a nonnegative integer and $c_0, c_1, \ldots, c_n$ are numbers. Then f is differentiable for all x, and

$$f'(x) = c_0 n x^{n-1} + c_1 (n - 1) x^{n-2} + \cdots + c_{n-1}.$$

Proof. Apply Theorem 4 and the Corollary of Theorem 3. □

Problem 1. Find dy/dx if

$$y = x^3 + 7x^2 - 5x + 4.$$

Solution. By the results just established, we may find the derivatives of the separate terms of a sum and add the results. Thus

$$\frac{dy}{dx} = \frac{d(x^3)}{dx} + \frac{d(7x^2)}{dx} + \frac{d(-5x)}{dx} + \frac{d(4)}{dx}$$

$$= 3x^2 + 14x - 5.$$

Problem 2. What is the slope of the curve

$$y = x^3 - 6x + 2$$

where it crosses the y-axis?

Solution. The slope at the point (x, y) is equal to

$$\frac{dy}{dx} = 3x^2 - 6.$$

The curve crosses the y-axis when $x = 0$. Hence its slope at that point is $m = (3x^2 - 6)_{x=0} = -6$.

Second- and higher-order derivatives

The derivative with respect to x of $y' = dy/dx$ is called the *second derivative* of y with respect to x and is denoted by y''. That is,

$$y' = \frac{dy}{dx}$$

is the first derivative of y with respect to x, and its derivative,

$$y'' = \frac{dy'}{dx} = \frac{d}{dx}\left(\frac{dy}{dx}\right),$$

is the second derivative of y with respect to x. The operation of taking the derivative of a function twice in succession, denoted by

$$\frac{d}{dx}\left(\frac{d}{dx}\cdots\right),$$

is also indicated by the notation

$$\frac{d^2}{dx^2}(\cdots).$$

In this notation, we write the second derivative of y with respect to x as

$$\frac{d^2y}{dx^2}.$$

More generally, the result of differentiating a function $y = f(x)$ n times in succession is denoted by $y^{(n)}$, by $f^{(n)}(x)$, or by $d^n y/dx^n$.

Example 2. If $y = x^3 - 3x^2 + 2$,

then $y' = \dfrac{dy}{dx} = 3x^2 - 6x$, $y'' = \dfrac{d^2y}{dx^2} = 6x - 6$,

$$y''' = \frac{d^3y}{dx^3} = 6, \quad y^{(iv)} = \frac{d^4y}{dx^4} = 0.$$

In mechanics, if $s = f(t)$ gives the position of a moving body at time t, then

(a) the first derivative ds/dt gives the *velocity*, and

(b) the second derivative d^2s/dt^2 gives the *acceleration*

of the body at time t.

Problem 3. A body moves in a straight line according to the law of motion

$$s = t^3 - 4t^2 - 3t.$$

Find its acceleration at each instant when the velocity is zero.

Solution. Here we find the velocity v and acceleration a are

$$v = \frac{ds}{dt} = 3t^2 - 8t - 3, \quad a = \frac{dv}{dt} = 6t - 8.$$

The velocity is zero when

$$3t^2 - 8t - 3 = (3t + 1)(t - 3) = 0,$$

that is, when

$$t = -\tfrac{1}{3} \quad \text{or} \quad t = 3.$$

The corresponding values of the acceleration are

$$t = -\tfrac{1}{3}, a = -10; \quad t = 3, a = 10.$$

EXERCISES

In Exercises 1 through 5, s represents the position of a moving body at time t. Find the velocity

$$v = ds/dt$$

and the acceleration

$$a = dv/dt = d^2s/dt^2.$$

1. $s = t^2 - 4t + 3$ 2. $s = 2t^3 - 5t^2 + 4t - 3$
3. $s = gt^2/2 + v_0 t + s_0$ (g, v_0, s_0 constants)
4. $s = 3 + 4t - t^2$ 5. $s = (2t + 3)^2$

Find both $y' = dy/dx$ and $y'' = dy'/dx$ in Exercises 6 through 15.

6. $y = x^4 - 7x^3 + 2x^2 + 5$
7. $y = 5x^3 - 3x^5$ 8. $y = 4x^2 - 8x + 1$
9. $y = \dfrac{x^4}{4} - \dfrac{x^3}{3} + \dfrac{x^2}{2} - x + 3$
10. $y = 2x^4 - 4x^2 - 8$
11. $12y = 6x^4 - 18x^2 - 12x$
12. $y = 3x^7 - 7x^3 + 21x^2$ 13. $y = x^2(x^3 - 1)$
14. $y = (x - 2)(x + 3)$ 15. $y = (3x - 1)(2x + 5)$

16. A particle projected vertically upward with a speed of 160 ft/sec reaches an elevation $s = 160t - 16t^2$ at the end of t seconds.

    (a) How high does it rise?

    (b) How fast is it traveling when it reaches an elevation of 256 feet going up and again when it reaches this elevation coming down?

17. Find the line tangent to the curve

    $$y = 2x^2 + 4x - 3$$

    at the point $(1, 3)$.

18. Find the lines tangent to the curve $y = x^3 + x$, where the slope is equal to 4. What is the smallest value the slope of this curve can ever have and where on the curve does the slope equal this smallest value?

19. Find the points on the curve

    $$y = 2x^3 - 3x^2 - 12x + 20$$

    at which the tangent is parallel to the x-axis.

20. Find the values of the constants a, b, and c if the curve $y = ax^2 + bx + c$ is to pass through the point $(1, 2)$ and is to be tangent to the line $y = x$ at the origin.

21. Find the constants a, b, and c so that the two curves

    $$y = x^2 + ax + b \quad \text{and} \quad y = cx - x^2$$

    shall be tangent to each other at the point $(1, 0)$.

22. Find the constant c if the curve $y = x^2 + c$ is to be tangent to the line $y = x$.

4.2 RATIONAL FUNCTIONS AND THEIR DERIVATIVES

In the preceding article, we learned how to find the derivative of a polynomial very quickly by using certain simple formulas. First we found the derivative of a monomial in x,

$$\frac{d}{dx}(cx^n) = cnx^{n-1},$$

and then we proved that the derivative of the sum of a finite number of such terms is the sum of their derivatives.

In this article we shall derive formulas for finding the derivative with respect to x of

$$\text{products} \quad y = uv,$$

$$\text{quotients} \quad y = u/v,$$

$$\text{powers} \quad y = u^n,$$

when u and v are any differentiable functions of x. For the present, this will mean that u and v may be polynomials in x, for example; but after we learn to differentiate other functions like $\sin x$ and $\log x$, the same basic formulas will apply to combinations of these as well.

The product of two polynomials in x is again a polynomial in x; hence if u and v are polynomials the product uv is also a polynomial. Similarly, if n is a positive integer and u is a polynomial, then u^n is again a polynomial. For example,

if $\qquad u = x^2 + 1, \quad v = x^3 + 3,$

then $\qquad uv = x^5 + x^3 + 3x^2 + 3,$

and if $\qquad u = x^2 + 1, \quad n = 2,$

then $\qquad u^n = x^4 + 2x^2 + 1.$

But the ratio u/v of two polynomials is, in general, not a polynomial in x. Such a function is called a *rational* function of x, where the word *ratio* is the key to the real meaning of the word *rational*.

Theorem 5. *The product of two differentiable functions u and v is differentiable, and*

$$\frac{d(uv)}{dx} = u\frac{dv}{dx} + v\frac{du}{dx}. \qquad (1)$$

Proof. Let

$$y = uv,$$

where u and v are differentiable functions of x. Let x be given an increment Δx, and let the corresponding increments in y, u, v be denoted by Δy, Δu, Δv. (These "increments" may be either positive or negative.) Then the new values of the variables satisfy the equation

$$y + \Delta y = (u + \Delta u)(v + \Delta v)$$
$$= uv + u\,\Delta v + v\,\Delta u + \Delta u\,\Delta v.$$

When we subtract from this the equation

$$y = uv,$$

we obtain

$$\Delta y = u\,\Delta v + v\,\Delta u + \Delta u\,\Delta v.$$

Next we must divide by Δx:

$$\frac{\Delta y}{\Delta x} = u\frac{\Delta v}{\Delta x} + v\frac{\Delta u}{\Delta x} + \Delta u\frac{\Delta v}{\Delta x}.$$

Finally, when Δx approaches zero, so will Δu and Δv, since

$$\lim \Delta u = \lim\left(\frac{\Delta u}{\Delta x}\,\Delta x\right)$$

$$= \lim\frac{\Delta u}{\Delta x}\lim \Delta x = \frac{du}{dx}\cdot 0.$$

Thus

$$\lim \frac{\Delta y}{\Delta x} = \lim\left(u\frac{\Delta v}{\Delta x} + v\frac{\Delta u}{\Delta x} + \Delta u\frac{\Delta v}{\Delta x}\right)$$

$$= \lim u\frac{\Delta v}{\Delta x} + \lim v\frac{\Delta u}{\Delta x} + \lim \Delta u\frac{\Delta v}{\Delta x}$$

$$= \lim u\lim\frac{\Delta v}{\Delta x} + \lim v\lim\frac{\Delta u}{\Delta x}$$

$$+ \lim \Delta u\lim\frac{\Delta v}{\Delta x}$$

$$= u\frac{dv}{dx} + v\frac{du}{dx} + 0\cdot\frac{dv}{dx}.$$

That is,

$$\frac{dy}{dx} = u\frac{dv}{dx} + v\frac{du}{dx},$$

which establishes (1). □

Corollary. *If u is a differentiable function of x and n is a positive integer, then u^n is differentiable and*

$$\frac{d}{dx}(u^n) = nu^{n-1}\frac{du}{dx}. \qquad (2)$$

Proof. For $n = 1$, the result is correct if we always interpret u^{n-1} as $u^0 = 1$. (One does not ordinarily so interpret it if u happens to be zero, because 0^0 is an indeterminate expression. But for $u \neq 0$, we would automatically have $u^0 = 1$.)

For $n = 2$, we apply Theorem 5 with $u = v$ and get

$$u\frac{du}{dx} + u\frac{du}{dx} = 2u\frac{du}{dx}$$

as the derivative of $uv = u^2$. Hence Eq. (2) is correct for $n = 2$.

We proceed by induction on n. Suppose that Eq. (2) is known to be true for $n = k$:

$$\frac{d}{dx}(u^k) = ku^{k-1}\frac{du}{dx}.$$

Then for $n = k + 1$, we apply Theorem 5 with $v = u^k$ and get

$$\frac{d}{dx}(uv) = u\frac{dv}{dx} + v\frac{du}{dx} = u\left(ku^{k-1}\frac{du}{dx}\right) + u^k\frac{du}{dx}$$

$$= (k+1)u^k\frac{du}{dx},$$

which is

$$\frac{d}{dx}(u^{k+1}) = (k+1)u^k\frac{du}{dx}.$$

Therefore, whenever Eq. (2) is true for $n = k$, it is also true for the next integer, $k + 1$. Knowing that it is true for $n = 1$ and $n = 2$, we conclude that it is true for all positive integers n. □

Note. The derivative of a product is *not* the product of the derivatives. Instead, we add together two terms $u(dv/dx)$ and $v(du/dx)$. In the first of these we leave u untouched and differentiate v, and in the second we differentiate u and leave v alone. In fact, it is possible to extend the formula, by the method of mathematical induction, to show that the derivative of a product

$$y = u_1 u_2 u_3 \cdots u_{n-1} u_n$$

of a finite number of differentiable functions is given by

$$\frac{d}{dx}(u_1 u_2 u_3 \cdots u_{n-1} u_n) = \frac{du_1}{dx}\cdot u_2 u_3 \cdots u_{n-1} u_n$$

$$+ u_1\frac{du_2}{dx}\cdot u_3 \cdots u_{n-1} u_n + \cdots$$

$$+ u_1 u_2 u_3 \cdots u_{n-1}\cdot\frac{du_n}{dx}, \qquad (3)$$

where the right side of the equation consists of the sum of the n terms obtained by multiplying the derivative of each one of the factors by the other $(n - 1)$ factors undifferentiated.

Theorem 6. *At a point where $v \neq 0$, the derivative of the quotient*

$$y = \frac{u}{v}$$

of two differentiable functions u and v is given by

$$\frac{d}{dx}\left(\frac{u}{v}\right) = \frac{v\dfrac{du}{dx} - u\dfrac{dv}{dx}}{v^2}. \tag{4}$$

Proof. Consider a point $x = c$ where $v \neq 0$ and where u and v are differentiable. Let x be given an increment Δx, and let Δy, Δu, Δv be the corresponding increments in y, u, v. Then as $\Delta x \to 0$,

$$\lim (v + \Delta v) = \lim v + \lim \Delta v,$$

while

$$\lim \Delta v = \lim \frac{\Delta v}{\Delta x} \cdot \Delta x = \frac{dv}{dx} \cdot 0 = 0.$$

Therefore the value of $v + \Delta v$ is close to the value of v when $x + \Delta x$ is close to c, that is, when Δx is near zero. In particular, since $v \neq 0$ at $x = c$, it follows that $v + \Delta v \neq 0$ when Δx is *near* zero, say when $0 < |\Delta x| < h$. Let Δx be so restricted. Then $v + \Delta v \neq 0$ and

$$y + \Delta y = \frac{u + \Delta u}{v + \Delta v}.$$

From this we subtract

$$y = \frac{u}{v}$$

and obtain

$$\begin{aligned}
\Delta y &= \frac{u + \Delta u}{v + \Delta v} - \frac{u}{v} \\
&= \frac{(vu + v\,\Delta u) - (uv + u\,\Delta v)}{v(v + \Delta v)} \\
&= \frac{v\,\Delta u - u\,\Delta v}{v(v + \Delta v)}.
\end{aligned}$$

We divide this by Δx by dividing the numerator of the fraction on the right by Δx and have

$$\frac{\Delta y}{\Delta x} = \frac{v\dfrac{\Delta u}{\Delta x} - u\dfrac{\Delta v}{\Delta x}}{v(v + \Delta v)}.$$

When Δx approaches zero, we obtain

$$\lim \frac{\Delta u}{\Delta x} = \frac{du}{dx};$$

$$\lim \frac{\Delta v}{\Delta x} = \frac{dv}{dx};$$

$$\lim v(v + \Delta v) = \lim v \lim (v + \Delta v) = v^2 \neq 0;$$

and

$$\lim \frac{\Delta y}{\Delta x} = \frac{\lim\left(v\dfrac{\Delta u}{\Delta x} - u\dfrac{\Delta v}{\Delta x}\right)}{\lim v(v + \Delta v)},$$

or

$$\frac{dy}{dx} = \frac{v\dfrac{du}{dx} - u\dfrac{dv}{dx}}{v^2},$$

which establishes Eq. (4). $\square$

Theorem 7. *At a point where $u = g(x)$ is differentiable and different from zero, the derivative of*

$$y = u^n$$

is given by

$$\frac{d(u^n)}{dx} = nu^{n-1}\frac{du}{dx} \tag{5}$$

if n is a negative integer.

Before we prove the theorem, we first note that formula (5) is the extension of (2) to the case where n is a *negative integer*.

Proof. To prove the theorem, we combine the results in Eqs. (2) and (4) as follows. Let

$$y = u^{-m} = \frac{1}{u^m},$$

where $n = -m$ is a negative integer, so that m is a positive integer. Then, using (4) for the derivative of a quotient, we have

$$\frac{dy}{dx} = \frac{d\left(\dfrac{1}{u^m}\right)}{dx} = \frac{u^m\dfrac{d(1)}{dx} - 1\dfrac{d(u^m)}{dx}}{(u^m)^2} \tag{6}$$

at any point where u is differentiable and different from zero. Now the various derivatives on the right side of (6) can be evaluated by formulas already proved, namely,

$$\frac{d(1)}{dx} = 0,$$

since 1 is a constant, and

$$\frac{d(u^m)}{dx} = mu^{m-1}\frac{du}{dx},$$

since m is a *positive integer*. Therefore

$$\frac{dy}{dx} = \frac{u^m \cdot 0 - 1 \cdot mu^{m-1}\frac{du}{dx}}{u^{2m}} = -mu^{-m-1}\frac{du}{dx}.$$

If $-m$ is replaced by its equivalent value n, the formula reduces to Eq. (5). □

Problem 1. Find the derivative of $y = x^2 + 1/x^2, x \neq 0$.

Solution. We may write

$$y = x^2 + x^{-2}.$$

Then

$$\frac{dy}{dx} = 2x^{2-1}\frac{dx}{dx} + (-2)x^{-2-1}\frac{dx}{dx}$$

$$= 2x - 2x^{-3}.$$

Problem 2. Find the derivative of

$$y = \frac{x^2+1}{x^2-1}, \quad x^2 \neq 1.$$

Solution. We apply the formula, Eq. (4), for the derivative of a quotient and have

$$\frac{dy}{dx} = \frac{(x^2-1)\cdot 2x - (x^2+1)\cdot 2x}{(x^2-1)^2}$$

$$= \frac{-4x}{(x^2-1)^2}.$$

Problem 3. Find the derivative of

$$y = (x^2+1)^3(x^3-1)^2.$$

Solution. We could, of course, expand everything here and write y as a polynomial in x, but this is not necessary. Instead we use Eq. (1) for the derivative of a product.

$$\frac{dy}{dx} = (x^2+1)^3\frac{d}{dx}(x^3-1)^2 + (x^3-1)^2\frac{d}{dx}(x^2+1)^3.$$

The derivatives which are now to be evaluated are of the type in Eq. (2).

$$\frac{d}{dx}(x^3-1)^2 = 2(x^3-1)\frac{d}{dx}(x^3-1)$$

$$= 2(x^3-1)\cdot 3x^2 = 6x^2(x^3-1),$$

and

$$\frac{d}{dx}(x^2+1)^3 = 3(x^2+1)^2\frac{d}{dx}(x^2+1)$$

$$= 3(x^2+1)^2 \cdot 2x = 6x(x^2+1)^2.$$

We substitute these into the earlier equation and have

$$\frac{dy}{dx} = (x^2+1)^3 6x^2(x^3-1) + (x^3-1)^2 6x(x^2+1)^2$$

$$= 6x(x^2+1)^2(x^3-1)[x(x^2+1) + (x^3-1)]$$

$$= 6x(x^2+1)^2(x^3-1)(2x^3+x-1).$$

EXERCISES

Find dy/dx in Exercises 1 through 8.

1. $y = x^3/3 - x^2/2 + x - 1$
2. $y = (x-1)^3(x+2)^4$
3. $y = (x^2+1)^5$ 4. $y = (x^3-3x)^4$
5. $y = (x+1)^2(x^2+1)^{-3}$ 6. $y = \dfrac{2x+1}{x^2-1}$
7. $y = \dfrac{2x+5}{\sqrt{3x-2}}$ 8. $y = \left(\dfrac{x+1}{x-1}\right)^2$

Find ds/dt in Exercises 9 through 15.

9. $s = \dfrac{t}{t^2+1}$ 10. $s = (2t+3)^3$
11. $s = (t^2-t)^{-2}$ 12. $s = t^2(t+1)^{-1}$
13. $s = \dfrac{2t}{3t^2+1}$ 14. $s = (t+t^{-1})^2$
15. $s = (t^2+3t)^3$

16. With the book closed, state and prove the formula for the derivative of the product of two differentiable functions u and v.

17. With the book closed, state and prove the formula for the derivative of the quotient u/v of two differentiable functions u and v.

18. With the book closed, state and prove the formula for the derivative with respect to x of u^n, n a positive integer and u a differentiable function of x.

19. Prove the formula in Eq. (3) for the derivative of the product of n differentiable functions by induction on n (for $n \geq 2$).

20. Use the formula in Eq. (3) with $u_1, u_2, u_3, \ldots, u_n$ all equal to u to establish Eq. (2) for $n \geq 2$.

4.2

4.3 INVERSE FUNCTIONS AND THEIR DERIVATIVES

For some functions it is not only true that to each x in the domain there corresponds a unique y in the range, but also that each such y is the *image* of only one x. For example, the mapping

$$f: x \to \sqrt{x} \tag{1}$$

is such a one-to-one mapping from the domain $x \geq 0$ to the range $y \geq 0$. Figure 4.2 illustrates how the graph of $y = \sqrt{x}$ can be used to go from any nonnegative x to its nonnegative square root: Start at x, go up to the curve, and then go across to the y-axis to $\sqrt{x}$. Since every nonnegative y is the image of just one x under this mapping, we can reverse the procedure. That is, we can start with $y \geq 0$, go over to the curve, and then go down to y^2 on the x-axis. This reverse mapping

$$g: y \to y^2, \quad y \geq 0, \tag{2}$$

describes a new function (the squaring function) that is called the *inverse* of the function f (which in this example is the square-root function).

Remark 1. The mapping g, as written in Eq. (2), has y as its independent variable (the domain variable for g). Any other letter could equally well be used if we were studying only g: e. g., any of

$$g(t) = t^2, \quad g(a) = a^2, \quad g(x) = x^2,$$

with the understanding that the domain is the set of nonnegative real numbers.

4.3

Remark 2. If the mapping g is expressed with x as independent variable, so that $g(x) = x^2$, the graph of g can be obtained by reflecting the graph of f in the 45° line $y = x$ as mirror (see Fig. 4.3). Any points $P(x_1, y_1)$ and $P'(y_1, x_1)$ are symmetric with respect to the line $y = x$. Thus $(a, \sqrt{a})$ and $(\sqrt{a}, a)$ are symmetric pairs. The first of these is on the graph of f, the second is on the graph of g.

If f and g are any pair of inverse functions, their graphs are mirror images of each other with respect to the 45° line $y = x$. Thus, if L_1 is the line tangent to the graph of f at (c, d) and L_2 is the mirror image of L_1 with respect to the 45° line, then it is reasonable to expect L_2 to be tangent to the graph of g at (d, c). (Figure 4.4 illustrates this idea.) Since (rise)/(run)

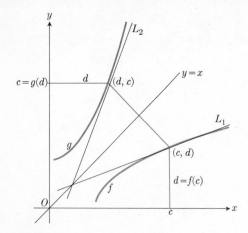

4.4 Graphs of inverse functions f and g and tangents L_1 and L_2 at corresponding points (c, d) and (d, c). Note that $d = f(c)$ and $c = g(d)$.

on L_2 corresponds to (run)/(rise) on L_1, we see that the slope of L_2 is just the reciprocal of the slope of L_1: $m' = 1/m$. Since L_1 is tangent to f at $(c, f(c))$,

$$m = f'(c).$$

And, if L_2 is tangent to the graph of g at $(d, g(d))$, then

$$m' = g'(d).$$

Hence the geometric evidence suggests that

$$g'(f(c)) = \frac{1}{f'(c)}. \qquad (3)$$

Naturally, Eq. (3) requires the existence of the derivative of f at c, and also requires that $f'(c) \neq 0$. In Fig. 4.4, f' is positive and f is a strictly increasing function.

The following two theorems are called *lemmas*. According to Webster, "lemma" means "a preliminary or auxiliary proposition or theorem demonstrated or accepted for immediate use in a demonstration of some other proposition." We shall use the two lemmas in establishing the validity of Eq. (3) when $f'(c)$ is positive. [The proof when $f'(c)$ is negative is only slightly different.] Briefly, what the first lemma says is that if dy/dx is positive at a point, then $\Delta y/\Delta x$ is also positive when Δx is near zero.

Lemma 1. *Let f be differentiable at c and $f'(c) > 0$. Then*

$$f(c + h) > f(c) \quad \text{and} \quad f(c - h) < f(c) \qquad (4)$$

for sufficiently small positive values of h.

Proof. Let $f'(c) = p$, where p is a positive number. When Δx is near zero, the difference quotient

$$\frac{f(c + \Delta x) - f(c)}{\Delta x} \qquad (5)$$

is very nearly equal to p, by definition of $f'(c)$ as a limit. In particular, since p is positive, we can take $\epsilon = p/2$ and be sure that the above quotient is between $p - \epsilon$ and $p + \epsilon$ when Δx is in a sufficiently small deleted neighborhood of zero. Let N be such a deleted neighborhood. Then

$$\frac{p}{2} < \frac{f(c + \Delta x) - f(c)}{\Delta x} < \frac{3p}{2} \quad \text{when } \Delta x \in N.$$

Since the interval $(p/2, 3p/2)$ contains only positive numbers, the numerator and denominator in the difference quotient (5) must have the same sign, both positive when $\Delta x = h$ is positive and both negative when $\Delta x = -h$ is negative. That is,

$$f(c + h) - f(c) > 0 \quad \text{for } h > 0,\ h \in N$$

and

$$f(c - h) - f(c) < 0 \quad \text{for } h > 0,\ -h \in N.$$

These inequalities establish Lemma 1. □

Lemma 2. *If f is a differentiable function at x, and if*

$$\Delta y = f(x + \Delta x) - f(x),$$

then $\quad \lim \Delta y = 0 \quad \text{as} \quad \Delta x \to 0.$

Proof. (This is left as an exercise. See the proof that $\Delta u \to 0$ as $\Delta x \to 0$ in the proof of Theorem 5.)

Theorem 8. *Let f be a one-to-one function with domain $[a, b]$ and range $[f(a), f(b)]$, whose derivative exists and is positive on (a, b). Then f has an inverse g, and if $y = f(x)$,*

then $\quad g'(y) = \dfrac{1}{f'(x)}, \quad \text{for } a < x < b. \qquad (6)$

Or, in another notation, if $y = f(x)$, then $x = g(y)$ and

$$\frac{dx}{dy} = \frac{1}{dy/dx}.$$

Proof. Because f is one-to-one from its domain D_f to its range R_f, the rule

$$g(y) = x \quad \text{if and only if} \quad y = f(x), \ x \in D_f$$

defines a function g whose domain D_g is the range of f:

$$D_g = R_f.$$

Figure 4.5 will help us to follow the remaining steps of the proof. Fix $y \in D_g$ and $x = g(y) \in D_f$. Then in Lemma 1 take $c = x$ and let N be a neighborhood of x contained in (a, b) and such that the inequalities (4) apply when $x + h$ and $x - h$ are in N and $h > 0$. This is possible because $a < x < b$. Also, let

$$y - k_1 = f(x - h), \quad y + k_2 = f(x + h).$$

Then k_1 and k_2 are positive numbers, so y is an inner point of the domain of g, and that domain contains the closed interval $[y - k, y + k]$, where

$$k = \min \{k_1, k_2\}.$$

For each $\Delta y \neq 0$ such that $|\Delta y| < k$, there exists $\Delta x \neq 0$ such that $|\Delta x| < h$ and

$$f(x + \Delta x) = y + \Delta y, \quad g(y + \Delta y) = x + \Delta x.$$

To prove that $g'(y)$ exists, we must show that the difference quotient

$$\frac{g(y + \Delta y) - g(y)}{\Delta y}$$

has a limit as $\Delta y \to 0$. But this is easy, because

$$g(y) = x, \quad g(y + \Delta y) = x + \Delta x,$$

$$y = f(x), \quad y + \Delta y = f(x + \Delta x),$$

so that

$$\frac{g(y + \Delta y) - g(y)}{\Delta y} = \frac{(x + \Delta x) - x}{f(x + \Delta x) - f(x)}$$

$$= \frac{\Delta x}{f(x + \Delta x) - f(x)}, \quad (7)$$

4.5

and

$$\lim_{\Delta x \to 0} \frac{f(x + \Delta x) - f(x)}{\Delta x} = f'(x). \quad (8a)$$

By hypothesis, $f'(x) \neq 0$. Therefore, taking reciprocals in Eq. (8a) we get

$$\lim_{\Delta x \to 0} \frac{\Delta x}{f(x + \Delta x) - f(x)} = \frac{1}{f'(x)}. \quad (8b)$$

By Lemma 2, $\Delta y \to 0$ when $\Delta x \to 0$. (The converse is also true because f and g are both one-to-one and continuous. Further discussion of continuity is postponed to the end of Chapter 4.) Therefore, if we let $\Delta x \to 0$ and use Eqs. (7) and (8b), we get

$$\lim_{\Delta y \to 0} \frac{g(y + \Delta y) - g(y)}{\Delta y} = \lim_{\Delta x \to 0} \frac{\Delta x}{f(x + \Delta x) - f(x)},$$

or

$$g'(y) = \frac{1}{f'(x)}. \quad \square$$

Example 1

Let $\qquad a = 0, \quad b > 0, \quad f(x) = x^2.$

Then $\qquad f'(x) = 2x > 0 \quad \text{for } a < x < b,$

and $\qquad$ if $y = x^2 = f(x),$ then $x = \sqrt{y} = g(y)$

for $0 < x < b$ and $0 < y < b^2$. By Theorem 8,

$$g'(y) = \frac{1}{f'(x)} = \frac{1}{2x} = \frac{1}{2\sqrt{y}}.$$

For $y = f(x) = x^2$, $x \geq 0$, the inverse (expressed as a function of y) is $x = g(y) = y^{1/2}$. Similarly, if n is any positive integer and if

$$y = f(x) = x^n, \quad x \geq 0,$$

then the inverse (expressed as a function of y) is

$$x = g(y) = y^{1/n}, \quad y \geq 0.$$

We have just seen illustrated that

$$\frac{d}{dy}(y^{1/2}) = \tfrac{1}{2}y^{-1/2}, \quad \text{if} \quad y > 0.$$

The following corollary extends this result.

Corollary 8.1. *Let n be a positive integer, $y > 0$,*

and let $$g(y) = y^{1/n}. \tag{9a}$$

Then $$g'(y) = \frac{1}{n}y^{(1/n)-1}. \tag{9b}$$

Proof. Let the inverse of g be f, defined for $x > 0$ such that $y = f(x)$, or $y = x^n$. Then by Theorem 8,

$$g'(y) = \frac{1}{f'(x)}, \quad \text{or} \quad g'(y) = \frac{1}{nx^{n-1}}.$$

Since $x^n = y$, we have

$$x = y^{1/n} \quad \text{and} \quad x^{n-1} = y^{(n-1)/n} = y^{1-(1/n)}.$$

Therefore

$$g'(y) = \frac{1}{ny^{1-(1/n)}} \quad \text{or} \quad g'(y) = \frac{1}{n}y^{(1/n)-1}. \quad \square$$

Remark 3. In Theorem 8, we assumed that $f'(x) > 0$ for $a < x < b$. We could equally well have proved the theorem under the assumption $f'(x) < 0$ on (a, b). Under the first hypothesis f is a strictly increasing function, while the second hypothesis fits a strictly decreasing function. Only minor changes in the proof are needed in this alternative form. Indeed, one can achieve the desired result by applying Theorem 8 to the functions $f_1 = -f$ and $g_1 = -g$:

$$g_1'(y) = \frac{1}{f_1'(x)} \Rightarrow g'(y) = \frac{1}{f'(x)}.$$

Henceforth, when we use Theorem 8, we may do so under either of the assumptions

$$f'(x) > 0 \quad \text{for all } x \in (a, b),$$

or

$$f'(x) < 0 \quad \text{for all } x \in (a, b),$$

Corollary 8.2. *Let n be a negative integer and*

let $$g(y) = y^{1/n}, \, y > 0.$$

Then $$g'(y) = \frac{1}{n}y^{(1/n)-1}.$$

Proof. For $x > 0$, let $f(x) = x^n$. Then

$$f'(x) = nx^{n-1} < 0 \quad \text{for } x > 0.$$

The functions f and g are inverses on $x > 0$, $y > 0$, because

$$y = x^n = f(x) \quad \text{if and only if} \quad x = y^{1/n} = g(y).$$

Hence

$$g'(y) = \frac{1}{f'(x)} = \frac{1}{nx^{n-1}} = \frac{1}{n}y^{(1/n)-1}. \quad \square$$

Remark 4. These applications of Theorem 8 have been made easier by using the notation $g(y) = y^{1/n}$. However, it is also true that if $g(x) = x^{1/n}$, then $g'(x) = (1/n)x^{(1/n)-1}$, because there is nothing sacred about which letter of the alphabet we use for the variable in the definition of g. Moreover, instead of writing the exponent as $1/n$, with n a positive or negative integer, we could write the exponent as n and say that n is the reciprocal of a positive or negative integer. In other words, Corollaries 8.1 and 8.2 simply extend the familiar formula

$$\frac{d}{dx}(x^n) = nx^{n-1} \tag{10}$$

from its earlier applications, where n was a positive integer (and all values of x), or a negative integer (and $x \neq 0$), to the situation where n is the reciprocal of a positive or negative integer (and $x > 0$). We are now in a position to extend Eq. (10) to any *rational* exponent n, for $x > 0$.

Theorem 9. *Let n be a rational number. Let f be the function*

$$f(x) = x^n, \quad x > 0.$$

Then

$$f'(x) = nx^{n-1}. \tag{11}$$

Proof. Because n is rational, there are integers p and q with $q > 0$, such that $n = p/q$. Let

$$u = x^{1/q}, \quad y = x^{p/q} = u^p.$$

By Corollaries 8.1 and 8.2,

$$\frac{du}{dx} = \frac{1}{q} x^{(1/q)-1}.$$

By the corollary of Theorem 5,

$$\begin{aligned}
\frac{dy}{dx} &= pu^{p-1}\frac{du}{dx} = pu^{p-1}\left(\frac{1}{q} x^{(1/q)-1}\right) \\
&= \frac{p}{q}(x^{(1/q)})^{p-1}x^{(1/q)-1} \\
&= \frac{p}{q} x^{((p/q)-(1/q)+(1/q)-1)} \\
&= nx^{n-1},
\end{aligned}$$

because $p/q = n$. $\square$

Example 2. If $\quad y = x^{2/3}, \quad x > 0,$

then $\qquad dy/dx = \frac{2}{3}x^{-1/3}.$

Remark 5. The restriction $x > 0$ is not necessary in Example 2, because either positive or negative values of x have real cube roots and Theorem 2 could be extended to cover negative as well as positive values of x for all rational values of n for which x^n is real valued. The corresponding change in Corollary 8.2 would be to allow y to be negative (or positive) when n is an odd integer. The key feature there is that the equation $y = x^n$, for n an odd integer, establishes a one-to-one correspondence between the set of all nonzero real numbers x and the set of all nonzero real numbers y. (This is true for $n = 1, 3, 5, \ldots$ or $n = -1, -3, -5, \ldots$)

The next examples illustrate a technique known as *implicit differentiation.* (We shall not be able to justify the method rigorously because it involves more sophisticated ideas than we take up in this book. Nevertheless the method is easy to understand and to apply.) If a relation between x and y is expressed by an equation such as

$$x^2 + y^2 = 1, \quad xy = 1, \quad x^2 + xy + y^5 = 3,$$

it may be difficult (or impossible) to solve the equation explicitly for y in terms of x. Or, the solution may not express y as a *function* of x. The next example will clarify some of these points, and show the *method of **implicit differentiation**.*

Example 3. If we solve the equation

$$x^2 + y^2 = 1 \tag{12}$$

for y, we get

$$y = \pm\sqrt{1-x^2}.$$

For each $x \in (-1, 1)$, there are two corresponding values of y, not just one as is required for a function. But we can look at two different functions

$$f(x) = +\sqrt{1-x^2}, \quad g(x) = -\sqrt{1-x^2}, \quad |x| < 1.$$

Focus attention on $f(x)$. Call it u and *assume* that it is differentiable. (This will be proved later when we prove the chain rule.) Then u^2 is also differentiable and we know that

$$\frac{d}{dx}(u^2) = 2u\frac{du}{dx}.$$

Also, since $u = \sqrt{1-x^2}$, it is clear that $u^2 + x^2$ is equal to the constant function 1 on the domain $|x| < 1$. Therefore

$$\frac{d}{dx}(u^2 + x^2) = \frac{d}{dx}(1) = 0 \quad \text{for } |x| < 1.$$

This implies that

$$2u\frac{du}{dx} + 2x = 0, \quad \text{so} \quad \frac{du}{dx} = \frac{-x}{u}.$$

Thus, if $u = \sqrt{1-x^2}$ is differentiable, its derivative is

$$u' = \frac{-x}{u} \quad \text{for } |x| < 1.$$

Had we chosen the other function, say

$$v = g(x) = -\sqrt{1-x^2},$$

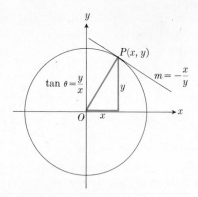

4.6 For the circle $x^2 + y^2 = 1$, the slope of the tangent at $P(x, y)$ is the negative reciprocal of the slope of OP: $dy/dx = -(x/y)$, $m_{OP} = y/x$.

the algebra would have been just the same:

$v^2 + x^2$ is the constant function 1 on $(-1, 1)$,

so, if v is differentiable, then

$$2vv' + 2x = 0, \quad v' = \frac{-x}{v}.$$

In practice, we would not have solved the original equation at all. We would have reasoned that if the original equation determines y as one or more functions of x, and if those functions are differentiable, then $x^2 + y^2$ is the sum of two differentiable functions and it is also the constant function 1 on $(-1, 1)$. Differentiating Eq. (12) implicitly with respect to x, we would get

$$\frac{d}{dx}(x^2 + y^2) = \frac{d}{dx}(1), \quad \text{or} \quad 2x + 2yy' = 0,$$

so

$$y' = -x/y.$$

See Fig. 4.6.

Example 4. If we differentiate both sides of the equation

$$xy = 1 \tag{13}$$

with respect to x, treating y as a differentiable function (which we happen in this case to know it is, for $x \neq 0$), then we get $xy' + y = 0$, or $y' = -y/x$. Here we could have done the problem differently:

$$y = x^{-1}, \quad y' = -1x^{-2}.$$

The answers agree, because $-y/x = -x^{-1}/x = -1x^{-2}$.

Example 5. In a more complicated equation, such as

$$x^2 + xy + y^5 = 3, \tag{14}$$

we cannot solve for y in terms of x. It is easy to verify that the point $(x_0, y_0) = (1, 1)$ is on the graph of Eq. (14). We proceed on faith, assuming that there is some neighborhood of x_0 throughout which $y = f(x)$ would satisfy the equation, with f a differentiable function at x_0. (There is nothing to be afraid of—go ahead and make the assumption.) Then y^5 is also differentiable and

$$\frac{d}{dx}(y^5) = 5y^4\frac{dy}{dx}.$$

Similarly xy is differentiable, and

$$\frac{d}{dx}(xy) = xy' + y.$$

Differentiating both sides of Eq. (14) implicitly with respect to x, we get

$$2x + (xy' + y) + 5y^4y' = 0.$$

This equation is linear in y', and can easily be solved to get

$$y' = -\frac{2x + y}{x + 5y^4}.$$

At the point $(x_0, y_0) = (1, 1)$, the slope of the curve is

$$y'(1, 1) = -\frac{2x + y}{x + 5y^4}\bigg]_{(1,1)} = -\frac{3}{6} = -\frac{1}{2}.$$

Example 6. If $y = x^{p/q}$,

then $y^q = x^p$,

and implicit differentiation with respect to x yields the familiar results

$$qy^{q-1}\frac{dy}{dx} = px^{p-1},$$

or

$$\frac{dy}{dx} = \frac{p}{q}y^{1-q}x^{p-1} = \frac{p}{q}(x^{p/q})^{1-q}x^{p-1} = \frac{p}{q}x^{(p/q)-1}.$$

Remark 6. It is not easy to establish the validity of implicit differentiation without using partial derivatives. (See, for example: Olmsted, *Advanced Calculus*, Appleton-Century-Crofts, 1961, p. 289; or Fine, *Calculus*, Macmillan, 1937, p. 248.)

The foregoing examples were intended to convince you that it is all right to go ahead and differentiate implicitly. But if you find that you are trying to divide by zero: Stop.

EXERCISES

Nov.5

In Exercises 1 through 23, find dy/dx.

1. $x^2 + y^2 = 1$

2. $y^2 = \dfrac{x-1}{x+1}$

3. $x^2 + xy = 2$

4. $x^2 y + xy^2 = 6$

5. $y^2 = x^3$

6. $x^{2/3} + y^{2/3} = 1$

7. $x^{1/2} + y^{1/2} = 1$

8. $x^3 - xy + y^3 = 1$

9. $x^2 = \dfrac{x-y}{x+y}$

10. $y = \dfrac{x}{\sqrt{x^2+1}}$

11. $y = x\sqrt{x^2+1}$

12. $y^2 = x^2 + \dfrac{1}{x^2}$

13. $2xy + y^2 = x + y$

14. $y = \sqrt{x} + \sqrt[3]{x} + \sqrt[4]{x}$

15. $y^2 = \dfrac{x^2-1}{x^2+1}$

16. $(x+y)^3 + (x-y)^3 = x^4 + y^4$

17. $(3x+7)^5 = 2y^3$

18. $y = (x+5)^4 (x^2-2)^3$

19. $\dfrac{1}{y} + \dfrac{1}{x} = 1$

20. $y = (x^2 + 5x)^3$

21. $y^2 = x^2 - x$

22. $x^2 y^2 = x^2 + y^2$

23. $y = \dfrac{\sqrt[3]{x^2+3}}{x}$

24. (a) By differentiating the equation $x^2 - y^2 = 1$ implicitly, show that $dy/dx = x/y$.

(b) By differentiating both sides of the equation $dy/dx = x/y$ implicitly, show that

$$\frac{d^2y}{dx^2} = \frac{y - x\left(\dfrac{dy}{dx}\right)}{y^2} = \frac{y - \dfrac{x^2}{y}}{y^2} = \frac{y^2 - x^2}{y^3},$$

or, since $y^2 - x^2 = -1$ from the original equation, that

$$\frac{d^2y}{dx^2} = \frac{-1}{y^3}.$$

Use the method outlined in Exercise 24 to find dy/dx and d^2y/dx^2 in Exercises 25 through 28.

25. $x^2 + y^2 = 1$

26. $x^3 + y^3 = 1$

27. $x^{2/3} + y^{2/3} = 1$

28. $xy + y^2 = 1$

29. A particle of mass m moves along the x-axis. The velocity $v = dx/dt$ and position x satisfy the equation

$$m(v^2 - v_0^2) = k(x_0^2 - x^2),$$

where k, v_0, and x_0 are constants. Show, by implicitly differentiating this equation with respect to t, that whenever $v \neq 0$,

$$m\frac{dv}{dt} = -kx.$$

Find the lines that are respectively *tangent* and *normal* to the following curves at the points indicated as P_0. (A line is said to be *normal* to a curve at a point P_0 if it is perpendicular to the tangent at P_0.)

30. $x^2 + xy - y^2 = 1$, $P_0(2, 3)$

31. $x^2 + y^2 = 25$, $P_0(3, -4)$

32. $x^2 y^2 = 9$, $P_0(-1, 3)$

33. $\dfrac{x-y}{x-2y} = 2$, $P_0(3, 1)$

34. $(y - x)^2 = 2x + 4$, $P_0(6, 2)$

35. (a) Sketch graphs of the curves $y = x^3$ and $y = x^{1/3}$ for $-2 \leq x \leq 2$, and sketch the lines tangent to them at the points $(1, 1)$ and $(-1, -1)$.

(b) Which of these two functions fails to have a derivative at $x = 0$? What is the slope of the other curve at that point? What lines are tangent to the two curves at that point?

36. Consider the functions $f_n(x) = x^n$ on $[0, 1]$. Sketch graphs (rough approximations will do) for $n = 1$, 3, 10, $\frac{1}{3}$, and $\frac{1}{10}$. [For $n = 10$, you may estimate

$$(0.5)^{10} = (1/1024) = 0.001,$$

and for $n = \frac{1}{10}$,

$$(0.5)^{0.1} = \sqrt[10]{0.5} = 0.933.$$

These also mean that the tenth root of 0.001 is approximately $\frac{1}{2}$ and the tenth power of 0.933 is approximately $\frac{1}{2}$.]

37. (Continuation of Exercise 36.) What do you think happens to $f_n(x)$ for fixed $x \in [0, 1)$ as $n \to \infty$? To $f_n(1)$? Is there a limit for each $x \in [0, 1]$? If so, let

$$g(x) = \lim_{n \to \infty} f_n(x),$$

and describe the graph of $y = g(x)$ on $[0, 1]$.

38. Which of the five functions described in Exercise 36 is (are) differentiable on $(0, 1)$? If the defining equation makes sense for $x \in (-\infty, \infty)$ or for $x \in [0, \infty)$, let the domains be so extended. Of these new functions, which ones are differentiable for all x's in their domains? Where do some of the new functions fail to be differentiable? Discuss.

39. Of the functions of Exercise 38 (those of Exercise 36 with extended domains), which have inverses that are functions? Is the inverse of each of these five functions always one of the five? Discuss.

4.4 THE INCREMENT OF A FUNCTION

In this article, we shall learn how to estimate the change Δy produced in a function $y = f(x)$ when x changes by a small amount Δx. To be precise, let us focus our attention on a portion of the graph of $y = f(x)$ in the neighborhood of a point $P(x, y)$ where the function is differentiable. Then, if $Q(x + \Delta x, y + \Delta y)$ is a second point on the curve, with $\Delta x \neq 0$, we know that

$$\text{the slope of the secant line } PQ = \frac{\Delta y}{\Delta x}$$

approaches the limiting value

$$\frac{dy}{dx} = f'(x)$$

as Δx approaches zero. Therefore, the difference

$$\frac{\Delta y}{\Delta x} - \frac{dy}{dx}$$

is numerically small when $|\Delta x|$ is small. Let us denote this difference by ϵ:

$$\frac{\Delta y}{\Delta x} - \frac{dy}{dx} = \epsilon. \tag{1}$$

Then, saying that

$$\lim_{\Delta x \to 0} \frac{\Delta y}{\Delta x} = \frac{dy}{dx} = f'(x) \tag{2}$$

is equivalent to saying that

$$\lim_{\Delta x \to 0} \epsilon = 0. \tag{3}$$

In other words, we may deduce from Eqs. (1), (2), and (3) that

$$\frac{\Delta y}{\Delta x} = \frac{dy}{dx} + \epsilon, \tag{4a}$$

where

$$\epsilon \to 0 \quad \text{as} \quad \Delta x \to 0. \tag{4b}$$

If we multiply both sides of (4a) by Δx, we also have

$$\Delta y = \frac{dy}{dx} \Delta x + \epsilon \, \Delta x. \tag{4c}$$

Although Eq. (4c) was derived under the assumption that $\Delta x \neq 0$, it is still a true equation even when $\Delta x = 0$. In fact, if we define ϵ by Eq. (1) when $\Delta x \neq 0$, and take $\epsilon = 0$ when $\Delta x = 0$, then Eqs. (4b, c) hold whether $\Delta x = 0$ or not.

If we compare Fig. 4.7 with Fig. 2.23, Article 2.8, we see that the first term on the right-hand side of Eq. (4c) is equal to the change $\Delta y_{\tan}$ that would be produced in y by a change Δx in x if the point (x, y) were to move along the tangent line. This is called the *linear part* of Δy, and for small values of Δx it usually is large in comparison with the second term $\epsilon \, \Delta x$.

The significance of Eqs. (4b, c) is that

$$\Delta y = \Delta y_{\tan} + \epsilon \, \Delta x$$
$$= \text{change in } y \text{ } along \text{ } the \text{ } curve$$

and

$$\Delta y_{\tan} = \frac{dy}{dx} \Delta x$$
$$= \text{change in } y \text{ } along \text{ } the \text{ } tangent \text{ } line$$

differ by an amount

$$\epsilon \, \Delta x,$$

which tends to zero more rapidly than Δx does when Δx approaches zero.

4.7

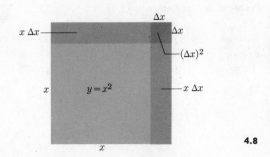

4.8

Example. If
$$y = x^2 = f(x),$$

then
$$\frac{dy}{dx} = 2x = f'(x),$$

and the linear part of Δy is

$$\frac{dy}{dx}\Delta x = 2x\,\Delta x.$$

On the other hand, the exact value of Δy is

$$\Delta y = 2x\,\Delta x + (\Delta x)^2.$$

We compare this with Eq. (4c) and see that for this particular example, the part which is denoted by $\epsilon\,\Delta x$ in (4c) is

$$\epsilon\,\Delta x = (\Delta x)^2.$$

When Δx is small, $(\Delta x)^2$ is the square of a small number and this is much smaller than Δx itself.

This example,

$$y = x^2, \quad \text{(linear part of } \Delta y) = 2x\,\Delta x,$$

also lends itself to a geometrical interpretation, as illustrated by Fig. 4.8. The original square, having sides x by x, has area $y = x^2$. When the sides are increased

to $x + \Delta x$ by $x + \Delta x$, the area is increased by

$$\Delta y = 2x\,\Delta x + (\Delta x)^2.$$

When Δx is small in comparison with x, most of the change in y is given by the two rectangular pieces x by Δx and only a very small part is given by the small square Δx by Δx. Thus, if the original square has sides

$$x = 2 \text{ (in.)}$$

and the larger square has sides

$$x + \Delta x = 2.01 \text{ (in.)},$$

so that

$$\Delta x = +0.01 \text{ (in.)},$$

the area of the original square is

$$y = x^2 = 4 \text{ (in}^2)$$

and the area of the larger square is

$$y + \Delta y = (x + \Delta x)^2 = x^2 + 2x\,\Delta x + (\Delta x)^2$$
$$= 4 + 0.04 + 0.0001 \text{ (in}^2).$$

The increment,

$$\Delta y = 0.04 + 0.0001 \text{ (in}^2),$$

has its linear part equal to

$$2x\,\Delta x = 0.04 \text{ (in}^2)$$

and its remainder

$$(\Delta x)^2 = 0.0001 \text{ (in}^2).$$

If we were to use only the linear part of Δy as an approximation to Δy itself, we would thereby introduce an error of magnitude 0.0001 (in²), which is just under one-fourth of one percent of Δy.

Since the linear part of Δy usually gives a good approximation to Δy itself (at least when Δx is small compared with dy/dx), it is customary to use the approximation

$$\Delta y \approx \frac{dy}{dx}\Delta x = \Delta y_{\text{tan}} \qquad (5)$$

in numerical calculations. (The symbol $\approx$ means "is approximately equal to.")

Problem 1. Use the approximation in Eq. (5) to approximate the change in $y = x^3$ when x changes from 3 to 2.98.

Solution. We take $x = 3$ and $x + \Delta x = 2.98$, so that $\Delta x = 2.98 - 3 = -0.02$. Since

$$\frac{dy}{dx} = 3x^2,$$

we find, using Eq. (5), that

$$\Delta y \approx 3x^2 \, \Delta x = 27(-0.02) = -0.54.$$

Problem 2. Using the approximation in Eq. (5), determine a reasonable approximation to $(2.98)^3$.

Solution. As in Problem 1, we consider

$$y = x^3.$$

Since 2.98 is near to 3 and $3^3 = 27$ is easily calculated, we think of starting from the point

$$(x = 3, \quad y = 27)$$

and trying to reach the point

$$(x + \Delta x = 2.98, \quad y + \Delta y = (2.98)^3 = ?).$$

Now instead of calculating $(2.98)^3$ exactly, we shall make use of the *approximation*

$$\Delta y \approx \frac{dy}{dx} \Delta x = 3x^2 \, \Delta x = -0.54.$$

Hence, adding this to $y = x^3 = 27$, we have

$$(2.98)^3 = y + \Delta y \approx y + \frac{dy}{dx} \Delta x = 27 - 0.54,$$

or

$$(2.98)^3 \approx 26.46.$$

Remark 1. Let f be a differentiable function in some neighborhood of $x = a$. Rewrite Eq. (4c) by setting

$$\Delta x = x - a, \quad \Delta y = f(x) - f(a),$$

and $dy/dx = f'(a)$. In the new equation, add $f(a)$ to both sides. You should get

$$f(x) = f(a) + f'(a)(x - a) + \epsilon(x - a). \quad (6a)$$

Condition (4b) translates into

$$\epsilon \to 0 \quad \text{as} \quad x \to a. \quad (6b)$$

The first two terms on the right-hand side of (6a) represent a linear function, called the *linearization*

of f at a:

$$L_a(x) = f(a) + f'(a)(x - a). \quad (7)$$

The graph of this linear function goes through the point $(a, f(a))$ and is tangent to the graph of f at that point. Because the difference between $f(x)$ and $L_a(x)$ is the part $\epsilon \, (x - a)$ in (6a), and (6b) says that ϵ is small when x is near a, the linearization of f at a can be used to estimate with considerable accuracy the values of $f(x)$ for x's near a.

Problem 3. Estimate $1/(2.04)^2$.

Solution. Let $f(x) = 1/x^2$, $a = 2$, and use the linearization of f at a. Differentiating, we get

$$f'(x) = -2x^{-3} = -2/x^3.$$

Therefore

$$f(a) = f(2) = \tfrac{1}{4}, \quad f'(a) = f'(2) = -\tfrac{2}{8} = -\tfrac{1}{4},$$

and

$$L_a(x) = L_2(x) = \tfrac{1}{4} - \tfrac{1}{4}(x - 2),$$

so that

$$L_2(2.04) = 0.25 - \tfrac{1}{4}(0.04) = 0.24.$$

EXERCISES

pg 80 #1-4   11/12

For each of the following functions, find

(a) Δy,

(b) the linear part of Δy, namely, $\Delta y_{\text{tan}} = (dy/dx) \, \Delta x$,

(c) the difference, $\Delta y - \Delta y_{\text{tan}}$.

1. $y = x^2 + 2x$ 2. $y = 2x^2 + 4x - 3$
3. $y = x^3 - x$ 4. $y = x^4$
5. $y = x^{-1}$

In Exercises 6 through 10, define a suitable function f, choose an appropriate value of a, and find the corresponding linearization of f at a for the purpose of estimating the indicated number. Then use that linearization to estimate the number.

6. $\sqrt{4.5}$ 7. $1/\sqrt{3.8}$ 8. $(7.5)^{1/3}$

9. $(34)^{-1/5}$ 10. $\dfrac{1.3}{1 + 1.3}$

4.9 The composition of g with h: $f(x) = g\big(h(x)\big)$, $f = g \circ h$.

11. A short table of squares is sometimes provided to be used with a small desk calculator. The instructions that come with it say something like this: To find $\sqrt{N}$, locate the nearest square in the table and compute $(N + a^2)/(2a)$. For instance, for $N = 7$, we might locate $(2.65)^2 = 7.0225$ and compute $14.0225/5.3$. (This division is easy to perform on the desk calculator. It comes out to approximately 2.64575. The CRC Mathematical Tables give $\sqrt{7} = 2.645751$.) Show that the above rule amounts to using the linearization of

$$f(x) = (x + a^2)^{1/2}$$

at 0 to estimate $\sqrt{N}$ with $x = N - a^2$.

12. The volume $y = x^3$ of a cube of edge x increases by an amount Δy when x increases by an amount Δx. Show that Δy may be represented geometrically as the sum of the volumes of

(a) three slabs of dimensions x by x by Δx,

(b) three bars of dimensions x by Δx by Δx,

(c) one cube of dimensions Δx by Δx by Δx.

Illustrate by a sketch.

4.5 COMPOSITE FUNCTIONS

Sometimes a function represents a mapping that can be achieved by performing two simpler mappings in succession. We illustrate this process of *composition of functions* with examples, and then give a general definition.

Example 1. The functions

$$f_1(x) = \sin(x^2), \quad -\infty < x < \infty, \tag{1a}$$

$$f_2(x) = \sin^2 x, \quad -\infty < x < \infty, \tag{1b}$$

are examples of composite functions. In Eq. (1a), we first square x, then find the sine of the result. Thus, if

$$g(x) = x^2 \tag{2a}$$

and

$$h(x) = \sin x, \tag{2b}$$

we can write Eq. (1a) in the form

$$f_1(x) = h\big(g(x)\big), \tag{3a}$$

or

$$f_1 = h \circ g, \tag{3b}$$

where (3a) is read "f_1 of x is equal to h of g of x," and (3b) is read "f_1 is the composition of h with g." The symbol $h \circ g$ is used to distinguish the composition of h with g from the ordinary product of h and g.

In the second equation, Eq. (1b), we first evaluate $\sin x$, then square the result. Using the notation of Eqs. (2a) and (2b), we can rewrite (1b) in the form

$$f_2(x) = g\big(h(x)\big), \tag{4a}$$

or, what amounts to the same thing,

$$f_2 = g \circ h. \tag{4b}$$

In both examples (1a) and (1b), the domains are the same—the set of all real numbers.

More generally, suppose we define the composition of g with h by the following rule:

$$f = g \circ h \tag{5a}$$

means that

$$f(x) = g\big(h(x)\big) \tag{5b}$$

for all values of x for which the right-hand side of Eq. (5b) is defined. Here g and h represent any two functions, no longer restricted as in (2a) and (2b). To evaluate (5b), we start with a value of x in the domain of h. (See Fig. 4.9, which illustrates the composition of g with h.) Then $h(x)$ is a number in the range of h. If this number $h(x)$ is also in the domain of g, then $g(h(x))$ is a number in the range of g. Thus, the domain of $g \circ h$ is a subset of the domain of h, and the range of $g \circ h$ is a subset of the range of g.

Example 2. Suppose that

$$g(x) = \sqrt{1-x}, \quad x \le 1, \qquad (6a)$$

and

$$h(x) = \sqrt{x}, \quad x \ge 0. \qquad (6b)$$

Then

$$g(h(x)) = \sqrt{1 - h(x)}, \quad x \ge 0, \, h(x) \le 1$$
$$= \sqrt{1 - \sqrt{x}}, \quad x \ge 0, \, \sqrt{x} \le 1.$$

From the restrictions $x \ge 0$, $\sqrt{x} \le 1$, we find that the domain of

$$f = g \circ h$$

is the interval $0 \le x \le 1$. Figure 4.10(a, b) shows the graphs of the functions h and g, respectively. Fig. 4.10(c) emphasizes the interval $[0, 1]$ of intersection of the domain of g and the range of h. Fig. 4.10(d) shows the graph of the composed function $f = g \circ h$ over the interval of intersection.

Definition 1. Composition of Functions. *Let g be a function with domain D_g and range R_g, and let h be a function with domain D_h and range R_h. The composition of g with h is the function f defined by*

$$f(x) = g(h(x))$$

with domain D_f consisting of those values x in D_h such that $h(x) \in D_g$.

Remark 1. Here is another way to look at the composite mapping $f = g \circ h$. Start with a number y in the intersection of D_g and R_h. Because this y is in the range of h, there is an x in D_h such that $h(x) = y$. And, because y is also in the domain of g, there is a number $z = g(y)$. Combining, we get

$$z = g(h(x)) = f(x).$$

Thus,

(x, y) is an element of the function h,

(y, z) is an element of the function g,

and

(x, z) is an element
of the composite function $f = g \circ h$.

Therefore the ordered pair (x, z) belongs to the composite function $f = g \circ h$ if (and only if) there is a number y such that

(x, y) belongs to h and (y, z) belongs to g.

Remark 2. By using a three-dimensional (x, y, z)-coordinate system, we can get a graphical representation of the composition:

$$y = h(x), \quad z = g(y),$$
$$f(x) = g(h(x)).$$

Figure 4.10(e) shows such a representation for the example

$$y = h(x) = \sqrt{x}, \quad x \ge 0,$$
$$z = g(y) = \sqrt{1-y},$$
$$f(x) = g(h(x)) = \sqrt{1 - \sqrt{x}}.$$

To find the value of $f(x)$ for a particular value of x, $0 \le x \le 1$, let Q be the point with abscissa x on the x-axis, and follow the diagram $Q \to R$, $R \to S$, $S \to T$, $T \to U$, $U \to P$. Here $R(x, y, 0)$ is on the graph of $y = h(x)$, $S(0, y, 0)$ has the same y-coordinate as R, and $T(0, y, z)$ is on the graph of $z = g(y)$. Because $U(0, 0, z)$ and $P(x, 0, z)$ have the same z-coordinates as T, the x- and z-coordinates of P satisfy the equations

$$z = g(y) = g(h(x)),$$

so that P is on the graph of $z = f(x)$ in the xz-coordinate plane (that is, $y = 0$). For the example shown in Fig. 4.10(d), the curve through A, P, and D is the graph of

$$z = \sqrt{1 - \sqrt{x}}, \quad 0 \le x \le 1.$$

See also Fig. 4.11, which illustrates the function $z = \sin(x^2)$ for $x \ge 0$.

a| $y = h(x) = \sqrt{x}$.

b| $y = g(x) = \sqrt{1-x}$ [or $z = g(y) = \sqrt{1-y}$].

c| The intersection of the domain of g and the range of h.

d| $y = f(x) = \sqrt{1-\sqrt{x}}$ [or $z = f(x) = \sqrt{1-\sqrt{x}}$].

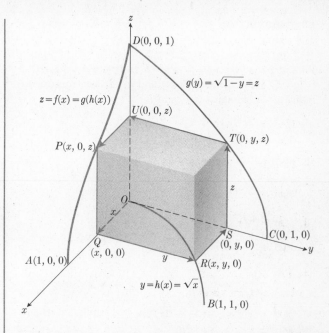

e| Representation of composition of functions in xyz-space: $\qquad y = \sqrt{x}$,
$$z = \sqrt{1-y}$$
$$= \sqrt{1-\sqrt{x}}.$$
4.10

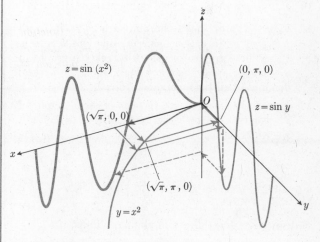

4.11 Composition: $\quad y = x^2$,
$$z = \sin y$$
$$= \sin(x^2).$$

EXERCISES

Find the compositions $f_1 = g \circ h$ and $f_2 = h \circ g$ for the following pairs of functions g and h. In each instance, indicate the domains of f_1 and f_2.

1. $g(x) = 2x + 1$, $x \in (-\infty, \infty)$
   $h(x) = \sqrt{x}$, $x \geq 0$

2. $g(x) = \dfrac{x}{x+1}$, $x \neq -1$

   $h(x) = \dfrac{1}{x}$, $x \neq 0$

3. $g(x) = \sqrt{x-1}$, $x \geq 1$

   $h(x) = \dfrac{1}{x}$, $x \neq 0$

4. $g(x) = \sin x$, $x \in (-\infty, \infty)$
   $h(x) = 1/x$, $x \neq 0$

5. $g(x) = \cos x$, $x \in [-2\pi, 2\pi]$
   $h(x) = 1/\sqrt{x}$, $x > 0$

6. $g(x) = |x|$, $h(x) = \sin x$, $x \in (-\infty, \infty)$
7. $g(x) = 2x + 4$, $h(x) = |x|$, $x \in (-\infty, \infty)$
8. $g: x \rightarrow \frac{1}{2}(x + |x|)$, $-\infty < x < \infty$
   $h: x \rightarrow \tan x$, $x \in (-\pi/2, \pi/2)$
9. $g(x) = x^3$, $h(x) = x^{1/3}$, $x \in (-\infty, \infty)$
10. $g(x) = x^2$, $h(x) = x^{1/2}$, on the natural domains

11. Figure 4.10(e) shows the graphs of $y = h(x)$ and $z = g(y)$ for a specific pair of functions h and g. Using these graphs (or otherwise), sketch graphs of $y = g(x)$, $z = h(y)$, and $z = h(g(x))$, for the natural domains of all the functions involved.

12. Figure 4.11 shows a portion of the graph of $z = \sin(x^2)$. Sketch the graph of $z = (\sin x)^2$ for $x \in [-2\pi, 2\pi]$.

4.6 DERIVATIVES OF COMPOSITE FUNCTIONS: THE CHAIN RULE

A derivative gives a rate of change. Thus, if

$$dy/dx = 5 \quad \text{and} \quad dx/dt = 3,$$

we might say "y changes five times as fast as x and x changes three times as fast as t," and conclude

that "y changes fifteen times as fast as t." This suggests that

$$\frac{dy}{dt} = \frac{dy}{dx} \cdot \frac{dx}{dt}. \tag{1}$$

In this section, we shall see that Eq. (1), which is sometimes called the *chain rule* for derivatives, is indeed valid when properly interpreted, and under appropriate conditions.

Problem 1. A particle moves along the line

$$y = 5x - 2$$

in such a way that, at time t, its x-coordinate satisfies $x = 3t$. Show that Eq. (1) holds.

Solution. From the given data, we get

$$\frac{dy}{dx} = 5, \quad \frac{dx}{dt} = 3. \tag{2a}$$

On the other hand, we also have

$$y = 5x - 2 = 15t - 2,$$

so that

$$\frac{dy}{dt} = 15. \tag{2b}$$

The numbers in Eqs. (2a, b) satisfy Eq. (1).

Problem 2. A particle moves along the curve $y = x^2$. Its x-coordinate satisfies

$$x = 2t^2 + t + 1.$$

Show that Eq. (1) is satisfied when $t = 2$.

Solution. When $t = 2$, we have $x = 11$, $y = 121$, $dy/dx = 2x = 22$, and $dx/dt = 4t + 1 = 9$. Therefore

$$\left(\frac{dy}{dx}\right)\left(\frac{dx}{dt}\right) = (22)(9) = 198.$$

On the other hand, by substitution we get

$$y = x^2 = (2t^2 + t + 1)^2$$
$$= 4t^4 + 4t^3 + 5t^2 + 2t + 1,$$

so that

$$\frac{dy}{dt} = 16t^3 + 12t^2 + 10t + 2.$$

At $t = 2$, we therefore have

$$\frac{dy}{dt} = 128 + 48 + 20 + 2 = 198 = \frac{dy}{dx} \cdot \frac{dx}{dt}.$$

Remark 1. In Problem 2, we verified the chain rule at time $t = 2$. For the same problem, Eq. (1) holds for any value of t, because

$$\frac{dy}{dt} = 16t^3 + 12t^2 + 10t + 2$$
$$= 2(2t^2 + t + 1)(4t + 1)$$
$$= 2x(4t + 1)$$
$$= \left(\frac{dy}{dx}\right)\left(\frac{dx}{dt}\right).$$

To prepare for a careful statement of the chain rule and its proof, we introduce some notation.

Let f be a function

$$f = \{(x, y) : y = f(x),\ x \in D_f\}, \qquad (3)$$

which is differentiable at an interior point x_0 of its domain D_f. Let g be a function

$$g = \{(t, x) : x = g(t),\ t \in D_g\}, \qquad (4a)$$

which is differentiable at an interior point t_0 of its domain such that

$$g(t_0) = x_0. \qquad (4b)$$

Let $h = f \circ g$ be the composition of f with g:

$$h = \{(t, y) : y = f(g(t)),\ t \in D_h\}. \qquad (5)$$

Theorem 10. *Under the hypotheses described in the preceding paragraph and Eqs. (3), (4), (5), if t_0 is an inner point of the domain of h, then*

$$h'(t_0) = f'(x_0) \cdot g'(t_0). \qquad (6)$$

Proof. Equations (3), (4), (5) say that, for any t in the domain of h, we have

$$y = h(t) = f(x),$$

provided

$$x = g(t).$$

By definition,

$$h'(t_0) = \lim_{t \to t_0} \frac{h(t) - h(t_0)}{t - t_0},$$

provided this limit exists. Now

$$h(t) - h(t_0) = f(g(t)) - f(g(t_0))$$
$$= f(x) - f(x_0),$$

so that

$$\frac{h(t) - h(t_0)}{t - t_0} = \frac{f(x) - f(x_0)}{t - t_0}. \qquad (7)$$

We would like to write the last term in Eq. (7) thus:

$$\frac{f(x) - f(x_0)}{t - t_0} = \frac{f(x) - f(x_0)}{x - x_0} \cdot \frac{x - x_0}{t - t_0}$$
$$= \frac{f(x) - f(x_0)}{x - x_0} \cdot \frac{g(t) - g(t_0)}{t - t_0}, \qquad (8)$$

but Eq. (8) is valid only if $x \neq x_0$ and $t \neq t_0$. We cannot guarantee this. However, by Eq. (4c) of Article 4.4, we can write

$$f(x) - f(x_0) = \Delta y = \frac{dy}{dx}\Delta x + \epsilon\,\Delta x \qquad (9a)$$

where

$$\frac{dy}{dx} = f'(x_0), \quad \Delta x = x - x_0, \qquad (9b)$$

and

$$\epsilon \to 0 \quad \text{as} \quad \Delta x \to 0. \qquad (9c)$$

Substitute from (9a, b) into the right-hand side of Eq. (7) and get

$$\frac{h(t) - h(t_0)}{t - t_0} = (f'(x_0) + \epsilon)\frac{x - x_0}{t - t_0}$$
$$= (f'(x_0) + \epsilon)\frac{g(t) - g(t_0)}{t - t_0}. \qquad (10)$$

Equation (10) brings us quickly to our goal, because $x = g(t)$ approaches $x_0 = g(t_0)$ when $t \to t_0$. (Why? You are asked to prove this statement in Exercise 11.) Therefore

$$\lim_{t \to t_0} \epsilon = \lim_{x \to x_0} \epsilon = 0$$

and

$$\lim_{t \to t_0} \frac{g(t) - g(t_0)}{t - t_0} = g'(t_0),$$

so that, from Eq. (10),

$$\lim_{t \to t_0} \frac{h(t) - h(t_0)}{t - t_0}$$
$$= \lim_{t \to t_0} [f'(x_0) + \epsilon] \cdot \lim_{t \to t_0} \frac{g(t) - g(t_0)}{t - t_0}$$
$$= f'(x_0)g'(t_0). \qquad (11)$$

Equation (11) says that h has a derivative at t_0 and

$$h'(t_0) = f'(x_0)g'(t_0). \quad \square$$

Remark 1. We have used subscripts on x_0 and t_0 to emphasize that these are held fixed while we take certain limits. The final result, Eq. (6), can equally well be written in either of the equivalent forms

$$h'(t) = f'(x)g'(t), \qquad (12a)$$

or

$$\frac{dy}{dt} = \frac{dy}{dx}\frac{dx}{dt}. \qquad (12b)$$

But it is understood that x is a function of t, so that dy/dx is also expressible as a function of t. When that has been done, the two sides of Eq. (12b) agree.

Problem 3. Find $\qquad dy/dt$

for $\qquad y = x^3 - 3x^2 + 5x - 4 = f(x)$,

where $\qquad x = t^2 + t = g(t)$.

Solution. From these equations, we find

$$f'(x) = \frac{dy}{dx} = 3x^2 - 6x + 5$$
$$= 3(t^2 + t)^2 - 6(t^2 + t) + 5,$$

$$g'(t) = \frac{dx}{dt} = 2t + 1,$$

so that Eq. (12b) becomes

$$\frac{dy}{dt} = \frac{dy}{dx}\frac{dx}{dt}$$
$$= [3(t^2 + t)^2 - 6(t^2 + t) + 5](2t + 1).$$

If, on the other hand, we first substitute the value of x in terms of t into the equation for y, we have

$$y = (t^2 + t)^3 - 3(t^2 + t)^2 + 5(t^2 + t) - 4.$$

When we differentiate this with respect to t, we get

$$\frac{dy}{dt} = 3(t^2 + t)^2(2t + 1)$$
$$- 6(t^2 + t)(2t + 1) + 5(2t + 1)$$
$$= [3(t^2 + t)^2 - 6(t^2 + t) + 5](2t + 1),$$

which agrees with the previous answer.

Remark 2. So far we have not defined dy and dx as separate entities, but have used the complete symbol dy/dx as the name for $\lim (\Delta y/\Delta x)$ as $\Delta x \to 0$. Now that we have established Eq. (12b), we are in a position where we can (and we shall in the next article) define dy and dx as separate quantities whose ratio is the derivative of y with respect to x. Then Eq. (12b) is the form of the chain rule which is most easily remembered, since it suggests that dx may be cancelled from the two fractions on the right.

Remark 3. If $dx/dt \neq 0$, we may divide both sides of Eq. (12b) by dx/dt and write it in the equivalent form

$$\frac{dy}{dx} = \frac{dy/dt}{dx/dt}. \qquad (13)$$

This form of the equation is particularly useful in dealing with the parametric equations

$$x = f(t), \quad y = g(t),$$

since it enables us to find the derivative of y with respect to x directly from these equations.

Example 1. The parametric equations

$$x = 2t + 3, \quad y = t^2 - 1$$

represent a curve whose equation in the form of $y = f(x)$ may be found by substituting

$$t = \frac{x - 3}{2}$$

from the first equation into the second; that is,

$$y = \tfrac{1}{4}(x - 3)^2 - 1.$$

If we work with the original equations and calculate

$$\frac{dx}{dt} = 2, \quad \frac{dy}{dt} = 2t,$$

then Eq. (13) gives

$$\frac{dy}{dx} = \frac{dy/dt}{dx/dt} = \frac{2t}{2} = t = \frac{x - 3}{2}.$$

On the other hand, from the equation for y in terms of x, we find

$$\frac{dy}{dx} = \frac{1}{2}(x-3) \cdot \frac{d}{dx}(x-3) = \frac{x-3}{2}.$$

Remark 4. The chain rule is also frequently expressed using other letters to represent the variables. Most common is the case where y is a function of u and u is a function of x,

$$y = F(u), \quad u = f(x).$$

Then the rule says

$$\frac{dy}{dx} = \frac{dy}{du}\frac{du}{dx}. \qquad (14)$$

We have already had an illustration of this formula in the case of the derivative with respect to x of

$$y = u^n.$$

Then

$$\frac{dy}{du} = nu^{n-1}$$

and

$$\frac{dy}{dx} = \frac{dy}{du}\frac{du}{dx} = nu^{n-1}\frac{du}{dx}. \qquad (15)$$

We have previously proved Eq. (15) for positive and negative integral exponents n. [See Article 4.2, Eqs. (2) and (5).] We can now extend it (at least for $u > 0$) to fractional exponents as well, for, in Article 4.3, Eq. (11), we established the result

$$\frac{d}{dx}(x^n) = nx^{n-1} \quad \text{for } n \text{ rational, } x > 0.$$

The same equation, written with u in place of x, says that

$$\frac{d}{du}(u^n) = nu^{n-1} \quad \text{for } n \text{ rational, } u > 0.$$

Combining this with the chain rule, Eq. (14), for u a differentiable function of x and n any rational number, we have the following theorem.

Theorem 11. *Let $u = f(x)$ be differentiable at $x = a$, and $f(a) > 0$. Let n be a rational number. Then $y = u^n$ is differentiable at $x = a$, and*

$$\frac{d}{dx}(u^n) = nu^{n-1}\frac{du}{dx}. \qquad (16)$$

Example 2. If $y = (x^2 - a^2)^{1/2}$, where a is a number,

then $\qquad \dfrac{dy}{dx} = \tfrac{1}{2}(x^2 - a^2)^{-1/2}(2x) = \dfrac{x}{y}.$

EXERCISES

1-9 odd   2-10 EVEN

In Exercises 1 through 4, each pair of equations represents a curve in parametric form. In each case, find the equation of the curve in the form $y = F(x)$ by eliminating t, then calculate

$$\frac{dy}{dt}, \quad \frac{dy}{dx}, \quad \frac{dx}{dt}$$

and verify that these derivatives satisfy the chain rule, Eq. (12b).

1. $x = 3t + 1, \quad y = t^2$ \qquad 2. $x = t^2, \quad y = t^3$

3. $x = \dfrac{t}{1-t}, \quad y = t^2$ \qquad 4. $x = \dfrac{t}{1+t}, \quad y = \dfrac{t^2}{1+t}$

5. If a point traces the circle $x^2 + y^2 = 25$ and if $dx/dt = 4$ when the point reaches $(3, 4)$, find dy/dt there.

In Exercises 6 through 10, find dy/dx

(a) by using the chain rule and also

(b) by first expressing y directly in terms of x, and then differentiating.

6. $y = u^2 + 3u - 7, \quad u = 2x + 1$

7. $y = \dfrac{u^2}{u^2 + 1}, \quad u = \sqrt{2x + 1}$

8. $y = z^{2/3}, \quad z = x^2 + 1$

9. $y = w^2 - w^{-1}, \quad w = 3x$

10. $y = 2v^3 + \dfrac{2}{v^3}, \quad v = (3x + 2)^{2/3}$

11. Prove that $x = g(t)$ approaches $x_0 = g(t_0)$ as $t \to t_0$ if g is differentiable at t_0.

4.7 THE DIFFERENTIALS dx AND dy

We are now prepared to define dx and dy in such a way that their ratio, when $dx \neq 0$, will be the same as the derivative of y with respect to x. This is very easy to do in the case where x is the *independent variable* and y is a function of x. When x is the independent variable and

$$y = f(x),$$

we shall adopt the following *definitions*.

Definition. *dx, called the "differential of x," may represent any real number whatever; that is, dx is another independent variable and its domain is*

$$-\infty < dx < +\infty.$$

Definition. *dy, called the "differential of y," represents the function of x and dx given by*

$$dy = f'(x)\, dx, \qquad (1)$$

where $f'(x)$ is the derivative at x of the function f.

It is clear from (1) that the differentials dx and dy have the properties

(1) (a) if $dx = 0$, then $dy = 0$, and

(2) (b) if $dx \neq 0$, then

$$\frac{dy}{dx} = \frac{\text{the differential of } y \text{ in terms of } x \text{ and } dx}{\text{the differential of } x}$$

$$= \frac{f'(x)\, dx}{dx} = f'(x) \qquad (2)$$

is the derivative of y with respect to x.

There is certainly nothing mysterious about this last result, since we deliberately defined dy by Eq. (1) so that Eq. (2) would be true. In other words, we planned it that way!

Example 1. If $y = x^3 = f(x)$,

then $f'(x) = 3x^2$,

and $dy = f'(x)\, dx = 3x^2\, dx.$

We also have been accustomed to writing

$$\frac{dy}{dx} = 3x^2,$$

and if we treat this as a fraction and multiply both sides by dx, we obtain again

$$dy = 3x^2\, dx.$$

Again, if $y = x = f(x)$,

then $f'(x) = 1,$

and $dy = f'(x)\, dx = dx.$

That is, the *function $f(x) = x$* has its differential, as given by Eq. (1), equal to the differential of the *independent variable x*. This is not a profound result; it simply shows that in the case where both (a) and (b) apply, the differential is the same whether given by (a) or by (b). That is, the two rules are *consistent*.

The geometric interpretation of dy becomes clear when we refer to Fig. 4.12, where in each part we indicate a curve $y = f(x)$ and a line segment PT tangent to the curve at P. The differential $dx = PR$ in each figure is considered positive if R is to the right of P [as in (a) and (c)], and negative when R is to the left of P [as in (b) and (d)]. The sign of dy is positive if T is above R [as in (a) and (d)] and negative if T is below R [as in (b) and (c)]. In any case, we find that

$$\frac{dy}{dx} = \frac{RT}{PR} = \tan \phi = f'(x)$$

gives the slope of the tangent to the curve at P, and

$$dy = f'(x)\, dx = (\tan \phi)(PR) = RT$$

is the *amount* of change in y along this tangent line that would be produced by a change dx in x. We thus have

(a) dy/dx is the *rate* of change of y per unit change in x, and

(b) dy is the *amount* of change of y for dx units of change in x along the *tangent* to the curve at P.

Therefore, if we take $dx = \Delta x$, then dy is the same as Δy_{tan} (Fig. 2.23), which is the principal part of Δy. In problems dealing with increments we therefore do take $dx = \Delta x$ and use dy as an approximation to Δy.

a|b

c|d

4.12

4.13

Remark 1. Equation (1) shows that at a point *a* where *f* is differentiable, the differential *dy* (or *df*) is directly proportional to *dx*. The proportionality coefficient is $f'(a)$. The function *df* is *linear* in *dx*. If we want to approximate the function *f* at *x*'s near *a*, we can take $dx = \Delta x = x - a$, and use $df = f'(a)\,dx$ as the linear part of the increment (which it is). This is just another way of using the tangent line to the graph of *f* at *a* to estimate values of *f* for *x*'s near *a*. The method is exactly the same as using the linearization of *f*, at *a*, as in Article 4.4, Eqs. (6) and (7), with a slight change in notation. You will find the differential notation widely used, as in the following problem.

Problem 1. Find a reasonable approximation to the value of

$$(1.001)^7 - 2(1.001)^{4/3} + 3.$$

Solution. At $x_0 = 1$, the function

$$f(x) = x^7 - 2x^{4/3} + 3$$

has the easily calculated value

$$y_0 = f(1) = 2.$$

The tangent to this curve $y = f(x)$ at $(1, 2)$ will remain near the curve for values of *x* close to x_0. See Fig. 4.13. As *x* changes from $x_0 = 1$ to $x_0 + dx = 1.001$, the change in *y* *along this tangent line will be*

$$dy = f'(x_0)\,dx.$$

Since

$$f'(x) = 7x^6 - \tfrac{8}{3}x^{1/3}$$

has the value

$$f'(x_0) = \tfrac{13}{3}$$

at $x_0 = 1$, when we take $dx = 0.001$, we have

$$dy = \tfrac{13}{3}(0.001) = 0.0043.$$

When this change in y is added to y_0, we have

$$y_0 + dy = 2.0043$$

as a good approximation to the value of y at the point on the curve for which $x = x_0 + dx$.

Suppose next that x is not the independent variable, but that x and y are both to be regarded as functions of t. Let

$$y = f(x), \quad x = g(t), \quad y = f(g(t)) = h(t), \quad (3)$$

where t is now the independent variable for the functions g and h. If these functions f, g, and h satisfy the differentiability conditions stated in Theorem 10 of Article 4.6, then dt is a new independent variable on $(-\infty, \infty)$, and in terms of t and dt, we have

$$dx = g'(t)\, dt, \quad dy = h'(t)\, dt. \quad (4a)$$

We can write Eq. (13) of Article 4.6 in the following form:

$$\frac{dy}{dx} = \frac{(dy/dt)}{(dx/dt)} = \frac{(dy/dt)\, dt}{(dx/dt)\, dt},$$

if

$$\frac{dx}{dt} \neq 0; \quad (4b)$$

or

$$f'(x) = \frac{h'(t)\, dt}{g'(t)\, dt}$$

$$= \frac{\text{differential of } y \text{ in terms of } t \text{ and } dt}{\text{differential of } x \text{ in terms of } t \text{ and } dt}. \quad (4c)$$

That is, the derivative of y with respect to x is equal to

$$\frac{\text{the differential of } y}{\text{the differential of } x}, \quad \text{if} \quad dx \neq 0,$$

whether the differentials are in terms of x and dx or in terms of t and dt.

It is this property of the differentials that makes it possible to treat the derivative as the ratio of dy and dx, whether x is the independent variable or not, and enables us to take full advantage of the Leibniz notation.

Example 2. Let $y = t^2$ and $x = t^3$.

Then

$$\frac{dy}{dt} = 2t, \quad \frac{dx}{dt} = 3t^2,$$

$$dy = 2t\, dt, \quad dx = 3t^2\, dt,$$

$$\frac{dy}{dx} = \frac{2t\, dt}{3t^2\, dt} = \frac{2}{3t} \quad (\text{if } t \neq 0, \ dt \neq 0).$$

If we eliminate t before taking derivatives,

$$y = x^{2/3},$$

$$\frac{dy}{dx} = \frac{2}{3} x^{-1/3} = \frac{2}{3x^{1/3}} = \frac{2}{3t} \quad (\text{if } x \neq 0),$$

in agreement with the answer above.

The second derivative

The second derivative of y with respect to x has been interpreted as the result obtained from y by doing the operation "differentiate with respect to x" twice in succession; that is,

$$\frac{d^2y}{dx^2} = \frac{d}{dx}\left[\frac{d}{dx}(y)\right].$$

It is also possible to define a second differential, d^2y, in such a way that the second derivative of y with respect to x is equal to d^2y divided by $(dx)^2$. However, things get rather complicated in the case of parametric equations like Eqs. (3) above. In such cases, it is simplest to calculate second- and higher-order derivatives by using such rules as

$$\frac{dy}{dx} = y' = \frac{dy/dt}{dx/dt},$$

$$\frac{d^2y}{dx^2} = y'' = \frac{dy'}{dx} = \frac{dy'/dt}{dx/dt}.$$

It is important to note that to get the second derivative of y with respect to x, when the first derivative $dy/dx = y'$ is expressed in terms of t, we may differentiate y' with respect to t, provided we divide the result by dx/dt. (See Exercise 21 at the end of Article 4.8 for the general formula.)

Problem 2. Find d^2y/dx^2 if $x = t - t^2$ and $y = t - t^3$.

Solution.
$$y' = \frac{dy}{dx} = \frac{dy/dt}{dx/dt} = \frac{1 - 3t^2}{1 - 2t},$$

$$\frac{d^2y}{dx^2} = y'' = \frac{dy'}{dx} = \frac{dy'/dt}{dx/dt} = \frac{\frac{d}{dt}\left[\frac{1 - 3t^2}{1 - 2t}\right]}{(1 - 2t)}$$

$$= \frac{(1 - 2t) \cdot (-6t) - (1 - 3t^2) \cdot (-2)}{(1 - 2t)^3}$$

$$= \frac{2 - 6t + 6t^2}{(1 - 2t)^3}.$$

4.8 FORMULAS FOR DIFFERENTIATION REPEATED IN THE NOTATION OF DIFFERENTIALS

Earlier in this chapter we derived formulas for the derivatives listed below on the left. By multiplying each one by dx, we now obtain the corresponding formulas for differentials.

Derivatives	Differentials
I. $\frac{dc}{dx} = 0$	I'. $dc = 0$
II. $\frac{d(cu)}{dx} = c\frac{du}{dx}$	II'. $d(cu) = c\,du$
III. $\frac{d(u + v)}{dx} = \frac{du}{dx} + \frac{dv}{dx}$	III'. $d(u + v) = du + dv$
IV. $\frac{d(uv)}{dx} = u\frac{dv}{dx} + v\frac{du}{dx}$	IV'. $d(uv) = u\,dv + v\,du$
V. $\frac{d\left(\frac{u}{v}\right)}{dx} = \frac{v\frac{du}{dx} - u\frac{dv}{dx}}{v^2}$	V'. $d\left(\frac{u}{v}\right) = \frac{v\,du - u\,dv}{v^2}$
VI. $\frac{du^n}{dx} = nu^{n-1}\frac{du}{dx}$	VI'. $d(u^n) = nu^{n-1}\,du$
VIa. $\frac{dcx^n}{dx} = cnx^{n-1}$	VI'a. $d(cx^n) = cnx^{n-1}\,dx$

We collect these formulas primarily for future reference. Any problem involving differentials, say that of finding dy when y is a given function of x, may be handled in either of the following ways:

(a) by finding the derivative dy/dx and then multiplying by dx, or

(b) by direct use of formulas I'–VI'a.

Example. If we let $y = x^3 + 5x^2 - 7x + 4$,

then
$$\frac{dy}{dx} = 3x^2 + 10x - 7,$$

and
$$dy = (3x^2 + 10x - 7)\,dx,$$

or we may calculate directly:

$$dy = d(x^3 + 5x^2 - 7x + 4)$$
$$= d(x^3) + d(5x^2) + d(-7x) + d(4) \quad \text{(III')}$$
$$= 3x^2\,dx + 10x\,dx - 7\,dx + 0 \quad \text{(VI'a)}$$
$$= (3x^2 + 10x - 7)\,dx.$$

It should be noted that a *differential* on the left side of an equation, say dy, also calls for a *differential*, usually dx, on the right side of the equation. Thus we never have $dy = 3x^2$, but instead $dy = 3x^2\,dx$.

The term "differentiate" means either to find the derivative or to find the differential and either operation is referred to as "differentiation."

EXERCISES

#2-20 EVEN
11/17 #1 11/18

In Exercises 1 through 8, find dy.

1. $y = x^3 - 3x^2 + 5x - 7$ 2. $y^2 = (3x^2 + 1)^{3/2}$

3. $xy^2 + x^2y = 4$ 4. $y = \frac{2x}{1 + x^2}$

5. $y = x\sqrt{1 - x^2}$ 6. $y = \frac{x + 1}{x^2 - 2x + 4}$

7. $y = \frac{(1 - x)^3}{2 - 3x}$ 8. $y = \frac{1 + x - x^2}{1 - x}$

Use differentials to obtain reasonable approximations to the following.

9. $\sqrt{145}$ 10. $(2.1)^3$

11. $\sqrt[4]{17}$ 12. $\sqrt[3]{0.126}$

13. $(8.01)^{4/3} + (8.01)^2 - \frac{1}{\sqrt[3]{8.01}}$

Given the following functions $x = f(t)$, $y = g(t)$:

(a) Express dx and dy in terms of t and dt.

(b) Use the results of (a) to find, at the point for which $t = 2$, the slope of the locus of the point (x, y).

(c) Use the results of (b) to find an equation of the line tangent to the curve at the point for which $t = 2$.

14. $x = t + \dfrac{1}{t}$, $\quad y = t - \dfrac{1}{t}$

15. $x = \sqrt{2t^2 + 1}$, $\quad y = (2t + 1)^2$

16. $x = t\sqrt{2t + 5}$, $\quad y = (4t)^{1/3}$

17. $x = \dfrac{t - 1}{t + 1}$, $\quad y = \dfrac{t + 1}{t - 1}$

18. $x = \dfrac{1}{t^2}$, $\quad y = \sqrt{t^2 + 12}$

19. Find d^2y/dx^2 from the parametric equations in Exercise 14.

20. Find d^2y/dx^2 from the parametric equations in Exercise 17.

21. Given the parametric equations $x = f(t)$, $y = g(t)$. Show that

$$\frac{d^2y}{dx^2} = \frac{\dfrac{dx}{dt}\dfrac{d^2y}{dt^2} - \dfrac{d^2x}{dt^2}\dfrac{dy}{dt}}{(dx/dt)^3}.$$

22. (Franklin: *Treatise on Advanced Calculus*. Wiley, 1940, p. 110.) Let

$$y = F(x), \quad x = f(t), \quad F[f(t)] = g(t).$$

Using a subscript to denote the independent variable, define second differentials as follows:

$$(d^2y)_x = F''(x) \cdot (dx)^2,$$

$$(d^2y)_t = g''(t) \cdot (dt)^2, \quad (d^2x)_t = f''(t) \cdot (dt)^2.$$

Then show that

$$(d^2y)_t = (d^2y)_x + F'(x)(d^2x)_t.$$

Hint. By the chain rule, $g'(t) = F'(x)f'(t)$. From this deduce that

$$g''(t) = F'(x)f''(t) + F''(x)[f'(t)]^2$$

4.9 CONTINUITY

Before we take up applications of differentiation (Chapter 5), it is desirable to discuss the *continuity* of a function. We shall see that continuity is even more basic than differentiability.

Definition. *A function f which is defined in some neighborhood of c is said to be continuous at c provided that*

(a) *the function has a definite finite value $f(c)$ at c, and*

(b) *as x approaches c, $f(x)$ approaches $f(c)$ as limit:*

$$\lim_{x \to c} f(x) = f(c). \tag{1}$$

If a function is continuous at all points of an interval $a \le x \le b$ (or $a < x < b$, etc.), then it is said to be continuous on, or in, that interval.

Remark 1. The foregoing definition does not apply to certain situations. For instance,

if $\qquad f(x) = \sqrt{x - x^2} \quad$ for $x \in [0, 1]$, $\qquad$ (2)

then only the one-sided limits of $f(x)$ exist as x approaches the endpoint 0, or 1. We still say that f is continuous at these endpoints, however, because these one-sided limits are equal to the values of the function at the respective endpoints:

$$\lim_{x \to 0+} f(x) = \lim_{x \to 0+} \sqrt{x - x^2} = 0 = f(0), \tag{3a}$$

$$\lim_{x \to 1-} f(x) = \lim_{x \to 1-} \sqrt{x - x^2} = 0 = f(1). \tag{3b}$$

Remark 2. Sometimes the domain of a function has certain *isolated* points. For instance, the natural domain of the function

$$f(x) = \sqrt{-|x|}$$

is just the single point $x = 0$. For the function

$$g(x) = \sqrt{|x|(x - 1)},$$

the natural domain consists of $x = 0$ and all $x \ge 1$. How should we decide about the continuity of f and g at 0? The decision that has been made by a substantial number of mathematicians is that both f and g are *continuous* at $x = 0$. The reason they have made that choice is that they like the following alternative definition because it includes all possible points in the domain of f.

Alternative definition. *Let f be a function and let c be a number in the domain of f. Then f is* continuous *at c if and only if to each $\epsilon > 0$ there corresponds a $\delta > 0$ such that*

$$|f(x) - f(c)| < \epsilon \text{ whenever } |x - c| < \delta \text{ and } x \in D_f.$$

In spite of its lack of generality, we prefer the first definition because we can apply all of our limit theorems directly when we use it. [Also, because those same theorems would be true if each were modified to restrict x to D_f whenever $f(x)$ is mentioned, the continuity at endpoints of D_f, as in Eqs. (3a) and (3b), presents no problem.] For isolated points of D_f, we can just go along with the others and say, "All right, if you say so, f is continuous there too."

Remark 3. When a function fails to be continuous at a point of its domain, we say that it is *discontinuous* at that point. For instance, sgn x is discontinuous at $x = 0$ because sgn $0 = 0$, whereas

$$\lim \text{sgn } x = -1, \quad \text{or} \quad +1,$$

when $x \to 0$ from the left, or from the right. Hence Eq. (1) is not satisfied.

Example 1. As an example of a continuous function, let us investigate

$$f(x) = x^2$$

at some fixed value $x = c$. Certainly requirement (a) of the definition is satisfied, since the function has the value

$$f(c) = c^2$$

at $x = c$. Furthermore, Eq. (1) is satisfied because

$$\lim_{x \to c} x^2 = c^2.$$

Therefore this function, $f(x) = x^2$, is continuous at *any* $x = c$; that is, it is continuous on $(-\infty, \infty)$.

The foregoing example is a special case of the following theorem.

Theorem 12. *Every polynomial function is continuous on $(-\infty, \infty)$.*

Proof. For any real number c,

$$\lim f(x) = f(c) \quad \text{when} \quad x \to c,$$

by Corollary 4.3, Chapter 3. ◻

The graph of a function which is continuous on an interval $a \leq x \leq b$ consists of an unbroken curve over that interval. This fact is of practical importance in using curves to represent functions. It makes it possible, for example, to sketch a curve by constructing a table of values (x, y), plotting relatively few points from this table, and then sketching a continuous (i.e., unbroken) curve through these points. For example, suppose we carry through the steps discussed for the simple case $y = x^2$.

4.14

We first make a short table of values:

x	0	± 0.5	± 1	± 2
y	0	0.25	1	4

then plot these points and draw a continuous curve through them, as shown in Fig. 4.14. Then we might go one step further and use the curve itself to find the value of x^2 corresponding to an x different from those used in making the table of values. For example, in Fig. 4.14, $x = 1.6$ is indicated on the

x-scale and the corresponding reading on the y-scale gives $x^2 \approx 2.6$. Of course, the graph probably won't give *exact* values except at those points which have been plotted exactly. But it will give values which are near the exact values, if the calculated points aren't spread too far apart.

To appreciate the concept of continuity more fully, it is desirable to have some examples of the opposite behavior which some functions exhibit at certain points, that is, discontinuity. For example, the function F such that $F(t) = 1/t$ is continuous for $t \neq 0$, but is not defined at $t = 0$. Nor can it be defined in any way at $t = 0$ to satisfy Eq. (1), because it has no limit as t approaches zero. It is customary to say that this function (Fig. 4.15) has an infinite discontinuity at $t = 0$.

The function

$$F(t) = \text{greatest integer in } t = [t],$$

on the other hand, is discontinuous at $t = n$ for every integer $n = 0, \pm 1, \pm 2, \ldots$, but its discontinuities are all finite. This function changes abruptly by unity when t decreases by ever so small an amount from 3 to $3 - \delta$, for example, no matter how small the positive number δ may be. (See Fig. 4.16.)

An extreme example of a discontinuous function is afforded by the function defined by the rule

$$f(x) = \begin{cases} 0, \text{ when } x \text{ is rational,} \\ 1, \text{ when } x \text{ is irrational.} \end{cases}$$

This function has a perfectly definite value for every x in the interval $0 \leq x \leq 1$. But no matter what c is chosen in this interval, there are points x which are arbitrarily close to c but having functional values $f(x)$ which differ from $f(c)$ by unity. That is,

$$|f(x) - f(c)|$$

is not arbitrarily small for all $x \neq c$ in some small neighborhood of c. This function is discontinuous at all points in the interval $(0, 1)$. Its graph cannot be drawn, but it can be described by saying that it consists of all the rational points on the x-axis from 0 to 1, with the irrational points all pushed up one unit above the x-axis. (See Fig. 4.17.) Thus it

4.15

4.16

4.17

consists of two parallel line segments, each of which is full of holes!

With these examples before us, the question arises as to how, in practice, we can tell whether or not a given function is continuous. When we sketch its graph, should we be sure to sketch a connected, unbroken curve, as for the graph of $y = x^2$, or must we be careful *not* to connect all of the points as, for example, in the case $y = 1/x$, where points in the third quadrant must not be connected with points in the first quadrant?

Since we have studied differentiation, the following theorem, which says that every function which has a derivative at a point is also continuous at that point, enables us to conclude that every polynomial is continuous for all x's, and every rational function is continuous for all x's in its domain. Thus, for example, the graphs of

$$y = x^3, \quad y = 2x^2 - x + 3, \quad y = \frac{x^2 - 1}{x^2 + 1}$$

are continuous, connected curves over the domain $-\infty < x < +\infty$. On the other hand, the graph of

$$y = \frac{x^2 + 1}{x^3 - 4x} \qquad (4)$$

goes shooting off toward $\pm\infty$ as x approaches one of the three values

$$x = -2, \quad x = 0, \quad x = +2,$$

where the denominator vanishes. But, over the intervals

$$-\infty < x < -2, \quad -2 < x < 0,$$

$$0 < x < 2, \quad 2 < x < +\infty,$$

the graph consists of separate continuous curves, since the denominator does not vanish in any of these intervals. The reader will find it instructive to work out the graph of Eq. (4) for himself on the basis of the discussion above.

Let us now state and prove the theorem we mentioned above.

Theorem 13. *If the function f has a finite derivative*

$$f'(c) = \lim_{\Delta x \to 0} \frac{f(c + \Delta x) - f(c)}{\Delta x} \qquad (5)$$

at $x = c$, then f is continuous at $x = c$.

Proof. For the limit in Eq. (5) to exist, it is necessary that $f(c)$ and $f(c + \Delta x)$ both exist, at least for all Δx near zero. We change the notation slightly by

writing x in place of $c + \Delta x$. Then

$$x = c + \Delta x$$

is near c when

$$\Delta x = x - c$$

is near zero. Equation (5) now may be written in the form

$$f'(c) = \lim_{x \to c} \frac{f(x) - f(c)}{x - c}.$$

Suppose then that $f'(c)$ exists and is finite. We want to prove that $f(x) - f(c)$ tends to zero as $x \to c$. This follows at once from

$$\lim_{x \to c} [f(x) - f(c)] = \lim_{x \to c} \left[(x - c) \frac{f(x) - f(c)}{x - c} \right]$$

$$= \lim_{x \to c} (x - c) \cdot \lim_{x \to c} \frac{f(x) - f(c)}{x - c}$$

$$= 0 \cdot f'(c) = 0. \quad \square$$

We have just shown that differentiability implies continuity. The converse, however, is not true, as is easily seen by considering the function

$$f(x) = |x|,$$

which is continuous at $x = 0$ but does not possess a derivative at that point. (See Fig. 4.18.)

4.18

Note. The fact that $f(x) = |x|$ has no derivative at $x = 0$ follows from the fact that

$$\frac{f(0 + \Delta x) - f(0)}{\Delta x} = \frac{|\Delta x|}{\Delta x} = \begin{cases} +1, & \text{when} \quad \Delta x > 0, \\ -1, & \text{when} \quad \Delta x < 0, \end{cases}$$

and

$$\lim_{\Delta x \to 0} \frac{|\Delta x|}{\Delta x} \text{ does not exist.}$$

4.19

Until the middle of the 19th century, it was generally believed that a continuous function would at least have a derivative at most places, even though there might be isolated points (as at $x = 0$, in our example) where the derivative does not exist. However, the German mathematicians Riemann (1826–1866) and Weierstrass (1815–1897) gave examples of functions which are continuous but which fail to have derivatives anywhere. For a readable account of this, see *World of Mathematics*, Vol. 3, p. 1963.

We conclude this chapter with some theorems which we shall state without proofs. Some of these theorems follow rather simply from the corresponding theorems on limits. Others require, for rigorous proofs, a more penetrating investigation of the properties of the real number system than we are able to make at this time.

Theorem 14. *Suppose f and g are two functions that are continuous at $x = c$. Then the functions F_1, F_2, F_3 defined by*

$$F_1(x) = f(x) + g(x),$$

$$F_2(x) = kf(x), \quad k \text{ any number},$$

$$F_3(x) = f(x) \cdot g(x)$$

are also continuous at $x = c$. Furthermore, if $g(c)$ is not zero, then F_4,

$$F_4(x) = \frac{f(x)}{g(x)},$$

is also continuous at $x = c$.

Theorem 15. *A function f that is continuous for all x in the closed interval $a \leq x \leq b$ has the following properties (See Fig. 4.19):*

(i) *It has a minimum value m and a maximum value M; that is, there are numbers α and β in the interval*

such that $m = f(\alpha)$ and $M = f(\beta)$, and such that for all x in the interval, the condition

$$m \leq f(x) \leq M$$

is satisfied.

(ii) *If N is any number between $f(a)$ and $f(b)$, then there is at least one number c between a and b such that $f(c) = N$.**

(iii) *Given any positive number ϵ there is a positive number δ (which may depend upon ϵ but does not depend upon x_1 or x_2) such that if x_1 and x_2 belong to the interval $a \leq x \leq b$ and $|x_1 - x_2| < \delta$, then $|f(x_1) - f(x_2)| < \epsilon$.*

Remark 4. A function that satisfies the condition (iii) above is said to be *uniformly continuous* for $a \leq x \leq b$, and the theorem says that a function that is *continuous* on a *closed* interval is automatically *uniformly* continuous there. The function $f(x) = 1/x$ is, on the other hand, continuous in the *open* interval $0 < x < 1$, but is not uniformly continuous there.

Example 2. The following physical interpretation of continuity may be of some value in throwing more light on the distinction between the notion of "continuous at every point of an interval" on the one hand and "uniformly continuous in an interval" on the other. We recall that a function is continuous at $x = c$ if $f(c)$ exists and $f(x) \to f(c)$ as $x \to c$. This means that if we are challenged with a positive "tolerance limit" ϵ and required to make

$$|f(x) - f(c)| < \epsilon \tag{6}$$

---

* This is known as the *intermediate value theorem*. Proofs of all parts of Theorem 15 can be found in Thomas, Moulton, Zelinka, *Elementary Calculus from an Advanced Viewpoint*, Addison-Wesley, 1967, Chapters 6 and 7.

4.20

for *all* x sufficiently close to c, we must produce a positive number δ such that condition (3) is met whenever

$$|x - c| < \delta. \qquad (7)$$

Let us translate this into physical terms.

Suppose we have a pair of dividers (Fig. 4.20) with a meter attached and having the property that when the points of the dividers are set at c and x respectively, the meter registers the numerical value of the difference in the functional values at c and x; that is,

the meter reads $|f(x) - f(c)|$
when the points touch x and c.

Suppose now we hold one prong of the dividers at c and move the other prong around near c, either to the left of c or to its right. Suppose that to *each* positive number ϵ we are able to assign an interval $(c - \delta, c + \delta)$ such that whenever the second prong is inside this interval, the meter reading is less than ϵ. Then the function is, by our definition, continuous at c.

Now the interval length 2δ will in general depend upon ϵ. That is, the smaller the tolerance limit ϵ that is required, the more narrowly must we restrict the range of x around c. Furthermore, the length 2δ will also, in general, depend upon c. That is, for a given function $f(x)$,

$$\delta = \delta(c, \epsilon)$$

is a function of both c and ϵ. But if the function $f(x)$ is continuous for all values of x in some domain, then with each x_0 in the domain and with each $\epsilon > 0$ we can associate a positive number $\delta = \delta(x_0, \epsilon)$, such that

if x is in the domain and if $|x - x_0| < \delta(x_0, \epsilon)$, then

$$|f(x) - f(x_0)| < \epsilon.$$

Finally, as we vary x_0, it may happen that all of these numbers $\delta(x_0, \epsilon)$ are at least as large as some positive number $k = k(\epsilon)$. Then, given $\epsilon > 0$, we could use an interval of constant width $2k$ around *any* x_0 of the domain, and have

$$|f(x) - f(x_0)| < \epsilon$$

whenever x is in the domain and $|x - x_0| < k$. For the interval $(x_0 - k, x_0 + k)$ surely lies inside the interval $x_0 - \delta(x_0, \epsilon) < x < x_0 + \delta(x_0, \epsilon)$, since $\delta(x_0, \epsilon) \geq k$. In other words, if the two prongs of the dividers are spread apart any distance smaller than this k and the dividers are then placed so that they touch *any two points* x_1, x_2, in the domain of x, in the circumstances described above it will turn out that the meter reading is less than ϵ. This exemplifies what is meant by *uniform continuity*.

To summarize these remarks we may say that

(a) *ordinary continuity* at a point c means that the interval width depends not only upon the tolerance ϵ but also upon c, whereas

(b) *uniform continuity* means that with any positive ϵ we may associate *one* interval width that works for *all* points in the domain.

EXERCISES

1-7 & 9   11/19

1. For what values of x is each of the following functions discontinuous?

   (a) $f(x) = \dfrac{x}{x + 1}$,   (b) $f(x) = \dfrac{x + 1}{x^2 - 4x + 3}$.

2. Is the function f defined by the rule

$$f(x) = \begin{cases} \dfrac{x^2 - 1}{x - 1}, & \text{when } x \neq 1, \\ 2, & \text{when } x = 1, \end{cases}$$

   continuous or discontinuous at $x = 1$? Prove your result.

3. The function $f(x) = |x|$ is continuous at $x = 0$. Given a positive number ϵ, how large may δ be in order that $|f(x) - 0| < \epsilon$ when $|x - 0| < \delta$?

4. What is the maximum of $f(x) = |x|$ for $-1 \le x \le 1$? What is the minimum? Sketch.

5. Does the function $f(x) = x^2$ have a maximum for $0 < x < 1$? Does it have a minimum? Give reasons for your answers.

6. A continuous function $y = f(x)$ is known to be negative at $x = 0$ and positive at $x = 1$. Why is it true that the equation $f(x) = 0$ has at least one root between $x = 0$ and $x = 1$? Illustrate with a sketch.

7. Is the function $f(x) = \sqrt[3]{x}$ continuous at $x = 0$? Is it differentiable there? Give reasons for your answers.

8. *Prove the following theorem.* Let f be continuous and positive at $x = c$. Prove that there is some interval around $x = c$, say $c - \delta < x < c + \delta$, throughout which $f(x)$ remains positive. Illustrate with a sketch. *Hint.* In the alternative definition of continuity, take $\epsilon = \frac{1}{2}f(c)$.

9. For $x \ne 2$, the function $f(x)$ is equal to

$$(x^2 + 3x - 10)/(x - 2).$$

What value should be assigned to $f(2)$ to make $f(x)$ continuous at $x = 2$?

10. Use the trigonometric identity

$$\sin x - \sin a = 2 \sin \frac{x - a}{2} \cos \frac{x + a}{2}$$

to prove that $\sin x$ is uniformly continuous on $(-\infty, \infty)$.

REVIEW QUESTIONS AND EXERCISES

1. Using the definition of the derivative, deduce the formula for the derivative of a product uv of two differentiable functions.

2. In the formula for the derivative of uv, let $v = u$, and thereby deduce a formula for the derivative of u^2. Repeat the process, with $v = u^2$, and get a formula for the derivative of u^3. Extend the result, by the method of mathematical induction, to deduce the formula for the derivative of u^n for every positive integer n.

3. Explain how the three formulas

(a) $\dfrac{d(x^n)}{dx} = nx^{n-1}$,   (b) $\dfrac{d(cu)}{dx} = c\dfrac{du}{dx}$,

(c) $\dfrac{d(u + v)}{dx} = \dfrac{du}{dx} + \dfrac{dv}{dx}$

are sufficient to differentiate any polynomial.

4. What formula do we need, in addition to the three listed in Exercise 3 above, to differentiate rational functions?

5. Does the derivative of a polynomial function exist at every point of its domain? What is the largest domain the function can have? Does the derivative of a rational function exist at every point in its domain? What real numbers, if any, must be excluded from the domain of a rational function?

Definition. **Algebraic Function.** *Let $y = f(x)$ define a function of x such that every pair of numbers (x, y) belonging to f satisfy an irreducible equation of the form*

$$P_0(x)y^n + P_1(x)y^{n-1} + \cdots + P_{n-1}(x)y + P_n(x) = 0$$

$$(\alpha)$$

for some positive integer n, with coefficients

$$P_0(x), \ldots, P_n(x)$$

polynomials in x, and $P_0(x)$ not identically zero. Then f is said to be an algebraic function.

6. What technique of this chapter can be used to find the derivative of an algebraic function if the polynomial coefficients $P_0(x), \ldots, P_n(x)$ in its defining equation (α) are given?

7. Show that the function f defined by $f(x) = x^{2/3}$ is an algebraic function by finding an appropriate equation of the type (α) in the definition above. On what domain of values of x is this function defined? Where is it continuous? Where is it differentiable?

8. Show that every rational function is algebraic. Do you think the converse is also true? Explain.

9. It can be shown (though not very easily) that sums, quotients, products, powers, and roots of algebraic functions are algebraic functions. Thus

$$f(x) = x\sqrt{3x^2 + 1} + 5x^{4/3}/(3x + 2), \quad x \ne -\frac{2}{3},$$

defines an algebraic function. Find its derivative. What formulas of this chapter are used in finding derivatives of functions like this one?

10. Show that $y = |x|$ satisfies the equation $y^2 - x^2 = 0$. Is the absolute value function algebraic? What is its derivative? Where does the derivative exist? Where is the absolute value function continuous?

11. Define differentials. If $y = f(x)$ defines a differentiable function, how are dy and dx related? Give geometrical interpretations of dx and dy.

12. State the chain rule for derivatives. Prove it, with the book closed.

13. Show how the chain rule is used to prove that the derivative of y with respect to x is the ratio of dy to dx when x and y are both differentiable functions of t, and $dx \neq 0$.

14. Suppose that the mapping $f: x \rightarrow f(x)$, $a \le x \le b$, is one-to-one from $[a, b]$ to $[f(a), f(b)]$. Describe the inverse mapping. What is its domain? its range?

15. (Continuation of 14.) If $g(y) = x$ whenever $f(x) = y$, where f is one-to-one from $[a, b]$ to $[f(a), f(b)]$, then we also have

$$g\big(f(x)\big) = x \quad \text{for } x \in [a, b].$$

By applying the chain rule to the composite function $h = g \circ f$, deduce a general formula for the derivative of an inverse function.

Note. g is the inverse of f on a suitable domain.

16. Give an example of a function that is defined and bounded on $0 \le t \le 1$, continuous in the open interval $0 < t < 1$, and discontinuous at $t = 0$.

17. State and prove a theorem about the relationship between continuity and differentiability of a function, at a point in its domain.

18. Read the article "The Lever of Mahomet" by R. Courant and H. Robbins, and the accompanying "Commentary on Continuity" by J. R. Newman, in *World of Mathematics*, Vol. 4, pp. 2410–2413.

MISCELLANEOUS EXERCISES

Find dy/dx in Exercises 1 through 33.

1. $y = \dfrac{x}{\sqrt{x^2 - 4}}$

2. $x^2 + xy + y^2 - 5x = 2$

3. $xy + y^2 = 1$

4. $x^3 + 4xy - 3y^3 = 2$

5. $x^2 y + y^2 = 6$

6. $y = (x + 1)^2 (x^2 + 2x)^{-2}$

7. $y = \dfrac{x}{\sqrt{1 - x^2}}$

8. $x^2 + 3xy^2 + y^3 = 2$

9. $y = \dfrac{x}{x + 1}$

10. $y = \sqrt{2x + 1}$

11. $y = x^2 \sqrt{x^2 - a^2}$

12. $y = \dfrac{2x + 1}{2x - 1}$

13. $y = \dfrac{x^2}{1 - x^2}$

14. $y = (x^2 + x + 1)^3$

15. $y = \dfrac{1}{\sqrt{x^2 + x - 1}}$

16. $y = \dfrac{x^3 - 1}{x - 1}$

17. $y = \dfrac{(2x^2 + 5x)^{3/2}}{3}$

18. $y = \dfrac{3}{(2x^2 + 5x)^{3/2}}$

19. $xy^2 + \sqrt{xy} = 2$

20. $x^2 + y^2 = xy$

21. $x^{2/3} + y^{2/3} = a^{2/3}$

22. $x^{1/2} + y^{1/2} = a^{1/2}$

23. $xy = 1$

24. $\sqrt{xy} = 1$

25. $(x + 2y)^2 + 2xy^2 = 6$

26. $y = \sqrt{\dfrac{1 - x}{1 + x^2}}$

27. $y^2 = \dfrac{x}{x + 1}$

28. $x^2 y + xy^2 = 6(x^2 + y^2)$

29. $xy + 2x + 3y = 1$

30. $y = u^2 - 1, \ x = u^2 + 1$

31. $y = \sqrt{2t + t^2}, \ t = 2x + 3$

32. $x = \dfrac{t}{1 + t^2}, y = 1 + t^2$

33. $t = \dfrac{x}{1 + x^2}, y = x^2 + t^2$

34. Find the slope of $y = x/(x^2 + 1)$ at the origin. Write an equation of the tangent line at the origin.

35. Write an equation of the tangent to the curve $x^2 - 2xy + y^2 + 2x + y - 6 = 0$ at $(2, 2)$.

36. Determine the constant c such that the straight line joining the points $(0, 3)$ and $(5, -2)$ is tangent to the curve $y = c/(x + 1)$.

37. What is the slope of the curve $y = 2x^2 - 6x + 3$ at the point on the curve where $x = 2$? What is an equation of the tangent line to the curve at this point?

38. Find the points on the curve

$$y = 2x^3 - 3x^2 - 12x + 20$$

where the tangent is parallel to the x-axis.

39. Find the derivatives of the following functions.

(a) $y = (x^2 + 2x)^5$

(b) $f(t) = \sqrt{3t^2 - 2t}$

(c) $f(r) = \sqrt{r^2 + 5} + \sqrt{r^2 - 5}$

(d) $f(x) = \dfrac{x^2 - 1}{x^2 + 1}$

40. Find an equation of the tangent to the curve

$$y = 2/\sqrt{x - 1}$$

at the point on the curve where $x = 10$.

41. Write an equation of the straight line passing through the point $(1, 2)$ and normal to the curve $x^2 = 4y$.

42. Use the definition of the derivative to find dy/dx for $y = \sqrt{2x + 3}$ and then check the result by finding the same derivative by the power formula.

43. Find the value of

$$\lim_{\Delta x \to 0} \frac{[2 - 3(x + \Delta x)]^2 - [2 - 3x]^2}{\Delta x}$$

and specify the function $f(x)$ of which this is the derivative.

44. Find the slope of the curve $x^2 y + xy^2 = 6$ at the point $(1, 2)$.

45. A cylindrical can of height 6 in. and radius r in. has volume $V = 6\pi r^2$ in^3. What is the difference between ΔV and its linear part as r varies? What is the geometric significance of the linear part?

46. If a hemispherical bowl of radius 10 in. is filled with water to a depth of x in., the volume of water is given by $v = \pi[10 - (x/3)]x^2$. Find the rate of increase of the volume per inch increase of the depth.

47. A bus will hold 60 people. If the number x of persons per trip who use the bus is related to the fare charged (p nickels), by the law $p = [3 - (x/40)]^2$, write the function expressing the total revenue per trip received by the bus company. What is the number x_1 of people per trip that will make the marginal revenue equal to zero? What is the corresponding fare?

48. Prove Eq. (3), Article 4.2, by mathematical induction.

49. Given $y = x - x^2$, find the rate of change of y^2 with respect to x^2 (expressed in terms of x).

50. If $x = 3t + 1$ and $y = t^2 + t$, find dy/dt, dx/dt, and dy/dx. Eliminate t to obtain y as a function of x, and then determine dy/dx directly. Do the results check?

51. A particle projected vertically upward with a speed of a ft/sec reaches an elevation $s = at - 16t^2$ ft at the end of t sec. What must the initial velocity be in order for the particle to travel exactly 49 ft upward before it starts coming back down? [What is the velocity at the 49-ft level?]

52. Find the rate of change of $\sqrt{x^2 + 16}$ with respect to $x/(x - 1)$ at $x = 3$.

53. The circle $(x - h)^2 + (y - k)^2 = r^2$, center at (h, k), radius $= r$, is tangent to the curve $y = x^2 + 1$ at the point $(1, 2)$.

(a) Find the locus of the point (h, k).

(b) If, also, the circle and the curve have the same second derivative at $(1, 2)$, find h, k, and r. Sketch the curve and the circle.

54. If $y = x^2 + 1$ and $u = \sqrt{x^2 + 1}$, find dy/du.

55. If $x = y^2 + y$ and $u = (x^2 + x)^{3/2}$, find dy/du.

56. If $f'(x) = \sqrt{3x^2 - 1}$ and $y = f(x^2)$, find dy/dx.

57. If

$$f'(x) = \sin(x^2) \quad \text{and} \quad y = f\left(\frac{2x - 1}{x + 1}\right),$$

find dy/dx.

58. Find $y' = dy/dx$ and $y'' = dy'/dx$

if $y = x^2 - 3x + 5$.

59. If s represents the distance a body moves in time t, determine the acceleration

$$a = d^2s/dt^2$$

if $s = 250 + 40t - 16t^2$.

60. If $y = x\sqrt{2x - 3}$,

find d^2y/dx^2.

61. Find the value of d^2y/dx^2 in the equation $y^3 + y = x$ at the point $(2, 1)$.

62. If $x = t - t^2$, $y = t - t^3$, find the values of dy/dx and d^2y/dx^2 at $t = 1$.

63. Prove Leibniz's rule:

(a) $\dfrac{d^2(uv)}{dx^2} = \dfrac{d^2u}{dx^2} \cdot v + 2\dfrac{du}{dx}\dfrac{dv}{dx} + u\dfrac{d^2v}{dx^2}$,

(b) $\dfrac{d^3(uv)}{dx^3} = \dfrac{d^3u}{dx^3} \cdot v + 3\dfrac{d^2u}{dx^2}\dfrac{dv}{dx} + 3\dfrac{du}{dx}\dfrac{d^2v}{dx^2} + u\dfrac{d^3v}{dx^3}$,

(c) $\dfrac{d^n(uv)}{dx^n} = \dfrac{d^n u}{dx^n} \cdot v + n \dfrac{d^{n-1}u}{dx^{n-1}} \dfrac{dv}{dx} + \cdots$

$\qquad + \dfrac{n(n-1)\cdots(n-k+1)}{k!} \dfrac{d^{n-k}u}{dx^{n-k}} \dfrac{d^k v}{dx^k}$

$\qquad + \cdots + u \dfrac{d^n v}{dx^n}.$

The terms on the right side of this equation may be obtained from the terms in the binomial expansion $(a + b)^n$ by replacing $a^{n-k}b^k$ by

$$(d^{n-k}u/dx^{n-k}) \cdot (d^k v/dx^k)$$

for $k = 0, 1, 2, \ldots, n$, and interpreting $d^0 u/dx^0$ as being u itself.

64. Find $d^3 y/dx^3$ in the following cases.

(a) $y = \sqrt{2x - 1}$ (b) $y = \dfrac{1}{3x + 2}$

(c) $y = ax^3 + bx^2 + cx + d$

65. If $f(x) = (x - a)^n g(x)$, where $g(x)$ is a polynomial and $g(a) \neq 0$, show that

$$f(a) = 0 = f'(a) = \cdots = f^{(n-1)}(a);$$

but that $f^{(n)}(a) = n!g(a) \neq 0$.

66. If $y = 2x^2 - 3x + 5$, find Δy for $x = 3$ and $\Delta x = 0.1$. Approximate Δy by finding its linear part.

67. Find an approximate value of $\sqrt{26}$ by considering the function $y = \sqrt{x}$ when $x = 25$ and $\Delta x = 1$. Also find an approximate value of $\sqrt[3]{26}$. (Specify the function used for the purpose and the values of x and Δx.)

68. By means of differentials, find an approximate value of $\sqrt[10]{0.999}$.

69. To compute the height h of a lamppost, the length a of the shadow of a six-foot pole is measured. The pole is 20 ft from the lamppost. If $a = 15$ ft, with a possible error of less than one inch, find the height of the lamppost and estimate the error in height.

70. Find the differential dy in the following cases.

(a) $y = x^2/(1 + x)$ (b) $x^2 - y^2 = 1$

(c) $xy + y^2 = 1$

71. Given a function f satisfying the following two conditions for all x and y:

(a) $f(x + y) = f(x) \cdot f(y)$,

(b) $f(x) = 1 + xg(x)$, where $\lim\limits_{x \to 0} g(x) = 1$.

Prove that

(a) the derivative $f'(x)$ exists, (b) $f'(x) = f(x)$.

72. Let $f(x) = x^2 + 1$. Given $\epsilon > 0$, find $\delta > 0$ such that $|f(x_1) - f(x_2)| < \epsilon$ whenever $|x_1 - x_2| < \delta$ and x_1, x_2 both lie in the closed interval $[-2, 2]$. State precisely what this means concerning the continuity of this function.

73. Given a function $f(x)$, defined for all real x, and a positive constant c such that $|f(x + h) - f(x)| \leq ch^2$ for all real h. Prove that

(a) $f(x)$ is uniformly continuous

(b) $f'(x) = 0$ for all x.

74. A function $f(x)$ is said to satisfy a Lipschitz condition of order m on the closed interval $[a, b]$ if there is a constant C such that

$$|f(x_2) - f(x_1)| \leq C|x_2 - x_1|^m$$

for all values of x_1, x_2 on $[a, b]$. Prove that a function which satisfies a Lipschitz condition of order $m > 0$ on $[a, b]$ is uniformly continuous there.

75. Suppose $[a, b]$ is the interval $[-1, 1]$ and

$$f(x) = \sqrt{1 - x^2}.$$

Find appropriate values of C and of m to satisfy the conditions in Exercise 74.

Hint. Show that if

$$y_2 > y_1 > 0 \quad \text{and} \quad y_2 - y_1 = h,$$

then

$$|\sqrt{y_2} - \sqrt{y_1}| \leq \sqrt{h}.$$

APPLICATIONS

CHAPTER 5

Some functions have the property that

$$f(x_1) > f(x_2) \quad \text{when} \quad x_1 > x_2. \qquad (1)$$

For instance, a linear function $f(x) = mx + b$ with positive slope m has this property on $(-\infty, \infty)$. For other functions, the condition expressed by (1) may hold only for a part of the domain. For example, $f(x) = \sin x$ (Fig. 5.1) has the property when x_1 and x_2 are in $[-\pi/2, \pi/2]$ but not in $[\pi/2, 3\pi/2]$. On the latter interval, $\sin x$ is decreasing.

5.1

Definition. *If* $f(x_1) > f(x_2)$ *when* $x_1 > x_2$ *for all* x_1 *and* x_2 *in* $[a, b]$, *we say that* f *is an increasing function on* $[a, b]$. *If* $f(x_1) < f(x_2)$ *for* $a \le x_2 < x_1 \le b$, *we say that* f *is a decreasing function on* $[a, b]$.

Remark 1. Sometimes we consider functions that are increasing or decreasing on open intervals such as (a, b) and $(-\infty, 0)$, or half-open intervals such as $[0, 1)$.

Example 1. (See Fig. 5.2.)

$$f(x) = x^3 \text{ increases on } (-\infty, \infty).$$

Example 2. (See Fig. 5.3.)

$$f(x) = \tan x \text{ increases on } (-\pi/2, \pi/2).$$

Example 3. (See Fig. 5.4.)

$$f(x) = \frac{1}{x} \text{ decreases on } (-\infty, 0) \text{ and on } (0, \infty).$$

Example 4. Let $F(x)$ for $x > 0$ be the area of the shaded region shown in Figure 5.5. Then the area increases as x moves to the right, so F is an increasing function on $(0, \infty)$.

5.2

5.5 $F(x) =$ area of tinted region. The area gets larger as x moves to the right.

Remark 2. It is also customary to say that f is increasing at each point in (a, b) if f is increasing on (a, b). In fact, we say that f is *increasing at a point* c if there is some neighborhood N of c such that $f(x) > f(c)$ when $x > c$ and $f(x) < f(c)$ when $x < c$, for all $x \in N$. For example, sgn x is increasing at $c = 0$ because sgn $0 = 0$, sgn $x = -1 < 0$ when $x < 0$, and sgn $x = +1 > 0$ when $x > 0$.

Remark 3. A function may oscillate so fast near a point that it is neither increasing nor decreasing there (nor remaining constant).

Example 5. Let f be the function defined by

$$f(x) = \begin{cases} x \sin (1/x) & \text{for } x \neq 0, \\ 0 & \text{for } x = 0. \end{cases}$$

No matter how small a neighborhood of zero N may be, there are x's in N for which $f(x)$ is positive and those for which it is negative. This function oscillates infinitely often between positive and negative values in every neighborhood of $x = 0$. It is neither increasing nor decreasing at 0.

Sign of *dy/dx*

For $y = x^3$, $dy/dx = 3x^2$ is positive when $x \neq 0$. Therefore, by Lemma 1 of Article 4.3, we can now

5.3

5.4

5.6

conclude that the function $f(x) = x^3$ is increasing at each $c \in (-\infty, 0)$ or in $(0, \infty)$. Because $f'(0) = 0$, the lemma does not apply at $c = 0$, although it is true that f is also increasing there, because x^3 is positive when x is greater than zero and is negative when x is less than zero.

At a point where $dy/dx > 0$, the tangent to the graph of $y = f(x)$ has positive slope, so the linearization of f at such a point is an increasing function. Since the tangent line stays close to the graph of f near the point of tangency, we also see geometrically the significance of Lemma 1 mentioned above: The curve rises as we go from left to right through this point. Of course, at a point where dy/dx is negative, the tangent line slopes downward and the curve falls as we go through the point of tangency from left to right.

Figure 5.6 shows a curve on which we have indicated certain points $A, B, C, D,$ and E. At A and E, the tangents have positive slopes and the curve is rising. At C, the tangent has negative slope and the curve is falling. At B and D, the tangents have zero slope and there is a transition between rising and falling portions of the curve. [Note, however, that such a transition doesn't always occur when the derivative is zero: The curve may cross its horizontal tangent and keep on rising, as $y = x^3$ does at $(0, 0)$.]

In relatively simple situations, $f'(x)$ is continuous and can only go from negative to positive values (or vice versa) by going through zero. [This is a consequence of the Intermediate Value Theorem, Theorem 15 (ii), Chapter 4.]

Example 6. We apply these ideas to the problem of sketching the curve $y = \frac{1}{3}x^3 - 2x^2 + 3x + 2$. The slope at (x, y) is

$$\frac{dy}{dx} = x^2 - 4x + 3 = (x - 1)(x - 3).$$

To determine where dy/dx is positive and where it is negative, we first determine where it is zero:

$$\frac{dy}{dx} = 0 \quad \text{when} \quad x = 1 \text{ or } x = 3,$$

since these points will mark the transition from positive to negative or from negative to positive slopes. The sign of dy/dx depends upon the signs of both factors $(x - 1)$ and $(x - 3)$, and since the sign of $(x - 1)$ is negative when x is to the left of 1 and positive to the right, we have the pattern of signs indicated in Fig 5.7(a). Similarly the sign of $(x - 3)$ is as shown in Fig. 5.7(b), and the sign of $dy/dx = (x - 1)(x - 3)$ as shown in Fig. 5.7(c). We can get a rough idea of the shape of the curve just from this pattern of signs of its slope, if we sketch a curve which is rising, falling, and rising again for $x < 1, 1 < x < 3,$ and $x > 3$, respectively (Fig. 5.8).

To get a more accurate curve, we would construct a table for some range of values extending, say, from $x = 0$ to $x = 4$, which includes the transition points between rising and falling portions of the curve (Fig. 5.9).

The terms "rising" and "falling," or "increasing" and "decreasing," are always taken to apply to the behavior of the curve as the point that is tracing it moves from left to right or, in other words, relative to its behavior as x increases.

The same concepts apply to functions that vary with time. For example, Fig. 5.10 represents a rope running through a pulley at P, bearing a weight W at one end. The other end is held in a man's hand M at a distance of 5 feet above the ground as he walks in a straight line at the rate of 6 ft/sec. If, as in the figure, x represents the distance in feet of the man's hand away from the vertical line PW, then x is an increasing function of t and we are given the rate at which it changes with t, namely, 6 ft/sec. This would be stated in mathematical terms by saying $dx/dt = +6$ (ft/sec). On the other hand, if the man were to walk toward the line PW at the rate of 6 ft/sec, we would have $dx/dt = -6$ (ft/sec), because x would be then a decreasing function of t.

sign of $x-1$

sign of $x-3$

sign of $(x-1)(x-3)$

5.7

rising | falling | rising

5.8

5.9

$6(ft/sec)$

$5(ft)$

5.10

EXERCISES

1-11 odd   1/29/76

In each of the following exercises, determine dy/dx and find the sets of values of x where the graph of y versus x is rising (to the right) and where it is falling. Sketch each curve, showing in particular the points of transition between falling and rising portions of the curve.

1. $y = x^2 - x + 1$ 2. $y = \dfrac{x^3}{3} - \dfrac{x^2}{2} - 2x + \dfrac{1}{3}$

3. $y = 2x^3 - 3x^2 + 3$ 4. $y = x^3 - 27x + 36$

5. $y = x^4 - 8x^2 + 16$ 6. $y = (x+1)(x-2)^2$

7. $y = \dfrac{(x-2)^2}{x+1}$ 8. $y = (x+1)(x-2)^{-2}$

9. $y = \sqrt{4 - x^2}$ 10. $y = \sqrt{x^2 - 4}$

11. $y = x|x|$

5.2 RELATED RATES

In the example at the end of Article 5.1, suppose that the pulley is 25 ft above the ground, the rope is 45 ft long, and at a given instant the distance x is 15 ft and the man is walking away from the pulley. How fast is the weight being raised at this particular instant?

In Fig. 5.11, M represents the man's hand, P the pulley, W the weight, and OM is a horizontal line at the level of the man's hand which is 5 ft above the ground, so that P is 20 ft above O. The figure is drawn to illustrate the situation at any time t and

P

y

$20(ft)$

W

z

h

O x M

5.11

not just at the instant in question. The reason for this is that certain of the distances, namely, x, y, z, and h in the illustration, are quantities which vary and it is important to treat them as such and not as constants.

Having drawn a figure to illustrate the relationship between the various variable quantities involved in the problem, let us now state what is given and what the problem asks for in terms of these variables.

Given: (a) Relationships between the variables which are to hold for all instants of time:

$$y + z = 45,$$
$$h + y = 20,$$
$$20^2 + x^2 = z^2.$$

(b) At a given instant, which we may take to be $t = 0$:

$$x = 15, \qquad \frac{dx}{dt} = 6.$$

Find: $dh/dt = (?)$ at the instant $t = 0$.

Such a problem involving rates of related variables is called "a problem in related rates." It is typical of such problems that

(a) certain variables are related in a definite way for all values of t under consideration,

(b) the values of some or all of these variables and the rates of change of some of them are given at some particular instant, and

(c) it is required to find the rate of change of one or more of them at this instant.

The variables may then all be considered to be functions of time, and if the equations which relate them for all values of t are differentiated with respect to t, the new equations so obtained will tell how their rates of change are related. From this information it should be possible to answer the question posed by the problem.

In our problem, we shall modify the procedure outlined above by first obtaining a single equation relating the variable x (whose rate is given) and the

variable h (whose rate is wanted) before we take derivatives. Using the equations given, we find successively:

$$z = 45 - y, \quad y = 20 - h,$$
$$z = 45 - (20 - h) = (25 + h),$$
$$20^2 + x^2 = z^2 = (25 + h)^2;$$

that is,

$$20^2 + x^2 = (25 + h)^2.$$

This last equation relates the variables x and h for all values of t under consideration (namely, in an interval of values of t near $t = 0$). Both sides of this equation are functions of t, and the equality says they represent the same function of t. Thus when we differentiate both sides of the equation with respect to t, we shall have another equation:

$$\frac{d}{dt}(20^2 + x^2) = \frac{d}{dt}(25 + h)^2,$$
$$0 + 2x\frac{dx}{dt} = 2(25 + h)\frac{dh}{dt}.$$

This may be solved for the rate we want, namely,

$$\frac{dh}{dt} = \frac{x}{25 + h}\frac{dx}{dt}.$$

Now at the given instant, we have

$$x = 15, \qquad \frac{dx}{dt} = 6,$$

and we find h at this instant from the equation

$$20^2 + 15^2 = (25 + h)^2, \quad 25 + h = 25.$$

When we substitute these values, we obtain

$$\frac{dh}{dt} = \frac{18}{5} = 3\tfrac{3}{5} \text{ (ft/sec)}$$

as the rate at which the weight is being raised at the instant in question.

As a second example, consider a ladder 26 ft long which leans against a vertical wall. At a particular instant, the foot of the ladder is 10 ft out from the base of the wall and is being drawn away from the wall at the rate of 4 ft/sec. How fast is the top of the ladder moving down the wall at this instant?

5.12

5.13

Figure 5.12 represents the position of the ladder, with the distance from the base of the wall to the foot of the ladder labeled x to indicate the fact that it is a variable, and the distance from the ground to the top of the ladder labeled y because it varies also. The statement of the problem may then be translated into mathematical terms as follows:

Given: $x^2 + y^2 = 26^2$.

Find: $\dfrac{dy}{dt} = (?)$

when

$$x = 10 \text{ (ft)} \quad \text{and} \quad \frac{dx}{dt} = 4 \text{ (ft/sec)}.$$

We differentiate the given equation implicitly with respect to t and get

$$2x \frac{dx}{dt} + 2y \frac{dy}{dt} = 0.$$

Hence

$$\frac{dy}{dt} = \frac{-x}{y} \frac{dx}{dt}.$$

When $x = 10$, $y = 24$, and $dx/dt = 4$, this leads to $dy/dt = -\frac{5}{3}$. That is, y is *decreasing* (the top of the ladder is moving *down*) at the rate of $\frac{5}{3}$ ft/sec.

As a final example, consider the conical reservoir, Fig. 5.13, into which water runs at the constant rate of 2 ft^3 per minute. How fast is the water level rising when it is 6 ft deep?

First, we must translate the problem into mathematical terms. To do this, we let

$v =$ volume (ft^3) of water in the tank at time t (min),

$x =$ radius (ft) of the section of the cone at the water line,

$y =$ depth (ft) of water in the tank at time t.

Then the statement that water runs into the tank at the rate of 2 ft^3/min becomes

$$\frac{dv}{dt} = 2.$$

The question we are to answer is

$$\frac{dy}{dt} = (?) \quad \text{when } y = 6.$$

The relationship between the volume of water v and depth y is expressed by the equation

$$v = \tfrac{1}{3}\pi x^2 y.$$

But this involves the additional variable x as well as v and y. However, we may eliminate x since, by similar triangles, we have

$$\frac{x}{y} = \frac{5}{10}, \quad \text{or} \quad x = \frac{1}{2}y.$$

Therefore

$$v = \tfrac{1}{12}\pi y^3,$$

and when we differentiate this with respect to t, we have

$$\frac{dv}{dt} = \frac{1}{4}\pi y^2 \frac{dy}{dt}.$$

Hence

$$\frac{dy}{dt} = \frac{4 \, dv/dt}{\pi y^2},$$

and when

$$\frac{dv}{dt} = 2 \quad \text{and} \quad y = 6,$$

this gives

$$\frac{dy}{dt} = \frac{2}{9\pi} \approx 0.071 \text{ ft/min.}$$

EXERCISES

11/30   # 1-15 odd

1. Let A be the area of a circle of radius r. How is dA/dt related to dr/dt?

2. Let V be the volume of a sphere of radius r. How is dV/dt related to dr/dt?

3. Sand falls onto a conical pile at the rate of 10 ft^3/min. The radius of the base of the pile is always equal to one-half of its altitude. How fast is the altitude of the pile increasing when it is 5 ft deep?

4. Suppose that a raindrop is a perfect sphere. Assume that through condensation, the raindrop accumulates moisture at a rate proportional to its surface area. Show that the radius increases at a constant rate.

5. Point A moves along the x-axis at the constant rate of a ft/sec while point B moves along the y-axis at the constant rate of b ft/sec. Find how fast the distance between them is changing when A is at the point $(x, 0)$ and B is at the point $(0, y)$.

6. A spherical balloon is inflated with gas at the rate of 100 ft^3/min. Assuming that the gas pressure remains constant, how fast is the radius of the balloon increasing at the instant when the radius is 3 ft?

7. A boat is pulled in to a dock by means of a rope with one end attached to the bow of the boat, the other end passing through a ring attached to the dock at a point 4 ft higher than the bow of the boat. If the rope is pulled in at the rate of 2 ft/sec, how fast is the boat approaching the dock when 10 ft of rope are out?

8. A balloon is 200 ft off the ground and rising vertically at the constant rate of 15 ft/sec. An automobile passes beneath it traveling along a straight road at the constant rate of 45 mi/hr = 66 ft/sec. How fast is the distance between them changing one second later?

9. Water is withdrawn from a conical reservoir 8 ft in diameter and 10 ft deep (vertex down) at the constant rate of 5 ft^3/min. How fast is the water level falling when the depth of water in the reservoir is 6 ft?

10. A particle moves around the circle $x^2 + y^2 = 1$ with an x-velocity component $dx/dt = y$. Find dy/dt. Does the particle travel in the clockwise or counterclockwise direction around the circle?

11. A man 6 ft tall walks at the rate of 5 ft/sec toward a street light that is 16 ft above the ground. At what rate is the tip of his shadow moving? At what rate is the length of his shadow changing when he is 10 ft from the base of the light?

12. When air expands adiabatically, the pressure p and volume v satisfy the relationship $pv^{1.4} = \text{constant}$. At a certain instant the pressure is 50 lb/in^2 and the volume 32 in^3 and is decreasing at the rate of 4 in^3/sec. How rapidly is the pressure changing at this instant?

13. A light is at the top of a pole 50 ft high. A ball is dropped from the same height from a point 30 ft away from the light. How fast is the shadow of the ball moving along the ground $\frac{1}{2}$ sec later? (Assume the ball falls a distance $s = 16t^2$ ft in t seconds.)

14. A girl flies a kite at a height of 300 ft, the wind carrying the kite horizontally away from the girl at a rate of 25 ft/sec. How fast must the girl pay out the string at the moment when the kite is 500 ft away from her?

15. A spherical iron ball 8 in. in diameter is coated with a layer of ice of uniform thickness. If the ice melts at the rate of 10 in^3 per minute, how fast is the thickness of the ice decreasing when it is 2 in. thick? At the same rate of melting, how fast is the outer surface area of ice decreasing?

16. Two ships A and B are sailing away from the point O along routes such that the angle $AOB = 120°$. How fast is the distance between them changing if, at a certain instant, $OA = 8$ mi, $OB = 6$ mi, ship A is sailing at the rate of 20 mi/hr, and ship B at the rate of 30 mi/hr?
Hint. Use the law of cosines.

5.14

5.15

a | b

|c|

5.16

5.3 SIGNIFICANCE OF THE SIGN OF THE SECOND DERIVATIVE

We have already seen how we may use the information given by dy/dx about the slope of the tangent to a curve to help in sketching it. We recall that in an interval where dy/dx is positive, the curve is rising to the right, while if dy/dx is negative the curve is falling to the right. Also it is evident that the regions of rise and fall are usually separated by high or low points where dy/dx is zero and the tangent is horizontal. However, it is possible for dy/dx to be zero at points which are neither high nor low points of the curve.

Example 1. If $\quad y = (x - 2)^3 + 1,$

then $\qquad \dfrac{dy}{dx} = 3(x - 2)^2,$

and although $\qquad \dfrac{dy}{dx} = 0 \quad$ at $\quad x = 2$

for all values of x other than 2, the slope is positive and y is an increasing function of x (Fig. 5.14).

The regions of rise and fall may also be separated by points where the derivative fails to exist.

Example 2. If $y = x^{2/3}$, then

$$\frac{dy}{dx} = \frac{2}{3} x^{-1/3} = \frac{2}{3\sqrt[3]{x}}$$

is positive when x is positive, and negative when x is negative. At the transition point $x = 0$, dy/dx does not exist, but $dx/dy = \frac{3}{2}x^{1/3}$ is zero, which means that the tangent to the curve at $(0, 0)$ is vertical instead of horizontal (Fig. 5.15).

Next we shall see that the sign of the second derivative tells whether the graph of $y = f(x)$ is concave upward (y'' positive) or downward (y'' negative).

Consider, for example, the curve in Fig. 5.16(a). The first and second derivatives are represented by the curves in Fig. 5.16 (b) and (c). The arc ABC of the y-curve is concave upward; CDE is concave downward; EF is again concave upward. To focus attention, let us consider a section near A on the arc ABC. Here y' is negative and the y-curve slopes downward to the right. But as we travel through A, moving from left to right, we find the slope becomes less negative. That is, y' is an *increasing* function of x. Therefore the y'-curve slopes upward at A'. Hence its slope (that is, y'') is positive there. The same kind of argument applies at all points along the arc ABC; namely, y' is an increasing function of x, so its derivative (that is, y'') is positive. This is indicated by drawing the arc $A''B''C''$ of the y''-curve above the x-axis.

Similarly, where the y-curve is concave downward (along CDE), the y'-curve is falling, so its slope (that is, y'') is negative.

The direction of concavity is therefore

upward if the second derivative is *positive*,

downward if the second derivative is *negative*.

In the first case, we could also say the curve is cupped so as to "hold water"; in the second case it would "spill water."

Points of inflection

A point where the curve changes the direction of its concavity from downward to upward or vice versa is called a *point of inflection*. Inflection points occur at C and E in Fig. 5.16(a), and are characterized by a change in the sign of d^2y/dx^2. Such a change of sign may occur where

(a) $d^2y/dx^2 = 0$, or

(b) d^2y/dx^2 fails to exist (for example, it may become infinite at such a point).

In Fig. 5.16, case (a) is shown. Case (b) is shown in Fig. 5.17, where the curve is

$$y = x^{1/3},$$

from which we find

$$y' = \tfrac{1}{3}x^{-(2/3)}, \quad y'' = -\tfrac{2}{9}x^{-(5/3)},$$

so that both y' and y'' become infinite when x approaches zero. On the other hand,

$$y' = \frac{1}{3x^{2/3}} = \frac{1}{3y^2}$$

5.17

5.18

5.19   The graph of $y = |x^2 - 4|$.

is always positive for both positive and negative values of x, so the curve is always rising and has a vertical tangent at $(0, 0)$. Also,

$$y'' = -\frac{2}{9}\left(\frac{1}{\sqrt[3]{x}}\right)^5 = \frac{-2}{9y^5}$$

is positive (the curve "holds water") when x is negative, and is negative (the curve "spills water") when x is positive, so that $(0, 0)$ is a point of inflection.

Note. The illustration just given would have been much simpler to discuss if we had written the equation in the form $x = y^3$. Then

$$\frac{dx}{dy} = 3y^2, \qquad \frac{d^2x}{dy^2} = 6y,$$

so that we have

$$\frac{dx}{dy} = 0 \quad \text{and} \quad \frac{d^2x}{dy^2} = 0$$

at $(0, 0)$. It is clear that dx/dy is positive for all y different from zero and d^2x/dy^2 has the same sign as y and therefore changes its sign at $y = 0$. If we interchange the x- and y-axes so as to take the x-axis to be vertical and the y-axis to be horizontal, the curve will be as shown in Fig. 5.18.

Remark. At a point of inflection, the curve should also have a unique tangent line, which the curve crosses there. Thus we rule out sharp corners, called *cusps*, such as points A and B on the graph of $y = |x^2 - 4|$, shown in Fig. 5.19. The curve to the left of A, and again to the right of B, has equation $y = x^2 - 4$, for which $y'' = +2$. Between A and B, the equation is $y = 4 - x^2$, for which $y'' = -2$. Thus the second derivative changes sign at A and again at B. However, there is not a (unique) tangent line to the graph at either A or B, and these points would not be called inflection points of the graph.

5.4 CURVE PLOTTING

The discussion in Article 5.3 may be summarized and stated in the following outline of procedure to apply in sketching the graph of an equation $y = f(x)$.

A. Calculate dy/dx and d^2y/dx^2.

B. Find the values of x for which dy/dx is positive and for which it is negative. Calculate y and d^2y/dx^2 at the points of transition between positive and negative values of dy/dx. These may give maximum or minimum points on the curve. (See Figs. 5.9, 5.15, 5.16, and 5.19.)

C. Find the values of x for which d^2y/dx^2 is positive and for which it is negative. Calculate y and dy/dx at the points of transition between positive and negative values of d^2y/dx^2. These may give points of inflection of the curve. (See Figs. 5.16 and 5.17.)

D. Plot a few additional points. In particular, points which lie between the transition points already determined or points which lie to the left and to the right of all of them will ordinarily be useful. The nature of the curve for large values of $|x|$ should also be indicated.

E. Sketch a smooth curve through the points found above, unless there are discontinuities in the curve or its slope. Have the curve pass through its points rising or falling as indicated by the sign of dy/dx, and concave upward or downward as indicated by the sign of d^2y/dx^2.

We shall now apply this technique to a few examples.

Problem 1. (See Fig. 5.20.) Sketch the curve of
$$y = \tfrac{1}{6}(x^3 - 6x^2 + 9x + 6).$$

Solution

$$\frac{dy}{dx} = \frac{1}{6}(3x^2 - 12x + 9) = \frac{1}{2}(x^2 - 4x + 3),$$

$$\frac{d^2y}{dx^2} = \frac{1}{2}(2x - 4) = x - 2.$$

In the factored form,

$$\frac{dy}{dx} = \frac{1}{2}(x - 1)(x - 3),$$

and the two factors change their signs at $x = 1$ and $x = 3$. (See Fig. 5.20a.)

5.20

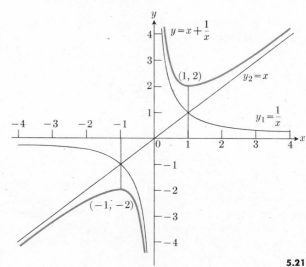

5.21

We readily see that $d^2y/dx^2 = x - 2$ is negative to the left of $x = 2$ and is positive to the right of $x = 2$, so that an inflection point occurs at $x = 2$. A fairly good sketch of the curve can now be made by using the information in the following table.

x	y	y'	y''	Remarks
-1	$-\frac{5}{3}$	$+$	$-$	Rising, concave down
0	1	$+\frac{3}{2}$	$-$	Rising, concave down
1	$\frac{5}{3}$	0	$-$	"Spills water", maximum
2	$\frac{4}{3}$	$-\frac{1}{2}$	0	Falling, point of inflection
3	1	0	$+$	"Holds water", minimum
4	$\frac{5}{3}$	$+\frac{3}{2}$	$+$	Rising, concave up

Problem 2. (See Fig. 5.21.) Sketch the curve of

$$y = x + \frac{1}{x} = x + x^{-1}.$$

Solution. $\quad \dfrac{dy}{dx} = 1 - x^{-2} = 1 - \dfrac{1}{x^2} = \dfrac{x^2 - 1}{x^2},$

$$\frac{d^2y}{dx^2} = 2x^{-3} = \frac{2}{x^3}.$$

The sign of dy/dx will be the same as the sign of

$$x^2 - 1 = (x - 1)(x + 1).$$

(See Fig. 5.21a.) But when x is near zero, $|y|$ will be large and y, dy/dx, d^2y/dx^2 all become infinite as x approaches zero. This curve is discontinuous at $x = 0$. Also, for large values of x, the $1/x$ term becomes small and $y \approx x$.

In fact,

$$\text{when } |x| \text{ is small,} \qquad y \approx \frac{1}{x},$$

$$\text{when } |x| \text{ is large,} \qquad y \approx x,$$

so that it is helpful to sketch (as can quickly be done) the curves

$$y_1 = \frac{1}{x}, \qquad y_2 = x,$$

as well as

$$y = x + \frac{1}{x} = y_1 + y_2.$$

Actually, replacing x by $-x$ merely changes the sign of y, so that it would suffice to sketch the portion of the curve in the first quadrant and then reflect the result with respect to the origin to get the portion in the third quadrant (Fig. 5.21b).

x	y_1	y_2	y	y'	y''	Remarks
-4	$-\frac{1}{4}$	-4	$-\frac{17}{4}$	$+$	$-$	Rising, concave down
-2	$-\frac{1}{2}$	-2	$-\frac{5}{2}$	$+$	$-$	Rising, concave down
-1	-1	-1	-2	0	-2	"Spills water," maximum
$-\frac{1}{2}$	-2	$-\frac{1}{2}$	$-\frac{5}{2}$	$-$	$-$	Falling, concave down
$-\frac{1}{4}$	-4	$-\frac{1}{4}$	$-\frac{17}{4}$	$-$	$-$	Falling, concave down
$+\frac{1}{4}$	4	$\frac{1}{4}$	$\frac{17}{4}$	$-$	$+$	Falling, concave up
$\frac{1}{2}$	2	$\frac{1}{2}$	$\frac{5}{2}$	$-$	$+$	Falling, concave up
1	1	1	2	0	$+2$	"Holds water", minimum
2	$\frac{1}{2}$	2	$\frac{5}{2}$	$+$	$+$	Rising, concave up
4	$\frac{1}{4}$	4	$\frac{17}{4}$	$+$	$+$	Rising, concave up

Remark. If $y = f(x)$ is the equation of a curve, and if $f(x) \to \infty$, or $f(x) \to -\infty$, as $x \to a$, or $x \to a-$, or $x \to a+$, then the graph of the curve will approach the line $x = a$ as an *asymptote*. For example, the line $x = 0$ (the y-axis) is an asymptote of the graph of $f(x) = x + x^{-1}$. When

$$f(x) = \frac{P(x)}{Q(x)},$$

where P and Q are polynomials with no common nonconstant factor, the asymptotes of the form $x = a$ are found by solving the equation $Q(x) = 0$. Thus

$$y = \frac{x^2 + 1}{x^3 - 4x}$$

has the lines

$$x = 0, \quad x = 2, \quad x = -2$$

as its vertical asymptotes.

EXERCISES

12/1   # 1-4, 6, 10, 12, 14, 16

In Exercises 1 through 6, find intervals of values of x for which the curve is (a) rising, (b) falling, (c) concave upward, (d) concave downward. Sketch the curves, showing the high turning points M, low turning points m, points of inflection I, and vertical asymptotes.

1. $y = x^2 - 4x + 3$ 2. $y = \dfrac{x}{x+1}$

3. $y = 4 + 3x - x^3$ 4. $y = \dfrac{x^3}{3} - \dfrac{x^2}{2} - 6x$

5. $y = x + \dfrac{4}{x}$ 6. $y = \dfrac{x^2}{x^2 - 1}$

7. Sketch a smooth curve $y = f(x)$, illustrating

$$f(1) = 0, \quad f'(x) < 0 \quad \text{for } x < 1,$$
$$f'(x) > 0 \quad \text{for } x > 1.$$

8. Sketch a smooth curve $y = f(x)$, illustrating

$$f(1) = 0, \quad f''(x) < 0 \quad \text{for } x < 1,$$
$$f''(x) > 0 \quad \text{for } x > 1.$$

12/2 # 17,19,20,21

Sketch curves 9 through 12, indicating high and low turning points and points of inflection

9. $y = 6 - 2x - x^2$ 10. $y = 12 - 12x + x^3$

11. $y = x^4 - 32x + 48$ 12. $y = x^3 - 3x^2 + 2$

For the curves 13 through 16, find vertical tangents and sketch the curves.

13. $x = y^3 + 3y^2 + 3y + 2$

14. $x = y^3 + 3y^2 - 9y - 11$

15. $x = y^4 - 2y^2 + 2$ 16. $x = y^2 + \dfrac{2}{y}$

17. Sketch a continuous curve $y = f(x)$ having the following characteristics:

$$f(-2) = 8, \quad f(0) = 4, \quad f(2) = 0,$$
$$f'(x) > 0 \quad \text{for } |x| > 2,$$
$$f'(2) = f'(-2) = 0,$$
$$f'(x) < 0 \quad \text{for } |x| < 2,$$
$$f''(x) < 0 \quad \text{for } x < 0, \quad f''(x) > 0 \quad \text{for } x > 0.$$

18. Sketch a continuous curve $y = f(x)$ having

$$f'(x) > 0 \quad \text{for } x < 2, \quad f'(x) < 0 \quad \text{for } x > 2,$$

(a) if $f'(x)$ is continuous at $x = 2$,

(b) if $f'(x) \to 1$ as $x \to 2-$,

$f'(x) \to -1$ as $x \to 2+$,

(c) if $f'(x) = 1$ for all $x < 2$,

$f'(x) = -1$ for all $x > 2$.

19. Sketch a continuous curve $y = f(x)$ for $x > 0$ if

$$f(1) = 0, \quad \text{and} \quad f'(x) = 1/x \quad \text{for all } x > 0.$$

Is such a curve necessarily concave upward or concave downward?

20. Show that the sum of any positive real number and its reciprocal is at least 2.

21. Sketch the curve

$$y = 2x^3 + 2x^2 - 2x - 1$$

after locating its maximum, minimum, and inflection points. Then answer the following questions from your graph:

(a) How many times and approximately where does the curve cross the x-axis?

(b) How many times and approximately where would the curve cross the x-axis if $+3$ were added to all the y-values?

(c) How many times and approximately where would the curve cross the x-axis if -3 were added to all the y-values?

5.5 MAXIMA AND MINIMA: THEORY

A function f is said to have a relative, or local, *maximum* at $x = a$ if

$$f(a) \geq f(a + h)$$

for all positive and negative values of h sufficiently near zero. For a local *minimum* at $x = b$,

SUCH THAT A+H IS D. OF F, $f(b) \leq f(b + h)$

for values of h close to zero. The word *relative* or *local* is used to distinguish such a point from an *absolute* maximum or minimum that would occur if we could say, for example, that

$$f(a) \geq f(x)$$

for all x and not just for all x close to a. In Fig. 5.21, for example, the point $(1, 2)$ is a *relative* minimum of the function

$$f(x) = x + \frac{1}{x}$$

because

$$x + \frac{1}{x} \geq 2$$

for all values of x close to 1. But certainly when x is negative, the inequality is no longer satisfied. Indeed, the function $f(x) = x + 1/x$ has no absolute minimum and no absolute maximum.

In Fig. 5.22 we indicate the graph of a function $y = f(x)$ defined only for the domain $[0, L]$. This function has a relative minimum at C, which is also an absolute minimum. It also has relative maxima at A and at B, and an absolute maximum at B.

5.22

5.23

We have encountered relative maxima and minima in sketching curves and have observed that they occur at transition points between rising and falling portions of a curve. At such transition points we have also observed that dy/dx is usually zero, but may in exceptional cases become infinite (Fig. 5.15). We shall now prove the following theorem.

Theorem 1. *Let the function f be defined for $a \leq x \leq b$ and have a relative maximum or minimum at $x = c$, where $a < c < b$. If the derivative $f'(x)$ exists as a finite number at $x = c$, then*

$$f'(c) = 0. \qquad (1)$$

Proof. By Lemma 1 of Article 4.3, we know that f would be increasing at c if $f'(c)$ were positive. But f is neither increasing nor decreasing at c because f has a local maximum or minimum at c. Hence $f'(c)$ cannot be positive. Likewise $f'(c)$ cannot be negative (because if it were, f would be decreasing at c). Therefore, $f'(c) = 0$. ◻

Remark 1. The reader is cautioned not to read into the theorem more than it says. It does not say what happens if a maximum or minimum occurs

(a) at a point c where the derivative fails to exist, or

(b) at an endpoint of the interval of definition of the function.

Neither does it say that the function necessarily does have a maximum or minimum at every place where the derivative is zero.

In Fig. 5.23, the graph represents the continuous function defined by

$$y = f(x) = \begin{cases} 3 - x & \text{for} \quad x \leq 2, \\ \frac{1}{2}x^2 - 1 & \text{for} \quad x > 2. \end{cases}$$

The slope is

$$\frac{dy}{dx} = \frac{d(3 - x)}{dx} = -1 \quad \text{for} \quad x < 2,$$

$$\frac{dy}{dx} = \frac{d(\frac{1}{2}x^2 - 1)}{dx} = x \quad \text{for} \quad x > 2.$$

At the point $x = 2$, the left-hand tangent has slope $m- = -1$ and the right-hand tangent has slope $m+ = 2$. Clearly, the curve is falling before $x = 2$ and rising after $x = 2$, and has a minimum at $x = 2$, $y = 1$. The derivative at $x = 2$ does not exist because $m+ \neq m-$. This shows that a minimum may occur where the derivative is not zero: where it doesn't even exist.

It is also easy to see from the proof of the theorem that when a maximum or minimum occurs at the *end* of a curve the derivative need not vanish at such a point. For example, suppose $g(x) = \sin x$ on $[-\pi/2, \pi/2]$ and that f is the inverse of g:

$$f(x) = \sin^{-1} x, \quad x \in [-1, 1].$$

The graphs of g and f are shown in Fig. 5.24. We know from elementary trigonometry that the minimum value of $\sin x$ is -1 and its maximum is $+1$, and that the sine is an increasing function on $[-\pi/2, \pi/2]$. Therefore its inverse function, $\sin^{-1} x$ (or, alternatively, arcsin x), is an increasing function

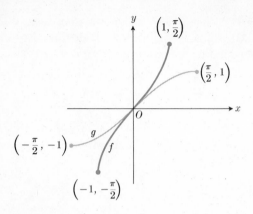

5.24 Graphs of $y = g(x) = \sin x$, $-\pi/2 \leq x \leq \pi/2$, and $y = f(x) = \sin^{-1} x$, $-1 \leq x \leq 1$.

on *its* domain $[-1, 1]$. Thus the minimum value of f is

$$f(-1) = -\pi/2,$$

and the maximum is $f(+1) = +\pi/2$. Although we don't yet have formulas for differentiating $\sin x$ and its inverse, it is clear from the graph that the slope of the inverse sine curve is not zero at its ends.

One-sided derivatives

Strictly, we can always say that $f'(a)$ and $f'(b)$ don't exist if $[a, b]$ is the domain of f, for in the definition of the derivative,

$$f'(x) = \lim_{h \to 0} \frac{f(x + h) - f(x)}{h}, \qquad (2)$$

we are supposed to let h approach zero through either positive or negative values. If we don't get the same answer for h positive and negative, we say that the indicated limit doesn't exist. (See Fig. 5.23 for $x = 2$.) When $x = a$ is the left endpoint of the domain of f we can't put $h < 0$, because $f(a + h)$ doesn't make sense unless $a + h$ is in $[a, b]$. But it is useful to define the right-hand derivative of f at a, which we write $f'(a+)$, as follows:

$$f'(a+) = \lim_{h \to 0+} \frac{f(a + h) - f(a)}{h}, \qquad (3a)$$

where $h \to 0+$ means that h approaches zero through positive values only. If this one-sided limit (3a)

exists, it is customary to say that it is the (right-hand) derivative of f at a.

Example 1. $f(x) = x^{3/2}$, $x \geq 0$,

$$f'(x) = \tfrac{3}{2}x^{1/2}, \quad x > 0,$$

$$f'(0+) = \lim_{h \to 0+} \frac{h^{3/2} - 0}{h} = \lim_{h \to 0+} h^{1/2} = 0.$$

It is a little bit sloppy to say that f is differentiable for $x \geq 0$ and that the formula $f'(x) = \tfrac{3}{2}x^{1/2}$ holds for all $x \geq 0$, but lots of mathematicians would go ahead and say it anyway. [They expect us to be smart enough to know that they mean $f'(0+) = 0$, and charitable enough to them for not saying it exactly that way.]

At the right-hand endpoint of the domain $[a, b]$, we can similarly define a left-hand derivative:

$$f'(b-) = \lim_{h \to 0-} \frac{f(b + h) - f(b)}{h}, \qquad (3b)$$

where the indicated limit is to be for h approaching zero through negative values, so that $b + h \in [a, b]$.

Remark 2. If f is defined on the domain $[a, b]$ and is differentiable on the open interval (a, b), and if $f'(a+)$ and $f'(b-)$ also exist, then we simply say that f is differentiable on $[a, b]$.

Example 2. $f(x) = (a^2 - x^2)^{3/2}$

is defined on the domain $[-a, a]$. For $x \in (-a, a)$, its derivative is

$$f'(x) = -3x(a^2 - x^2)^{1/2}. \qquad (4)$$

The right-hand derivative at $-a$ is

$$f'(-a+) = \lim \frac{f(x) - f(-a)}{x + a}$$

$$= \lim \frac{(a - x)(a + x)(a^2 - x^2)^{1/2}}{a + x}$$

$$= 0, \quad \text{where } x \to -a \text{ from the right.}$$

Similarly, if we use the definition of the derivative $f'(a-)$, we find that

$$f'(a-) = 0.$$

The formula of Eq. (4) is also zero at $\pm a$. So we would say, in this example, that f is differentiable on $[-a, a]$ and that its derivative is given by Eq. (4).

Endpoint extrema

If the domain of f is the bounded, closed interval $[a, b]$ and if $f'(a+)$ and $f'(b-)$ exist, then it is easy to verify that

$$f \text{ has a local } \begin{Bmatrix} \text{maximum} \\ \text{minimum} \end{Bmatrix} \text{ at } a \text{ if } \begin{cases} f'(a+) < 0, \\ f'(a+) > 0, \end{cases}$$

$$\text{(5a)}$$

and

$$f \text{ has a local } \begin{Bmatrix} \text{minimum} \\ \text{maximum} \end{Bmatrix} \text{ at } b \text{ if } \begin{cases} f'(b-) < 0, \\ f'(b-) > 0. \end{cases}$$

$$\text{(5b)}$$

Summary

How does one find the maximum and minimum values of a function? Locate the points where

(1) the derivative is zero,

(2) the derivative fails to exist,

(3) the domain of the function has an end.

These are the candidates for values of the independent variable where f has an extremum. They are called the *critical points* for maximizing or minimizing f. By comparing the values of f at these points with each other and with the behavior at nearby points, we decide which of them, if any, give the local (or absolute) maxima and minima.

Problem. Let $f(x) = |4 - x^2|$ on $[-3, 3]$. Find the local (and absolute) maxima and minima.

Solution. We rewrite the formula for f:

$$f(x) = \begin{cases} 4 - x^2 & \text{for } |x| \le 2, \\ x^2 - 4 & \text{for } 2 < |x| \le 3. \end{cases}$$

The derivative is then given by

$$f'(x) = \begin{cases} -2x & \text{for } x \in (-2, 2) \\ 2x & \text{for } x \in (-3, -2) \text{ or } x \in (2, 3). \end{cases}$$

Hence the critical points are

(1) $x = 0$, where the derivative is zero;

(2) $x = -2$ and $x = +2$. Here the derivative fails to exist because $f'(2-) = -4$, whereas $f'(2+) = +4$, and $f'(-2-) = -4$, $f'(-2+) = +4$;

(3) $x = -3$ and $x = +3$, the endpoints of the domain.

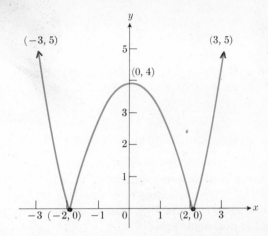

5.25 The graph of $y = |4 - x^2|$, $-3 \le x \le 3$.

The corresponding values of the function are

$$f(0) = 4, \quad f(2) = f(-2) = 0,$$

$$f(3) = f(-3) = 5.$$

There are minima (relative and absolute) at $x = \pm 2$, maxima (relative and absolute) at $x = \pm 3$, and a relative maximum at $x = 0$. The graph is shown in Fig. 5.25.

EXERCISES

12/2   #1,2,3 12/3 4-10 EVEN

Find the critical points for each of the following functions. For each critical point, determine whether the function has a local maximum or a local minimum there, or neither. If possible, find the absolute maximum and minimum values of the function on the indicated domain.

1. $f(x) = x - x^2$ on $[0, 1]$ 2. $f(x) = x - x^3$ on $[0, 1]$

3. $f(x) = |x - x^2|$ on $[-2, 2]$

4. $f(x) = x(1 + x^2)^{-1}$ on $(-\infty, \infty)$

5. $f(x) = \dfrac{x}{1 + |x|}$ on $(-\infty, \infty)$

6. $f(x) = \dfrac{|x|}{1 + |x|}$ on $[0, \infty)$

7. $f(x) = x - [x]$ on $(-\infty, \infty)$, where $[x]$ is equal to the greatest integer in x

if second deri. is ZERO it doesn't tell you anything

8. $f(x) = \text{sgn}(\sin x)$ on $[-2\pi, 2\pi]$. Answer this question without using derivatives.

9. $f(x) = (x - x^2)^{-1}$ on $(0, 1)$

10. $f(x) = |x^3|$ on $[-2, 3]$. What would occur if the domain were changed to $[-2, 3)$?

5.6 MAXIMA AND MINIMA: PROBLEMS

The differential calculus is a powerful tool for solving problems that call for minimizing or maximizing a function. We shall illustrate how this is done in several instances, and then summarize the technique in a list of specific rules.

Problem 1. Find two positive numbers whose sum is 20 and such that their product is as large as possible.

Solution. If one of the numbers is x, the other is $(20 - x)$, and their product is

$$y = x(20 - x) = 20x - x^2. \qquad (1)$$

Since both numbers are to be positive,

$$x > 0 \quad \text{and} \quad 20 - x > 0,$$

or

$$0 < x < 20.$$

From (1), we find

$$dy/dx = 20 - 2x = 2(10 - x),$$

which is

$$\text{positive when } x < 10,$$
$$\text{negative when } x > 10,$$
$$\text{zero when } x = 10.$$

$y' = 20 - 2x = 0$, $= y'$ $x = 10$

$y'' = -2 < 0$ max point

$(10, 10)$

Furthermore

$$\frac{d^2y}{dx^2} = -2$$

is always negative, and the curve representing (1) is concave downward at every point on it. The graph is the curve shown in Fig. 5.26, which has an absolute maximum at $x = 10$. The two numbers are thus $x = 10$, $20 - x = 10$.

Problem 2. A square sheet of tin a inches on a side is to be used to make an open-top box by cutting a small square of tin from each corner and bending up the sides. How large a square should be cut from each corner for the box to have as large a volume as possible?

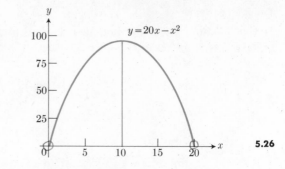

$y = 20x - x^2$

5.26

$a - 2x$

a

$a - 2x$

x

x

5.27

Solution. We first draw a figure to illustrate the problem (Fig. 5.27). In the figure, the side of the square cut from each corner is taken to be x inches and the volume of the box in cubic inches is then given by

$$y = x(a - 2x)^2, \quad 0 \le x \le a/2. \qquad (2)$$

The restrictions placed on x in (2) are clearly those imposed by the fact that one can neither cut a negative amount of material from a corner, nor can one cut away an amount which is more than the total amount present. It is also evident that $y = 0$ when $x = 0$ or when $x = a/2$, so that the maximum volume y must occur at some value of x between 0 and $a/2$. The function in (2) possesses a derivative at *every* such point, hence

when y is a maximum, dy/dx must be zero.

From (2), we find that

$$y = a^2x - 4ax^2 + 4x^3,$$

$$\frac{dy}{dx} = a^2 - 8ax + 12x^2 = (a - 2x)(a - 6x).$$

y

$\dfrac{a}{6}$ $\dfrac{a}{3}$ $\dfrac{a}{2}$ x

O

5.28

2r

h

5.29

From the factored form of the equation for the derivative, it follows that

$$\frac{dy}{dx} = 0 \quad \text{when} \quad x = \frac{a}{2} \text{ or } \frac{a}{6}.$$

We gain additional information about the shape of the curve representing (2) from

$$\frac{d^2y}{dx^2} = 24x - 8a = 24\left(x - \frac{a}{3}\right),$$

which shows that the curve is

concave downward   for $x < \dfrac{a}{3}$,

concave upward   for $x > \dfrac{a}{3}$.

In particular,

at $x = \dfrac{a}{6}$: $\dfrac{dy}{dx} = 0$, $\dfrac{d^2y}{dx^2} = -4a$,

at $x = \dfrac{a}{2}$: $\dfrac{dy}{dx} = 0$, $\dfrac{d^2y}{dx^2} = +4a$.

     (3)

From (3) we see that if we were to draw the graph of the curve (2) it would "spill water" at $x = (a/6)$, and this is the only point between $x = 0$ and $x = (a/2)$ where a relative maximum of the volume y may occur (Fig. 5.28). Each corner square should thus have dimensions $a/6$ by $a/6$ to produce a box of maximum volume.

Problem 3. An oil can is to be made in the form of a right circular cylinder and is to contain one quart of oil. What dimensions of the can will require the least amount of material?

Solution. Again we start with a figure to illustrate the problem (Fig. 5.29). Clearly, the requirement that the can hold a quart of oil is the same as

$$V = \pi r^2 h = a^3, \quad\quad\quad (4a)$$

if the radius r and altitude h are in inches and a^3 is the number of cubic inches in a quart ($a^3 = 57.75$). How shall we interpret the phrase "least amount of material"? A reasonable interpretation arises from neglecting the thickness of the material and the waste due to the manufacturing process. Then we ask for dimensions r and h that make the total surface area

$$A = 2\pi r^2 + 2\pi rh \quad\quad\quad (4b)$$

as small as possible while still satisfying (4a).

We are not quite ready to apply the methods used in Problems 1 and 2, because Eq. (4b) expresses A as a function of *two* variables, r and h, and our methods call for A to be expressed as a function of just *one* variable. However, Eq. (4a) may be used to express one of the variables r or h in terms of the other; in fact, we find

$$h = \frac{a^3}{\pi r^2}, \qu\quad\quad\quad (4c)$$

or

$$r = \sqrt{\frac{a^3}{\pi h}}. \qu\quad\quad\quad (4d)$$

The division in (4c) and (4d) is legitimate because neither r nor h can be zero, and only the positive square root is used in (4d) because the radius r can never be negative. If we substitute from (4c) into (4b), we have

$$A = 2\pi r^2 + \frac{2a^3}{r}, \quad 0 < r < \infty, \qu\quad\quad (4e)$$

and now we may apply our previous methods. A minimum of A can occur only at a point where

$$\frac{dA}{dr} = 4\pi r - 2a^3 r^{-2} \qquad (4f)$$

is zero, that is, where

$$4\pi r = \frac{2a^3}{r^2}, \quad r = \frac{a}{\sqrt[3]{2\pi}} \cdot \qquad (4g)$$

At such a value of r, we shall have

$$\frac{d^2 A}{dr^2} = 4\pi + 4a^3 r^{-3} = 12\pi > 0,$$

so the curve representing A as a function of r has $dA/dr = 0$ and $d^2 A/dr^2$ positive ("holds water") at $r = a/\sqrt[3]{2\pi}$, which must therefore produce a relative minimum. Since the second derivative is *always positive* for $0 < r < \infty$, the curve is concave upward everywhere, and there can be no other relative minimum, so we have also found the *absolute* minimum. From (4g) and (4c), we find

$$r = a/\sqrt[3]{2\pi} = \sqrt[3]{V/2\pi},$$

$$h = 2a/\sqrt[3]{2\pi} = 2\sqrt[3]{V/2\pi}$$

as the dimensions of the can of volume V having minimal surface area. Figure 5.30 shows a curve representing A as a function of r as given by (4e).

There is an alternative method of solving problems of this type. Namely, instead of solving (4a) for h in terms of r, say, we differentiate both (4a) and (4b) with respect to r, remembering that h is a function of r. Thus, we have

$$V = \pi r^2 h,$$

$$A = 2\pi r^2 + 2\pi r h,$$

and because V is a constant,

$$dV/dr = 0.$$

Since we want to find when A will be a minimum, we put

$$\frac{dA}{dr} = 0$$

also. Hence

$$\frac{dV}{dr} = \pi\left(r^2 \frac{dh}{dr} + 2rh\right) = 0, \quad \frac{dh}{dr} = -\frac{2h}{r}, \quad (4h)$$

$$\frac{dA}{dr} = 2\pi\left(2r + r\frac{dh}{dr} + h\right) = 2\pi(2r - h). \quad (4i)$$

5.30

5.31

5.32

Therefore dA/dr is zero when

$$h = 2r. \qquad (4j)$$

When this is substituted into (4a), we have

$$V = \pi r^2 h = 2\pi r^3,$$

so that

$$r = \sqrt[3]{V/2\pi}, \quad h = 2r = 2\sqrt[3]{V/2\pi}$$

give the critical dimensions for a cylindrical can of volume V.

We may use $d^2 A/dr^2$ to test these critical values. We have

$$\frac{dA}{dr} = 2\pi(2r - h),$$

so that, if we take account of (4h), we find

$$\frac{d^2 A}{dr^2} = 2\pi \left(2 - \frac{dh}{dr} \right) = 2\pi \left(2 + \frac{2h}{r} \right).$$

This is positive for all positive values of r and h, and hence A has a minimum at $r = r_{\text{crit}}$ where $dA/dr = 0$ and $d^2 A/dr^2$ is positive.

Problem 4. A wire of length L is to be cut into two pieces, one of which is bent to form a circle and the other to form a square. How should the wire be cut if the sum of the areas enclosed by the two pieces is to be a maximum?

Solution. In the notation of Fig. 5.31, the sum of the combined areas is

$$A = \pi r^2 + x^2, \tag{5a}$$

where r and x must satisfy the equation

$$L = 2\pi r + 4x. \tag{5b}$$

We could solve (5b) for x in terms of r, but instead we shall differentiate both (5a) and (5b), treating A and x as functions of r for $0 \leq 2\pi r \leq L$. Then

$$\frac{dA}{dr} = 2\pi r + 2x \frac{dx}{dr}, \tag{5c}$$

and

$$\frac{dL}{dr} = 2\pi + 4 \frac{dx}{dr} = 0, \quad \frac{dx}{dr} = -\frac{\pi}{2}, \tag{5d}$$

where dL/dr is zero because L is a constant. If we substitute dx/dr from (5d) into (5c), we get

$$\frac{dA}{dr} = \pi(2r - x) \tag{5e}$$

and, for future reference, we note that

$$\frac{d^2 A}{dr^2} = \pi \left(2 - \frac{dx}{dr} \right) = \pi \left(2 + \frac{\pi}{2} \right) \tag{5f}$$

is a positive constant, so that the curve which represents A as a function of r is always concave upward (Fig. 5.32). Now

$$\frac{dA}{dr} = 0 \quad \text{when} \quad x = 2r,$$

and when we substitute this into (5b),

$$L = 2\pi r + 4(2r) = (2\pi + 8)r,$$

we have

$$\frac{dA}{dr} = 0 \quad \text{when} \quad r = \frac{L}{2\pi + 8}, \quad x = \frac{L}{\pi + 4}.$$

But the fact that the second derivative is positive means that this value of r gives a *minimum* for A. The problem asks for the *maximum* of A.

Since r is limited to

$$0 \leq r \leq \frac{L}{2\pi},$$

we examine the values of A at the ends of this interval. When

$r = 0$: $x = \dfrac{L}{4}, \quad A = \dfrac{1}{16} L^2,$

and when

$r = \dfrac{L}{2\pi}$: $x = 0, \quad A = \dfrac{1}{4\pi} L^2.$

At the minimum,

$$r = \frac{1}{2} \frac{L}{\pi + 4}, \quad x = \frac{L}{\pi + 4}, \quad A = \frac{1}{4\pi + 16} L^2.$$

Using these values to make a rough sketch of A as a function of r (Fig. 5.32), we readily see that the maximum value of A occurs when $r = L/2\pi$, which means that the wire should not be cut at all, but all of it should be bent into the circle for maximum total area. Or, if we adopt the point of view that the wire *must* be cut, then there is no answer to the problem. For no matter how little of it is used for the square, we could always get a larger total area by using still less of it for the square.

Problem 5. Fermat's principle in optics states that light travels from a point A to a point B along that path for which the time of travel is a minimum. Let us find the path that a ray of light will follow in going from a point A in a medium where the velocity of light is c_1 to a point B in a second medium where the velocity of light is c_2, when both points lie in the xy-plane and the x-axis separates the two media. (See Fig. 5.33).

Solution. In either medium where the velocity of light remains constant, the light ray will follow a straight path, since then "shortest time" and "shortest distance" amount to the same thing. Hence the path will consist of a straight line segment from A to P in the first medium and another line segment PB in the second medium.

5.33

5.34

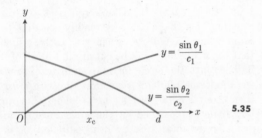

5.35

The time required for the light to travel from A to P is

$$t_1 = \frac{\sqrt{a^2 + x^2}}{c_1},$$

and from P to B the time required is

$$t_2 = \frac{\sqrt{b^2 + (d - x)^2}}{c_2}.$$

We therefore seek to minimize

$$t = t_1 + t_2 = \frac{\sqrt{a^2 + x^2}}{c_1} + \frac{\sqrt{b^2 + (d - x)^2}}{c_2}. \quad (6a)$$

We find

$$\frac{dt}{dx} = \frac{x}{c_1 \sqrt{a^2 + x^2}} - \frac{(d - x)}{c_2 \sqrt{b^2 + (d - x)^2}}, \quad (6b)$$

or

$$\frac{dt}{dx} = \frac{\sin \theta_1}{c_1} - \frac{\sin \theta_2}{c_2}, \quad (6c)$$

if we make use of the angles θ_1 and θ_2 in the figure.

If we restrict x to the interval $0 \leq x \leq d$, t has a negative derivative at $x = 0$ and a positive derivative at $x = d$, while at the value of x, say x_c, for which

$$\frac{\sin \theta_1}{c_1} = \frac{\sin \theta_2}{c_2}, \quad (6d)$$

dt/dx is zero. Figure 5.34 indicates the directions of the tangents to the curve giving t as a function of x, at these three points, and suggests that t will indeed be a minimum at $x = x_c$. If we want further information on this point, by referring to Fig. 5.33 we see that a decrease in x will cause P to move to the left, making θ_1 smaller, and hence also making $\sin \theta_1$ smaller, but will have the opposite effect on θ_2 and $\sin \theta_2$. Figure 5.35 shows that since $(\sin \theta_1)/c_1$ is an increasing function of x which is zero at $x = 0$, while $(\sin \theta_2)/c_2$ is a decreasing function of x which is zero at $x = d$, the two curves can cross at only one point, $x = x_c$, between 0 and d. To the right of x_c, the curve for $(\sin \theta_1)/c_1$ is above the curve for $(\sin \theta_2)/c_2$, but these roles are reversed to the left of x_c, so that

$$\frac{dt}{dx} = \frac{\sin \theta_1}{c_1} - \frac{\sin \theta_2}{c_2} \begin{cases} \text{is negative for } x < x_c, \\ \text{is zero for } x = x_c, \\ \text{is positive for } x > x_c, \end{cases}$$

and the minimum of t does indeed occur at $x = x_c$.

Instead of determining this value of x explicitly, it is customary to characterize the path followed by the ray of light by leaving the equation for $dt/dx = 0$ in the form (6d), which is known as the law of refraction, or Snell's law. (See Sears, *Optics*, 3rd edition, p. 27.)

The reader will very likely have noticed that the techniques summarized in the following rules have been used in the above problems.

First. When possible, draw a figure to illustrate the problem and label those parts that are important in the problem. Constants and variables should be clearly distinguished.

Second. Write an equation for the quantity that is to be a maximum or a minimum. If this quantity is denoted by y, it is desirable to express it in terms of a single independent variable x. This may require some algebraic manipulation to make use of auxiliary conditions of the problem.

Third. If $y = f(x)$ is the quantity to be a maximum or a minimum, find those values of x for which

$$\frac{dy}{dx} = f'(x) = 0.$$

Fourth. Test each value of x for which $f'(x) = 0$ to determine whether it provides a maximum or minimum or neither. The usual tests are:

(a) If $\dfrac{d^2y}{dx^2}$ is positive when $\dfrac{dy}{dx} = 0$,

then y is a minimum.

If $\dfrac{d^2y}{dx^2}$ is negative when $\dfrac{dy}{dx} = 0$,

then y is a maximum.

If $\dfrac{d^2y}{dx^2} = 0$ when $\dfrac{dy}{dx} = 0$,

then the test fails.

(b) If

$$\frac{dy}{dx} \text{ is } \begin{cases} \text{positive} & \text{for } x < x_c, \\ \text{zero} & \text{for } x = x_c, \\ \text{negative} & \text{for } x > x_c, \end{cases}$$

then a maximum occurs at x_c. But if dy/dx changes from negative to zero to positive as x advances through x_c, there is a minimum. If dy/dx does not change its sign, neither a maximum nor a minimum need occur.

Fifth. If the derivative fails to exist at some point, examine this point as possible maximum or minimum. (See Fig. 5.23.)

Sixth. If the function $y = f(x)$ is defined for only a limited range of values $a \le x \le b$, examine $x = a$ and $x = b$ for possible extreme values of y. (See Fig. 5.32.)

Remark. The following useful argument applies in many problems: It is often obvious from the formulas, or from physical conditions, that we have a continuous and everywhere-differentiable function that does not attain its maximum at an end point. Hence it has at least one maximum at an interior point, at which its derivative must be zero. So if we find just one zero for the derivative, we have the maximum without any appeal to second-derivative or other tests.

Problem 6. Suppose a manufacturer can sell x items per week at a price $P = 200 - 0.01x$ cents, and that it costs $y = 50x + 20,000$ cents to produce the x items. What is the production level for maximum profits?

Solution. The total revenue per week on x items is

$$xP = 200x - 0.01x^2.$$

The manufacturer's profit T is revenue minus cost:

$$T = xP - y = (200x - 0.01x^2) - (50x + 20,000)$$
$$= 150x - 0.01x^2 - 20,000.$$

To maximize T, we find

$$dT/dx = 150 - 0.02x,$$

which is zero when

$$x = 7500.$$

We know that this production level gives maximum profit, since the second derivative $d^2T/dx^2 = -0.02$ is negative; this is also clear from the argument in the *Remark* above. To sell the 7500 items, the manufacturer should charge $1.25 per item.

12/10 21,24,25 STUDY (5,7,5,15)
12/9 14-20

EXERCISES

12/7 # 1-6   12/8 7-11 & 13

1. Show that the rectangle that has maximum area for a given perimeter is a square.

2. Find the dimensions of the rectangle of greatest area that can be inscribed in a semicircle of radius r.

3. Find the area of the largest rectangle with lower base on the x-axis and upper vertices on the curve

$$y = 12 - x^2.$$

4. An open rectangular box is to be made from a piece of cardboard 8 in. wide and 15 in. long by cutting a square from each corner and bending up the sides. Find the dimensions of the box of largest volume.

5. One side of an open field is bounded by a straight river. How would you put a fence around the other three sides of a rectangular plot in order to enclose as great an area as possible with a given length of fence?

6. An open storage bin with square base and vertical sides is to be constructed from a given amount of material. Determine its dimensions if its volume is to be a maximum. Neglect the thickness of the material and waste in construction.

7. A box with square base and open top is to hold 32 in^3. Find the dimensions that require the least amount of material. Neglect the thickness of the material and waste in construction.

8. A variable line through the point $(1, 2)$ intersects the x-axis at $A(a, 0)$ and the y-axis at $B(0, b)$. Find the area of the triangle AOB of least area if both a and b are positive.

9. A poster is to contain 50 in^2 of printed matter with margins of 4 in. each at top and bottom and 2 in. at each side. Find the overall dimensions if the total area of the poster is to be a minimum.

10. A right triangle of given hypotenuse is rotated about one of its legs to generate a right circular cone. Find the cone of greatest volume.

11. It costs a manufacturer c dollars each to manufacture and distribute a certain item. If he sells it at x dollars each, he estimates that the number he can sell is given by

$$n = a/(x - c) + b(100 - x),$$

where a and b are certain positive constants. What selling price will bring him a maximum profit?

12. One end of a cantilever beam of length L is built into a wall, while the other end is simply supported. If the beam weighs w lb per unit length, its deflection y at distance x from the built-in end satisfies the equation

$$48EIy = w(2x^4 - 5Lx^3 + 3L^2x^2),$$

where E and I are constants that depend on the material of the beam and the shape of its cross section. How far from the built-in end does the maximum deflection occur?

13. Determine the constant a so that the function

$$f(x) = x^2 + \frac{a}{x}$$

may have

(a) a relative minimum at $x = 2$,

(b) a relative minimum at $x = -3$,

(c) a point of inflection at $x = 1$.

Show that the function cannot have a relative maximum for any value of a.

14. Determine the constants a and b so that the function

$$f(x) = x^3 + ax^2 + bx + c$$

may have

(a) a relative maximum at $x = -1$ and a relative minimum at $x = 3$,

(b) a relative minimum at $x = 4$ and a point of inflection at $x = 1$.

15. A wire of length L is cut into two pieces, one being bent to form a square and the other to form an equilateral triangle. How should the wire be cut

(a) if the sum of the two areas is to be a minimum,

(b) if the sum of the areas is to be a maximum?

16. Find the points on the curve $5x^2 - 6xy + 5y^2 = 4$ that are nearest the origin.

17. The distance between the points (x_1, y_1) and (x_1, y_2) is

$$\sqrt{(x_2 - x_1)^2 + (y_2 - y_1)^2}.$$

Find the point on the curve $y = \sqrt{x}$ nearest the point $(c, 0)$

(a) if $c \geq \frac{1}{2}$,   (b) if $c < \frac{1}{2}$.

18. Find the volume of the largest right circular cone that can be inscribed in a sphere of radius r.

19. Find the volume of the largest right circular cylinder that can be inscribed in a sphere of radius r.

20. Show that the volume of the largest right circular cylinder that can be inscribed in a given right circular cone is $\frac{4}{9} \times$ volume of the cone.

21. The strength of a rectangular beam is proportional to the product of its width and the square of its depth. Find the dimensions of the strongest beam that can be cut from a circular cylindrical log of radius r.

22. The stiffness of a rectangular beam is proportional to the product of its breadth and the cube of its

depth. Find the stiffest beam that can be cut from a log of given diameter.

23. The intensity of illumination at any point is proportional to the product of the strength of the light source and the inverse of the square of the distance from the source. If two sources of relative strengths a and b are a distance c apart, at what point on the line joining them will the intensity be a minimum? Assume the intensity at any point is the sum of intensities from the two sources.

24. A window is in the form of a rectangle surmounted by a semicircle. If the rectangle is of clear glass while the semicircle is of colored glass which transmits only half as much light per square foot as clear glass does, and the total perimeter is fixed, find the proportions of the window that will admit the most light.

25. Right circular cylindrical tin cans are to be manufactured to contain a given volume. There is no waste involved in cutting the tin that goes into the vertical sides of the can, but each end piece is to be cut from a square and the corners of the square wasted. Find the ratio of height to diameter for the most economical cans.

26. A silo is to be made in the form of a cylinder surmounted by a hemisphere. The cost of construction per square foot of surface area is twice as great for the hemisphere as for the cylinder. Determine the dimensions to be used if the volume is fixed and the cost of construction is to be a minimum. Neglect the thickness of the silo and waste in construction.

27. If the sum of the areas of a cube and a sphere is constant, what is the ratio of an edge of the cube to the diameter of the sphere when

(a) the sum of their volumes is a minimum,

(b) the sum of their volumes is a maximum?

*28. Two towns, located on the same side of a straight river, agree to construct a pumping station and filtering plant at the river's edge, to be used jointly to supply the towns with water. If the distances of the two towns from the river are a and b and the distance between them is c, show that the sum of the lengths of the pipe lines joining them to the pumping stations is at least as great as $\sqrt{c^2 + 4ab}$.

---

* You may find it easier to do these problems without calculus.

*29. Light emanating from a source A is reflected to a point B by a plane mirror. If the time required for the light to travel from A to the mirror and then to B is a minimum, show that the angle of incidence is equal to the angle of reflection.

30. Show that a manufacturer's profit is maximized (or minimized) at a level of production where his marginal revenue equals marginal cost.

31. Suppose the government imposes a tax of ten cents, for each item sold, on the product of Problem 6, but other features are unchanged. How much of the tax should the manufacturer absorb and how much should he pass on to the customer? Why? Compare his profits before and after the tax.

5.7 ROLLE'S THEOREM

There is strong geometrical evidence to support the belief that between two points where a smooth curve $y = f(x)$ crosses the x-axis there must be at least one point where it has a horizontal tangent (Fig. 5.36a). But such is not the case if the curve has a corner, as in Fig. 5.36(b), where the derivative fails to exist. More precisely, we have the following theorem.

a|b

5.36

Rolle's Theorem.* *Let the function f be defined and continuous on the closed interval [a, b] and differentiable in the open interval (a, b). Furthermore, let*

$$f(a) = f(b) = 0.$$

Then there is at least one number c between a and b where f'(x) is zero; that is,

$$f'(c) = 0 \quad \text{for some } c \text{ in } (a, b).$$

Proof. Either $f(x)$ is identically equal to zero for all x in $[a, b]$, or else $f(x)$ is different from zero for some values of x in this interval. In the former case, $f'(x)$ is also identically zero and the theorem is true for this case.

But if $f(x)$ is not zero everywhere between a and b, then either it is positive someplace, or negative someplace, or both. In any case, the function will then have a maximum positive value or a minimum negative value, or both. That is, it has an extreme value at a point c where $f(c)$ is negative (in the case of a minimum) or $f(c)$ is positive (in the case of a maximum). In either case, c is neither a nor b, since

$$f(a) = f(b) = 0, \qquad f(c) \neq 0.$$

Therefore c is between a and b, and Theorem 1 applies, showing that the derivative must be zero at $x = c$:

$$\cdot f'(c) = 0 \quad \text{for some } c, \quad a < c < b. \ \square$$

Remark 1. There may be more than one place between a and b where the derivative is zero. In Fig. 5.36(a), for example, dy/dx is zero at c_1 and at c_2, and both points lie between $a = -2$ and $b = +2$.

Example. The polynomial

$$y = x^3 - 4x = f(x)$$

is continuous and differentiable for all $x, -\infty < x < +\infty$.

---

* Published in 1691 in *Méthode pour Résoudre les Egalités* by the French mathematician Michel Rolle. See D. E. Smith, *Source Book in Mathematics*, p. 253.

If we choose values

$$a = -2, \qquad b = +2,$$

the hypotheses of Rolle's Theorem are satisfied, since

$$f(-2) = f(+2) = 0.$$

Thus $\qquad f'(x) = 3x^2 - 4$

must be zero at least once between -2 and $+2$. In fact, we find

$$3x^2 - 4 = 0$$

at

$$x = c_1 = -2\sqrt{3}/3 \quad \text{and} \quad x = c_2 = +2\sqrt{3}/3.$$

Remark 2. The reader may combine Rolle's Theorem with part (ii) of Theorem 15, Chapter 4 to obtain the following criterion for isolating the real roots of an equation $f(x) = 0$. Suppose a and b are two real numbers such that

(a) $f(x)$ is continuous on $[a, b]$ and its first derivative $f'(x)$ exists on (a, b),

(b) $f(a)$ and $f(b)$ have opposite signs, and

(c) $f'(x)$ is different from zero for all values of x in (a, b).

Then there is one and only one real root of the equation $f(x) = 0$ between a and b.

To see the significance of this, suppose the equation is

$$f(x) = x^3 + 3x + 1 = 0$$

(see Fig. 4.37). Then

$$f'(x) = 3x^2 + 3$$

is always positive, so that the equation $f'(x) = 0$ can have no real roots. Hence the original equation $f(x) = 0$ cannot have as many as two real roots. It does, in fact, have exactly one real root, since the graph of

$$y = x^3 + 3x + 1$$

crosses the x-axis between $x = -1$ and $x = 0$ but can never cross the x-axis at any other point. (If it did, the derivative would have to be zero at some point between.)

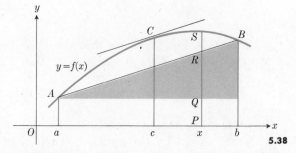

5.37

5.38

EXERCISES

12/16 # 1,3,5

Without trying to solve the equations exactly, show that the equation $f(x) = 0$ has one and only one real root between the numbers of the pair given for each of the following functions $f(x)$.

1. $x^4 + 3x + 1$, $(-2, -1)$ 2. $x^4 + 2x^3 - 2$, $(0, 1)$

3. $2x^3 - 3x^2 - 12x - 6$, $(-1, 0)$

4. Let $f(x)$, together with its first two derivatives $f'(x)$ and $f''(x)$, be continuous for $a \le x \le b$. Suppose the curve $y = f(x)$ intersects the x-axis in at least three different places between a and b, inclusive. Using Rolle's Theorem, show that the equation $f''(x) = 0$ has at least one real root between a and b. Generalize this result.

5. Assume that $\sin x$ is differentiable. (This is true and will be proved later. You don't need the formula for the derivative to answer this question.) From elementary trigonometry we know that

$$\sin 0 = \sin \pi = 0,$$

and that the maximum of $\sin x$ is 1. What do you conclude about the value of c in Rolle's Theorem for $f(x) = \sin x$ on $[a, b] = [0, \pi]$?

5.8 THE MEAN VALUE THEOREM

In this article we shall prove the Mean Value Theorem, which is a generalization of Rolle's Theorem. Again we shall be concerned with a function $y = f(x)$ which is continuous on $[a, b]$ and which has a nonvertical tangent at each point between $A(a, f(a))$ and $B(b, f(b))$, although the tangent may be vertical at one or both of the end points A and B (Fig. 4.38). For example, the function might be

$$f(x) = \sqrt{a^2 - x^2} \quad \text{on} \quad [-a, a],$$

which represents a semicircle that fulfills the requirements above.

Demonstration

Geometrically, the Mean Value Theorem states that if the function f is continuous on $[a, b]$ and differentiable on (a, b), then there is at least one number c in (a, b) where the tangent to the curve is parallel to the chord through A and B. This is intuitively plausible, for if we consider displacing the chord AB in Fig. 5.38, upward, keeping it parallel to its original position, there will be a transition between a position where it cuts the curve in two nearby points and a position where it will fail to touch the curve, and this transition will take place at a point C where the line will be tangent to this curve. This transition will occur where the vertical distance between the chord AB and the curve is a maximum.

The analytic proof of the Mean Value Theorem has its key idea in this last statement. The vertical distance between the chord and the curve is measured by RS in Fig. 5.38, and

$$RS = PS - PR.$$

Now PS is simply the ordinate y on the curve $y = f(x)$, so that

$$PS = f(x).$$

On the other hand, PR is the ordinate on the chord AB, and its value is given by

$$g(x) = f(a) + m(x - a), \tag{1a}$$

from the equation of the straight line through $A(a, f(a))$ with slope

$$m = \frac{f(b) - f(a)}{b - a}. \tag{1b}$$

Therefore $RS = f(x) - g(x)$

measures the vertical displacement from the chord AB to the curve $y = f(x)$ for any x on $[a, b]$. Note that $f(a) - g(a) = 0$ and $f(b) - g(b) = 0$ because this vertical displacement is zero at the ends of the arc where the curve and chord meet. To complete this demonstration of the theorem, we apply Rolle's Theorem to the function

$$F(x) = f(x) - g(x). \tag{2}$$

Because both f and g are continuous on $[a, b]$, F is also continuous there. Likewise f and g are differentiable in (a, b), so F is also differentiable there. Hence F satisfies the hypotheses of Rolle's Theorem. From Rolle's theorem we therefore conclude that $F'(c) = 0$ for some $c \in (a, b)$. From Eq. (2),

$$F'(x) = f'(x) - g'(x),$$

so the conclusion is that

$$f'(c) = g'(c).$$

But from Eqs. (1a, b) we see that $g'(c) = m$. Therefore

$$f'(c) = \frac{f(b) - f(a)}{b - a} \quad \text{for some } c \in (a, b). \tag{3}$$

The result (3) is equivalent to stating that

$$f(b) - f(a) = f'(c)(b - a)$$

for some c,

$$a < c < b.$$

These results are summarized in the following theorem.

Rolle's Theorem on a slant

The Mean Value Theorem. *Let $y = f(x)$ be continuous on $[a, b]$ and be differentiable in the open interval (a, b). Then there is at least one number c between a and b such that*

$$f(b) - f(a) = f'(c)(b - a). \tag{4}$$

slope of curve $(b - A)$ *m of l_1 = m of l* *m of l_1 = m of l* *$(a, f(a))$* *$(b, f(b))$*

5.39

We note that Eq. (3) states that the slope $f'(c)$ of the curve at $C(c, f(c))$ is the same as the slope $[f(b) - f(a)]/(b - a)$ of the chord joining the point $A(a, f(a))$ and $B(b, f(b))$; this is a form that is easily recalled.

Equation (4) contains a symbol c which is not very well defined except by this equation itself. For a specific function f and specific values of a and b, however, the equation can be used to find one or more values of c.

Example 1. (See Fig. 5.39.) Let

$$f(x) = x^3, \quad a = -2, \quad \text{and} \quad b = +2.$$

Then

$$f'(x) = 3x^2, \qquad f'(c) = 3c^2,$$

$$f(b) = 2^3 = 8, \qquad f(a) = (-2)^3 = -8,$$

$$\frac{f(b) - f(a)}{b - a} = \frac{8 - (-8)}{2 - (-2)} = \frac{16}{4} = 4,$$

so that

$$f'(c) = \frac{f(b) - f(a)}{b - a}$$

becomes

$$3c^2 = 4, \qquad c = \pm\tfrac{2}{3}\sqrt{3}.$$

There are thus two values of c, namely,

$$c_1 = -\tfrac{2}{3}\sqrt{3}, \qquad c_2 = +\tfrac{2}{3}\sqrt{3},$$

between $a = -2$ and $b = +2$, where the tangent to the curve $y = x^3$ is parallel to the chord through the points $(-2, -8)$ and $(+2, +8)$.

Example 2. (See Fig. 5.40.) Let

$$f(x) = x^{2/3}, \quad a = -8, \quad \text{and} \quad b = +8.$$

Then

$$f'(x) = \frac{2}{3} x^{-1/3} = \frac{2}{3\sqrt[3]{x}}$$

exists everywhere between a and b *except at* $x = 0$. We find that

$$\frac{f(b) - f(a)}{b - a} = \frac{(8)^{2/3} - (-8)^{2/3}}{8 - (-8)} = \frac{4 - 4}{16} = 0,$$

and that

$$f'(c) = \frac{2}{3\sqrt[3]{c}}$$

is not zero for any finite value of c. The result (3) need not hold, and does not hold, in this case due to the failure of the derivative to exist at a point, namely $x = 0$, between $a = -8$ and $b = +8$.

$y = x^{2/3}$

$(-8, 4)$ $(8, 4)$

5.40

Remark. The Mean Value Theorem has the following interpretation when applied to an equation of motion $s = f(t)$. The quantity $\Delta s = f(b) - f(a)$ is the change in s corresponding to $\Delta t = b - a$, and the right-hand side of Eq. (3) is

$$\frac{\Delta s}{\Delta t} = \frac{f(b) - f(a)}{b - a}$$

$$= \text{average velocity from } t = a \text{ to } t = b. \quad (5)$$

The equation then tells us that there is an instant $t = c$ between a and b at which the *instantaneous* velocity $f'(c)$ is equal to the *average* velocity. The theorem may therefore be paraphrased as follows: If a motorist makes a trip in which his *average* velocity is 30 mi/hr, then at least once during the trip his speedometer must also have registered precisely 30 mi/hr.

Corollary 1. *If a function F has a derivative which is equal to zero for all values of x in an interval (a, b), that is, if*

$$F'(x) \equiv 0 \quad \text{for } x \in (a, b), \quad (6a)$$

then the function is constant throughout the interval:

$$F(x) \equiv \text{constant} \quad \text{for } x \in (a, b). \quad (6b)$$

Proof. Suppose (6a) is satisfied. Let x_1 and x_2 be any two points in the interval with

$$a < x_1 < x_2 < b.$$

Then, since the function is differentiable for

$$x_1 \le x \le x_2,$$

it is also continuous in the same closed interval. Hence the Mean Value Theorem applies. That is, there is at least one number c, $x_1 < c < x_2$, such that

$$F(x_1) - F(x_2) = F'(c)(x_1 - x_2).$$

But $F'(c)$ is zero by hypothesis. Therefore

$$F(x_1) = F(x_2).$$

That is, the value of the function at any point x_1 is the same as its value at any other point x_2, for all x_1, x_2 in the interval (a, b). This is what is meant by Eq. (6b). ☐

Corollary 2. *If F_1 and F_2 are two functions each of which has its derivative equal to $f(x)$ for $a < x < b$, that is,*

$$\text{if} \quad \frac{dF_1(x)}{dx} = \frac{dF_2(x)}{dx} = f(x) \quad \text{for } a < x < b,$$

$$\text{then} \quad F_1(x) - F_2(x) \equiv \text{constant} \quad \text{in } (a, b).$$

Proof. Apply Corollary 1 to the function

$$F(x) = F_1(x) - F_2(x).$$

Corollary 3. *Let f be continuous on $[a, b]$ and differentiable on (a, b). If $f'(x)$ is positive throughout (a, b), then f is an increasing function on $[a, b]$, and if $f'(x)$ is negative throughout (a, b), then f is decreasing on $[a, b]$.*

8

Proof. Let x_1 and x_2 be any two numbers in $[a, b]$, such that $x_1 < x_2$. Apply the Mean Value Theorem to f on $[x_1, x_2]$:

$$f(x_2) - f(x_1) = f'(c)(x_2 - x_1) \quad \text{for some } c \in (x_1, x_2).$$

The sign of the right-hand side is the same as the sign of $f'(c)$ because $x_2 - x_1$ is positive. Therefore

$$f(x_2) > f(x_1) \quad \text{if} \quad f'(x) \text{ is positive on } (a, b),$$

and

$$f(x_2) < f(x_1) \quad \text{if} \quad f'(x) \text{ is negative on } (a, b). \quad \square$$

EXERCISES

In Exercises 1 through 5, a, b, and c refer to the equation $f(b) - f(a) = (b - a)f'(c)$, which expresses the Mean Value Theorem. Given $f(x)$, a, and b, find c.

1. $f(x) = x^2 + 2x - 1$, $\quad a = 0$, $\quad b = 1$.
2. $f(x) = x^3$, $\quad a = 0$, $\quad b = 3$.
3. $f(x) = x^{2/3}$, $\quad a = 0$, $\quad b = 1$.
4. $f(x) = x + \dfrac{1}{x}$, $\quad a = \frac{1}{2}$, $b = 2$.
5. $f(x) = \sqrt{x - 1}$, $\quad a = 1$, $b = 3$.

6. Suppose you know that $f'(x)$ always has a value between -1 and $+1$. Show that

$$|f(x) - f(a)| \leq |x - a|.$$

7. Let $P_1(x_1, y_1)$ and $P_2(x_2, y_2)$ be any two points on the parabola $y = ax^2 + bx + c$, and let $P_3(x_3, y_3)$ be the point on the arc P_1P_2 where the tangent is parallel to the chord P_1P_2. Show that

$$x_3 = (x_1 + x_2)/2.$$

8. Inequalities can often be established using the Mean Value Theorem. For example, if we know that $m < f'(x) < M$ when $a < x < b$, we can apply the Theorem to conclude that

$$f(a) + m(x - a) < f(x) < f(a) + M(x - a)$$

for all $x \in (a, b)$. Prove this result.

9. Suppose that f is a function that is differentiable for all $x \in (0, \infty)$, with $f'(x) = 1/x$. (You won't

need any more information than this to answer the question. Such a function exists, even if we don't know yet what it is.) If $f(1) = 0$, prove that $0.5 < f(2) < 1.0$.

10. (a) If $f'(x) = 1/(x^2 + 1)$ for all x, and $f(0) = 0$, prove that $0.4 < f(2) < 2.0$.

(b) What better estimate of $f(2)$ could you give if you were given the further information that $f(1) = \pi/4$? (You should be able to prove that $0.2 < f(2) - f(1) < 0.5$.)

5.9 EXTENSION OF THE MEAN VALUE THEOREM

In Article 5.8 we established the existence of a number c between a and b, such that

$$f(b) - f(a) = f'(c)(b - a) \tag{1}$$

under suitable hypotheses on the function f. If the number c is replaced by a on the right side of Eq. (1), the equality must be changed to an approximation, which turns out to be the approximation we obtain by using the line tangent to the curve at $(a, f(a))$ to approximate the curve $y = f(x)$ at $x = b$. When b is close to a, we expect the approximation to be quite good. The following theorem tells us that if the function has a second derivative, as well as a first, then the difference between the tangent approximation and the function itself is approximately proportional to $(b - a)^2$.

Extended Mean Value Theorem. *Let $f(x)$ and its first derivative $f'(x)$ be continuous on the closed interval $[a, b]$, and suppose its second derivative $f''(x)$ exists in the open interval (a, b). Then there is a number c_2 between a and b such that*

$$f(b) = f(a) + f'(a)(b - a) + \tfrac{1}{2}f''(c_2)(b - a)^2. \tag{2}$$

Proof. Let K be the number defined by the equation

$$f(b) = f(a) + f'(a)(b - a) + K(b - a)^2. \tag{3}$$

Consider the function $F(x)$ that we get by replacing b by x in Eq. (3) and subtracting the right-hand side from the left:

$$F(x) = f(x) - f(a) - f'(a)(x - a) - K(x - a)^2. \tag{4}$$

Then, by substitution in (4), we find

$$F(a) = 0.$$

Also, from (3), we have

$$F(b) = 0.$$

Moreover, F and its first derivative are continuous on $[a, b]$, and

$$F'(x) = f'(x) - f'(a) - 2K(x - a). \qquad (5)$$

Therefore F satisfies the hypotheses of Rolle's Theorem. Hence there is a number c_1 between a and b such that

$$F'(c_1) = 0.$$

And, by substitution in (5), we also have

$$F'(a) = 0.$$

The derived function F' satisfies Rolle's Theorem on the interval $[a, c_1]$. Hence there is a number c_2 between a and c_1 such that

$$F''(c_2) = 0.$$

We differentiate (5) and get

$$F''(x) = f''(x) - 2K. \qquad (6)$$

If we put $x = c_2$ in (6), set the result equal to zero, and solve for K, we have

$$K = \tfrac{1}{2} f''(c_2).$$

When this is substituted into Eq. (3), we have Eq. (2). □

By a similar method, it is easy to prove a more general Extended Mean Value Theorem (see Miscellaneous Exercise 74 at the end of this chapter.)

Remark 1. Equation (2) can be used to estimate the size of the error that is made when we use the linearization of f at a to estimate $f(b)$, as in the following problem.

Problem 1. Use the linearization of $f(x) = \sqrt{x}$ at $a = 4$ to approximate $\sqrt{5}$, and estimate the size of the error in the approximation.

Solution. The linearization of f at a is

$$L_a(x) = f(a) + f'(a)(x - a),$$

as in Eq. (7), Article 4.4. For $f(x) = \sqrt{x}$ we have

$$f'(x) = 1/(2\sqrt{x}).$$

Hence $f(a) = \sqrt{4} = 2$ and

$$f'(a) = 1/(2\sqrt{4}) = 1/4,$$

so that

$$L_4(x) = 2 + \tfrac{1}{4}(x - 4). \qquad (7a)$$

Substituting $x = 5$ in this gives $L(5) = 2.25$ as the approximation to $\sqrt{5}$ that we get by using Eq. (7a).

Now Eq. (2), with $a = 4$, $b = 5$, and $f(x) = \sqrt{x}$, says that

$$f(b) - L_a(b) = \tfrac{1}{2} f''(c_2)(b - a)^2, \qquad (7b)$$

because the first two terms on the right side of Eq. (2) are just the same as $L_a(b)$. For the present problem,

$$f''(x) = -1/(4x^{3/2}) \qquad (7c)$$

and $4 < c_2 < 5$. We don't know just what number to substitute for c_2, but it is clear that $f''(c_2)$ lies between $f''(4)$ and $f''(5)$, and we compute these by substituting into (7c):

$$f''(4) = -1/32, \qquad f''(5) = -1/(20\sqrt{5}).$$

Because $2 < \sqrt{5} < 2.25$, we estimate $20\sqrt{5}$ to be between 40 and 45; thus $f''(c_2)$ is between $-1/32$ and $-1/45$. Therefore, when $a = 4$ and $b = 5$, the right side of Eq. (7b) is between $-1/64$ and $-1/90$, which, in turn, are between -0.016 and -0.011. This means that the linear approximation 2.25 is too large by something between 0.01 and 0.02, so the error is less than one percent. As a practical matter, we would correct our estimate from 2.25 to 2.23 or 2.24. (A table in three decimals gives 2.236.)

Remark 2. If the hypotheses of the Extended Mean Value Theorem are satisfied on $[a, b]$, then they also hold on $[a, x]$ for any $x \in (a, b)$, and Eq. (2) can be rewritten with x in place of b, as follows:

$$f(x) = f(a) + f'(a)(x - a) + \tfrac{1}{2} f''(c)(x - a)^2 \\ \text{for some } c \in (a, x). \qquad (8)$$

The first two terms on the right-hand side of Eq. (8) are the same as $L_a(x)$, the linearization of f at a.

5.41 The graph of $f(x) = \sqrt{x}$ and its linearization at $a = 4$. Here $f(x) - L_4(x)$ is negative because $f''(x) < 0$.

The last term, therefore, shows that the difference

$$f(x) - L_a(x) = \tfrac{1}{2}f''(c)(x - a)^2 \qquad (9)$$

is, as we announced just before the statement of the Extended Mean Value Theorem, approximately proportional to $(x - a)^2$. We have to say "approximately" because the coefficient $(\tfrac{1}{2})f''(c)$ is not constant when x varies. But if x stays close to a, then c also stays close to a, and the quadratic function

$$Q_a(x) = f(a) + f'(a)(x - a) + \tfrac{1}{2}f''(a)(x - a)^2 \qquad (10)$$

has a graph which should stay close to the graph of f near a. (For a further discussion of this feature, see Article 14.3.)

Remark 3. If the second derivative is continuous and positive at $x = a$, then it is positive throughout a small neighborhood of a, and Eq. (8) shows that near a, the graph of f lies above its tangent (at a). This validates our earlier conclusion, and replaces our geometrical argument, that the graph of f is concave upward (holds water) when its second derivative is positive. Similarly, if $f''(a)$ is negative, and the second derivative is continuous at a, the graph of f is concave downward at a because it lies below the tangent to the curve. In Fig. 5.41, for example, we see that near $a = 4$ the graph of $f(x) = \sqrt{x}$ lies below the graph of $L_a(x)$. Also, from Eq. (9), we have a quantitative measure of the difference $f(x) - L_a(x)$. That difference, which

we previously wrote in the form $\epsilon(x - a)$, with $\lim \epsilon = 0$ as $x \to a$, is now seen to be very nearly equal to $\tfrac{1}{2}f''(a)(x - a)^2$ when x is near a.

EXERCISES

12/17/76 # 1, 2, 3a, 3b

1. Use the linearization of $f(x) = \sqrt{x}$ at $a = 25$ to estimate $\sqrt{24}$, and use the Extended Mean Value Theorem to determine limits on the error.

2. If $f(x) = 3x^2 + 2x + 4$ and $a = 1$, show that the quadratic approximation of Eq. (10), and the exact expression of Eq. (8), are identical. Explain.

3. Use both the linear approximation $L_4(x)$ and the quadratic approximation $Q_4(x)$ of the function $\sqrt{x}$ to estimate

   (a) $\sqrt{4.4}$,   (b) $\sqrt{2}$,
   (c) $\sqrt{3.6}$,   (d) $\sqrt{5.3}$.

   (The five-decimal values are 2.09762, 1.41421, 1.89737, and 2.30217.)

4. In Fig. 5.41, the vertical displacement between the curve and the tangent line at the abscissa x is $|f(x) - L_4(x)|$. From the solution of Problem 1 in Remark 1, we saw that this is about $0.02(x - 4)^2$. In one figure, sketch portions of the graphs of the parabola $y = 0.02(x - 4)^2$, the curve $y = \sqrt{x}$, and the line $y = 2 + (\tfrac{1}{4})(x - 4)$, for $x \in [3, 5]$. (To three decimals, $\sqrt{3} = 1.732$ and $\sqrt{5} = 2.236$.)

5. If f and its first two derivatives are continuous functions in some neighborhood of $x = a$, what can you say about the existence and the values of the following limits? [$L_a(x)$ is the linearization of f at a.]

   (a) $\displaystyle\lim_{x \to a} |f(x) - f(a)|$ (b) $\displaystyle\lim_{x \to a} \frac{f(x) - f(a)}{x - a}$

   (c) $\displaystyle\lim_{x \to a} \frac{f(x) - L_a(x)}{x - a}$ (d) $\displaystyle\lim_{x \to a} \frac{f(x) - L_a(x)}{(x - a)^2}$

6. Use Eq. (10) to prove that if f and its first two derivatives are continuous in some neighborhood of $x = a$, and $f''(x)$ changes its sign when x increases through a, then the graph of f lies above the tangent line (at a) on one side of a and below it on the other side of a. (This is another way of saying that there is a *point of inflection* at a.)

7. Prove that a polynomial $f(x)$ of degree n may be written, precisely, in the form

$$f(x) = f(a) + f'(a)(x - a) + \frac{f''(a)}{2}(x - a)^2$$
$$+ \cdots + \frac{f^{(n)}(a)}{n!}(x - a)^n.$$

Suggestion. Write the polynomial in the form

$$f(x) = a_0 + a_1(x - a) + a_2(x - a)^2 + \cdots$$
$$+ a_n(x - a)^n,$$

and evaluate the function and its derivatives at $x = a$.

8. Use the Extended Mean Value Theorem, Eq. (2), to prove the following: Let $f(x)$ be continuous and have continuous first and second derivatives. Suppose that $f'(a) = 0$. Then $f(x)$ has

(a) a relative maximum at a if its second derivative is less than or equal to zero throughout some neighborhood of a, and

(b) a relative minimum at a if its second derivative is greater than or equal to zero throughout some neighborhood of a.

9. The Extended Mean Value Theorem can be further extended as follows: Suppose that f, f', and f'' are continuous on $[a, b]$, and that f''' exists on (a, b). Let K be the number for which it is true that

$$f(b) = f(a) + f'(a)(b - a)$$
$$+ \tfrac{1}{2}f''(a)(b - a)^2 + K(b - a)^3.$$

By an argument like the one used in the proof of the Extended Mean Value Theorem, show that

$$K = \tfrac{1}{6}f'''(c_3) \quad \text{for some } c_3 \text{ in } (a, b).$$

REVIEW QUESTIONS AND EXERCISES

1. Discuss the significance of the signs of first and second derivatives. Sketch a small portion of a curve, illustrating how it looks near a point where

(a) both y' and y'' are positive;

(b) $y' > 0$, $y'' < 0$;   (c) $y' < 0$, $y'' > 0$;

(d) $y' < 0$, $y'' < 0$.

2. Define *point of inflection.* How do you find points of inflection from an equation of a curve?

3. How do you locate local maximum and minimum points of a curve? Discuss exceptional points, such as end points and points where the derivative fails to exist, in addition to the nonexceptional type. Illustrate with graphs.

4. Let n be a positive integer. For which values of n does the curve $y = x^n$ have

(a) a local minimum at the origin,

(b) a point of inflection at the origin?

5. Outline a general method of attack for solving "related rates" problems.

6. Outline a general method of attack for solving "max-min" problems.

7. What are the hypotheses of Rolle's theorem? What is the conclusion?

8. Is the converse of Rolle's theorem true?

9. With the book closed, state and prove the Mean Value Theorem. What is its geometrical interpretation?

10. We know that if $F(x) = x^2$, then $F'(x) = 2x$. If someone knows a function G such that $G'(x) = 2x$ but $G(x) \neq x^2$, what can be said about the difference $G(2) - G(1)$? Explain.

11. Use the Extended Mean Value Theorem to estimate $\sqrt[3]{9}$. Compare the answer with what you get using a linear approximation.

12. Read the article "Mathematics in Warfare" by F. W. Lanchester, *World of Mathematics*, Vol. 4, pp. 2138–2157, as a discussion of a practical problem in "related rates."

MISCELLANEOUS EXERCISES

12/14 2, 6, 7, 10, 15   12/15 20, 31, 32, 34, 50

In Exercises 1 through 14, find y' and y''. Determine in each case the sets of values of x for which

(a) y is increasing (as x increases),

(b) y is decreasing (as x increases),

(c) the graph is concave upward,

(d) the graph is concave downward.

Also sketch the graph in each case, indicating *high* and *low* turning points and points of inflection.

1. $y = 9x - x^2$

2. $y = x^3 - 5x^2 + 3x$

3. $y = 4x^3 - x^4$

4. $y = 4x + x^{-1}$

5. $y = x^2 + 4x^{-1}$

6. $y = x + 4x^{-2}$

7. $y = 5 - x^{2/3}$

8. $y = \dfrac{x - 1}{x + 1}$

9. $y = x - \dfrac{4}{x}$

10. $y = x^4 - 2x^2$

11. $y = \dfrac{x^2}{ax + b}$, $\quad a > 0, \; b > 0$

12. $y = 2x^3 - 9x^2 + 12x$ 13. $y = (x - 1)(x + 1)^2$

14. $y = x^2 - \frac{1}{6}x^3$

15. The slope of a curve at any point (x, y) is given by the equation

$$\frac{dy}{dx} = 6(x - 1)(x - 2)^2(x - 3)^3(x - 4)^4.$$

(a) For what value (or values) of x is y a maximum? Why?

(b) For what value (or values) of x is y a minimum? Why?

16. A particle moves along the x-axis with velocity $v = dx/dt = f(x)$. Show that its acceleration is $f(x)f'(x)$.

17. A meteorite entering the earth's atmosphere has velocity inversely proportional to $\sqrt{s}$ when at distance s from the center of the earth. Show that its acceleration is inversely proportional to s^2.

18. If the velocity of a falling body is $k\sqrt{s}$ at the instant when the body has fallen a distance s, find its acceleration.

19. The volume of a cube is increasing at a rate of $300 \text{ in}^3/\text{min}$ at the instant when the edge is 20 in. Find the rate at which the edge is changing.

20. Sand falling at the rate of $3 \text{ ft}^3/\text{min}$ forms a conical pile whose radius always equals twice the height. Find the rate at which the height is changing at the instant when the height is 10 ft.

21. The volume of a sphere is decreasing at the rate of $12\pi \text{ ft}^3/\text{min}$. Find the rates at which the radius and the surface area are changing at the instant when the radius is 20 ft. Also find approximately how much the radius and surface area may be expected to change in the following 6 sec.

22. At a certain instant, airplane A is flying a level course at 500 mi/hr. At the same time, airplane B is straight above airplane A and flying at the rate of 700 mi/hr on a slant course that intercepts A's course at a point C that is 4 mi from B and 2 mi from A.

(a) At the instant in question, how fast is the distance between the airplanes decreasing?

(b) What is the minimum distance between the airplanes, if they continue on the present courses at constant speed?

23. A point moves along the curve $y^2 = x^3$ in such a way that its distance from the origin increases at the constant rate of 2 units per second. Find dx/dt at $(2, 2\sqrt{2})$.

24. Refer to the triangle in Fig. 5.12. How fast is its area changing when $x = 17\sqrt{2}$?

25. Suppose the cone in Fig. 5.13 has a small opening at the vertex through which the water escapes at the rate of $0.08\sqrt{y} \text{ ft}^3/\text{min}$ when its depth is y. Water is also running into the cone at a constant rate of $c \text{ ft}^3/\text{min}$. When the depth is $6\frac{1}{4}$ ft it is observed to be increasing at the rate 0.02 ft/min. Under these conditions, will the tank fill? Give a reason for your answer.

26. A particle projected vertically upward from the surface of the earth with initial velocity v_0 has velocity $\sqrt{v_0^2 - 2gR[1 - (R/s)]}$ when it reaches a distance s from the *center* of the earth. Here R is the radius of the earth. Show that the acceleration is inversely proportional to s^2.

27. Given a triangle ABC. Let D and E be points on the sides AB and AC, respectively, such that DE is parallel to BC. Let the distance between BC and DE equal x. Show that the derivative, with respect to x, of the area $BCED$ is equal to the length of DE.

28. Points A and B move along the x- and y-axes, respectively, in such a way that the perpendicular distance r (inches) from the origin to AB remains constant. How fast is OA changing, and is it increasing or decreasing, when $OB = 2r$ and B is moving toward O at the rate of $0.3r$ in/sec?

29. Ships A and B start from O at the same time. Ship A travels due east at a rate of 15 mi/hr. Ship B travels in a straight course making an angle of 60° with the

path of ship A at a rate of 20 mi/hr. How fast are they separating at the end of 2 hr?

30. Water is being poured into an inverted conical tank (vertex down) at the rate of $2\,\text{ft}^3/\text{min}$. How fast is the water level rising when the depth of the water is 5 ft? The radius of the base of the cone is 3 ft and the altitude is 10 ft.

31. Divide 20 into two parts (not necessarily integers) such that the product of one part with the square of the other shall be a maximum.

32. Find the largest value of

$$f(x) = 4x^3 - 8x^2 + 5x \quad \text{for} \quad 0 \le x \le 2.$$

Give reasons for your answer.

33. Find two *positive* numbers whose sum is 36 and such that their product is as large as possible. Can the problem be solved if the product is to be as small as possible?

34. Determine the coefficients a, b, c, d so that the curve whose equation is

$$y = ax^3 + bx^2 + cx + d$$

has a maximum at $(-1, 10)$ and an inflection point at $(1, -6)$.

35. Find that number which most exceeds its square.

36. The perimeter p and area A of a circular sector ("piece of pie") of radius r and arc length s are given by

$$p = 2r + s \quad \text{and} \quad A = \tfrac{1}{2}rs,$$

respectively. If the perimeter is known to be 100 ft, what value of r will produce a maximum area?

37. If a ball is thrown vertically upward with a velocity of 32 ft/sec, its height after t sec is given by the equation $s = 32t - 16t^2$. At what instant will the ball be at its highest point, and how high will it rise?

38. A right circular cone has altitude 12 ft and radius of base 6 ft. A cone is inscribed with its vertex at the center of the base of the given cone and its base parallel to the base of the given cone. Find the dimensions of the cone of maximum volume that can be so inscribed.

39. An oil can is to be made in the form of a right circular cylinder to contain $16\pi\,\text{in}^3$. What dimensions of the can will require the least amount of material to be used?

40. An isosceles triangle is drawn with its vertex at the origin, its base parallel to and above the x-axis and, the vertices of its base on the curve $12y = 36 - x^2$. Determine the area of the largest such triangle.

41. A tire manufacturer is able to make x (hundred) grade A tires and y (hundred) grade B tires per day, where

$$y = \frac{40 - 10x}{5 - x}, \quad 0 \le x \le 4.$$

If the profit on each grade A tire is twice the profit on a grade B tire, how many grade A tires per day should she make?

42. Find the points on the curve $x^2 - y^2 = 1$ which are nearest the point $P(a, 0)$ if

(a) $a = 4$,   (b) $a = 2$,

(c) $a = \sqrt{2}$.

43. A motorist is located in a desert 5 mi from a point A, which is the point on a long straight road nearest to him. He wishes to get to a point B on the road. If he can travel at 15 mi/hr on the desert and 39 mi/hr on the road, find the point at which he must meet the road to get to B in the shortest possible time if

(a) B is 5 mi from A,   (b) B is 10 mi from A,

(c) B is 1 mi from A.

44. Points A and B are ends of a diameter of a circle and C is a point on the circumference. Which of the following statements about triangle ABC is (or are) true?

(a) The area is a maximum when the triangle is isosceles.

(b) The area is a minimum when the triangle is isosceles.

(c) The perimeter is a maximum when the triangle is isosceles.

(d) The perimeter is a minimum when the triangle is isosceles.

45. The base and the perimeter of a triangle are fixed. Determine the remaining two sides if the area is to be a maximum.

46. The base b and the area k of a triangle are fixed. Determine the base angles if the angle at the vertex opposite b is to be a maximum.

47. A line is drawn through a fixed point (a, b) to meet the axes Ox, Oy in P and Q. Show that the minimum values of PQ, $OP + OQ$, and $OP \cdot OQ$ are respectively $(a^{2/3} + b^{2/3})^{3/2}$, $(\sqrt{a} + \sqrt{b})^2$, and $4ab$.

48. Find the smallest value of the constant m if

$$mx - 1 + \frac{1}{x}$$

is to be greater than or equal to zero for all positive values of x.

49. Let s be the distance from the fixed point $P_1(x_1, y_1)$ to a point $P(x, y)$ on the line $L: ax + by + c = 0$. Using calculus methods,

(a) show that s^2 is a minimum when $P_1 P$ is perpendicular to L, and

(b) show that the minimum distance is

$$|ax_1 + by_1 + c| / \sqrt{a^2 + b^2}.$$

50. A playing field is to be built in the shape of a rectangle plus a semicircular area at each end. A 440-yd race track is to form the perimeter of the field. Find the dimensions of the field if the rectangular part is to have as large an area as possible.

51. If $ax + (b/x) \geq c$ for all positive values of x, where a, b, and c are positive constants, show that

$$ab \geq c^2/4.$$

52. Prove that if

$$ax^2 + (b/x) \geq c$$

for all positive values of x, where a, b, and c are positive constants, then

$$27ab^2 \geq 4c^3.$$

53. Given $f(x) = ax^2 + 2bx + c$ with $a > 0$. By considering the minimum, prove that $f(x) \geq 0$ for all real x if, and only if,

$$b^2 - ac \leq 0.$$

54. In Exercise 53, take

$$f(x) = (a_1 x + b_1)^2 + (a_2 x + b_2)^2 + \cdots + (a_n x + b_n)^2,$$

and deduce Schwarz's inequality:

$$(a_1 b_1 + a_2 b_2 + \cdots + a_n b_n)^2$$
$$\leq (a_1^2 + a_2^2 + \cdots + a_n^2)(b_1^2 + b_2^2 + \cdots + b_n^2).$$

55. In Exercise 54, prove that equality can hold only in case there is a real number x such that $b_i = -a_i x$ for every $i = 1, 2, \ldots, n$.

56. If x is positive and m is greater than one, prove that

$$x^m - 1 - m(x - 1)$$

is not negative.

57. What are the dimensions of the rectangular plot of greatest area which can be laid out within a triangle of base 36 ft and altitude 12 ft? Assume that one side of the rectangle lies on the base of the triangle.

58. Find the width across the top of an isosceles trapezoid of base 12 in. and slant sides 6 in. if its area is a maximum.

59. A fence h ft high runs parallel to and w ft from a vertical wall. Find the length of the shortest ladder which will reach from the ground across the top of the fence to the wall.

60. Assuming that the cost per hour of running an ocean liner is $a + bv^n$, where a, b, and n are positive constants, $n > 1$, and v is the velocity through the water, find the speed for making the run from Liverpool to New York at minimum cost.

61. A flower bed is to be in the shape of a circular sector of radius r and central angle θ (i.e., like a piece of pie). Find r and θ if the area is fixed and the perimeter is a minimum.

62. A reservoir is to be built in the form of a right circular cone and the lateral area waterproofed. If the capacity of the reservoir is to be 72π ft^3 and one gallon of waterproofing material will cover 80 ft^2, how many gallons are required?

63. Given two concentric circles, C_1 of radius r_1 and C_2 of radius r_2, $r_2 > r_1 > 0$. Let A be the area between them.

(a) How fast is A increasing (or decreasing), when $r_1 = 4$ in. and is increasing at the rate of 0.02 in/sec while $r_2 = 6$ in. and is increasing at the rate of 0.01 in/sec?

(b) Suppose that at time $t = 0$, r_1 is 3 in. and r_2 is 5 in., and that for $t > 0$, r_1 increases at the constant rate of a in/sec and r_2 increases at the constant rate of b in/sec. If

$$\tfrac{3}{5}a < b < a,$$

find when the area A will be a maximum.

64. Given two concentric spheres, S_1 of radius r_1 and S_2 of radius r_2, $r_2 > r_1 > 0$. Let V be the volume between them. Suppose that at time $t = 0$, $r_1 = r$ in.

and $r_2 = R$ in., and that for $t > 0$, r_1 increases at the constant rate of a in/sec and r_2 increases at the constant rate of b in/sec. If

$$a > b > ar^2/R^2,$$

find when V will be a maximum.

65. The motion of a particle in a straight line is given by $s = \lambda t - (1 + \lambda^4)t^2$. Show that the particle moves forward initially when λ is positive but ultimately retreats. Show also that for different values of λ the maximum possible distance that the particle can move forward is $\frac{1}{8}$.

66. Let $h(x) = f(x)g(x)$ be the product of two functions that have first and second derivatives and are positive; that is,

$$f(x) > 0, \; g(x) > 0.$$

(a) Is it true, if f and g both have a relative maximum at $x = a$, that h has a relative maximum at $x = a$?

(b) Is it true, if f and g both have a point of inflection at $x = a$, that h has a point of inflection at $x = a$?

For both (a) and (b) either give a proof or construct a numerical example showing the statement false.

67. The numbers $c_1, c_2, \ldots, c_n$ are recorded in an experiment. It is desired to determine a number x with the property that

$$(c_1 - x)^2 + (c_2 - x)^2 + (c_3 - x)^2 + \cdots + (c_n - x)^2$$

shall be a minimum. Find x.

68. The 4 points

$$(-2, -\tfrac{1}{2}), \quad (0, 1), \quad (1, 2), \quad \text{and} \quad (3, 3)$$

are observed to lie more or less close to a straight line of equation $y = mx + 1$. Find m if the sum

$$(y_1 - mx_1 - 1)^2 + (y_2 - mx_2 - 1)^2 + (y_3 - mx_3 - 1)^2 + (y_4 - mx_4 - 1)^2$$

is to be a minimum, where $(x_1, y_1), \ldots, (x_4, y_4)$ are the coordinates of the given points.

69. The *geometric mean* of the n positive numbers $a_1, a_2, \ldots, a_n$ is the nth root of $a_1 a_2 \ldots a_n$ and the arithmetic mean is $(a_1 + a_2 + \cdots + a_n)/n$. Show that if $a_1, a_2, \ldots, a_{n-1}$ are fixed and $a_n = x$ is permitted to vary over the set of positive real numbers, the ratio of the arithmetic mean to the geometric mean is a minimum when x is the arithmetic mean of $a_1, a_2, \ldots, a_{n-1}$.

70. The curve $(y + 1)^3 = x^2$ passes through the points $(1, 0)$ and $(-1, 0)$. Does Rolle's Theorem justify the conclusion that dy/dx vanishes for some value of x in the interval $-1 \le x \le 1$? Give reasons for your answer.

71. If $a < 0 < b$ and $f(x) = x^{-1/3}$, show that there is no c that satisfies Eq. (3), Article 5.8. Illustrate with a sketch of the graph.

72. If $a < 0 < b$ and $f(x) = x^{1/3}$, show that there is a value of c that satisfies Eq. (3), Article 5.8, even though the function fails to have a derivative at $x = 0$. Illustrate with a sketch of the graph.

73. Show that the equation

$$f(x) = 2x^3 - 3x^2 + 6x + 6 = 0$$

has exactly one real root and find its value accurate to two significant figures. [*Hint.* $f(-1) = -5$, $f(0) = +6$, and $f'(x) > 0$ for all real x.]

74. General Extended Mean Value Theorem. Suppose $f(x)$ and its derivatives $f'(x), f''(x), \ldots, f^{(n-1)}(x)$ of order one through $n - 1$ are continuous on $a \le x \le b$, and $f^{(n)}(x)$ exists for $a < x < b$. If

$$F(x) = f(x) - f(a) - (x - a)f'(a)$$
$$- \frac{(x-a)^2 f''(a)}{2!} - \cdots$$
$$- \frac{(x-a)^{n-1} f^{(n-1)}(a)}{(n-1)!} - K(x-a)^n,$$

where K is chosen so that $F(b) = 0$, show that

(a) $F(a) = F(b) = 0$,

(b) $F'(a) = F''(a) = \cdots = F^{(n-1)}(a) = 0$,

(c) there exist numbers $c_1, c_2, c_3, \ldots, c_n$ such that

$$a < c_n < c_{n-1} < \cdots < c_2 < c_1 < b$$

and such that

$$F'(c_1) = 0 = F''(c_2)$$
$$= F'''(c_3) = \cdots = F^{(n-1)}(c_{n-1})$$
$$= F^{(n)}(c_n).$$

(d) Hence, deduce that

$$K = \frac{f^{(n)}(c_n)}{n!}$$

for c_n as in (c); or, in other words, since $F(b) = 0$,

$$f(b) = f(a) + f'(a)(b - a)$$
$$+ \frac{f''(a)}{2!}(b - a)^2 + \cdots$$
$$+ \frac{f^{(n-1)}(a)}{(n - 1)!}(b - a)^{n-1}$$
$$+ \frac{f^{(n)}(c_n)}{n!}(b - a)^n$$

for some c_n, $a < c_n < b$. [*Amer. Math. Monthly,* Vol. 60 (1953), p. 415, James Wolfe.]

75. Suppose that it costs a manufacturer $y = a + bx$ dollars to produce x units per week. Assume that the price, P dollars per item, at which he can sell x items per week is $P = c - ex$.

(a) What level of production maximizes his profits?

(b) What is the corresponding price?

(c) What is his profit (per week) at this level of production?

(d) If a tax of t dollars per item sold is imposed on this product, and the manufacturer still wishes to maximize his profit, at what price should he sell each item? Comment on the difference between this price and the price before tax.

76. Sketch the region R of points (x, y) that satisfy the simultaneous inequalities $y \geqq x$ and $y \leqq x + 2$.

Find: (a) the maximum value, and

(b) the minimum value

of the function $2x + 3y$ for points in R.
Hint: Visualize how lines of the family $2x + 3y = c$ cover the plane as c is assigned different values. You want to know how big (or small) c can be and have the line touch R. Experiment. Try numbers like -6, 0, 6, 12, 18 for c. Do you think there are values for c for which the line $2x + 3y = c$ touches R in a single boundary point? Observe that on the boundary of R, $2x + 3y$ can be expressed in terms of x.

77. Sketch the region R of points (x, y) that satisfy the simultaneous inequalities $x > 0$, $y > 0$, $2x + 3y \leqq 6$, $x + y \geqq 1$, $3x + 2y \leqq 6$. Find: (a) the maximum

value, and (b) the minimum value of the function $f = 3x + 4y$ for points in R.
Hint: Visualize how lines of the family $3x + 4y = c$ cover the plane as different values are assigned to c. Experiment with specific values of c. Calculate the values of $3x + 4y$ at the vertices of R and sketch the lines of the form $3x + 4y = c$ that go through these points.

INTEGRATION

CHAPTER 6

6.1 INTRODUCTION

In the preceding chapters we have pursued one of the two main branches of the calculus, namely, *differential calculus*. We shall now turn our attention to the other main branch of the subject, *integral calculus*. Today, "to integrate" has two meanings when used in connection with calculus. The deeper and more fundamental meaning is nearly the same as the nontechnical definition: "to indicate the whole of; to give the sum or total of" (Webster). The mathematical meaning of the word in this sense will be amply illustrated in finding areas bounded by curves, volumes of various solids, lengths of curves, and centers of gravity, and in other applications.

The second mathematical meaning of the verb "to integrate" is "to find a function whose derivative is given." This is the aspect of integration that we shall discuss in the next two articles.

The two kinds of integration are called respectively *definite* and *indefinite*, and the connection between the two is given by a theorem which is called the *fundamental theorem* of integral calculus.

6.2 THE INDEFINITE INTEGRAL

Suppose that we are given the derivative dy/dx as a function

$$\frac{dy}{dx} = f(x), \quad x \in (a, b), \tag{1}$$

and are asked to find $y = F(x)$.

Example 1. We might be asked to find y as a function of x if

$$\frac{dy}{dx} = 2x.$$

From our experience with derivatives, we can guess one answer, namely,

$$y = x^2.$$

On the other hand, we realize that this is not the only answer, since

$$y = x^2 + 1,$$
$$y = x^2 - \sqrt{2},$$
$$y = x^2 + 5\pi$$

are also valid answers. Indeed,

$$y = x^2 + C$$

is an answer if C is any constant.

Definition 1. *An equation such as* (1), *which specifies the derivative as a function of x (or as a function of x and y), is called a differential equation.*

Example 2. $$\frac{dy}{dx} = 2xy^2$$

is a differential equation. Second-, third-, and higher-order derivatives may also occur in differential equations, such as

$$\frac{d^2y}{dx^2} + 6xy\,\frac{dy}{dx} + 3x^2y^3 = 0,$$

and so on. For the time being we shall restrict attention to the special type of differential equation considered in Eq. (1). Differential equations of more general types will be considered in Chapter 15.

Definition 2. *A function* $y = F(x)$ *is called a solution of the differential equation* (1), *if over the domain* $a < x < b$, $F(x)$ *is differentiable and*

$$\frac{dF(x)}{dx} = f(x). \qquad (2)$$

We also say, in these circumstances, that $F(x)$ *is an integral of* $f(x)$ *with respect to x.*

Remark 1. It is clear from this definition that if $F(x)$ is an integral of $f(x)$ with respect to x, then $F(x) + C$ is also such an integral when C is any constant whatever. For if Eq. (2) is satisfied, then we also have

$$\frac{d}{dx}\,[F(x) + C] = \frac{dF(x)}{dx} + \frac{dC}{dx}$$
$$= f(x) + 0 = f(x).$$

What is not clear, however, is whether there are other integrals of $f(x)$ not contained in this collection given by the formula $F(x) + C$. Specifically, we know that $y = x^2 + C$ is a solution, for any constant C, of the differential equation $dy/dx = 2x$. But are there any other solutions?

This question is answered by the second corollary of the Mean Value Theorem, Article 5.8. For if both $F_1(x)$ and $F_2(x)$ are integrals of $f(x)$,

then $$\frac{dF_1(x)}{dx} = \frac{dF_2(x)}{dx} = f(x)$$

or $$\frac{d[F_1(x) - F_2(x)]}{dx} = 0,$$

and hence $$F_1(x) - F_2(x) = C,$$

where C is a constant. Hence, if we take

$$F_2(x) = F(x),$$

we have $$F_1(x) = F(x) + C.$$

Therefore, if $y = F(x)$ is any solution whatever of Eq. (1), then *all* solutions are contained in the formula

$$y = F(x) + C,$$

where C is an arbitrary constant. This is indicated by writing

$$\int f(x)\,dx = F(x) + C, \qquad (3)$$

where the symbol $\int$ is called an "integral sign," and Eq. (3) is read "The integral of $f(x)\,dx$ is $F(x)$ plus C." This is a standard notation. We may interpret it in either of two ways:

1. We may think of the symbol

$$\int \ldots dx \qquad (4)$$

as meaning "integral, with respect to x, of $\ldots$" The symbol (4) is then interpreted as the inverse of the symbol

$$\frac{d}{dx}\ldots,$$

which means "derivative, with respect to x, of $\ldots$" In this interpretation the integral sign and the dx go together; the integral sign specifies the operation of integration, and the dx tells us that the "variable of integration" is x.

2. Or, we may think of Eq. (2) as written in *differential* form:

$$dF(x) = f(x)\,dx, \qquad (5)$$

before the operation indicated by the integral sign is performed. Then, when we introduce the integral sign in Eq. (5) (that is, when we "integrate" both sides of the equation), we get

$$\int dF(x) = \int f(x)\, dx.$$

If we compare this with Eq. (3), we have

$$\int dF(x) = F(x) + C. \qquad (6)$$

In other words, when we integrate the *differential* of a function we get that function plus an arbitrary constant. In this interpretation, we therefore think of the symbol $\int$ for integration (without absorbing the dx as part of the symbol) as meaning the operation which is the inverse of the operation denoted by the symbol d for differentiation. This is the interpretation which we shall adopt in this book.

Example 3. If we want to solve the differential equation

$$\frac{dy}{dx} = 3x^2,$$

we use the definition of the differential

$$dy = \frac{dy}{dx}\, dx$$

to change it to the differential form

$$dy = 3x^2\, dx.$$

Now we know, from past experience, that

$$d(x^3) = 3x^2\, dx.$$

Hence we have

$$y = \int 3x^2\, dx = \int d(x^3) = x^3 + C.$$

If both x and y occur in the differential equation, but in such a way that we can separate the variables so as to combine all y terms with dy and all x terms with dx, then we can integrate as in the following problem.

Problem 1. Solve the differential equation

$$\frac{dy}{dx} = x^2\sqrt{y}, \quad y > 0. \qquad (7)$$

Solution. We change to differentials

$$dy = x^2\sqrt{y}\, dx$$

and then divide by $\sqrt{y}$ to obtain

$$y^{-(1/2)}\, dy = x^2\, dx,$$

in which the variables have been separated. The left side of this equation is

$$d(2y^{1/2}) = y^{-(1/2)}\, dy,$$

while the right side is

$$d(x^3/3) = x^2\, dx.$$

Therefore

$$d(2y^{1/2}) = d(x^3/3).$$

When we integrate this equation, we may write

$$2y^{1/2} + C_1 = \frac{x^3}{3} + C_2, \quad \text{or} \quad 2y^{1/2} = \frac{x^3}{3} + C, \quad (8a)$$

where we have combined the two constants C_1 and C_2 into a single constant

$$C = C_2 - C_1.$$

In fact, when we integrate the two sides of a differential equation, it always suffices to add the arbitrary constant C to just one side of the equation since, in any case, if we add constants to both sides of the equation they may always be combined into a single constant.

Remark 2. We readily verify that Eq. (8a) applies to a family of functions

$$y = F(x) = \frac{1}{4}\left(\frac{x^3}{3} + C\right)^2. \qquad (8b)$$

To make $y > 0$, we would restrict the domain of F to

$$x^3 + 3C > 0 \quad \text{or} \quad x^3 + 3C < 0.$$

If we choose the former, then Eq. (7) is satisfied in the form

$$F'(x) = x^2\sqrt{F(x)}, \qquad (8c)$$

because

$$2\left[\frac{1}{4}\left(\frac{x^3}{3} + C\right)\right]x^2 = x^2\sqrt{\frac{1}{4}\left(\frac{x^3}{3} + C\right)^2},$$

if

$$x^3 + 3C > 0.$$

6.1   Solution of $dy/dx = x^2\sqrt{y}$ through $(3, 4)$.

If, in addition to the differential equation (7), we want the graph of F to contain some given point, say $(3, 4)$, we must choose C so that these coordinates satisfy Eqs. (8a, b):

$$2(4)^{1/2} = \frac{27}{3} + C, \quad \text{or} \quad C = -5.$$

The corresponding function F is defined by

$$F(x) = \frac{1}{4}\left(\frac{x^3}{3} - 5\right)^2, \quad x^3 - 15 > 0. \qquad (9)$$

Figure 6.1 shows part of the graph of this function.

Remark 3. If in Eq. (7) we remove the restriction to positive values of y, and also allow $y = 0$, then we cannot divide when $y = 0$. However, we can see from the solution in Eq. (9), that the original form of the equation is satisfied in the sense of zero slope at $x = \sqrt[3]{15}$, $y = 0$. Observe also that the constant function $y = 0$ satisfies Eq. (7). Therefore, if we extend the graph to the left of $x = \sqrt[3]{15}$, not according to the algebraic formula of Eq. (9), but by following the x-axis, then we obtain a new function defined as

$$F(x) = \begin{cases} 0 & \text{for} \quad x \le \sqrt[3]{15}, \\ \frac{1}{36}(x^3 - 15)^2 & \text{for} \quad x > \sqrt[3]{15}. \end{cases} \qquad (10)$$

For every point (x, y) on the graph of (10), the slope satisfies the equation $dy/dx = x^2\sqrt{y}$.

Integration, as defined above, requires the ability to guess the answer. But the following formulas help to reduce the amount of guesswork in many cases. In these formulas, u and v denote differentiable functions of some independent variable (say of x) and a, n, and C are constants.

$$\int du = u + C, \qquad\qquad \text{(a)}$$

$$\int a\, du = a\int du, \qquad\qquad \text{(b)}$$

$$\int (du + dv) = \int du + \int dv, \qquad \text{(c)}$$

$$\int u^n\, du = \frac{u^{n+1}}{n+1} + C, \quad (n \ne -1). \quad \text{(d)}$$

In words, these formulas say that:

(a) The integral of the differential of a function u is u plus an arbitrary constant C.

(b) A constant may be moved across the integral sign. [*Caution.* Variables must *not* be moved across the integral sign.]

(c) The integral of the sum of two differentials is the sum of their integrals. We note that formula (c) may be extended to the sum of any *finite* number of differentials:

$$\int (du_1 + du_2 + \cdots + du_n)$$
$$= \int du_1 + \int du_2 + \cdots + \int du_n.$$

(d) If n is not equal to minus one, the integral of $u^n\, du$ is obtained by adding one to the exponent and dividing by the new exponent. For example,

$$\int x^{1/2}\, dx = \frac{x^{3/2}}{3/2} + C = \tfrac{2}{3}x^{3/2} + C.$$

Caution. One *must* have precisely du as well as u^n to use this formula.

Example 4.
$$\int \sqrt{2x+1}\, dx$$

does not fit the formula if we let

$$u = 2x + 1, \qquad n = \tfrac{1}{2},$$

because then

$$du = \frac{du}{dx}\cdot dx = 2\, dx$$

is *not* present precisely. But only the constant factor 2 is missing, and this factor can be introduced after the integral sign provided we compensate for it by a factor of $\frac{1}{2}$ in front of the integral sign [by (b)]. Thus we write

$$\int \sqrt{2x+1}\, dx = \frac{1}{2}\int \sqrt{2x+1}\cdot 2\, dx$$

$$= \frac{1}{2}\int u^{1/2}\, du, \quad (u = 2x+1,\ du = 2\, dx)$$

$$= \frac{1}{2}\,\frac{u^{3/2}}{3/2} + C$$

$$= \frac{1}{3}\,(2x+1)^{3/2} + C.$$

Remark 4. The word *antidifferentiation* is also used as a synonym for indefinite *integration*. Thus one *antiderivative* of $\sqrt{x}$ is $(\frac{2}{3})x^{3/2}$, and every antiderivative is obtained from this one by adding a constant. Another synonym for *antiderivative*, or *indefinite integral*, is *primitive*. Thus a function F of which f is the derivative is called a *primitive* of f.

Example 5. The derivative of $F(x) = \sqrt{x^2+1}$ is $f(x) = x/\sqrt{x^2+1}$. Therefore, for any constant C,

$$\sqrt{x^2+1} + C \quad \text{is a primitive of} \quad \frac{x}{\sqrt{x^2+1}}.$$

EXERCISES

12/21   #1-6 12/22 7-19 12/23 20,21,22,24

Solve the following differential equations.

1. $\dfrac{dy}{dx} = x^2 + 1$ 　　　　2. $\dfrac{dy}{dx} = \dfrac{1}{x^2} + x, \quad x > 0$

3. $\dfrac{dy}{dx} = \dfrac{x}{y}, \quad y > 0$

4. $\dfrac{dy}{dx} = \sqrt{xy}, \quad x > 0, \quad y > 0$

5. $\dfrac{dy}{dx} = \sqrt[3]{y/x}, \quad x > 0, \quad y > 0$

6. $\dfrac{dy}{dx} = 2xy^2,\ y > 0$ 　　7. $\dfrac{dy}{dx} = 3x^2 - 2x + 5$

8. $\dfrac{ds}{dt} = 3t^2 + 4t - 6$ 　　9. $\dfrac{dr}{dz} = (2z+1)^3$

10. $\dfrac{du}{dv} = 2u^2(4v^3 + 4v^{-3}), \quad v > 0, \quad u > 0$

11. $\dfrac{dx}{dt} = 8\sqrt{x}, \quad x > 0$ 　12. $\dfrac{dy}{dt} = (2t + t^{-1})^2, \quad t > 0$

13. $\dfrac{dy}{dz} = \sqrt{(z^2 - z^{-2})^2 + 4}, \quad z > 0$

Evaluate the following integrals.

14. $\displaystyle\int (2x+3)\, dx$ 　　15. $\displaystyle\int (x^2 - \sqrt{x})\, dx$

16. $\displaystyle\int (3x-1)^{234}\, dx$ 　17. $\displaystyle\int (2 - 7t)^{2/3}\, dt$

18. $\displaystyle\int \sqrt{2 + 5y}\, dy$ 　19. $\displaystyle\int \dfrac{dx}{(3x+2)^2}$

20. $\displaystyle\int \dfrac{3r\, dr}{\sqrt{1 - r^2}}$ 　　21. $\displaystyle\int \sqrt{2x^2 + 1}\ x\, dx$

22. $\displaystyle\int t^2(1 + 2t^3)^{-(2/3)}\, dt$ 　23. $\displaystyle\int \dfrac{y\, dy}{\sqrt{2y^2 + 1}}$

24. $\displaystyle\int \left(\sqrt{x} + \dfrac{1}{\sqrt{x}}\right) dx$ 　25. $\displaystyle\int \dfrac{(z+1)\, dz}{\sqrt[3]{z^2 + 2z + 2}}$

6.3 APPLICATIONS OF INDEFINITE INTEGRATION

Differential equations, such as Eq. (1) or (7) of Article 6.2, arise in chemistry, physics, mathematics, and all branches of engineering. Some of these applications will be illustrated in the examples that follow. Before proceeding with these, however, let us consider the meaning of the arbitrary constant C, which always enters when we integrate a differential equation. If we draw one of the integral

6.2

curves $y = F(x)$ (corresponding to taking $C = 0$), then any other integral curve $y = F(x) + C$ is obtained by simply shifting this curve through a vertical displacement C. Thus we obtain a family of "parallel" curves, as in Fig. 6.2. They are parallel in the sense that the slope of the tangent to any one of them, at the point of abscissa x, is $f(x)$, the same for all curves $y = F(x) + C$. Now clearly this family of parallel curves has the property that, given any point (x_0, y_0) with x_0 in the allowed domain of the independent variable x, there is one and only one curve of the family that passes through this particular point. For if that curve is to pass through the point, the equation must be satisfied by these particular coordinates. This uniquely specifies the value of C, namely,

$$C = y_0 - F(x_0).$$

With C thus determined, we get a definite function expressing y in terms of x.

The condition imposed that $y = y_0$ when $x = x_0$ is often referred to as an "initial condition." This terminology is particularly appropriate in connection with physical problems, where time is the independent variable and initial velocities or initial positions of moving bodies are specified.

Problem 1. The velocity, at time t, of a moving body is given by

$$v = at,$$

where a is a constant. If the body's coordinate is s_0 at time $t = 0$, find the distance s as a function of t.

Solution. The velocity v is the same as the derivative ds/dt. Hence we want to solve the problem that consists of

the differential equation $\qquad \dfrac{ds}{dt} = at$ $\qquad$ (1)

and the initial condition $\qquad s = s_0$ when $t = 0$. (2)

From Eq. (1), we have

$$ds = at \, dt,$$

$$s = \int at \, dt = a\frac{t^2}{2} + C.$$

The constant of integration may now be determined from the initial condition, which requires that $s_0 = C$. Hence, the solution of the problem is

$$s = a\frac{t^2}{2} + s_0.$$

Problem 2. (See Fig. 6.2.) Find the curve whose slope at the point (x, y) is $3x^2$ if the curve is also required to pass through the point $(1, -1)$.

Solution. In mathematical language, we have the following problem:

differential equation: $\qquad \dfrac{dy}{dx} = 3x^2$,

initial condition: $\qquad y = -1$ when $x = 1$.

First, we integrate the differential equation.

$$dy = 3x^2 \, dx,$$

$$y = \int 3x^2 \, dx = x^3 + C.$$

Then we impose the initial condition to evaluate the constant C:

$$-1 = 1^3 + C; \quad C = -2.$$

We substitute the value of C into the solution of the differential equation, and obtain the particular integral curve that passes through the given point, namely,

$$y = x^3 - 2.$$

$$\frac{ds}{dt} = 2t + 1$$
$$\int ds = (2t+1)\,dt$$
$$s = t^2 + 5 \cdot t$$

EXERCISES

12/   1/4   1-15 odd

In Exercises 1 through 6, find the position s as a function of t from the given velocity $v = ds/dt$. Evaluate the constant of integration so as to have $s = s_0$ when $t = 0$.

1. $v = 3t^2$ 2. $v = 2t + 1$

3. $v = (t+1)^2$ 4. $v = (t^2+1)^2$

5. $v = (t+1)^{-2}$ 6. $v = \sqrt{2gs}$ (g constant)

In Exercises 7 through 11, find the velocity v and position s as functions of t from the given acceleration $a = dv/dt$. Evaluate the constants of integration so as to have $v = v_0$ and $s = s_0$ when $t = 0$.

7. $a = g$ (constant)   8. $a = t$

9. $a = \sqrt[3]{2t+1}$ 10. $a = (2t+1)^{-3}$

11. $a = (t^2+1)^2$

12. The gravitational attraction exerted by the earth on a particle of mass m at distance s from the center is given by $F = -mgR^2s^{-2}$, where R is the radius of the earth and F is negative because the force acts in opposition to increasing s. If a particle is projected vertically upward from the surface of the earth with initial velocity $v_0 = \sqrt{2gR}$, apply Newton's second law $F = ma$ with $a = v(dv/ds)$ to show that

$$v = v_0\sqrt{R/s} \quad \text{and} \quad s^{3/2} = R^{3/2}[1 + (3v_0t/2R)].$$

Remark. The initial velocity $v_0 = \sqrt{2gR}$ (approximately 7 miles per second) is known as the "velocity of escape," since the displacement s tends to infinity with increasing t provided the initial velocity is this large. Actually, a somewhat larger initial velocity is required for escape from the earth's gravitational attraction, due to the retardation effect of air resistance, which we have here neglected for the sake of simplicity.

Solve the following differential equations subject to the prescribed initial conditions.

13. $\dfrac{dy}{dx} = x\sqrt{y}$, $x = 0, y = 1$

14. $\dfrac{dy}{dx} = 2xy^2$, $x = 1, y = 1$

15. $\dfrac{dy}{dx} = x\sqrt{1+x^2}$, $x = 0, y = -3$

16. $\dfrac{dy}{dx} = \dfrac{4\sqrt{(1+y^2)^3}}{y}$, $x = 0, y = 1$

Christmas review

6.4 BRIEF REVIEW OF TRIGONOMETRY

Many natural phenomena are periodic; that is, they repeat after definite periods of time. Such phenomena are most readily studied through the use of the trigonometric functions, particularly sines and cosines. Our object in this article and the next is to apply the operations of the calculus to these functions, but before we do so, we shall review some of their properties.

When an angle of measure θ is placed in standard position at the center of a circle of radius r, as in Fig. 6.3, the trigonometric functions of θ are defined by the equations

$$\sin\theta = \frac{y}{r}, \quad \cos\theta = \frac{x}{r}, \quad \tan\theta = \frac{y}{x},$$
$$\csc\theta = \frac{r}{y}, \quad \sec\theta = \frac{r}{x}, \quad \cot\theta = \frac{x}{y}. \tag{1}$$

Observe that $\tan\theta$ and $\sec\theta$ are not defined for values of θ such that $x = 0$. In radian measure, this means that $\pi/2, 3\pi/2, \ldots, -\pi/2, -3\pi/2, \ldots$ are excluded from the domains of the tangent and the secant functions. Similarly $\cot\theta$ and $\csc\theta$ are not defined for values of θ corresponding to $y = 0$: that is, for $\theta = 0, \pi, 2\pi, \ldots, -\pi, -2\pi, \ldots$ For those values of θ where the functions are defined, it follows from Eqs. (1) that

$$\csc\theta = \frac{1}{\sin\theta}, \quad \sec\theta = \frac{1}{\cos\theta}, \quad \cot\theta = \frac{1}{\tan\theta}.$$

Since, by the theorem of Pythagoras, we have

$$x^2 + y^2 = r^2,$$

it follows that

$$\cos^2\theta + \sin^2\theta = 1. \tag{2}$$

It is also useful to express the coordinates of P in terms of r and θ as follows:

$$x = r\cos\theta,$$
$$y = r\sin\theta. \tag{3}$$

When $\theta = 0$ in Fig. 6.3, we have $y = 0$ and $x = r$; hence, from the definitions (1), we obtain

$$\sin 0 = 0, \quad \cos 0 = 1.$$

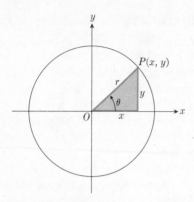

6.3   Angle θ in standard position.

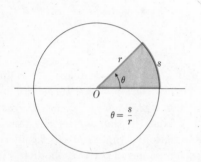

6.4   In radian measure, $\theta = s/r$.

Similarly, for a right angle, $\theta = \pi/2$, we have $x = 0,\ y = r$; hence

$$\sin \frac{\pi}{2} = 1, \qquad \cos \frac{\pi}{2} = 0.$$

Radian measure

In all work with the trigonometric functions in the calculus, it is desirable to measure the angle in *radians*. The number of radians θ in the angle in Fig. 6.4 is defined as the number of "radius units" contained in the arc s subtended by the central angle θ; that is

$$\theta \text{ (in radians)} = \frac{s}{r}. \tag{4a}$$

This also implies that

$$s = r\theta \qquad (\theta \text{ in radians}). \tag{4b}$$

Another useful interpretation of radian measure is easy to get if we take $r = 1$ in (4b). Then the central angle θ, in radians, is just equal to the arc s subtended by θ. We may imagine the circumference of the circle marked off with a scale from which we may read θ. We think of a number scale, like the y-axis shifted one unit to the right, as having been wrapped around the circle. The unit on this number scale is the same as the unit radius. We put the zero of the scale at the place where the initial ray crosses the circle, and then we wrap the positive end of the scale around the circle in the counterclockwise direction, and wrap the negative end around in the opposite direction (see Fig. 6.5). Then θ can be read from this curved s-"axis."

Two points on the s-axis that are exactly 2π units apart will map onto the same point on the unit circle when the wrapping is carried out. For example, if $P_1(x_1, y_1)$ is the point to which an arc of length s_1 reaches, then arcs of length $s_1 + 2\pi$, $s_1 + 4\pi$, and so on, will reach exactly the same point after going completely around the circle one, or two, or more, times. Similarly P_1 will be the image of points on the negative s-axis at $s_1 - 2\pi$, $s_1 - 4\pi$, and so on. Thus, from the wrapped s-axis, we could read

$$\theta_1 = s_1,$$

or

$$\theta_1 + 2\pi,\ \theta_1 + 4\pi,\ \ldots,\ \theta_1 - 2\pi,\ \theta_1 - 4\pi,\ \ldots$$

A unit of arc length $s = 1$ radius subtends a central angle of $57°18'$ (approximately); so

$$1 \text{ radian} \approx 57°18'. \tag{5}$$

We find this, and other relations between degree measure and radian measure, by using the fact that the full circumference has arc length $s = 2\pi r$ and central angle $360°$. Therefore

$$360° = 2\pi \text{ radians}, \tag{6a}$$

$$180° = \pi = 3.14159\ldots \text{ radians}, \tag{6b}$$

$$\left(\frac{360}{2\pi}\right)^{\circ} = 1 \text{ radian} \approx 57°17'44.8'', \tag{6c}$$

$$1° = \frac{2\pi}{360} = \frac{\pi}{180} \approx 0.01745 \text{ radian}. \tag{6d}$$

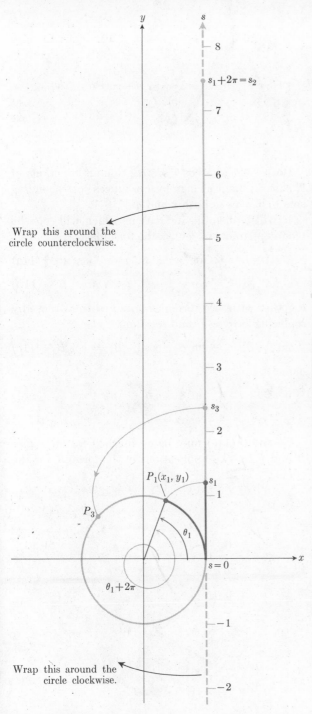

Wrap this around the
circle counterclockwise.

Wrap this around the
circle clockwise.

6.5 The curved s-"axis" wrapped around the unit circle.

It should be emphasized, however, that the radian measure of an angle is dimensionless, since r and s in Eqs. (4a, b) both represent lengths measured in identical units, for instance feet, inches, centimeters, or light-years. Thus $\theta = 2.7$ is to be interpreted as a pure number. The sine and cosine of 2.7 are the ordinate and abscissa, respectively, of the point $P(x, y)$ on a circle of radius r at the end of an arc of length 2.7 radii. For practical purposes we would convert 2.7 radians to 2.7 $(360/2\pi)$ degrees and say

$$\sin 2.7 = \sin \left[2.7 \left(\frac{360}{2\pi} \right)^{\circ} \right] \approx \sin \left[154°41'55'' \right]$$

$$\approx 0.42738.$$

We include here a short table of the angles most frequently used, their radian measures, and their sines and cosines.

Degrees	0°	30°	45°	60°	90°	180°	270°	360°
Radians	0	$\frac{\pi}{6}$	$\frac{\pi}{4}$	$\frac{\pi}{3}$	$\frac{\pi}{2}$	π	$\frac{3\pi}{2}$	2π
Sine	0	$\frac{1}{2}$	$\frac{\sqrt{2}}{2}$	$\frac{\sqrt{3}}{2}$	1	0	-1	0
Cosine	1	$\frac{\sqrt{3}}{2}$	$\frac{\sqrt{2}}{2}$	$\frac{1}{2}$	0	-1	0	1
TAN	O	$\frac{\sqrt{3}}{3}$	1	$\sqrt{3}$	UN	O	UND	O

Periodicity

The mapping from the real numbers s onto points $P(x, y)$ on the unit circle by the wrapping process described above and illustrated in Fig. 6.5 defines the coordinates as functions of s because Eqs. (1) apply, with $\theta = s$ and $r = 1$:

$$x = \cos \theta = \cos s, \qquad y = \sin \theta = \sin s.$$

Because $s + 2\pi$ maps onto the same point that s does, it follows that

$$\cos (\theta + 2\pi) = \cos \theta,$$
$$\sin (\theta + 2\pi) = \sin \theta. \tag{7}$$

Equations (7) are *identities;* that is, they are true for all real numbers θ. These identities would be

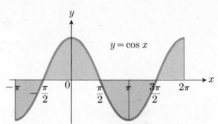

a | b

6.6

true for $\theta' = \theta + 2\pi$:

$$\cos \theta' = \cos (\theta' - 2\pi) \quad \text{and} \quad \sin \theta' = \sin (\theta' - 2\pi). \tag{8}$$

Equations (7) and (8) say that 2π can be added to or subtracted from the domain variable of the sine or cosine functions with no change in the function values. The same process could be repeated any number of times. Consequently

$$\cos (\theta + 2n\pi) = \cos \theta,$$
$$\sin (\theta + 2n\pi) = \sin \theta, \quad n = 0, \pm 1, \pm 2, \ldots \tag{9}$$

Figure 6.6(a, b) shows graphs of the curves

$$y = \sin x \quad \text{and} \quad y = \cos x.$$

The portion of either curve between 0 and 2π is repeated endlessly to the left and to the right. We also note that the cosine curve is the same as the sine curve shifted to the left an amount $\pi/2$.

More trigonometric identities

Figure 6.7 shows two angles of opposite sign but of equal magnitude. By symmetry, the points $P(x, y)$ and $P'(x, -y)$, where the rays of the two angles θ and $-\theta$ intersect the circle, have equal abscissas and ordinates that differ only in sign. Hence we have

$$\sin (-\theta) = -\frac{y}{r} = -\sin \theta, \tag{10a}$$

$$\cos (-\theta) = \frac{x}{r} = \cos \theta. \tag{10b}$$

In particular,

$$\sin \left(-\frac{\pi}{2}\right) = -\sin \frac{\pi}{2} = -1,$$

$$\cos \left(-\frac{\pi}{2}\right) = \cos \frac{\pi}{2} = 0.$$

Both $\sin \theta$ and $\cos \theta$ are continuous functions of θ, since a small change in θ produces corresponding small changes in both x and y.

It will be helpful, for reasons which will soon be made apparent, to review the formulas

$$\sin (A + B) = \sin A \cos B + \cos A \sin B, \tag{11a}$$

$$\cos (A + B) = \cos A \cos B - \sin A \sin B, \tag{11b}$$

together with two formulas obtained from these by replacing B by $-B$ and recalling that

$$\sin (-B) = -\sin B, \quad \cos (-B) = \cos B, \tag{11c}$$

namely,

$$\sin (A - B) = \sin A \cos B - \cos A \sin B, \tag{11d}$$

$$\cos (A - B) = \cos A \cos B + \sin A \sin B. \tag{11e}$$

Equation (11e) may be established for all angles A and B by two applications of the formula for the

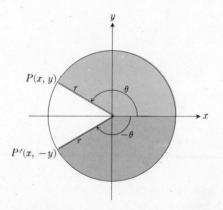

6.7   Angles of opposite sign.

$$\text{TAN A+B} = \frac{\tan A - \tan B}{1 + \tan A \tan B}$$

$$\text{TAN A-B} = \frac{\tan A + \tan B}{1 - \tan A \tan B}$$

6.8 **a**| Law of cosines.

b| Diagram for cos $(A - B)$.

distance between two points:

$$d = \sqrt{(x_2 - x_1)^2 + (y_2 - y_1)^2}.$$

The first application gives the law of cosines. The second then yields the identity (11e). The other formulas (11a, b, d) can be derived from (11e) as shown below.

Law of cosines. In Fig. 6.8(a), triangle OAB has been placed with one vertex O at the origin, and a second vertex A on the x-axis at $A(b, 0)$. The third vertex B has coordinates

$$x = a \cos \theta, \qquad y = a \sin \theta,$$

as given by Eq. (3) with $r = a$. The angle AOB has measure θ. By the formula for the distance between two points, the square of the distance c from A to B is

$$c^2 = (a \cos \theta - b)^2 + (a \sin \theta)^2$$
$$= a^2 (\cos^2 \theta + \sin^2 \theta) + b^2 - 2ab \cos \theta,$$

or

$$c^2 = a^2 + b^2 - 2ab \cos \theta. \qquad (12)$$

Equation (12) is called the *law of cosines.* In words, it says: "The square of any side of a triangle is equal to the sum of the squares of the other two sides minus twice the product of those two sides and the

cosine of the angle between them." When the angle θ is a right angle, its cosine is zero, and Eq. (12) reduces to the theorem of Pythagoras. Equation (12) holds for a general angle θ, since it is based solely on the distance formula and on Eqs. (3) for the coordinates of a point. The same equation works with the exterior angle $(2\pi - \theta)$, or the opposite of $(2\pi - \theta)$, in place of θ, because

$$\cos (2\pi - \theta) = \cos (\theta - 2\pi) = \cos \theta.$$

It is still a valid formula when B is on the x-axis and $\theta = \pi$ or $\theta = 0$, as we can easily verify if we remember that $\cos 0 = 1$ and $\cos \pi = -1$. In these special cases, the right side of Eq. (12) becomes $(a - b)^2$ or $(a + b)^2$.

Addition formulas. Equation (11e) follows from the law of cosines applied to the triangle OPQ in Fig. 6.8(b). We take $OP = OQ = r = 1$. Then the coordinates of P are

$$x_P = \cos A, \qquad y_P = \sin A$$

and of Q,

$$x_Q = \cos B, \qquad y_Q = \sin B.$$

Hence the square of the distance between P and Q is

$$(PQ)^2 = (x_Q - x_P)^2 + (y_Q - y_P)^2$$
$$= (x_Q^2 + y_Q^2) + (x_P^2 + y_P^2) - 2(x_Q x_P + y_Q y_P)$$
$$= 2 - 2 (\cos A \cos B + \sin A \sin B).$$

Next, imagine that a new set of axes is introduced in such a way that the x'-axis contains the point Q. In other words, rotate the original axes through an angle B to obtain the x'- and y'-axes. Relative to these axes, P has new coordinates

$$x' = \cos(A - B),$$
$$y' = \sin(A - B),$$

and Q has coordinates $(1, 0)$. The distance formula applies just as well in this coordinate system as in the original and gives the result

$$(PQ)^2 = (OP)^2 + (OQ)^2 - 2(OP)(OQ)\cos(A - B)$$
$$= 2 - 2\cos(A - B).$$

When we equate these two expressions for $(PQ)^2$, we obtain

$$\cos(A - B) = \cos A \cos B + \sin A \sin B. \quad (11e)$$

We now deduce Eqs. (11a, b, d) from Eq. (11e). We shall also need the results

$$\sin 0 = 0, \quad \sin(\pi/2) = 1, \quad \sin(-\pi/2) = -1,$$
$$\cos 0 = 1, \quad \cos(\pi/2) = 0, \quad \cos(-\pi/2) = 0. \quad (13)$$

1. In Eq. (11e), we put $A = \pi/2$ and use Eqs. (13) to get

$$\cos\left(\frac{\pi}{2} - B\right) = \sin B. \quad (14a)$$

In this equation, if we replace B by $\pi/2 - B$ and $\pi/2 - B$ by $\pi/2 - (\pi/2 - B)$, we get

$$\cos B = \sin\left(\frac{\pi}{2} - B\right). \quad (14b)$$

Equations (14a, b) express the familiar results that the sine and cosine of an angle are the cosine and sine, respectively, of the complementary angle.

2. We next put $B = -\pi/2$ in Eq. (11e) and use (13) to get

$$\cos\left(A + \frac{\pi}{2}\right) = -\sin A. \quad (14c)$$

3. We can get the formula for $\cos(A + B)$ from Eq. (11e) by substituting $-B$ for B everywhere:

$$\cos(A + B) = \cos[A - (-B)]$$
$$= \cos A \cos(-B) + \sin A \sin(-B)$$
$$= \cos A \cos B - \sin A \sin B, \quad (11b)$$

where the final equality uses Eqs. (11c), established earlier.

4. To derive formulas for $\sin(A \pm B)$, we use the identity (14a) with B replaced by

$$A + B \quad \text{or} \quad A - B.$$

Thus we have

$$\sin(A + B) = \cos[\pi/2 - (A + B)]$$
$$= \cos(\pi/2 - A - B)$$
$$= \cos(\pi/2 - A)\cos B$$
$$\quad + \sin(\pi/2 - A)\sin B$$
$$= \sin A \cos B + \cos A \sin B. \quad (11a)$$

Equation (11d) follows from this if we replace B by $-B$.

These are the key results of analytic trigonometry, and all have been derived simply from the distance formula and the definitions of sine and cosine. The most important formulas to remember are the following ones:

$$\sin(A + B) = \sin A \cos B + \cos A \sin B, \quad (11a)$$
$$\cos(A + B) = \cos A \cos B - \sin A \sin B, \quad (11b)$$
$$\sin(-B) = -\sin B, \quad \cos(-B) = \cos B. \quad (11c)$$

If we let

$$\alpha = A + B \quad \text{and} \quad \beta = A - B,$$

so that

$$A = \tfrac{1}{2}(\alpha + \beta),$$
$$B = \tfrac{1}{2}(\alpha - \beta),$$

and subtract Eq. (11d) from Eq. (11a), we obtain the further useful identity

$$\sin\alpha - \sin\beta = 2\cos\frac{\alpha + \beta}{2}\sin\frac{\alpha - \beta}{2}. \quad (15)$$

EXERCISES

_+4 +π,2,5_

In Exercises 1 through 6, sketch the graph of the given equation.

1. $y = 2 \sin x$

2. $y = 3 \sin 2x$

3. $y = A \sin (Bx + C)$, A, B, C constants $\neq 0$

4. $y = 2 \cos 3x$

5. $y = 3 \cos (2x + \pi/4)$

6. $y = 2 \tan x/3$

7. Show that the area of a sector of a circle having central angle θ and radius r is $\frac{1}{2}r^2\theta$, if θ is measured in radians.

8. Let $A(r, 0)$ be the point where the positive x-axis cuts a circle of radius r, center at the origin O. Let $P(r \cos \theta, r \sin \theta)$ be a point on the circle in the first quadrant, with angle $AOP = \theta$ radians. Let AT be tangent to the circle at A and suppose it intersects the line OP at T. By considering the areas of triangle AOP, sector AOP, and triangle AOT, prove the following inequality:

$$\sin \theta < \theta < \tan \theta \quad \text{if} \quad 0 < \theta < \pi/2.$$

9. In Eq. (11e) take $B = A$. Does the result agree with something else you know?

10. In Eq. (11d) take $B = A$. Does the result agree with something you already know?

11. Derive a formula for $\tan (A - B)$ from Eqs. (11d, e).

12. Derive a formula for $\tan (A + B)$ from Eqs. (11a, b).

13. Express all of the trigonometric functions of a general angle θ in terms of $\sin \theta$ and $\cos \theta$.

14. A function $f(\theta)$ is said to be

an even function of θ if $f(-\theta) = f(\theta)$,

an odd function of θ if $f(-\theta) = -f(\theta)$.

Which of the six trigonometric functions are even, and which are odd?

15. Deduce formulas for $\cos 2A$ and $\sin 2A$ from Eqs. (11a, b).

16. Let P and Q be points on a circle with radius $r = 1$, center at the origin O, and such that OP makes an angle $-B$ with the positive x-axis, OQ an angle A. Use the law of cosines to derive a formula for $\cos (A + B)$ directly from this configuration.

6.5 DIFFERENTIATION AND INTEGRATION OF SINES AND COSINES

We shall now apply the operations of the calculus to the sine and cosine functions. We need the results given by the following theorem.

Theorem. _Let θ be measured in radians. Then_

$$\lim_{\theta \to 0} \sin \theta = 0, \tag{1a}$$

$$\lim_{\theta \to 0} \cos \theta = 1, \tag{1b}$$

$$\lim_{\theta \to 0} \frac{\sin \theta}{\theta} = 1. \tag{1c}$$

These results were established in Article 3.3, Eqs. (9a, b, c).

Derivative of sin _u_

We now consider a function defined by

$$y = \sin u,$$

and calculate the derivative from the definition

$$\frac{dy}{du} = \lim_{\Delta u \to 0} \frac{\Delta y}{\Delta u}.$$

Let u be given an increment Δu and y a corresponding increment Δy. Then

$$y + \Delta y = \sin (u + \Delta u),$$

and hence

$$\Delta y = \sin (u + \Delta u) - \sin u \tag{a}$$

$$= 2 \cos \left(u + \frac{\Delta u}{2} \right) \sin \frac{\Delta u}{2}, \tag{b}$$

where we have made use of Eq. (15) of Article 6.4, with $\alpha = u + \Delta u$ and $\beta = u$, in going from (a) to (b). If we divide (b) by Δu, we have

$$\frac{\Delta y}{\Delta u} = 2 \cos \left(u + \frac{\Delta u}{2} \right) \frac{\sin (\Delta u/2)}{\Delta u}$$

$$= \cos (u + \theta) \frac{\sin \theta}{\theta}$$

$$= [\cos u \cos \theta - \sin u \sin \theta] \frac{\sin \theta}{\theta},$$

where $\theta = \Delta u/2$. We now let Δu and θ approach zero and make use of Eqs. (1a, b, c):

$$\lim_{\Delta u \to 0} \frac{\Delta y}{\Delta u} = [\cos u \cdot 1 - \sin u \cdot 0] \cdot 1 = \cos u.$$

But since $y = \sin u$, this means that

$$\frac{dy}{du} = \frac{d(\sin u)}{du} = \cos u.$$

If u is a differentiable function of x, we may apply the chain rule

$$\frac{dy}{dx} = \frac{dy}{du}\frac{du}{dx}$$

to this, with the result that we obtain

$$\frac{d(\sin u)}{dx} = \cos u \cdot \frac{du}{dx}. \qquad \text{(VII)}$$

Thus to find the derivative of the sine of a function, we take the cosine of the same function and multiply it by the derivative of the function.

Example 1. If

$$y = \sin 2x,$$

then

$$\frac{dy}{dx} = \cos 2x \cdot \frac{d(2x)}{dx} = 2\cos 2x.$$

Derivative of cos u

To obtain a formula for the derivative of $\cos u$, we make use of the identities

$$\cos u = \sin\left(\frac{\pi}{2} - u\right), \qquad \sin u = \cos\left(\frac{\pi}{2} - u\right).$$

Thus

$$\frac{d(\cos u)}{dx} = \frac{d\sin\left(\frac{\pi}{2} - u\right)}{dx}$$

$$= \cos\left(\frac{\pi}{2} - u\right)\frac{d\left(\frac{\pi}{2} - u\right)}{dx}$$

$$= \sin u \cdot -\frac{du}{dx},$$

or

$$\frac{d(\cos u)}{dx} = -\sin u\frac{du}{dx}. \qquad \text{(VIII)}$$

This equation tells us that the derivative of the cosine of a function is minus the sine of the same function, times the derivative of the function.

Example 2. Let

$$y = \cos(x^2).$$

Then

$$\frac{dy}{dx} = -\sin(x^2)\frac{d(x^2)}{dx} = -2x\sin(x^2).$$

The formulas (VII) and (VIII) may be combined with the formulas given previously, as in the following problems.

Problem 1. Find dy/dx if

$$y = \sin^2(3x) = u^2, \qquad u = \sin 3x.$$

Solution.
$$\frac{dy}{dx} = 2u\frac{du}{dx} = 2\sin 3x\frac{d(\sin 3x)}{dx}$$

$$= 2\sin 3x \cdot \cos 3x\frac{d(3x)}{dx}$$

$$= 6\sin 3x\cos 3x.$$

Problem 2. Find dy/dx if

$$y = \sec^2 5x = (\cos 5x)^{-2}.$$

Solution. First we must apply the formula for the derivative of a function to a power,

$$\frac{d(u^n)}{dx} = nu^{n-1}\frac{du}{dx}.$$

We then would have

$$\frac{dy}{dx} = -2(\cos 5x)^{-3}\frac{d(\cos 5x)}{dx}$$

$$= (-2\sec^3 5x)\left(-\sin 5x\frac{d(5x)}{dx}\right)$$

$$= +10\sec^3 5x\sin 5x.$$

Problem 3. Show that the function

$$f(x) = \tan x$$

is an increasing function of x at any point where

$$\cos x \neq 0.$$

Solution. (See Fig. 6.9.) To show this, we let

$$y = f(x) = \tan x, \quad \text{or} \quad y = \frac{\sin x}{\cos x}.$$

6.9. $y = \tan x$.

Then
$$\frac{dy}{dx} = \frac{\cos x \dfrac{d\,(\sin x)}{dx} - \sin x \dfrac{d\,(\cos x)}{dx}}{\cos^2 x}$$

$$= \frac{\cos x \cdot \cos x \dfrac{dx}{dx} - \sin x \left(-\sin x \dfrac{dx}{dx}\right)}{\cos^2 x}$$

$$= \frac{\cos^2 x + \sin^2 x}{\cos^2 x} = \frac{1}{\cos^2 x} = f'(x)$$

exists and is positive at any point where $\cos x \neq 0$. Since $f'(x)$ is positive, $f(x)$ is an increasing function of x. In fact, since $\cos^2 x \leq 1$, we observe that $dy/dx \geq 1$ at every point on the curve $y = \tan x$. (When $\cos x = 0$, $\tan x$ does not exist.)

Problem 4. Find the velocity and acceleration of a particle moving in a circle of radius r with constant angular velocity ω, $\omega > 0$.

Solution. (See Fig. 6.10.) If the position of the particle at time t is $P(x, y)$, then

$$x = r \cos \theta, \qquad y = r \sin \theta, \tag{2a}$$

and it is given that the angular velocity

$$d\theta/dt = \omega \tag{2b}$$

is constant. The velocity is a vector with components

$$v_x = \frac{dx}{dt} = \frac{dx}{d\theta}\frac{d\theta}{dt}, \qquad v_y = \frac{dy}{dt} = \frac{dy}{d\theta}\frac{d\theta}{dt}, \tag{2c}$$

a | b

|c|

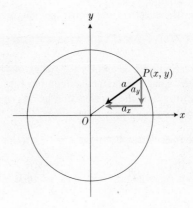

6.10

$$\sin Ax = A \sin x \cos x$$

parallel to the x- and y-axes respectively. Also, the acceleration is a vector with components

$$a_x = \frac{dv_x}{dt}, \qquad a_y = \frac{dv_y}{dt} \qquad (2d)$$

parallel to the coordinate axes. From (2a) and (2b), we find

$$v_x = \frac{dx}{dt} = -r \sin\theta \frac{d\theta}{dt} = -\omega r \sin\theta = -\omega y,$$

$$v_y = \frac{dy}{dt} = r \cos\theta \frac{d\theta}{dt} = \omega r \cos\theta = \omega x, \qquad (2e)$$

and from these we find in turn

$$a_x = \frac{dv_x}{dt} = -\omega \frac{dy}{dt} = -\omega^2 x,$$

$$a_y = \frac{dv_y}{dt} = \omega \frac{dx}{dt} = -\omega^2 y. \qquad (2f)$$

The velocity vector has both magnitude and direction. Its magnitude is

$$\sqrt{v_x^2 + v_y^2} = \sqrt{\omega^2 y^2 + \omega^2 x^2} = \omega\sqrt{y^2 + x^2} = \omega r,$$

which is the angular velocity ω times the radius of the circle. Its direction is specified, except for sense, by its slope, which is given by

$$\frac{v_y}{v_x} = \frac{dy/dt}{dx/dt} = \frac{dy}{dx},$$

which is the same as the slope of the tangent to the curve at P. In Fig. 6.10(b), the sense is seen graphically to be in the counterclockwise direction, since from (2e) the x-component has a sign opposite to the sign of y if, as we assume, ω is positive.

Similarly, the acceleration vector has magnitude

$$\sqrt{a_x^2 + a_y^2} = \omega^2\sqrt{x^2 + y^2} = \omega^2 r,$$

and its direction will be opposite to that of the vector from O to P, since the latter has components x and y, while (2f) shows that the acceleration has its corresponding components just $(-\omega^2)$ times these; that is,

the acceleration vector $\mathbf{a} = -\omega^2 \overrightarrow{OP}$.

This shows that the acceleration is toward the center of the circle at each instant and has a constant magnitude $\omega^2 r$.

To summarize: If a particle moves in a circle of radius r with constant angular velocity ω, then its velocity vector is tangent to the circle and has magnitude ωr, while its acceleration vector points toward the center of the circle and has magnitude $\omega^2 r$. Hence (by Newton's second law) the force needed to keep a particle of mass m moving at constant speed ωr in a circle of radius r is $m\omega^2 r$, directed toward the center of the circle.

Integration of sines and cosines

Corresponding to the derivative formulas (VII) and (VIII), we also have the differential formulas

$$d(\sin u) = \cos u \, du, \qquad \text{(VII')}$$

$$d(\cos u) = -\sin u \, du, \qquad \text{(VIII')}$$

and the integration formulas

$$\int \cos u \, du = \sin u + C,$$

$$\int \sin u \, du = -\cos u + C. \qquad (3)$$

Example. $\int \cos 2t \, dt = \frac{1}{2}\int \cos 2t \cdot 2 \, dt$

$$= \frac{1}{2}\int \cos u \, du \quad (u = 2t)$$

$$= \frac{1}{2}\sin 2t + C.$$

Problem 5. Evaluate the integral

$$\int \frac{\cos 2x}{\sin^3 2x} \, dx.$$

Solution. Since

$$d(\sin 2x) = 2\cos 2x \, dx,$$

we recognize the numerator as being

$$\frac{1}{2}d(\sin 2x).$$

Hence we have

$$\int \frac{\cos 2x \, dx}{\sin^3 2x} = \int (\sin 2x)^{-3} \cdot \frac{1}{2}d(\sin 2x)$$

$$= \frac{1}{2}\int u^{-3} \, du \quad (u = \sin 2x)$$

$$= \frac{1}{2}\frac{u^{-2}}{-2} + C$$

$$= \frac{-1}{4\sin^2 2x} + C.$$

$$\frac{\sin^2\theta}{1+\cos\theta} = 1-\cos\theta$$

#5 35, 56, 58, 60

EXERCISES

1/4/77 1, 9, 17, 25, 33   1/5/   21, 23, 27, 29, 31, 35,

Evaluate limits 1 through 20 by making use of Eq. (1) together with appropriate trigonometric identities and theorems on limits.

1. $\lim\limits_{\theta\to 0} \dfrac{\tan\theta}{\theta}$

2. $\lim\limits_{\theta\to\pi} \dfrac{\sin\theta}{\pi-\theta}$
   [Hint. Let $x = \pi - \theta$.]

3. $\lim\limits_{\theta\to 0} \dfrac{\sin 2\theta}{\theta}$

4. $\lim\limits_{x\to 0} \dfrac{\sin x}{3x}$

5. $\lim\limits_{x\to 0} \dfrac{\sin 5x}{\sin 3x}$

6. $\lim\limits_{x\to 0} \tan 2x \csc 4x$

7. $\lim\limits_{\theta\to 0} \dfrac{\sin^2\theta}{\theta}$

8. $\lim\limits_{\theta\to 0} \dfrac{1-\cos\theta}{\theta}$

$\left[\text{Hint. If } |\theta| < \pi, \text{ then } 1 - \cos\theta = \dfrac{\sin^2\theta}{1+\cos\theta}.\right]$

9. $\lim\limits_{\theta\to 0} \dfrac{1-\cos\theta}{\theta^2}$

10. $\lim\limits_{y\to 0} \dfrac{\tan 2y}{3y}$

11. $\lim\limits_{u\to 0} \dfrac{3u}{\sin 5u}$

12. $\lim\limits_{x\to\infty} x\sin\dfrac{1}{x}$
    [Hint. Let $1/x = u$.]

13. $\lim\limits_{y\to\infty} 2y\tan\dfrac{\pi}{y}$

14. $\lim\limits_{x\to\pi/2} \dfrac{2x-\pi}{\cos x}$

15. $\lim\limits_{\theta\to 0} \theta\cot 2\theta$

16. $\lim\limits_{x\to 0} \dfrac{x^2+2x}{\sin 2x}$

17. $\lim\limits_{x\to 0} \dfrac{\sin 2x}{2x^2+x}$

18. $\lim\limits_{h\to 0} \dfrac{\sin(a+h)-\sin a}{h}$

19. $\lim\limits_{h\to 0} \dfrac{\cos(a+h)-\cos a}{h}$

20. $\lim\limits_{h\to 2} \dfrac{\cos(\pi/h)}{h-2}$

In Exercises 21 through 36, find dy/dx.

21. $y = \sin(3x+4)$

22. $y = x\sin x$

23. $y = \dfrac{\sin x}{x}$

24. $y = \cos 5x$

25. $y = x^2\sin 3x$

26. $y = \sqrt{2+\cos 2x}$

27. $y = \sin^2 x + \cos^2 x$

28. $y = \dfrac{2}{\cos 3x}$

29. $y = 3\sin 2x - 4\cos 2x$

30. $y = 3\cos^2 2x - 3\sin^2 2x$

31. $y = 2\sin x\cos x$

32. $y = \dfrac{1}{\sin x}$

33. $y = \cos^2 3x$

34. $y = \cot x$

35. $x\sin 2y = y\cos 2x$

36. $y^2 = \sin^4 2x + \cos^4 2x$

37. Using the Mean Value Theorem, prove that
$$|\sin b - \sin a| \le |b - a|.$$

38. Show that the curve
$$y = x + \sin x$$
has no relative maxima or minima even though it does have points where dy/dx is zero. Sketch the curve.

39. A particle moves on the curve
$$x = a\cos\omega t, \qquad y = b\sin\omega t,$$
where a, b, and ω are constants. Show that the acceleration components are
$$a_x = -\omega^2 x \quad \text{and} \quad a_y = -\omega^2 y.$$

Evaluate the integrals in Exercises 40 through 60.

40. $\displaystyle\int \sin 3x\, dx$

41. $\displaystyle\int \cos(2x+4)\, dx$

42. $\displaystyle\int x\sin(2x^2)\, dx$

43. $\displaystyle\int (\cos\sqrt{x})\,\dfrac{dx}{\sqrt{x}}$

44. $\displaystyle\int \sin 2t\, dt$

45. $\displaystyle\int \cos(3\theta-1)\, d\theta$

46. $\displaystyle\int 4\cos 3y\, dy$

47. $\displaystyle\int 2\sin z\cos z\, dz$

48. $\displaystyle\int \sin^2 x\cos x\, dx$

49. $\displaystyle\int \cos^2 2y\sin 2y\, dy$

50. $\displaystyle\int (1-\sin^2 3t)\cos 3t\, dt$

51. $\displaystyle\int \dfrac{\sin x\, dx}{\cos^2 x}$

52. $\displaystyle\int \dfrac{\cos x\, dx}{\sin^2 x}$

53. $\displaystyle\int \sqrt{2+\sin 3t}\cos 3t\, dt$

54. $\displaystyle\int \dfrac{\sin 2t\, dt}{\sqrt{2-\cos 2t}}$

55. $\displaystyle\int \sin^3\dfrac{y}{2}\cos\dfrac{y}{2}\, dy$

56. $\displaystyle\int \dfrac{\sin\dfrac{z-1}{3}\, dz}{\cos^2\dfrac{z-1}{3}}$

57. $\displaystyle\int \cos^2\dfrac{2x}{3}\sin\dfrac{2x}{3}\, dx$

58. $\displaystyle\int (1 + \sin 2t)^{3/2} \cos 2t \, dt$

59. $\displaystyle\int (3 \sin 2x + 4 \cos 3x) \, dx$

60. $\displaystyle\int \sin t \cos t \, (\sin t + \cos t) \, dt$

6.6 AREA UNDER A CURVE

In geometry we learned how to find areas of certain polygons: rectangles, triangles, parallelograms, trapezoids. Indeed, the area of any polygon can be found by cutting it into triangles.

The area of a circle is easily computed from the familiar formula $A = \pi r^2$. But the idea behind this simple formula isn't so simple. In fact, it is the subtle concept of a *limit*, the area of the circle being *defined* as the limit of areas of inscribed (or circumscribed) regular polygons as the number of sides increases without bound. A similar idea is involved in the definition we now introduce for other plane areas.

Let $y = f(x)$ define a continuous function of x on the closed interval $[a, b]$. For simplicity, we shall also suppose that $f(x)$ is nonnegative over $[a, b]$. We consider the problem of calculating the area bounded above by the graph of the function, on the sides by vertical lines through $x = a$ and $x = b$, and below by the x-axis (Fig. 6.11).

We divide the area into n thin strips of uniform width $\Delta x = (b - a)/n$ by lines perpendicular to the x-axis through the end points $x = a$ and $x = b$ and many intermediate points, which we number as $x_1, x_2, \ldots, x_{n-1}$ (Fig. 6.12). We use an inscribed rectangle to approximate the area in each strip. For instance, in the figure, we approximate the area of the strip $aP_0P_1x_1$ by the shaded rectangle of altitude aP_0 and base $a \ldots x_1$. The area of this rectangle is

$$f(a) \cdot (x_1 - a) = f(a) \cdot \Delta x,$$

since the length of the altitude aP_0 is the value of f at $x = a$, and the length of the base is $x_1 - a = \Delta x$. Similarly the inscribed rectangle in the second strip

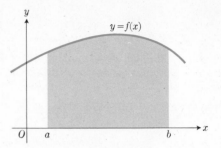

6.11 The area under a curve.

6.12 The area under a curve $y = f(x)$ divided into strips. Each strip is approximated by a rectangle.

6.13 Rectangles under the graph of an increasing function.

has an area equal to

$$f(x_1) \cdot \Delta x.$$

Continuing in this fashion, we inscribe a rectangle in each strip.

In the special case where the function increases with x, as in Fig. 6.13, we always use the ordinate

$y = 1 + x^2,\ 0 \le x \le 1$

$(1, 2)$

$(\tfrac{1}{2}, \tfrac{5}{4})$

$(0, 1)$

6.14

6.15 Rectangles under the graph of a decreasing function.

6.16 Rectangles under a curve that rises and falls between a and b.

at the left edge of the strip as the altitude of the corresponding rectangle. Then we have

$$\text{area of first rectangle} = f(a) \cdot \Delta x,$$
$$\text{area of second rectangle} = f(x_1) \cdot \Delta x,$$
$$\text{area of third rectangle} = f(x_2) \cdot \Delta x,$$
$$\vdots$$
$$\text{area of } n\text{th and last rectangle} = f(x_{n-1}) \cdot \Delta x.$$

Example. (See Fig. 6.14.) Suppose $f(x) = 1 + x^2$; $a = 0$, $b = 1$, and $n = 4$. There are $n - 1 = 3$ intermediate points, $x_1 = \tfrac{1}{4}$, $x_2 = \tfrac{1}{2}$, and $x_3 = \tfrac{3}{4}$, which divide the interval $[0, 1]$ into $n = 4$ subintervals, each of length $\Delta x = \tfrac{1}{4}$. The inscribed rectangles have areas

$$
\begin{aligned}
f(0) \cdot \Delta x &= 1 \cdot \tfrac{1}{4} = \tfrac{16}{64} \\
f(\tfrac{1}{4}) \cdot \Delta x &= \tfrac{17}{16} \cdot \tfrac{1}{4} = \tfrac{17}{64} \\
f(\tfrac{1}{2}) \cdot \Delta x &= \tfrac{5}{4} \cdot \tfrac{1}{4} = \tfrac{20}{64} \\
f(\tfrac{3}{4}) \cdot \Delta x &= \tfrac{25}{16} \cdot \tfrac{1}{4} = \tfrac{25}{64} \\
\hline
\text{Sum} &= \tfrac{78}{64} = 1.21875.
\end{aligned}
$$

Since the area under the curve is larger than the sum of the areas of these inscribed rectangles, we may expect it to be somewhat larger than 1.22. (In fact, by using methods we shall soon develop, we shall find that the area is exactly $\tfrac{4}{3}$.) Thus our estimate of 1.22 is about 8% too small. There are easy ways of improving the accuracy, for example by using trapezoids in place of rectangles to approximate each strip, but we defer that to a later time.

If the curve slopes downward, as in Fig. 6.15, the inscribed rectangles have areas as follows:

$$\text{first rectangle} \quad f(x_1) \cdot \Delta x,$$
$$\text{second rectangle} \quad f(x_2) \cdot \Delta x,$$
$$\text{third rectangle} \quad f(x_3) \cdot \Delta x,$$
$$\vdots$$
$$n\text{th and last} \quad f(b) \cdot \Delta x.$$

More generally, the curve may rise and fall between $x = a$ and $x = b$, as in Fig. 6.16. But there is a number c_1 between a and x_1 inclusive such that the first inscribed rectangle has area $f(c_1) \cdot \Delta x$; and a number c_2 in the second closed subinterval such that the area of the second inscribed rectangle is $f(c_2) \cdot \Delta x$; and so on. The number c_1 is the place between a and x_1 inclusive where f is minimized for the first subinterval. Similarly the minimum value of f for x in the second subinterval is attained at c_2, and so on.

The sum of the areas of these inscribed rectangles is

$$S_n = f(c_1) \cdot \Delta x + f(c_2) \cdot \Delta x + \cdots + f(c_n) \cdot \Delta x. \quad (1)$$

We may also write this in more abbreviated form by using the sigma notation:

$$S_n = \sum_{k=1}^{n} f(c_k) \cdot \Delta x. \tag{2}$$

The Greek letter $\sum$ (capital sigma) is used this way in mathematics to denote a sum. Note that each term of the sum in (1) is of the form $f(c_k) \cdot \Delta x$, with only the subscript on c changing from one term to another. We have indicated the subscript by k, but we could equally well have used i or j or any other symbol except a letter which is already in use for something else. In the first term in the sum on the right side of Eq. (1), the subscript is $k = 1$; in the second, $k = 2$; and so on to the last, or nth, in which $k = n$. We indicate this by writing $k = 1$ below the $\sum$ in (2), to say that the sum is to *start* with the term we get by replacing k by 1 in the expression that follows. The n above the sigma tells us where to *stop*. For instance, if $n = 4$, we have

$$\sum_{k=1}^{4} f(c_k) \cdot \Delta x = f(c_1) \cdot \Delta x + f(c_2) \cdot \Delta x$$
$$+ f(c_3) \cdot \Delta x + f(c_4) \cdot \Delta x.$$

The only thing that changes from one summand to the next is the numeral in the place indicated by k. First we replace k by 1, then by 2, then 3, then 4. Then we add.

Here we give a few other sums as examples of the $\sum$-notation:

(a) $\displaystyle\sum_{k=1}^{5} k^2 = 1^2 + 2^2 + 3^2 + 4^2 + 5^2,$

(b) $\displaystyle\sum_{k=1}^{3} \frac{k}{k+1} = \frac{1}{1+1} + \frac{2}{2+1} + \frac{3}{3+1},$

(c) $\displaystyle\sum_{j=0}^{2} \frac{j+1}{j+2} = \frac{0+1}{0+2} + \frac{1+1}{1+2} + \frac{2+1}{2+2},$

(d) $\displaystyle\sum_{i=1}^{4} x_i = x_1 + x_2 + x_3 + x_4,$

(e) $\displaystyle\sum_{k=1}^{4} x^k = x + x^2 + x^3 + x^4.$

We turn our attention once more to the area under a curve. We *define* it to be

> the limit of the sums of the areas of inscribed rectangles as their number increases without bound. In symbols,
>
> $$A = \lim_{n \to \infty} [f(c_1)\,\Delta x + f(c_2)\,\Delta x + \cdots + f(c_n)\,\Delta x]$$
> $$= \lim_{n \to \infty} \sum_{k=1}^{n} f(c_k)\,\Delta x. \tag{3}$$

Remark 1. The limit indicated in Eq. (3) exists, provided f is continuous. That is, by taking larger and larger values of n and computing the sum of the areas of inscribed rectangles for each n, we get answers which differ from one another (and from what we would intuitively call the area under the curve) by amounts that become arbitrarily small as n increases.

Remark 2. We could have used circumscribed instead of inscribed rectangles. We would then replace the c_k in Eq. (3) by other numbers, say e_k. These would be the places in the subintervals where the function takes on its *maximum* instead of minimum values. The corresponding sums would tend to overestimate the exact area, but in the limit we would get the same answer whether we used inscribed or circumscribed rectangles. The fact that the two kinds of sums of areas of rectangles give the same limit is a consequence of the *uniform continuity* of the function f over the domain $a \leq x \leq b$. It is a theorem which is usually proved in more advanced courses in mathematical analysis. A substantial part of the proof goes as follows: Let

$$m_k = f(c_k)$$
$$= \min \{f(x) \text{ for } x \text{ in the } k\text{th subinterval}\},$$
$$M_k = f(e_k)$$
$$= \max \{f(x) \text{ for } x \text{ in the } k\text{th subinterval}\}.$$

The expression $m_k\,\Delta x$ gives the area of the inscribed rectangle, and the expression $M_k\,\Delta x$ gives the area of the circumscribed rectangle.

The exact area A, then, is a number between the *lower sum*

$$L = m_1 \Delta x + m_2 \Delta x + \cdots + m_n \Delta x = \sum_{k=1}^{n} m_k \Delta x$$

$$(4a)$$

and the *upper sum*

$$U = M_1 \Delta x + M_2 \Delta x + \cdots + M_n \Delta x = \sum_{k=1}^{n} M_k \Delta x.$$

$$(4b)$$

By subtraction, we can see that since

$$L \leq A \leq U, \qquad (5)$$

we have

$$|A - L| \leq U - L \quad \text{and} \quad |U - A| \leq U - L,$$

$$(6a)$$

where

$$U - L = (M_1 - m_1) \Delta x + (M_2 - m_2) \Delta x$$
$$+ \cdots + (M_n - m_n) \Delta x. \quad (6b)$$

The right-hand side of (6b) will be small if the differences $M_k - m_k$ are *all* small, for $k = 1, 2, \ldots, n$. Here is where the *uniform* continuity of f over $[a, b]$ is important. [See part (iii) of Theorem 15, Article 4.9.] Suppose that ϵ is an arbitrary positive number. Then $\epsilon' = \epsilon/(b - a)$ is also positive, and by the theorem cited there exists a number $\delta > 0$ such that for any $x, x' \epsilon [a, b]$,

$$|f(x) - f(x')| < \frac{\epsilon}{b - a} \quad \text{if} \quad |x - x'| < \delta. \quad (7)$$

Let n be any positive integer large enough so that

$$\Delta x = \frac{b - a}{n} < \delta, \quad \text{that is,} \quad n > \frac{b - a}{\delta}. \quad (8)$$

Then each subinterval is so short that c_k and e_k are within δ-distance of each other for each $k = 1, 2, \ldots, n$. Hence, by (7),

$$|M_k - m_k| = |f(e_k) - f(c_k)| < \frac{\epsilon}{b - a}$$
$$\text{for } k = 1, 2, \ldots, n. \quad (9)$$

Therefore each of the n summands on the right-hand side of Eq. (6b) is less than $\epsilon \Delta x/(b - a)$. Consequently, whenever condition (8) is satisfied,

$$U - L < \frac{n \cdot \epsilon \cdot \Delta x}{b - a} = \epsilon \frac{n \Delta x}{b - a} = \epsilon \frac{b - a}{b - a} = \epsilon. \quad (10)$$

It is this inequality, and the inequalities in (6a), that justifies the conclusions

$$\lim_{\Delta x \to 0} U = A \quad \text{and} \quad \lim_{\Delta x \to 0} L = A.$$

Remark 3. Just as we use the simple formula $A = \pi r^2$ to find the area of a circle, rather than resorting to a calculation of the limit of areas of inscribed polygons, so with the area under a curve. We shall not actually compute many areas directly from the definition in Eq. (3). Rather, we shall develop from it a method for getting answers very quickly and simply. But first we need some definition of area, as given above, as a starting place.

Remark 4. Our definition of area as the limit of sums of areas of inscribed rectangles is less general than definitions you will find in more advanced books. For more sophisticated approaches, you may wish to consult one of the following references:

(1) Thomas, Moulton, and Zelinka, *Elementary Calculus from an Advanced Viewpoint*. Addison-Wesley Publishing Co., Inc. (1967), Chapter 12.

(2) R. C. Buck and E. F. Buck, *Advanced Calculus*. McGraw Hill (1965), Section 3.1.

(3) J. M. H. Olmsted, *Advanced Calculus*. Appleton-Century-Crofts, Inc. (1961), pp. 337–342.

For the types of regions considered here, the definition given in Eq. (3) and these more advanced definitions lead to the same numerical results.

EXERCISES

1-6# 2, 3   1-7# 6, 9

In Exercises 1 through 5, sketch the graph of the given equation over the interval $a \leq x \leq b$. Divide the interval into $n = 4$ subintervals each of length $\Delta x = (b - a)/4$.

(a) Sketch the inscribed rectangles and compute the sum of their areas.

(b) Do the same using the circumscribed in place of the inscribed rectangle on each subinterval.

1. $y = 2x + 1$, $a = 0$, $b = 1$.
2. $y = x^2$, $a = -1$, $b = 1$.

$y = f(x)$

a | b

|c|

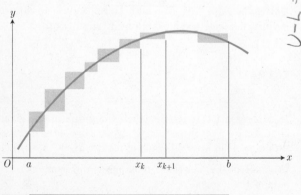

6.17

U—L = ERROR

3. $y = \sin x$, $a = 0$, $b = \pi$.

4. $y = 1/x$, $a = 1$, $b = 2$.

5. $y = \sqrt{x}$, $a = 0$, $b = 4$.

6. Suppose that f is continuous and nonnegative over $[a, b]$, as in Fig. 6.17(a). By inserting points

$$x_1, x_2, \ldots, x_{k-1}, x_k, \ldots, x_{n-1}$$

as shown, divide $[a, b]$ into n subintervals of lengths $\Delta x_1 = x_1 - a, \Delta x_2 = x_2 - x_1, \ldots, \Delta x_n = b - x_{n-1}$, which need not be equal.

(a) If $m_k = \min \{f(x)$ for x in the kth subinterval$\}$, explain the connection between the *lower sum*

$$L = m_1 \Delta x_1 + m_2 \Delta x_2 + \cdots + m_n \Delta x_n$$

and the shaded region in one of the parts of Figs. 6.17.

(b) If $M_k = \max \{f(x)$ for x in the kth subinterval$\}$, explain the connection between the *upper sum*

$$U = M_1 \Delta x_1 + M_2 \Delta x_2 + \cdots + M_n \Delta x_n$$

and the shaded region in one of the parts of Fig. 6.17.

(c) Explain the connection between $U - L$ and the shaded regions along the curve in Fig. 6.17(c).

(d) If $\epsilon > 0$ is given, why is it possible to make $U - L \leq \epsilon \cdot (b - a)$ by making the largest of the Δx_k's sufficiently small?

7. Suppose that the graph of f is always rising toward the right between $x = a$ and $x = b$, as in Fig. 6.18. Take $\Delta x = (b - a)/n$. Show, by reference to Fig. 6.18, that the difference between the upper and lower sums is representable graphically as the area $[f(b) - f(a)] \Delta x$ of the rectangle R. [*Hint.* The

$y = f(x)$

$f(b) - f(a)$

R

P_0 P_1 P_2

Δx

6.18

difference $U - L$ is the sum of areas of rectangles with diagonals P_0P_1, P_1P_2, and so forth along the curve, and there is no overlapping when these are all displaced horizontally into the rectangle R.]

8. Draw a figure to represent a continuous curve $y = f(x)$ which is always falling to the right between $x = a$ and $x = b$. Suppose the subdivisions Δx_k are again equal, $\Delta x_k = \Delta x = (b - a)/n$. Obtain an expression for the difference $U - L$ analogous to the expression in Exercise 7.

9. In Exercise 7 or 8, if the Δx_k's are not all equal, show that $U - L \leq |f(b) - f(a)|(\Delta x_{\max})$, where $\Delta x_{\max}$ is the largest of the Δx_k's for $k = 1, 2, \ldots, n$.

6.7 COMPUTATION OF AREAS AS LIMITS

In Article 6.6 we defined the area under the graph of $y = f(x)$ over the interval $a \leq x \leq b$ as the *limit* of sums of areas of inscribed rectangles. We computed a few sums, but no limits. To compute the limits we need some algebraic formulas. We now develop these. Then we compute some areas as limits to show how it can be done. In Article 6.8 we show how much easier it is using calculus.

We need the following formulas:

$$\sum_{k=1}^{n} k = 1 + 2 + 3 + \cdots + n = \frac{n(n + 1)}{2}$$

$$\sum_{k=1}^{n} k^2 = 1^2 + 2^2 + 3^2 + \cdots + n^2$$
$$= \frac{n(n + 1)(2n + 1)}{6},$$

which we shall prove by the method of mathematical induction. This consists in showing that each formula is true when $n = 1$, and that if the formula is true for any integer n, then it is also true for the next integer, $n + 1$. We shall also show how such formulas might be discovered.

First, consider the sum of first powers:

$$F(n) = 1 + 2 + 3 + \cdots + n.$$

Here is a short table that shows how $F(n)$ increases with n. The last column exhibits $F(n)/n$, the ratio of $F(n)$ to n.

n	$F(n)$	$F(n)/n$
1	1	$1 = \frac{2}{2}$
2	$1 + 2 = 3$	$\frac{3}{2} = \frac{3}{2}$
3	$1 + 2 + 3 = 6$	$\frac{6}{3} = \frac{4}{2}$
4	$1 + 2 + 3 + 4 = 10$	$\frac{10}{4} = \frac{5}{2}$
5	$1 + 2 + 3 + 4 + 5 = 15$	$\frac{15}{5} = \frac{6}{2}$
6	$1 + 2 + 3 + 4 + 5 + 6 = 21$	$\frac{21}{6} = \frac{7}{2}$

The last column seems to indicate that the ratio $F(n)/n$ is equal to $(n + 1)/2$. At least such is the case for all the entries in the table ($n = 1, 2, 3, 4, 5, 6$). In other words, the formula $F(n)/n = (n + 1)/2$ or

$$\sum_{k=1}^{n} k = 1 + 2 + 3 + \cdots + n = \frac{n(n + 1)}{2} \qquad (1)$$

is true for $n = 1, 2, 3, 4, 5, 6$. Suppose now that n is any integer for which (1) is known to be true (at the moment, n could be any integer from 1 through 6). Then if $(n + 1)$ were added to both sides of the equation, the new equation

$$1 + 2 + 3 + \cdots + n + (n + 1)$$
$$= \frac{n(n + 1)}{2} + (n + 1) \qquad (2)$$

would also be true for the same n. But the right side of (2) is

$$\frac{n(n + 1)}{2} + (n + 1) = \frac{(n + 1)}{2}(n + 2)$$
$$= \frac{(n + 1)(n + 2)}{2},$$

so that (2) becomes

$$1 + 2 + 3 + \cdots + n + (n + 1)$$
$$= \frac{(n + 1)[(n + 1) + 1]}{2},$$

which is just like Eq. (1) except that n is replaced by $n + 1$. Thus if Eq. (1) is true for an integer n, it is also true for the next integer $n + 1$. Hence we now know that it is true for $n + 1 = 7$, since it was true for $n = 6$. Then we can say it is true for

$n + 1 = 8$, since it is true for $n = 7$. By the principle of mathematical induction, then, it is true for every positive integer n.

Now let's consider the squares. Let

$$Q(n) = 1^2 + 2^2 + 3^2 + \cdots + n^2$$

be the sum of the squares of the first n positive integers. Obviously this grows faster than the sum of first powers, but let us look at the ratio to compare them.

n	$F(n)$	$Q(n)$	$Q(n)/F(n)$
1	1	$1^2 = 1$	$\frac{1}{1} = \frac{3}{3}$
2	3	$1^2 + 2^2 = 5$	$\frac{5}{3} = \frac{5}{3}$
3	6	$1^2 + 2^2 + 3^2 = 14$	$\frac{14}{6} = \frac{7}{3}$
4	10	$1^2 + 2^2 + 3^2 + 4^2 = 30$	$\frac{30}{10} = \frac{9}{3}$
5	15	$1^2 + 2^2 + 3^2 + 4^2 + 5^2 = 55$	$\frac{55}{15} = \frac{11}{3}$
6	21	$1^2 + 2^2 + 3^2 + 4^2 + 5^2 + 6^2 = 91$	$\frac{91}{21} = \frac{13}{3}$

We note how regular the last column is: $\frac{3}{3}, \frac{5}{3}, \frac{7}{3}$, and so on. In fact it is just $(2n + 1)/3$ for $n = 1, 2, 3, 4, 5, 6$; that is,

$$Q(n) = F(n) \cdot \frac{2n + 1}{3}.$$

But from Eq. (1), $F(n) = n(n + 1)/2$, and hence

$$Q(n) = 1^2 + 2^2 + 3^2 + \cdots + n^2$$
$$= \frac{n(n + 1)(2n + 1)}{6} \tag{3}$$

is true for the integers n from 1 through 6. To establish it for all other positive integers, we proceed as before. Start with any n for which (3) is true and add $(n + 1)^2$. Then

$$1^2 + 2^2 + 3^2 + \cdots + n^2 + (n + 1)^2$$
$$= \frac{n(n + 1)(2n + 1)}{6} + (n + 1)^2$$
$$= \frac{(n + 1)}{6}[n(2n + 1) + 6(n + 1)]$$
$$= \frac{(n + 1)}{6}(2n^2 + 7n + 6)$$
$$= \frac{(n + 1)(n + 2)(2n + 3)}{6}. \tag{4}$$

We note that the last expression in (4) is the same as the last expression in (3) with n replaced by $n + 1$. In other words, if the formula in (3) is true for any integer n, we have just shown that it is true for $n + 1$. Since we know it is true for $n = 6$, it is also true for $n + 1 = 7$. And now that we know it is true for $n = 7$, it follows that it is true for $n + 1 = 8$, and so on. It is true for every positive integer n by the principle of mathematical induction.

We now apply these formulas to find areas under two graphs.

Example 1. Consider the line $y = mx$ (Fig. 6.19). Let b and a be any positive numbers, $b > a$. Let n be a positive integer and divide the interval $a \ldots b$ into n subintervals each of length $\Delta x = (b - a)/n$, by inserting the points

$$x_1 = a + \Delta x,$$
$$x_2 = a + 2\,\Delta x,$$
$$x_3 = a + 3\,\Delta x,$$
$$\vdots$$
$$x_{n-1} = a + (n - 1)\,\Delta x.$$

The inscribed rectangles have areas

$$f(a)\,\Delta x = ma \cdot \Delta x,$$
$$f(x_1)\,\Delta x = m(a + \Delta x) \cdot \Delta x,$$
$$f(x_2)\,\Delta x = m(a + 2\,\Delta x) \cdot \Delta x,$$
$$\vdots$$
$$f(x_{n-1})\,\Delta x = m[a + (n - 1)\,\Delta x] \cdot \Delta x,$$

whose sum is

$$S_n = m[a + (a + \Delta x) + (a + 2\,\Delta x) + \cdots$$
$$+ (a + (n - 1)\,\Delta x)] \cdot \Delta x$$
$$= m[na + (1 + 2 + \cdots + (n - 1))\,\Delta x]\,\Delta x$$
$$= m\left[na + \frac{(n - 1)n}{2}\,\Delta x\right]\Delta x$$
$$= m\left[a + \frac{n - 1}{2}\,\Delta x\right]n\,\Delta x \quad \left(\Delta x = \frac{b - a}{n}\right)$$
$$= m\left[a + \frac{b - a}{2} \cdot \frac{n - 1}{n}\right] \cdot (b - a).$$

The area under the graph is defined to be the limit of S_n as $n \to \infty$. In the final form, the only place n appears is in the fraction

$$\frac{n - 1}{n} = 1 - \frac{1}{n},$$

$y = mx, a \leq x \leq b$

6.19

$y = x^2, 0 \leq x \leq b$

6.20

and $1/n \to 0$ as $n \to \infty$, so

$$\lim \frac{n-1}{n} = 1.$$

Therefore,

$$\lim S_n = m\left(a + \frac{b-a}{2}\right) \cdot (b-a)$$
$$= \frac{ma + mb}{2} \cdot (b-a).$$

This is easily interpreted as the area of a trapezoid, with "bases" (in this case vertical) ma and mb and with altitude $(b-a)$.

Example 2. Consider the graph of $y = x^2$, $0 \leq x \leq b$, Fig. 6.20. Let n be a positive integer; divide the interval $0 \leq x \leq b$ into n subintervals each of length $\Delta x = b/n$, by inserting the points

$$x_1 = \Delta x, \quad x_2 = 2\Delta x, \quad x_3 = 3\Delta x, \quad \ldots,$$
$$x_{n-1} = (n-1)\Delta x.$$

The inscribed rectangles have areas

$$f(0)\,\Delta x = 0,$$
$$f(x_1)\,\Delta x = (\Delta x)^2\,\Delta x,$$
$$f(x_2)\,\Delta x = (2\,\Delta x)^2\,\Delta x,$$
$$f(x_3)\,\Delta x = (3\,\Delta x)^2\,\Delta x,$$
$$\vdots$$
$$f(x_{n-1})\,\Delta x = ((n-1)\,\Delta x)^2\,\Delta x.$$

The sum of these areas is

$$S_n = (1^2 + 2^2 + 3^2 + \cdots + (n-1)^2)(\Delta x)^3$$
$$= \frac{(n+1)n(2n+1)}{6} \cdot \left(\frac{b}{n}\right)^3$$
$$= \frac{b^3}{6} \cdot \frac{n+1}{n} \cdot \frac{n}{n} \cdot \frac{2n+1}{n}$$
$$= \frac{b^3}{6} \cdot \left(1 + \frac{1}{n}\right) \cdot \left(2 + \frac{1}{n}\right).$$

To find the area under the graph, we let n increase without bound and get

$$A = \lim S_n = \frac{b^3}{3}.$$

Therefore the area under the curve is $\frac{1}{3}$ the base b times the "altitude" b^2. The triangle OBP, Fig. 6.20, has area $\frac{1}{2}b \cdot b^2 = b^3/2$, and the area under the curve turns out to be somewhat smaller, as we should expect.

EXERCISES 1-7 #2

1. Verify the formula

$$\sum_{k=1}^{n} k^3 = 1^3 + 2^3 + \cdots + n^3 = \left(\frac{n(n+1)}{2}\right)^2$$

for $n = 1, 2, 3$. Then add $(n+1)^3$ and thereby prove by mathematical induction (as in the text) that the formula is true for all positive integers n.

2. Using the result of Exercise 1 and the method of Example 2 in the text, show that the area under the graph of $y = x^3$ over the interval $0 \leq x \leq b$ is $b^4/4$.

3. Find the area under the graph of $y = mx$ over the interval $a \leq x \leq b$ by using *circumscribed* rectangles in place of the inscribed rectangles of Example 1 in the text.

1-12

4. Find the area under the curve $y = x^2$ over the interval $0 \leq x \leq b$ by using circumscribed rectangles in place of the inscribed rectangles of Example 2 in the text.

5. Do Exercise 2 above by using circumscribed rectangles instead of inscribed rectangles.

6. Establish the formulas given below, for every positive integer n, by showing

   (a) that the formula is correct for $n = 1$, and

   (b) if true for n, the formula is also true for $n + 1$.

$$\sum_{k=1}^{n} (2k - 1) = 1 + 3 + 5 + \cdots + (2n - 1) = n^2,$$

$$\sum_{k=1}^{n} \frac{1}{k(k+1)}$$

$$= \frac{1}{1 \cdot 2} + \frac{1}{2 \cdot 3} + \cdots + \frac{1}{n \cdot (n+1)} = \frac{n}{n+1}.$$

6.8 AREAS BY CALCULUS

In Article 6.6, we defined the area under a curve and showed how we could estimate it by computing sums of areas of rectangles. Nothing more than arithmetic is involved in these calculations, but we pay the price of getting only an estimate of the true area. On the other hand, in Article 6.7, we used algebraic techniques and actually computed *limits*, thus getting exact areas at the cost of fairly extensive algebraic preliminaires. In this article we shall follow the path blazed by Leibniz and Newton to show how exact areas can be easily computed by using calculus.

To begin we need some preliminary results. We consider a function f which is continuous and non-negative over the domain $[a, b]$. Let A_a^c, A_c^b, A_a^b denote the areas under the graph and above the x-axis from a to c, from c to b, and from a to b, respectively (Fig. 6.21). If c is between a and b, we have

$$A_a^c + A_c^b = A_a^b. \tag{1}$$

And this is also true when $c = a$ if we define the area from a to a to be zero,

$$A_a^a = 0. \tag{2}$$

Equation (1) is also true if c is beyond b, provided we adopt some conventions about signed areas. Let

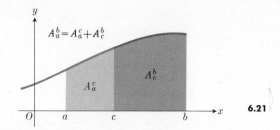

6.21

us say that area above the x-axis is positive if we go from left to right, and negative if we go from right to left. Thus, in Fig. 6.21, A_a^c, A_c^b, and A_a^b are all positive, while

$$A_c^a = -A_a^c, \quad A_b^c = -A_c^b, \quad A_b^a = -A_a^b \tag{3}$$

are negative. So formula (1) is also true in the form

$$A_a^b + A_b^c = A_a^c, \tag{4}$$

because adding A_b^c to A_a^b just subtracts A_c^b from the latter, leaving A_a^c.

The following theorem will also be used.

Theorem 1. The Mean Value Theorem for Areas. *Let f be a nonnegative continuous function over the domain $[a, b]$. Let A_a^b denote the area under the graph of f over the domain. Then there is at least one number c between a and b such that*

$$A_a^b = f(c) \cdot (b - a). \tag{5}$$

Proof. Suppose m and M are respectively the minimum and maximum values of f over the domain $[a, b]$. Then

$$m(b - a) \leq A_a^b \leq M(b - a),$$

and therefore

$$m \leq \frac{A_a^b}{b - a} \leq M.$$

Since $A_a^b/(b - a)$ lies between the minimum and maximum values of $f(x)$ for $a \leq x \leq b$, there is at least one place c between a and b where $f(c)$ is equal to this number:

$$f(c) = \frac{A_a^b}{b - a} \quad \text{[Theorem 15, Article 4.9]}.$$

Equation (5) follows. ☐

Remark. The geometric interpretation of this Mean Value Theorem is this: A line drawn parallel to the x-axis at the right place between m and M units above the x-axis will serve as upper boundary of a rectangle having the same area as that under the curve, and it will surely cut the curve at least once between $x = a$ and $x = b$. The abscissa of that cut is a suitable value of c in Eq. (5) (see Fig. 6.22).

Theorem 2. *Let f be a nonnegative continuous function over $[a, b]$. Let P be a set of points*

$$P = \{a = x_0 < x_1 < x_2 < \cdots < x_{n-1} < x_n = b\}$$

that partitions $[a, b]$ into n subintervals, not necessarily of equal lengths. Let c_k be any number in the kth subinterval $[x_{k-1}, x_k]$, and let $\Delta x_k = x_k - x_{k-1}$, for $k = 1, 2, \ldots, n$. Then

$$\lim_{\max \Delta x_k \to 0} \sum_{k=1}^{n} f(c_k)\, \Delta x_k = A_a^b. \qquad (6)$$

Proof. We apply the Mean Value Theorem for areas to each of the subintervals. If ΔA_k is the exact area under the curve on the kth subinterval, there exists a number d_k on the segment $[x_{k-1}, x_k]$ such that

$$\Delta A_k = f(d_k)\, \Delta x_k, \quad k = 1, 2, \ldots, n. \qquad (7a)$$

Thus, if we choose $d_1, d_2, \ldots, d_n$ to satisfy Eq. (7a), and add, we get

$$A_a^b = \sum_{k=1}^{n} f(d_k)\, \Delta x_k. \qquad (7b)$$

We compare this with the sum we would obtain if we used the numbers c_k, $k = 1, 2, \ldots, n$, as on the left-hand side of (6), by computing the difference

$$A_a^b - \sum_{k=1}^{n} f(c_k)\, \Delta x_k = \sum_{k=1}^{n} [f(d_k) - f(c_k)]\, \Delta x_k. \qquad (8)$$

Because f is assumed to be continuous on the closed interval $[a, b]$ it is *uniformly* continuous there. Hence, if $\epsilon > 0$, there exists $\delta > 0$ such that

$$|f(d_k) - f(c_k)| < \frac{\epsilon}{b-a} \quad \text{if} \quad \max \Delta x_k < \delta. \qquad (9)$$

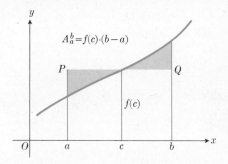

6.22 The area under the curve is equal to the area of the rectangle $aPQb$: the shaded regions above and below the curve have equal areas.

6.23 Increment of area function.

When $\max \Delta x_k \to 0$, therefore, conditions (9) are satisfied, and from Eq. (8) we see that

$$\left| A_a^b - \sum_{k=1}^{n} f(c_k)\, \Delta x_k \right| < \frac{\epsilon}{b-a} \sum_{k=1}^{n} \Delta x_k$$

$$= \frac{\epsilon}{b-a}(b-a) = \epsilon. \qquad (10)$$

This inequality is just what the limit statement in Eq. (6) means. □

This theorem says that whether we use inscribed rectangles, circumscribed rectangles, or intermediate rectangles anywhere between, the sum of the areas $f(c_k)\, \Delta x_k$ approaches the exact area under the curve, provided we make the lengths of all the subintervals approach zero.

To *compute* the area A_a^b, we now consider any abscissa x between a and b, the area A_a^x, and the area $A_a^{x+\Delta x}$, where $\Delta x \neq 0$ (Fig. 6.23). We shall derive a differential equation for the area function A_a^x. The solution of this differential equation, with the initial condition

$$A_a^a = 0,$$

will enable us to compute the area from a to any x and, in particular, from a to b.

From Eq. (1) we have

$$A_a^x + A_x^{x+\Delta x} = A_a^{x+\Delta x},$$

so that

$$\Delta(A_a^x) = A_a^{x+\Delta x} - A_a^x = A_x^{x+\Delta x}. \quad (11a)$$

Then, by Eq. (5),

$$A_x^{x+\Delta x} = f(c) \cdot \Delta x, \quad (11b)$$

where c is a number between x and $x + \Delta x$, which must therefore approach x as Δx approaches zero. Combining (11a) and (11b) and dividing by Δx, we get

$$\frac{\Delta A_a^x}{\Delta x} = f(c), \quad (11c)$$

and therefore

$$\begin{aligned}
\frac{dA_a^x}{dx} &= \lim_{\Delta x \to 0} \frac{\Delta A_a^x}{\Delta x} \\
&= \lim_{c \to x} f(c) \\
&= f(x),
\end{aligned}$$

where the last line follows from the fact that f is continuous.

Therefore the area function A_a^x satisfies the differential equation

$$\frac{dA_a^x}{dx} = f(x) \quad (12a)$$

and the initial condition

$$A_a^a = 0. \quad (12b)$$

Thus if $F(x)$ is any integral of $f(x)\,dx$, we have

$$A_a^x = \int f(x)\,dx = F(x) + C, \quad (13a)$$

$$A_a^a = 0 = F(a) + C.$$

Hence $\qquad\qquad C = -F(a)$

and $\qquad\qquad A_a^x = F(x) - F(a).$

Finally, by taking $x = b$, we get

$$A_a^b = F(b) - F(a). \quad (13b)$$

Equations (13a) and (13b) summarize the method for finding the area under a curve by integration. If the equation of the curve is $y = f(x)$, we integrate this function f to find

$$F(x) + C = \int f(x)\,dx. \quad (14a)$$

If the interval is $a \le x \le b$, we then compute

$$A_a^b = F(x)]_a^b = F(b) - F(a). \quad (14b)$$

The standard notation $F(x)]_a^b$ in Eq. (14b) simply means: First replace x by the upper value b to calculate $F(b)$, and from this subtract the value $F(a)$ obtained by setting $x = a$. For example,

$$2x + 3]_1^5 = 13 - 5 = 8.$$

It is worth noting that the constant of integration may be omitted in evaluating Eq. (14b). For if we use $F(x) + C$ in place of $F(x)$ in (14b), we find

$$\begin{aligned}
F(x) + C]_a^b &= [F(b) + C] - [F(a) + C] \\
&= F(b) - F(a) \\
&= F(x)]_a^b.
\end{aligned}$$

Example 1. (See Fig. 6.19.) The area under the graph of $y = mx$, $a \le x \le b$, is

$$\int mx\,dx \Big]_a^b = \frac{mx^2}{2} \Big]_a^b = \frac{mb^2}{2} - \frac{ma^2}{2}$$

$$= \frac{mb + ma}{2} \cdot (b - a).$$

Example 2. (See Fig. 6.20.) The area under the graph of

$$y = x^2, \quad 0 \le x \le b,$$

is

$$\int x^2\,dx \Big]_0^b = \frac{x^3}{3} \Big]_0^b = \frac{b^3}{3}.$$

Compare both the results and the methods with Examples 1 and 2 of Article 6.7.

6.24

Problem 1. As another illustration of the method of finding areas, calculate the area bounded by the parabola $y = 6 - x - x^2$ and the x-axis.

Solution. We find where the curve crosses the x-axis by setting

$$y = 0 = 6 - x - x^2 = (3 + x)(2 - x),$$

which gives

$$x = -3 \quad \text{or} \quad x = 2.$$

The curve is sketched in Fig. 6.24.

According to Eqs. (14a, b), the area is

$$A_{-3}^{2} = \int (6 - x - x^2) \, dx \Big]_{-3}^{2}$$

$$= 6x - \frac{x^2}{2} - \frac{x^3}{3} \Big]_{-3}^{2}$$

$$= (12 - 2 - \tfrac{8}{3}) - (-18 - \tfrac{9}{2} + \tfrac{27}{3})$$

$$= 20\tfrac{5}{6}.$$

The curve in Fig. 6.24 is an arch of a parabola, and it is interesting to note that the area is exactly equal to two-thirds the base times the altitude:

$$\tfrac{2}{3}(5)(\tfrac{25}{4}) = \tfrac{125}{6} = 20\tfrac{5}{6}.$$

Problem 2. Show that the area under one arch of the curve $y = \sin x$ is 2.

Solution. One arch of the sine curve extends from $x = 0$ to $x = \pi$ (Fig. 6.6a). Therefore the area is

$$A_{0}^{\pi} = \int \sin x \, dx \Big]_{0}^{\pi} = -\cos x \Big]_{0}^{\pi}$$

$$= -\cos \pi + \cos 0.$$

Since $\cos \pi = -1$ while $\cos 0 = +1$, this gives $A_{0}^{\pi} = 2$.

EXERCISES

1-12

In Exercises 1 through 10, find the area bounded by the x-axis, the given curve $y = f(x)$, and the given vertical lines.

1. $y = x^2 + 1$, $x = 0$, $x = 3$.
2. $y = 2x + 3$, $x = 0$, $x = 1$.
3. $y = \sqrt{2x + 1}$, $x = 0$, $x = 4$.
4. $y = \dfrac{1}{\sqrt{2x + 1}}$, $x = 0$, $x = 4$.
5. $y = \dfrac{1}{(2x + 1)^2}$, $x = 1$, $x = 2$.
6. $y = (2x + 1)^2$, $x = -1$, $x = 3$.
7. $y = x^3 + 2x + 1$, $x = 0$, $x = 2$.
8. $y = x\sqrt{2x^2 + 1}$, $x = 0$, $x = 2$.
9. $y = \dfrac{x}{\sqrt{2x^2 + 1}}$, $x = 0$, $x = 2$.
10. $y = \dfrac{x}{(2x^2 + 1)^2}$, $x = 0$, $x = 2$.

11. Find the area bounded by the coordinate axes and the line $x + y = 1$.

12. Find the area between the curve $y = 4 - x^2$ and the x-axis.

13. Find the area between the curve $y = 1/\sqrt{x}$, the x-axis, and the lines $x = 1$, $x = 4$.

14. Find the area between the curve $y = \sqrt{1 - x}$ and the coordinate axes.

15. Find the area between the curve $x = 1 - y^2$ and the y-axis.

16. Find the area contained between the x-axis and one arch of the curve $y = \cos 3x$.

*17. Take $B = A$ in Eq. (11b), Article 6.4, and show that

$$\cos 2A = \cos^2 A - \sin^2 A.$$

Combine this with the identity

$$1 = \cos^2 A + \sin^2 A$$

---

* The method used in this problem should be used in several later problems involving integration of squares of sines and cosines.

[handwritten margin notes: $a_0 x^v + a_2 x^{v-1} + a_3 x^{v-2} + \ldots + a_{v-1} x + a_v = 0$ / Fundamental Theorem of Algebra states that a polynomial has 1 root. / polynomial equation of vth power has v roots]

[handwritten left margin, vertical: An integer can be factored in one and only one way (except for order of going)]

to show that

$$\cos^2 A = \tfrac{1}{2}(1 + \cos 2A), \quad \sin^2 A = \tfrac{1}{2}(1 - \cos 2A).$$

Make use of the last of these identities to find the area contained between the x-axis and one arch of the curve $y = \sin^2 3x$.

18. The graph of $y = \sqrt{a^2 - x^2}$ over $-a \le x \le a$ is a semicircle of radius a.

(a) Using this fact, explain why it is true that

$$\int \sqrt{a^2 - x^2}\, dx \Big]_{-a}^{a} = \frac{1}{2}\pi a^2.$$

(b) Evaluate $\int \sqrt{a^2 - x^2}\, dx]_0^a$.

19. The integral in Exercise 18 can be evaluated by using the substitution

$$x = a \cos\theta, \qquad \pi \ge \theta \ge 0,$$

to replace $\sqrt{a^2 - x^2}\, dx$ by $-a^2 \sin^2\theta\, d\theta$. Combine this with Exercise 17 to show that

$$\int \sqrt{a^2 - x^2}\, dx \Big]_{-a}^{a} = \int -a^2 \sin^2\theta\, d\theta \Big]_{\pi}^{0}$$

$$= -\frac{a^2}{2} \int (1 - \cos 2\theta)\, d\theta \Big]_{\pi}^{0},$$

and thus verify the result given in Exercise 18(a) by evaluating this final integral.

6.9   THE DEFINITE INTEGRAL AND THE FUNDAMENTAL THEOREMS OF INTEGRAL CALCULUS

In Articles 6.6, 6.7, and 6.8, we made a systematic study of the area problem. We have arrived at the following result.

If the function f is nonnegative and continuous over the domain $[a, b]$, then the area under its graph is

$$A_a^b = \lim \sum f(c_k)\, \Delta x = \int f(x)\, dx]_a^b$$

$$= F(x)]_a^b$$

$$= F(b) - F(a). \tag{1}$$

The first part of this equation is like the definition of the area as the limit of the sum of areas of con-

structed rectangles. The last part of the equation gives a short way of evaluating this limit, that is, by calculus. Therein lies one of the most powerful ideas of "modern" mathematics ("modern" in the sense of post-Renaissance); for the key idea is this: that the limit can be evaluated by integration. This, essentially, is what is known as the *First Fundamental Theorem* of integral calculus. It ties together the summation process (which Archimedes used over two thousand years ago for finding areas, volumes, and centers of gravity) and the differentiation process, from which one may find the tangent to a curve. It is a remarkable fact that the inverse of the "tangent problem" (that is, the inverse of differentiation) provides a ready tool for solving the summation problem. Its applications extend far beyond the finding of areas; they include finding volumes of solids, lengths of curves, areas of surfaces of revolution, centers of gravity, work done by a variable force, and gravitational and electrical potential.

While Eq. (1) is expressed in terms of area, and up until now has been restricted to nonnegative functions, the Fundamental Theorem is less restrictive.

First fundamental theorem of integral calculus. *Let f be a function which is continuous over the domain $[a, b]$. Let*

$$a, x_1, x_2, \ldots, x_{n-1}, b \tag{2}$$

be a set of numbers $a < x_1 < x_2 < \cdots < x_{n-1} < b$ that partition the interval $a \ldots b$ into n equal subintervals each of length

$$\Delta x = (b - a)/n. \tag{3}$$

Let $c_1, c_2, \ldots, c_n$ be a set of n numbers, one in each subinterval,

$$a \le c_1 \le x_1,$$
$$x_1 \le c_2 \le x_2,$$
$$\vdots$$
$$x_{n-1} \le c_n \le b. \tag{4}$$

Let

$$S_n = f(c_1)\, \Delta x + f(c_2)\, \Delta x + \cdots + f(c_n)\, \Delta x$$

$$= \sum_{k=1}^{n} f(c_k)\, \Delta x. \tag{5}$$

Finally, let $F(x)$ be any primitive of $f(x)$, so that

$$f(x) = F'(x). \qquad (6)$$

Then, as $n \to \infty$,

$$\lim S_n = \lim \sum f(c_k)\,\Delta x = F(b) - F(a). \qquad (7)$$

Proof. We shall first prove (7) for the special set of numbers $c_1, c_2, \ldots, c_n$ that we get by applying the Mean Value Theorem of Article 5.8 to the function F in each subinterval. We can do this because F is differentiable and continuous. Thus, remembering that $F'(x) = f(x)$, we have

$$F(x_1) - F(a) \doteq F'(c_1) \cdot (x_1 - a) = f(c_1)\,\Delta x,$$
$$F(x_2) - F(x_1) \doteq F'(c_2) \cdot (x_2 - x_1) = f(c_2)\,\Delta x,$$
$$F(x_3) - F(x_2) \doteq F'(c_3) \cdot (x_3 - x_2) = f(c_3)\,\Delta x,$$
$$\vdots \qquad (8)$$
$$F(x_{n-1}) - F(x_{n-2}) = F'(c_{n-1}) \cdot (x_{n-1} - x_{n-2})$$
$$= f(c_{n-1})\,\Delta x,$$
$$F(b) - F(x_{n-1}) = F'(c_n) \cdot (b - x_{n-1})$$
$$= f(c_n)\,\Delta x.$$

We add Eqs. (8), and note that

$$F(x_1), F(x_2), \ldots, F(x_{n-1})$$

all appear twice on the left side, once positive and once negative. Hence these terms cancel out, leaving only $F(b) - F(a)$ in the sum. Thus we get

$$F(b) - F(a) = f(c_1)\,\Delta x + f(c_2)\,\Delta x + \cdots + f(c_n)\,\Delta x. \qquad (9)$$

Since the left side of this equation does not in any way involve n, it remains fixed as we let $n \to \infty$, thus establishing Eq. (7), for this particular way of choosing the numbers $c_1, c_2, \ldots, c_n$.

But the theorem states that the same answer is obtained no matter how the c's are chosen in the subintervals, so long as there is one c in each subinterval. To establish this final result, we recall that the function f is continuous on the closed interval $[a, b]$ and therefore is *uniformly* continuous there

[Theorem 15 (iii), Chapter 4]. Hence, if ϵ is any positive number, there exists a positive number δ, depending only upon ϵ, such that

$$|f(c_k) - f(c'_k)| < \epsilon \qquad (10)$$

whenever

$$|c_k - c'_k| < \delta. \qquad (11)$$

And we can make $\Delta x = (b - a)/n < \delta$ by making

$$n > (b - a)/\delta. \qquad (12)$$

For all sufficiently large n, (12) is satisfied. Now let c_1, c'_1 be two numbers in the first subinterval, c_2, c'_2 in the second, and so on. Form the sums

$$S_n = \sum_{k=1}^{n} f(c_k)\,\Delta x, \qquad S'_n = \sum_{k=1}^{n} f(c'_k)\,\Delta x.$$

Their difference is less than or equal to

$$|f(c_1) - f(c'_1)|\,\Delta x + |f(c_2) - f(c'_2)|\,\Delta x + \cdots$$
$$+ |f(c_n) - f(c'_n)|\,\Delta x. \qquad (13a)$$

Every term in (13a) is less than $\epsilon \cdot \Delta x$, by (10), and there are n terms. Therefore

$$|S_n - S'_n| < n \cdot (\epsilon \cdot \Delta x) = \epsilon \cdot (n\,\Delta x)$$
$$= \epsilon \cdot (b - a), \qquad (13b)$$

provided condition (12) is satisfied. This inequality, (13b), says that the sums S_n and S'_n that we get from two different choices of the c's in the subintervals can be made to differ by as little as we please [no more than $\epsilon \cdot (b - a)$] by making n sufficiently large. But for the particular choice of the c's in Eqs. (8), we have

$$S_n = F(b) - F(a).$$

Therefore S'_n differs arbitrarily little from

$$F(b) - F(a)$$

when n is sufficiently large. This means that

$$\lim S'_n = F(b) - F(a). \qquad (14)$$

Equation (14) completes the proof. $\square$

Remark 1. The integral sign, $\int$, is a modified capital S (for sum), intended to remind us of the close connection between integration and summation.

Remark 2. The limit in Eq. (7),

$$\lim \sum f(c_k) \, \Delta x,$$

is called the *definite integral* of f from a to b. It is denoted by the symbol $\int_a^b f(x) \, dx$. The first Fundamental Theorem of integral calculus thus says that

$$\int_a^b F'(x) \, dx = F(b) - F(a). \qquad (15)$$

Remark 3. It really isn't necessary to make the subdivisions of $[a, b]$ regular. We could equally well have put

$$\Delta x_1 = x_1 - a,$$
$$\Delta x_2 = x_2 - x_1, \; \ldots,$$
$$\Delta x_n = b - x_{n-1},$$

and

$$S = \sum_{k=1}^n f(c_k) \, \Delta x_k.$$

The uniform continuity of f on $[a, b]$ guarantees that if the largest Δx_k is made to approach zero, then all sums S of this form approach the same number as limit: namely, $F(b) - F(a)$, where F is any primitive of f. Since any two primitives of the same function f differ at most by a constant, and since

$$F(x) + C]_a^b = F(b) - F(a),$$

the same answer is obtained no matter which primitive is used.

Remark 4. If the function has only nonnegative values over $[a, b]$, then the definite integral

$$\int_a^b f(x) \, dx = F(x)]_a^b = F(b) - F(a) \qquad (16)$$

represents the area under its graph, above the x-axis, between the ordinates at $x = a$ and $x = b$. If, on the other hand, the function f were everywhere negative between a and b, the summands $f(c_k) \, \Delta x$ would

a | b

6.25

all be negative [assuming $b > a$ and $\Delta x = (b - a)/n$ is positive], and the integral in Eq. (16) would be negative.

Example 1. For $|x| < 2$, $f(x) = x^2 - 4$ is negative (see Fig. 6.25a):

$$\int_{-2}^2 f(x) \, dx = \frac{x^3}{3} - 4x \Big]_{-2}^2 = (\tfrac{8}{3} - 8) - (-\tfrac{8}{3} + 8)$$
$$= -\tfrac{32}{3}.$$

The area between the curve and the x-axis, from $x = -2$ to $x = +2$, contains $\tfrac{32}{3}$ units of area. The sign is negative because the area is below the x-axis. Clearly, the graph in Fig. 6.25(b) of

$$y = g(x) = -f(x) = 4 - x^2, \quad -2 \leq x \leq 2,$$

is just the mirror image, with respect to the x-axis as mirror, of the curve in Fig. 6.25(a). The area between the graph of $y = g(x)$ and the x-axis is

$$\int_{-2}^2 g(x) \, dx = 4x - \frac{x^3}{3} \Big]_{-2}^2 = \tfrac{32}{3}.$$

The absolute value is the same as for the integral of $f(x) \, dx$ between the same limits. For $g(x) \, dx$ the sign is positive, since the area between the g-curve and the x-axis is above the axis.

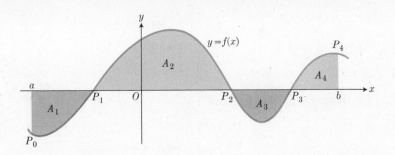

6.26

Remark 5. If the graph of $y = f(x)$, $a \leq x \leq b$, is partly below and partly above the x-axis, as in Fig. 6.26, then

$$\lim \sum f(c_k)\, \Delta x = \int_a^b f(x)\, dx = F(x)]_a^b$$
$$= F(b) - F(a)$$

is the algebraic sum of *signed* areas, positive areas above the x-axis, negative areas below. For example, if the absolute values of the areas between the curve and the x-axis in Fig. 6.26 are A_1, A_2, A_3, A_4, then the definite integral of f from a to b is equal to

$$\int_a^b f(x)\, dx = -A_1 + A_2 - A_3 + A_4.$$

Thus, if we wanted the sum of the absolute values of these signed areas, that is

$$A = |-A_1| + A_2 + |-A_3| + A_4,$$

then we should need to find the abscissas s_1, s_2, s_3 of the points P_1, P_2, P_3 where the curve crosses the x-axis. We would then compute, separately,

$$-A_1 = \int_a^{s_1} f(x)\, dx, \qquad A_2 = \int_{s_1}^{s_2} f(x)\, dx,$$

$$-A_3 = \int_{s_2}^{s_3} f(x)\, dx, \qquad A_4 = \int_{s_3}^b f(x)\, dx,$$

and add their absolute values.

Problem 1. Find the total area bounded by the curve $y = x^3 - 4x$ and the x-axis.

Solution. The graph, shown in Fig. 6.27 lies above the x-axis from -2 to 0, below from 0 to $+2$. [The polynomial $x^3 - 4x$ factors as

$$x^3 - 4x = x(x - 2)(x + 2).$$

It is easy to determine the sign of the product from the signs of the three factors.]

$$A_1 = \int_{-2}^0 (x^3 - 4x)\, dx = \frac{x^4}{4} - 2x^2 \Big]_{-2}^0$$
$$= 0 - (4 - 8) = +4,$$

$$-A_2 = \int_0^2 (x^3 - 4x)\, dx = \frac{x^4}{4} - 2x^2 \Big]_0^2$$
$$= (4 - 8) - 0 = -4,$$

$$A_1 + |-A_2| = 4 + |-4| = 8.$$

Remark 6. The definite integral, as a limit of sums, provides a new way of defining functions. The integral of any continuous function $f(t)$ from $t = a$

6.27

$$F(x) = \int_1^{x^2} \frac{dt}{1 + \sqrt{1-x}} \quad \leftarrow \text{drops out}$$

$$F'(x) = (1 + \sqrt{1-x^2})\, 2x$$

to $t = x$ defines a number

$$F(x) = \int_a^x f(t)\, dt,$$

which can be computed as a limit (at least in theory). The function F defined by this formula has certain rather obvious properties:

1. $F(a) = 0$.

2. F is an increasing function of x over intervals where f is positive.

3. When x changes from x_0 by a small amount, say when it changes to $x_0 + \Delta x$, $F(x)$ changes by an amount that is approximately $f(x_0)\,\Delta x$. These properties lead us to conjecture that F is differentiable and that its derivative is f. This conjecture is true (for continuous functions f). It is stated as the Second Fundamental Theorem of Integral Calculus.

Second fundamental theorem of integral calculus. *Let f be continuous on $[a, b]$, and let* (REPLACE x w/ x max; Mvlpi By deR. of x)

$$F(x) = \int_a^x f(t)\, dt \quad \text{for } x \in [a, b]. \qquad (17a)$$

($\leftarrow$ CONSTANT)

Then F is differentiable on (a, b), and

$$F'(x) = f(x) \quad \text{for } a < x < b. \qquad (17b)$$

Proof. The same argument that led to Eq. (5), Article 6.8 can be applied to obtain the following:

$$F(x + \Delta x) - F(x) = \int_x^{x+\Delta x} f(t)\, dt = f(c)\, \Delta x$$

for some c between x and $x + \Delta x$. Divide by Δx and take limits:

$$\lim_{\Delta x \to 0} \frac{F(x + \Delta x) - F(x)}{\Delta x} = \lim_{c \to x} f(c),$$

or

$$F'(x) = f(x). \quad \square$$

Example 2. Suppose

$$F(x) = \int_0^x \sqrt{1 - t^2}\, dt, \quad 0 < x < 1.$$

Then

$$F'(x) = \sqrt{1 - x^2}.$$

Problem 2. Let $F(x) = \int_0^{\sqrt{x}} (t + 1)^{1/2}\, dt$ for $x > 0$. Find $F'(x)$.

Solution 1. By direct integration, we get

$$\int (t + 1)^{1/2}\, dt = \tfrac{2}{3}(t + 1)^{3/2} + C,$$

and

$$F(x) = \tfrac{2}{3}(\sqrt{x} + 1)^{3/2} - \tfrac{2}{3}.$$

When we differentiate this we get

$$F'(x) = (\sqrt{x} + 1)^{1/2} \frac{d}{dx}(\sqrt{x} + 1)$$

$$= (\sqrt{x} + 1)^{1/2}(\tfrac{1}{2}x^{-1/2}). \qquad (18a)$$

Solution 2. In the original integral, call the upper limit u and apply the chain rule:

$$F(x) = G(u) = \int_0^u (t + 1)^{1/2}\, dt \quad \text{with } u = \sqrt{x}.$$

The Second Fundamental Theorem applies to $G'(u)$:

$$G'(u) = (u + 1)^{1/2}.$$

Now apply the chain rule:

$$F'(x) = G'(u)\frac{du}{dx} = (u + 1)^{1/2}(\tfrac{1}{2}x^{-1/2}). \qquad (18b)$$

Eqs. (18a) and (18b) are equivalent because $u = \sqrt{x}$.

Remark 7. The First Fundamental Theorem is sometimes used as a tool for approximating sums. This is the reverse of what we did in Article 6.7. There we found formulas for sums of first powers, and of squares, of the positive integers 1 through n. Then we used these formulas to compute limits of sums of areas of inscribed rectangles for the graphs of $y = mx$, $a \le x \le b$, and of $y = x^2$, $0 \le x \le b$. In the following example, we work back from the definite integral (or, what amounts to the same thing, the area under the graph) to an approximation for the sum of the square roots of the integers 1 through n. The process is not completely reversible. We can go from exact formulas for sums to definite integrals by way of limits, but we cannot go back from the definite integral to an exact formula for the sum, because we don't know which terms went to zero in the limit process, and hence we cannot recover them.

Example 3. Consider the function defined by $f(x) = \sqrt{x}$, $0 \le x \le 1$. Let n be a positive integer, and $\Delta x = 1/n$. In Eq. (7), take $c_1 = x_1 = \Delta x$, $c_2 = x_2 = 2\,\Delta x, \ldots$, $c_n = b = 1 = n\,\Delta x$. Then

$$S_n = \sqrt{c_1}\,\Delta x + \sqrt{c_2}\,\Delta x + \cdots + \sqrt{c_n}\,\Delta x$$

$$= \frac{\sqrt{1} + \sqrt{2} + \cdots + \sqrt{n}}{n^{3/2}}.$$

$$\to \int \sqrt{x}\,dx\Big]_0^1 = \frac{x^{3/2}}{3/2}\Big]_0^1 = \frac{2}{3} \quad \text{as } n \to \infty.$$

When n is large, S_n will be close to its limit $\frac{2}{3}$. This means that the numerator

$$\sqrt{1} + \sqrt{2} + \cdots + \sqrt{n}$$

is approximately equal to $\frac{2}{3}n^{3/2}$. For $n = 10$, the sum of the square roots is 22.5^-, while $\frac{2}{3}n^{3/2}$ is 21.1^-, so that the approximation is in error by about 6%.

C

EXERCISES

1-17-77 6-24 EVEN

1. For each of the following cases, integrate the given function f to find a new function F, defined by $F(x) = \int f(x)\,dx$. Apply the Mean Value Theorem to this new function F to find an expression for c_k in terms of x_k and x_{k-1} such that

$$F(x_k) - F(x_{k-1}) = F'(c_k)(x_k - x_{k-1}).$$

   (a) $f(x) = x$ (b) $f(x) = x^2$
   (c) $f(x) = x^3$ (d) $f(x) = 1/\sqrt{x}$

2. Consider the function defined by $f(x) = x$, and take $a = 0$, $b > 0$. Show that by taking

$$c_k = \tfrac{1}{2}(x_k + x_{k-1})$$

in Eq. (5), the resulting sum has the constant value $S_n = \frac{1}{2}b^2$, independently of the value of n. (Let $a = x_0$ and $b = x_n$.)

3. Take $f(x) = x^2$, $a = 0$, $b > 0$ and form S_n, Eq. (5), using

$$c_k = \sqrt{\frac{x_k^2 + x_k x_{k-1} + x_{k-1}^2}{3}}.$$

Show that no matter what value n has, the resulting sum S_n has the constant value $S_n = \frac{1}{3}b^3$.

(Let $a = x_0$ and $b = x_n$.) What is the limit of S_n as $n \to \infty$? Note that one should substitute $x_k - x_{k-1}$ for Δx and recognize that

$$\left(\frac{x_k^2 + x_k x_{k-1} + x_{k-1}^2}{3}\right)\Delta x = \frac{x_k^3 - x_{k-1}^3}{3}.$$

4. Take $f(x) = x^3$, $a = 0$, $b > 0$, and calculate S_n, Eq. (5), taking

$$c_k = \sqrt[3]{\frac{x_k^3 + x_k^2 x_{k-1} + x_k x_{k-1}^2 + x_{k-1}^3}{4}}.$$

Express the result in a form which is independent of the number of subdivisions n. (Let $a = x_0$ and $b = x_n$.)

5. Take $f(x) = 1/\sqrt{x}$, $a = 1$, $b > 1$. Use the intermediate values

$$c_k = \left(\frac{\sqrt{x_{k-1}} + \sqrt{x_k}}{2}\right)^2$$

and calculate S_n, Eq. (5). Express the result in a form which is independent of the number of subdivisions. (Let $a = x_0$ and $b = x_n$.)

Evaluate the definite integrals 6 through 16.

6. $\displaystyle\int_1^2 (2x + 5)\,dx$ 7. $\displaystyle\int_0^1 (x^2 - 2x + 3)\,dx$

8. $\displaystyle\int_{-1}^1 (x + 1)^2\,dx$ 9. $\displaystyle\int_0^2 \sqrt{4x + 1}\,dx$

10. $\displaystyle\int_0^\pi \sin x\,dx$ 11. $\displaystyle\int_0^\pi \cos x\,dx$

12. $\displaystyle\int_{\pi/4}^{\pi/2} \frac{\cos x\,dx}{\sin^2 x}$ (Let $u = \sin x$.)

13. $\displaystyle\int_0^{\pi/6} \frac{\sin 2x}{\cos^2 2x}\,dx$ *14. $\displaystyle\int_0^\pi \sin^2 x\,dx$

*15. $\displaystyle\int_0^{2\pi/\omega} \cos^2(\omega t)\,dt$ (ω constant)

16. $\displaystyle\int_0^1 \frac{dx}{(2x + 1)^3}$

---

* See Exercise 17, Article 6.8.

17. (a) Express the area between the curves $y = x^2$, $y = 18 - x^2$ as a *limit of a sum* of areas of rectangles. (b) Evaluate the area of (a) by Eq. (7).

18. Approximate the area under the curve $y = 1/x$ between $x = 1$ and $x = 2$ by five rectangles, each of base $\Delta x = 0.2$. Use the ordinate of the curve at the *midpoint* of each subinterval as the altitude of the approximating rectangle. The following short table of reciprocals may be used for convenience:

x	1.1	1.3	1.5	1.7	1.9
$1/x$	0.909	0.769	0.667	0.588	0.526

(Compare your answer with 0.693, which is the value $\int_1^2 dx/x$ to 3 decimals.)

In Exercises 19 through 25, use Eqs. (17a, b) to find $F'(x)$ for the given functions F:

19. $F(x) = \int_0^x \sqrt{1 + t^2}\, dt$ 20. $F(x) = \int_1^x \dfrac{dt}{t}$

21. $F(x) = \int_x^1 \sqrt{1 - t^2}\, dt$ 22. $F(x) = \int_0^x \dfrac{dt}{1 + t^2}$

23. $F(x) = \int_1^{2x} \cos(t^2)\, dt$

Hint. Use the chain rule with $u = 2x$.

24. $F(x) = \int_1^{x^2} \dfrac{dt}{1 + \sqrt{1 - t}}$ 25. $F(x) = \int_{\sin x}^0 \dfrac{dt}{2 + t}$

6.10 THE TRAPEZOIDAL RULE FOR APPROXIMATING AN INTEGRAL

Any definite integral may be thought of as an area, or an algebraic sum of signed areas, as discussed in Article 6.9. We know how to evaluate a definite integral when an indefinite integral of the integrand is known. But there are simple integrands, for example $(\sin x)/x$, for which no simple indefinite integral is known. In such instances, if the integrand is continuous, the definite integral still exists and we may wish to evaluate it numerically. We can often obtain good accuracy by using numerical methods for approximating a definite integral. These

6.28 The sum of the areas of trapezoids approximates the area under the curve.

methods are also important for computations done by machines. One of the simplest of these numerical methods is the *trapezoidal rule*, which we shall now derive. (See Fig. 6.28.)

Suppose that the definite integral $\int_a^b f(x)\, dx$ is to be evaluated. We divide the interval $a \le x \le b$ into n subintervals, each of length $\Delta x = (b - a)/n$, in the usual way by inserting the points

$$\begin{aligned} x_1 &= a + \Delta x, \\ x_2 &= a + 2\,\Delta x, \\ &\vdots \\ x_{n-1} &= a + (n - 1)\,\Delta x \end{aligned}$$

between $x_0 = a$ and $x_n = b$.

The integral from a to b is just the sum of the integrals from a to x_1, from x_1 to x_2, and so on, and, finally, the integral from x_{n-1} to b:

$$\int_a^b f(x)\, dx = \int_a^{x_1} f(x)\, dx + \int_{x_1}^{x_2} f(x)\, dx + \cdots$$
$$+ \int_{x_{n-1}}^b f(x)\, dx$$
$$= \sum_{k=1}^n \int_{x_{k-1}}^{x_k} f(x)\, dx.$$

The integral over the first subinterval is now *approximated* by the area of the trapezoid $aP_0P_1x_1$, which equals $\frac{1}{2}(y_0 + y_1)\,\Delta x$; over the second subinterval by the area of the trapezoid $x_1P_1P_2x_2$, which is $\frac{1}{2}(y_1 + y_2)\,\Delta x$; and so on. The *trapezoidal rule* is: To estimate the definite integral $\int_a^b f(x)\,dx$, use the *trapezoidal approximation* T given by

$$T = \tfrac{1}{2}(y_0 + y_1)\,\Delta x + \tfrac{1}{2}(y_1 + y_2)\,\Delta x + \cdots$$
$$+ \tfrac{1}{2}(y_{n-2} + y_{n-1})\,\Delta x + \tfrac{1}{2}(y_{n-1} + y_n)\,\Delta x \quad (1a)$$
$$= (\tfrac{1}{2}y_0 + y_1 + y_2 + \cdots + y_{n-1} + \tfrac{1}{2}y_n)\,\Delta x,$$

where

$$y_0 = f(x_0),$$
$$y_1 = f(x_1),\ \ldots,\ y_{n-1} = f(x_{n-1}), \quad (1b)$$
$$y_n = f(x_n).$$

Problem 1. Use the trapezoidal rule with $n = 4$ to estimate $\int_1^2 x^2\,dx$ and compare this approximation with the exact value of the integral.

Solution. The exact value of this integral is

$$\int_1^2 x^2\,dx = \frac{x^3}{3}\Big]_1^2 = \frac{7}{3}.$$

For the trapezoidal approximation we have

$$x_0 = a = 1,\quad x_n = b = 2,\quad n = 4,$$
$$\Delta x = (b - a)/n = (2 - 1)/4 = \tfrac{1}{4},$$

so that

$$x_0 = a \qquad\quad = 1,\qquad y_0 = f(x_0) = \ \ 1^2 = \tfrac{16}{16},$$
$$x_1 = a + \ \Delta x = \tfrac{5}{4},\qquad y_1 = f(x_1) = (\tfrac{5}{4})^2 = \tfrac{25}{16},$$
$$x_2 = a + 2\,\Delta x = \tfrac{6}{4},\qquad y_2 = f(x_2) = (\tfrac{6}{4})^2 = \tfrac{36}{16},$$
$$x_3 = a + 3\,\Delta x = \tfrac{7}{4},\qquad y_3 = f(x_3) = (\tfrac{7}{4})^2 = \tfrac{49}{16},$$
$$x_4 = b \qquad\quad = 2,\qquad y_4 = f(x_4) = (\tfrac{8}{4})^2 = \tfrac{64}{16},$$

and

$$T = (\tfrac{1}{2}y_0 + y_1 + y_2 + y_3 + \tfrac{1}{2}y_4)\,\Delta x$$
$$= (\tfrac{75}{8})\,\Delta x = \tfrac{75}{32} = 2.34375.$$

Thus the approximation is too large by about 1 part in 233, or less than one-half of one percent.

The graph in Fig. 6.29 shows clearly that each approximating trapezoid contains slightly more area than the corresponding strip of area under the curve. But the polygonal line $P_0P_1P_2P_3P_4$ lies very close to the curve, so we would expect the area under the curve to be quite close to the area of the polygon $AP_0P_1P_2P_3P_4BA$, which is the trapezoidal approximation.

6.29 Trapezoidal approximation of the area under the curve.

Accuracy of the trapezoidal approximation

It is easy to demonstrate that as n increases and Δx approaches zero, the trapezoidal approximation approaches the exact value of the definite integral as limit. For we have

$$T = (y_1 + y_2 + \cdots + y_n)\,\Delta x + \tfrac{1}{2}(y_0 - y_n)\,\Delta x$$

$$= \sum_{k=1}^{n} f(x_k)\,\Delta x + \tfrac{1}{2}[f(a) - f(b)]\,\Delta x. \quad (2)$$

When n increases without bound and Δx approaches zero, the sum that is indicated by the sigma approaches $\int_a^b f(x)\,dx$ as limit, and the last term in (2) approaches zero. Therefore

$$\lim T = \int_a^b f(x)\,dx.$$

This means, of course, that by taking n sufficiently large the difference between T and the integral can be made as small as desired.

By methods studied in more advanced calculus (an extension of the Mean Value Theorem), it is possible to prove* that if f is continuous on

$$a \leq x \leq b,$$

and twice differentiable on $a < x < b$, then there is a number e between a and b such that

$$\int_a^b f(x) \, dx = T - \frac{b-a}{12} f''(e) \cdot (\Delta x)^2. \quad (3)$$

Thus as Δx approaches zero the "error," that is, the difference between the integral and the trapezoidal approximation, approaches zero as the *square* of Δx. By estimating the size of the second derivative between a and b, we can get a good estimate of how accurate T is as an approximation to the integral.

Example 2. In Problem 1 above, $f(x) = x^2$, $f''(x) = 2$, and the predicted error in (3) with $a = 1$, $b = 2$ is

$$-\frac{b-a}{12} f''(e) \cdot (\Delta x)^2 = -\frac{2-1}{12} \cdot 2 \cdot \frac{1}{16} = -\frac{1}{96}.$$

This is precisely what we find when we subtract $T = \frac{75}{32}$ from $\int_1^2 x^2 \, dx = \frac{7}{3}$, since $\frac{7}{3} - \frac{75}{32} = -\frac{1}{96}$. Here we are able to give the error *exactly*, since the second derivative of $f(x) = x^2$ is a constant and we have no uncertainty caused by not knowing e in the term $f''(e)$. Of course we are not always this lucky; in most cases the best we can do is *estimate* the difference between the integral and T.

Problem 2. Suppose the trapezoidal rule, with $n = 5$, is used to approximate $\int_1^2 (1/x) \, dx$. Estimate the error.

Solution. Here

$$f(x) = x^{-1}, \quad f'(x) = -x^{-2}, \quad f''(x) = 2x^{-3} = 2/x^3.$$

Since $f''(x)$ steadily decreases

$$\text{from} \quad f''(1) = 2 \quad \text{to} \quad f''(2) = \tfrac{1}{4},$$

we can estimate the error only as lying between

$$-\tfrac{1}{12} \cdot 2 \cdot \tfrac{1}{25} = -\tfrac{1}{150} \approx -0.0067$$

and

$$-\tfrac{1}{12} \cdot \tfrac{1}{4} \cdot \tfrac{1}{25} = -\tfrac{1}{1200} \approx -0.0008.$$

---

* See, for example, J. M. H. Olmsted, *Intermediate Analysis*, Appleton-Century-Crofts, 1956, p. 145.

Therefore the integral lies between

$$T - \tfrac{1}{150} \quad \text{and} \quad T - \tfrac{1}{1200},$$

so that it is slightly less than T, but differs from it by less than 0.01. In other words, we can get about two-decimal place accuracy for the integral by using the trapezoidal rule with $n = 5$, $\Delta x = \tfrac{1}{5}$. By taking $n = 10$, $\Delta x = \tfrac{1}{10}$, the error is cut by a factor of approximately 4. [The e of $f''(e)$ in the error may change when n does, and hence we cannot say that the error is cut precisely by a factor of 4.]

EXERCISES

1-19   #3

1. Interpret the meaning of the sign of the correction term in Eq. (3) if the graph of $y = f(x)$ is

   (a) concave upward over $a < x < b$,

   (b) concave downward.

   Illustrate both cases with sketches.

Test the accuracy of the trapezoidal approximation to the definite integral $\int_b^a f(x) \, dx$ in Exercises 2 through 5.

2. $f(x) = x$, $\quad a = 0$, $\quad b = 2$, $\quad n = 4$.

3. $f(x) = x^3$, $\quad a = 0$, $\quad b = 2$, $\quad n = 4$.

4. $f(x) = \sqrt{x}$, $\quad a = 0$, $\quad b = 2$, $\quad n = 4$.

5. $f(x) = 1/x^2$, $\quad a = 1$, $\quad b = 2$, $\quad n = 2$.

6.11 SOME COMMENTS ON NOTATION

In each application of the definite integral it is reasonably easy to set up sums that approximate the answer to some physical problem. In general, it will even be possible (though not necessary) to find *particular* choices of the points c_k such that the *particular* sums

$$S_n = \sum_{k=1}^n f(c_k) \, \Delta x$$

give the *exact* value. Then

$$\lim_{n \to \infty} S_n = \int_a^b f(x) \, dx = F(x)\big]_a^b = F(b) - F(a)$$

also gives the *exact* value. But since all sums S_n give the *same* answer in the limit [provided that the function $f(x)$ is continuous for $a \leq x \leq b$; this condition will usually be satisfied by the functions we shall encounter], we could get the same limit from

$$S_n = \sum_{k=1}^{n} f(x_k) \, \Delta x. \tag{1a}$$

Finally, we modify this notation slightly by dropping the subscript k entirely and writing simply

$$S_a^b = \sum_{a}^{b} f(x) \, \Delta x, \tag{1b}$$

where we write a and b to indicate that we have a sum of expressions, each of the form $f(x) \, \Delta x$, extending over a set of subintervals from $x = a$ to $x = b$. Of course it is not the *sum* (1b) that we are interested in, but rather the *limit* of the sum as given by the definite integral, and the notation (1b) is most suggestive of the final form, namely,

$$\lim_{\Delta x \to 0} S_a^b = \lim_{\Delta x \to 0} \sum_{a}^{b} f(x) \, \Delta x$$

$$= \int_a^b f(x) \, dx = F(x) \Big]_a^b. \tag{2}$$

As remarked in Article 6.9, it is the close relationship between sums and integrals which leads to the adoption of the symbol $\int$ (a modified S) to denote integration.

It should also be noted that *since it is the integral* that gives the *exact* answer in (2), and since the expression $f(x) \, dx$ after the integral sign is the same as the differential of $F(x)$,

$$\frac{dF(x)}{dx} = f(x), \tag{3a}$$

$$dF(x) = f(x) \, dx, \tag{3b}$$

we would arrive at the *correct final result* for the area under the curve $y = f(x)$ between $x = a$ and $x = b$, say, if we were to write

$$dA = f(x) \, dx, \qquad A = \int_a^b f(x) \, dx. \tag{4}$$

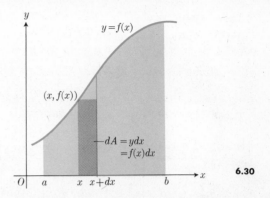

6.30

It is easy to attach a geometric interpretation to (4), but it is also easy to be misled by this interpretation into feeling that the integral in (4) gives only an approximation to the area, rather than giving its exact value. Enough has already been said on this latter point, however, so that the careful reader need not be a victim of this delusion. If we accept the interpretation simply as a short cut for setting up the *integral whose value gives the exact result*, we may thereby gain from its simplicity. Explicitly, if we again think of the area from the left boundary a to a right boundary x, this area is a function of x, with derivative $dA/dx = y = f(x)$, as we found in Article 6.8. When we multiply both sides of this equation by dx, we get the result $dA = f(x) \, dx$, as in (4). But if we think of dx as a small increment in x, we may also interpret this as the area of a small rectangle with base extending along the x-axis from x to $x + dx$, and with altitude $f(x) = y$ equal to the ordinate of the curve (see Fig. 6.30). Then this rectangle gives an *approximation* to that portion of the area under the curve lying between x and $x + dx$, and we think of the integral

$$A = \int_a^b f(x) \, dx$$

as adding together all of these small rectangles from $x = a$ to $x = b$ and then taking the *limit* of the sum so as to give the *exact value*.

It should be borne in mind that what has just been discussed should in no way obscure the fact that a *precise* formulation of the problem would involve a process of

(a) subdividing the interval (a, b),

(b) forming a sum $\sum_a^b f(x)\,\Delta x$,

(c) taking the limit $\lim_{\Delta x \to 0} \sum_a^b f(x)\,\Delta x$, and

(d) applying the fundamental theorem to evaluate this limit:

$$\lim_{\Delta x \to 0} \sum_a^b f(x)\,\Delta x = \int_a^b f(x)\,dx = F(x)]_a^b.$$

Insofar as the short cut described above leads to the same final answer, without leading to confusion or feelings of misgiving, it may be helpful and time-saving. But whenever there is doubt that the final answer may only be an approximation instead of a mathematically exact answer, a reconsideration should be made, along the lines which led up to the fundamental theorem. It is probably desirable, at least in the beginning, to go through the precise formulation first, and then it is but a matter of seconds to repeat the setup of the problem by the short-cut method.

6.12 SUMMARY

Much that we have done in this chapter is related to area. This is useful and gives us a way of interpreting sums like those in Eq. (5), Article 6.9, and Eq. (1a) in Article 6.11. But it is also good to express the main results in ways that don't depend upon area. In this article we shall summarize six results of major importance. Although we have appealed to the notion of area in presenting them in earlier sections, they can all be proved by purely analytical methods, with no reference to area. (See, for example, Apostol, *Modern Mathematical Analysis;* Buck, *Advanced Calculus;* or Rudin, *Principles of Analysis.*)

Once again we start with a function $f(x)$ defined on an interval $[a, b]$. We partition the interval into n subintervals by inserting points $x_1, x_2, \ldots, x_{n-1}$ between $a = x_0$ and $b = x_n$. We do not require that the points be uniformly spaced. The kth subinterval

has length

$$\Delta x_k = x_k - x_{k-1},$$

which may vary with k. In the kth subinterval a number c_k is chosen arbitrarily, for each k from 1 through n. Then we form the sum

$$\sum_{k=1}^n f(c_k) \cdot (x_k - x_{k-1}), \tag{1}$$

This sum depends on the function f, on the points $x_0, x_1, x_2, \ldots, x_n$, and on the c's. However, for a given function f and interval $[a, b]$ it may happen that all sums like (1) are nearly equal to some constant, provided that the subintervals are all sufficiently short. If this is true, then that constant is called the *Riemann integral* of f from a to b, and is variously denoted by $R_a^b(f)$, or $\int_a^b f$, or $\int_a^b f(x)\,dx$, or $\int_a^b f(t)\,dt$, or $\int_a^b f(u)\,du$, and so on.

Definition of Riemann Integral. *Let f be a function whose domain includes the interval $[a, b]$, $a < b$. Let f have the property that there exists a number $R_a^b(f)$ so related to f that to each positive number ϵ there corresponds a positive number δ such that every sum (1) differs from $R_a^b(f)$ by less than ϵ whenever all subintervals have lengths Δx_k less than δ. Then:*

(a) *f is said to be Riemann-integrable (or, more briefly, integrable) over $[a, b]$, and*

(b) *$R_a^b(f)$ is called the Riemann integral (or, more briefly, the integral) of f from a to b.*

Theorem 3. *If f is Riemann-integrable over an interval $[a, b]$, then it is also integrable over any subinterval contained in $[a, b]$.*

Theorem 4. *Every function that is continuous on a closed bounded interval $[a, b]$ is Riemann-integrable there.*

Remark. Although we are mainly interested in continuous functions, they are not the only ones that are integrable. All bounded functions that are *piecewise*-continuous are also integrable. "Piecewise-continuous" means that the interval can be divided into a finite number of nonoverlapping open subintervals over each of which the function is continuous. "Bounded" means that, for some finite

6.31   Graph of a piecewise-continuous function.

constant M, $|f(x)| \leq M$ for all values of x in the interval. Figure 6.31 shows the graph of a bounded piecewise-continuous function over $[a, b]$. For this example, the integral $R_a^b(f)$ would be computed as the sum

$$R_a^b(f) = R_a^u(f) + R_u^v(f) + R_v^w(f) + R_w^z(f) + R_z^b(f).$$

If $b < a$ and $R_b^a(f)$ exists, then we define $R_a^b(f)$ to be its negative:

$$R_a^b(f) = -R_b^a(f). \qquad (2)$$

If $a = b$, we define $R_a^a(f)$ to be zero.

Theorem 5.   *Let a, b, c be three numbers belonging to an interval over which the Riemann integral f exists. Then*

$$R_a^c(f) = R_a^b(f) + R_b^c(f). \qquad (3)$$

Theorem 6.   *Let f be Riemann-integrable over $[a, b]$. Let x be any number between a and b at which f is continuous. Then $R_a^x(f)$ is differentiable at x and its derivative there is $f(x)$:*

$$\frac{d}{dx} R_a^x(f) = f(x). \qquad (4)$$

Theorem 7.   The Mean Value Theorem for Integrals.   *Let f be continuous on $[a, b]$. Then there exists at least one number c between a and b such that*

$$R_a^b(f) = f(c) \cdot (b - a). \qquad (5)$$

Theorem 8.   Fundamental Theorem of Integral Calculus. *Let f be Riemann-integrable over $[a, b]$. Let F be any continuous indefinite integral of f, that is,*

$$F'(x) = f(x) \quad for \ a < x < b.$$

Then

$$R_a^b(f) = F(b) - F(a). \qquad (6)$$

EXERCISES

1. Rewrite Equations (2) through (6), Article 6.12, using the notation $\int_a^b f(t) \, dt$ in place of $R_a^b(f)$ for the Riemann integral of f from a to b.

2. Sketch graphs of the following piecewise-continuous functions on $(0, 2)$ and compute $\int_0^2 f(x) \, dx$.

   (a) $f(x) = \begin{cases} x & \text{for } 0 \leq x < 1 \\ \sin(\pi x) & \text{for } 1 \leq x \leq 2 \end{cases}$

   (b) $f(x) = \begin{cases} \sqrt{1-x} & \text{for } 0 \leq x \leq 1 \\ (7x-6)^{-1/3} & \text{for } 1 < x \leq 2 \end{cases}$

3. Find $F'(x)$ for $x = \frac{1}{2}$ and for $x = \frac{3}{2}$

   if $\qquad F(x) = \int_0^x f(t) \, dt$

   and

   (a) f is defined as in Exercise 2(a) above,

   (b) f is defined as in Exercise 2(b) above, and

   (c) $f(t) = \dfrac{\sin(\pi t)}{1+t}.$

REVIEW QUESTIONS AND EXERCISES

1. The process of "indefinite integration" is sometimes called "antidifferentiation." Explain why the two terms should be synonymous.

2. Can there be more than one indefinite integral of a given function? If more than one exist, how are they related? What theorem of Chapter 5 is the key to this relationship?

3. If the acceleration of a moving body is given as a function of time (t), what further information do you need to find the law of motion, $s = f(t)$? How is s found?

4. Develop the law of cosines from the formula for the distance between two points.

5. Develop the formula for $\cos (A - B)$ from the law of cosines.

6. Write expressions for $\sin (A + B)$ and $\sin (A - B)$. Set $\alpha = A + B, \beta = A - B$ and develop a formula for $\sin \alpha - \sin \beta$.

7. Under what assumptions is it true that

$$\lim (\sin \theta / \theta) = 1?$$

Prove the result.

8. Write expressions for $\cos (A + B)$ and $\cos (A - B)$. Set $\alpha = A + B, \beta = A - B$ and develop a formula for $\cos \alpha - \cos \beta$. Then use this result to develop a formula for the derivative of $\cos x$, from the definition

$$\frac{d (\cos x)}{dx} = \lim_{\Delta x \to 0} \frac{\cos (x + \Delta x) - \cos x}{\Delta x}.$$

9. Let A_n be the area bounded by a regular n-sided polygon inscribed in a circle of radius r. Show that $A_n = (n/2)r^2 \sin (2\pi/n)$. Find $\lim A_n$ as $n \to \infty$. Does the result agree with what you know about the area of a circle?

10. A function G is defined by

$$G(x) = \int_0^x (1 + t^2)^{1/2} \, dt.$$

What is the largest possible domain for G? For which values of x in this domain is G continuous? Differentiable? For what values of x does $G'(x) = 3$? Where is $G'(x) = 0$? What is the minimum value of $G'(x)$?

11. Write a formula for the area bounded above by the semicircle $y = \sqrt{r^2 - t^2}$, below by the t-axis, on the left by the y-axis, and on the right by the line $t = x$. Without making any calculations, what do you know must be the derivative, with respect to x, of this expression? Explain.

12. What property of continuous functions is used in the proof of the Mean Value Theorem for Areas?

13. Is every Riemann-integrable function also differentiable? Give a reason for your answer.

14. Is the function f, defined on the domain $0 \le x \le 1$ by

$$f(x) = \begin{cases} 0 \text{ when } x \text{ is rational,} \\ 1 \text{ when } x \text{ is irrational,} \end{cases}$$

Riemann-integrable over $(0, 1)$? Give a reason for your answer.

15. If you could not find an indefinite integral of $f(x) \, dx$, how could you still calculate $\int_a^b f(x) \, dx$ to any specified number of decimal places of accuracy, assuming f is continuous over $a \le x \le b$? Illustrate for

$$f(x) = 1/x, \quad a = 1, \quad b = 2,$$

and one-decimal-place accuracy.

MISCELLANEOUS EXERCISES

Solve the differential equations in Exercises 1 through 5.

1. $\dfrac{dy}{dx} = xy^2$

2. $\dfrac{dy}{dx} = \sqrt{1 + x + y + xy}$

3. $\dfrac{dy}{dx} = \dfrac{x^2 - 1}{y^2 + 1}$

4. $\dfrac{dx}{dy} = \dfrac{y - \sqrt{y}}{x + \sqrt{x}}$

5. $\dfrac{dx}{dy} = \left(\dfrac{2 + x}{3 - y}\right)^2$

6. Solve each of the following differential equations subject to the prescribed initial conditions.

   (a) $\dfrac{dy}{dx} = x\sqrt{x^2 - 4}, \quad x = 2, \quad y = 3$

   (b) $\dfrac{dy}{dx} = xy^3, \quad x = 0, \quad y = 1$

7. Can there be a curve satisfying the following conditions? When $x = 0$, then $y = 0$ and $dy/dx = 1$, and also d^2y/dx^2 is everywhere equal to zero. Give a reason for your answer.

8. Find an equation of the curve whose slope at the point (x, y) is $3x^2 + 2$, if the curve is required to pass through the point $(1, -1)$.

9. A particle moves along the x-axis. Its acceleration is $a = -t^2$. At $t = 0$, the particle is at the origin. In the course of its motion, it reaches the point $x = b$, where $b > 0$, but no point beyond b. Determine its velocity at $t = 0$.

10. A particle moves with acceleration $a = \sqrt{t} - (1/\sqrt{t})$. Assuming that the velocity $v = 2$ and the distance $s = 5$ when $t = 0$, find

   (a) the velocity v in terms of t,
   (b) the distance s in terms of t.

11. A particle is accelerated with acceleration $3 + 2t$, where t is the time. At $t = 0$, the velocity is 4. Find the velocity as a function of time and the distance between the position of the particle at time zero and at time 4.

12. The acceleration of a particle moving along the x-axis is given by $d^2x/dt^2 = -4x$. If the particle starts from rest at $x = 5$, find the velocity when it first reaches $x = 3$.

13. Let $f(x)$, $g(x)$ be two continuously differentiable functions satisfying the relationships

$$f'(x) = g(x), \qquad f''(x) = -f(x).$$

Let $$h(x) = f^2(x) + g^2(x).$$

If $h(0) = 5$, find $h(10)$.

14. The family of straight lines $y = ax + b$ (a, b arbitrary constants) can be characterized by the relation $y'' = 0$. Find a similar relation satisfied by the family of all circles $(x - h)^2 + (y - h)^2 = r^2$, where h and r are arbitrary constants. [*Hint.* Eliminate h and r from the set of three equations including the given one and two obtained by successive differentiation.]

15. Assume that the brakes of an automobile produce a constant deceleration of k ft/sec^2.

(a) Determine what k must be to bring an automobile traveling 60 mi/hr (88 ft/sec) to rest in a distance of 100 ft from the point where the brakes are applied.

(b) With the same k, how far would a car traveling 30 mi/hr travel before being brought to a stop?

16. Solve the differential equation $dy/dx = x\sqrt{1+x^2}$ subject to the condition that $y = -2$ when $x = 0$.

17. The acceleration due to gravity is -32 ft/sec^2. A stone is thrown upward from the ground with a speed of 96 ft/sec. Find the height to which the stone rises in t sec. What is the maximum height reached by the stone?

18. Show that the following procedure will produce a continuous polygonal "curve" whose slope at the point (x_k, y_k) will be $f(x_k)$. First, sketch the auxiliary curve $C: y = xf(x)$. Then through the point $P_0(x_0, y_0)$, draw the ordinate $x = x_0$ intersecting C in

$$Q_0(x_0, x_0 f(x_0)).$$

Through P_0 draw a line segment P_0P_1 parallel to OQ_0. Then the slope of P_0P_1 is $f(x_0)$. Now take $P_1(x_1, y_1)$ on this segment to lie close to P_0. For example, take $x_1 = x_0 + h$, where h is small. Then find $Q_1(x_1, x_1 f(x_1))$ on C, and through P_1 draw a line segment P_1P_2 parallel to OQ_1. Continue the process by taking $P_2(x_2, y_2)$ close to P_1, with $x_2 = x_1 + h$; then find $Q_2(x_2, x_2 f(x_2))$ on C, and through P_2 draw a line segment P_2P_3 parallel to OQ_2; and so on. M. S. Klamkin, *Amer. Math. Monthly*, 1955.

19. (a) Apply the procedure of Exercise 18 to the case $f(x) = 1/x$ with $x_0 = 1$, $y_0 = 1$, and $h = \frac{1}{4}$. Continue the process until you reach the point $P_4(x_4, y_4)$. What is your value of y_4?

(b) Repeat the construction of part (a), but with $h = \frac{1}{8}$, and continue until you reach $x_8 = 2$. What is your value of y_8?

20. A body is moving with velocity 16 ft/sec when it is suddenly subjected to a deceleration. If the deceleration is proportional to the square root of the velocity, and the body comes to rest in 4 sec,

(a) how fast is the body moving 2 sec after it begins decelerating, and

(b) how far does the body travel before coming to rest?

Evaluate the integrals 21 through 33.

21. $\int \dfrac{x^3 + 1}{x^2}\, dx$

22. $\int y\sqrt{1+y^2}\, dy$

23. $\int t^{1/3}(1 + t^{4/3})^{-7}\, dt$

24. $\int \dfrac{(1 + \sqrt{u})^{1/2}\, du}{\sqrt{u}}$

25. $\int \dfrac{dr}{\sqrt[3]{(7 - 5r)^2}}$

26. $\int \cos 4x\, dx$

27. $\int \sin^2 3x \cos 3x\, dx$

28. $\int \dfrac{\cos x\, dx}{\sqrt{\sin x}}$

29. $\int \cos(2x - 1)\, dx$

30. $\int \dfrac{y\, dy}{\sqrt{25 - 4y^2}}$

31. $\int \dfrac{dt}{t\sqrt{2t}}$

32. $\int (x^2 - \sqrt{x})\, dx$

33. $\int \dfrac{dx}{(2 - 3x)^2}$

Find dy/dx in Exercises 34 through 38.

34. $y = \cos(1 - 2x)$

35. $y = \dfrac{\cos x}{\sin x}$

36. $y = \sec^2(5x)$

37. $y = \sin^4 5x$

38. $y^3 = \sin^3 x + \cos^3 x$

39. Given $y = 3\sin 2x$ and $x = u^2 + \pi$, find the value of dy/du when $u = 0$.

40. If $0 < x < \pi/2$, prove that $x > \sin x > 2x/\pi$.

41. If one side and the opposite angle of a triangle are fixed, prove that the area is a maximum when the triangle is isosceles.

42. A light hangs above the center of a table of radius r ft. The illumination at any point on the table is directly proportional to the cosine of the angle of incidence (i.e., the angle a ray of light makes with the normal) and is inversely proportional to the square of the distance from the light. How far should the light be above the table in order to give the strongest illumination at the edge of the table?

43. If A, B, C are constants, $AB \neq 0$, prove that the graph of the curve $y = A\sin(Bx + C)$ is always concave toward the x-axis and that its points of inflection coincide with its points of intersection with the x-axis.

44. Two particles move on the same straight line so that their distances from a fixed point O, at any time t, are

$$x_1 = a\sin bt \quad \text{and} \quad x_2 = a\sin[bt + (\pi/3)],$$

where a and b are constants, $ab \neq 0$. Find the greatest distance between them.

45. If the identity $\sin(x + a) = \sin x \cos a + \cos x \sin a$ is differentiated with respect to x, is the resulting equation also an identity? Does this principle apply to the equation $x^2 - 2x - 8 = 0$? Explain why or why not.

46. A revolving beacon light in a lighthouse $\frac{1}{2}$ mile offshore makes two revolutions per minute. If the shoreline is a straight line, how fast is the ray of light moving along the shore when it passes a point one mile from the lighthouse?

47. The coordinates of a moving particle are

$$x = a\cos^3\theta, \quad y = a\sin^3\theta.$$

If a is a positive constant and θ increases at the constant rate of ω rad/sec, find the magnitude of the velocity vector.

48. The area bounded by the x-axis, the curve $y = f(x)$, and the lines $x = 1$, $x = b$ is equal to

$$\sqrt{b^2 + 1} - \sqrt{2} \quad \text{for all } b > 1.$$

Find $f(x)$.

49. Evaluate the following limits.

(a) $\displaystyle \lim_{x \to 0} \frac{2\sin 5x}{3x}$

(b) $\displaystyle \lim_{x \to 0} \sin 5x \cot 3x$

(c) $\displaystyle \lim_{x \to 0} x\csc^2 \sqrt{2x}$

50. Find dy/dx and d^2y/dx^2 if

$$x = \cos 3t, \quad y = \sin^2 3t.$$

51. Let $f(x)$ be a continuous function. Express

$$\lim_{n \to \infty} \frac{1}{n}\left[f\left(\frac{1}{n}\right) + f\left(\frac{2}{n}\right) + \cdots + f\left(\frac{n}{n}\right) \right]$$

as a definite integral.

52. Use the result of Exercise 51 to evaluate

(a) $\displaystyle \lim_{n \to \infty} \frac{1}{n^{16}}[1^{15} + 2^{15} + 3^{15} + \cdots + n^{15}]$,

(b) $\displaystyle \lim_{n \to \infty} \frac{\sqrt{1} + \sqrt{2} + \sqrt{3} + \cdots + \sqrt{n}}{n^{3/2}}$,

(c) $\displaystyle \lim_{n \to \infty} \frac{1}{n}\left[\sin\frac{\pi}{n} + \sin\frac{2\pi}{n} + \sin\frac{3\pi}{n} + \cdots + \sin\frac{n\pi}{n} \right]$.

53. Find

(a) $\displaystyle \lim_{h \to 0} \frac{1}{h}\int_x^{x+h} \frac{du}{u + \sqrt{u^2 + 1}}$,

(b) $\displaystyle \lim_{x \to x_1}\left[\frac{x}{x - x_1}\int_{x_1}^x f(t)\, dt \right]$.

54. Variables x and y are related by the equation

$$x = \int_0^y \frac{1}{\sqrt{1 + 4t^2}}\, dt.$$

Show that d^2y/dx^2 is proportional to y and find the constant of proportionality.

55. (a) Show that the perimeter P_n of an n-sided regular polygon inscribed in a circle of radius r is

$$P_n = 2nr\sin(\pi/n).$$

(b) Find the limit of P_n as $n \to \infty$. Is the answer consistent with what you know about the circumference of a circle?

APPLICATIONS OF THE DEFINITE INTEGRAL

CHAPTER 7

7.1 INTRODUCTION

In Chapter 6 we discovered a close connection between sums of the form

$$S_a^b = \sum_a^b f(x)\,\Delta x \qquad (1)$$

and integration, the inverse of differentiation. When f is continuous on $[a, b]$, we found that the *limit* of S_a^b as Δx approaches zero is just $F(b) - F(a)$, where F is any integral or primitive of f:

$$F(x) = \int f(x)\,dx. \qquad (2)$$

We applied this to the problem of computing the area between the x-axis and the graph of $y = f(x)$, $a \leq x \leq b$. In this chapter we shall extend the applications to the following topics: area between two curves, distance, volumes, lengths of curves, areas of surfaces of revolution, average value of a function, center of mass, centroid, work, and hydrostatic force. (Further applications will be taken up in Chapter 11 in connection with polar coordinates.) integrals.

7.2 AREA BETWEEN TWO CURVES

Suppose that

$$y_1 = f_1(x), \qquad y_2 = f_2(x)$$

define two functions of x that are continuous on $[a,b]$, and furthermore suppose that

$$f_1(x) \geq f_2(x) \quad \text{for } a \leq x \leq b.$$

Then the y_1-curve is above the y_2-curve from a to b (Fig. 7.1), and we consider the problem of finding the area bounded above by the y_1-curve, below by the y_2-curve, and on the sides by the vertical lines $x = a$, $x = b$.

If the x-interval from a to b is divided into n equal subintervals, each of width

$$\Delta x = \frac{b - a}{n},$$

and a rectangle of width Δx and altitude extending from the y_2-curve to the y_1-curve is used to approximate that portion of the area between the curves

7.1

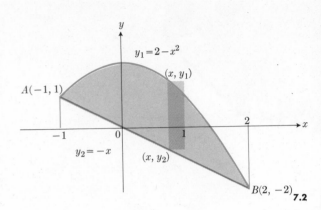

B(2, -2) 7.2

that lies between x and $x + \Delta x$, we find the area of such a rectangle is

$$(y_1 - y_2)\,\Delta x = [f_1(x) - f_2(x)]\,\Delta x.$$

The total area in question is *approximated* by adding together the areas of all such rectangles:

$$A \approx \sum_a^b [f_1(x) - f_2(x)]\,\Delta x.$$

Finally, if we let $\Delta x \to 0$, we obtain the exact area:

$$A = \lim_{\Delta x \to 0} \sum_a^b [f_1(x) - f_2(x)]\,\Delta x$$
$$= \int_a^b [f_1(x) - f_2(x)]\,dx. \qquad (1)$$

Problem. Find the area (Fig. 7.2) bounded by the parabola

$$y = 2 - x^2$$

and the straight line

$$y = -x.$$

Solution. We first find where the curves intersect by finding points that satisfy both equations simultaneously. That is, we solve

$$2 - x^2 = -x, \quad \text{or} \quad x^2 - x - 2 = 0:$$
$$(x - 2)(x + 1) = 0, \qquad x = -1, 2.$$

The points of intersection are thus $A(-1, 1)$ and $B(2, -2)$. For all values of x between -1 and $+2$,

the curve $\qquad y_1 = 2 - x^2$

is above the line $\qquad y_2 = -x$

by an amount

$$y_1 - y_2 = (2 - x^2) - (-x) = 2 - x^2 + x.$$

This is the altitude of a typical rectangle used to approximate that portion of the area lying between x and $x + \Delta x$. The total area is approximated by

$$A_{-1}^2 \approx \sum_{-1}^2 (y_1 - y_2)\,\Delta x = \sum_{-1}^2 (2 - x^2 + x)\,\Delta x,$$

and is given exactly by

$$A_{-1}^2 = \lim_{\Delta x \to 0} \sum_{-1}^2 (2 - x^2 + x)\,\Delta x$$
$$= \int_{-1}^2 (2 - x^2 + x)\,dx = 4\tfrac{1}{2}.$$

EXERCISES

1-19 #1,2,3   1-20, #4,5

1. Make a sketch to represent a region that is bounded on the right by a continuous curve $x = f(y)$, on the left by a continuous curve $x = g(y)$, below by the line $y = a$, and above by the line $y = b$. Divide the region into n horizontal strips each of altitude $\Delta y = (b - a)/n$ and express the area of the enclosed region

   (a) as a limit of a sum of areas of rectangles, and

   (b) as an appropriate definite integral.

2. Find the area bounded by

  (a) the x-axis and the curve $y = 2x - x^2$,

  (b) the y-axis and the curve $x = y^2 - y^3$,

  (c) the curve $y^2 = x$ and the line $x = 4$,

  (d) the curve $y = 2x - x^2$ and the line $y = -3$,

  (e) the curve $y = x^2$ and the line $y = x$,

  (f) the curve $x = 3y - y^2$ and the line $x + y = 3$,

  (g) the curves $y = x^4 - 2x^2$ and $y = 2x^2$.

3. Find the area of the "triangular" shaped region in the first quadrant bounded by the y-axis and the curves $y = \sin x$, $y = \cos x$.

4. The area bounded by the curve $y = x^2$ and the line $y = 4$ is divided into two equal portions by the line $y = c$. Find c.

5. Find the area bounded by the curve $\sqrt{x} + \sqrt{y} = 1$ and the coordinate axes.

6. Make a sketch to illustrate the following alternative way of arriving at Eq. (1) for the area between two curves $y = f_1(x)$ and $y = f_2(x)$. Draw a line parallel to the x-axis and below both curves for $a \leq x \leq b$. With no loss of generality, we may take this line to be C units below the x-axis for some positive number C.

  (a) If this line is taken as a new x-axis, show that the ordinates on the curves are given by

$$y = f_1(x) + C \quad \text{and} \quad y = f_2(x) + C. \quad \text{(i)}$$

Let A_1 be the area under the curve $f_1(x) + C$ over $[a, b]$, and let A_2 be the corresponding area under the curve $f_2(x) + C$. By results of Chapter 6, we know that

$$A_1 = \int_a^b [f_1(x) + C]\, dx$$

and

$$A_2 = \int_a^b [f_2(x) + C]\, dx.$$

Since the area between the two curves is $A_1 - A_2$,

  (b) subtract the two integrals of (i) above and deduce Eq. (1).

  (c) Show that the technique described above is equivalent to shifting both original curves upward C units, and therefore does not change the area between the curves.

7.3 DISTANCE

As a second application of the basic principles involved in the use of the Fundamental Theorem of the calculus, we shall calculate the distance traveled by a body moving with velocity

$$v = f(t). \quad \text{(1)}$$

To simplify the discussion we shall assume that $f(t)$ is positive, as well as being continuous, for $a \leq t \leq b$. This means that the body moves only in one direction and does no backing up.

Now there are two ways in which we can calculate the distance traveled by the body between $t = a$ and $t = b$.

First method. If we can integrate the differential equation

$$ds = f(t)\, dt, \quad \text{(2)}$$

which we get by substituting ds/dt for v in Eq. (1), then we can determine the position s of the body as a function of t, say

$$s = F(t) + C. \quad \text{(3)}$$

The distance traveled by the body between $t = a$ and $t = b$ is then given by

$$s]_{t=a}^{t=b} = F(t) + C]_a^b = F(b) - F(a).$$

We recognize this, of course, as saying that the distance is given by the definite integral

$$s]_{t=a}^{t=b} = \int_a^b f(t)\, dt = F(t)]_a^b = F(b) - F(a). \quad \text{(4)}$$

Second method. In this method, we imagine the total time interval $a \leq t \leq b$ as divided into n subintervals, each of duration $\Delta t = (b - a)/n$. The velocity at the beginning of the first subinterval is

$$v_1 = f(t_1) = f(a).$$

If Δt is small, the velocity remains nearly constant throughout the time from a to $a + \Delta t$. Hence during the first subinterval of time, the body travels a distance Δs_1, which is approximately equal to $v_1 \Delta t$:

$$\Delta s_1 \approx v_1 \Delta t = f(t_1) \Delta t. \quad \text{(5)}$$

If, instead of using the velocity v_1 at time t_1, we were to use the *average* velocity

$$\overline{v_1} = \frac{\Delta s_1}{\Delta t}, \tag{6a}$$

we could write

$$\Delta s_1 = \overline{v_1}\, \Delta t \tag{6b}$$

exactly. Now, by the Mean Value Theorem, we know that there is some instant, say T_1, between t_1 and $t_1 + \Delta t$ where the instantaneous velocity is equal to the average velocity $\overline{v_1}$. In other words,

$$f(T_1) = \overline{v_1} \quad \text{for some } T_1,\ t_1 < T_1 < t_1 + \Delta t, \tag{6c}$$

and therefore

$$\Delta s_1 = f(T_1)\, \Delta t$$

exactly. Reasoning in the same manner for the second, third, ..., nth subintervals, we conclude that there are instants of time $T_2, T_3, \ldots, T_n$ in these respective intervals such that

$$\Delta s_2 = f(T_2)\, \Delta t,$$
$$\Delta s_3 = f(T_3)\, \Delta t,$$
$$\vdots$$
$$\Delta s_n = f(T_n)\, \Delta t,$$

where $\Delta s_2, \Delta s_3, \ldots, \Delta s_n$ represent the distances traveled during these respective time subintervals. Therefore the total distance traveled between $t = a$ and $t = b$ is

$$\begin{aligned} s]_{t=a}^{t=b} &= \Delta s_1 + \Delta s_2 + \Delta s_3 + \cdots + \Delta s_n \\ &= f(T_1)\, \Delta t + f(T_2)\, \Delta t + \cdots + f(T_n)\, \Delta t \\ &= \sum_{k=1}^{n} f(T_k)\, \Delta t. \end{aligned} \tag{7}$$

Let us now take finer and finer subdivisions Δt and let n increase without limit. For each n we select the appropriate instants of time $T_1, T_2, \ldots, T_n$, according to the method described above. Then the particular sums used in Eq. (7) tend to the definite integral

$$\lim_{n\to\infty} \sum_{k=1}^{n} f(T_k)\, \Delta t = \int_a^b f(t)\, dt \tag{8}$$

as limit, by virtue of the Fundamental Theorem. On the other hand, these sums all give the distance traveled by the body. Therefore the distance traveled is equal to the integral in Eq. (8) (or the one in Eq. 4).

Remark 1. If, instead of using the velocities at the instants of time $T_1, T_2, \ldots, T_n$ described above, we had used the velocities

$$v_1 = f(t_1), \quad v_2 = f(t_2), \quad \ldots, \quad v_n = f(t_n)$$

at the beginnings of the various subintervals, then we would have had n *approximations* like (5) with subscripts $1, 2, \ldots, n$. Then we would have obtained an *approximation*

$$\Delta s_1 + \Delta s_2 + \cdots + \Delta s_n$$
$$\approx f(t_1)\, \Delta t + f(t_2)\, \Delta t + \cdots + f(t_n)\, \Delta t,$$

or

$$s]_{t=a}^{t=b} = \sum_{k=1}^{n} f(t_k)\, \Delta t. \tag{9}$$

Now since $f(t)$ is continuous, the sums (7) and (9) have the same *limit* as $n \to \infty$. In other words, the approximation (9) gets better as n increases, and the *limit* again gives the exact value, namely, the integral in Eq. (8).

Remark 2. Of course, the two methods give the same result, Eqs. (4) and (8). The second method is useful primarily

(a) because it shows how the simple formula

$$\text{distance} = \text{velocity} \times \text{time},$$

which applies only to the case of *constant* velocity, can be extended to the case of variable velocity, provided we apply it to short subintervals Δt; and

(b) because it can be used [in the form of the approximation (9)] to estimate the distance in cases where the velocity is given empirically by a table of values or a graph instead of by a formula $f(t)$ with known indefinite integral $F(t)$.

Remark 3. If the velocity changes sign during the interval (a, b), then the integral in Eq. (4) gives only the *net* change in s. This permits cancellation of distances traveled forwards and backwards. For example, it would give an answer of 2 miles if the body traveled forward 7 miles and backed up 5 miles.

a|b

7.3

If we want to determine the actual total distance traveled, we should calculate the integral of the *absolute value* of the velocity,

$$\int_a^b |f(t)|\, dt. \tag{10}$$

This would be done by integrating separately over the intervals where v is positive and where v is negative and adding the absolute values of the results.

Remark 4. The preceding discussion shows that the distance traveled is given by precisely the same expression as that for the area bounded by the curve

$$v = f(t)$$

and the t-axis from a to b. All of the discussion above can be interpreted geometrically. For example, T is chosen between t and $t + \Delta t$ in such a way that the area of the rectangle of base Δt and altitude $f(T)$ (Fig. 7.3a) is precisely equal to the area under the velocity curve between t and $t + \Delta t$. This is also the place where the slope of the curve $s = F(t)$ (Fig. 7.3b) is equal to the slope of the chord.

EXERCISES

1-20 #1,2   1-21 #3-13 odd

In Exercises 1 through 8, the function $v = f(t)$ represents the velocity v (ft/sec) of a moving body as a function of the time t (sec). Sketch the graph of v versus t and find that portion of the given time interval $a \le t \le b$ in which the velocity is (a) positive, and (b) negative. Then find the total distance traveled by the body between $t = a$ and $t = b$.

1. $v = 2t + 1, \quad 0 \le t \le 2$

2. $v = t^2 - t - 2, \quad 0 \le t \le 3$

3. $v = t - \dfrac{8}{t^2}, \quad 1 \le t \le 3$

4. $v = |t - 1|, \quad 0 \le t \le 2$

5. $v = 6 \sin 3t, \quad 0 \le t \le \dfrac{\pi}{2}$

6. $v = 4 \cos 2t, \quad 0 \le t \le \pi$

7. $v = \sin t + \cos t, \quad 0 \le t \le \pi$

8. $v = \sin t \sqrt{2 + 2 \cos t}, \quad 0 \le t \le \pi$

In Exercises 9 through 13, the function $a = f(t)$ represents the acceleration (ft/sec^2) of a moving body and v_0 is its velocity at time $t = 0$. Find the *distance* traveled by the body between time $t = 0$ and $t = 2$.

9. $a = \sin t, \quad v_0 = 2$

10. $a = 1 - \cos t, \quad v_0 = 0$

11. $a = g$ (constant), $\quad v_0 = 0$

12. $a = \sqrt{4t + 1}, \quad v_0 = -4\frac{1}{3}$

13. $a = \dfrac{1}{\sqrt{4t + 1}}, \quad v_0 = 1$

14. Suppose water flows into a tank at the rate of $f(t)$ (gal/min), where f is a given, positive, continuous function of t. Let the amount of water in the tank at time $t = 0$ be Q_0 (gal). Apply the Fundamental Theorem to show that the amount of water in the tank at any later time $t = b$ is

$$Q = Q_0 + \int_0^b f(t)\, dt.$$

15. Use the trapezoidal rule, Article 6.10, to find (approximately) the distance traveled between $t = 0$ and $t = 2$ by a body whose velocity is given by the following table of values.

v (ft/sec)	2.2	2.5	3.0	3.8	5.0
t (sec)	0	0.5	1.0	1.5	2.0

Also find (approximately) the average velocity during the time $t = 0$ to $t = 2$.

7.4 VOLUMES

Method of slicing

The volumes of many solids can be found by an application of the *method of slicing*. Suppose, for example, that the solid is bounded by two parallel planes perpendicular to the x-axis at $x = a$ and $x = b$. Imagine the solid cut into thin slices of thickness Δx by planes perpendicular to the x-axis. Then the total volume V of the solid is the sum of the volumes of these slices (see Fig. 7.4).

Let ΔV be the volume of the representative slice between x and $x + \Delta x$. Then if A' and A'' are respectively the smallest and largest cross-sectional areas of the solid between x and $x + \Delta x$, it will be

seen at once that

$$A' \, \Delta x \leq \Delta V \leq A'' \, \Delta x,$$

or

$$\Delta V = A(\bar{x}) \, \Delta x,$$

where $A(\bar{x})$ denotes an appropriate intermediate cross-sectional area of the solid at some $\bar{x}$ between x and $x + \Delta x$. Then

$$V = \sum_a^b A(\bar{x}) \, \Delta x$$

will give the total volume of the solid exactly. If, instead of choosing the exactly appropriate intermediate point $\bar{x}$ in the typical subinterval, we use the area $A(x)$ of the cross section at x, we have only an approximation

$$V \approx \sum_a^b A(x) \, \Delta x.$$

But now let $\Delta x \to 0$. Then, if the cross-sectional area is a continuous function of x, all these sums will approach the same limit. Since one sequence of sums always gives the value V, it will have this value as its limit. Hence the other sums will also give the value V in the limit, that is,

$$V = \lim_{\Delta x \to 0} \sum_a^b A(x) \, \Delta x = \int_a^b A(x) \, dx. \quad (1)$$

Volume of a solid of revolution

The solid generated by rotating a plane region about an axis on its plane is called a *solid of revolution*. To find the volume of such a solid, as shown in Fig. 7.5, we need only observe that the cross-sectional area $A(x)$ in Eq. (1) is the area of a circle of radius $r = y = f(x)$, so that

$$A(x) = \pi r^2 = \pi [f(x)]^2. \quad (2)$$

Example 1. Suppose the curve in Fig. 7.5 represents the graph of

$$y = \sqrt{x}$$

from $(0, 0)$ to $(4, 2)$. Then the volume of the representative slice is

$$\Delta V \approx \pi y^2 \, \Delta x = \pi (\sqrt{x})^2 \, \Delta x,$$

and the total volume is approximately

$$V \approx \sum_0^4 \pi x \, \Delta x.$$

Exactly, we have

$$V = \lim_{\Delta x \to 0} \sum_0^4 \pi x \, \Delta x = \int_0^4 \pi x \, dx = \pi \frac{x^2}{2}\Big]_0^4 = 8\pi.$$

Method of cylindrical shells

Suppose the region $PQRS$ in Fig. 7.6 is revolved around the y-axis. We can compute the generated volume in the following way. Consider a strip of area between the ordinate at x and the ordinate at $x + \Delta x$. When this strip is revolved around the y-axis, it generates a hollow, thin-walled shell of inner radius x, outer radius $x + \Delta x$, and volume ΔV. The base of this shell is a ring bounded by two concentric circles. The inner radius is

$$r_1 = x$$

and the outer radius is

$$r_2 = x + \Delta x.$$

The area of the ring is

$$\Delta A = \pi(r_2^2 - r_1^2) = 2\pi\left(\frac{r_2 + r_1}{2}\right)(r_2 - r_1)$$

$$= 2\pi r \, \Delta x.$$

Here $\quad r = \dfrac{r_2 + r_1}{2} = x + \dfrac{\Delta x}{2}$

is the radius of the circle midway between the inner and outer boundaries of the ring, and $2\pi r$ is its circumference.

Now if we had a cylindrical shell of constant altitude y standing on this base, its volume would be

$$\text{altitude} \times \text{base} = y \, \Delta A.$$

In the present case, the altitude of the shell varies between the minimum value of y and the maximum value of y between x and $x + \Delta x$. For an increasing function such as the one shown in Fig. 7.6, the volume therefore lies between $y \, \Delta A$ and $(y + \Delta y) \, \Delta A$.

7.5

7.6

That is,

$$y \, \Delta A \leq \Delta V \leq (y + \Delta y) \, \Delta A,$$

or

$$y \cdot 2\pi r \, \Delta x \leq \Delta V \leq (y + \Delta y) \cdot 2\pi r \, \Delta x.$$

The total volume V is contained between the lower sum

$$s = \sum_{a}^{b} y \cdot 2\pi \left(x + \frac{\Delta x}{2} \right) \Delta x$$

and the upper sum

$$S = \sum_{a}^{b} (y + \Delta y) \cdot 2\pi \left(x + \frac{\Delta x}{2} \right) \Delta x.$$

As Δx approaches zero, both of these sums approach the following integral as limit (see Article 7.5). Hence this limit must also be equal to the volume V, namely,

$$V = \lim_{\Delta x \to 0} s = \lim_{\Delta x \to 0} S = \int_{a}^{b} y \cdot 2\pi x \, dx$$

$$= \int_{a}^{b} 2\pi x f(x) \, dx.$$

Remark. An easy way to visualize this result is to imagine that the volume element ΔV has been cut along a generator of the cylinder and that the shell has been rolled out flat like a thin sheet of tin. The sheet then has dimensions very nearly equal to $2\pi x$ by $y = f(x)$ by Δx. Hence

$$\Delta V \approx 2\pi x \cdot f(x) \cdot \Delta x,$$

and the total volume is given approximately by

$$V \approx \sum_{a}^{b} 2\pi x \cdot f(x) \cdot \Delta x.$$

As Δx approaches zero, we obtain a limit that is equal to the exact volume:

$$V = \lim_{\Delta x \to 0} \sum_{a}^{b} 2\pi x \cdot f(x) \cdot \Delta x$$

$$= \int_{a}^{b} 2\pi x f(x) \, dx.$$

Example 2. In Example 1, where the area under the curve $y = \sqrt{x}$ is revolved around the x-axis, we may

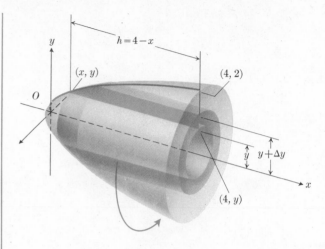

7.7 The solid of revolution generated by rotating the curve $y = \sqrt{x}$, $[0, 4]$, about the x-axis.

take a horizontal strip of area between the lines at distances y and $y + \Delta y$ above the x-axis. The volume generated by revolving this strip around the x-axis is a hollow cylindrical shell of inner circumference $2\pi y$, inner length $4 - x$, and wall thickness Δy (see Fig. 7.7). Hence the total volume V is approximately

$$V \approx \sum_{y=0}^{2} 2\pi y (4 - x) \, \Delta y,$$

and is exactly equal to the limit of this sum as Δy approaches zero:

$$V = \lim_{\Delta y \to 0} \sum_{y=0}^{2} 2\pi y (4 - x) \, \Delta y$$

$$= \int_{0}^{2} 2\pi y (4 - y^2) \, dy$$

$$= 2\pi \left[2y^2 - \frac{y^4}{4} \right]_{0}^{2} = 8\pi.$$

Illustrations

Various methods for finding volumes are illustrated in the following problems.

Problem 1. The region inside the circle

$$x^2 + y^2 = a^2$$

is rotated about the x-axis to generate a solid sphere. Find its volume.

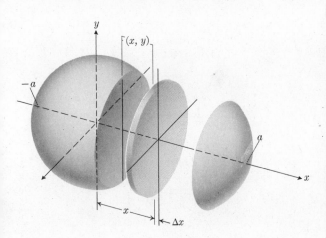

7.8 The sphere generated by rotating the circle $x^2 + y^2 = a^2$ about the x-axis.

Solution. We imagine the sphere cut into thin slices by planes perpendicular to the x-axis (Fig. 7.8). The volume of a typical slice between two planes at x and $x + \Delta x$ is approximately

$$\pi y^2 \, \Delta x = \pi(a^2 - x^2) \, \Delta x,$$

and the sum of all slices is approximately

$$V_{-a}^{a} \approx \sum_{-a}^{a} \pi(a^2 - x^2) \, \Delta x.$$

The exact volume is given by

$$V_{-a}^{a} = \lim_{\Delta x \to 0} \sum_{-a}^{a} \pi(a^2 - x^2) \, \Delta x$$

$$= \int_{-a}^{a} \pi(a^2 - x^2) \, dx$$

$$= \pi \left[a^2 x - \frac{x^3}{3} \right]_{-a}^{a} = \tfrac{4}{3}\pi a^3.$$

Problem 2. A hole of diameter a is bored through the center of the sphere of Problem 1. Find the remaining volume.

Solution. The volume in question could be generated by rotating about the y-axis the area inside the circle $x^2 + y^2 = a^2$ lying to the right of the line $x = a/2$ (Fig. 7.9a). The line and the circle intersect at the points

$(a/2, \pm a\sqrt{3}/2)$. There are at least three methods for finding the required volume.

Method 1. Figure 7.9(b) shows an exploded view of the solid sphere with the core pulled out. Note that the core is a cylinder with a spherical cap at each end. Essentially, what we shall do is subtract the volume of this core from the volume of the sphere, but we shall simplify matters slightly by imagining that the two caps have been sliced off first, by planes perpendicular to the y-axis at $y = \pm a\sqrt{3}/2$. When these two caps have been removed, the truncated sphere has a volume V_1. From this truncated sphere we remove a right circular cylinder of radius $a/2$ and altitude $2(a\sqrt{3}/2) = a\sqrt{3}$. Then the volume of this flat-ended cylinder is

$$V_2 = \pi \left(\frac{a}{2} \right)^2 (a\sqrt{3}) = \frac{\sqrt{3}}{4}\pi a^3.$$

The desired volume is $V = V_1 - V_2$. We find V_1 by the same method we used for the spherical ball in Problem 1, but we keep in mind that the two caps have been removed at top and bottom. Imagine the solid as cut into slices by planes perpendicular to the y-axis. The slice between y and $y + \Delta y$ is approximated by a cylinder of altitude Δy and cross-sectional area

$$\pi x^2 = \pi(a^2 - y^2),$$

so that we have the approximation

$$V_1 \approx \sum_{-a\sqrt{3}/2}^{a\sqrt{3}/2} \pi(a^2 - y^2) \, \Delta y$$

and the exact value

$$V_1 = \int_{-a\sqrt{3}/2}^{a\sqrt{3}/2} \pi(a^2 - y^2) \, dy = \frac{3\sqrt{3}}{4}\pi a^3.$$

Thus

$$V = V_1 - V_2 = \frac{3\sqrt{3}}{4}\pi a^3 - \frac{\sqrt{3}}{4}\pi a^3 = \frac{\sqrt{3}}{2}\pi a^3.$$

Method 2. Instead of subtracting volumes, we may work directly with the volume required. Again, we imagine the solid to be cut into thin slices by planes perpendicular to the y-axis. Each slice (Fig. 7.9c) is now like a washer of thickness Δy, inner radius

$$r_1 = \frac{a}{2},$$

and outer radius

$$r_2 = x = \sqrt{a^2 - y^2}.$$

a|b

c|d

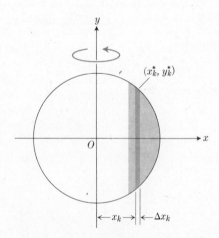

7.9 **a|** The tinted region generates the volume of revolution.

b| An exploded view showing the sphere with the core removed.

c| A phantom view showing a cross-sectional slice of the sphere with core removed.

d| The strip of area indicated by darker tint generates a cylindrical shell.

The area of a face of such a washer is

$$\pi r_2^2 - \pi r_1^2 = \pi(\tfrac{3}{4}a^2 - y^2)$$

and the volume of the solid is approximately

$$V \approx \sum_{-a\sqrt{3}/2}^{a\sqrt{3}/2} \pi(\tfrac{3}{4}a^2 - y^2)\,\Delta y,$$

while its exact value is

$$V = \lim_{\Delta y \to 0} \sum_{-a\sqrt{3}/2}^{a\sqrt{3}/2} \pi(\tfrac{3}{4}a^2 - y^2)\,\Delta y$$

$$= \int_{-a\sqrt{3}/2}^{a\sqrt{3}/2} \pi(\tfrac{3}{4}a^2 - y^2)\,dy$$

$$= \frac{\sqrt{3}}{2}\pi a^3.$$

Method 3. This time we shall use the cylindrical-shell approach (see Fig. 7.9a). We imagine the solid to be cut into a number of hollow cylindrical shells by cylinders having the y-axis as their common axis and having radii

$$x_1 = \frac{a}{2}, \quad x_2, \quad x_3, \quad \ldots, \quad x_n, \quad x_{n+1} = a.$$

The first shell has inner radius x_1 and outer radius x_2, the second shell has inner radius x_2 and outer radius x_3, and so on, the kth shell having inner radius x_k and outer radius x_{k+1}. This kth shell fills the region swept out when the dark strip in Fig. 7.9(d) is revolved about the y-axis. If we imagine this region to have been cut along a line parallel to the y-axis and flattened out, we see that the volume ΔV_k of the kth cylindrical shell is approximately

$$2\pi x_k^* \cdot \Delta x_k \cdot 2y_k^* = 4\pi x_k^* \sqrt{a^2 - (x_k^*)^2}\,\Delta x_k,$$

where (x_k^*, y_k^*), Fig. 7.9(d), is the point of abscissa

$$x_k^* = \tfrac{1}{2}(x_k + x_{k+1})$$

on the circle in the first quadrant. Then the entire volume will be approximated by

$$V \approx \sum_{k=1}^{n} 4\pi x_k^* \sqrt{a^2 - (x_k^*)^2}\,\Delta x_k$$

$$\approx \sum_{a/2}^{a} 4\pi x \sqrt{a^2 - x^2}\,\Delta x.$$

7.10

The exact value will be the *limit* of this sum, namely,

$$V = \lim_{x \to 0} \sum_{a/2}^{a} 4\pi x \sqrt{a^2 - x^2}\,\Delta x$$

$$= \int_{a/2}^{a} 4\pi x \sqrt{a^2 - x^2}\,dx.$$

To evaluate this integral, we let

$$u = a^2 - x^2;$$

then

$$V = 4\pi \int_{a/2}^{a} \sqrt{a^2 - x^2}\,(x\,dx)$$

$$= 4\pi \int u^{1/2}(-\tfrac{1}{2}\,du) = -\frac{4\pi}{3}\Big[(a^2 - x^2)^{3/2}\Big]_{a/2}^{a}$$

$$= \frac{\sqrt{3}}{2}\pi a^3.$$

Problem 3. A wedge is cut from a right circular cylinder of radius r by two planes. One is perpendicular to the axis of the cylinder while the second makes an angle α with the first and intersects it at the center of the cylinder. Find the volume of the wedge.

Solution. The volume ΔV of the slice between y and $y + \Delta y$ in Fig. 7.10 is approximately

$$\Delta V \approx A(y)\,\Delta y,$$

where

$$A(y) = \tfrac{1}{2}xh$$

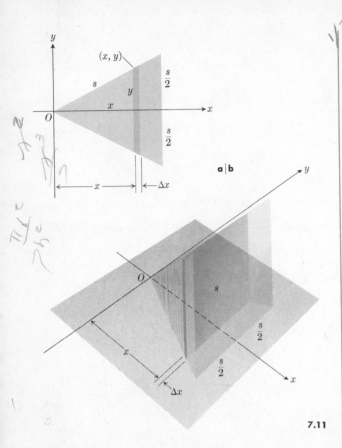

7.11

is the area of the triangle that forms one face of the slice and is to be expressed as a function of y. By trigonometry,

$$h = x \tan \alpha,$$

and by the theorem of Pythagoras,

$$x^2 + y^2 = r^2, \quad \text{or} \quad x^2 = r^2 - y^2.$$

Hence

$$A(y) = \tfrac{1}{2}x^2 \tan \alpha = \tfrac{1}{2}\tan \alpha \, (r^2 - y^2).$$

The total volume is given by

$$V = \lim_{\Delta y \to 0} \sum_{-r}^{r} A(y) \, \Delta y$$

$$= \int_{-r}^{r} \tfrac{1}{2} \tan \alpha (r^2 - y^2) \, dy.$$

Remembering that the factor $\tfrac{1}{2} \tan \alpha$ is a constant, we find

$$V = \tfrac{2}{3} r^3 \tan \alpha.$$

Problem 4. The base of a certain solid is an equilateral triangle of side s, with one vertex at the origin and an altitude along the x-axis. Each plane section perpendicular to the x-axis is a square, one side of which lies in the base of the solid. Find the volume of the solid.

Solution. Figure 7.11(a) represents the base of the solid with a strip of width Δx, which corresponds to a slice of the solid of volume

$$\Delta V \approx A(x) \, \Delta x,$$

where

$$A(x) = (2y)^2 = 4y^2$$

is the area of a face of the slice. The slice extends upward from the plane of the paper in Fig. 7.11(a). It is possible to find the required volume from the statement of the problem by reference to this figure and without visualizing the actual solid. A perspective view of the solid is, however, given in Fig. 7.11(b). It is required to find y in terms of x so that the area $A(x)$ will be given as a function of x. Since the base triangle is equilateral, its altitude h is given by

$$h^2 = s^2 - (s/2)^2 = \tfrac{3}{4}s^2,$$

or

$$h = \frac{s}{2}\sqrt{3}.$$

Then, by similar triangles, we find

$$\frac{2y}{x} = \frac{\tfrac{s}{2}}{h} = \frac{2}{\sqrt{3}}, \quad \text{or} \quad y = \frac{x}{\sqrt{3}}.$$

Then

$$V = \int_0^h A(x) \, dx = \int_0^{s\sqrt{3}/2} \tfrac{4}{3} x^2 \, dx$$

$$= \frac{s^3}{2\sqrt{3}} = \frac{1}{3} hs^2.$$

EXERCISES

In Exercises 1 through 8, find the volumes generated when the areas bounded by the given curves and lines are rotated about the x-axis. [*Note.* $x = 0$ is the y-axis and $y = 0$ is the x-axis.]

1. $x + y = 2$, $x = 0$, $y = 0$
2. $y = \sin x$, $y = 0$ $(0 \le x \le \pi)$
[See Exercise 17, Article 6.8.]

3. $y = x - x^2$, $y = 0$ 4. $y = 3x - x^2$, $y = x$

5. $x = 2y - y^2$, $x = 0$ 6. $y = x$, $y = 1$, $x = 0$
   (Use cylindrical shells.)

7. $y = x^2$, $y = 4$ 8. $y = 3 + x^2$, $y = 4$

9. By integration find the volume generated by the triangle with vertices at $(0, 0)$, $(h, 0)$, (h, r) when it is rotated

   (a) about the x-axis,   (b) about the y-axis.

10. (a) The area bounded by the curve $y = x^2$ and the line $y = x$ is revolved around the y-axis. Find the volume generated.

    (b) Find the volume generated if the area is revolved around the x-axis.

11. The area bounded by the curve $y = x^2$ and the line $y = 4$ generates various solids of revolution when rotated

    (a) about the y-axis,   (b) about the line $y = 4$,
    (c) about the x-axis,   (d) about the line $y = -1$,
    (e) about the line $x = 2$.

    Find the volume generated in each case.

12. (a) A hemispherical bowl of radius a contains water to a depth h. Find the volume of water in the bowl.

    (b) (Review exercise on related rates.) Water runs into a hemispherical bowl of radius 5 ft at the rate of 0.2 ft³/sec. How fast is the water level in the bowl rising when the water is 4 ft. deep?

13. A football has a volume that is approximately the same as the volume generated by rotating the area inside the ellipse $b^2x^2 + a^2y^2 = a^2b^2$ (where a and b are constants) about the x-axis. Find the volume so generated.

14. The cross sections of a certain solid by planes perpendicular to the x-axis are circles with diameters extending from the curve $y = x^2$ to the curve $y = 8 - x^2$. The solid lies between the points of intersection of these two curves. Find its volume.

15. The base of a certain solid is the circle $x^2 + y^2 = a^2$. Each plane section of the solid cut out by a plane perpendicular to the x-axis is a square with one edge of the square in the base of the solid. Find the volume of the solid.

16. Two great circles, lying in planes that are perpendicular to each other, are marked on a sphere of radius a. A portion of the sphere is then shaved off in such a manner that any plane section of the

remaining solid, perpendicular to the common diameter of the two great circles, is a square with vertices on these circles. Find the volume of the solid that remains.

17. The base of a certain solid is the circle $x^2 + y^2 = a^2$. Each plane section of the solid cut out by a plane perpendicular to the y-axis is an isosceles right triangle with one leg in the base of the solid. Find the volume.

18. The base of a certain solid is the region between the x-axis and the curve $y = \sin x$ between $x = 0$ and $x = \pi/2$. Each plane section of the solid perpendicular to the x-axis is an equilateral triangle with one side in the base of the solid. Find the volume.

19. A rectangular swimming pool is 30 ft wide and 50 ft long. The depth of water h (ft) at distance x (ft) from one end of the pool is measured at 5-ft intervals and found to be as follows:

x (ft)	0	5	10	15	20	25
h (ft)	6.0	8.2	9.1	9.9	10.5	11.0

x (ft)	30	35	40	45	50
h (ft)	11.5	11.9	12.3	12.7	13.0

Use the trapezoidal rule to find (approximately) the volume of water in the pool.

20. The circle $x^2 + y^2 = a^2$ is rotated about the line $x = b$ ($b > a$) to generate a torus. Find the volume generated.

Hint. $\int_{-a}^{a} \sqrt{a^2 - x^2} \, dx = \pi a^2/2,$

since it is the area of a semicircle of radius a.

7.5 APPROXIMATIONS

By now it is apparent that each application of the Fundamental Theorem that we have so far made has involved the following steps.

1. Select an independent variable, say x, such that the quantity U to be computed can be represented as a sum of pieces ΔU, where ΔU is that part of U that is associated with the subinterval $(x, x + \Delta x)$ of the domain $a \le x \le b$ of the variable x.

2. Subdivide the domain $[a, b]$ into n subintervals. For the sake of simplicity we usually take the lengths all to be the same, namely, equal to $\Delta x = (b - a)/n$.

3. Approximate that portion ΔU of U that is associated with the subinterval $(x, x + \Delta x)$ by an expression of the form

$$\Delta U \approx f(X) \, \Delta x. \tag{1}$$

In this expression, X is to be some point in the subinterval $(x, x + \Delta x)$ and the function f is to be continuous over the entire domain $a \leq x \leq b$.

4. Observe that the total quantity U is given *approximately* by

$$U \approx \sum_a^b f(X) \, \Delta x. \tag{2}$$

5. Take the limit, as Δx approaches zero, of the sum in Eq. (2). This limit is the definite integral

$$\lim_{\Delta x \to 0} \sum_a^b f(X) \, \Delta x = \int_a^b f(x) \, dx. \tag{3}$$

Is this limit also an approximation to U or does it give U exactly?

In the case of area, distance, and volume we have seen that the *limit* in (3) does give U exactly. In order for us to be able to apply these methods to new situations as they arise, we need an answer to the following question.

Question. How accurate must the approximations in (1) and (2) be if we are to be able to say that all of the error is squeezed out in going to the limit (3), with the result that the exact value of U is given by the limit

$$U = \lim_{\Delta x \to 0} \sum_a^b f(X) \, \Delta x = \int_a^b f(x) \, dx? \tag{4}$$

Answer. Denote by $\alpha \, \Delta x$ the correction that must be added to the right side of Eq. (1) to give ΔU exactly. That is, suppose that

$$\Delta U = f(X) \, \Delta x + \alpha \, \Delta x, \tag{5}$$

exactly.

Case 1. Suppose these correction terms are no larger than a constant K times $(\Delta x)^2$:

$$|\alpha \, \Delta x| \leq K \, (\Delta x)^2$$

where K is a constant the same for all subintervals and all methods of subdivision. Then we have

$$\Delta U = f(X) \, \Delta x + \alpha \, \Delta x,$$

$$U = \sum_a^b f(X) \, \Delta x + \sum_a^b \alpha \, \Delta x;$$

and

$$\left| U - \sum_a^b f(X) \, \Delta x \right| = \left| \sum_a^b \alpha \, \Delta x \right| \leq \sum_a^b K \, (\Delta x)^2. \tag{6}$$

This last sum consists of n terms, each of which is equal to $K \, (\Delta x)^2$, where $\Delta x = (b - a)/n$. Therefore

$$\sum_a^b K \, (\Delta x)^2 = nK(b - a)^2/n^2$$

$$= K(b - a)^2/n = K(b - a) \, \Delta x,$$

and (6) becomes

$$\left| U - \sum_a^b f(X) \, \Delta x \right| \leq K(b - a) \, \Delta x. \tag{7}$$

In other words, if the error in the approximation (1) to each individual ΔU is no more than a constant times the *square* of Δx, then the error in the approximation (2) to the *total* U is no more than a constant times the *first power* of Δx. Now let Δx approach zero in (7). The sum on the left becomes the definite integral (3), and the term on the right becomes zero. In other words, U is exactly equal to the definite integral in this case.

Case 2. Suppose the correction terms are numerically no larger than a constant K' times Δx times δy:

$$|\alpha \, \Delta x| \leq K' \, \Delta x \, \delta y,$$

where K' is the same for all subintervals and all methods of subdivision, and where δy is the oscillation in the interval $(x, x + \Delta x)$ of a function $y = \phi(x)$ that is continuous over the closed interval $[a, b]$.

Then one finds in this case that the total error in the approximation (2) is no larger than

$$K'(b - a) \text{ times } (\max \delta y).$$

But the maximum δy also approaches zero when Δx does, so again we find that U is given exactly by the definite integral.

We have given criteria such as

$$|\alpha \, \Delta x| \leq K \, (\Delta x)^2 \quad \text{and} \quad |\alpha \, \Delta x| \leq K' \, \Delta x \, \delta y,$$

where K and K' are constants. Usually, in an application, we have a function of x in place of K or K' in these inequalities. But a function of x that is continuous over the closed interval $[a, b]$ has a maximum absolute value M on that interval, and we could take K (or K') equal to M in such a case. Also, the correction terms $\alpha \, \Delta x$ could involve finite combinations of the two cases discussed above, provided that the inequality

$$|\alpha \, \Delta x| \leq K \, (\Delta x)^2 + K' \, \Delta x \, \delta y$$

is satisfied for some choice of the constants K and K'.

Roughly speaking, we may say that in the approximation

$$\Delta U \approx f(X) \, \Delta x$$

we must include all first power Δx terms but we may omit higher power terms like $(\Delta x)^2$, $(\Delta x)^3$, and so on, or we may omit such mixed terms as $(\Delta x, \Delta y)$, $(\Delta x)^2(\Delta y)$, $(\Delta x)(\Delta y)^2$, and so on. If each separate piece ΔU is estimated to this degree of accuracy, then the total quantity U which is given approximately by the sum (2) will be given exactly by the limit of the sum, namely, by the integral (4).

In discussing the cylindrical shell method of finding a volume of revolution (Article 7.4), we found that we could estimate the volume ΔV in a hollow shell as follows:

$$2\pi \left(x + \frac{\Delta x}{2} \right) y \, \Delta x \leq \Delta V \leq 2\pi \left(x + \frac{\Delta x}{2} \right) (y + \Delta y) \, \Delta x. \quad (8)$$

Multiplied out, this becomes

$$2\pi x y \, \Delta x + \pi y \, (\Delta x)^2 \leq \Delta V,$$
$$\Delta V \leq 2\pi x y \, \Delta x + \pi y \, (\Delta x)^2 + 2\pi x \, \Delta x \, \Delta y + \pi \, \Delta y \, (\Delta x)^2.$$

If we ignore all except the first power terms in Δx, we have the approximation

$$\Delta V \approx 2\pi x y \, \Delta x,$$

with an error that involves combinations such as $\pi y \, (\Delta x)^2$, $2\pi x \, \Delta y \, \Delta x$, $\pi \, \Delta y \, (\Delta x)^2$. All such terms may be safely ignored when we go to the *limit* of the sum as Δx approaches zero:

$$V = \lim_{\Delta x \to 0} \sum_a^b 2\pi x y \, \Delta x$$
$$= \int_a^b 2\pi x y \, dx = \int_a^b 2\pi x f(x) \, dx.$$

Infinitesimals

A variable, such as Δx above, that approaches zero as a limit is called an *infinitesimal*. Terms that approach zero as the first power of Δx are said to be of the *same order* as Δx, but terms which approach zero as $(\Delta x)^2$ or as $\Delta y \, \Delta x$ are called infinitesimals of *higher order* than Δx. In setting up a definite integral, we must retain those infinitesimals that are of the same order as Δx, but we may omit those infinitesimals that are of higher order than Δx. Thus we may omit the term $\alpha \, \Delta x$, Eq. (5), if α is an infinitesimal of the same order as Δx (or higher order) or of the same order as δy (or higher order), and the *limit* in (4) will give the exact value of U.

As a further illustration of these ideas, we give here a proof of Bliss's theorem, a theorem which is often useful.

Bliss's Theorem.[*] Let f and g be continuous functions on $[a, b]$, where $a < b$, and a and b are finite real numbers. Let P be a partition of $[a, b]$ into n subintervals by points

$$a = x_0 < x_1 < x_2 < \cdots < x_n = b, \quad (9a)$$

and let

$$\delta = \max \, (x_i - x_{i-1}), \quad i = 1, 2, \ldots, n. \quad (9b)$$

---

[*] Olmsted, J. M. H., *Advanced Calculus*, Appleton-Century-Crofts, 1961, p. 116.

Let t_i and t_i' be in the subinterval $[x_{i-1}, x_i]$, and form the sum

$$S = \sum_{i=1}^{n} f(t_i) g(t_i') \, \Delta x_i. \tag{10}$$

Then, as $n \to \infty$ and $\delta \to 0$,

$$\lim S = \int_a^b f(x) g(x) \, dx. \tag{11}$$

Proof. The result follows from the fact that f is bounded, g is uniformly continuous on $[a, b]$, and the sum

$$S^* = \sum_{i=1}^{n} f(t_i) g(t_i) \, \Delta x_i \tag{12}$$

approaches the integral in Eq. (11) when $n \to \infty$ and $\delta \to 0$. First we see that because f is bounded, there exists a positive number K such that

$$|f(x)| < K \quad \text{for } a \le x \le b. \tag{13}$$

Second, if $\epsilon > 0$, there exists $\delta' > 0$ such that

$$|g(t_i') - g(t_i)| < \frac{\epsilon}{K(b-a)} \quad \text{if} \quad |t_i' - t_i| < \delta'.$$

Therefore, if $\delta \le \delta'$,

$$|S - S^*| \le \sum_{i=1}^{n} |f(t_i)| \cdot |g(t_i') - g(t_i)| \, \Delta x_i$$

$$\le \sum_{i=1}^{n} K \cdot \frac{\epsilon}{K(b-a)} \, \Delta x_i$$

$$= \frac{\epsilon}{b-a} \sum \Delta x_i = \epsilon. \tag{14}$$

As $n \to \infty$ and $\delta \to 0$, therefore, S^* approaches the integral on the right side of Eq. (11); and $S - S^*$ approaches zero. Hence S approaches the integral, as required. □

Remark. Bliss's theorem can be extended to products of more than two functions. For instance, instead of $f(t_i) g(t_i')$, as in Eq. (10), we might have three functions and three points in the ith subinterval: $f(t_i) g(t_i') h(t_i'')$. If the three functions f, g, and h are all continuous on $[a, b]$, the limit of the corresponding sum would be the integral

$$\int_a^b f(x) g(x) h(x) \, dx.$$

Other combinations of functions than products, such as sums and quotients (denominators nonzero, of course), behave in a similar manner. For the arc length of a curve, we encounter a sum of the form

$$\sum \sqrt{[f(t_i)]^2 + [g(t_i')]^2},$$

where f and g are continuous on $[a, b]$. Again, that sum has for its limit the same integral we would get if t_i' were replaced by t_i. In other words, the evaluation of one of the functions at t_i and the other at t_i' is of no consequence *in the limit* for continuous functions.

EXERCISES

1. In Fig. 7.6, Article 7.4, let V_a^x denote the volume generated by rotating about the y-axis the area under the curve $y = f(x)$ between the ordinate at a and the ordinate at x, $(x > a)$. By making use of the inequality (8) in this section, show that

$$\frac{dV_a^x}{dx} = \lim_{\Delta x \to 0} \frac{\Delta V_a^x}{\Delta x} = 2\pi x f(x).$$

From this, deduce that

$$V_a^b = \int_a^b 2\pi x f(x) \, dx.$$

2. Let U_a^x denote the amount of the quantity U associated with the interval (a, x), and let ΔU in Eq. (5) represent

$$U_a^{x+\Delta x} - U_a^x = U_x^{x+\Delta x}.$$

If the function $f(x)$ in Eq. (5) is continuous over the closed interval $a \le x \le b$ and $|\alpha \, \Delta x| \le K \, (\Delta x)^2$, where K is a constant, show that

$$\frac{dU_a^x}{dx} = \lim_{\Delta x \to 0} \frac{\Delta U}{\Delta x} = f(x).$$

From this, deduce that $U_a^b = \int_a^b f(x) \, dx$.

3. In Exercise 2, replace the condition $|\alpha \Delta x| \leq K(\Delta x)^2$ by the condition

$$|\alpha \Delta x| \leq |K' \Delta x \, \delta y|,$$

where K' is a constant and δy is the oscillation over the interval $(x, x + \Delta x)$ of a function $y = g(x)$ that is continuous over the closed interval $a \leq x \leq b$. Derive the same conclusion as in Exercise 2.

7.6   LENGTH OF A PLANE CURVE

Divide the arc AB, Fig. 7.12, into n pieces and join the successive points of division by straight lines. A representative line, such as PQ, will have length

$$PQ = \sqrt{(\Delta x_k)^2 + (\Delta y_k)^2}.$$

The length of the curve AB is approximately

$$L_A^B \approx \sum_{k=1}^{n} \sqrt{(\Delta x_k)^2 + (\Delta y_k)^2}.$$

When the number of division points is increased indefinitely and the lengths of the individual segments there tend to zero, we obtain

$$L_A^B = \lim_{n \to \infty} \sum_{k=1}^{n} \sqrt{(\Delta x_k)^2 + (\Delta y_k)^2}, \qquad (1)$$

provided that the limit exists.* The sum on the right side of (1) is not in the standard form to which we can apply the Fundamental Theorem of the integral calculus, but it can be put into such a form, as follows.

Suppose that the function $y = f(x)$ is continuous and possesses a continuous derivative at each point of the curve from $A(a, f(a))$ to $B(b, f(b))$. Then, by the Mean Value Theorem, there is some point $P^*(x_k^*, y_k^*)$ between P and Q on the curve where the

---

* For most smooth curves encountered in practice, the limit does exist. Such curves are called rectifiable. An example of a continuous curve that is not rectifiable is

$$y = \begin{cases} x \sin 1/x & \text{when } x \neq 0, \\ 0 & \text{when } x = 0, \end{cases} \quad \frac{-\pi}{2} \leq x \leq \frac{\pi}{2}.$$

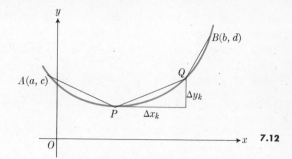

7.12

tangent to the curve is parallel to the chord PQ. That is,

$$f'(x_k^*) = \frac{\Delta y_k}{\Delta x_k}, \quad \text{or} \quad \Delta y_k = f'(x_k^*) \, \Delta x_k.$$

Hence (1) may also be written in the form

$$L_A^B = \lim_{n \to \infty} \sum_{k=1}^{n} \sqrt{(\Delta x_k)^2 + [f'(x_k^*) \, \Delta x_k]^2}$$

$$= \lim_{\Delta x \to 0} \left(\sum_a^b \sqrt{1 + [f'(x^*)]^2} \, \Delta x \right),$$

or

$$L_A^B = \int_a^b \sqrt{1 + \left(\frac{dy}{dx}\right)^2} \, dx, \qquad (2a)$$

where we have written dy/dx for $f'(x)$.

We may remark that it is sometimes convenient, if x may be expressed as a single-valued function of y, to interchange the roles of x and y (indeed, the *length* of a curve does not depend on the particular axes used), and the length is also given by

$$L_A^B = \int_c^d \sqrt{1 + \left(\frac{dx}{dy}\right)^2} \, dy. \qquad (2b)$$

In many applications, the curve is traced by a moving particle whose coordinates x and y are given as functions of some third variable, such as the time t. Let the equations of motion be

$$x = g(t), \qquad y = h(t), \qquad (3)$$

and let t_k, t_{k+1} be the values of t at P and Q respectively. Suppose the arc AB is described just once by $P(x, y)$ as t goes from t_a at A to t_b at B. If the functions $g(t)$ and $h(t)$ are continuously differentiable for t between t_a and t_b inclusive, the Mean Value Theorem may be applied to Eq. (3) to give

$$\Delta x_k = x_{k+1} - x_k = g(t_{k+1}) - g(t_k) = g'(t_k') \, \Delta t_k,$$

$$\Delta y_k = y_{k+1} - y_k = h(t_{k+1}) - h(t_k) = h'(t_k'') \, \Delta t_k,$$

where t_k' and t_k'' are two suitably chosen values of t between t_k and t_{k+1}. Then (1) becomes

$$L_A^B = \lim_{n \to \infty} \sum_{k=1}^{n} \sqrt{[g'(t_k')]^2 + [h'(t_k'')]^2} \, \Delta t_k$$

$$= \int_{t_a}^{t_b} \sqrt{\left(\frac{dx}{dt}\right)^2 + \left(\frac{dy}{dt}\right)^2} \, dt. \qquad (4)$$

Clearly, nothing inherently depends on the fact that t stands for time in Eqs. (3) and (4). Any other variable could serve as well, and if θ is used instead of t in (3) in representing the curve, then we need only replace t by θ in (4) as well.

Example 1. The coordinates (x, y) of a point on a circle of radius r can be expressed in terms of the central angle θ, Fig. 7.13, as follows:

$$x = r \cos \theta, \qquad y = r \sin \theta.$$

The point $P(x, y)$ moves once around the circle as θ varies from 0 to 2π, so that the circumference of the circle is given by

$$C = \int_0^{2\pi} \sqrt{\left(\frac{dx}{d\theta}\right)^2 + \left(\frac{dy}{d\theta}\right)^2} \, d\theta.$$

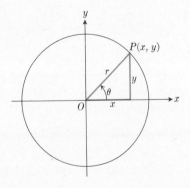

7.13

We find

$$\frac{dx}{d\theta} = -r \sin \theta, \qquad \frac{dy}{d\theta} = r \cos \theta,$$

so that

$$\left(\frac{dx}{d\theta}\right)^2 + \left(\frac{dy}{d\theta}\right)^2 = r^2 (\sin^2 \theta + \cos^2 \theta) = r^2,$$

and hence

$$C = \int_0^{2\pi} r \, d\theta = r[\theta]_0^{2\pi} = 2\pi r.$$

It should be remarked that Eq. (4) is frequently written in terms of differentials in place of derivatives. This is done formally by writing $(dt)^2$ under the radical in place of the dt outside the radical, and then writing

$$(dx)^2 = \left(\frac{dx}{dt} \, dt\right)^2 = \left(\frac{dx}{dt}\right)^2 (dt)^2$$

and

$$(dy)^2 = \left(\frac{dy}{dt} \, dt\right)^2 = \left(\frac{dy}{dt}\right)^2 (dt)^2.$$

It is also customary to eliminate the parentheses in $(dx)^2$ and write dx^2 instead, so that Eq. (4) is written

$$L = \int \sqrt{dx^2 + dy^2}. \qquad (5)$$

Of course, dx and dy must both be expressed in terms of one and the same variable, and appropriate limits must be supplied in (5) before the integration can be performed.

Note. A useful mnemonic device is also associated with (5). It is customary to write

$$ds = \sqrt{dx^2 + dy^2}, \qquad (6)$$

and treat ds as the differential of arc length, which can be integrated (between appropriate limits) to give the total length of a curve. Figure 7.14(a) gives the exact interpretation of ds corresponding to Eq. (6). Figure 7.14(b) is not strictly accurate, but is to be thought of as a simplified version of Fig. 7.14(a), with the arc of the curve treated as the hypotenuse ds of a right triangle of sides dx and dy.

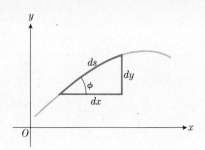

a|b

7.14

Problem 1. Find the length of the curve $y = x^{2/3}$ between $x = -1$ and $x = 8$.

Solution. From the equation of the curve, we find

$$\frac{dy}{dx} = \frac{2}{3} x^{-1/3}.$$

Since this becomes infinite at the origin (see Fig. 7.15), we use Eq. (2b) instead of (2a) to find the length of the curve. Then we need to find dx/dy. Since the equation of the curve,

$$y = x^{2/3},$$

can also be written as

$$x = \pm y^{3/2},$$

we find

$$\frac{dx}{dy} = \pm \frac{3}{2} y^{1/2}, \quad \text{or} \quad dx = \pm \frac{3}{2} y^{1/2}\, dy.$$

Then

$$ds^2 = dx^2 + dy^2 = \left(\tfrac{9}{4}y + 1\right) dy^2,$$

so that

$$ds = \sqrt{\tfrac{9}{4}y + 1}\, dy.$$

The portion of the curve between $A(-1, 1)$ and the origin has length

$$L_1 = \int_0^1 \sqrt{\tfrac{9}{4}y + 1}\, dy,$$

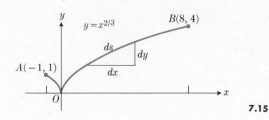

$y = x^{2/3}$

$B(8, 4)$

$A(-1, 1)$

7.15

while the rest of the curve from the origin to $B(8, 4)$ has length

$$L_2 = \int_0^4 \sqrt{\tfrac{9}{4}y + 1}\, dy,$$

and the total length is

$$L = L_1 + L_2.$$

It is necessary to calculate the two lengths L_1 and L_2 as separate integrals, since $x = \pm y^{3/2}$ needs to be separated into two distinct functions of y. For the portion AO of the curve, we have $x = -y^{3/2}$, $0 \le y \le 1$; while on the arc OB, we have $x = +y^{3/2}$, $0 \le y \le 4$.

To evaluate the given integrals, we let

$$u = \tfrac{9}{4}y + 1;$$

then

$$du = \tfrac{9}{4}\, dy, \qquad dy = \tfrac{4}{9}\, du,$$

and

$$\int \left(\tfrac{9}{4}y + 1\right)^{1/2} dy = \tfrac{4}{9} \int u^{1/2}\, du = \tfrac{8}{27} u^{3/2}.$$

Therefore

$$L = \tfrac{8}{27} \left\{ \left(\tfrac{9}{4}y + 1\right)^{3/2} \Big]_0^1 + \left(\tfrac{9}{4}y + 1\right)^{3/2} \Big]_0^4 \right\}$$

$$= \tfrac{1}{27}(13\sqrt{13} + 80\sqrt{10} - 16) = 10.5.$$

As a check against gross errors, we calculate the sum of the lengths of the two inscribed chords:

$$AO + OB = \sqrt{2} + \sqrt{80} = 10.4.$$

The check appears to be satisfactory.

The curve in Fig. 7.15 has a cusp at $(0, 0)$ where the slope becomes infinite. If we were to reconstruct the derivation of Eq. (2) for this particular curve, we would see that the crucial step that required an application of

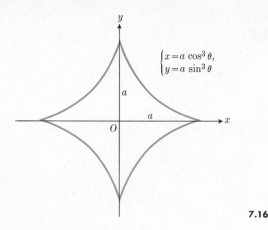

$$\begin{cases} x = a \cos^3 \theta, \\ y = a \sin^3 \theta \end{cases}$$

7.16

the Mean Value Theorem could not have been taken for the case of a chord PQ from a point P to the left of the cusp to a point Q to its right. For this reason, if for no other, when one or more cusps occur between the ends of a portion of a curve whose length is to be calculated, it is best to calculate the lengths of portions of the curve between cusps and add the results. We recall that the Mean Value Theorem is still valid even when the derivative becomes infinite at an extremity of the interval where it is to be applied, so that the derivation of Eq. (2) would be valid for the separate portions of a curve lying *between* cusps (or other discontinuities of dy/dx, such as occur at corners). Thus in the example just worked, we find the lengths L_1 from $A(-1, 1)$ to O (up to the cusp) and L_2 from O to $B(8, 4)$, then add the results to obtain $L = L_1 + L_2$. This was done by the sum of the two integrals. Had there been no point of discontinuity of dy/dx, it would not have been necessary to take two separate integrals, and Eq. (2a) could have been used.

Problem 2. The coordinates of the point $P(x, y)$ on the four-cusped hypocycloid (Fig. 7.16) are given by

$$x = a \cos^3 \theta, \qquad y = a \sin^3 \theta.$$

Find the total length of the curve.

Solution. When θ varies from 0 to $\pi/2$, P traces out the portion of the curve in the first quadrant. Also, from the fact that

$$x^{2/3} + y^{2/3} = a^{2/3} (\cos^2 \theta + \sin^2 \theta)$$
$$= a^{2/3}(1) = a^{2/3},$$

it will be seen that for every point (x, y) on the curve in the first quadrant, the corresponding points $(-x, y)$ $(-x, -y)$, and $(x, -y)$ in the other three quadrants are also on the curve, which is therefore symmetrical about both axes. The portion of the curve in the first quadrant lies *between* two cusps and is one-quarter of the total length of the curve. Therefore

$$L = 4 \int_{\theta=0}^{\theta=\pi/2} \sqrt{dx^2 + dy^2}.$$

From the equation of the curve, we find

$$\frac{dx}{d\theta} = -3a \cos^2 \theta \sin \theta, \quad dx = 3a \cos \theta \sin \theta \,(-\cos \theta)\, d\theta,$$

$$\frac{dy}{d\theta} = 3a \sin^2 \theta \cos \theta, \quad dy = 3a \cos \theta \sin \theta \,(\sin \theta)\, d\theta,$$

and hence

$$ds^2 = dx^2 + dy^2$$
$$= (3a \cos \theta \sin \theta)^2 (\cos^2 \theta + \sin^2 \theta)(d\theta)^2,$$
or
$$ds^2 = (3a \cos \theta \sin \theta \, d\theta)^2.$$

Hence, for θ between 0 and $\pi/2$,

$$ds = 3a \cos \theta \sin \theta \, d\theta$$
and
$$L = 4 \int_0^{\pi/2} 3a \cos \theta \sin \theta \, d\theta.$$

To evaluate this integral, we let

$$u = \sin \theta, \qquad du = \cos \theta \, d\theta;$$
then
$$\int \cos \theta \sin \theta \, d\theta = \int u \, du = \tfrac{1}{2} u^2 = \tfrac{1}{2} \sin^2 \theta,$$

so that

$$L = (12a)(\tfrac{1}{2} \sin^2 \theta) \Big]_0^{\pi/2} = 6a.$$

EXERCISES

2/7/77 #1-9 odd

In Exercises 1 through 6, find the length of the segment of the curve described.

1. $y = \frac{1}{3}(x^2 + 2)^{3/2}$, from $x = 0$ to $x = 3$
2. $y = x^{3/2}$, from $(0, 0)$ to $(4, 8)$

3. $9x^2 = 4y^3$ from $(0, 0)$ to $(2\sqrt{3}, 3)$

4. $y = x^3/3 + 1/(4x)$, from $x = 1$ to $x = 3$

5. $x = y^4/4 + 1/(8y^2)$, from $y = 1$ to $y = 2$

6. $(y + 1)^2 = 4x^3$, from $x = 0$ to $x = 1$

7. Find the distance traveled between $t = 0$ and $t = \pi/2$ by a particle $P(x, y)$ whose position at time t is given by

$$x = a\cos t + at\sin t, \quad y = a\sin t - at\cos t,$$

where a is a positive constant.

8. Find the distance traveled by the particle $P(x, y)$ between $t = 0$ and $t = 4$ if the position at time t is given by

$$x = t^2/2, \quad y = \tfrac{1}{3}(2t + 1)^{3/2}.$$

9. The position of a particle $P(x, y)$ at time t is given by

$$x = \tfrac{1}{3}(2t + 3)^{3/2}, \quad y = t^2/2 + t.$$

Find the distance it travels between $t = 0$ and $t = 3$.

7.17

7.18

7.7 AREA OF A SURFACE OF REVOLUTION

Suppose that the curve in Fig. 7.17 is rotated about the x-axis. It will generate a surface in space. We approximate the curve by an inscribed polygon and also rotate it about the x-axis. The surface area generated by the curve is defined to be the limit of the surface areas generated by the inscribed polygons as their lengths approach the length of the arc of the curve; that is, as the number of segments approaches infinity and the lengths of the individual segments approach zero.

The inscribed polygonal line segments will generate inscribed frustums of cones. The sum of the lateral areas of these frustums will be an approximation to the area of the surface. To obtain an analytic expression for this approximation, we require the formula

$$A = \pi(r_1 + r_2)l \tag{1}$$

for the lateral area A of a frustum of slant height l, where r_1 and r_2 are the radii of its bases.

To establish Eq. (1), we may imagine the frustum of a cone to be the limit of inscribed frustums of pyramids (see Fig. 7.18). If each base of an inscribed frustum of a pyramid is a regular polygon of n sides, and b_1 is the length of one side in the upper face, while b_2 is the length of a side in the lower face, then the lateral area will consist of n trapezoids each having an area

$$\tfrac{1}{2}(b_1 + b_2)h.$$

Hence the n trapezoids have area

$$\tfrac{1}{2}(nb_1 + nb_2)h.$$

As n increases indefinitely, we have

$$\lim_{n \to \infty} nb_1 = 2\pi r_1, \quad \lim_{n \to \infty} nb_2 = 2\pi r_2;$$

now

$$\lim_{n \to \infty} h = l,$$

so that

$$A = \lim_{n\to\infty} \tfrac{1}{2}(nb_1 + nb_2)h$$
$$= \tfrac{1}{2}(2\pi r_1 + 2\pi r_2)l = \pi(r_1 + r_2)l,$$

which establishes Eq. (1). Note that if $r_1 = r_2$, Eq. (1) reduces to the correct formula for the lateral area of a cylinder, and if $r_1 = 0$, it gives the correct result for the lateral area of a cone. It can also be put into the form

$$A = 2\pi rl,$$

where $r = \tfrac{1}{2}(r_1 + r_2)$ is the radius of the midsection of the frustum. In this form, (1) says that the lateral area of a frustum of a cone is equal to (circumference of mid-section) $\times$ (slant height).

We now consider the portion of the surface ΔS generated by the arc PQ, and its inscribed frustum of a cone generated by the chord PQ. Call the co-ordinates of P: (x, y), and of Q: $(x + \Delta x, y + \Delta y)$, and take

$$r_1 = y, \quad r_2 = y + \Delta y, \quad l = \sqrt{(\Delta x)^2 + (\Delta y)^2}$$

in Eq. (1). Then we have the approximation

$$S \approx \sum_{x=a}^{b} \pi(2y + \Delta y)\sqrt{(\Delta x)^2 + (\Delta y)^2},$$

or

$$S \approx \sum_{a}^{b} 2\pi\left(y + \frac{1}{2}\Delta y\right)\sqrt{1 + \left(\frac{\Delta y}{\Delta x}\right)^2}\,\Delta x.$$

In more formal notation, suppose that the curve is the graph of a function f that is continuous, together with its derived function f', on $[a, b]$. Let the segment $[a, b]$ be partitioned by points

$$a = x_0 < x_1 < x_2 < \cdots < x_n = b.$$

Then, by part (ii) of the Intermediate Value Theorem (Theorem 15, Article 4.9), there exists t_i on the ith subinterval such that

$$f(t_i) = y_i + \tfrac{1}{2}(\Delta y_i).$$

By the Mean Value Theorem (Article 5.8), there also exists t_i' on the ith subinterval such that

$$f'(t_i') = \frac{\Delta y_i}{\Delta x_i}.$$

Therefore, by the definition of S,

$$S = \lim_{n\to\infty} \sum_{i=1}^{n} 2\pi f(t_i)\sqrt{1 + [f'(t_i')]^2}\,\Delta x_i,$$

and, by Bliss's Theorem (Article 7.5), this leads to the result

$$S = \int_a^b 2\pi f(x)\sqrt{1 + [f'(x)]^2}\,dx,$$

or

$$S = \int_a^b 2\pi y\sqrt{1 + \left(\frac{dy}{dx}\right)^2}\,dx. \tag{2}$$

Our end result, Eq. (2), is easily remembered if we write

$$\sqrt{1 + \left(\frac{dy}{dx}\right)^2}\,dx = ds$$

and take

$$S = \int 2\pi y\,ds. \tag{3}$$

If we let

$$dS = 2\pi y\,ds,$$

so that

$$S = \int dS,$$

we may interpret dS as the product of

a circumference $2\pi y$ and a slant height ds.

Thus dS gives the lateral area of a frustum of a cone slant height ds if the point (x, y) is the midpoint of the element of arc length ds (Fig. 7.19).

Note. The following question often occurs to the alert student: Why not approximate the surface area S by inscribed *cylinders* and arrive at a result

$$S = \int 2\pi y\,dx,$$

having dx instead of ds, to replace Eq. (3)? This is a reasonable question. Since we know from our discussion on volume that inscribed cylinders work perfectly well for *volumes* of revolution, why not use them for *surfaces* of revolution also? The answer hinges on the fact that the approximation

$$\Delta V \approx \pi y^2\,\Delta x$$

for the volume of a slice involves, at worst, terms which are products like $(\Delta x)(\Delta y)$ and higher powers of Δx, and

7.19

7.20

these contribute zero to the *limit* of the sum of volumes of the inscribed cylinders (see Article 7.5). But the approximations

$$\Delta S \approx 2\pi y \, \Delta x \qquad (a)$$

and

$$\Delta S \approx 2\pi y \sqrt{(\Delta x)^2 + (\Delta y)^2} \qquad (b)$$

for the surface area of a slice cannot *both* be this accurate, for the following reason: Their ratio is

$$\frac{2\pi y \sqrt{(\Delta x)^2 + (\Delta y)^2}}{2\pi y \, \Delta x} = \sqrt{1 + \left(\frac{\Delta y}{\Delta x}\right)^2},$$

which has the limiting value

$$\lim_{\Delta x \to 0} \sqrt{1 + \left(\frac{\Delta y}{\Delta x}\right)^2} = \sqrt{1 + \left(\frac{dy}{dx}\right)^2},$$

and this will be different from one (unless $dy/dx = 0$, which would not be generally true), whereas two approximations that differ only by terms involving products like $(\Delta y)(\Delta x)$ and higher powers of Δx have a ratio whose limiting value is unity. Since the approximations (a) and (b) above will usually lead to different answers when we pass to the corresponding definite integrals,

they cannot both be correct, and we must abandon one or both of them. But the approximation (b) is clearly the one that corresponds to a natural way of defining the surface area of a surface of revolution, and it leads to (3).

If the axis of revolution is the y-axis, the corresponding formula that replaces (3) is

$$S = \int 2\pi x \, ds,$$

while more generally we may write

$$S = \int 2\pi \rho \, ds, \qquad (4)$$

if ρ is the distance from the axis of revolution to the element of arc length ds. Both ρ and ds must be expressed in terms of some one variable and proper limits must be supplied to (4) in any particular problem.

Problem 1. The circle

$$x^2 + y^2 = r^2$$

is revolved about the x-axis (Fig. 7.20). Find the area of the sphere generated.

Solution. We write

$$dS = 2\pi y \, ds, \qquad ds = \sqrt{dx^2 + dy^2},$$

and use

$$x = r \cos \theta, \qquad y = r \sin \theta$$

to represent the circle. Then

$$dx = -r \sin \theta \, d\theta, \qquad dy = r \cos \theta \, d\theta,$$

so that

$$ds = r \, d\theta$$

and

$$dS = 2\pi y \, ds = 2\pi (r \sin \theta) r \, d\theta$$
$$= 2\pi r^2 \sin \theta \, d\theta.$$

The top half of the circle generates the entire sphere, and the representative point (x, y) traces out this upper semicircle as θ varies from 0 to π. Hence

$$S = \int_0^\pi 2\pi r^2 \sin \theta \, d\theta$$

$$= 2\pi r^2 \left[-\cos \theta\right]_0^\pi = 4\pi r^2.$$

7.21

BAGEL

Problem 2. The circle in Problem 1 is revolved about the line $y = -r$, which is tangent to the circle at the point $(0, -r)$ (Fig. 7.21). Find the area of the surface generated.

Solution. Here it takes the whole circle to generate the surface, and in terms of the previous example, this means that we must let θ vary from 0 to 2π. The radius of rotation now becomes $\rho = y + r$, and we have

$$dS = 2\pi\rho \, ds = 2\pi(y + r)r \, d\theta = 2\pi(r \sin\theta + r)r \, d\theta.$$

Hence

$$S = \int_0^{2\pi} 2\pi (\sin\theta + 1)r^2 \, d\theta$$

$$= 2\pi r^2 \left[-\cos\theta + \theta \right]_0^{2\pi} = 4\pi^2 r^2.$$

EXERCISES

7/8 #1,2,3,9 4,5,7

1. Find the area of the surface generated by rotating the hypocycloid $x = a \cos^3\theta$, $y = a \sin^3\theta$ about the x-axis.

2. Find the area of the surface generated by rotating the portion of the curve $y = \frac{1}{3}(x^2 + 2)^{3/2}$ between $x = 0$ and $x = 3$ about the y-axis.

3. Find the area of the surface generated by rotating about the x-axis the arc of the curve $y = x^3$ between $x = 0$ and $x = 1$.

4. Find the area of the surface generated by rotating about the y-axis the arc of the curve $y = x^2$ between $(0, 0)$ and $(2, 4)$.

5. The arc of the curve $y = x^3/3 + 1/(4x)$ from $x = 1$ to $x = 3$ is rotated about the line $y = -1$. Find the surface area generated.

6. The arc of the curve $x = y^4/4 + 1/(8y^2)$ from $y = 1$ to $y = 2$ is rotated about the x-axis. Find the surface area generated.

7. The curve described by the particle $P(x, y)$,

$$x = t + 1, \qquad y = \frac{t^2}{2} + t,$$

from $t = 0$ to $t = 4$, is rotated about the y-axis. Find the surface area that is generated.

8. The loop of the curve $9x^2 = y(3 - y)^2$ is rotated about the x-axis. Find the surface area generated.

7.8 AVERAGE VALUE OF A FUNCTION

The process of finding the average value of a finite number of data is familiar to all students. For example, if $y_1, y_2, \ldots, y_n$ are the grades of a class of n students on a certain calculus quiz, then the class average on that quiz is

$$y_{av} = \frac{y_1 + y_2 + \cdots + y_n}{n}. \qquad (1)$$

When the number of data is infinite, it is not feasible to use Eq. (1) (since it is likely to take on the meaningless form ∞/∞). This situation arises, in particular, when the data y are given by a continuous function

$$y = f(x), \quad a \leq x \leq b.$$

In this case, the average value of y, with respect to x, is defined to be

$$(y_{av})_x = \frac{1}{b - a} \int_a^b f(x) \, dx. \qquad (2)$$

7.22

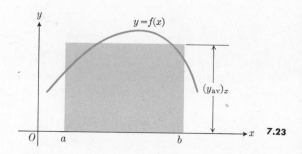

7.23

The right side of Eq. (3) represents the area bounded above by the curve $y = f(x)$, below by the x-axis, and on the sides by the ordinates $x = a$, $x = b$. The left side of the equation can be interpreted as the area of a rectangle of altitude $(y_{av})_x$ and of base $b - a$. Hence Eq. (3) provides a geometric interpretation of $(y_{av})_x$ as that ordinate of the curve $y = f(x)$ that should be used as altitude if one wishes to construct a rectangle whose base is the interval $a \leq x \leq b$ and whose area is equal to the area under the curve (Fig. 7.23). In the narrower sense of area, this statement is only valid when the curve lies above the x-axis. In case the curve lies partly or entirely below the x-axis, we would count areas below the x-axis as negative. In such a case there might well be a certain amount of canceling of positive and negative areas.

Remark 3. Equation (2) is a *definition*, and hence is not subject to proof. Nevertheless, some discussion may help to explain why this particular formula is used to define the average. One might arrive at it as follows. From the total "population" of x-values, $a \leq x \leq b$, we select a representative "sample," $x_1, x_2, \ldots, x_n$, uniformly distributed between a and b. Then, using Eq. (1), we calculate the average of the functional values

$$y_1 = f(x_1), \quad y_2 = f(x_2), \quad \ldots, \quad y_n = f(x_n)$$

associated with these representative x's. This gives us

$$\frac{y_1 + y_2 + \cdots + y_n}{n}$$
$$= \frac{f(x_1) + f(x_2) + \cdots + f(x_n)}{n}. \quad (4)$$

Since we require that the x's be uniformly distributed between a and b, let us take the spacing to be Δx, with

$$x_2 - x_1 = x_3 - x_2 = \cdots = x_n - x_{n-1} = \Delta x,$$

$$\Delta x = \frac{b - a}{n}.$$

The curve in Fig. 7.22, for example, might represent temperature as a function of time over a twenty-four hour period. Equation (2) would then give the "average temperature" for the day.

Remark 1. It may be possible to express y as a function of x, or, alternatively, as a function of u. Then $(y_{av})_x$ and $(y_{av})_u$ need not be equal. For example, for a freely falling body starting from rest,

$$s = \tfrac{1}{2}gt^2, \quad v = gt, \quad v = \sqrt{2gs}.$$

Suppose we calculate the average velocity, first with respect to t and second with respect to s, from $t_1 = 0$, $s_1 = 0$ to $t_2 > 0$, $s_2 = \tfrac{1}{2}gt_2^2$. Then, by definition,

$$(v_{av})_t = \frac{1}{t_2 - 0} \int_0^{t_2} gt \, dt = \tfrac{1}{2}gt_2 = \tfrac{1}{2}v_2,$$

$$(v_{av})_s = \frac{1}{s_2 - 0} \int_0^{s_2} \sqrt{2gs} \, ds = \tfrac{2}{3}\sqrt{2gs_2} = \tfrac{2}{3}v_2.$$

Remark 2. If both sides of Eq. (2) are multiplied by $b - a$, we have

$$(y_{av})_x \cdot (b - a) = \int_a^b f(x) \, dx. \quad (3)$$

Then, in (4), let us replace the n in the denominator by $(b - a)/\Delta x$, thus obtaining

$$\frac{f(x_1) + f(x_2) + \cdots + f(x_n)}{(b - a)/\Delta x}$$

$$= \frac{f(x_1)\, \Delta x + f(x_2)\, \Delta x + \cdots + f(x_n)\, \Delta x}{b - a}.$$

Now if n is very large (Δx small), the expression

$$f(x_1)\, \Delta x + f(x_2)\, \Delta x + \cdots + f(x_n)\, \Delta x = \sum_{k=1}^{n} f(x_k)\, \Delta x$$

is very nearly equal to $\int_a^b f(x)\, dx$. In fact, if we take limits, letting $n \to \infty$, we obtain precisely

$$\lim_{n \to \infty} \frac{f(x_1)\, \Delta x + f(x_2)\, \Delta x + \cdots + f(x_n)\, \Delta x}{b - a},$$

which is equal to

$$\frac{1}{b - a} \int_a^b f(x)\, dx.$$

This is the expression used to define the average value of y in Eq. (2).

EXERCISES

1 & 3

In Exercises 1 through 5, find the average value with respect to x, over the given domain, of the given function $f(x)$. In each case, draw a graph of the curve $y = f(x)$, and sketch a rectangle whose altitude is the average ordinate.

1. (a) $\sin x$, $0 \le x \le \pi/2$
   (b) $\sin x$, $0 \le x \le 2\pi$
2. (a) $\sin^2 x$, $0 \le x \le \pi/2$
   (b) $\sin^2 x$, $\pi \le x \le 2\pi$
3. $\sqrt{2x + 1}$, $4 \le x \le 12$
4. $\frac{1}{2} + \frac{1}{2}\cos 2x$, $0 \le x \le \pi$
5. $\alpha x + \beta$; $a \le x \le b$ (α, β, a, b, constants)
6. Given a circle C of radius a, and a diameter AB of C. Chords are drawn perpendicular to AB, intercepting equal segments along AB. Find the limit of the average of the lengths of these chords, as the number

of chords tends to infinity. [*Hint.* $\int_{-a}^{a} \sqrt{a^2 - x^2}\, dx$ is $\frac{1}{2}\pi a^2$, since it is the area of a semicircle of radius a.]

7. Solve Exercise 6 under the modified assumption that the chords intercept equal arcs along the circumference of C.
8. Solve Exercise 6 using the *squares* of the lengths, in place of the lengths of the chords.
9. Solve Exercise 7 using the *squares* of the lengths, in place of the lengths of the chords.

7.9 MOMENTS AND CENTER OF MASS

If several masses $m_1, m_2, \ldots, m_n$ are placed along the x-axis at distances $x_1, x_2, \ldots, x_n$, respectively, from the origin (Fig. 7.24), then their moment about

7.24

the origin is defined by the following equality:

$$x_1 m_1 + x_2 m_2 + \cdots + x_n m_n = \sum_{k=1}^{n} x_k m_k. \quad (1)$$

If all the mass

$$m_1 + m_2 + \cdots + m_n = \sum_{k=1}^{n} m_k \quad (2)$$

is concentrated at one point of abscissa $\bar{x}$, the total moment is

$$\bar{x}\left(\sum_{k=1}^{n} m_k \right).$$

The position of $\bar{x}$ for which this is the same as the total moment in (1) is called the *center of mass*. The condition

$$\bar{x} \sum_{k=1}^{n} m_k = \sum_{k=1}^{n} x_k m_k$$

thus determines

$$\bar{x} = \frac{\displaystyle\sum_{k=1}^{n} x_k m_k}{\displaystyle\sum_{k=1}^{n} m_k}. \quad (3)$$

7.25

the points

$$(x_1, y_1, z_1), \quad (x_2, y_2, z_2), \ldots, \quad (x_n, y_n, z_n),$$

we define their moments with respect to the various coordinate planes as

$$M_{yz} = x_1 m_1 + x_2 m_2 + \cdots + x_n m_n = \sum_{k=1}^{n} x_k m_k,$$

$$M_{zx} = y_1 m_1 + y_2 m_2 + \cdots + y_n m_n = \sum_{k=1}^{n} y_k m_k,$$

$$M_{xy} = z_1 m_1 + z_2 m_2 + \cdots + z_n m_n = \sum_{k=1}^{n} z_k m_k.$$

(M_{yz} = moment with respect to the yz-plane, etc.)

The center of mass $(\bar{x}, \bar{y}, \bar{z})$ is the point where the total mass could be concentrated without altering these moments. Its coordinates therefore are given by

$$\bar{x} = \frac{\sum x_k m_k}{\sum m_k}, \qquad \bar{y} = \frac{\sum y_k m_k}{\sum m_k}, \qquad \bar{z} = \frac{\sum z_k m_k}{\sum m_k}. \tag{5}$$

Now most physical objects with which we deal are composed of enormously large numbers of molecules. It would be extremely difficult, and in most cases unnecessary, for us to concern ourselves with the molecular structure of a physical object, such as a pendulum, whose motion as a whole is to be studied. Instead, we make certain simplifying assumptions which we recognize as being only approximately correct. One such assumption is that the matter in a given solid is continuously distributed throughout the solid. Furthermore, if P is a point in the solid and ΔV is an element of volume which contains P, and if Δm is the mass of ΔV, then we assume that the ratio $\Delta m/\Delta V$ tends to a definite limit

$$\delta = \lim_{\Delta V \to 0} \frac{\Delta m}{\Delta V} \tag{6}$$

as the largest dimension of ΔV approaches zero. The limit δ is called the *density* of the solid at the point P. It is customary to write Eq. (6) in the alternative forms

$$\delta = dm/dV, \qquad dm = \delta \, dV. \tag{7}$$

Example 1. The principle of a moment underlies the simple seesaw. For instance (Fig. 7.25), suppose one child weighs 80 lb and sits 5 ft from the point O, while the other child weighs 100 lb and is 4 ft from O. Then the child at the left end of the seesaw produces a moment of $80 \times 5 = 400$ (lb-ft), which tends to rotate the plank counterclockwise about O. The child at the right end of the plank produces a moment of $100 \times 4 = 400$ (lb-ft), which tends to rotate the plank clockwise around O. If we introduce coordinates $x_1 = -5$ and $x_2 = +4$, we find

$$x_1 m_1 + x_2 m_2 = (-5)(80) + (4)(100)$$
$$= -400 + 400 = 0$$

as the resultant moment about O. The same moment, zero, would be obtained if both children were at O, which is the center of their combined mass.

If, instead of being placed on the x-axis, the masses are located in the xy-plane at points

$$(x_1, y_1), \quad (x_2, y_2), \ldots, \quad (x_n, y_n),$$

in that order, then we define their moments with respect to the y-axis and with respect to the x-axis as

$$M_y = x_1 m_1 + x_2 m_2 + \cdots + x_n m_n = \sum_{k=1}^{n} x_k m_k,$$

$$M_x = y_1 m_1 + y_2 m_2 + \cdots + y_n m_n = \sum_{k=1}^{n} y_k m_k.$$

The center of mass is the point $(\bar{x}, \bar{y})$,

$$\bar{x} = \frac{\sum x_k m_k}{\sum m_k}, \qquad \bar{y} = \frac{\sum y_k m_k}{\sum m_k}, \tag{4}$$

where the total mass could be concentrated and still give the same total moments M_y and M_x.

In space, three coordinates are needed to specify the position of a point. If the masses are located at

Now if a solid is divided into small pieces ΔV of mass Δm and if $P(\tilde{x}, \tilde{y}, \tilde{z})$ is a point in ΔV and δ is the density at P, then

$$\Delta m \approx \delta \, \Delta V.$$

The moments of Δm with respect to the coordinate planes are not defined by what we have done thus far. But now we may think of replacing the Δm that fills the volume ΔV by an equal mass all of which is concentrated at the point P. The moments of this concentrated mass with respect to the coordinate planes are

$$\tilde{x} \, \Delta m, \qquad \tilde{y} \, \Delta m, \qquad \tilde{z} \, \Delta m.$$

Now we add the moments of all the concentrated masses in all the volume elements ΔV and take the limit as the ΔV's approach zero. This leads us to the following *definitions* of the moments M_{yz}, etc., for the mass as a whole:

$$M_{yz} = \lim_{\Delta m \to 0} \sum \tilde{x} \, \Delta m = \int \tilde{x} \, dm,$$

$$M_{zx} = \lim_{\Delta m \to 0} \sum \tilde{y} \, \Delta m = \int \tilde{y} \, dm,$$

$$M_{xy} = \lim_{\Delta m \to 0} \sum \tilde{z} \, \Delta m = \int \tilde{z} \, dm.$$

From these, we then deduce the equations

$$\bar{x} = \frac{\int \tilde{x} \, dm}{\int dm}, \qquad \bar{y} = \frac{\int \tilde{y} \, dm}{\int dm}, \qquad \bar{z} = \frac{\int \tilde{z} \, dm}{\int dm} \qquad (8)$$

for the center of mass of the solid as a whole.

In theory, the element dm is approximately the mass of a volume element dV which has three small dimensions, as in Fig. 7.26. In a later chapter we shall see how to evaluate the integrals (8) which arise when this is done. In practice, however, we can usually take

$$dm = \delta \, dV,$$

with a volume element dV which has only one small dimension. Then we must interpret $\tilde{x}, \tilde{y}, \tilde{z}$ in the integrands in (8) as *the coordinates of the center of mass of the element dm*.

In many problems of practical importance, the density δ is constant and the solid possesses a plane of symmetry. Then it is easy to see that the center

7.26

of mass lies in this plane of symmetry. For we may, with no loss of generality, choose our coordinate reference frame in such a way that the yz-plane is the plane of symmetry. Then for every element of mass Δm with a positive $\tilde{x}$ there is a symmetrically located element of mass with a corresponding negative $\tilde{x}$. These two elements have moments which are equal in magnitude and of opposite signs. The whole mass is made up of such symmetric pairs of elements and the sum of their moments about the yz-plane is zero. Therefore $\bar{x} = 0$; that is, the center of mass lies in the plane of symmetry. If there are two planes of symmetry, their intersection is an axis of symmetry and the center of mass must lie on this axis, since it lies in both planes of symmetry.

The most frequently encountered distributions of mass are

(a) along a thin wire or filament: $dm = \delta_1 \, ds$,

(b) in a thin plate or shell: $dm = \delta_2 \, dA$ or $\delta_2 \, dS$,

(c) in a solid: $dm = \delta_3 \, dV$,

where

$$ds = \text{element of arc length,}$$
$$\delta_1 = \underline{\text{mass per unit}} \text{ length of wire,}$$
$$dA \text{ or } dS = \text{element of area,}$$
$$\delta_2 = \underline{\text{mass per unit}} \text{ area of plate or shell,}$$
$$dV = \text{element of volume,}$$
$$\delta_3 = \underline{\text{mass per unit}} \text{ volume of solid.}$$

δ is density

Problem 1. Find the center of mass of a thin homogeneous triangular plate of base b and altitude h.

Solution. Divide the triangle into strips of width dy parallel to the x-axis. A representative strip is shown in Fig. 7.27. The mass of the strip is approximately

$$dm = \delta_2\, dA,$$

where

$$dA = l\, dy$$

7.27

and l is the width of the triangle at distance y above its base. By similar triangles,

$$\frac{l}{b} = \frac{h - y}{h}, \quad \text{or} \quad l = \frac{b}{h}(h - y),$$

so that

$$dm = \delta_2 \frac{b}{h}(h - y)\, dy.$$

For the y-coordinate of the center of mass of the element dm, we have $\tilde{y} = y$. For the entire plate,

$$\bar{y} = \frac{\displaystyle\int y\, dm}{\displaystyle\int dm} = \frac{\displaystyle\int_0^h \delta_2 \frac{b}{h} y(h - y)\, dy}{\displaystyle\int_0^h \delta_2 \frac{b}{h}(h - y)\, dy} = \frac{1}{3}h.$$

Thus the center of mass lies above the base of the triangle at a distance one-third of the way toward the opposite vertex. By considering each side in turn as being a base of the triangle, this result shows that the center of gravity lies at the intersection of the medians.

Problem 2. A thin homogeneous wire is bent to form a semicircle of radius r (Fig. 7.28). Find its center of mass.

Solution. Here we take

$$dm = \delta_1\, ds,$$

where ds is an element of arc length of the wire and

$$\delta_1 = \frac{M}{L} = \frac{M}{\pi r}$$

is the mass per unit length of the wire. In terms of the central angle θ measured in radians (as usual), we have

$$ds = r\, d\theta$$

and

$$\tilde{x} = r\cos\theta, \quad \tilde{y} = r\sin\theta.$$

7.28

Hence

$$\bar{x} = \frac{\int_0^\pi r\cos\theta\, \delta_1 r\, d\theta}{\int_0^\pi \delta_1 r\, d\theta} = \frac{\delta_1 r^2\, [\sin\theta]_0^\pi}{\delta_1 r[\theta]_0^\pi} = 0,$$

$$\bar{y} = \frac{\int_0^\pi r\sin\theta\, \delta_1 r\, d\theta}{\int_0^\pi \delta_1 r\, d\theta} = \frac{\delta_1 r^2\, [-\cos\theta]_0^\pi}{\delta_1 r[\theta]_0^\pi} = \frac{2}{\pi}r.$$

The center of mass is therefore on the y-axis at a distance $2/\pi$ (roughly $\frac{2}{3}$) of the way up from the origin toward the intercept $(0, r)$.

Problem 3. Find the center of mass of a solid hemisphere of radius r if its density at any point P is proportional to the distance of P from the base of the hemisphere.

Solution. Imagine the solid cut into slices of thickness dy by planes perpendicular to the y-axis (Fig. 7.29), and take

$$dm = \delta_3\, dV,$$

where

$$dV = A(y)\, dy$$

is the volume of the representative slice at distance y above the base of the hemisphere, which is in the xz-plane, and where

$$\delta_3 = ky \quad (k = \text{constant})$$

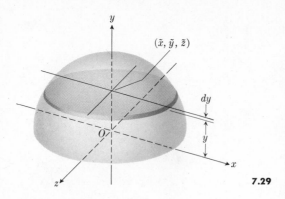

7.29

is the density of the solid in this slice. The area of a face of the slice dV is $A(y) = \pi x^2$, where $x^2 + y^2 = r^2$, that is,

$$dV = A(y)\,dy = \pi(r^2 - y^2)\,dy,$$

so that

$$dm = k\pi(r^2 - y^2)y\,dy.$$

The center of mass of the slice may be taken at its geometrical center, that is

$$(\tilde{x}, \tilde{y}, \tilde{z}) = (0, y, 0),$$

so that

$$\bar{x} = \bar{z} = 0$$

and

$$\bar{y} = \frac{\int y\,dm}{\int dm} = \frac{\int_0^r k\pi(r^2 - y^2)y^2\,dy}{\int_0^r k\pi(r^2 - y^2)y\,dy}$$

$$= \frac{k\pi\left[\dfrac{r^2 y^3}{3} - \dfrac{y^5}{5}\right]_0^r}{k\pi\left[\dfrac{r^2 y^2}{2} - \dfrac{y^4}{4}\right]_0^r} = \frac{8}{15}r.$$

EXERCISES

In Exercises 1 through 5, find the center of mass of a thin homogeneous plate covering the given portion of the xy-plane.

1. The first quadrant of the circle $x^2 + y^2 = a^2$.

2. The area bounded by the parabola $y = h^2 - x^2$ and the x-axis.

3. The "triangular" shaped area in the first quadrant between the circle $x^2 + y^2 = a^2$ and the lines $x = a$, $y = a$.

4. The area that lies between the x-axis and the curve $y = \sin x$ between $x = 0$ and $x = \pi$.
   Hint. Take $dA = y\,dx$ and $\tilde{y} = \frac{1}{2}y$.

5. The area that lies between the y-axis and the curve $x = 2y - y^2$.

6. Find the distance, from the base, of the center of mass of a thin triangular plate of base b and altitude h if its density varies as the square root of the distance from the base.

7. In Exercise 6, suppose that the density varies as the square of the distance.

8. Find the center of mass of a homogeneous solid right circular cone.

9. Find the center of mass of a solid right circular cone if the density varies as the distance from the base.

10. In Exercise 9, suppose that the density varies as the square of the distance.

11. In Problem 2 (see Fig. 7.28), suppose that the density is $\delta_1 = k \sin \theta$, k being constant. Find the center of mass.

7.10 THE CENTROID

If a mass has uniform density, Eqs. (8), Article 7.9, reduce to

$$\bar{x} = \frac{\int \tilde{x}\delta_3\,dV}{\int \delta_3\,dV} = \frac{\delta_3 \int \tilde{x}\,dV}{\delta_3 \int dV} = \frac{\int \tilde{x}\,dV}{\int dV},$$

$$\bar{y} = \frac{\int \tilde{y}\,dV}{\int dV}, \qquad \bar{z} = \frac{\int \tilde{z}\,dV}{\int dV} \tag{1}$$

for a solid, with similar equations having dA or ds in place of dV for a plate or a wire. Since these expressions involve only the geometric objects, namely, volumes, areas, and curves, we speak of the point $(\bar{x}, \bar{y}, \bar{z})$ in such cases as the *centroid* of the object.

Problem 1. Find the centroid of a solid hemisphere of radius r.

Solution. As in Problem 3, Article 7.9, imagine the solid (Fig. 7.29) cut into slices of thickness dy by planes perpendicular to the y-axis. The centroid of a slice is its geometrical center, which lies on the y-axis at $(0, y, 0)$. Its moment with respect to the xz-plane is

$$dM_{xz} = y\, dV$$
$$= y\pi(r^2 - y^2)\, dy.$$

Hence

$$M_{xz} = \pi \int_0^r (r^2 y - y^3)\, dy = \frac{\pi r^4}{4}.$$

Since the volume of the hemisphere is

$$V = \frac{2}{3}\pi r^3,$$

we have

$$\bar{y} = \frac{M_{xz}}{V} = \frac{3}{8} r.$$

STUDY

Problem 2. Find the centroid of a thin hemispherical shell of inner radius r and thickness t.

Solution. We shall first solve this problem exactly (A), by using the results of the preceding example. Second (B), we shall see how the position of the centroid changes as we hold r fixed and let $t \to 0$. Finally (C), we shall solve the problem approximately without using the results of Problem 1, by considering the center of mass of an imaginary distribution of mass over the surface of the hemisphere of radius r, assuming that the thickness t is negligible in comparison with r (as, for example, the gold leaf covering the dome of the State House in Boston).

A. Let M_1, M_2 and M; V_1, V_2, and V denote respectively the moments with respect to the xz-plane and the volumes of the solid hemisphere of radius r, the solid hemisphere of radius $(r + t)$, and the hemispherical shell of thickness t and inner radius r. Since the moment of the sum of two masses is the sum of their moments and

$$V_1 + V = V_2,$$

we also have

$$M_1 + M = M_2, \quad \text{or} \quad M = M_2 - M_1.$$

But by Problem 1,

$$M_2 = \frac{\pi}{4}(r + t)^4, \qquad M_1 = \frac{\pi}{4} r^4,$$

so that

$$M = \frac{\pi}{4}[(r + t)^4 - r^4]$$
$$= \frac{\pi}{4}[4r^3 t + 6r^2 t^2 + 4rt^3 + t^4],$$

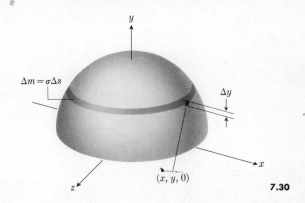

7.30

while

$$V = V_2 - V_1 = \frac{2}{3}\pi[(r + t)^3 - r^3]$$
$$= \frac{2}{3}\pi(3r^2 t + 3rt^2 + t^3);$$

hence

$$\bar{y} = \frac{M}{V} = \frac{1}{2}\frac{[r^3 + \frac{3}{2}r^2 t + rt^2 + \frac{1}{4}t^3]}{[r^2 + rt + \frac{1}{3}t^2]}.$$

B. In the case of a shell where the thickness t is negligible in comparison with r, this reduces to $\bar{y} = \frac{1}{2}r$ if we write

$$\bar{y} = \frac{1}{2}\frac{r^3\left[1 + \frac{3}{2}\left(\frac{t}{r}\right) + \left(\frac{t}{r}\right)^2 + \frac{1}{4}\left(\frac{t}{r}\right)^3\right]}{r^2\left[1 + \left(\frac{t}{r}\right) + \frac{1}{3}\left(\frac{t}{r}\right)^2\right]},$$

and then let

$$(t/r) \to 0.$$

C. To solve the problem directly, without reference to Problem 1, consider the mass of the shell as being uniformly distributed over its surface so that the mass of any portion cut from the shell will be proportional to its (inner) surface area. The proportionality factor,

$$\sigma = \delta t,$$

where δ is the volume density and t the thickness of the shell, is frequently referred to as a surface density factor. (Thus in working with sheet metal stock, say aluminum of uniform thickness and density, we might speak of it as weighing so many pounds *per square foot*. This would be our σ, and A square feet of this particular stock would weigh σA pounds.) Then the slice of shell between planes perpendicular to the y-axis at distances y and $y + \Delta y$ respectively above the xz-plane has mass

$$\Delta m = \sigma\, \Delta S,$$

where ΔS is the surface area of the slice (see Fig. 7.30).

The moment of this slice with respect to the xz-plane then lies between

$$y \, \Delta m \quad \text{and} \quad (y + \Delta y) \, \Delta m,$$

and hence differs from $y \, \Delta m$ by at most $\Delta y \, \Delta m$. The sum of the moments of the slices has a limit, as Δy approaches zero, equal to $\int y \, dm$. We are thus led to

$$\bar{y} = \frac{\int y \, dm}{\int dm} = \frac{\int \sigma y \, dS}{\int \sigma \, dS} = \frac{\sigma \int y \, dS}{\sigma \int dS},$$

since σ is constant by our hypotheses. Here

$$dS = 2\pi x \, ds = 2\pi (r \cos \theta) r \, d\theta$$

if we use

$$x = r \cos \theta, \qquad y = r \sin \theta$$

to represent the circle $x^2 + y^2 = r^2$. Hence

$$
\begin{aligned}
\bar{y} &= \frac{\int_0^{\pi/2} r \sin \theta \cdot 2\pi (r \cos \theta) \cdot r \, d\theta}{\int_0^{\pi/2} 2\pi (r \cos \theta) r \, d\theta} \\
&= \frac{2\pi r^3 \int_0^{\pi/2} \sin \theta \cos \theta \, d\theta}{2\pi r^2 \int_0^{\pi/2} \cos \theta \, d\theta} \\
&= r \frac{[\frac{1}{2} \sin^2 \theta]_0^{\pi/2}}{[\sin \theta]_0^{\pi/2}} = \frac{1}{2} r.
\end{aligned}
$$

Observe that the element of arc ds which, when rotated about the y-axis generates dS, need only move along the arc of the circle in the first quadrant, namely, $0 \le \theta \le \pi/2$, to give us the entire hemisphere.

By the symmetry of the shell, the centroid lies on the y-axis; that is,

$$(\bar{x}, \bar{y}, \bar{z}) = (0, \tfrac{1}{2} r, 0).$$

Remark. The *centroid* of a body is also called its *center of gravity.*

EXERCISES |17#1–3   2/22 5, 7, 8, 9, 12

In Exercises 1 through 5, find the centroid of the areas bounded by the given curves and lines.

1. The x-axis and the curve $y = c^2 - x^2$.

2. The y-axis and the curve $x = y - y^3, 0 \le y \le 1$.

3. The curve $y = x^2$ and the line $y = 4$.

4. The curve $y = x - x^2$ and the line $x + y = 0$.

5. The curve $x = y^2 - y$ and the line $y = x$.

6. Find the center of gravity of a solid right circular cone of altitude h and base-radius r.

7. Find the center of gravity of the solid generated by rotating, about the y-axis, the area bounded by the curve $y = x^2$ and the line $y = 4$.

8. The area bounded by the curve $x = y^2 - y$ and the line $y = x$ is rotated about the x-axis. Find the center of gravity of the solid thus generated.

9. Find the center of gravity of a very thin right circular conical shell of base-radius r and altitude h.

10. Find the center of gravity of the surface area generated by rotating, about the line $x = -r$, the arc of the circle $x^2 + y^2 = r^2$ that lies in the first quadrant. [*Suggestion.* Use $x = r \cos \theta, y = r \sin \theta$ to represent the circle.]

11. Find the moment, about the x-axis, of the arc of the parabola $y = \sqrt{x}$ lying between the points $(0, 0)$ and $(4, 2)$.

12. Find the center of gravity of the arc length of one quadrant of a circle.

7.11 WORK

When a constant force F (pounds) acts throughout a distance s (feet), the *work* done (in foot-pounds) is the product of force and distance:

$$W = Fs. \tag{1}$$

When the force is not constant, as for instance in stretching or compressing a spring, then Eq. (1) cannot be used directly to give the work done. The law in (1) can be used, however, to find approximately the work done over a *short* interval Δs if the force is a continuous function of s. The integral process then enables us to extend the law in (1) to find the total work done.

To illustrate, suppose we consider the work done in compressing a spring from its natural unstressed length L to a length $\frac{3}{4}L$ (Fig. 7.31) if the force required to hold it under compression is

$$F = cx, \tag{2}$$

where x is the amount it has been compressed and c is a proportionality factor (called the "spring constant"). Thus to compress the spring by an amount

7.31

7.32

for appropriate choices of the $\tilde{x}$ between x and $x + \Delta x$. In the limit as Δx tends to zero, we have

$$W = \lim_{\Delta x \to 0} \sum_{x=0}^{L/4} cx\,\Delta x = \int_0^{L/4} cx\,dx$$

$$= \frac{cL^2}{32} = \frac{1}{2}\,\frac{cL}{4}\,\frac{L}{4}.$$

In this last form, the factor $\frac{1}{2}c(L/4)$ is one-half the final value reached by F when the spring has been compressed to $\frac{3}{4}$ of its original length, and the factor $L/4$ is the total distance through which the variable force has acted. This suggests

$$W = \overline{F}s \tag{3}$$

as a suitable modification of Eq. (1) when the force is variable, where $\overline{F}$ represents the *average* value of the variable force throughout the total displacement. However, the determination of $\overline{F}$ itself involves an integration in the general case, so that it is usually as easy to apply the principles illustrated in the example just considered as it is to apply Eq. (3). In fact, Eq. (3) may be interpreted as *defining* $\overline{F}$.

In a manner entirely analogous to that in the above example, it is easily seen that

$$W = \int_a^b F\,ds \tag{4}$$

gives the work done by a variable force (which, however, always acts along a given direction) as the point of application undergoes a displacement from $s = a$ to $s = b$. This leads to the following interesting theorem of mechanics.

Theorem 3. *Let F denote the resultant of all forces acting on a particle of mass m. Let the direction of F remain constant. Then whether the magnitude of F is constant or variable, the work done on the particle by the force F is equal to the change in the kinetic energy of the particle.*

The ingredients required for a proof of this theorem are:

(a) Eq. (4), which gives the work,

(b) the definition of kinetic energy: K.E. $= \frac{1}{2}mv^2$,

(c) Newton's second law: $F = m(dv/dt)$.

$L/4$, the force must be increased from

$$F_0 = c \times 0 = 0$$

to

$$F_1 = c\,\frac{L}{4},$$

and as it does so the point of application of the force will move from $x = 0$ to $x = L/4$ (Fig. 7.32). How then shall we find the *work* done during the process? We imagine the x-interval from 0 to $L/4$ to be divided into a large number of subintervals, each of length Δx. As the spring is compressed an amount Δx, so that its left end moves across the representative subinterval from x to $x + \Delta x$, the *force* will vary from cx to $c(x + \Delta x)$, and since it acts through a *distance* Δx, the work done for this small compression will lie between

$$cx\,\Delta x \quad \text{and} \quad c(x + \Delta x)\,\Delta x,$$

so that the total work will be given approximately by

$$W \approx \sum_{x=0}^{L/4} cx\,\Delta x,$$

or

$$W = \sum_{x=0}^{L/4} c\tilde{x}\,\Delta x,$$

The fact that

$$v = \frac{ds}{dt} \quad \text{and} \quad \frac{dv}{dt} = \frac{dv}{ds}\frac{ds}{dt} = \frac{dv}{ds}v,$$

together with Newton's second law, enables us to write Eq. (4) in the form

$$W = \int_{s=a}^{s=b} mv\frac{dv}{ds}\,ds = \int_{v=v_a}^{v=v_b} mv\,dv,$$

which leads to

$$W = \frac{1}{2}mv^2\bigg]_{v_a}^{v_b} = \frac{1}{2}mv_b^2 - \frac{1}{2}mv_a^2.$$

That is, the work done by the force F is the kinetic energy at b minus the kinetic energy at a or, more simply, the change in kinetic energy:

$$W = \Delta(\text{K.E.}).$$

As a second example of work in a situation where the simple Eq. (1) cannot be applied to the *total* but can be applied to a *small piece*, we consider the problem of pumping all the water from a full hemispherical bowl of radius r (feet) to a distance h (feet) above the top of the bowl (see Fig. 7.33).

7.33

We introduce coordinate axes as shown in Fig. 7.33 and imagine the bowl to be divided into a large number of thin slices by planes perpendicular to the x-axis between $x = 0$ and $x = r$. The representative slice between the planes at x and $x + \Delta x$

has volume ΔV which, if we neglect only infinitesimals of higher order than Δx, is given approximately by

$$\Delta V \approx \pi y^2\,\Delta x = \pi(r^2 - x^2)\,\Delta x.$$

To the same order of approximation, the force F required to lift *this slice* is equal to its weight:

$$w\,\Delta V \approx \pi w(r^2 - x^2)\,\Delta x,$$

where w is the weight of a cubic foot of water. Finally, the *distance* through which this force must act lies between

$$h + x \quad \text{and} \quad h + x + \Delta x,$$

so that the work ΔW done in *lifting this one slice* is approximately

$$\Delta W \approx \pi w(r^2 - x^2)(h + x)\,\Delta x,$$

where we again have suppressed all higher powers of Δx. This is justified in the *limit* of the sum, and the total work is

$$\begin{aligned}
W &= \lim_{\Delta x \to 0} \sum_0^r \pi w(r^2 - x^2)(h + x)\,\Delta x \\
&= \int_0^r \pi w(h + x)(r^2 - x^2)\,dx \\
&= hw\int_0^r \pi(r^2 - x^2)\,dx + w\int_0^r \pi x(r^2 - x^2)\,dx \\
&= hwV + \bar{x}wV.
\end{aligned}$$

Here (wV) is the weight of the whole bowlful of water of volume V, and the second integral may be interpreted physically as giving the work required in pumping *all* the water from the depth of the center of gravity of the bowl to the level $x = 0$, while the first integral gives the work done in pumping the whole bowlful of water from the level $x = 0$ up a distance of h feet. The actual evaluation of the integrals leads to

$$W = \tfrac{2}{3}\pi r^3 w(h + \tfrac{3}{8}r).$$

Can you prove the following fact to yourself? No matter what the shape of the container in Fig. 7.33, the total work is the sum of two terms: One of these is

$$W_1 = hw\int dV,$$

and represents the total work done in lifting a bowl-ful of water a distance h, while the other is

$$W_2 = w \int x \, dV$$

and represents the work done in lifting a bowlful of water a distance equal to the depth of the center of gravity of the bowl.

EXERCISES 4/23 1, 6, 9, 10

1. If the spring in Fig. 7.31 has natural length $L = 18$ in., and a force of 10 lb is sufficient to compress it to a length of 16 in., what is the value of the "spring constant" c for the particular spring in question? How much work is done in compressing it from a length of 16 in. to a length of 12 in.?

2. Answer the questions of Exercise 1 if the law of force is $F = c \sin (\pi x/2L)$ rather than Eq. (2).

3. Two electrons repel each other with a force inversely proportional to the square of the distance between them. Suppose one electron is held fixed at the point $(1, 0)$ on the x-axis. Find the work required to move a second electron along the x-axis from the point $(-1, 0)$ to the origin.

4. If two electrons are held stationary at the points $(-1, 0)$ and $(1, 0)$ on the x-axis, find the work done in moving a third electron from $(5, 0)$ to $(3, 0)$ along the x-axis.

5. If a straight hole could be bored through the center of the earth, a particle of mass m falling in this hole would be attracted toward the center of the earth with force $mg\,r/R$ when it is at distance r from the center. (R is the radius of earth; g is the acceleration due to gravity at the surface of the earth.) How much work is done on the particle as it falls from the surface to the center of the earth?

6. A bag of sand originally weighing 144 lb is lifted at a constant rate of 3 ft/min. The sand leaks out uniformly at such a rate that half of the sand is lost when the bag has been lifted 18 ft. Find the work done in lifting the bag this distance.

7. Gas in a cylinder of constant cross-sectional area A expands or is compressed by the motion of a piston. If p is the pressure of the gas in pounds per square inch and v is its volume in cubic inches, show that the work done by the gas as it goes from an initial state (p_1, v_1) to a second state (p_2, v_2) is

$$W = \int_{(p_1, v_1)}^{(p_2, v_2)} p \, dv \text{ (inch-pounds)}.$$

[*Hint*. Take the x-axis perpendicular to the face of the piston. Then $dv = A \, dx$ and $F = pA$.]

8. Use the result of Exercise 7 to find the work done on the gas in compressing it from $v_1 = 243$ in^3 to $v_2 = 32$ in^3 if the initial pressure $p_1 = 50$ lb/in^2 and the pressure and volume satisfy the law for adiabatic change of state, $pv^{1.4} = $ constant.

9. Find the work done in pumping all the water out of a conical reservoir of radius 10 ft at the top, altitude 8 ft, to a height of 6 ft above the top of the reservoir.

10. Find the work done in Exercise 9 if at the beginning the reservoir is filled to a depth of 5 ft and the water is pumped just to the top of the reservoir.

REVIEW QUESTIONS AND EXERCISES

1. List nine applications of the definite integral presented in this chapter.

2. How do you define the area bounded above by a curve $y = f_1(x)$, below by a curve $y = f_2(x)$, and on the sides by $x = a$ and $x = b$, $a < b$?

3. How do you define the volume generated by rotating a plane area about an axis in its plane and not intersecting the area?

4. How do you define the length of a plane curve? Can you extend this to a curve in three-dimensional space?

5. How do you define the surface area of a sphere? Of other surfaces of revolution?

6. How do you define the average value of a function over an interval?

7. How do you define center of mass?

8. How do you define work done by a variable force?

MISCELLANEOUS EXERCISES

1. Sketch the graphs of the equations $y = 2 - x^2$ and $x + y = 0$ in one diagram, and find the area bounded by them.

2. Find the maximum and minimum points of the curve $y = x^3 - 3x^2$ and find the total area bounded by this curve and the x-axis. Sketch.

In the following exercises (3–15), find the area bounded by the given curves and lines. Use the trapezoidal rule, Article 6.10, to approximate any integral you cannot evaluate by the Fundamental Theorem. A sketch is usually helpful.

3. $y = x$, $y = \dfrac{1}{x^2}$, $x = 2$

4. $y = x$, $y = \dfrac{1}{\sqrt{x}}$, $x = 2$

5. $y = x + 1$, $y = 3 - x^2$

6. $y = 2x^2$, $y = x^2 + 2x + 3$

7. $x = 2y^2$, $x = 0$, $y = 3$

8. $4x = y^2 - 4$, $4x = y + 16$

9. $x^{1/2} + y^{1/2} = a^{1/2}$, $x = 0$, $y = 0$

10. $y = \sqrt{9 + x^2}$, $y = 0$, $x = 0$, $x = 4$

11. $y^2 = 9x$, $y = \dfrac{3x^2}{8}$

12. $y = \dfrac{1}{1 + x^2}$, $y = 0$, $x = 0$, $x = 1$

13. $y = x\sqrt{2x^2 + 1}$, $x = 0$, $x = 2$

14. $y^2 = 4x$ and $y = 4x - 2$

15. $y = 2 - x^2$ and $y = x^2 - 6$

16. The function $v = 3t^2 - 15t + 18$ represents the velocity v (ft/sec) of a moving body as a function of the time t (sec). (a) Find that portion of the time interval $0 \le t \le 3$ in which the velocity is positive. (b) Find that portion where v is negative. (c) Find the total distance traveled by the body from $t = 0$ to $t = 3$.

17. The area from 0 to x under a certain graph is given to be

$$A = (1 + 3x)^{1/2} - 1, \quad x \ge 0.$$

(a) Find the *average* rate of change of A with respect to x as x increases from 1 to 8. (b) Find the *instantaneous* rate of change of A with respect to x at $x = 5$. (c) Find the ordinate (height) y of the graph as a function of x. (d) Find the average value of the ordinate (height) y, with respect to x, as x increases from 1 to 8.

18. A solid is generated by rotating, about the x-axis, the area bounded by the curve $y = f(x)$, the x-axis, and the lines $x = a$, $x = b$. Its volume, for all $b > a$, is $b^2 - ab$. Find $f(x)$.

19. Find the volume generated by rotating the area bounded by the given curves and lines about the line indicated:

(a) $y = x^2$, $y = 0$, $x = 3$; about the x-axis.

(b) $y = x^2$, $y = 0$, $x = 3$; about the line $x = -3$.

(c) $y = x^2$, $y = 0$, $x = 3$; about the y-axis, first integrating with respect to x and then integrating with respect to y.

(d) $x = 4y - y^2$, $x = 0$; about the y-axis.

(e) $x = 4y - y^2$, $x = 0$; about the x-axis.

20. A solid is generated by rotating $f(x)$, $(0 \le x \le a)$, about the x-axis. Its volume for all a is $a^2 + a$; find $f(x)$.

21. The area bounded by the curve $y^2 = 4x$ and the straight line $y = x$ is rotated about the x-axis. Find the volume generated.

22. Sketch the area bounded by the curve $y^2 = 4ax$, the line $x = a$, and the x-axis. Find the respective volumes generated ·by rotating this area in the following ways: (a) about the x-axis, (b) about the line $x = a$, (c) about the y-axis.

23. The area bounded by the curve $y = x/\sqrt{x^3 + 8}$, the x-axis, and the line $x = 2$ is rotated about the y-axis, generating a certain volume. Set up the integral that should be used to evaluate the volume and then evaluate the integral.

24. Find the volume of the solid generated by rotating the larger area bounded by

$$y^2 = x - 1, \ x = 3, \ \text{and} \ y = 1$$

about the y-axis.

25. The area bounded by the curve $y^2 = 4ax$ and the line $x = a$ is rotated about the line $x = 2a$. Find the volume generated.

26. Two circles have a common diameter and lie in perpendicular planes. A square moves in such a way that its plane is perpendicular to this diameter and its diagonals are chords of the circles. Find the volume generated.

27. Find the volume generated by rotating about the x-axis the area bounded by the x-axis and one arch of the curve $y = \sin 2x$.

28. A round hole of radius $\sqrt{3}$ ft is bored through the center of a solid sphere of radius 2 ft. Find the volume cut out.

29. The base of a solid is the area bounded by $y^2 = 4ax$ and $x = a$. Each cross section perpendicular to the x-axis is an equilateral triangle. Find the volume of the solid.

30. Find the length of the curve $x = (\frac{3}{5})y^{5/3} - (\frac{3}{4})y^{1/3}$ from $y = 0$ to $y = 1$.

31. Find the surface area generated when the curve of Problem 30 is rotated about the line $y = -1$.

32. Find the length of the curve $y = (2x^{3/2}/3) - (x^{1/2}/2)$ from $x = 0$ to $x = 4$ and the surface area generated when the curve is rotated about the y-axis.

33. Find the average value of y with respect to x for that part of the curve $y = \sqrt{ax}$ between $x = a$ and $x = 3a$.

34. Find the average value of y^2 with respect to x for the curve $ay = b\sqrt{a^2 - x^2}$ between $x = 0$ and $x = a$. Also find the average value of y with respect to x^2 for $0 \le x \le a$.

35. Consider the curve $y = f(x)$, $x \ge 0$ such that $f(0) = a$. Let $s(x)$ denote the arc length along the curve from $(0, a)$ to $(x, f(x))$. Find $f(x)$ if (a) $s(x) = Ax$. (What are the permissible values of A?) (b) Is it possible for $s(x) = x^n$, $n > 1$? Give a reason for your answer.

36. A point moves in a straight line during the time from $t = 0$ to $t = 3$ according to the law $s = 120t - 16t^2$. (a) Find the average value of the velocity, with respect to time, for these three seconds. [Compare with the "average velocity," Article 2.8, Eq. (6).] (b) Find the average value of the velocity with respect to the distance s during the three seconds.

37. Sketch a smooth curve through the points $A(1, 3)$, $B(3, 5)$, $C(5, 6)$, $D(7, 6)$, $E(9, 7)$, $F(11, 10)$. The area bounded by this curve, the x-axis, and the lines $x = 1$, $x = 11$ is rotated about the x-axis to generate a solid. Use the trapezoidal rule to approximate the volume generated. Also determine approximately the average value of the circular cross-sectional area (with respect to x).

38. Determine the center of mass of a thin homogeneous plate covering the area enclosed by the curves $y^2 = 8x$ and $y = x^2$.

39. Find the center of mass of a homogeneous plate covering the area in the first quadrant bounded by the curve $4y = x^2$, the y-axis, and the line $y = 4$.

40. Find the center of gravity of the area bounded by the curve $y = 4x - x^2$ and the line $2x - y = 0$.

41. Find the center of mass of a thin homogeneous plate covering the portion of the xy-plane, in the first quadrant, bounded by the curve $y = x^2$, the x-axis, and the line $x = 1$.

42. Consider a thin metal plate of area A and constant density and thickness. Show that if its first moment about the y-axis is M, its moment about the line $x = b$ is $M - bA$. Indicate why this result actually shows that the center of gravity is a physical property of the body, independent of the coordinate system used for finding its location.

43. Find the center of mass of a thin plate covering the region bounded by the curve $y^2 = 4ax$ and the line $x = a$, a = positive constant, if the density at (x, y) is directly proportional to (a) x, (b) $|y|$.

44. A particle of mass M starts from rest at time $t = 0$ and is moved with constant acceleration a from $x = 0$ to $x = h$ against a variable force $F(t) = t^2$. Find the work done.

45. Below the surface of the earth the force of its gravitational attraction is directly proportional to the distance from its center. Find the work done in lifting an object, whose weight at the surface is w lb, from a distance r ft below the earth's surface to the surface.

46. A storage tank is a right circular cylinder 20 ft long and 8 ft in diameter with its axis horizontal. If the tank is half full of oil weighing w lb/ft^3, find the work done in emptying it through a pipe that runs from the bottom of the tank to an outlet that is 6 ft above the top of the tank.

TRANSCENDENTAL FUNCTIONS

CHAPTER 8

We have learned how to differentiate and integrate polynomials and certain other algebraic functions, including some rational functions and fractional powers. By definition, y is an *algebraic* function of x if it is a function that satisfies an irreducible algebraic equation of the form

$$P_0(x)y^n + P_1(x)y^{n-1} + \cdots + P_{n-1}(x)y + P_n(x) = 0,$$

with n a positive integer and with coefficients

$$P_0(x), \ P_1(x), \ldots$$

that are polynomials in x. For instance, $y = \sqrt{x}$, $x > 0$, defines an algebraic function whose elements (x, y) satisfy the irreducible equation

$$y^2 - x = 0.$$

Sums, products, quotients, powers, and roots of algebraic functions are in turn algebraic functions.

A function that is not algebraic is called *transcendental*. The class of transcendental functions includes the trigonometric, logarithmic, exponential, and inverse trigonometric functions, and many more which are less familiar.

We have learned how to differentiate and integrate two transcendental functions—the sine and cosine. In this chapter we shall add to this list the derivatives of the remaining trigonometric functions, their inverse functions, and the logarithmic and exponential functions.

At this stage it is well to recall the list of formulas for derivatives and differentials given in Chapter 4, which we present in expanded form here. The first six pairs of functions, (I, I′) through (VI, VI′), by themselves enable us to differentiate the *algebraic* functions, which include polynomials, ratios of polynomials, and roots or powers of either of these types. VII, VII′, VIII, and VIII′ are discussed in Article 6.5.

When we combine formulas V, VII, and VIII and apply them to the trigonometric identities

$$\tan u = \frac{\sin u}{\cos u}, \quad \cot u = \frac{\cos u}{\sin u},$$

$$\sec u = \frac{1}{\cos u}, \quad \csc u = \frac{1}{\sin u}, \tag{1}$$

Derivatives	Differentials
I. $\dfrac{dc}{dx} = 0.$	I'. $dc = 0.$
II. $\dfrac{d(cu)}{dx} = c\dfrac{du}{dx}.$	II'. $d(cu) = c\,du.$
III. $\dfrac{d(u+v)}{dx} = \dfrac{du}{dx} + \dfrac{dv}{dx}.$	III'. $d(u+v) = du + dv.$
IV. $\dfrac{d(uv)}{dx} = u\dfrac{dv}{dx} + v\dfrac{du}{dx}.$	IV'. $d(uv) = u\,dv + v\,du.$
V. $\dfrac{d\left(\dfrac{u}{v}\right)}{dx} = \dfrac{v\dfrac{du}{dx} - u\dfrac{dv}{dx}}{v^2}.$	V'. $d\left(\dfrac{u}{v}\right) = \dfrac{v\,du - u\,dv}{v^2}.$
VI. $\dfrac{d(u^n)}{dx} = nu^{n-1}\dfrac{du}{dx}.$	VI'. $d(u^n) = nu^{n-1}\,du.$
VII. $\dfrac{d(\sin u)}{dx} = \cos u\dfrac{du}{dx}.$	VII'. $d(\sin u) = \cos u\,du.$
VIII. $\dfrac{d(\cos u)}{dx} = -\sin u\dfrac{du}{dx}.$	VIII'. $d(\cos u) = -\sin u\,du.$
IX. $\dfrac{d(\tan u)}{dx} = \sec^2 u\dfrac{du}{dx}.$	IX'. $d(\tan u) = \sec^2 u\,du.$
X. $\dfrac{d(\cot u)}{dx} = -\csc^2 u\dfrac{du}{dx}.$	X'. $d(\cot u) = -\csc^2 u\,du.$
XI. $\dfrac{d(\sec u)}{dx} = \sec u\tan u\dfrac{du}{dx}.$	XI'. $d(\sec u) = \sec u\tan u\,du.$
XII. $\dfrac{d(\csc u)}{dx} = -\csc u\cot u\dfrac{du}{dx}.$	XII'. $d(\csc u) = -\csc u\cot u\,du.$

it is a simple matter to complete the list of formulas for differentiating the trigonometric functions and, doing so, we obtain the formulas that appear as the pairs (IX, IX') through (XII, XII'). The proofs of these eight formulas should be carried through by the reader.

These formulas are in the forms that are customarily used, though there are alternate forms, such as the formula

$$\frac{d(\sec u)}{dx} = \frac{\sin u}{\cos^2 u}\frac{du}{dx},$$

which are obtained from the expressions given by using some trigonometric identities. One reason for preferring the forms above is that they are quite easy to remember if we note that *the derivative of every cofunction* (cos, cot, csc) *can be obtained from the derivative of the corresponding function* (sin, tan, sec) *by*

(a) *introducing a minus sign, and*

(b) *replacing each function by its cofunction.*

Apply this, for example, to the formula

$$\frac{d\,(\sec u)}{dx} = \sec u \tan u \frac{du}{dx}.$$

Replace sec u and tan u by their *cofunctions* on *both sides* of the equation and put in a *minus* sign; the result is

$$\frac{d\,(\csc u)}{dx} = -\csc u \cot u \frac{du}{dx}.$$

Thus it is really only necessary to "memorize" the two new formulas

$$\frac{d\,(\tan u)}{dx} = \sec^2 u \frac{du}{dx},$$

$$\frac{d\,(\sec u)}{dx} = \sec u \tan u \frac{du}{dx};$$

the above rule produces the other two.

The formulas IX′–XII′ for differentials immediately produce the four new integration formulas

$$\int \sec^2 u \, du = \tan u + C,$$

$$\int \csc^2 u \, du = -\cot u + C,$$

$$\int \sec u \tan u \, du = \sec u + C,$$

$$\int \csc u \cot u \, du = -\csc u + C.$$

(2)

Problem 1. Find dy/dx if $y = \tan^2 3x$.

Solution. First we apply the power formula (VI:)

$$\frac{dy}{dx} = 2 \tan 3x \frac{d\,(\tan 3x)}{dx},$$

and then IX:

$$\frac{d\,(\tan 3x)}{dx} = \sec^2 3x \frac{d(3x)}{dx},$$

and then II:

$$\frac{d(3x)}{dx} = 3 \frac{dx}{dx} = 3.$$

When these are combined, we get

$$\frac{dy}{dx} = 6 \tan 3x \sec^2 3x.$$

Problem 2. Integrate

$$\int \tan^2 3x \, dx.$$

Solution. At first sight, this seems to be impossible with the formulas we have for integration. However, we see that the trigonometric identity

$$\sin^2 3x + \cos^2 3x = 1$$

becomes

$$\tan^2 3x + 1 = \sec^2 3x$$

when we divide both sides by $\cos^2 3x$. Hence,

$$\tan^2 3x = \sec^2 3x - 1,$$

and

$$\int \tan^2 3x \, dx = \int (\sec^2 3x - 1) \, dx$$

$$= \int \sec^2 3x \, dx - \int 1 \, dx$$

$$= \tfrac{1}{3} \int \sec^2 3x \, d(3x) - \int 1 \, dx$$

$$= \tfrac{1}{3} \tan 3x - x + C.$$

EXERCISES

Sketch the graphs of the equations in Exercises 1 through 10.

1. $y = \sin x$ 2. $y = \cos x$

3. $y = \tan x$ 4. $y = \cot x$

5. $y = \sec x$ 6. $y = \csc x$

7. $y = 3 \sin 2x$ 8. $y = 4 \cos (x/3)$

9. $y = \sin^2 x$ 10. $y = \tfrac{1}{2} + \tfrac{1}{2} \cos 2x$

11. (a) Derive formula IX.   12. (a) Derive formula X.

    (b) Derive formula XI.   (b) Derive formula XII.

34,36,38,48, @8.2 2-8

2/25
odd 13-33   41-47

Find dy/dx in Exercises 13 through 33.

13. $y = \tan(3x^2)$

14. $y = \tan^2(\cos x)$

15. $y = \cot(3x+5)$

16. $y = \sqrt{\cot x}$

17. $y = \sec^2 x - \tan^2 x$

18. $y = \frac{1}{3}\sec^3 x$

19. $y = 3x + \tan 3x$

20. $y = 3\tan 2x$

21. $y = x - \tan x$

22. $y = \sec^4 x - \tan^4 x$

23. $y = (\csc x + \cot x)^2$

24. $y = 2\sin^2 3x$

25. $y = \frac{1}{2}x - \frac{1}{4}\sin 2x$

26. $y = \frac{1}{2}x + \frac{1}{4}\sin 2x$

27. $y = \sin^3\frac{x}{3} - 3\sin\frac{x}{3}$

28. $y = 3\cos^2\frac{x}{2}$

29. $y = 2\sin\frac{1}{2}x - x\cos\frac{1}{2}x$

30. $x^2 = \sin y + \sin 2y$

31. $y = \sin^3 x - \sin 3x$

32. $y = \frac{1}{3}\sin^3 5x - \sin 5x$

33. $x + \tan(xy) = 0$

34. Find the maximum height of the curve

$$y = 6\cos x - 8\sin x$$

above the x-axis.

35. Find the maximum and minimum values of the function $y = 2\sin x + \cos 2x$ for $0 \le x \le \pi/2$.

36. Show that the function $f(x) = x + \sin x$ has no relative maxima or minima.

37. Show that the curve $y = x\sin x$ is tangent to the line $y = x$ whenever $\sin x = 1$, and is tangent to the line $y = -x$ whenever $\sin x = -1$.

38. A revolving light 3 miles from a straight shoreline makes 8 revolutions per minute. Find the velocity of the beam of light along the shore at the instant when it makes an angle of 45° with the shoreline.

39. A rope with a ring in one end is looped over two pegs in a horizontal line. The free end, after being passed through the ring, has a weight suspended from it, so that the rope hangs taut. If the rope slips freely through the ring, the weight will descend as far as possible. Find the angle formed at the bottom of the loop. (Assume that the length of the rope is at least four times the distance between the pegs.)

Evaluate the following integrals.

40. $\int \sin 3t\, dt$

41. $\int \sec^2 2\theta\, d\theta$

42. $\int \tan^3 x\sec^2 x\, dx$

43. $\int \sec^3 x\tan x\, dx$

44. $\int \sec\frac{x}{2}\tan\frac{x}{2}\, dx$

45. $\int \cos^2 y\, dy$

46. $\int \frac{d\theta}{\cos^2\theta}$

47. $\int \frac{d\theta}{\sin^2(\theta/3)}$

48. Find the area bounded by the curve

$$y = \tan x\sec^2 x,$$

the x-axis, and the line $x = \pi/3$.

49. The area bounded above by the curve $y = \tan x$, below by the x-axis, and on the right by the line $x = \pi/4$ is revolved about the x-axis. Find the volume generated.

50. Prove that $\tan x > x$ for $0 < x < \pi/2$ by applying the Mean Value Theorem to $f(t) = \tan t - t$ on $[0, x]$.

51. Prove that (a) $t\sec^2 t - \tan t > 0$, $0 < t < \pi/2$, (b) $(\tan x)/x$ is an increasing function on $(0, \pi/2)$.

8.2 THE INVERSE TRIGONOMETRIC FUNCTIONS

The equation

$$x = \sin y \qquad (1)$$

determines infinitely many real values of y for each x in the range $-1 \le x \le 1$.

Example. If $x = \frac{1}{2}$, then we ask for all angles y such that $\sin y = \frac{1}{2}$. The two angles 30° and 150° in the first and second quadrants occur to us immediately. But any whole multiple of 360° may be either added to or subtracted from these and the sine of the resulting angle will still be $\frac{1}{2}$. (See Fig. 8.1.) Expressing these facts in mathematical language and using radian measure for the angles, we have $\sin y = \frac{1}{2}$ if

$$y = \begin{cases} \dfrac{\pi}{6} + 2n\pi, \\[2mm] \dfrac{5\pi}{6} + 2n\pi, \end{cases} \qquad n = 0, \pm 1, \pm 2, \ldots$$

Similarly, we find that $\sin y = -\frac{1}{2}$ if

$$y = \begin{cases} -\dfrac{\pi}{6} + 2n\pi, \\[2mm] -\dfrac{5\pi}{6} + 2n\pi, \end{cases} \qquad n = 0, \pm 1, \pm 2, \ldots$$

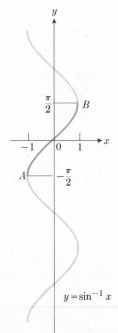

8.2 The principle values of the function $y = \sin^{-1} x$ lie on the portion of the curve printed in darker color.

Now it is desirable, for some of our later applications, to adopt a rule for picking a *principal value* of y. We shall require that the rule

(a) give one and only one value of y for each x, $-1 \leq x \leq 1$, such that $\sin y = x$; and

(b) give two "nearly equal" values of y for two "nearly equal" values of x.

To state requirement (b) more specifically, we require that if x_1 and x_2 are two values of x both between -1 and $+1$, and y_1 and y_2 are the corresponding values of y such that $\sin y = x$, then $y_2 - y_1$ should tend to zero if $x_2 - x_1$ does. The portion AOB of the curve, shown in darker color in Fig. 8.2, fulfills these requirements. For any x between -1 and $+1$ there is one and only one corresponding point (x, y) on this portion of the curve, and the y-value satisfies $\sin y = x$. Furthermore, this is a continuous curve, so that if (x_1, y_1) and (x_2, y_2) are two points on it and $(x_2 - x_1) \to 0$, then also $(y_2 - y_1) \to 0$.

To be sure that the point (x, y) stays on the portion AOB of the curve, we need only restrict y:

$$\sin y = x, \quad -\frac{\pi}{2} \leq y \leq \frac{\pi}{2}. \qquad (2)$$

The restrictions placed on y give a continuous function

$$y = \sin^{-1} x, \quad -\frac{\pi}{2} \leq y \leq \frac{\pi}{2}, \qquad (3)$$

called the "inverse sine of x," which is defined on the domain $-1 \leq x \leq 1$ and has values on the range $-\pi/2 \leq y \leq \pi/2$.

Notation. The minus one in Eq. (3), although written as an exponent, does *not* mean

$$(\sin x)^{-1} = \frac{1}{\sin x} = \csc x.$$

Actually, Eq. (3) merely gives a name to a new function that is defined implicitly by Eq. (2). The symbol $f^{-1}(x)$ is often used to denote the function y

defined implicitly by $f(y) = x$; that is,

$$y = f^{-1}(x).$$

The notation "arcsin" x is also used to represent the function that we have denoted by $\sin^{-1} x$, but the latter notation is now more commonly used. Thus,

$$\sin^{-1}\left(\frac{1}{2}\right) = \frac{\pi}{6}, \qquad \sin^{-1}\left(-\frac{1}{2}\right) = -\frac{\pi}{6}.$$

Note. In terms of angles referred to standard position in the various quadrants, Eq. (2) and the restriction $-\pi/2 \le y \le \pi/2$ mean that the answer to the question: "What is the angle y whose sine is x?" is always an angle in the *first* or *fourth* quadrant, but if it is in the *fourth* quadrant, it is to be expressed as the *negative* of an angle between 0 and $\pi/2$ and not as a positive angle $\ge 3\pi/2$, since the latter would violate the restriction in (2).

At the risk of appearing to labor a point which is already clear, we also note that the inverse sine is an *odd* function of x. This means that

$$\sin^{-1}(-x) = -\sin^{-1}(x).$$

Keeping this fact firmly in mind will prevent us from using values of y corresponding to points on the discontinuous curve composed of the portions OB and CD on the curve in Fig. 8.3. The objection to using these is that for a small positive value of x, say $x_1 = +0.01$, the point is near O and $y_1 \approx 0.01$; while for a small negative value of x, say $x_2 = -0.01$, the point is near D and $y_2 \approx 2\pi - 0.01$. The difference $y_2 - y_1$ is nearly $2\pi = 6.28+$, whereas the difference $x_1 - x_2$ is, in this case, only 0.02. This difficulty is not encountered if we restrict the value of y as in (3), which confines us to the *continuous curve AOB* of Fig. 8.2.

To each of the other trigonometric functions there also corresponds an *inverse* trigonometric function. In each case, we restrict the angle in such a way that the function is *single-valued*.

The same reasoning that led us to adopt the particular range

$$-\frac{\pi}{2} \le y \le \frac{\pi}{2} \qquad y = \sin^{-1} x$$

for the principal value of $y = \sin^{-1} x$ prompts us to adopt a similar range for the principal value of y satisfying the equation $x = \tan y$ (see Fig. 8.4).

$x = \sin y$

8.3

$y = \tan^{-1} x$

8.4

Thus we write

$$y = \tan^{-1} x, \quad -\frac{\pi}{2} < y < \frac{\pi}{2} \qquad (4)$$

to mean the same as

$$\tan y = x, \quad -\frac{\pi}{2} < y < \frac{\pi}{2}. \qquad (5)$$

The inverse tangent function, (4), is defined on the *domain* $-\infty < x < +\infty$, that is, for all real x. Its *range* is $-\pi/2 < y < +\pi/2$. The values $y = \pm\pi/2$ are to be excluded, since the tangent becomes infinite as the angle approaches $\pm\pi/2$.

When we come to the inverse cosine function, we simply *define* it by the equation

$$\cos^{-1} x = \frac{\pi}{2} - \sin^{-1} x. \qquad (6)$$

Since

$$-\frac{\pi}{2} \le \sin^{-1} x \le \frac{\pi}{2},$$

the range of principal values for (6) is

$$0 \le \cos^{-1} x \le \pi. \qquad (7)$$

The *domain* of the inverse cosine function is

$$-1 \le x \le 1.$$

Its *range* is $0 \le y \le \pi$. The principal value is thus represented by the heavily marked portion of the curve $x = \cos y$ shown in Fig. 8.5.

The reason for defining $\cos^{-1} x$ by Eq. (6) is as follows. In the right triangle in Fig. 8.6, the acute angles α and β are complementary, that is

$$\alpha + \beta = \frac{\pi}{2}.$$

But we also have

$$\sin \alpha = x = \cos \beta,$$

so that

$$\alpha = \sin^{-1} x, \qquad \beta = \cos^{-1} x,$$

and the relation $\alpha + \beta = \pi/2$ is the same as $\beta = \pi/2 - \alpha$. That is,

$$\cos^{-1} x = \frac{\pi}{2} - \sin^{-1} x.$$

8.5

$$y = \sec^{-1} x, \quad 0 \le \sec^{-1} x \le \pi$$

8.6

8.7

Thus Eq. (6) expresses the fact that the angle whose cosine is x is the complement of the angle whose sine is x.

For exactly analogous reasons, we also define the inverse cotangent to be

$$\cot^{-1} x = \frac{\pi}{2} - \tan^{-1} x, \qquad (8)$$

and we thus restrict the principal value to

$$0 < \cot^{-1} x < \pi. \qquad (9)$$

The inverse secant and inverse cosecant functions will be single-valued functions of x on the domain $|x| \geq 1$ if we adopt the definitions

$$\sec^{-1} x = \cos^{-1}\left(\frac{1}{x}\right), \qquad (10a)$$

$$\csc^{-1} x = \sin^{-1}\left(\frac{1}{x}\right), \qquad (10b)$$

with their principal values confined to the ranges

$$0 \leq \sec^{-1} x < \frac{\pi}{2}, \qquad (11a)$$

$$-\frac{\pi}{2} \leq \csc^{-1} x < 0. \qquad (11b)$$

(Figure 8.7 illustrates the principle values of $\sec^{-1} x$.) We adopt the definition (10a) for the following reason:

$$\text{If} \quad \sec y = x, \quad \text{then} \quad \cos y = \frac{1}{x}.$$

We simply ask that the principal values of y be the same in these two cases, that is, that

$$y = \sec^{-1} x = \cos^{-1}\left(\frac{1}{x}\right).$$

A similar reason explains the choice of (10b) and (11b).

Remark. From the graphs of the inverse sine, inverse tangent, and inverse secant, all of which are increasing functions on the domains specified, we expect that their derivatives will be positive. This is a consequence of the relation

$$dy/dx = (dx/dy)^{-1}$$

that connects the derivative of a function with its inverse. For example, the secant function has a nonnegative derivative on $[0, \pi]$, excluding $\pi/2$; hence it has an inverse there, and that inverse also has a nonnegative derivative. It should be noted, however, that some writers choose the principal value of the inverse secant of x to lie between 0 and $\pi/2$ when x is positive, and between $-\pi$ and $-\pi/2$ (hence, as a negative angle in the third quadrant) when x is negative. This latter method has an advantage in simplifying the formula for the derivative of $\sec^{-1} x$, but has the disadvantage of failing to satisfy the relationship expressed in Eq. (10a) when x is negative. Either method leads to a function which is discontinuous, as is inherent in the nature of the secant function itself, since to pass from a point where the secant is negative to a point where the secant is positive requires crossing one of the discontinuities of the curve.

EXERCISES

3|1 2,4,6,8

1. Given that $\alpha = \sin^{-1}\frac{1}{2}$, find $\cos\alpha$, $\tan\alpha$, $\sec\alpha$, $\csc\alpha$.
2. Given that $\alpha = \cos^{-1}\left(-\frac{1}{2}\right)$, find $\sin\alpha$, $\tan\alpha$, $\sec\alpha$, $\csc\alpha$.
3. Evaluate $\sin^{-1}(1) - \sin^{-1}(-1)$.
4. Evaluate $\tan^{-1}(1) - \tan^{-1}(-1)$.
5. Evaluate $\sec^{-1}(2) - \sec^{-1}(-2)$.
6. A picture a feet high is placed on a wall with its base b feet above the level of an observer's eye. If the observer stands x feet from the wall, show that the angle of vision α subtended by the picture is given by

$$\alpha = \cot^{-1}\frac{x}{a+b} - \cot^{-1}\frac{x}{b}.$$

7. Prove
   (a) $\tan^{-1}(-x) = -\tan^{-1} x$,
   (b) $\cos^{-1}(-x) = \pi - \cos^{-1} x$,
   (c) $\sec^{-1}(-x) = \pi - \sec^{-1}(x)$.

8. Simplify each of the following expressions.
   (a) $\sin(\sin^{-1} 0.735)$ (b) $\cos(\sin^{-1} 0.8)$
   (c) $\sin(2\sin^{-1} 0.8)$ (d) $\tan^{-1}(\tan\pi/3)$
   (e) $\cos^{-1}(-\sin\pi/6)$ (f) $\sec^{-1}[\sec(-30°)]$

8.3 DERIVATIVES OF THE INVERSE TRIGONOMETRIC FUNCTIONS

Note the formulas for derivatives and differentials at the bottom of the page. To illustrate how these are derived, we shall derive formulas XIII and XVII. Let

$$y = \sin^{-1} u, \quad -\frac{\pi}{2} \le y \le \frac{\pi}{2}.$$

Then

$$\sin y = u,$$

$$\cos y \frac{dy}{dx} = \frac{du}{dx}, \qquad \frac{dy}{dx} = \frac{1}{\cos y} \frac{du}{dx}.$$

To express the right-hand side in terms of u, we use the fact that

$$\cos y = \pm\sqrt{1 - \sin^2 y} = \pm\sqrt{1 - u^2}.$$

When $-\pi/2 \le y \le \pi/2$, $\cos y$ is not negative;

hence

$$\cos y = +\sqrt{1 - u^2}$$

and

$$\frac{dy}{dx} = \frac{1}{\sqrt{1 - u^2}} \frac{du}{dx},$$

which establishes XIII.

Next, let us take

$$y = \sec^{-1} u, \quad 0 \le y \le \pi.$$

Then

$$\sec y = u, \qquad \sec y \tan y \frac{dy}{dx} = \frac{du}{dx},$$

$$\frac{dy}{dx} = \frac{1}{\sec y \tan y} \frac{du}{dx}.$$

Substituting

$$\sec y = u,$$

$$\tan y = \pm\sqrt{\sec^2 y - 1} = \pm\sqrt{u^2 - 1},$$

we have

$$\frac{dy}{dx} = \frac{1}{u(\pm\sqrt{u^2 - 1})} \frac{du}{dx}.$$

The ambiguous sign is determined by the sign of $\tan y$, and hence is

$+$ if $0 < y < \dfrac{\pi}{2}$; that is, if u is $+$,

$-$ if $\dfrac{\pi}{2} < y < \pi$; that is, if u is $-$.

Derivatives	*Differentials*
XIII. $\dfrac{d\,(\sin^{-1} u)}{dx} = \dfrac{1}{\sqrt{1 - u^2}} \dfrac{du}{dx}.$	XIII$'$. $d\,(\sin^{-1} u) = \dfrac{1}{\sqrt{1 - u^2}} du.$
XIV. $\dfrac{d\,(\cos^{-1} u)}{dx} = -\dfrac{1}{\sqrt{1 - u^2}} \dfrac{du}{dx}.$	XIV$'$. $d\,(\cos^{-1} u) = -\dfrac{1}{\sqrt{1 - u^2}} du.$
XV. $\dfrac{d\,(\tan^{-1} u)}{dx} = \dfrac{1}{1 + u^2} \dfrac{du}{dx}.$	XV$'$. $d\,(\tan^{-1} u) = \dfrac{1}{1 + u^2} du.$
XVI. $\dfrac{d\,(\cot^{-1} u)}{dx} = -\dfrac{1}{1 + u^2} \dfrac{du}{dx}.$	XVI$'$. $d\,(\cot^{-1} u) = -\dfrac{1}{1 + u^2} du.$
XVII. $\dfrac{d\,(\sec^{-1} u)}{dx} = \dfrac{1}{|u|\sqrt{u^2 - 1}} \dfrac{du}{dx}.$	XVII$'$. $d\,(\sec^{-1} u) = \dfrac{1}{|u|\sqrt{u^2 - 1}} du.$
XVIII. $\dfrac{d\,(\csc^{-1} u)}{dx} = \dfrac{-1}{|u|\sqrt{u^2 - 1}} \dfrac{du}{dx}.$	XVIII$'$. $d\,(\csc^{-1} u) = \dfrac{-1}{|u|\sqrt{u^2 - 1}} du.$

In other words,

$$\frac{dy}{dx} = \frac{1}{u\sqrt{u^2 - 1}}\frac{du}{dx} \quad \text{if} \quad u > 1$$

$$= \frac{1}{-u\sqrt{u^2 - 1}}\frac{du}{dx} \quad \text{if} \quad u < -1;$$

both of these are summarized in the single formula

$$\frac{dy}{dx} = \frac{1}{|u|\sqrt{u^2 - 1}}\frac{du}{dx}.$$

Remark 1. In some calculus books and handbooks of mathematical formulas (such as *CRC Standard Mathematical Tables*, 14th edition, pp. 504, 305) the principal value of $\sec^{-1} x$, or $\text{arcsec } x$ is defined to be between 0 and $\pi/2$ for $x \geq 1$, and between $-\pi$ and $-\pi/2$ for $x \leq -1$. When this convention is adopted the absolute value signs, as used in formula XVII, are not required in the formula for the derivative.

The formulas XIII to XVIII are used directly as given, but even more important are the integration formulas obtained immediately from the differential formulas XIII′ to XVIII′, namely,

$$\int \frac{du}{\sqrt{1 - u^2}} = \sin^{-1} u + C,$$

$$\int \frac{du}{1 + u^2} = \tan^{-1} u + C,$$

$$\int \frac{du}{u\sqrt{u^2 - 1}} = \int \frac{d(-u)}{(-u)\sqrt{u^2 - 1}}$$

$$= \sec^{-1} |u| + C. \qquad (1)$$

Note that $\sec^{-1} u$ and $\sec^{-1} |u|$ are meaningless unless $|u| \geq 1$ (see Fig. 8.7).

Example

$$\int_0^1 \frac{dx}{1 + x^2} = \tan^{-1} x \Big]_0^1$$

$$= \tan^{-1} 1 - \tan^{-1} 0 = \frac{\pi}{4}.$$

Remark 2. When u is positive, both of the commonly used definitions of $\sec^{-1} u$ agree that

$$0 \leq \sec^{-1} u < \pi/2$$

and

$$d(\sec^{-1} u) = \frac{du}{u\sqrt{u^2 - 1}}.$$

Therefore, for $u > 1$,

$$\int \frac{du}{u\sqrt{u^2 - 1}} = \sec^{-1} u + C. \qquad (2a)$$

Although the definitions of $\sec^{-1} u$ disagree when u is negative, the integral in (2a) can be evaluated for $u < -1$ by making the simple substitution $u = -v$:

$$\int \frac{du}{u\sqrt{u^2 - 1}} = \int \frac{-dv}{-v\sqrt{v^2 - 1}} \quad (v > 1)$$

$$= \int \frac{dv}{v\sqrt{v^2 - 1}}$$

$$= \sec^{-1} v + C. \qquad (2b)$$

But, since $v = -u$, Eq. (2b) becomes

$$\int \frac{du}{u\sqrt{u^2 - 1}} = \sec^{-1}(-u) + C \quad \text{when } u < -1.$$
$$\qquad (2c)$$

We can combine Eqs. (2a) and (2c) into one equation if we introduce $|u|$:

$$\int \frac{du}{u\sqrt{u^2 - 1}} = \sec^{-1} |u| + C, \quad \text{if} \quad u^2 > 1, \quad (3)$$

because $|u| = u$ if u is positive and $|u| = -u$ if u is negative.

Problem. Sketch a portion of the graph of

$$f(x) = \frac{1}{x\sqrt{x^2 - 1}}, \quad 1 < |x| < 3,$$

and compare

$$\int_{-2}^{-\sqrt{2}} f(x)\, dx \quad \text{and} \quad \int_{\sqrt{2}}^{2} f(x)\, dx.$$

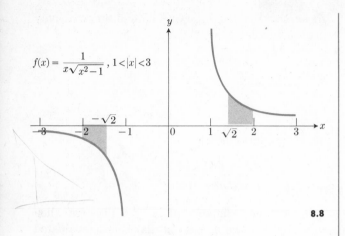

$f(x) = \dfrac{1}{x\sqrt{x^2-1}}, \; 1 < |x| < 3$

8.8

Solution. Figure 8.8 shows that the graph is below the x-axis for $x < -1$ and above the x-axis for $x > 1$. For the two integrals, we have

$$I_1 = \sec^{-1}|x|]_{-2}^{-\sqrt{2}} = \sec^{-1}\sqrt{2} - \sec^{-1}2$$
$$= \frac{\pi}{4} - \frac{\pi}{3} = -\frac{\pi}{12}$$

and

$$I_2 = \sec^{-1}|x|]_{\sqrt{2}}^{2} = \sec^{-1}2 - \sec^{-1}\sqrt{2}$$
$$= \frac{\pi}{3} - \frac{\pi}{4} = \frac{\pi}{12}.$$

The two tinted regions shown in Fig. 8.8 have equal areas, $\pi/12$.

EXERCISES

3/2 # 1-13 odd   17-21

1. Derive formula XIV.   2. Derive formula XV.

3. Derive formula XVI.   4. Derive formula XVIII.

Find dy/dx in Exercises 5 through 14.

5. $y = \sin^{-1}\dfrac{x}{2}$ 6. $y = \dfrac{1}{3}\tan^{-1}\dfrac{x}{3}$

7. $y = \sec^{-1}5x$ 8. $y = \cos^{-1}2x$

9. $y = \cot^{-1}\dfrac{2}{x} + \tan^{-1}\dfrac{x}{2}$ 10. $y = \sin^{-1}\dfrac{x-1}{x+1}$

11. $y = \tan^{-1}\dfrac{x-1}{x+1}$

12. $y = x\sin^{-1}x + \sqrt{1-x^2}$

13. $y = x(\sin^{-1}x)^2 - 2x + 2\sqrt{1-x^2}\sin^{-1}x$

14. $y = x\cos^{-1}2x - \frac{1}{2}\sqrt{1-4x^2}$

15. How far from the wall should the observer stand in order to maximize the angle of vision α in Exercise 6, Article 8.2?

Evaluate the following integrals.

16. $\displaystyle\int_0^{1/2} \frac{dx}{\sqrt{1-x^2}}$ 17. $\displaystyle\int_{-1}^{1} \frac{dx}{1+x^2}$

18. $\displaystyle\int_{\sqrt{2}}^{2/\sqrt{3}} \frac{dx}{x\sqrt{x^2-1}}$ 19. $\displaystyle\int_{-2}^{-2/\sqrt{3}} \frac{dx}{x\sqrt{x^2-1}}$

20. $\displaystyle\int \frac{dx}{\sqrt{1-4x^2}}$ 21. $\displaystyle\int_{1/\sqrt{3}}^{1} \frac{dx}{x\sqrt{4x^2-1}}$

8.4 THE NATURAL LOGARITHM

We have so far studied functions which are fairly familiar. Polynomials, rational functions, and other algebraic functions result from the familiar operations of arithmetic and algebra. The trigonometric functions can be identified with coordinates of points on a unit circle and with their ratios and reciprocals. The inverse trigonometric functions are probably less familiar, but neverthless they can be understood without any knowledge of the calculus. But we are now going to study a function, the natural logarithm, which depends on calculus for its very definition.

Definition. *The natural logarithm* of x, which is indicated by the notation ln x, is defined, for positive x, as the integral*

$$\ln x = \int_1^x \frac{1}{t}\,dt. \tag{1}$$

---

* The first discovery of logarithms is credited to a Scottish nobleman, John Napier (1550–1617). For a biographical sketch of Napier, see the *World of Mathematics*, Vol. 1, "The Great Mathematicians," by H. W. Turnbull, pp. 121–125.

Handwritten annotations at top of figure:

COMMON log

if #■ + log is [to] infin.

" #○ log is 1

#○ 1

x	$\log x$
>1	$+$
$=1$	0
$0<x<1$	$-$
$0<x$	$\emptyset$

$y = \dfrac{1}{t}$

ln x

8.9 The tinted area represents ln x.

For any x greater than 1, this integral represents the area bounded above by the curve $y = 1/t$, below by the t-axis, on the left by the line $t = 1$, and on the right by the line $t = x$ (see Fig. 8.9).

If $x = 1$, the left and right boundaries of the area are identical and the area is zero:

$$\ln 1 = \int_1^1 \frac{1}{t}\, dt = 0 \qquad (2)$$

If x is less than 1, then the left boundary is the line $t = x$ and the right boundary is $t = 1$. In this case,

$$\ln x = \int_1^x \frac{1}{t}\, dt = -\int_x^1 \frac{1}{t}\, dt \qquad (3)$$

is the negative of the area under the curve between x and 1.

In all cases, if x is any positive number, the value of the definite integral in Eq. (1) can be calculated to as many decimal places as desired by using inscribed rectangles, circumscribed rectangles, or trapezoids to approximate the appropriate area. (See Chapter 6. Also see Exercise 8 below.) In any event, Eq. (1) defines a function that is computable over the domain $(0, \infty)$, since the integrand $1/t$ is continuous over this domain. We study its range in Article 8.7.

$\log A = a \Rightarrow 10^a = A$

EXERCISES

3/2 # 2, 4

Obtain approximations to the natural logarithms, given in Exercises 1 through 4. Use trapezoids of altitude $\Delta t = 0.1$ to approximate the appropriate areas.

1. ln 1.2   2. ln 1.4

3. ln 2   4. ln 0.5

5. (a) Suppose h is small and positive. Does the approximation $\ln (1 + h) \approx h$ correspond to using an inscribed rectangle or a circumscribed rectangle to approximate the area from 1 to $1 + h$ under the curve $y = 1/t$?

  (b) Answer the same question in case h is negative.

6. Approximate $\ln (1 + h)$ by using the line L that is tangent to the curve $y = 1/t$ at $A(1, 1)$ as upper boundary of a trapezoid of altitude $|h|$. Sketch. Show that this leads to the approximation

$$\ln (1 + h) \approx h - \frac{h^2}{2}.$$

Use this result to approximate

  (a) ln 1.04,   (b) ln 0.96.

7. Let $aACBb$ be the polygon whose vertices are

$$a(1, 0),\quad A(1, 1),\quad C(\tfrac{4}{3}, \tfrac{2}{3}),\quad B(2, \tfrac{1}{2}),\quad \text{and}\quad b(2, 0).$$

Show that AC and CB are tangent to the hyperbola $y = 1/t$ at A and at B, respectively. Use the area of the polygon to find an approximation to ln 2. Sketch.

8. (a) Show, by long division or otherwise, that

$$\frac{1}{1 + u} = 1 - u + u^2 - \frac{u^3}{1 + u}.$$

(The division could be continued. We stop here only for convenience.)

  (b) In Eq. (1), make the substitution

$$t = 1 + u, \qquad dt = du,$$

and make the corresponding change in the limits of integration, thus obtaining

$$\ln x = \int_0^{x-1} \frac{du}{1 + u}.$$

(c) Combine the results of (a) and (b) to obtain

$$\ln x = \int_0^{x-1} \left(1 - u + u^2 - \frac{u^3}{1+u}\right) du,$$

or $\ln x = (x - 1) - \frac{1}{2}(x - 1)^2 + \frac{1}{3}(x - 1)^3 - R,$

where

$$R = \int_0^{x-1} \frac{u^3}{1+u}\, du.$$

(d) Show that, if $x > 1$ and $0 \le u \le x - 1$, then

$$u^3/(1 + u) \le u^3.$$

Deduce that therefore

$$R \le \int_0^{x-1} u^3 \, du = \frac{(x-1)^4}{4}.$$

(e) Combining the results of (c) and (d), show that the approximation

$$\ln x \approx (x - 1) - \frac{1}{2}(x - 1)^2 + \frac{1}{3}(x - 1)^3$$

tends to overestimate the value of $\ln x$, but with an error not greater than $(x - 1)^4/4$.

(f) Use the result of (e) to estimate $\ln 1.2$.

9. Explain how Theorem 4, Article 6.12 ensures the existence of the integral that defines $\ln x$

(a) for $x > 1$,   (b) for $0 < x < 1$.

8.5 THE DERIVATIVE OF ln x

Since the function $F(x) = \ln x$ is defined by the integral

$$F(x) = \int_1^x \frac{1}{t} \, dt \quad (x > 0) \tag{1}$$

(see Fig. 8.10), it follows at once, from the Second Fundamental Theorem of integral calculus (Article 6.9) that $F'(x) = 1/x$. That is,

$$d (\ln x)/dx = 1/x. \tag{2}$$

We can obtain a slightly more general formula by considering $\ln u$, where u is a positive, differentiable, function of x. By the chain rule for derivatives,

$$\frac{d \ln u}{dx} = \frac{d \ln u}{du} \frac{du}{dx} = \frac{1}{u} \frac{du}{dx}, \tag{XIX}$$

8.10 Area of inscribed rectangle $= \frac{1}{2}$, area of circumscribed rectangle $= 1$; $\frac{1}{2} < \ln 2 < 1$.

or, in terms of differentials,

$$d \ln u = \frac{du}{u}. \tag{XIX$'$}$$

Problem 1. Find $\dfrac{dy}{dx}$ if $y = \ln (3x^2 + 4)$.

Solution.
$$\frac{dy}{dx} = \frac{1}{3x^2 + 4} \frac{d(3x^2 + 4)}{dx}$$

$$= \frac{6x}{3x^2 + 4}.$$

Formula XIX$'$ leads at once to the integration formula

$$\int \frac{du}{u} = \ln u + C, \tag{3a}$$

provided that u is positive. On the other hand, if u is negative, then $-u$ is positive and

$$\int \frac{du}{u} = \int \frac{d(-u)}{-u} = \ln (-u) + C. \tag{3b}$$

The two results (3a, b) can be combined into a single result, namely,

$$\int \frac{du}{u} = \begin{cases} \ln u + C & \text{if } u > 0, \\ \ln (-u) + C & \text{if } u < 0, \end{cases}$$

or

$$\int \frac{du}{u} = \ln |u| + C. \tag{4}$$

We recall that the formula

$$\int u^n \, du = \frac{u^{n+1}}{n+1} + C, \quad n \neq -1$$

failed to cover one case, namely, $n = -1$. Now Eq. (4) covers this case for us, since it tells us that

$$\int u^{-1} \, du = \int \frac{du}{u} = \ln |u| + C.$$

It is important, of course, to remember that

$$\int \frac{dx}{x^2} = \int x^{-2} \, dx = \frac{x^{-1}}{-1} + C$$

is *not* a logarithm.

Problem 2. Integrate

$$\int \frac{\cos \theta \, d\theta}{1 + \sin \theta}.$$

Solution. In Eq. (4), let

$$u = 1 + \sin \theta.$$

Then

$$du = \frac{du}{d\theta} \, d\theta = \cos \theta \, d\theta,$$

so that

$$\int \frac{\cos \theta \, d\theta}{1 + \sin \theta} = \int \frac{du}{u} = \ln |u| + C$$
$$= \ln |1 + \sin \theta| + C.$$

Remark. Because $1 + \sin \theta$ is never negative, we can also write $\ln (1 + \sin \theta)$ in place of $\ln |1 + \sin \theta|$. Either answer is correct.

EXERCISES

Find dy/dx in Exercises 1 through 18.

1. $y = \ln (x^2 + 2x)$
2. $y = (\ln x)^3$
3. $y = \ln (\cos x)$
4. $y = \ln (\tan x + \sec x)$
5. $y = \ln (x\sqrt{x^2 + 1})$
6. $y = \ln (3x\sqrt{x+2})$
7. $y = x \ln x - x$
8. $y = x^3 \ln (2x)$
9. $y = \frac{1}{2} \ln \frac{1+x}{1-x}$
10. $y = \frac{1}{3} \ln \frac{x^3}{1+x^3}$

11. $y = \ln \frac{x}{2+3x}$
12. $y = \ln (x^2 + 4) - x \tan^{-1} \frac{x}{2}$
13. $y = \ln x - \frac{1}{2} \ln (1 + x^2) - \frac{\tan^{-1} x}{x}$
14. $y = x (\ln x)^3$
15. $y = x [\sin (\ln x) + \cos (\ln x)]$
16. $y = x \sec^{-1} x - \ln (x + \sqrt{x^2 - 1}), \quad (x > 1)$
17. $y = x \ln (a^2 + x^2) - 2x + 2a \tan^{-1} \frac{x}{a}$
18. $y = \ln (\ln x)$

Evaluate the integrals in Exercises 19 through 30.

19. $\int \frac{dx}{2x+3}$
20. $\int \frac{dx}{2-3x}$
21. $\int \frac{x \, dx}{4x^2 + 1}$
22. $\int \frac{\sin x \, dx}{2 - \cos x}$
23. $\int \frac{\cos x \, dx}{\sin x}$
24. $\int \frac{2x - 5}{x} \, dx$
25. $\int \frac{x \, dx}{x+1}$
26. $\int \frac{x^2 \, dx}{4 - x^3}$
27. $\int \frac{x \, dx}{1 - x^2}$
28. $\int \frac{dx}{\sqrt{x}(1 + \sqrt{x})}$
29. $\int (\ln x)^2 \frac{dx}{x}$
30. $\int \frac{dx}{(2x+3)^2}$

8.6 PROPERTIES OF NATURAL LOGARITHMS

In this article we shall establish the following properties of the natural logarithm:

$$\ln ax = \ln a + \ln x, \tag{1}$$

$$\ln \frac{x}{a} = \ln x - \ln a, \tag{2}$$

$$\ln x^n = n \ln x, \tag{3}$$

provided x and a are positive and n is a rational number.

The demonstrations of these results are all based on the fact that

$$y = \ln x$$

satisfies the differential equation

$$\frac{dy}{dx} = \frac{1}{x} \qquad \text{for all} \quad x > 0,$$

plus the fact that if two functions have the same derivative for all $x > 0$, then the two functions can differ only by a constant. That is, if

$$\frac{dy_1}{dx} = \frac{dy_2}{dx} \qquad \text{for all} \quad x > 0,$$

then

$$y_1 = y_2 + \text{constant} \qquad \text{for all} \quad x > 0.$$

Now to prove Eq. (1), let

$$y_1 = \ln ax, \qquad y_2 = \ln x.$$

Then

$$\frac{dy_1}{dx} = \frac{1}{ax}\frac{d(ax)}{dx} = \frac{a}{ax} = \frac{1}{x} = \frac{dy_2}{dx}. \qquad (4)$$

Therefore we have

$$\ln ax = \ln x + C. \qquad (5)$$

To evaluate C it suffices to substitute $x = 1$:

$$\ln a = \ln 1 + C = 0 + C,$$

which gives

$$C = \ln a.$$

Hence, by (5)

$$\ln ax = \ln x + \ln a. \ \square$$

To demonstrate Eq. (2), we first put $x = 1/a$ in Eq. (1) and recall that $\ln 1 = 0$:

$$0 = \ln 1 = \ln a + \ln (1/a),$$

so that

$$\boxed{\ln \frac{1}{a} = -\ln a.} \qquad (6)$$

Now apply Eq. (1) with a replaced by $1/a$ and $\ln a$ replaced by $\ln (1/a) = -\ln a$. The result is Eq. (2).

To demonstrate Eq. (3), let

$$y_1 = \ln x^n.$$

Then

$$\frac{dy_1}{dx} = \frac{1}{x^n} \cdot nx^{n-1} = \frac{n}{x} = \frac{d}{dx}(n \ln x).$$

Hence $y_1 = \ln x^n$ and $y_2 = n \ln x$ have equal derivatives, so they differ at most by a constant:

$$\ln x^n = n \ln x + C. \qquad (7)$$

But by taking $x = 1$, and remembering that $\ln 1 = 0$, we find $C = 0$, which gives Eq. (3). In particular, if $n = 1/m$, where m is a positive integer, we have

$$\ln \sqrt[m]{x} = \ln x^{1/m} = \frac{1}{m} \ln x. \qquad (8)$$

EXERCISES

Express the following logarithms in terms of the two given logarithms $a = \ln 2$, $b = \ln 3$. [For example: $\ln 1.5 = \ln \frac{3}{2} = \ln 3 - \ln 2 = b - a$.]

1. $\ln 16$ 2. $\ln \sqrt[3]{9}$ 3. $\ln 2\sqrt{2}$

4. $\ln 0.25$ 5. $\ln \frac{4}{9}$ 6. $\ln 12$

7. $\ln \frac{9}{8}$ 8. $\ln 36$ 9. $\ln 4.5$

10. $\ln \sqrt{13.5}$

8.7 GRAPH OF $y = \ln x$

The slope of the curve

$$y = \ln x \qquad (1)$$

is given by

$$\frac{dy}{dx} = \frac{1}{x}. \qquad (2)$$

Two conclusions can be drawn immediately from Eq. (2).

1. The natural logarithm is a *differentiable* function, and therefore is *continuous*, on $(0, \infty)$.

2. The graph of $y = \ln x$ steadily rises from left to right because the slope is positive.

Also, since the derivative is continuous the curve has a continuously turning tangent. The second derivative,

$$\frac{d^2y}{dx^2} = -\frac{1}{x^2}, \qquad (3)$$

8.11

is always negative, so the curve (1) is everywhere concave downward.

The curve passes through the point $(1, 0)$, since $\ln 1 = 0$. At this point its slope is $+1$, so the tangent line at this point makes an angle of $45°$ with the x-axis (if we use equal units on the x- and y-axes).

If we refer to the definition of $\ln 2$ as an integral,

$$\ln 2 = \int_1^2 \frac{1}{t}\, dt,$$

we see that it may be interpreted as the area in Fig. 8.10 with $x = 2$. By considering the areas of rectangles of base 1 and altitudes 1 or $\frac{1}{2}$, respectively circumscribed over or inscribed under the given area, we see that

$$0.5 < \ln 2 < 1.0.$$

In fact, by more extensive calculations, the value of $\ln 2$ to 5 decimal places is found to be

$$\ln 2 \approx 0.69315.$$

By Eq. (3) of Article 8.6, we have

$\ln 4 = \ln 2^2 = 2 \ln 2 \approx 1.38630,$
$\ln 8 = \ln 2^3 = 3 \ln 2 \approx 2.07945,$
$\ln \frac{1}{2} = \ln 2^{-1} = -\ln 2 \approx -0.69315,$
$\ln \frac{1}{4} = \ln 2^{-2} = -2 \ln 2 \approx -1.38630, \ldots$

We now plot the points that correspond to $x = \frac{1}{4}$, $\frac{1}{2}$, 1, 2, 4, 8 on the curve $y = \ln x$ and connect them with a smooth curve. The curve we draw should have slope $1/x$ at the point of abscissa x and should everywhere be concave downward. The curve is shown in Fig. 8.11.

Since $\ln 2$ is greater than 0.5 and $\ln 2^n = n \ln 2$, it is clear that

$$\ln 2^n > 0.5n,$$

and hence $\ln x$ increases without limit as x does. That is,

$$\ln x \to +\infty \quad \text{as} \quad x \to +\infty. \tag{4}$$

On the other hand, as x approaches zero through positive values, $1/x$ tends to plus infinity. Hence, taking Eq. (6) of Article 8.6 into account, we have

$$\ln x = -\ln \frac{1}{x} \to -\infty \quad \text{as} \quad x \to 0+. \tag{5}$$

Summary

The natural logarithm, $y = \ln x$, is a function with the following properties.

1. Its *domain* is the set of positive real numbers, $x > 0$.

2. Its *range* is the set of all real numbers,

$$-\infty < y < +\infty.$$

3. It is a *continuous, increasing* function of x everywhere on its domain:

$$\text{If} \quad x_1 > x_2 > 0, \quad \text{then} \quad \ln x_1 > \ln x_2.$$

It provides a one-to-one mapping from its domain to its range.

4. *Multiplication* of numbers in the domain corresponds to *addition* of numbers in the range. That is,

$$\text{if} \quad \begin{cases} x_1 > 0, & y_1 = \ln x_1, \\ x_2 > 0, & y_2 = \ln x_2, \end{cases}$$

$$\text{then} \quad x_1 x_2 > 0 \quad \text{and} \quad y_1 + y_2 = \ln (x_1 x_2).$$

5. The *derivative* of $y = \ln x$ is $dy/dx = 1/x$.

EXERCISES

$1 \& 3$

1. Take $\ln 3 = 1.09861$ as known. Plot the points corresponding to $x = \frac{1}{9}, \frac{1}{3}, 1, 3,$ and 9 on the curve $y = \ln x$. Also, through each of these points construct a line segment tangent to the curve. Then sketch the curve itself. From the curve, read off $\ln 2$.

2. Let x_0 be the abscissa of the point $(x_0, 1)$ in which the line $y = 1$ intersects the curve $y = \ln x$. Show that the curve $y = x \ln x$ has a minimum at

$$(1/x_0, - 1/x_0)$$

and sketch the curve for $x > 0$. Does this curve possess a point of inflection? If so, find it (or them), and if not, state why not. (See Exercise 5.)

3. Sketch the curve $x = \ln y$ for $y > 0$. What is its slope at the point (x, y)? Is it always concave upward, or downward, or does it have inflection points? Give reasons for your answers.

4. The curve $y = \ln x$ in Fig. 8.11 has the property that y becomes infinite when x does. But the ratio $(\ln x)/x$ approaches zero as x becomes infinite. Prove this latter statement by showing, first, that for $x > 1$,

$$\ln x = \int_1^x \frac{1}{t}\, dt \le \int_1^x \frac{1}{\sqrt{t}}\, dt = 2(\sqrt{x} - 1).$$

Hint. Compare the areas under the curves $y_1 = 1/t$ and $y_2 = 1/\sqrt{t}$ for $1 \le t \le x$.

5. From the result of Exercise 4, that

$$\lim_{x \to +\infty} \frac{\ln x}{x} = 0,$$

deduce that $\lim_{x \to 0+} x \ln x = 0$.

Hint. Let $x = 1/u, u \to +\infty$.

6. Show that the curve

$$y = \ln x - (x - 1) + \tfrac{1}{2}(x - 1)^2$$

has a point of inflection and a horizontal tangent at $(1, 0)$. Sketch the curve for $0 < x < 2$. (Compare Exercise 8, Article 8.4.)

7. Suppose you had a table of natural logarithms giving $\ln x$ for each $x > 0$. How could you use this to find $\log_{10} N$, where $\log_{10} N = b$ means $N = 10^b$?

8.8 THE EXPONENTIAL FUNCTION

Does the natural logarithmic function have an inverse, and, if so, what are its main properties? The answers are most easily understood in terms of the graphs of the curves

$$y = \ln x, \qquad x > 0 \qquad\qquad (1a)$$

$$x = \ln y, \qquad y > 0. \qquad\qquad (1b)$$

These two graphs are shown in Fig. 8.12. We know quite a bit about the graph of Eq. (1a).

1. Its slope at the point $(x, \ln x)$ is $1/x$.

2. Because the derivative of $\ln x$ is positive, the graph constantly rises from left to right.

3. The function $\ln x$ is positive for $x > 1$, zero for $x = 1$, negative for $x < 1$.

4. Since

$$\ln (2^n) = n \ln 2 \approx (0.693)n,$$

the points having abscissas

$$x_n = 2^n, \quad n = 1, 2, 3, \ldots,$$

have ordinates y_n that increase without bound as $n \to \infty$. Combining this with the fact that $\ln x$ is continuous and monotone increasing, we see that the portion of the domain where

$$1 \le x < \infty$$

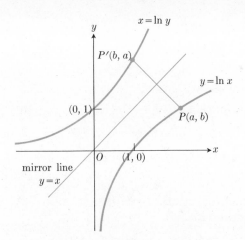

8.12 Each curve is the reflection of the other with respect to the line $y = x$. The points $P(a, b)$, with $b = \ln a$, and $P'(b, a)$ are symmetric with respect to the mirror line.

maps one-to-one onto

$$0 \leq y < \infty$$

under the natural logarithmic mapping $y = \ln x$.

5. Because $\ln (1/x) = -\ln x$, the last-named property means that the part of the domain where

$$0 < x \leq 1$$

maps one-to-one onto

$$-\infty < y \leq 0.$$

Thus, as x increases through the domain between 0 and $+\infty$, $\ln x$ increases between $-\infty$ and $+\infty$. Every real number y is the natural logarithm of precisely one positive real number x. The *inverse relation* that we get from ln by interchanging x and y in the set of ordered pairs

$$\ln = \{(x, y) : y = \ln x, \quad x > 0\}$$

is, therefore, a function—the *inverse natural logarithmic function*, which we shall temporarily denote by $\ln^{-1}$. Thus

$$y = \ln^{-1}(x) \tag{2a}$$

means just the same as

$$x = \ln y, \quad y > 0, \quad -\infty < x < \infty. \tag{2b}$$

The *domain* of $\ln^{-1}$ is the *range* of ln, hence is the set of all real numbers, $-\infty < x < \infty$. Thus, Eqs. (2a) and (2b) both correspond to the upper curve in Fig. 8.12.

The number whose natural logarithm is 1 plays a special role, and is the famous number e (for Euler):

$$e = \ln^{-1}(1), \quad 1 = \ln e. \tag{3}$$

Equations (3) *define* e. In a later chapter we shall find that e can be found from an infinite series. Using that series, it is possible to compute as many significant places in the decimal expansion of e as we want. In the early 1960's, it was computed to 100,000 decimal places by Daniel Shanks and John W. Wrench, Jr., using an IBM 7090 computer. The computation took 2.5 hours, as compared with 8.7 hours for π. See Shanks and Wrench, "Calculation of π to 100,000 Decimals," in *Mathematics of Computation*, **16**, No. 77, January 1962, p. 78. To 15 places,

$$e = 2.7\ 1828\ 1828\ 45\ 90\ 45. \tag{4}$$

Without using the infinite series, we can approximate e by finding numbers $a, b, c, \ldots$ such that

$$\ln a + \ln b + \ln c + \cdots = 1.00000. \tag{5}$$

Assuming, for example, that $\ln 2 = 0.69315$, we can find logarithms of the square root, fourth root, eighth root, ... of 2 by successive divisions of $\ln 2$. The arithmetic is easy:

$$\ln 2 \approx 0.69315;$$
$$\ln 2^{1/2} \approx 0.34658, \quad 2^{1/2} \approx 1.414214;$$
$$\ln 2^{1/4} \approx 0.17329, \quad 2^{1/4} \approx 1.189207;$$
$$\ln 2^{1/8} \approx 0.08664, \quad 2^{1/8} \approx 1.090508;$$
$$\ln 2^{1/16} \approx 0.04332, \quad 2^{1/16} \approx 1.044274.$$

To find which of these logarithms have a sum close to 1.00000, we subtract from 1 the largest logarithm we can without getting a negative result (0.69315, in this case), and then repeat the subtraction process. This leads to

$$1.00000 = 0.69315 + 0.17329$$
$$+ 0.08664 + 0.04332 + R,$$

where the remainder R is

$$R = 0.00360 < \ln 2^{1/160} \approx 0.00433.$$

This leads to the estimation

$$2 \cdot 2^{1/4} \cdot 2^{1/8} \cdot 2^{1/16} < e < 2 \cdot 2^{1/4} \cdot 2^{1/8} \cdot 2^{1/16} \cdot 2^{1/160} \tag{6}$$

We get further information about $\ln^{-1}$ by studying rational powers of e. Because

$$\ln(e^x) = x \ln e \quad \text{for } x \text{ rational,}$$

and

$$\ln e = 1,$$

we have

$$\ln e^x = x \quad \text{for } x \text{ rational.} \tag{7}$$

When we compare Eq. (7) with Eqs. (2b) and (2a) we see that

$$e^x = \ln^{-1}(x) \quad \text{for all rational values of } x. \tag{8}$$

The right-hand side of Eq. (8) has a perfectly well-defined meaning for *any real number* x (not just for the rationals). When x happens to be *rational*, both sides of Eq. (8) are well defined, and are equal. When x is *irrational*, we use Eq. (8) to *define* e^x.

Definition 1. *For any real number x, we define e^x to be the same as $\ln^{-1}(x)$:*

$$e^x = \ln^{-1}(x). \tag{9}$$

Notation. The notation exp (exponential function) is also used to represent the inverse of the natural logarithm:

$$\exp(x) = \ln^{-1}(x), \quad x \text{ real.} \tag{10}$$

Thus Eq. (9) becomes

$$e^x = \exp(x).$$

The use of the exp-notation is particularly helpful when working with composite functions, such as

$$e^{(\sin^{-1} x)} = \exp(\sin^{-1} x),$$

or other expressions leading to complicated typography.

Summary

So far, we have

1. defined ln and studied it,
2. defined exp $= \ln^{-1}$,
3. shown that

$$e^x = \exp(x) \quad \text{for } x \text{ rational,}$$

4. *defined e^x for x irrational to be* exp (x).

Result. The exponential function (base e) is the inverse of the natural logarithmic function. All of its properties are derived from that fact.

Theorem 1. *For every real x,*

$$\frac{d}{dx}(e^x) = e^x, \tag{11a}$$

or

$$\exp'(x) = \exp(x). \tag{11b}$$

Proof. From the general theory of inverse functions, Theorem 8, Article 4.3, we can write

$$y = e^x \Leftrightarrow x = \ln y$$

and

$$\frac{dy}{dx} = \frac{1}{dx/dy} = \frac{1}{(1/y)} = y. \quad \square$$

Corollary. *If u is a differentiable function of x, then*

$$\frac{d}{dx}(e^u) = e^u \frac{du}{dx}; \tag{XX}$$

in terms of differentials,

$$d(e^u) = e^u \, du. \tag{XX'}$$

Proof. For formula XX, apply the chain rule and Theorem 1:

$$\frac{d}{dx}(e^u) = \frac{d}{du}(e^u)\frac{du}{dx} = e^u \frac{du}{dx}.$$

The formula for the differential follows from this if we multiply both sides of the equation by dx and use the definition

$$dy = \frac{dy}{dx} \, dx. \quad \square$$

Problem 1. Let $P(x, y)$ be a point on the graph of $y = e^x$. Let Q be the point where the tangent to the graph at P intersects the x-axis. Find the length of the segment QP.

Solution. The slope of the tangent at P is equal to the ordinate of P because

$$\frac{dy}{dx} = e^x = y.$$

Since the slope of QP is also rise/run, and the rise is y, the run must equal 1. Therefore

$$|QP| = \sqrt{y^2 + 1}.$$

See Fig. 8.13.

Problem 2. Find dy/dx if $y = e^{\tan^{-1} x}$.

Solution.
$$\frac{dy}{dx} = e^{\tan^{-1} x} \frac{d \tan^{-1} x}{dx}$$

$$= e^{\tan^{-1} x} \cdot \frac{1}{1 + x^2} \cdot \frac{dx}{dx}$$

$$= \frac{e^{\tan^{-1} x}}{1 + x^2}.$$

The differential formula XX′ leads to the integration formula

$$\int e^u \, du = e^u + C. \tag{12}$$

Problem 3. Find the area under the curve $y = e^{-x}$ from $x = 0$ to $x = b (>0)$ and show that this area *remains finite* as $b \to +\infty$.

Solution. The area from $x = 0$ to $x = b$ is given by

$$A_0^b = \int_0^b y \, dx = \int_0^b e^{-x} \, dx.$$

To evaluate this integral, we compare it with our standard forms and see that it is almost, but not exactly, like

$$\int e^u \, du = e^u + C.$$

To bring it into precisely this form, we let

$$u = -x, \qquad du = -dx,$$

or

$$dx = -du,$$

8.13

8.14

so that

$$\int e^{-x} \, dx = \int e^u (-du) = -\int e^u \, du$$

$$= -e^u + C = -e^{-x} + C.$$

Therefore

$$A_0^b = -e^{-x}]_0^b = -e^{-b} + e^0 = 1 - e^{-b}.$$

From this we see that the number of square units of area in the tinted region of Fig. 8.14 is somewhat less than one for b large and positive. Moreover, as b increases without bound, so does e^b. Hence

$$\lim_{b \to \infty} e^{-b} = \lim_{b \to \infty} (1/e^b) = 0,$$

and

$$\lim_{b \to \infty} A_0^b = \lim_{b \to \infty} (1 - e^{-b}) = 1.$$

We summarize this by writing

$$\int_0^\infty e^{-x}\,dx = \lim_{b\to\infty}\int_0^b e^{-x}\,dx = 1.$$

The area from 0 to b remains finite and approaches 1 as $b \to \infty$.

Some properties of the function

$$y = e^x$$

are worthy of additional comment.

Theorem 2. *For all real x_1 and x_2,*

$$e^{x_1}e^{x_2} = e^{x_1+x_2}, \qquad (13a)$$

or

$$\exp(x_1)\cdot\exp(x_2) = \exp(x_1+x_2). \qquad (13b)$$

Proof. Let $\quad y_1 = e^{x_1}, \quad y_2 = e^{x_2}.$
Then, by definition,

$$x_1 = \ln y_1, \quad x_2 = \ln y_2,$$

and

$$x_1 + x_2 = \ln y_1 + \ln y_2 = \ln(y_1 y_2).$$

Therefore

$$y_1 y_2 = \ln^{-1}(x_1 + x_2) = \exp(x_1 + x_2),$$

so that, by substitution,

$$e^{x_1}e^{x_2} = \exp(x_1 + x_2) = e^{(x_1+x_2)}. \;\square$$

Corollary. *For every real x,*

$$e^{-x} = \frac{1}{e^x},$$

or

$$\exp(-x) = [\exp(x)]^{-1}. \qquad (14)$$

Proof. Let $x_1 = -x$ and $x_2 = x$ in Eq. (13a) or (13b):

$$e^{-x}e^{x} = e^{-x+x} = e^0 = \ln^{-1}(0) = 1.$$

Therefore, by division,

$$e^{-x} = \frac{1}{e^x}. \;\square$$

Remark. In Exercise 4, Article 8.7, it is shown that

$$\lim_{x\to\infty}\frac{\ln x}{x} = 0.$$

From this it also follows that for any real number n,

$$\lim_{x\to\infty}\frac{\ln(x^n)}{x} = \lim_{x\to\infty}\frac{n\ln x}{x} = 0. \qquad (15)$$

If n is a positive integer and

$$u = x^n, \qquad x = \sqrt[n]{u},$$

where both x and u are positive, then Eq. (15) implies

$$\lim_{u\to\infty}\frac{\ln u}{u^{1/n}} = 0. \qquad (16)$$

Equation (16) says that the logarithm function increases more slowly than the nth root function, for any positive integer n. It can also be made to give information about the rate of growth of the exponential function. In Eq. (16), let

$$u^{1/n} = e^y,$$

or

$$y = (\ln u)/n.$$

Because the limit of a product of a finite number of factors is the product of their limits, we also have

$$\lim_{u\to\infty}\frac{(\ln u)^n}{u} = \left[\lim_{u\to\infty}\frac{\ln u}{u^{1/n}}\right]^n \qquad (17)$$

$$= 0^n = 0$$

for any positive integer n. This form is one that easily gives us a comparison between the rates of growth of the exponential function and the nth power function. In Eq. (17), we let

$$\ln u = y \quad \text{and} \quad u = e^y,$$

and get

$$\lim_{y\to\infty}\frac{y^n}{e^y} = 0 \quad \text{for any positive integer } n. \qquad (18)$$

The limit result (18) says that as $y \to \infty$, e^y increases more rapidly than any fixed positive integral power of y.

8.15

Problem 4. Find a number c such that $e^y > y^{10}$ for $y > c$.

Solution. The condition to be met is equivalent to the condition that $y > 10 \ln y$. Consider the function $g(y) = y - 10 \ln y$ for $y > 0$. Its derivative is

$$g'(y) = 1 - 10/y,$$

which is positive for $y > 10$. Because we know something about $\ln 2$, we look for $y = 2^k$, such that $2^k > 10$ and

$$2^k > 10 \ln 2^k = (10k) \ln 2 = 6.9315k.$$

By trial and error, we see that $k = 5$ is too small but $k = 6$ is large enough. In other words,

$$\begin{aligned} g(2^6) = g(64) &= 64 - 10 \ln 64 \\ &= 64 - 60 \ln 2 \\ &> 64 - 60(0.694) > 0. \end{aligned}$$

Therefore $c = 64$ is sufficiently large to guarantee that $g(y)$ is positive for $y > c$, because

$$g(64) > 0 \quad \text{and} \quad g'(y) > 0 \quad \text{for } y > 10$$

together imply that

$$g(y) > 0 \quad \text{for all } y > 64.$$

As a check, observe that $e > 2$, so that

$$e^{64} > 2^{64} \quad \text{and} \quad 64^{10} = 2^{60} < 2^{64}.$$

Theorem 3. *For every real x and rational r,*

$$(e^x)^r = e^{rx}, \tag{19a}$$

or

$$[\exp(x)]^r = \exp(rx). \tag{19b}$$

Proof. Let

$$y = e^x, \quad \text{or} \quad x = \ln y.$$

Then, for any rational r,

$$rx = r \ln y = \ln(y^r),$$

so that

$$y^r = \ln^{-1}(rx) = \exp(rx) = e^{rx}.$$

But $y = e^x$. Therefore

$$(e^x)^r = e^{rx}. \ \square$$

Powers of e are tabulated in many mathematical tables, such as *CRC* and Burington's. They may also be read directly from the LL-scales of a log-log slide rule. For example, if the number x on the D-scale in Fig. 8.15 is $x = 2$, then the corresponding readings on the LL-scales are:

$$e^2 = 7.4 \qquad \text{on LL 3,}$$
$$e^{0.2} = 1.2215 \quad \text{on LL 2,}$$
$$e^{0.02} = 1.0202 \quad \text{on LL 1.}$$

The value of e^{-2} can be read from the LL00-scale on the reverse side of the slide rule opposite the 2 on the right half of the A-scale (the reading gives $e^{-2} = 0.135$). It is also possible to use

$$e^{-2} = \frac{1}{e^2} = \frac{1}{7.4} = 0.135$$

to arrive at the same result. The use of the LL-scales is described in the manual of instructions that comes with the log-log slide rule.

A table of e^x and e^{-x} is included at the end of the book for convenience and to give an appreciation of the rapid rate of increase of the exponential function for positive values of x.

$\log_{10} 10^A = A$ $\quad 10^{\log_{10} B} = B$ $\quad \ln e^A = A$

$e^{\ln B} = B$

$e^w = e^w \frac{dw}{dx}$

EXERCISES

1. Simplify each of the following expressions.

(a) $e^{\ln x}$ (b) $\ln (e^x)$ (c) $e^{-\ln(x^2)}$

(d) $\ln (e^{-x^2})$ (e) $\ln (e^{1/x})$ (f) $\ln (1/e^x)$

(g) $e^{\ln (1/x)}$ (h) $e^{-\ln(1/x)} \ln x$ (i) $e^{\ln 2 + \ln x}$

(j) $e^{2\ln x}$ (k) $\ln (e^{x - x^2})$ (l) $\ln (x^2 e^{-2x})$

(m) $e^{x + \ln x}$ (n) $\exp (\ln x - 2 \ln y)$

Find dy/dx in Exercises 2 through 19.

2. $y = x^2 e^x$ $\ln x e^x \cdot e^{-x}$

3. $y = e^{2x}(2 \cos 3x + 3 \sin 3x)$ $2 \ln x + 2x$

4. $y = \ln \dfrac{e^x}{1 + e^x}$

5. $y = \frac{1}{2}(e^x - e^{-x})$

6. $y = \frac{1}{2}(e^x + e^{-x})$

7. $y = \dfrac{e^x - e^{-x}}{e^x + e^{-x}}$

8. $y = e^{\sin^{-1} x}$

9. $y = (1 + 2x)e^{-2x}$

10. $y = (9x^2 - 6x + 2)e^{3x}$

11. $y = \dfrac{ax - 1}{a^2} e^{ax}$

12. $y = e^{-x^2}$

13. $y = x^2 e^{-x^2}$

14. $y = e^x \ln x$

15. $y = \tan^{-1} (e^x)$

16. $y = \sec^{-1} (e^{2x})$

17. $e^{2x} = \sin (x + 3y)$

18. $y = e^{1/x}$

19. $\tan y = e^x + \ln x$

20. Let h be a number between $\frac{1}{2}$ and 1. (For example, $h = \ln 2$ would qualify.) Consider the set S of numbers

$$a_1 = h,$$
$$a_2 = h/2,$$
$$a_3 = h/4, \ldots,$$
$$a_n = h/2^{n-1}, \ldots$$

Given any $\epsilon > 0$, you could find a finite subset of S whose sum would lie between $1 - \epsilon$ and $1 + \epsilon$. Explain how this could be done if you had access to a computer.

21. Recall that $\sqrt{a}$ can be approximated by the following procedure: From a table of squares, locate a number x such that x^2 is reasonably near a. For example, for $a = 2$ you might use the squares $1.4^2 = 1.96$ and $1.5^2 = 2.25$ to give the estimate $x = 1.4$. Then get an improved estimate

$$x' = \frac{1}{2}(x + a/x).$$

These operations are easy for a computer, and the process can be repeated with x replaced by the improved estimate to get a still better estimate. When $a = 1 + h$ and h is small, you could begin with the approximation $x = 1 + h/2$. Using these ideas, explain how you could compute good approximations, successively, for the square root, fourth root, eighth root, and so on, of 2, if you had access to a computer.

22. (a) Show that $y = Ce^{ax}$ is a solution of the differential equation $dy/dx = ay$ for any choice of the constant C.

(b) Using the result of (a), find a solution of the differential equation $dy/dt = -2y$ satisfying the initial condition $y = 3$ when $t = 0$.

23. Show that $y = e^{-ax} u$ is a solution of the differential equation

$$\frac{d^2y}{dx^2} + 2a \frac{dy}{dx} + (a^2 + b^2)y = 0$$

if and only if u satisfies the equation

$$\frac{d^2u}{dx^2} + b^2 u = 0,$$

provided that a and b are constants.

Evaluate the integrals in Exercises 24 through 31.

24. $\displaystyle\int e^{2x} \, dx$

25. $\displaystyle\int x e^{x^2} \, dx$

26. $\displaystyle\int e^{\sin x} \cos x \, dx$

27. $\displaystyle\int e^{x/3} \, dx$

28. $\displaystyle\int \dfrac{4 \, dx}{e^{3x}}$

29. $\displaystyle\int \dfrac{e^x \, dx}{1 + 2e^x}$

30. $\displaystyle\int_e^{e^2} \dfrac{dx}{x \ln x}$

31. $\displaystyle\int \dfrac{(e^x - e^{-x}) \, dx}{(e^x + e^{-x})}$

32. If a particle moves along the x-axis so that its position at time t is given by

$$x = ae^{\omega t} + be^{-\omega t},$$

where a, b, ω, are constants, show that it is repelled from the origin with a force proportional to the displacement. Assume that

$$\text{force} = \text{mass} \times \text{acceleration}.$$

33. Find a positive number p such that $e^x > x^{20}$ for $x > p$.

34. Find a positive number b such that $e^u > 20u^{10}$ for $u > b$. [*Suggestion.* Observe that $u^{11} > 20u^{10}$ when u is sufficiently large.]

8.9 THE FUNCTION a^u

If a is any positive real number and

$$b = \ln a, \tag{1a}$$

then

$$a = e^b. \tag{1b}$$

The two equations (1a, b) may be combined to give the result

$$a = e^{\ln a}. \tag{2}$$

In words, $\ln a$ *is the power to which the base e may be raised to give a.*

Suppose we now raise both sides of Eq. (2) to the power u, where u is any real number. We would like to have the law of exponents

$$(e^{\ln a})^u = e^{u \ln a}$$

be true. Hence we now make the following *definition:*

$$a^u = e^{u \ln a}. \tag{3}$$

This definition is equivalent to saying that

$$\ln a^u = u \ln a, \tag{3'}$$

since both Eqs. (3) and (3') say that $u \ln a$ is the power to which e may be raised to produce a^u. But (3') is the same as Eq. (3), Article 8.6, in case $u = n$ is a rational number. What we are now considering is the case where u may be any real number, rational or irrational, $-\infty < u < +\infty$. Our new definition of a^u includes the old case but goes beyond and extends it.

Properties of a^u

By making use of the law of exponents, Eq. (13a), Article 8.8,

$$e^{x_1} \cdot e^{x_2} = e^{x_1 + x_2}, \tag{4}$$

and the law of logarithms, Eq. (1), Article 8.6,

$$\ln ab = \ln a + \ln b, \tag{5}$$

together with the definition (3) and Eq. (2) above, the following laws may be established.

$$\left.\begin{array}{l} \text{(a)} \ \ a^0 = 1 \\[4pt] \text{(b)} \ \ a^1 = a \\[4pt] \text{(c)} \ \ a^u \cdot a^v = a^{u+v} \\[4pt] \text{(d)} \ \ a^{-u} = \dfrac{1}{a^u} \\[4pt] \text{(e)} \ \ (a^u)^v = a^{uv} \\[4pt] \text{(f)} \ \ (ab)^u = a^u b^u \end{array}\right\} \tag{6}$$

The first two properties, $a^0 = 1$ and $a^1 = a$, are trivial consequences of Eqs. (2) and (3). To prove (6c), we use the definition

$$a^u \cdot a^v = e^{u \ln a} \cdot e^{v \ln a},$$

then Eq. (4),

$$e^{u \ln a} \cdot e^{v \ln a} = e^{(u+v) \ln a},$$

and then the definition

$$a^{u+v} = e^{(u+v) \ln a},$$

and combine the results into the following:

$$a^u \cdot a^v = e^{u \ln a} \cdot e^{v \ln a} = e^{(u+v) \ln a} = a^{u+v},$$

which establishes the result

$$a^u \cdot a^v = a^{u+v}.$$

Equation (6d) is a consequence of (6a) and (6b):

$$a^{-u} \cdot a^u = a^{-u+u} = a^0 = 1.$$

Equation (6e) is established as follows. Let

$$b = a^u = e^{u \ln a}, \tag{7a}$$

so that

$$(a^u)^v = b^v = e^{v \ln b}. \tag{7b}$$

But

$$\ln b = u \ln a, \tag{7c}$$

since $u \ln a$ is the power to which e may be raised to produce b, Eq. (7a). Now substitute from (7c) into (7b),

$$(a^u)^v = e^{v \ln b} = e^{vu \ln a}, \tag{7d}$$

and make use of the definition, Eq. (3),

$$a^{uv} = e^{uv \ln a}. \tag{7e}$$

When we compare Eqs. (7d, e), we see that we have

$$(a^u)^v = a^{uv},$$

since both expressions are equal to

$$e^{uv \ln a}.$$

The proof of (6f) is left as a problem.

With the definition of a^u now clarified, we are ready to calculate its derivative in case u is a differentiable function of x. We apply formula XX, Article 8.8, and remembering that $\ln a$ is constant when a is, we obtain

$$\frac{da^u}{dx} = \frac{de^{u \ln a}}{dx}$$

$$= e^{u \ln a} \cdot \frac{du}{dx} \cdot \ln a,$$

$$\frac{da^u}{dx} = a^u \cdot \frac{du}{dx} \cdot \ln a. \tag{8}$$

This gives us a formula for the derivative of any positive constant a raised to a variable power. There is very little reason to memorize the result, since it may always be derived very quickly by the method of logarithmic differentiation, which will presently be discussed. It illustrates the fact that the base e is the most desirable one to encounter, since $\ln e = 1$ and Eq. (8) is the same as formula XX in case $a = e$. It also enables us to write down a formula for the integral of $a^u \, du$. For, if we multiply both sides of Eq. (8) by dx to change it to differential form,

$$da^u = \ln a \cdot a^u \, du,$$

and then divide by $\ln a$, provided $a \neq 1$, we see that

$$\int a^u \, du = \int \frac{1}{\ln a} \, da^u = \frac{a^u}{\ln a} + C,$$

$$(a > 0, \ a \neq 1). \tag{9}$$

Logarithmic differentiation

The properties

$$
\left.
\begin{array}{ll}
\text{(a)} & \ln uv = \ln u + \ln v \\[4pt]
\text{(b)} & \ln \dfrac{u}{v} = \ln u - \ln v \\[4pt]
\text{(c)} & \ln u^n = n \ln u \\[4pt]
\text{(d)} & \ln a^u = u \ln a
\end{array}
\right\} \tag{10}
$$

can be used to advantage in calculating derivatives of products, quotients, roots, and powers, as illustrated in the examples that follow. The method, known as logarithmic differentiation, is to take the natural logarithm of both sides of an equation

$$y = f(x),$$
$$\ln y = \ln f(x),$$

simplify $\ln f(x)$ as much as possible by making use of the properties in Eq. (10), and then differentiate implicitly with respect to x:

$$\frac{d}{dx} \ln y = \frac{1}{y} \frac{dy}{dx}.$$

Example 1. Derive Eq. (8).

Solution. Let $y = a^u$. Then

$$\ln y = \ln a^u = u \ln a,$$

$$\frac{1}{y} \frac{dy}{dx} = \frac{du}{dx} \ln a,$$

$$\frac{dy}{dx} = y \frac{du}{dx} \ln a,$$

or, since $y = a^u$,

$$\frac{da^u}{dx} = a^u \frac{du}{dx} \ln a.$$

Example 2. If n is a real constant and u is a positive differentiable function of x, show that

$$\frac{du^n}{dx} = nu^{n-1} \frac{du}{dx}.$$

Solution. Let $y = u^n$. Then

$$\ln y = \ln u^n = n \ln u,$$

$$\frac{1}{y}\frac{dy}{dx} = n\frac{1}{u}\frac{du}{dx},$$

$$\frac{dy}{dx} = n\frac{y}{u}\frac{du}{dx} = n\frac{u^n}{u}\frac{du}{dx}$$

$$= nu^{n-1}\frac{du}{dx}. \qquad \text{Q.E.D.}$$

Example 3. Find dy/dx if $y = x^x$, $x > 0$.

Solution. $\ln y = \ln x^x = x\ln x$,

$$\frac{1}{y}\frac{dy}{dx} = x\cdot\frac{1}{x} + \ln x = 1 + \ln x,$$

$$\frac{dy}{dx} = y(1 + \ln x) = x^x(1 + \ln x).$$

Example 4. Find dy/dx if

$$y^{2/3} = \frac{(x^2 + 1)(3x + 4)^{1/2}}{\sqrt[5]{(2x - 3)(x^2 - 4)}}, \qquad (x > 2).$$

Solution

$$\ln y^{2/3} = \tfrac{2}{3}\ln y$$
$$= \ln(x^2 + 1) + \tfrac{1}{2}\ln(3x + 4)$$
$$\qquad - \tfrac{1}{5}\ln(2x - 3) - \tfrac{1}{5}\ln(x^2 - 4) \qquad \text{(a)}$$

and

$$\frac{2}{3}\cdot\frac{1}{y}\frac{dy}{dx}$$

$$= \frac{2x}{x^2 + 1} + \frac{1}{2}\cdot\frac{3}{3x + 4} - \frac{1}{5}\cdot\frac{2}{2x - 3} - \frac{1}{5}\cdot\frac{2x}{x^2 - 4},$$

so that

$$\frac{dy}{dx} = \frac{3y}{2}\left[\frac{2x}{x^2 + 1} + \frac{\frac{3}{2}}{3x + 4} - \frac{\frac{2}{5}}{2x - 3} - \frac{2x/5}{x^2 - 4}\right].$$

Remark. The restriction $x > 2$ ensures that all the quantities whose logarithms are indicated in (a) above are positive. If we want dy/dx at a point where y is negative, we may multiply our equation by -1 before taking logarithms; for if y is negative, then $-y$ is positive and $\ln(-y)$ is well defined.

Economists define the ratio of "marginal cost" to "average cost" as the "elasticity of total cost." That is, if the total cost of producing x units of a given product is $y = f(x)$ dollars, then the "average cost" is y/x dollars per unit. The "marginal cost," which is, roughly speaking, the additional cost of producing one more unit, is dy/dx. Then, by definition,

$$\text{elasticity of total cost} = \frac{dy/dx}{y/x} = \frac{dy/y}{dx/x} = \frac{d(\ln y)}{d(\ln x)}.$$

When the elasticity of total cost equals one, then marginal cost equals average cost (that is, $dy/dx = y/x$) and average cost has a stationary value [that is, $d(y/x)/dx = 0$]. [For further discussion, see R. G. D. Allen, *Mathematical Analysis for Economists* (Macmillan, 1939), p. 260ff.]

EXERCISES

3/ 8 # 1-15 odd

Use the method of logarithmic differentiation to find dy/dx in each of the following exercises (1 through 8).

1. $y^2 = x(x + 1)$ $(x > 0)$

2. $y = \sqrt[3]{\dfrac{x + 1}{x - 1}}$ $(x > 1)$

3. $y = \dfrac{x\sqrt{x^2 + 1}}{(x + 1)^{2/3}}$ $(x > 0)$

4. $y = \sqrt[3]{\dfrac{x(x + 1)(x - 2)}{(x^2 + 1)(2x + 3)}}$ $(x > 2)$

5. $y = x^{\sin x}$ $(x > 0)$

6. $y = (\sin x)^{\tan x}$ $(\sin x > 0)$

7. $y = 2^{\sec x}$

8. $y = x^{\ln x}$ $(x > 0)$

9. Show that $(ab)^u = a^u b^u$ if a and b are any positive numbers and u is any real number.

10. Show that the derivative of average cost is zero when marginal cost and average cost are equal.

Evaluate the following integrals (11–15):

11. $\displaystyle\int_0^{\ln 2} e^{-2x}\,dx$

12. $\displaystyle\int_0^{1.2} 3^x\,dx$

13. $\displaystyle\int_1^{\sqrt{2}} x\,2^{-x^2}\,dx$

14. $\displaystyle\int_0^1 5^{2t-2}\,dt$

15. $\displaystyle\int_0^{\pi/6} (\cos\theta)4^{-\sin\theta}\,d\theta$

16. Let a be a number greater than one. Prove that the graph of $y = a^x$ has the following characteristics:

(a) If $x_1 > x_2$, then $a^{x_1} > a^{x_2}$.

(b) The graph is everywhere concave upward.

(c) The graph lies entirely above the x-axis.

(d) The slope at any point is proportional to the ordinate there, and the proportionality factor is the slope at the y-intercept of the graph.

(e) The curve approaches the negative x-axis as $x \to -\infty$.

8.10 THE FUNCTION $\text{LOG}_a u$

We know that $\ln u$ is the power to which e may be raised to give u. For that reason, we say that e is the base of the system of natural logarithms in keeping with the following definition.

Definition. *If u is positive and a is a positive number different from 1, we say that y is the logarithm of u to the base a, and write*

$$y = \log_a u, \qquad (1a)$$

provided y is the power to which a may be raised to give u:

$$a^y = u. \qquad (1b)$$

Example

$$\log_5 25 = 2 \quad \text{since} \quad 5^2 = 25,$$
$$\log_2 \tfrac{1}{4} = -2 \quad \text{since} \quad 2^{-2} = \tfrac{1}{4}.$$

To find $x = \log_4 8$, we rewrite the equation as

$$4^x = 2^{2x} = 8 = 2^3,$$

from which we read $2x = 3$, $x = \frac{3}{2}$. In other words,

$$\log_4 8 = \tfrac{3}{2} \quad \text{since} \quad 4^{3/2} = (\sqrt{4})^3 = 8.$$

We may solve Eq. (1b) for y, and thereby obtain an expression for $\log_a u$, by taking natural logarithms and applying Eq. (3') of Article 8.9:

$$\ln u = \ln a^y = y \ln a.$$

If $\ln a \neq 0$ (which is the case when a is different from 1), we may solve for y. The result is that

$$y = \frac{\ln u}{\ln a}$$

is the power to which a may be raised to produce u. In other words,

$$\log_a u = \frac{\ln u}{\ln a}. \qquad (2)$$

Properties of $\log_a u$

The following properties follow readily from Eq. (2) above and the analogous properties of $\ln u$.

$$
\begin{aligned}
&\text{(a)} \;\; \log_a uv = \log_a u + \log_a v \\
&\text{(b)} \;\; \log_a \frac{u}{v} = \log_a u - \log_a v \\
&\text{(c)} \;\; \log_a u^v = v \log_a u
\end{aligned}
\qquad (3)
$$

Equation (3c), for example, is derived as follows:

$$\log_a u^v = \frac{\ln u^v}{\ln a} = \frac{v \ln u}{\ln a} = v \log_a u,$$

where we make use of Eq. (2), then Eq. (3') of Article 8.9, and then Eq. (2) again.

If u is a differentiable positive function of x, we may differentiate both sides of Eq. (2) and thus obtain

$$\frac{d \log_a u}{dx} = \frac{1}{u \ln a} \frac{du}{dx}. \qquad (4)$$

It is clear that this formula is simpler for logarithms to the base e than for any other base. The only bases of practical importance are $a = e$ (natural logarithms) and $a = 10$ (common logarithms). Since $\ln 10 = 2.30259 \ldots$, Eq. (4) is certainly less attractive for the case $a = 10$ than it is for the case $a = e$. This is the primary reason why natural logarithms are to be preferred over common logarithms in applications of the calculus.

Logarithms to the base 10 are used primarily as aids in performing arithmetical calculations such as multiplication, division, and raising numbers to powers. The use of slide rules, desk calculators, and new high-speed computing machinery is rapidly making this use of logarithms less and less important. Natural logarithms, on the other hand, are not in any immediate danger of becoming obsolete, since they occur naturally when some common kinds of differential equations are solved. (See Examples 1 and 2, Article 8.11.)

EXERCISES
3/8 #1+2   3/9 #7,8

Determine the following logarithms:

1. (a) $\log_4 16$,   (b) $\log_8 32$,
   (c) $\log_5 0.04$,   (d) $\log_{0.5} 4$.

2. (a) $\log_2 4$,   (b) $\log_4 2$,
   (c) $\log_8 16$,   (d) $\log_{32} 4$.

3. Find x if $3^x = 2^{x+1}$.

4. Find x if $3^{\log_3 7} + 2^{\log_2 5} = 5^{\log_5 x}$.

5. Show that $\log_b u = \log_a u \cdot \log_b a$ if a, b, and u are positive numbers, $a \neq 1$, $b \neq 1$.

6. Given $\ln 2 = 0.69315$, $\ln 10 = 2.30259$, $\log_{10} 2 = 0.30103$. Find
   (a) $\log_{10} 20$, $\log_{10} 200$, $\log_{10} 0.2$, $\log_{10} 0.02$,
   (b) $\ln 20$, $\ln 200$, $\ln 0.2$, $\ln 0.02$.

7. Use the table of natural logarithms at the end of the book to evaluate the following logarithms to two significant figures:
   (a) $\log_3 5$,   (b) $\log_5 3$,
   (c) $\log_{1.4} 2.3$.

8. Use the tables at the end of the book to evaluate the following to two significant figures:
   (a) $(1.6)^{1.5}$,   (b) $\dfrac{\ln 0.7}{\ln 1.3}$.

9. Find the derivatives of the following:
   (a) $y = 3^{\tan x}$,   (b) $y = (x^2 + 1)^{\ln x}$,
   (c) $s = 2^{-t^2}$,   (d) $r = \theta e^{-2\theta}$.

8.11 DIFFERENTIAL EQUATIONS

Suppose a quantity x changes at a rate that at any instant of time t is proportional to the amount of x present at that instant. This is expressed by the differential equation

$$\frac{dx}{dt} = kx, \qquad (1)$$

where k is the proportionality constant. If the amount of x present at time $t = 0$ is x_0, the initial condition

$$x = x_0 \qquad \text{when} \qquad t = 0 \qquad (2)$$

enables us to evaluate the constant of integration that enters when we integrate Eq. (1). The method of solution will be illustrated by an example.

Example 1. As a result of leakage, an electrical condenser discharges at a rate proportional to the charge. If the charge Q has the value Q_0 at the time $t = 0$, find Q as a function of t.

Solution. The mathematical statement of the problem consists of the differential equation $dQ/dt = -kQ$ and the initial condition $t = 0$, $Q = Q_0$. Then

$$\frac{dQ}{Q} = -k\,dt,$$

$$\int \frac{dQ}{Q} = -k \int dt,$$

$$\ln Q = -kt + C. \qquad (3)$$

The constant of integration C is evaluated by using the initial conditions:

$$t = 0, \quad Q = Q_0; \qquad \ln Q_0 = C.$$

Substituting this value of C back into (3) and transposing it to the left of the equation, we get

$$\ln Q - \ln Q_0 = -kt$$

or

$$\ln \frac{Q}{Q_0} = -kt.$$

Hence, $-kt$ is the power to which e must be raised to give Q/Q_0, that is,

$$\frac{Q}{Q_0} = e^{-kt} \qquad \text{or} \qquad Q = Q_0 e^{-kt}.$$

According to this equation, Q is never zero; that is, some charge would always remain. But when $kt = 10$, say, then $Q = Q_0 e^{-10}$ so that the charge Q has by then diminished to less than 5/1000 of 1 percent of its original value Q_0.

Remark. In this example, the function integrated was positive, so that we were able to omit the absolute value symbols and write simply $\ln Q$ in place of $\ln |Q|$. Occasionally we encounter a problem where the quantity whose logarithm we require is an unknown function which presumably could be either positive or negative. To change sign from one to the other, however, would mean that the quantity would become zero at the transition point, provided it is a *continuous* function (Fig. 8.16). An integral of the form

$$\int \frac{du}{u} \qquad (4)$$

between points where u changes continuously from positive to negative or from negative to positive is a so-called *improper integral*, because the integrand $1/u$ becomes infinite at $u = 0$. We shall discuss improper integrals in more detail in a later chapter. At present we shall assume that any physical problems we encounter that lead to integrals of the form of (4) arise from physical situations in which infinities are excluded. Then if we know the sign of u at one point of the interval of integration, we shall assume that it always has the same sign throughout the whole interval.

WRITE **Example 2.** Ohm's law, $E = Ri$, requires modification in a circuit containing self-inductance, as in a coil. The modified form is

$$L \frac{di}{dt} + Ri = E \qquad (5)$$

for the series circuit shown in Fig. 8.17, where R denotes the resistance of the circuit in ohms, L is the self-inductance in henries, E is the impressed electromotive force (emf) in volts, i is the current in amperes, and t is the time in seconds. (See Sears, *Electricity and Magnetism*, Chapter 13.) We shall solve the differential equation (5) under the assumption that E is constant and

$$i = 0 \quad \text{when} \quad t = 0. \qquad (6)$$

To integrate (5), we first separate the variables in order to have the terms involving the variable current i combined with di for purposes of integration. Thus

$$L \, di = (E - Ri) \, dt$$

and

$$\int \frac{L \, di}{E - Ri} = \int dt. \qquad (7)$$

We let

$$u = E - Ri, \qquad (8)$$

then

$$du = -R \, di, \quad di = -\frac{1}{R} \, du,$$

8.16

8.17

so that (7) becomes

$$-\frac{L}{R} \int \frac{du}{u} = \int dt. \qquad (9)$$

From (8) and the initial conditions (6) we see that $u = E - Ri$ has the positive value $u_0 = E$ at $t = 0$. We therefore assume that it remains positive, so that $|u| = u$ and the integral in (9) then gives

$$-\frac{L}{R} \ln u = t + C$$

or

$$-\frac{L}{R} \ln (E - Ri) = t + C. \qquad (10)$$

The initial conditions $t = 0$, $i = 0$ enable us to evaluate the constant of integration:

$$C = -\frac{L}{R} \ln E.$$

When we substitute this back into (10) and transpose it to the left side of the equation, we obtain

$$\frac{L}{R} \left[\ln E - \ln (E - Ri) \right] = t,$$

$$\ln \frac{E}{E - Ri} = \frac{Rt}{L},$$

$$\frac{E}{E - Ri} = e^{(Rt)/L},$$

$$\frac{E - Ri}{E} = e^{-(Rt)/L},$$

$$1 - \frac{R}{E}i = e^{-(Rt)/L},$$

$$i = \frac{E}{R}\left(1 - e^{-(Rt)/L}\right). \qquad (11)$$

We see from this that the current (for $t > 0$) is always less than, but increases toward, the steady state value

$$i_{s.s.} = \frac{E}{R}, \qquad (12)$$

which is the current that would flow in the circuit if either $L = 0$ (no inductance) or $di/dt = 0$ (steady current, i = constant) in Eq. (5). Indeed, if $L \to 0$, then for all $t > 0$ the exponent [in (11)]

$$-\frac{Rt}{L} \to -\infty \quad \text{and} \quad i \to \frac{E}{R}.$$

A graph of the current versus time relation (11) is shown in Fig. 8.18.

8.18

Incidentally, in problems involving electrical circuits, the letter e is usually used to denote an emf and the letter ϵ is then used to denote the constant which we have called (and shall continue to call) e. Mathematicians have become accustomed to the use of ϵ to denote an arbitrarily small positive number, so they are not likely to change their notation; nor are the electrical engineers likely to change theirs. However, this lack of uniformity should not cause confusion, since the meaning of the symbols will usually be clear from the context.

EXERCISES

3/9 #4,8

1. Suppose a body of mass m moving in a straight line with velocity v encounters a resistance proportional to the velocity and this is the only force acting on the body. If the body starts with velocity v_0, how far does it travel in time t? Assume $F = d(mv)/dt$.

2. A radioactive substance disintegrates at a rate proportional to the amount present. How much of the substance remains at time t if the initial amount is Q_0?

3. If the bacteria in a culture increase continuously at a rate proportional to the number present, and the initial number is N_0, find the number at time t.

In Exercises 4–7, substitute $y = e^{rx}$ and find values of the constant r for which $y = e^{rx}$ is a solution of the given differential equation.

4. $\dfrac{d^2y}{dx^2} - 4\dfrac{dy}{dx} + 3y = 0$ 5. $\dfrac{d^2y}{dx^2} - \dfrac{dy}{dx} - 2y = 0$

6. $\dfrac{d^3y}{dx^3} + 6\dfrac{d^2y}{dx^2} + 5\dfrac{dy}{dx} = 0$

7. $\dfrac{d^4y}{dx^4} - 13\dfrac{d^2y}{dx^2} + 36y = 0$

8. By substitution, verify that

$$y = (c_1 + c_2 x)e^{r_1 x}$$

satisfies the differential equation

$$\frac{d^2y}{dx^2} - 2r_1\frac{dy}{dx} + r_1^2 y = 0$$

for all values of the constants c_1, c_2, and r_1.

9. By substitution, verify that $y = e^{ax}(c_1 \cos bx + c_2 \sin bx)$ satisfies the differential equation

$$\frac{d^2y}{dx^2} - 2a\frac{dy}{dx} + (a^2 + b^2)y = 0$$

for all values of the constants c_1, c_2, a, and b.

10. Sketch the curve $y = e^{-x}\cos 2x$ for $x \geq 0$. Show that it is tangent to the curves $y = \pm e^{-x}$ when $\cos 2x = \pm 1$.

REVIEW QUESTIONS AND EXERCISES

1. Review the formulas for derivatives of sums, products, quotients, powers, sines, and cosines. Using these, develop formulas for derivatives of the other trigonometric functions.

2. Define the inverse sine, inverse cosine, inverse tangent, and inverse secant functions. What is the *domain* of each? What is its *range*? What is the derivative of each? Sketch the graph of each.

π, e are

3. Define the natural logarithm function. What is its domain? What is its range? What is its derivative? Sketch its graph.

4. What is the inverse function of the natural logarithm called? What is the domain of this function? What is its range? What is its derivative? Sketch its graph.

5. Define the term "algebraic function." Define "transcendental function." To which class (algebraic or transcendental) do you think the "greatest integer" step-function (Fig. 2.5) belongs?

[It is often difficult to prove that a particular function belongs to one class or the other. Numbers are also classified as algebraic and transcendental. *References.* (1) W. J. Le Veque, *Topics in Number Theory*, Addison-Wesley, Vol. II, Chap. 5, pp. 161–200; (2) I. M. Niven, *Irrational Numbers*, Carus monograph number 11 of the Mathematical Association of America, (1956). Both π and e are transcendental numbers, and proofs may be found in the references cited. That π is transcendental was first proved by Ferdinand Lindemann in 1882. One result that follows from the transcendence of π is that it is impossible to construct, with unmarked straightedge and compass alone, a square whose area is equal to the area of a given circle. The first proof that e is transcendental was published by Charles Hermite in 1873. You may also enjoy reading about an interesting related feature of the graph of $y = \ln x$ in the article on logarithms on p. 301 of Vol. 14 of the *Encyclopaedia Britannica* (1956 edition).]

6. Let n be an integer greater than 1. Divide the interval $1 \le x \le n$ into n equal subintervals and write an expression for the trapezoidal approximation to the area under the graph of $y = 1/x$, $1 \le x \le n$, based on this subdivision. Is this approximation less than, equal to, or greater than $\ln n$? Give a reason for your answer.

7. Prove that $\lim_{x \to \infty} (\ln x)/x = 0$, starting with the definition of $\ln x$ as an integral.

8. The *Encyclopaedia Britannica* article on logarithms begins with the statement: "By shortening processes of computation, logarithms have doubled the working speed of astronomers and engineers." What property or properties of logarithms do you think the author of the article had in mind when he made that statement?

9. What is the meaning of the differential equation $dy/dt = ky$? What is the solution of this equation that satisfies the initial condition $y = y_0$ when $t = 0$?

MISCELLANEOUS EXERCISES

In each of the following exercises (1 through 25), (a) find dy/dx, and (b) sketch the curve.

1. $y = \sin 2x$
2. $y = 4 \cos (2x + \pi/4)$
3. $y = 2 \sin x + \sin 2x$
4. $y = \dfrac{\sin x}{1 + \cos x}$
5. $x = \cos y$
6. $x = \tan y$
7. $y = 4 \sin \left(\dfrac{x}{2} + \pi\right)$
8. $y = 1 - \sin x$
9. $y = x - \sin x$
10. $y = \dfrac{\sin x}{x}$ (What happens as $x \to 0$? As $x \to \infty$?)
11. $y = \dfrac{\sin x}{x}$ (What happens as $x \to 0$? As $x \to \infty$?)
12. $y = x \sin \dfrac{1}{x}$ (What happens as $x \to \infty$? As $x \to 0$?)
13. $y = x^2 \sin \dfrac{1}{x}$ (What happens as $x \to \infty$? As $x \to 0$?)
14. $x = \tan \dfrac{\pi y}{2}$
15. (a) $y = \frac{1}{2}(e^x + e^{-x})$,
    (b) $y = \frac{1}{2}(e^x - e^{-x})$,
    (c) $y = \dfrac{e^x - e^{-x}}{e^x + e^{-x}}$
16. $y = xe^{-x}$
17. (a) $y = x \ln x$, (b) $y = \sqrt{x} \ln x$
18. (a) $y = \dfrac{\ln x}{x}$, (b) $y = \dfrac{\ln x}{\sqrt{x}}$, (c) $y = \dfrac{\ln x}{x^2}$
19. $y = e^{-x} \sin 2x$
20. (a) $y = 2x - \frac{1}{2}e^{2x}$, (b) $y = e^{(2x - \frac{1}{2}e^{2x})}$
21. (a) $y = x - e^x$, (b) $y = e^{(x - e^x)}$

22. $y = \ln (x + \sqrt{x^2 + 1})$

23. $y = \dfrac{1}{2} \ln \dfrac{1 + x}{1 - x}$

24. $y = \ln (x^2 + 4)$

25. $y = x \tan^{-1} \dfrac{x}{2}$

Find dy/dx in Problems 26–42.

26. $y = \dfrac{e^{2x} - e^{-2x}}{e^{2x} + e^{-2x}}$

27. $y = \ln \dfrac{\sec x + \tan x}{\sec x - \tan x}$

28. $y = x^2 e^{2x} \sin 3x$

29. $y = \sin^{-1}(x^2) - xe^{x^2}$

30. $y = \ln \left(\dfrac{x^4}{1 + x^3} \right) + 7^{x^{2/3}}$

31. $y = (x^2 + 2)^{2 - x}$

32. $y = \dfrac{\ln x}{e^x}$

33. $y = \ln \dfrac{x}{\sqrt{x^2 + 1}}$

34. $y = \ln (4 - 3x)$

35. $y = \ln (3x^2 + 4x)$

36. $y = x (\ln x)^3$ 37. $y = x \ln (x^3)$

38. $y = x^3 \ln x$ 39. $y = \ln e^x$

40. $y = x^2 e^x$ 41. $x = \ln y$

42. $y = \ln (\ln x)$

43. Find dx/dy by logarithmic differentiation for

(a) $y = \dfrac{x}{x^2 + 1}, \quad x > 0$;

(b) $y = \sqrt[3]{\dfrac{x(x - 2)}{x^2 + 1}}, \quad x > 2$.

44. If $f(x) = x + e^{4x}$, find $f(0)$ and $f'(0)$, and find an approximation for $f(0.01)$.

45. Find dy/dx for each of the following:

(a) $y = a^{x^2 - x}$,   (b) $y = \ln \dfrac{e^x}{1 + e^x}$,

(c) $y = x^x$,   (d) $y = x^{1/x}$.

46. Sketch the graphs of $y = \ln (1 - x)$ and $y = \ln (1/x)$.

47. Sketch (in a common figure) the graphs of $y = e^{-x}$ and $y = -e^{-x}$.

48. Solve for x: $\tan^{-1} x - \cot^{-1} x = \pi/4$.

49. If

$$\frac{dy}{dx} = \frac{e^x - e^{-x}}{e^x + e^{-x}},$$

find $\dfrac{d^2 y}{dx^2}$ and y.

50. If $dy/dx = 2/e^y$ and $y = 0$ when $x = 5$, find y as a function of x.

51. $P(x_1, y_1)$ and $Q(x_2, y_2)$ are any two points (in the first quadrant) lying on the hyperbola $xy = R$ (R positive). Show that the area bounded by the arc PQ, the lines $x = x_1$, $x = x_2$, and the x-axis is equal to the area bounded by the arc PQ, the lines $y = y_1$, $y = y_2$, and the y-axis.

52. By the trapezoidal rule, find $\int_0^2 e^{-x^2} dx$, using $n = 4$.

53. In a condenser discharging electricity the rate of change of the voltage in volts per second is proportional to the voltage, being numerically equal to minus one-fortieth of the voltage. Express the voltage as a function of the time. In how many seconds will the voltage decrease to 10 percent of its original value?

54. (a) Sketch the graph $2y = (e^x + e^{-x})$. Observe that whenever $P_1(x_1, y_1)$ is on the graph, so is the point $P_1'(-x_1, y_1)$. This implies a certain symmetry property of the graph. What is it? (b) Find the length of the curve from its lowest point to an arbitrary point $P_1(x_1, y_1)$ on it.

55. The area bounded by the x-axis and one arch of the curve $y = \sin x$ is revolved around the x-axis. Find the volume of the solid of revolution thus generated. Compare its volume with that of two inscribed cones.

56. A curve $y = f(x)$ goes through the points $(0, 0)$ and (x_1, y_1). It divides the rectangle $0 \le x \le x_1$, $0 \le y \le y_1$ into two regions: A above the curve and B below. Find the curve if the area of A is twice the area of B for all choices of $x_1 > 0$ and $y_1 > 0$.

57. Find a curve passing through the origin and such that the length s of the curve between the origin and any point (x, y) of the curve is given by

$$s = e^x + y - 1.$$

58. A particle starts at the origin and moves along the x-axis in such a way that its velocity at the point $(x, 0)$ is given by the formula $dx/dt = \cos^2 \pi x$. How long will it take to cover the distance from the origin to the point $x = \frac{1}{4}$? Will it ever reach the point $x = \frac{1}{2}$? Why?

59. A particle moves in a straight line with acceleration $a = 4/(4 - t)^2$. If when $t = 0$ the velocity is equal to 2, find how far the particle moves between $t = 1$ and $t = 2$.

60. The velocity of a certain particle moving along the x-axis is proportional to x. At time $t = 0$ the particle is located at $x = 2$ and at time $t = 10$ it is at $x = 4$. Find its position at $t = 5$.

61. Solve the differential equation $dy/dx = y^2 e^{-x}$ if $y = 2$ when $x = 0$.

62. It is estimated that the population of a certain country is now increasing at a rate of 2% per year. Assuming that this (instantaneous) rate will continue indefinitely, estimate what the population N will be t years from now, if the population now is N_0. How many years will it take for the population to double?

63. If $y = (e^{2x} - 1)/(e^{2x} + 1)$, show that $dy/dx = 1 - y^2$.

64. Determine the inflection points of the curve $y = e^{-(x/a)^2}$, where a is a positive constant. Sketch the curve. (This is closely related to the normal curve used in statistics.)

65. Find the volume generated when the area bounded by $y = e^{-x}$, $x = 0$, $x = \ln 2$, $y = 0$ is rotated about the x-axis.

66. Find the volume generated when the area bounded by $x = \sec y$, $x = 0$, $y = 0$, $y = \pi/3$ is rotated about the y-axis.

67. (a) Find dy/dx if $y = \ln (\sec x + \tan x)$. (b) Find the length of arc of the curve $y = \ln \sec x$ from $x = 0$ to $\pi/4$, using, at some stage, the result of part (a).

68. Find the length of the curve $x/a = (y/b)^2 - \frac{1}{8}(b^2/a^2) \ln (y/b)$ from $y = b$ to $y = 3b$, assuming a and b to be positive constants.

69. Find the volume generated by rotating about the x-axis the area bounded by

$$y = e^x, \quad y = 0, \quad x = 0, \quad x = 2.$$

70. Find the area bounded by the curve $y = (a/2) \times (e^{x/a} + e^{-x/a})$, the x-axis, and the lines $x = -a$ and $x = +a$.

71. The portion of a tangent to a curve included between the x-axis and the point of tangency is bisected by the y-axis. If the curve passes through $(1, 2)$, find its equation.

72. Use the trapezoidal rule with $n = 5$ to approximate the value of (a) $\ln 0.5$, (b) $\ln 3$.

73. (a) If $y = x \ln x - x$, find y'. (b) Use the results of 73(a) and 72(b) to evaluate $\int_1^3 \ln x \, dx$ approximately.

Evaluate the integrals in Exercises 74 and 75.

74. (a) $\int \dfrac{dx}{4 - 3x}$ (b) $\dfrac{5 \, dx}{x - 3}$ (c) $\int_0^2 \dfrac{x \, dx}{x^2 + 2}$

75. (a) $\int_0^2 \dfrac{x \, dx}{(x^2 + 2)^2}$ (b) $\int \dfrac{x + 1}{x} \, dx$ (c) $\int \dfrac{x}{2x + 1} \, dx$

76. Given $\ln 2 = 0.6932$ and $\ln 5 = 1.6094$. Use the properties of logarithms to find numerical values for $\ln 0.1$, $\ln 0.25$, $\ln 10$, and $\ln 20$.

77. Find the volume generated by rotating about the x-axis the area in the first quadrant bounded by the curve $xy^2 = 1$, the x-axis, the line $x = 1$, and the line $x = 4$.

78. Find the volume generated if the area in Exercise 78 is rotated about the y-axis.

Evaluate the integrals in Exercises 79–80.

79. (a) $\int_0^1 \dfrac{x^2 \, dx}{2 - x^3}$ (b) $\int_0^3 x(e^{x^2 - 1}) \, dx$ (c) $\int_1^3 \dfrac{dx}{x}$

80. (a) $\int_0^5 \dfrac{x \, dx}{x^2 + 1}$ (b) $\int_0^1 (e^x + 1) \, dx$

81. In the inversion of raw sugar the time rate of change of the amount of raw sugar present varies as the amount of raw sugar remaining. If after 10 hr 1000 lb of raw sugar has been reduced to 800 lb, how much raw sugar will remain after 24 hr?

82. A cylindrical tank of radius 10 ft and height 20 ft, with its axis vertical, is full of water but has a leak at the bottom. Assuming that water escapes at a rate proportional to the depth of water in the tank and that 10% escapes during the first hour, find a formula for the volume of water left in the tank after t hr.

83. Let p be a positive integer ≥ 2. Show that

$$\lim_{n\to\infty}\left(\frac{1}{n+1}+\frac{1}{n+2}+\cdots+\frac{1}{p\cdot n}\right)=\ln p.$$

84. (a) If $(\ln x)/x = (\ln 2)/2$, does it necessarily follow that $x = 2$? (b) If $(\ln x)/x = -2\ln 2$, does it necessarily follow that $x = \frac{1}{2}$? Give reasons for your answers.

85. Given that $\lim_{x\to\infty} (\ln x)/x = 0$ (see Article 8.7, Exercise 4). Prove that (a) $\lim_{x\to\infty} (\ln x)/x^h = 0$ if h is any positive constant, (b) $\lim_{x\to+\infty} x^n/e^x = 0$ if n is any constant.

86. Show that $\lim_{h\to 0} (e^h - 1)/h = 1$, by considering the definition of the derivative of e^x at $x = 0$.

87. Prove that if x is any positive number,

$$\lim_{n\to\infty} n(\sqrt[n]{x} - 1) = \ln x.$$

[*Hint.* Take $x = e^{nh}$ and apply Exercise 86.] *Remark.* This result provides a method for finding $\ln x$ (to any desired finite number of decimal places) using nothing fancier than repeated use of the operation of extracting square roots. For we may take $n = 2^k$, and then $\sqrt[n]{x}$ is obtained from x by taking k successive square roots.

88. Show that $(x^2/4) < x - \ln (1 + x) < (x^2/2)$ if $0 < x < 1$. [*Hint.* Let $f(x) = x - \ln (1 + x)$ and show that $(x/2) < f'(x) < x$.]

89. Prove that the area under the graph of $y = 1/x$ over the interval $a \leq x \leq b$ ($a > 0$) is the same as the area over the interval $ka \leq x \leq kb$, for any $k > 0$.

90. Find the limit, as $n \to \infty$, of

$$\frac{e^{1/n} + e^{2/n} + \cdots + e^{(n-1)/n} + e^{n/n}}{n}.$$

In considering the ratio of two functions $f(x)$ and $g(x)$, we sometimes wish to know the value of $\lim_{x\to a} f(x)/g(x)$ at a point where both $f(x)$ and $g(x)$ approach zero or both approach ∞. In such cases we are led to meaningless expressions $0/0$ or ∞/∞ if we substitute $x = a$ in the numerator and denominator of the fraction. Thus: $\lim_{t\to\infty} (t^2 + t)/(2t^2 + 1)$ assumes the form ∞/∞ as $t \to \infty$, and $\lim_{t\to 0} \sin x/x$ assumes the form $0/0$ as $t \to 0$.

The following theorem, which we shall state without proof,* is very useful in finding limits of this kind.

Theorem (*l'Hôpital's rule*). *If $f(a) = g(a) = 0$ or if $f(a) = g(a) = \infty$ and if the limit of the ratio $f'(t)/g'(t)$ as t approaches a exists, then*

$$\lim_{t\to a}\frac{f(t)}{g(t)} = \lim_{t\to a}\frac{f'(t)}{g'(t)}.$$

For our first example we have

$$\lim_{t\to\infty}\frac{t^2+t}{2t^2+1} = \lim_{t\to\infty}\frac{2t+1}{4t}\left[\text{still} = \frac{\infty}{\infty}\right] = \lim_{t\to\infty}\frac{2}{4} = \frac{1}{2}.$$

(Note that the method discussed in the problems for Article 3.4 could also be used.) For our second example

$$\lim_{x\to 0}\frac{\sin x}{x} = \lim_{x\to 0}\frac{\cos x}{1} = \frac{1}{1} = 1.$$

Use l'Hôpital's rule to evaluate the following limits.

91. $\lim_{t\to\infty} \dfrac{t^2 + 2t}{3t^2}$

92. $\lim_{x\to 1} \dfrac{x^3 - 3x + 2}{x^3 - x^2 - x + 1}$

93. $\lim_{x\to 0} \dfrac{\sin 7x}{x}$

94. $\lim_{t\to 0} \dfrac{1 - \cos t - \frac{1}{2}t^2}{t^4}$

95. $\lim_{x\to 0} \dfrac{e^x - 1}{x^2}$

96. $\lim_{x\to+\infty} \dfrac{\ln x}{x}$

97. $\lim_{x\to\infty} \dfrac{x^3}{e^x}$

98. $\lim_{x\to 0} \dfrac{\sin^2 x}{1 - \cos x}$

99. $\lim_{y\to 0} \dfrac{\sin^{-1} y - y}{y^3}$

100. $\lim_{t\to 0} \dfrac{5^t - e^t}{t}$

---

* For a proof see "L'Hôpital's Rule," by A. E. Taylor, *American Mathematical Monthly*, 59, pp. 20–24 (1952).

METHODS OF INTEGRATION

CHAPTER 9

9.1 BASIC FORMULAS

Since indefinite integration is defined as the inverse of differentiation, the problem of evaluating an integral

$$\int f(x)\ dx \tag{1}$$

is equivalent to finding a function F such that

$$dF(x) = f(x)\ dx. \tag{2}$$

At first sight, this may seem like a hopeless task when we think of adopting a "trial-and-error" approach and realize that it is simply impossible to try *all functions* as F in Eq. (2) hoping that we find one that does the job.* In fact, it is even possible to write down fairly simple integrals, such as

$$\int e^{-x^2}\ dx, \tag{3}$$

which cannot be expressed in terms of finite combinations of the so-called "elementary functions" which we have studied thus far. We shall leave a discussion of such integrals as (3) to a later time, and say simply that the words "finite combinations" must give way and an integral like (3) may then be expressed in terms of an infinite series.

To cut down on the amount of trial-and-error involved in integration, it is useful to build up a table of standard types of integral formulas by inverting formulas for differentials as we have done in the previous chapters. Then we try to match any integral that confronts us against one of the standard types. This usually involves a certain amount of algebraic manipulation.

A table of integrals, more extensive than the list of basic formulas given here, probably is, or will be,

---

* If f is continuous, then an integral function F satisfying Eq. (2) always exists. For example, for $F(x)$ we could take the area A_a^x discussed in Article 6.8. Theoretically, this, together with the fact that such an area can be calculated as a limit of sums of areas of rectangles, gives us a rule for computing $F(x)$. However, we are interested in avoiding these arithmetical calculations whenever possible. We prefer to find simple closed-form expressions for the integral whenever possible.

a part of your library. To use such a table intelligently, it is necessary to become familiar with certain basic techniques that one can apply to reduce a given integral to a form that matches an entry in the tables. The examples and problems in this book should serve to develop our skill with these techniques. So that we may concentrate on the techniques without becoming entangled in a mass of algebra, these problems and examples have been kept fairly simple. This in turn means that *these particular* problems can frequently be solved immediately by consulting an integral table. But you should realize that if you adopt such a course, you will defeat the intended purpose of developing your own power. And it is this power which is important, rather than the specific answer to any given problem.

Perhaps a good way to develop the skill we are aiming for is for each of you to build your own table of integrals. You may, for example, make a notebook in which the various sections are headed by the standard forms such as $\int u^n\, du$, $\int du/u$, $\int e^u\, du$, and so on, and then under each heading you may include several examples to illustrate the range of application of the particular formula.

Making such a notebook probably has educational value. But once it is made, it should rarely be necessary to refer to it!

Your success in integration hinges on your ability to spot the particular part of the integrand that you ought to call u. If you pick u skillfully, then you will have du so that you can apply a formula that you already know. This means that the *first requirement* for skill in integration is a thorough mastery of the formulas for differentiation. If you will look on the following page, you will see that we have listed certain formulas for differentials that have been derived in previous chapters, together with their integral counterparts.

At present, let us just consider this list a handy reference and *not* a challenge to our memories! A bit of examination will probably convince us that we are already rather familiar with the first twelve formulas for *differentials* and, so far as *integration* is concerned, part of our training in technique will

show how we can get the *integrals* in the last six cases without memorizing the formulas for the differentials of the inverse trigonometric functions.

Just what types of functions can we integrate directly by use of this short table of integrals?

Powers $\qquad \int u^n\, du,\quad \int \dfrac{du}{u}$

Exponentials $\qquad \int e^u\, du,\quad \int a^u\, du$

Trigonometric functions

$$\int \sin u\, du,\quad \int \cos u\, du.$$

Algebraic functions

$$\int \frac{du}{\sqrt{1 - u^2}},\quad \int \frac{du}{1 + u^2},\quad \int \frac{du}{u\sqrt{u^2 - 1}}$$

Of course, there are additional combinations of trigonometric functions, such as $\int \sec^2 u\, du$, which are integrable accidentally, so to speak.

What common types of functions are *not* included in the table?

Logarithms $\qquad \int \ln u\, du,\quad \int \log_a u\, du$

Trigonometric functions

$$\int \tan u\, du,\quad \int \cot u\, du,\quad \int \sec u\, du,\quad \int \csc u\, du$$

Algebraic functions

$$\int \frac{du}{a^2 + u^2},\quad \text{etc., with } a^2 \neq 1$$

$$\int \sqrt{a^2 \pm u^2}\, du,\quad \int \sqrt{u^2 - a^2}\, du,\quad \text{etc.}$$

Inverse functions

$$\int \sin^{-1} u\, du,\quad \int \tan^{-1} u\, du,\quad \text{etc.}$$

We shall eventually see how to handle all of these and some others, but there are no methods which will solve *all* integration problems in terms of elementary functions.

Differentials	*Integrals*
1. $du = \dfrac{du}{dx} \, dx$	1. $\displaystyle\int du = u + C$
2. $d(au) = a \, du$	2. $\displaystyle\int a \, du = a \int du$
3. $d(u + v) = du + dv$	3. $\displaystyle\int (du + dv) = \int du + \int dv$
4. $d(u^n) = nu^{n-1} \, du$	4. $\displaystyle\int u^n \, du = \dfrac{u^{n+1}}{n+1} + C, \quad n \neq -1$
5. $d\,(\ln u) = \dfrac{du}{u}$	5. $\displaystyle\int \dfrac{du}{u} = \ln |u| + C$
6. (a) $d(e^u) = e^u \, du$	6. (a) $\displaystyle\int e^u \, du = e^u + C$
(b) $d(a^u) = a^u \ln a \, du$	✓(b) $\displaystyle\int a^u \, du = \dfrac{a^u}{\ln a} + C$
7. $d\,(\sin u) = \cos u \, du$	7. $\displaystyle\int \cos u \, du = \sin u + C$
8. $d\,(\cos u) = -\sin u \, du$	8. $\displaystyle\int \sin u \, du = -\cos u + C$
9. $d\,(\tan u) = \sec^2 u \, du$	✓9. $\displaystyle\int \sec^2 u \, du = \tan u + C$
10. $d\,(\cot u) = -\csc^2 u \, du$	✓10. $\displaystyle\int \csc^2 u \, du = -\cot u + C$
11. $d\,(\sec u) = \sec u \tan u \, du$	✓11. $\displaystyle\int \sec u \tan u \, du = \sec u + C$
12. $d\,(\csc u) = -\csc u \cot u \, du$	✓12. $\displaystyle\int \csc u \cot u \, du = -\csc u + C$
13. $d\,(\sin^{-1} u) = \dfrac{du}{\sqrt{1 - u^2}}$ 14. $d\,(\cos^{-1} u) = \dfrac{-du}{\sqrt{1 - u^2}}$	✓ 13. and 14. $\displaystyle\int \dfrac{du}{\sqrt{1 - u^2}} = \begin{cases} \sin^{-1} u + C \\ -\cos^{-1} u + C' \end{cases}$
15. $d\,(\tan^{-1} u) = \dfrac{du}{1 + u^2}$ 16. $d\,(\cot^{-1} u) = \dfrac{-du}{1 + u^2}$	✓ 15. and 16. $\displaystyle\int \dfrac{du}{1 + u^2} = \begin{cases} \tan^{-1} u + C \\ -\cot^{-1} u + C' \end{cases}$
17. $d\,(\sec^{-1} u) = \dfrac{du}{|u|\sqrt{u^2 - 1}}$ 18. $d\,(\csc^{-1} u) = \dfrac{-du}{|u|\sqrt{u^2 - 1}}$	✓ 17. and 18. $\displaystyle\int \dfrac{du}{u\sqrt{u^2 - 1}} = \begin{cases} \sec^{-1} |u| + C \\ -\csc^{-1} |u| + C \end{cases}$

EXERCISES

Evaluate each of the following integrals by reducing the integrand to one of the standard forms 1 through 18. In each case, indicate what you have called u and refer by number to the standard formula used.

1. $\int \sqrt{2x+3}\, dx$

2. $\int \dfrac{dx}{3x+5}$

3. $\int \dfrac{dx}{(2x-7)^2}$

4. $\int \dfrac{(x+1)\, dx}{x^2+2x+3}$

5. $\int \dfrac{\sin x\, dx}{2+\cos x}$

6. $\int \tan^3 2x \sec^2 2x\, dx$

7. $\int \dfrac{x\, dx}{\sqrt{1-4x^2}}$

8. $\int x^{1/3}\sqrt{x^{4/3}-1}\, dx$

9. $\int \dfrac{x\, dx}{(3x^2+4)^3}$

10. $\int x^2\sqrt{x^3+5}\, dx$

11. $\int \dfrac{x^2\, dx}{\sqrt{x^3+5}}$

12. $\int \dfrac{x\, dx}{4x^2+1}$

13. $\int e^{2x}\, dx$

14. $\int \sin x\, e^{\cos x}\, dx$

15. $\int \dfrac{dx}{e^{3x}}$

16. $\int \dfrac{e^{\sqrt{x+1}}}{\sqrt{x+1}}\, dx$

17. $\int \cos^2 x \sin x\, dx$

18. $\int \dfrac{\cos x\, dx}{\sin^3 x}$

19. $\int \cot^3 x \csc^2 x\, dx$

20. $\int \tan 3x \sec^2 3x\, dx$

21. $\int \dfrac{e^{2x}+e^{-2x}}{e^{2x}-e^{-2x}}\, dx$

22. $\int \sin 2x \cos^2 2x\, dx$

23. $\int (1+\cos\theta)^3 \sin\theta\, d\theta$

24. $\int te^{-t^2}\, dt$

25. $\int \dfrac{\cos x\, dx}{\sin x}$

26. $\int \dfrac{\cos x\, dx}{1+\sin x}$

27. $\int \sec^3 x \tan x\, dx$

28. $\int \dfrac{\sin\theta\, d\theta}{\sqrt{1+\cos\theta}}$

29. $\int \sec^2 3x\, e^{\tan 3x}\, dx$

30. $\int \cos 2t\sqrt{4-\sin 2t}\, dt$

31. $\int \dfrac{1+\cos 2x}{\sin^2 2x}\, dx$

32. $\int \dfrac{\sin^2 2x}{1+\cos 2x}\, dx$

33. $\int \dfrac{\csc^2 2t}{\sqrt{1+\cot 2t}}\, dt$

34. $\int e^{3x}\, dx$

35. $\int \dfrac{e^{\tan^{-1}2t}}{1+4t^2}\, dt$

36. $\int xe^{-x^2}\, dx$

37. $\int 3^x\, dx$

38. $\int 10^{2x}\, dx$

39. Each of the following integrals may be easily evaluated for a particular numerical value of n. Choose this value and integrate. For example,

$$\int x^n \cos(x^2)\, dx$$

is easily evaluated for $n=1$:

$$\int x \cos(x^2)\, dx = \tfrac{1}{2}\sin(x^2)+C.$$

(a) $\int x^n \ln x\, dx$ (b) $\int x^n e^{x^3}\, dx$ (c) $\int x^n \sin\sqrt{x}\, dx$

40. The integral $\int_a^\infty e^{-x^2}\, dx$ arises in statistics and elsewhere. It is defined to mean the same thing as

$$\lim_{b\to+\infty}\int_a^b e^{-x^2}\, dx.$$

Show that if $x > a \geq 1$, then $e^{-x^2} < e^{-ax}$. Hence, by comparing the integral from a to ∞ of e^{-x^2} with the integral of e^{-ax} and evaluating the latter integral, show that

$$\int_a^\infty e^{-x^2}\, dx < \frac{1}{a}e^{-a^2} \quad \text{if } a\geq 1.$$

9.2 POWERS OF TRIGONOMETRIC FUNCTIONS

The formula

$$\int u^n\, du = \begin{cases} \dfrac{u^{n+1}}{n+1}+C, & n\neq -1, \\[2mm] \ln|u|+C, & n=-1 \end{cases}$$

may be used to evaluate certain integrals involving powers of the trigonometric functions, as illustrated by the examples that follow. The same methods work for powers of other functions. The reader should pay attention to the *methods* rather than trying to remember specific results.

Problem 1. $\displaystyle\int \sin^n ax \cos ax \, dx$.

Solution. If we let $u = \sin ax$, then

$$du = \cos ax \, d(ax) = a \cos ax \, dx,$$

so that we need only multiply the integral by unity in the form of a times $1/a$. Since a and $1/a$ are constants, we may write a inside the integral sign and $1/a$ in front of the integral sign, so that we have

$$\int \sin^n ax \cos ax \, dx = \frac{1}{a} \int (\sin ax)^n (a \cos ax \, dx)$$

$$= \frac{1}{a} \int u^n \, du$$

$$= \begin{cases} \dfrac{1}{a}\dfrac{u^{n+1}}{n+1} + C, & n \neq -1, \\ \dfrac{1}{a}\ln |u| + C, & n = -1; \end{cases}$$

that is,

$$\int \sin^n ax \cos ax \, dx = \frac{\sin^{n+1} ax}{(n+1)a} + C, \quad n \neq -1, \quad (1a)$$

and if $n = -1$, we get

$$\int \cot ax \, dx = \frac{1}{a} \ln |\sin ax| + C. \quad (1b)$$

Note that the success of the method depended upon having $\cos ax$ to go with the dx as part of du.

Problem 2. $\displaystyle\int \sin^3 x \, dx$.

Solution. The method of the previous example does not work because there is no $\cos x$ to go with dx to give du if we try letting $u = \sin x$. But if we write

$$\sin^3 x = \sin^2 x \cdot \sin x = (1 - \cos^2 x) \cdot \sin x$$

and let

$$u = \cos x, \qquad du = -\sin x \, dx,$$

we have

$$\int \sin^3 x \, dx = \int (1 - \cos^2 x) \cdot \sin x \, dx$$

$$= \int (1 - u^2) \cdot (-du) = \int (u^2 - 1) \, du$$

$$= \tfrac{1}{3} u^3 - u + C = \tfrac{1}{3} \cos^3 x - \cos x + C.$$

This *method* may be applied whenever an *odd* power of $\sin x$ or $\cos x$ is to be integrated. For example, any positive odd power of $\cos x$ has the form

$$\cos^{2n+1} x = \cos^{2n} x \cdot \cos x = (\cos^2 x)^n \cdot \cos x$$
$$= (1 - \sin^2 x)^n \cdot \cos x,$$

with n an integer ≥ 0. Then, if we let $u = \sin x$, $du = \cos x \, dx$, we have

$$\int \cos^{2n+1} x \, dx = \int (1 - \sin^2 x)^n \cdot \cos x \, dx$$

$$= \int (1 - u^2)^n \cdot du.$$

The expression $(1 - u^2)^n$ may now be expanded by the binomial theorem and the result evaluated as a sum of individual integrals of the type $\int u^m \, du$.

Problem 3. $\displaystyle\int \sec x \tan x \, dx$.

Solution. Of course this is a standard form already, so there is no real problem in finding an answer. But in trigonometry we often express all trigonometric functions in terms of sines and cosines, and we now investigate what this does to the integral in question.

$$\int \sec x \tan x \, dx = \int \frac{1}{\cos x}\frac{\sin x}{\cos x} \, dx = \int \frac{\sin x \, dx}{\cos^2 x}.$$

Taking a clue from the previous examples (keeping in mind du as well as u), we let

$$u = \cos x, \qquad du = -\sin x \, dx,$$

and then

$$\int \frac{\sin x \, dx}{\cos^2 x} = \int \frac{-du}{u^2}$$

$$= -\int u^{-2} \, du = \frac{-u^{-1}}{-1} + C = \frac{1}{u} + C$$

$$= \frac{1}{\cos x} + C = \sec x + C.$$

Problem 4. $\displaystyle\int \tan^4 x \, dx$.

Solution. This does not lend itself readily to the use of sines and cosines, since both of them occur to even powers. We say: $u = \tan x$ would require $du = \sec^2 x \, dx$. Is there some way to include $\sec^2 x$? Yes; there is an identity involving tangents and secants. How does it go? Since

$$\sin^2 x + \cos^2 x = 1,$$

if we divide through by $\cos^2 x$ we get

$$\tan^2 x + 1 = \sec^2 x \quad \text{or} \quad \tan^2 x = \sec^2 x - 1.$$

Then

$$\int \tan^4 x \, dx = \int \tan^2 x \cdot \tan^2 x \, dx$$
$$= \int \tan^2 x \cdot (\sec^2 x - 1) \, dx$$
$$= \int \tan^2 x \sec^2 x \, dx - \int \tan^2 x \, dx.$$

The first of these is all set. But how about the $\tan^2 x$? Oh, yes,

$$\tan^2 x = \sec^2 x - 1.$$

So

$$\int \tan^4 x \, dx = \int \tan^2 x \sec^2 x \, dx - \int \tan^2 x \, dx$$
$$= \int \tan^2 x \sec^2 x \, dx - \int (\sec^2 x - 1) \, dx$$
$$= \int \tan^2 x \sec^2 x \, dx - \int \sec^2 x \, dx + \int dx.$$

In the first two of these, we let

$$u = \tan x, \quad du = \sec^2 x \, dx$$

and we have

$$\int u^2 \, du - \int du = \tfrac{1}{3} u^3 - u + C'.$$

The other is a standard form, so

$$\int \tan^4 x \, dx = \tfrac{1}{3} \tan^3 x - \tan x + x + C.$$

The *method* works for any *even* power of $\tan x$, but what is still better is a *reduction formula*, derived as follows:

$$\int \tan^n x \, dx = \int \tan^{n-2} x \, (\sec^2 x - 1) \, dx$$
$$= \int \tan^{n-2} x \sec^2 x \, dx - \int \tan^{n-2} x \, dx$$
$$= \frac{\tan^{n-1} x}{n - 1} - \int \tan^{n-2} x \, dx.$$

This reduces the problem of integrating $\tan^n x \, dx$ to the problem of integrating $\tan^{n-2} x \, dx$. Since this decreases the exponent on $\tan x$ by 2, a repetition with the same formula will reduce the exponent by 2 again, and so on. Applying this to the problem above, we have

$$n = 4: \quad \int \tan^4 x \, dx = \frac{\tan^3 x}{3} - \int \tan^2 x \, dx,$$
$$n = 2: \quad \int \tan^2 x \, dx = \frac{\tan x}{1} - \int \tan^0 x \, dx,$$
$$n = 0: \quad \int \tan^0 x \, dx = \int 1 \, dx = x + C.$$

Therefore

$$\int \tan^4 x \, dx = \tfrac{1}{3} \tan^3 x - (\tan x - x + C)$$
$$= \tfrac{1}{3} \tan^3 x - \tan x + x + C'.$$

This reduction formula works whether the original exponent n is even or odd, but if the exponent is odd, say $2m + 1$, after m steps it will be reduced by $2m$, leaving

$$\int \tan x \, dx = \int \frac{\sin x}{\cos x} \, dx = -\int \frac{d(\cos x)}{\cos x}$$
$$= -\ln |\cos x| + C \quad (2)$$

as the final integral to be evaluated.

These examples illustrate how it is possible, by using the trigonometric identities

$$\sin^2 x + \cos^2 x = 1, \quad \tan^2 x + 1 = \sec^2 x,$$

and others readily derived from these, to evaluate the integrals of

(a) *odd* powers of $\sin x$ or $\cos x$,

(b) *any* integral powers of $\tan x$ (or $\cot x$), and

(c) *even* powers of $\sec x$ (or $\csc x$).

The even powers of $\sec x$, say $\sec^{2n} x$, can all be reduced to powers of $\tan x$ by employing the substitution $\sec^2 x = 1 + \tan^2 x$, and then using the reduction formula for integrating powers of $\tan x$ after expanding $\sec^{2n} x = (1 + \tan^2 x)^n$ by the binomial theorem. But it is even simpler to use the method below:

$$\int \sec^{2n} x \, dx = \int \sec^{2n-2} x \sec^2 x \, dx$$

$$= \int (\sec^2 x)^{n-1} \sec^2 x \, dx$$

$$= \int (1 + \tan^2 x)^{n-1} \sec^2 x \, dx$$

$$= \int (1 + u^2)^{n-1} \, du \qquad (u = \tan x).$$

When $(1 + u^2)^{n-1}$ is expanded by the binomial theorem, the resulting polynomial in u may be integrated term by term.

Example

$$\int \sec^6 x \, dx = \int \sec^4 x \cdot \sec^2 x \, dx$$

$$= \int (1 + \tan^2 x)^2 \cdot \sec^2 x \, dx$$

$$= \int (1 + 2u^2 + u^4) \, du \quad (u = \tan x)$$

$$= u + \frac{2u^3}{3} + \frac{u^5}{5} + C$$

$$= \tan x + 2 \frac{\tan^3 x}{3} + \frac{\tan^5 x}{5} + C.$$

Problem 5. $\qquad \int \sec x \, dx.$

Solution. This is hard to evaluate unless one has seen the following trick!

$$\sec x = \frac{\sec x \, (\tan x + \sec x)}{\sec x + \tan x}$$

$$= \frac{\sec x \tan x + \sec^2 x}{\sec x + \tan x}.$$

In this form the numerator is the derivative of the denominator. Therefore

$$\int \sec x \, dx = \int \frac{\sec x \tan x + \sec^2 x}{\sec x + \tan x} \, dx$$

$$= \int \frac{du}{u} \quad (u = \sec x + \tan x)$$

$$= \ln |u| + C.$$

That is,

$$\int \sec x \, dx = \ln |\sec x + \tan x| + C. \qquad (3)$$

EXERCISES

3/15 #1-19 odd   3/16 #21-35 odd

1. $\displaystyle\int \sin t \sqrt{1 + \cos t} \, dt$

2. $\displaystyle\int \frac{\sin \theta \, d\theta}{2 - \cos \theta}$

3. $\displaystyle\int \frac{\sec^2 2x \, dx}{1 + \tan 2x}$

4. $\displaystyle\int \tan 3x \, dx$

5. $\displaystyle\int \cos^3 x \, dx$

6. $\displaystyle\int \tan^2 4\theta \, d\theta$

7. (a) $\displaystyle\int \sin^3 x \cos^2 x \, dx$ (b) $\displaystyle\int \frac{\sin^3 x \, dx}{\cos^2 x}$

8. $\displaystyle\int \sec^n x \tan x \, dx$

9. $\displaystyle\int \tan^n x \sec^2 x \, dx$

10. $\displaystyle\int \sin^n x \cos x \, dx$

11. $\displaystyle\int \cos^n x \sin x \, dx$

12. $\displaystyle\int \sin^2 3x \cos 3x \, dx$

13. $\displaystyle\int \cos^3 2x \sin 2x \, dx$

14. $\displaystyle\int \sec^4 3x \tan 3x \, dx$

15. $\displaystyle\int \sec^4 3x \, dx$

16. $\displaystyle\int \cos^3 2x \, dx$

17. $\displaystyle\int \tan^3 2x \, dx$

18. $\displaystyle\int \tan^3 x \sec x \, dx$

19. $\displaystyle\int \sin^3 x \, dx$

20. $\displaystyle\int \frac{\cos x \, dx}{(1 + \sin x)^2}$

21. $\displaystyle\int \frac{\sec^2 x \, dx}{2 + \tan x}$

22. $\displaystyle\int \frac{\cos^3 t \, dt}{\sin^2 t}$

23. $\displaystyle\int \frac{e^x \, dx}{1 + e^x}$

24. $\displaystyle\int (\ln ax)^n \frac{dx}{x}$

25. $\displaystyle\int \frac{dx}{x \ln 3x}$

26. $\displaystyle\int \cot^3 x \, dx$

27. $\displaystyle\int \csc^3 2t \cot 2t \, dt$

28. $\displaystyle\int \csc^4 x \, dx$

29. $\displaystyle\int \frac{dx}{\cos^4 x}$

30. $\displaystyle\int \frac{\sin x \, dx}{(1 + \cos x)^2}$

31. $\displaystyle\int \csc 3x \cot^3 3x \, dx$

32. $\displaystyle\int \frac{\cos^3 u \, du}{\sin^5 u}$

33. $\displaystyle\int \frac{e^{\tan x}}{\cos^2 x} \, dx$

34. $\displaystyle\int \frac{1 + \cos 2x}{1 - \cos 2x} \, dx$

35. $\displaystyle\int \frac{1 + \sin 2x}{1 - \sin 2x} \, dx$

36. Derive a reduction formula for $\int \cot^n ax \, dx$ and use the result to evaluate $\int \cot^4 3x \, dx$.

9.3 EVEN POWERS OF SINES AND COSINES

In Article 9.2, we saw how we could evaluate integrals of odd powers of sines and cosines. Indeed, any integral of the form

$$\int \sin^m x \cos^n x \, dx \qquad (1)$$

in which at least one of the exponents m and n is a positive odd integer may be evaluated by these methods.

Problem. $\int \cos^{2/3} x \sin^5 x \, dx$.

Solution. Here we have $\sin x$ to an *odd* power. So we put one factor of $\sin x$ with dx and the remaining sine factors, namely $\sin^4 x$, can be expressed in terms of $\cos x$ without introducing any square roots, as follows:

$$\sin^4 x = (\sin^2 x)^2 = (1 - \cos^2 x)^2.$$

The $\sin x$ goes well with dx when we take

$$u = \cos x, \qquad du = -\sin x \, dx$$

and evaluate the integral as follows:

$$\int \cos^{2/3} x \sin^5 x \, dx = \int \cos^{2/3} x (1 - \cos^2 x)^2 \sin x \, dx$$
$$= \int u^{2/3}(1 - u^2)^2(-du)$$
$$= -\int (u^{2/3} - 2u^{8/3} + u^{14/3}) \, du$$
$$= -[\tfrac{3}{5}u^{5/3} - \tfrac{6}{11}u^{11/3} + \tfrac{3}{17}u^{17/3}] + C,$$

so that we have

$$-\cos^{5/3} x[\tfrac{3}{5} - \tfrac{6}{11}\cos^2 x + \tfrac{3}{17}\cos^4 x] + C.$$

If both the exponents m and n in the integral (1) are even integers, the method illustrated above won't work. So we use one or both of the following trigonometric identities:

$$\sin^2 A = \tfrac{1}{2}(1 - \cos 2A), \qquad (2a)$$
$$\cos^2 A = \tfrac{1}{2}(1 + \cos 2A). \qquad (2b)$$

These identities may be derived very quickly by adding or subtracting the equations

$$\cos^2 A + \sin^2 A = 1,$$
$$\cos^2 A - \sin^2 A = \cos 2A,$$

and dividing by two.

Example 1

$$\int \cos^4 x \, dx = \int (\cos^2 x)^2 \, dx = \int \tfrac{1}{4}(1 + \cos 2x)^2 \, dx \quad (a)$$
$$= \tfrac{1}{4}\int (1 + 2\cos 2x + \cos^2 2x) \, dx \qquad (b)$$
$$= \tfrac{1}{4}\int [1 + 2\cos 2x + \tfrac{1}{2}(1 + \cos 4x)] \, dx$$
$$= \tfrac{3}{8}x + \tfrac{1}{4}\sin 2x + \tfrac{1}{32}\sin 4x + C.$$

In (a), we used Eq. (2b) with $A = x$, and in (b), we used Eq. (2b) with $A = 2x$. The final integrations involve

$$\int \cos ax \, dx = \frac{1}{a}\int \cos ax \, d(ax) = \frac{1}{a}\sin ax + C'.$$

Remark. An integral such as $\int \sin^2 x \cos^4 x \, dx$, which involves even powers of both $\sin x$ and $\cos x$, can be changed to a sum of integrals each of which involves only powers of one of them. Then these may be handled by the method illustrated above.

Example 2

$$\int \sin^2 x \cos^4 x \, dx = \int (1 - \cos^2 x) \cos^4 x \, dx$$
$$= \int \cos^4 x \, dx - \int \cos^6 x \, dx.$$

We evaluated $\int \cos^4 x \, dx$ above, and

$$\int \cos^6 x \, dx = \int (\cos^2 x)^3 \, dx = \tfrac{1}{8}\int (1 + \cos 2x)^3 \, dx$$
$$= \tfrac{1}{8}\int (1 + 3\cos 2x + 3\cos^2 2x + \cos^3 2x) \, dx.$$

We now know how to handle each term of this integral. The reader may supply the details and show that the result is

$$\int \cos^6 x \, dx = \tfrac{5}{16}x + \tfrac{1}{4}\sin 2x + \tfrac{3}{64}\sin 4x - \tfrac{1}{48}\sin^3 2x + C.$$

EXERCISES
3/17 #1–17 odd

Evaluate the following integrals.

1. $\int \sin^2 x \cos^3 x \, dx$

2. $\int \dfrac{\sin^3 x \, dx}{\cos^2 x}$

3. $\int \sin^2 2t \, dt$

4. $\int \cos^2 3\theta \, d\theta$

5. $\displaystyle\int \sin^4 ax \, dx$

6. $\displaystyle\int \sin^2 y \cos^2 y \, dy$

7. $\displaystyle\int \frac{dx}{\cos^2 x}$

8. $\displaystyle\int \frac{dx}{\sin^4 x}$

9. $\displaystyle\int \frac{\cos 2t \, dt}{\sin^4 2t}$

10. $\displaystyle\int \sin^6 x \, dx$

11. $\displaystyle\int \cos^2 3x \sin^3 3x \, dx$

12. $\displaystyle\int \frac{\cos^3 2t}{\sin^2 2t} \, dt$

13. $\displaystyle\int \frac{\sin^2 x}{\cos^4 x} \, dx$

14. $\displaystyle\int \sec^2 \theta \tan^{2/3} \theta \, d\theta$

15. $\displaystyle\int (\cos^2 5x - \sin^2 5x) \, dx$

16. $\displaystyle\int (\cos^2 t - \sin^2 t)^3 \, dt$

17. $\displaystyle\int_0^{\pi/2} \sqrt{1 + \cos t} \, dt$

18. $\displaystyle\int_0^{\pi/2} \sqrt{1 - \cos x} \, dx$

9.4 INTEGRALS WITH TERMS $\sqrt{a^2 - u^2}$, $\sqrt{a^2 + u^2}$, $\sqrt{u^2 - a^2}$, $a^2 + u^2$, $a^2 - u^2$

Sometimes an integral with one of these terms may be treated directly by an integral formula from the list in Article 9.1 if we change the integral around so that $a = 1$. For example, we have

$$\int \frac{du}{1 + u^2} = \tan^{-1} u + C, \qquad (1)$$

and to evaluate

$$\int \frac{du}{a^2 + u^2} \qquad (2)$$

we factor a^2 out of the denominator and proceed as follows:

$$\int \frac{du}{a^2 + u^2} = \int \frac{du}{a^2 \left[1 + \left(\dfrac{u}{a}\right)^2\right]}$$

$$= \frac{1}{a^2} \int \frac{ad\left(\dfrac{u}{a}\right)}{1 + \left(\dfrac{u}{a}\right)^2} = \frac{1}{a} \int \frac{dz}{1 + z^2}$$

$$= \frac{1}{a} \tan^{-1} z + C$$

$$= \frac{1}{a} \tan^{-1} \frac{u}{a} + C \qquad \left(z = \frac{u}{a}\right).$$

That is,

$$\int \frac{du}{a^2 + u^2} = \frac{1}{a} \tan^{-1} \frac{u}{a} + C. \qquad (3)$$

The essential feature here was the introduction of a new variable by means of the substitution

$$z = \frac{u}{a}, \quad \text{or} \quad u = az.$$

Such a substitution allows the a-terms to be brought outside the integral sign, and the resulting integral may then match one of the inverse trigonometric formulas.

An alternative approach will show, however, that one may bypass the job of learning these formulas. In addition, this method, which we shall soon illustrate, permits the evaluation of many additional integrals.

The method leans primarily upon the following identities:

$$1 - \sin^2 \theta = \cos^2 \theta,$$
$$1 + \tan^2 \theta = \sec^2 \theta, \qquad (4)$$
$$\sec^2 \theta - 1 = \tan^2 \theta.$$

These identities may be multiplied by a^2, with the result that the substitutions listed below have the following effects:

if $\quad u = a \sin \theta,$

then $\qquad a^2 \cos^2 \theta \quad$ replaces $\quad a^2 - u^2;$ (5a)

if $\quad u = a \tan \theta,$

then $\qquad a^2 \sec^2 \theta \quad$ replaces $\quad a^2 + u^2;$ (5b)

if $\quad u = a \sec \theta,$

then $\qquad a^2 \tan^2 \theta \quad$ replaces $\quad u^2 - a^2.$ (5c)

Thus we see that corresponding to each of the *binomial* expressions $a^2 - u^2$, $a^2 + u^2$, and $u^2 - a^2$, we have a substitution that replaces the binomial by a single squared term. The particular substitution to use depends on the form of the integrand. In the problems that follow, a is a positive constant.

Problem 1. $\displaystyle\int \frac{du}{\sqrt{a^2 - u^2}}, \quad a > 0.$

Solution. We try the substitution (5a):

$$u = a \sin \theta,$$
$$du = a \cos \theta \, d\theta,$$
$$\theta = \sin^{-1}(u/a).$$

Thus

$$a^2 - u^2 = a^2(1 - \sin^2 \theta) = a^2 \cos^2 \theta.$$

Then

$$\int \frac{du}{\sqrt{a^2 - u^2}} = \int \frac{a \cos \theta \, d\theta}{\sqrt{a^2 \cos^2 \theta}} = \int \frac{a \cos \theta \, d\theta}{\pm a \cos \theta},$$

the sign depending on the sign of $\cos \theta$; continuing,

$$\int \frac{du}{\sqrt{a^2 - u^2}} = \pm \int d\theta = \pm(\theta + C).$$

Using only the *principal value* of $\sin^{-1} u/a$ means that θ will lie between $-\pi/2$ and $\pi/2$; hence $\cos \theta \geq 0$ and the ambiguous sign is $+$. That is,

$$\int \frac{du}{\sqrt{a^2 - u^2}} = \sin^{-1}\frac{u}{a} + C. \qquad (6)$$

Problem 2. $\displaystyle\int \frac{du}{\sqrt{a^2 + u^2}}, \quad a > 0.$

Solution. This time we try

$$u = a \tan \theta,$$
$$du = a \sec^2 \theta \, d\theta,$$
$$\theta = \tan^{-1}(u/a).$$

Thus

$$a^2 + u^2 = a^2(1 + \tan^2 \theta) = a^2 \sec^2 \theta.$$

Then

$$\int \frac{du}{\sqrt{a^2 + u^2}} = \int \frac{a \sec^2 \theta \, d\theta}{\sqrt{a^2 \sec^2 \theta}} = \pm \int \sec \theta \, d\theta,$$

the sign depending on the sign of $\sec \theta$.

By Eq. (3), Article 9.2, we know that

$$\int \sec \theta \, d\theta = \ln |\sec \theta + \tan \theta| + C.$$

If we take $\theta = \tan^{-1}\dfrac{u}{a}, \quad -\dfrac{\pi}{2} < \theta < \dfrac{\pi}{2},$

then $\sec \theta$ is positive, and

$$\int \frac{du}{\sqrt{a^2 + u^2}} = \int \sec \theta \, d\theta$$
$$= \ln |\sec \theta + \tan \theta| + C$$
$$= \ln \left| \frac{\sqrt{a^2 + u^2}}{a} + \frac{u}{a} \right| + C \qquad (7)$$
$$= \ln |\sqrt{a^2 + u^2} + u| + C',$$

where

$$C' = C - \ln a.$$

Problem 3. $\displaystyle\int \frac{du}{\sqrt{u^2 - a^2}}, \quad |u| > a > 0.$

Solution. We try the substitution

$$u = a \sec \theta,$$
$$du = a \sec \theta \tan \theta \, d\theta,$$
$$\theta = \sec^{-1}(u/a).$$

Thus

$$u^2 - a^2 = a^2(\sec^2 \theta - 1) = a^2 \tan^2 \theta.$$

Then

$$\int \frac{du}{\sqrt{u^2 - a^2}} = \int \frac{a \sec \theta \tan \theta \, d\theta}{\sqrt{a^2 \tan^2 \theta}}$$
$$= \pm \int \sec \theta \, d\theta,$$

the sign depending on the sign of $\tan \theta$. If we take

$$\theta = \sec^{-1}\frac{u}{a}, \quad 0 \leq \theta \leq \pi,$$

then

$$\tan \theta \text{ is positive} \quad \text{if} \quad 0 < \theta < \pi/2,$$
$$\tan \theta \text{ is negative} \quad \text{if} \quad \pi/2 < \theta < \pi,$$

and, from Eq. (3), Article 9.2,

$$\pm \int \sec \theta \, d\theta = \pm \ln |\sec \theta + \tan \theta| + C.$$

When $\tan \theta$ is positive, we must use the plus sign; when $\tan \theta$ is negative, the minus sign. Moreover,

$$\sec \theta = \frac{u}{a}, \quad \tan \theta = \pm \frac{\sqrt{u^2 - a^2}}{a}.$$

So we have

$$\int \frac{du}{\sqrt{u^2 - a^2}} = \pm\ln\left|\frac{u}{a} \pm \frac{\sqrt{u^2 - a^2}}{a}\right| + C$$

$$= \begin{cases} \ln\left|\dfrac{u}{a} + \dfrac{\sqrt{u^2 - a^2}}{a}\right| + C \\ \text{or} \\ -\ln\left|\dfrac{u}{a} - \dfrac{\sqrt{u^2 - a^2}}{a}\right| + C. \end{cases}$$

But the two forms are actually equal, because

$$-\ln\left|\frac{u}{a} - \frac{\sqrt{u^2 - a^2}}{a}\right|$$

$$= \ln\left|\frac{a}{u - \sqrt{u^2 - a^2}}\right|$$

$$= \ln\left|\frac{a(u + \sqrt{u^2 - a^2})}{(u - \sqrt{u^2 - a^2})(u + \sqrt{u^2 - a^2})}\right|$$

$$= \ln\left|\frac{a(u + \sqrt{u^2 - a^2})}{a^2}\right|$$

$$= \ln\left|\frac{u + \sqrt{u^2 - a^2}}{a}\right|.$$

Therefore

$$\int \frac{du}{\sqrt{u^2 - a^2}} = \ln|u + \sqrt{u^2 - a^2}| + C', \qquad (8)$$

where we have replaced $C - \ln a$ by C' in this final form.

Problem 4. $\displaystyle\int \frac{du}{a^2 + u^2}, \quad a > 0.$

Solution. $u = a \tan\theta, \qquad du = a\sec^2\theta\,d\theta,$

$$a^2 + u^2 = a^2(1 + \tan^2\theta) = a^2\sec^2\theta.$$

Then

$$\int \frac{du}{a^2 + u^2} = \int \frac{a\sec^2\theta\,d\theta}{a^2\sec^2\theta} = \frac{1}{a}\int d\theta = \frac{1}{a}\theta + C.$$

Since $u = a\tan\theta$, we have

$$\tan\theta = \frac{u}{a}, \qquad \theta = \tan^{-1}\frac{u}{a},$$

and

$$\int \frac{du}{a^2 + u^2} = \frac{1}{a}\tan^{-1}\frac{u}{a} + C. \qquad (9)$$

Problem 5. $\displaystyle\int \frac{x^2\,dx}{\sqrt{9 - x^2}}.$

Solution. If we substitute

$$x = 3\sin\theta, \quad -\frac{\pi}{2} < \theta = \sin^{-1}\left(\frac{x}{3}\right) < \frac{\pi}{2},$$

$$dx = 3\cos\theta\,d\theta,$$

$$9 - x^2 = 9(1 - \sin^2\theta) = 9\cos^2\theta,$$

then we find

$$\int \frac{x^2\,dx}{\sqrt{9 - x^2}} = \int \frac{9\sin^2\theta \cdot 3\cos\theta\,d\theta}{3\cos\theta} = 9\int \sin^2\theta\,d\theta.$$

This is considerably simpler than the integral we started with. To evaluate it, we make use of the identity

$$\sin^2\theta = \tfrac{1}{2}(1 - \cos 2\theta).$$

Then

$$\int \sin^2\theta\,d\theta = \tfrac{1}{2}\int (1 - \cos 2\theta)\,d\theta$$

$$= \tfrac{1}{2}[\theta - \tfrac{1}{2}\sin 2\theta] + C$$

$$= \tfrac{1}{2}[\theta - \sin\theta\cos\theta] + C.$$

Substituting this above, we get

$$\int \frac{x^2\,dx}{\sqrt{9 - x^2}} = \frac{9}{2}[\theta - \sin\theta\cos\theta] + C$$

$$= \frac{9}{2}\left[\sin^{-1}\frac{x}{3} - \frac{x\sqrt{9 - x^2}}{9}\right] + C.$$

The trigonometric substitutions (a), (b), and (c) of Eq. (5) can be easily remembered by thinking of the theorem of Pythagoras and taking a and u as two of the sides and θ as an angle in a right triangle. Thus $\sqrt{a^2 - u^2}$ suggests a as hypotenuse and u as a leg, $\sqrt{a^2 + u^2}$ suggests a and u as the legs, and $\sqrt{u^2 - a^2}$ suggests u as hypotenuse and a as a leg. These situations are shown in Fig. 9.1.

The trigonometric identities, Eqs. (4), are simply equivalent expressions of the theorem of Pythagoras applied to the right triangles in Fig. 9.2. The triangles in Figs. 9.2(b, c) are obtained from the basic triangle in Fig. 9.2(a) by dividing its sides all by $\cos\theta$ and by $\sin\theta$, respectively, to obtain similar triangles.

$u = a \sin \theta$
$\sqrt{a^2 - u^2} = a \cos \theta$

a|b

$u = a \tan \theta$
$\sqrt{u^2 + a^2} = a \sec \theta$

$u = a \sec \theta$
$\sqrt{u^2 - a^2} = a \tan \theta$

|c|

9.1

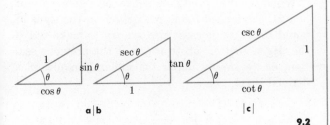

a|b

|c|

9.2

When we make a trigonometric substitution in a definite integral, it is often useful to introduce the corresponding new limits of integration. The following example illustrates the method.

Problem 6. Evaluate

$$\int_{-a}^{a} \sqrt{a^2 - x^2}\, dx$$

by using the substitution

$$x = a \cos \theta,$$

assuming $a > 0$.

Solution. The substitution $x = a \cos \theta$ maps the set of numbers $-a \le x \le a$ one-to-one onto the set of numbers $-1 \le \cos \theta \le 1$ or $\pi \ge \theta \ge 0$. Thus

$$\int_{-a}^{a} \sqrt{a^2 - x^2}\, dx = \int_{\pi}^{0} \sqrt{a^2 - a^2 \cos^2 \theta}\,(-a \sin \theta)\, d\theta$$

$$= a^2 \int_{0}^{\pi} \sqrt{1 - \cos^2 \theta}\, \sin \theta\, d\theta,$$

where the negative sign has been used in reversing the order of the limits and the constant a^2 has been placed outside the integral sign. Now

$$\sqrt{1 - \cos^2 \theta} = \sqrt{\sin^2 \theta} = |\sin \theta|$$

and, for $0 \le \theta \le \dot\pi$, $\sin \theta \ge 0$, so

$$|\sin \theta| = \sin \theta,$$

and we have

$$a^2 \int_{0}^{\pi} \sin^2 \theta\, d\theta = \frac{a^2}{2} \int_{0}^{\pi} (1 - \cos 2\theta)\, d\theta$$

$$= \frac{a^2}{2} [\theta - \tfrac{1}{2} \sin 2\theta]_0^{\pi} = \tfrac{1}{2}\pi a^2.$$

The definite integral that we have evaluated in Problem 6 represents the area of the region bounded above by the semicircle

$$y = \sqrt{a^2 - x^2}, \quad -a \le x \le a,$$

and below by the x-axis. The result, $\tfrac{1}{2}\pi a^2$, is just what we ought to get.

EXERCISES

3/21 # 1 - 19 odd

Evaluate the following integrals.

1. $\displaystyle\int_{0}^{0.6a} \frac{x\, dx}{\sqrt{a^2 - x^2}}$

2. $\displaystyle\int \frac{dx}{\sqrt{1 - 4x^2}}$

3. $\displaystyle\int_{0}^{a} \sqrt{a^2 - x^2}\, dx$

4. $\displaystyle\int \frac{dx}{\sqrt{4 - (x - 1)^2}}$

5. $\displaystyle\int \sec 2t\, dt$

6. $\displaystyle\int_{0}^{2} \frac{dx}{\sqrt{4 + x^2}}$

7. $\displaystyle\int_{0}^{1} \frac{dx}{\sqrt{4 - x^2}}$

8. $\displaystyle\int \frac{x\, dx}{\sqrt{4 + x^2}}$

9. $\displaystyle\int_{0}^{2} \frac{x\, dx}{4 + x^2}$

10. $\displaystyle\int_{0}^{2} \frac{dx}{4 + x^2}$

11. $\displaystyle\int_{0}^{1} \frac{dx}{4 - x^2}$

12. $\displaystyle\int \csc u\, du$

13. $\displaystyle\int \frac{dx}{x\sqrt{a^2 + x^2}}$

14. $\displaystyle\int \frac{x + 1}{\sqrt{4 - x^2}}\, dx$

15. $\displaystyle\int \frac{dx}{\sqrt{2 - 5x^2}}$

16. $\displaystyle\int \frac{\sin \theta\, d\theta}{\sqrt{2 - \cos^2 \theta}}$

17. $\displaystyle\int \frac{dx}{x\sqrt{x^2 - a^2}}$ **18.** $\displaystyle\int \frac{dx}{x\sqrt{a^2 - x^2}}$

19. $\displaystyle\int \frac{dx}{(a^2 - x^2)^{3/2}}$ **20.** $\displaystyle\int \frac{dx}{(a^2 + x^2)^2}$

9.5 INTEGRALS WITH $ax^2 + bx + c$

The general quadratic

$$f(x) = ax^2 + bx + c, \quad a \neq 0, \qquad (1)$$

can be reduced to the form $a(u^2 + B)$ by completing the square:

$$
\begin{aligned}
ax^2 + bx + c &= a\left(x^2 + \frac{b}{a}\,x\right) + c \\
&= a\left(x^2 + \frac{b}{a}\,x + \frac{b^2}{4a^2}\right) + c - \frac{b^2}{4a} \\
&= a\left(x + \frac{b}{2a}\right)^2 + \frac{4ac - b^2}{4a},
\end{aligned}
$$

and then substituting

$$u = x + \frac{b}{2a}, \qquad B = \frac{4ac - b^2}{4a}. \qquad (2)$$

When the integrand involves the square root of

$$f(x) = ax^2 + bx + c,$$

we restrict attention to the case where $f(x)$ is not negative. If a is negative and B is positive, the square root is imaginary. We disregard this case and consider

$$\sqrt{a(u^2 + B)}$$

(1) when a is positive, and

(2) when a and B are both negative.

In the first case, the relation

$$\sqrt{a(u^2 + B)} = \sqrt{a}\,\sqrt{u^2 + B}$$

allows us to reduce the problem to a consideration of $\sqrt{u^2 + B}$, which we handle by the methods of Article 9.4. In the second case, when a and B are

both negative, then $-a$ and $-B$ are positive and

$$
\begin{aligned}
\sqrt{a(u^2 + B)} &= \sqrt{-a(-B - u^2)} \\
&= \sqrt{-a}\,\sqrt{-B - u^2} \\
&\qquad (-a > 0, \quad -B > 0),
\end{aligned}
$$

and taking $-B = A^2$, say, we consider $\sqrt{A^2 - u^2}$ as in Article 9.4.

When the integrand does not involve an even root of $f(x)$, there need be no restriction on the signs of a and B. In these cases also, we try to make use of the trigonometric substitutions of the previous section, or we simply apply the integration formulas derived there.

Problem 1. $\displaystyle\int \frac{dx}{\sqrt{2x - x^2}}.$

Solution. The algebraic transformations proceed as follows:

$$
\begin{aligned}
\sqrt{2x - x^2} &= \sqrt{-(x^2 - 2x)} \\
&= \sqrt{-(x^2 - 2x + 1) + 1} \\
&= \sqrt{1 - u^2} \quad (u = x - 1).
\end{aligned}
$$

Then, with $u = x - 1$,

$$du = dx$$

and

$$\int \frac{dx}{\sqrt{2x - x^2}} = \int \frac{du}{\sqrt{1 - u^2}} = \sin^{-1} u + C;$$

that is,

$$\int \frac{dx}{\sqrt{2x - x^2}} = \sin^{-1}(x - 1) + C.$$

Problem 2. $\displaystyle\int \frac{dx}{4x^2 + 4x + 2}.$

Solution. Again we start with the algebraic transformations:

$$
\begin{aligned}
4x^2 + 4x + 2 &= 4(x^2 + x) + 2 \\
&= 4(x^2 + x + \tfrac{1}{4}) + (2 - \tfrac{4}{4}) \\
&= 4u^2 + 1 \quad (u = x + \tfrac{1}{2}).
\end{aligned}
$$

Then we let

$$u = x + \tfrac{1}{2}, \qquad du = dx$$

and perform the integration as follows:

$$\int \frac{dx}{4x^2 + 4x + 2} = \int \frac{du}{4u^2 + 1} = \frac{1}{4} \int \frac{du}{u^2 + \frac{1}{4}} = \frac{1}{4} \int \frac{du}{u^2 + a^2} \quad (a = \tfrac{1}{2})$$

$$= \frac{1}{4} \left(\frac{1}{a} \tan^{-1} \frac{u}{a} + C \right) = \frac{1}{2} \tan^{-1} (2x + 1) + C.$$

Problem 3. Integrate the expression $\displaystyle \int \frac{(x + 1)\, dx}{\sqrt{2x^2 - 6x + 4}}$.

Solution. The quadratic part may be reduced as follows:

$$2x^2 - 6x + 4 = 2(x^2 - 3x) + 4 = 2(x^2 - 3x + \tfrac{9}{4}) + 4 - \tfrac{9}{2} = 2(u^2 - a^2), \quad \text{with} \quad u = x - \tfrac{3}{2},\ a = \tfrac{1}{2}.$$

Then
$$x = u + \tfrac{3}{2}, \quad dx = du, \quad x + 1 = u + \tfrac{5}{2},$$

and
$$\int \frac{(x + 1)\, dx}{\sqrt{2x^2 - 6x + 4}} = \int \frac{(u + \tfrac{5}{2})\, du}{\sqrt{2(u^2 - a^2)}} = \frac{1}{\sqrt{2}} \int \frac{u\, du}{\sqrt{u^2 - a^2}} + \frac{5}{2\sqrt{2}} \int \frac{du}{\sqrt{u^2 - a^2}}.$$

In the first term on the right-hand side of the last equation, we let

$$z = u^2 - a^2, \quad dz = 2u\, du, \quad u\, du = \tfrac{1}{2} dz,$$

and to the second we apply Eq. (8), Article 9.4:

$$\frac{1}{\sqrt{2}} \int \frac{u\, du}{\sqrt{u^2 - a^2}} = \frac{1}{2\sqrt{2}} \int \frac{dz}{\sqrt{z}} = \frac{1}{2\sqrt{2}} \int z^{-(1/2)}\, dz = \frac{1}{2\sqrt{2}} \cdot 2 z^{1/2} + C_1 = \sqrt{\frac{u^2 - a^2}{2}} + C_1$$

and

$$\frac{5}{2\sqrt{2}} \int \frac{du}{\sqrt{u^2 - a^2}} = \frac{5}{2\sqrt{2}} \ln |u + \sqrt{u^2 - a^2}| + C_2,$$

so that

$$\int \frac{(x + 1)\, dx}{\sqrt{2x^2 - 6x + 4}} = \sqrt{\frac{u^2 - a^2}{2}} + \frac{5}{2\sqrt{2}} \ln |u + \sqrt{u^2 - a^2}| + C$$

$$= \sqrt{\frac{x^2 - 3x + 2}{2}} + \frac{5}{2\sqrt{2}} \ln |x - \tfrac{3}{2} + \sqrt{x^2 - 3x + 2}| + C.$$

EXERCISES

3/22 #1,3,5   2/23 6,8,10

1. $\displaystyle \int_1^3 \frac{dx}{x^2 - 2x + 5}$

2. $\displaystyle \int \frac{x\, dx}{\sqrt{x^2 - 2x + 5}}$

3. $\displaystyle \int \frac{(x + 1)\, dx}{\sqrt{2x - x^2}}$

4. $\displaystyle \int \frac{(x - 1)\, dx}{\sqrt{x^2 - 4x + 3}}$

5. $\displaystyle \int \frac{x\, dx}{\sqrt{5 + 4x - x^2}}$

6. $\displaystyle \int \frac{dx}{\sqrt{x^2 - 2x - 8}}$

7. $\displaystyle \int \frac{(1 - x)\, dx}{\sqrt{8 + 2x - x^2}}$

8. $\displaystyle \int \frac{x\, dx}{\sqrt{x^2 + 4x + 5}}$

9. $\displaystyle \int \frac{x\, dx}{x^2 + 4x + 5}$

10. $\displaystyle \int \frac{(2x + 3)\, dx}{4x^2 + 4x + 5}$

9.6 INTEGRATION BY THE METHOD OF PARTIAL FRACTIONS

In algebra we learned how to combine fractions over a common denominator. In integration, it is desirable to reverse the process and split a fraction into a sum of fractions having simpler denominators. The technique of doing this is known as the *method of partial fractions*.

Example

$$\frac{2}{x+1} + \frac{3}{x-3} = \frac{2(x-3) + 3(x+1)}{(x+1)(x-3)}$$
$$= \frac{5x-3}{(x+1)(x-3)}.$$

The reverse process consists in finding constants A and B such that

$$\frac{5x-3}{(x+1)(x-3)} = \frac{A}{x+1} + \frac{B}{x-3}.$$

(Pretend, for a moment, that we don't know that $A = 2$, $B = 3$ will work. Then we call A and B *undetermined coefficients*.) Clearing of fractions, we have

$$5x - 3 = A(x - 3) + B(x + 1)$$
$$= (A + B)x - 3A + B.$$

This will be an identity in x if and only if coefficients of like powers of x on the two sides of the equation are equal:

$$A + B = 5, \qquad -3A + B = -3.$$

These two equations in two unknowns determine

$$A = 2, \qquad B = 3.$$

More generally, suppose we wish to separate a rational function

$$\frac{f(x)}{g(x)} \tag{1}$$

into a sum of partial fractions. Success in doing so hinges upon two things:

1. The degree of $f(x)$ should be less than the degree of $g(x)$. If this is not the case, we first perform a long division, then work with the remainder term. This remainder can always be put into the required form.

2. The factors of $g(x)$ should be known. Theoretically, any polynomial $g(x)$ with real coefficients can be expressed as a product of real linear and quadratic factors. In practice, it may be difficult to perform the factorization.

Let us assume that these two conditions prevail. Let $x - r$ be a linear factor of $g(x)$. Suppose $(x - r)^m$ is the highest power of $x - r$ that divides $g(x)$. Then, to this factor, assign the sum of m partial fractions as follows:

$$\frac{A_1}{x-r} + \frac{A_2}{(x-r)^2} + \cdots + \frac{A_m}{(x-r)^m}.$$

Next, let $x^2 + px + q$ be a quadratic factor of $g(x)$. Suppose

$$(x^2 + px + q)^n$$

is the highest power of this factor that divides $g(x)$. Then, to this factor, assign the sum of n partial fractions:

$$\frac{B_1 x + C_1}{x^2 + px + q} + \frac{B_2 x + C_2}{(x^2 + px + q)^2} + \cdots$$
$$+ \frac{B_n x + C_n}{(x^2 + px + q)^n}.$$

Do this for each of the distinct linear and quadratic factors of $g(x)$. Then set the original fraction $f(x)/g(x)$ equal to the sum of all these partial fractions. Clear the resulting equation of fractions and arrange the terms in decreasing powers of x. Equate the coefficients of corresponding powers of x, and solve the resulting equations for the undetermined coefficients.

Problem 1. Express

$$\frac{4 - 2x}{(x^2 + 1)(x - 1)^2}$$

as a sum of partial fractions.

Solution. Let

$$\frac{-2x + 4}{(x^2 + 1)(x - 1)^2} = \frac{Ax + B}{x^2 + 1} + \frac{C}{x - 1} + \frac{D}{(x - 1)^2}.$$

Then we have

$$-2x + 4 = (Ax + B)(x - 1)^2 + C(x - 1)(x^2 + 1)$$
$$+ D(x^2 + 1)$$
$$= (A + C)x^3 + (-2A + B - C + D)x^2$$
$$+ (A - 2B + C)x + (B - C + D).$$

If this is to be an identity in x, it is both necessary and sufficient that the coefficient of each power of x that occurs should be the same on the left-hand side of the equation as it is on the right-hand side. Imposing this condition successively on the coefficients of x^3, x^2, x, and x^0, respectively, we have

$$0 = A + C,$$
$$0 = -2A + B - C + D,$$
$$-2 = A - 2B + C,$$
$$4 = B - C + D.$$

If we subtract the second equation from the fourth, we can solve for A:

$$2A = 4, \qquad A = 2.$$

Then from the first equation, we have

$$C = -A = -2.$$

Knowing A and C, we find B from the third equation:

$$B = 1.$$

Finally, from the fourth equation, we have

$$D = 4 - B + C = 1.$$

Hence

$$\frac{-2x + 4}{(x^2 + 1)(x - 1)^2} = \frac{2x + 1}{x^2 + 1} - \frac{2}{x - 1} + \frac{1}{(x - 1)^2}.$$

Problem 2. Evaluate

$$\int \frac{x^5 - x^4 - 3x + 5}{x^4 - 2x^3 + 2x^2 - 2x + 1}\, dx.$$

Solution. The integrand is a fraction, but not a proper fraction. Hence we divide first, thus obtaining

$$\frac{x^5 - x^4 - 3x + 5}{x^4 - 2x^3 + 2x^2 - 2x + 1}$$
$$= x + 1 + \frac{-2x + 4}{x^4 - 2x^3 + 2x^2 - 2x + 1}. \quad (2)$$

The denominator factors as follows:

$$x^4 - 2x^3 + 2x^2 - 2x + 1 = (x^2 + 1)(x - 1)^2.$$

By the result of Example 2, we have for the remainder term

$$\frac{-2x + 4}{(x^2 + 1)(x - 1)^2} = \frac{2x + 1}{x^2 + 1} - \frac{2}{x - 1} + \frac{1}{(x - 1)^2}. \quad (3)$$

Hence, substituting from (3) into (2), multiplying by dx, and integrating, we have

$$\int \frac{x^5 - x^4 - 3x + 5}{x^4 - 2x^3 + 2x^2 - 2x + 1}\, dx$$
$$= \int \left[x + 1 + \frac{2x + 1}{x^2 + 1} - \frac{2}{x - 1} + \frac{1}{(x - 1)^2} \right] dx$$
$$= \frac{x^2}{2} + x + \ln(x^2 + 1) + \tan^{-1} x - 2\ln|x - 1|$$
$$- \frac{1}{x - 1} + K.$$

In theory, any rational function of x can be integrated by the method of partial fractions. Once the necessary algebra has been done, the problem reduces to evaluating integrals of the following two types:

$$\int \frac{dx}{(x - r)^h}, \quad (4a)$$

$$\int \frac{(ax + b)\, dx}{(x^2 + px + q)^k}. \quad (4b)$$

The first of these becomes simply $\int u^{-h}\, du$ when we let $u = x - r$. In the second type it is preferable to complete the square in the denominator:

$$x^2 + px + q = \left(x + \frac{p}{2} \right)^2 + q - \frac{p^2}{4},$$

and then let

$$u = x + \frac{p}{2}, \qquad c^2 = q - \frac{p^2}{4}.$$

Then

$$ax + b = a\left(u - \frac{p}{2} \right) + b = au + b',$$

$$b' = b - a\frac{p}{2},$$

and we consider

$$\int \frac{au + b'}{(u^2 + c^2)^k}\, du = \frac{a}{2}\int (u^2 + c^2)^{-k}(2u\, du)$$

$$+ b'\int \frac{du}{(u^2 + c^2)^k}.\qquad (5)$$

The first integral on the right in (5) readily yields to the substitution $z = u^2 + c^2$. In the second integral, we let

$$u = c\tan\theta, \quad\text{or}\quad \theta = \tan^{-1}\frac{u}{c},$$

$$du = c\sec^2\theta\, d\theta,$$

$$u^2 + c^2 = c^2\sec^2\theta,$$

and obtain

$$\int \frac{du}{(u^2 + c^2)^k} = c^{1-2k}\int \cos^{2k-2}\theta\, d\theta.\qquad (6)$$

In the next article we shall obtain a reduction formula for $\int \cos^n\theta\, d\theta$, which may be used to evaluate the integral in (6). The trigonometric identity

$$\cos^2\theta = \frac{1 + \cos 2\theta}{2}\qquad (7)$$

may also be used to advantage.

Problem 3. $\qquad \int \dfrac{dx}{1 - x^2}.$

Solution. By partial fractions,

$$\frac{1}{1 - x^2} = \frac{A}{1 - x} + \frac{B}{1 + x},$$

$$\begin{aligned}1 &= A(1 + x) + B(1 - x)\\ &= A + B + (A - B)x,\end{aligned}$$

$$A + B = 1,\quad A - B = 0,$$

$$A = B = \tfrac{1}{2}.$$

Therefore

$$\int \frac{1}{1 - x^2}\, dx = \int \left(\frac{\tfrac{1}{2}}{1 - x} + \frac{\tfrac{1}{2}}{1 + x}\right) dx$$

$$= -\tfrac{1}{2}\ln|1 - x| + \tfrac{1}{2}\ln|1 + x| + C$$

$$= \tfrac{1}{2}\ln\left|\frac{1 + x}{1 - x}\right| + C.\qquad (8)$$

Problem 4. $\qquad \int \sec\theta\, d\theta.$

Solution. We did this in Problem 5, Article 9.2, by a trick. We can now do it in a more straightforward manner by writing $\sec\theta$ as $1/\cos\theta$ and proceeding as follows:

$$\int \sec\theta\, d\theta = \int \frac{d\theta}{\cos\theta} = \int \frac{\cos\theta\, d\theta}{\cos^2\theta}$$

$$= \int \frac{dx}{1 - x^2}\qquad (x = \sin\theta)$$

$$= \tfrac{1}{2}\ln\left|\frac{1 + x}{1 - x}\right| + C\quad\text{(Eq. 8)}$$

$$= \ln\sqrt{\frac{1 + \sin\theta}{1 - \sin\theta}} + C.\qquad (9)$$

This answer is equivalent to Eq. (3), Article 9.2, as may be seen by multiplying numerator and denominator by $1 + \sin\theta$:

$$\sqrt{\frac{1 + \sin\theta}{1 - \sin\theta}} = \sqrt{\frac{(1 + \sin\theta)^2}{1 - \sin^2\theta}}$$

$$= \left|\frac{1 + \sin\theta}{\cos\theta}\right|$$

$$= |\sec\theta + \tan\theta|.$$

EXERCISES

1. $\displaystyle\int \frac{x\, dx}{x^2 + 4x - 5}$

2. $\displaystyle\int \frac{x\, dx}{x^2 - 2x - 3}$

3. $\displaystyle\int \frac{(x + 1)\, dx}{x^2 + 4x - 5}$

4. $\displaystyle\int \frac{x^2\, dx}{x^2 + 2x + 1}$

5. $\displaystyle\int \frac{dx}{x(x + 1)^2}$

6. $\displaystyle\int \frac{dx}{(x + 1)(x^2 + 1)}$

7. $\displaystyle\int \frac{dx}{x(x^2 + x + 1)}$

8. $\displaystyle\int \frac{\sin\theta\, d\theta}{\cos^2\theta + \cos\theta - 2}$

9. $\displaystyle\int \frac{e^t\, dt}{e^{2t} + 3e^t + 2}$

10. $\displaystyle\int \frac{dx}{(x^2 + 1)^2}$

11. $\displaystyle\int \frac{x^4\, dx}{(x^2 + 1)^2}$

9.7 INTEGRATION BY PARTS

There are really just two general methods of integration. One of these is the method of substitution, which we have illustrated in Articles 9.2 through 9.5. The method of partial fractions is really not a method of *integration* so much as it is a method of *algebraic transformation* of a rational function into an integrable form. The second general method of integration, called *integration by parts*, depends on the formula for the differential of a product:

$$d(uv) = u\,dv + v\,du \quad \text{or} \quad u\,dv = d(uv) - v\,du.$$

When this is integrated, we have

$$\int u\,dv = uv - \int v\,du + C. \qquad (1)$$

By way of comment on the formula (1) for integration by parts, we observe that it expresses one integral $\int u\,dv$ in terms of a second integral $\int v\,du$. If, by proper choice of u and dv, the second integral is simpler than the first, we may be able to evaluate it quite simply and thus arrive at an answer.

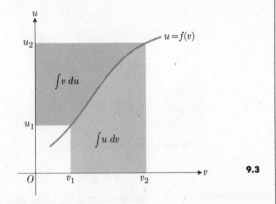

9.3

Note. In a definite integral, appropriate limits must be supplied. We may then interpret the formula for integration by parts,

$$\int_{(1)}^{(2)} u\,dv = uv \Big]_{(1)}^{(2)} - \int_{(1)}^{(2)} v\,du,$$

geometrically in terms of areas (see Fig. 9.3).

Problem 1. $\int \ln x\,dx.$

Solution. If we try to match $\ln x\,dx$ with $u\,dv$, we may take

$$u = \ln x \quad \text{and} \quad dv = dx.$$

Then, to use (1), we see that we also require

$$du = d(\ln x) = \frac{dx}{x},$$

$$v = \int dv = \int dx = x + C_1,$$

so that

$$\int \ln x\,dx = (\ln x)(x + C_1) - \int (x + C_1)\frac{dx}{x} + C_2$$

$$= x \ln x + C_1 \ln x - \int dx - \int C_1 \frac{dx}{x} + C_2$$

$$= x \ln x + C_1 \ln x - x - C_1 \ln x + C_2$$

$$= x \ln x - x + C_2.$$

Note that the first constant of integration C_1 does not appear in the final answer. This is generally true, for if we write $v + C_1$ in place of v in the right side of (1), we obtain

$$u(v + C_1) - \int (v + C_1)\,du$$

$$= uv + C_1 u - \int v\,du - \int C_1\,du = uv - \int v\,du,$$

where it is understood that a constant of integration must still be added in the final result. It is therefore customary to drop the first constant of integration when determining v as $\int dv$. On the other hand, there is occasionally an advantage in taking C_1 equal to some specific constant. For instance, if we consider

$$\int \ln(x+1)\,dx$$

and let

$$u = \ln(x+1) \quad \text{and} \quad dv = dx,$$

then

$$du = \frac{dx}{x+1} \quad \text{and} \quad v = x + C_1.$$

Equation (1) then gives

$$\int \ln(x+1)\,dx = (x + C_1)\ln(x+1) - \int \frac{x + C_1}{x+1}\,dx.$$

Now taking $C_1 = 1$ greatly simplifies the second integral and leads to the result

$$\int \ln (x+1) \, dx = (x+1) \ln (x+1) - x + C_2.$$

Problem 2. $\int \tan^{-1} x \, dx.$

Solution. This is typical of the inverse trigonometric functions. Let

$$u = \tan^{-1} x, \qquad dv = dx.$$

Then

$$du = \frac{dx}{1+x^2} \quad \text{and} \quad v = x,$$

so that

$$\int \tan^{-1} x \, dx = x \tan^{-1} x - \int \frac{x \, dx}{1+x^2}$$
$$= x \tan^{-1} x - \tfrac{1}{2} \ln (1+x^2) + C.$$

Sometimes an integration by parts must be repeated to obtain an answer, as in the following example.

Problem 3. $\int x^2 e^x \, dx.$

Solution. Let $u = x^2, \qquad dv = e^x \, dx.$

Then $du = 2x \, dx \quad \text{and} \quad v = e^x,$

so that $\int x^2 e^x \, dx = x^2 e^x - 2 \int x e^x \, dx.$

The integral on the right is similar to the original integral, except that we have reduced the power of x from 2 to 1. If we could now reduce it from 1 to 0, we could see success ahead. In $\int x e^x \, dx$, we therefore let

$$U = x, \qquad dV = e^x \, dx,$$

so that

$$dU = dx \quad \text{and} \quad V = e^x.$$

Then

$$\int x e^x \, dx = x e^x - \int e^x \, dx = x e^x - e^x + c,$$

and

$$\int x^2 e^x \, dx = x^2 e^x - 2x e^x + 2e^x + C.$$

Problem 4. Obtain a reduction formula for

$$J_n \equiv \int \cos^n x \, dx.$$

Solution. We may think of $\cos^n x$ as $\cos^{n-1} x \cdot \cos x$. Then we let

$$u = \cos^{n-1} x, \qquad dv = \cos x \, dx,$$

so that

$$du = (n-1) \cos^{n-2} x (-\sin x \, dx) \quad \text{and} \quad v = \sin x.$$

Hence

$$J_n = \cos^{n-1} x \sin x + (n-1) \int \sin^2 x \cos^{n-2} x \, dx$$
$$= \cos^{n-1} x \sin x + (n-1) \int (1 - \cos^2 x) \cos^{n-2} x \, dx,$$

or

$$\int \cos^n x \, dx = \cos^{n-1} x \sin x + (n-1) \int \cos^{n-2} x \, dx$$
$$- (n-1) \int \cos^n x \, dx.$$

The last integral on the right may now be transposed to the left to give

$$[1 + (n-1)] J_n = n J_n.$$

We then divide by n, and the final result is

$$\int \cos^n x \, dx = \frac{\cos^{n-1} x \sin x}{n} + \frac{n-1}{n} \int \cos^{n-2} x \, dx.$$

$$(2)$$

This allows us to reduce the exponent on $\cos x$ by 2, and is a very useful formula. When n is a positive integer, we may apply the formula repeatedly until the remaining integral is either

$$\int \cos x \, dx = \sin x + C$$

or

$$\int \cos^0 x \, dx = \int dx = x + C.$$

For example, with $n = 4$, we get

$$\int \cos^4 x \, dx = \frac{\cos^3 x \sin x}{4} + \frac{3}{4} \int \cos^2 x \, dx,$$

and with $n = 2$,

$$\int \cos^2 x \, dx = \frac{\cos x \sin x}{2} + \frac{1}{2} \int dx.$$

Therefore

$$\int \cos^4 x \, dx = \frac{\cos^3 x \sin x}{4} + \frac{3}{4} \left(\frac{\cos x \sin x}{2} + \frac{1}{2} x \right) + C.$$

The reader may find it instructive to derive the companion formula:

$$\int \sin^n x \, dx = -\frac{\sin^{n-1} x \cos x}{n} + \frac{n-1}{n} \int \sin^{n-2} x \, dx. \tag{3}$$

The integral in the following example occurs in electrical engineering problems. Its evaluation requires two integrations by parts, followed by solving for the unknown integral in a method analogous to that used above in finding reduction formulas.

Problem 5. $\int e^{ax} \cos bx \, dx$.

Solution. Let $u = e^{ax}$, $dv = \cos bx \, dx$.

Then $du = ae^{ax} \, dx$ and $v = \frac{1}{b} \sin bx$,

so that

$$\int e^{ax} \cos bx \, dx = \frac{e^{ax} \sin bx}{b} - \frac{a}{b} \int e^{ax} \sin bx \, dx.$$

The second integral is like the first except that it has $\sin bx$ in place of $\cos bx$. If we apply integration by parts to it, letting

$$U = e^{ax} \quad \text{and} \quad dV = \sin bx \, dx,$$

then

$$dU = ae^{ax} \, dx \quad \text{and} \quad V = -\frac{1}{b} \cos bx,$$

so that

$$\int e^{ax} \cos bx \, dx = \frac{e^{ax} \sin bx}{b} - \frac{a}{b}\left[-\frac{e^{ax} \cos bx}{b} + \frac{a}{b} \int e^{ax} \cos bx \, dx \right].$$

Now the unknown integral appears on the left with a coefficient of unity and on the right with a coefficient of $-a^2/b^2$. Transposing this term to the left and dividing by the new coefficient

$$1 + \frac{a^2}{b^2} = \frac{a^2 + b^2}{b^2},$$

we have

$$\int e^{ax} \cos bx \, dx = e^{ax}\left(\frac{b \sin bx + a \cos bx}{a^2 + b^2} \right) + C. \tag{4}$$

EXERCISES

1–17 odd   3/28 13, 15, 17

1. $\int x \ln x \, dx$

2. $\int x^n \ln ax \, dx \quad (n \neq -1)$

3. $\int x \tan^{-1} x \, dx$

4. $\int \sin^{-1} ax \, dx$

5. $\int x \sin ax \, dx$

6. $\int x^2 \cos ax \, dx$

7. $\int x \sec^2 ax \, dx$

8. $\int e^{ax} \sin bx \, dx$

9. $\int \sin (\ln x) \, dx$

10. $\int \cos (\ln x) \, dx$

11. $\int \ln (a^2 + x^2) \, dx$

12. $\int x \cos (2x + 1) \, dx$

13. $\int x \sin^{-1} x \, dx$

14. $\int_1^2 x \sec^{-1} x \, dx$

15. $\int_1^4 \sec^{-1} \sqrt{x} \, dx$

16. $\int x^2 \tan^{-1} x \, dx$

Derive the following reduction formulas and apply each one to the specific problem given.

17. (a) $\int x^m (\ln x)^n \, dx = \frac{x^{m+1}(\ln x)^n}{m+1} - \frac{n}{m+1} \int x^m (\ln x)^{n-1} \, dx$

(b) $\int x^3 (\ln x)^2 \, dx$

18. (a) $\int \sin^n x \, dx = -\frac{\sin^{n-1} x \cos x}{n} + \frac{n-1}{n} \int \sin^{n-2} x \, dx$

(b) $\int_0^{\pi/6} \sin^4 3x \, dx$

19. (a) $\int x^n e^x \, dx = x^n e^x - n \int x^{n-1} e^x \, dx,$

(b) $\int x^3 e^x \, dx$

20. (a) $\int \sec^n x \, dx = \frac{\sec^{n-2} x \tan x}{(n-1)} + \frac{n-2}{n-1} \int \sec^{n-2} x \, dx$

(b) $\int \sec^3 x \, dx$ [See Eq. (3), Article 9.2.]

(c) $\int \sqrt{a^2 + x^2} \, dx$ [*Hint.* Let $x = a \tan \theta$.]

21. Find the second-degree polynomial $P(x)$ that has the following properties:

(a) $P(0) = 1$,   (b) $P'(0) = 0$,

(c) the indefinite integral

$$\int \frac{P(x)\, dx}{x^3(x-1)^2}$$

is a rational function (that is, no logarithmic terms occur in the answer). .

9.8 INTEGRATION OF RATIONAL FUNCTIONS OF $\sin x$ AND $\cos x$, AND OTHER TRIGONOMETRIC INTEGRALS

It has been discovered that the substitution

$$z = \tan \frac{x}{2} \tag{1}$$

enables one to reduce the problem of integrating any rational function of $\sin x$ and $\cos x$ to a problem involving a rational function of z. This in turn can be integrated by the method of partial fractions discussed in Article 9.6. Thus the substitution (1) is a very powerful tool. This method is cumbersome, however, and is used only when the simpler methods outlined previously have failed.

To see the effect of the substitution, we calculate

$$\cos x = 2 \cos^2 \frac{x}{2} - 1 = \frac{2}{\sec^2 \frac{x}{2}} - 1$$

$$= \frac{2}{1 + \tan^2 \frac{x}{2}} - 1 = \frac{2}{1 + z^2} - 1,$$

or

$$\cos x = \frac{1 - z^2}{1 + z^2}; \tag{2a}$$

and

$$\sin x = 2 \sin \frac{x}{2} \cos \frac{x}{2} = 2 \frac{\sin \frac{x}{2}}{\cos \frac{x}{2}} \cdot \cos^2 \frac{x}{2}$$

$$= 2 \tan \frac{x}{2} \cdot \frac{1}{\sec^2 \frac{x}{2}} = \frac{2 \tan \frac{x}{2}}{1 + \tan^2 \frac{x}{2}},$$

or

$$\sin x = \frac{2z}{1 + z^2}. \tag{2b}$$

Finally, $x = 2 \tan^{-1} z,$

so that $dx = \dfrac{2\, dz}{1 + z^2}. \tag{2c}$

Example 1. $\displaystyle\int \sec x \, dx = \int \frac{dx}{\cos x}$

becomes

$$\int \frac{2\, dz}{1 + z^2} \cdot \frac{1 + z^2}{1 - z^2} = \int \frac{2\, dz}{1 - z^2}.$$

To this we apply the method of partial fractions:

$$\frac{2}{1 - z^2} = \frac{A}{1 - z} + \frac{B}{1 + z},$$

$$2 = A(1 + z) + B(1 - z)$$

$$= (A + B) + (A - B)z,$$

which requires

$$A + B = 2, \qquad A - B = 0.$$

Hence

$$A = B = 1$$

and

$$\int \frac{2\, dz}{1 - z^2} = \int \frac{dz}{1 - z} + \int \frac{dz}{1 + z}$$

$$= -\ln |1 - z| + \ln |1 + z| + C$$

$$= \ln \left| \frac{1 + z}{1 - z} \right| + C$$

$$= \ln \left| \frac{1 + \tan \frac{x}{2}}{1 - \tan \frac{x}{2}} \right| + C$$

$$= \ln \left| \frac{\tan \frac{\pi}{4} + \tan \frac{x}{2}}{1 - \tan \frac{\pi}{4} \tan \frac{x}{2}} \right| + C$$

$$= \ln \left| \tan \left(\frac{\pi}{4} + \frac{x}{2} \right) \right| + C.$$

That is,

$$\int \sec x \, dx = \ln \left| \tan \left(\frac{\pi}{4} + \frac{x}{2} \right) \right| + C \tag{3}$$

is an alternative form, which may be used in place of Eq. (3), Article 9.2, or Eq. (9), Article 9.6.

Example 2. $$\int \frac{dx}{1 + \cos x}$$

becomes

$$\int \frac{2\,dz}{1 + z^2}\,\frac{1 + z^2}{2} = \int dz = z + C = \tan \frac{x}{2} + C.$$

Example 3. $$\int \frac{dx}{2 + \sin x}$$

becomes

$$\int \frac{2\,dz}{1 + z^2} \left[\frac{1 + z^2}{2 + 2z + 2z^2} \right] = \int \frac{dz}{z^2 + z + 1}$$

$$= \int \frac{dz}{(z + \tfrac{1}{2})^2 + \tfrac{3}{4}}$$

$$= \int \frac{du}{u^2 + a^2} \qquad [u = z + \tfrac{1}{2},\ a = \sqrt{3}/2]$$

$$= \frac{1}{a} \tan^{-1} \frac{u}{a} + C$$

$$= \frac{2}{\sqrt{3}} \tan^{-1} \frac{2z + 1}{\sqrt{3}} + C$$

$$= \frac{2}{\sqrt{3}} \tan^{-1} \frac{1 + 2 \tan \frac{x}{2}}{\sqrt{3}} + C.$$

We have already made repeated use of trigonometric identities to aid us in evaluating integrals. The following types of integrals:

$$\int \sin mx \sin nx\, dx,$$

$$\int \sin mx \cos nx\, dx, \qquad (4)$$

$$\int \cos mx \cos nx\, dx,$$

arise in connection with alternating-current theory, heat transfer problems, bending of beams, cable stress analysis in suspension bridges, and many other places where trigonometric series (or Fourier series) are applied to problems in mathematics, science, and engineering. The integrals in (4) can be evaluated by the method of integration by parts, but two such integrations are required in each case.

A simpler way to evaluate them is to exploit the trigonometric identities

$$\sin mx \sin nx = \tfrac{1}{2}[\cos (m - n)x - \cos (m + n)x], \qquad (5a)$$

$$\sin mx \cos nx = \tfrac{1}{2}[\sin (m - n)x + \sin (m + n)x], \qquad (5b)$$

$$\cos mx \cos nx = \tfrac{1}{2}[\cos (m - n)x + \cos (m + n)x]. \qquad (5c)$$

These identities follow at once from

$$\cos (A + B) = \cos A \cos B - \sin A \sin B,$$
$$\cos (A - B) = \cos A \cos B + \sin A \sin B, \qquad (6a)$$

and

$$\sin (A + B) = \sin A \cos B + \cos A \sin B,$$
$$\sin (A - B) = \sin A \cos B - \cos A \sin B. \qquad (6b)$$

If, for example, we add the two equations in (6a) and then divide by 2, we obtain (5c) by taking $A = mx$ and $B = nx$. The identity in (5a) is obtained in a similar fashion by subtracting the first equation in (6a) from the second equation. Finally, if we add the two equations in (6b) we are led to the identity in (5b).

Example 4

$$\int \sin 3x \cos 5x\, dx = \tfrac{1}{2} \int [\sin (-2x) + \sin 8x]\, dx$$

$$= \tfrac{1}{2} \int (\sin 8x - \sin 2x)\, dx$$

$$= -\frac{\cos 8x}{16} + \frac{\cos 2x}{4} + C.$$

EXERCISES

1. $$\int_0^\pi \frac{dx}{1 + \sin x}$$ 2. $$\int_{\pi/2}^\pi \frac{dx}{1 - \cos x}$$

3. $$\int \frac{dx}{1 - \sin x}$$ 4. $$\int_0^{\pi/2} \frac{dx}{2 + \cos x}$$

5. $\int \dfrac{\cos x \, dx}{2 - \cos x}$ 6. $\displaystyle\int_0^{\pi/2} \cos 3x \sin 2x \, dx$

7. $\displaystyle\int_{-\pi}^{\pi} \sin 3x \sin 2x \, dx$ 8. $\displaystyle\int_{-\pi}^{\pi} \sin^2 3x \, dx$

9. Two functions f and g are said to be *orthogonal* on an interval $[a, b]$ if

$$\int_a^b f(x) \, g(x) \, dx = 0.$$

(a) Prove that $\sin mx$ and $\sin nx$ are orthogonal on any interval of length 2π provided that m and n are integers such that $m^2 \neq n^2$.

(b) Prove the same for $\sin mx$ and $\cos nx$.

(c) Prove the same for $\cos mx$ and $\cos nx$.

9.9 FURTHER SUBSTITUTIONS

Some integrals involving fractional powers of the variable x may be simplified by substituting $x = z^n$, where n is the least common multiple of the denominators of the exponents.

Example.
$$\int \frac{\sqrt{x} \, dx}{1 + \sqrt[4]{x}}$$

may be simplified by taking

$$x = z^4, \qquad dx = 4z^3 \, dz.$$

This leads to

$$\int \frac{\sqrt{x} \, dx}{1 + \sqrt[4]{x}} = \int \frac{z^2 \cdot 4z^3 \, dz}{1 + z}$$

$$= 4 \int \left(z^4 - z^3 + z^2 - z + 1 - \frac{1}{z + 1} \right) dz$$

$$= 4 \left[\frac{z^5}{5} - \frac{z^4}{4} + \frac{z^3}{3} - \frac{z^2}{2} + z - \ln |z + 1| \right] + C$$

$$= \tfrac{4}{5} x^{5/4} - x + \tfrac{4}{3} x^{3/4} - 2x^{1/2} + 4x^{1/4}$$

$$\qquad\qquad - 4 \ln |1 + \sqrt[4]{x}| + C.$$

In $\int x^3 \sqrt{x^2 + a^2} \, dx$, on the other hand, the substitutions

$$z^2 = x^2 + a^2, \quad \text{or} \quad x^2 = z^2 - a^2,$$

and

$$2x \, dx = 2z \, dz$$

lead to

$$\int x^3 \sqrt{x^2 + a^2} \, dx = \int x^2 \sqrt{x^2 + a^2} \cdot x \, dx$$

$$= \int (z^2 - a^2) \cdot z^2 \cdot dz$$

$$= \int (z^4 - a^2 z^2) \, dz$$

$$= \frac{(x^2 + a^2)^{5/2}}{5} - \frac{a^2 (x^2 + a^2)^{3/2}}{3} + C$$

$$= \frac{3x^2 - 2a^2}{15} (x^2 + a^2)^{3/2} + C.$$

Even when it is not clear at the start that a substitution will work, it is advisable to try one that seems reasonable and pursue it until it either gives results or appears to make matters worse. In the latter case, try something else! Sometimes a chain of substitutions $u = f(x)$, $v = g(u)$, $z = h(v)$, and so on, will produce results when it is by no means obvious that this will work. The criterion of success is whether the new integrals so obtained appear to be simpler than the original integral. Here it is handy to remember that any rational function of x can be integrated by the method of partial fractions and that any rational function of $\sin x$ and $\cos x$ can be integrated by using the substitution $z = \tan x/2$. If we can reduce a given integral to one of these types, we then know how to finish the job.

Even in these cases, however, it is frequently simpler to use special methods suggested by the particular integrand rather than to use the general methods. For instance, one would hardly let $z = \tan x/2$ to evaluate $\int \sin x \, dx = -\cos x + C$. And reference to Eqs. (5) and (6), Article 9.6 and the accompanying discussion shows that a trigonometric substitution is used to evaluate certain of the integrals that arise in the method of partial fractions. It may be more convenient to use the same substitution *before* going through the algebraic reductions instead of *after* doing so.

Example. Consider the integral

$$\int_{-1}^{+1} \sqrt{\frac{1 + x}{1 - x}} \, dx, \qquad\qquad (1)$$

which appears in the so-called "lifting line theory" in aerodynamics. If we let

$$\frac{1+x}{1-x} = z^2, \tag{2}$$

we shall, of course, get rid of the radical. Whether this is really a good substitution or not depends upon how complicated the expression is for dx in terms of z and dz. To settle this question, we solve for x as follows:

$$1 + x = z^2 - xz^2,$$

$$x(z^2 + 1) = z^2 - 1,$$

$$x = \frac{z^2 - 1}{z^2 + 1}. \tag{3}$$

Hence

$$dx = \frac{4z\,dz}{(z^2 + 1)^2}$$

and the integral becomes

$$\int \sqrt{\frac{1+x}{1-x}}\,dx = \int \frac{4z^2\,dz}{(z^2 + 1)^2}.$$

Now the integrand on the right is a rational function of z and we could proceed by the method of partial fractions. But the $z^2 + 1$ in the denominator also lends itself to the substitution

$$z = \tan\theta. \tag{4}$$

We try this, and have

$$dz = \sec^2\theta\,d\theta,$$

$$z^2 + 1 = \tan^2\theta + 1 = \sec^2\theta,$$

so that

$$\int \frac{4z^2\,dz}{(z^2 + 1)^2} = \int \frac{4\tan^2\theta \cdot \sec^2\theta\,d\theta}{\sec^4\theta}$$

$$= 4\int \frac{\sin^2\theta}{\cos^2\theta}\cdot\frac{1}{\sec^2\theta}\,d\theta$$

$$= 4\int \sin^2\theta\,d\theta,$$

and the last integral can now be evaluated at once to give

$$4\int \sin^2\theta\,d\theta = 2\left[\theta - \frac{\sin 2\theta}{2}\right] + C. \tag{5}$$

We now have two alternative courses of action for evaluating the *definite integral* (1):

(a) We may reverse the substitutions (3) and (4) and replace (5) by its equivalent in terms of x. Then the definite integral (1) could be evaluated by substituting the limits of integration. Or,

(b) we may determine new limits of integration corresponding to the new variable of integration.

We illustrate the second line of attack. In the original integral (1), x varies from -1 to $+1$. As this happens, the left side of (2) varies from 0 to $+\infty$, and since we have tacitly taken

$$z = \sqrt{\frac{1+x}{1-x}}$$

as the *positive* square root, we see that then z varies from 0 to $+\infty$. Finally, from (4), we have $\theta = \tan^{-1} z$, so that θ varies from 0 to $\pi/2$ as z varies from 0 to $+\infty$. Combining these results, we have

$$\int_{-1}^{+1} \sqrt{\frac{1+x}{1-x}}\,dx = \int_0^\infty \frac{4z^2\,dz}{(z^2 + 1)^2}$$

$$= 4\int_0^{\pi/2} \sin^2\theta\,d\theta$$

$$= 2\left[\theta - \frac{\sin 2\theta}{2}\right]_0^{\pi/2} = \pi.$$

The reader will find it instructive to evaluate the integral in (1) by making the alternative substitution

$$x = \cos 2t,$$

$$dx = -2\sin 2t\,dt = -4\sin t\cos t\,dt,$$

which is particularly well adapted to the integrand in question, since

$$1 + \cos 2t = 2\cos^2 t,$$

$$1 - \cos 2t = 2\sin^2 t.$$

But the shortest way of all is to notice that for

$$-1 < x < 1,$$

we have

$$\sqrt{\frac{1+x}{1-x}} = \frac{1+x}{\sqrt{1-x^2}},$$

and hence

$$\int \sqrt{\frac{1+x}{1-x}}\,dx = \int \frac{1+x}{\sqrt{1-x^2}}\,dx$$

$$= \sin^{-1} x - \sqrt{1-x^2} + C. \tag{6}$$

EXERCISES

4/13 2-8 even   4/14   10-20 even

1. $\int \dfrac{1 - \sqrt{x}}{1 + \sqrt{x}}\, dx$

2. $\int \dfrac{dx}{a + b\sqrt{x}}$

   (a, b constant)

3. $\int x^2 \sqrt{x + a}\, dx$

4. $\int \dfrac{\sqrt{x + a}\, dx}{x + b}$ (b > a)

5. $\int \sqrt{\dfrac{a + x}{b + x}}\, dx$ (b ≠ a)

6. $\int \dfrac{dx}{x + \sqrt{x^2 + a^2}}$

   (a > 0)

7. $\int_0^1 \dfrac{x^3\, dx}{(x^2 + 1)^{3/2}}$

8. $\int \dfrac{dx}{x(ax^n + c)}$

   (anc ≠ 0)

9. $\int_3^8 \dfrac{(t + 2)\, dt}{t\sqrt{t + 1}}$

10. $\int \dfrac{dx}{x - x^{2/3}}$

11. $\int_0^3 \dfrac{\sqrt{x + 1} - 1}{\sqrt{x + 1} + 1}\, dx$

12. $\int \dfrac{dx}{x(1 - \sqrt[3]{x})}$

13. $\int \dfrac{y^{2/3}\, dy}{y + 1}$

14. $\int \dfrac{z^5\, dz}{\sqrt{1 + z^3}}$

15. $\int \dfrac{\sqrt{t^3 - 1}}{t}\, dt$

16. $\int_0^{\ln 2} \dfrac{dw}{(1 + e^w)}$

17. $\int_0^{\pi/2} \dfrac{\sin 2\theta\, d\theta}{2 + \cos \theta}$

18. $\int \dfrac{\sin x\, dx}{\tan x + \cos x}$

19. $\int \dfrac{dx}{x^3 + 1}$

20. $\int \dfrac{dy}{y^{1/3} - y^{1/2}}$

9.10 IMPROPER INTEGRALS

An integral of the type discussed in the previous article,

$$\int_{-1}^{+1} \sqrt{\dfrac{1 + x}{1 - x}}\, dx,$$

is called an *improper* integral because the function

$$f(x) = \sqrt{\dfrac{1 + x}{1 - x}}$$

which appears after the integral sign becomes infinite at one of the limits of integration, in this case at $x = +1$. In general, integrals of the following two types are called improper integrals:

(a) $$\int_a^b f(x)\, dx,$$

where $f(x)$ becomes infinite at a value of x in $[a, b]$,

(b) $$\int_a^\infty f(x)\, dx \quad \text{or} \quad \int_{-\infty}^b f(x)\, dx,$$

where one or both of the limits of integration are infinite.

In the Example, Article 9.9, we had

$$\int_{-1}^1 \sqrt{\dfrac{1 + x}{1 - x}}\, dx = \int_0^\infty \dfrac{4z^2\, dz}{(z^2 + 1)^2}$$

for

$$z = \sqrt{\dfrac{1 + x}{1 - x}},$$

where the integral on the left is an improper integral of the first type and the integral on the right is an improper integral of the second type.

Figure 9.4 (a) illustrates the case where the function becomes infinite at one of the limits of integration. If we interpret the integral in terms of area under the curve $y = f(x)$, say from -1 to $+1$ as in the figure, we see that the curve extends to infinity as x approaches 1 and the area from -1 to $+1$ is not well defined. Nevertheless, we can certainly define the area from $x = -1$ to $x = b$, where b is any positive number *less* than one; for example, we can take $b = 0.999$. This defines a function of b:

$$g(b) = \int_{-1}^b f(x)\, dx.$$

If this function has a finite limit as b approaches $+1$ from the left, we *define* this limit to be the value of the improper integral

$$\int_{-1}^{+1} f(x)\, dx = \lim_{b \to 1-} \int_{-1}^b f(x)\, dx.$$

In this case we also say that the improper integral *converges*. On the other hand, we say that the inte-

9.4

gral *diverges* if the function g has no definite finite limit as $b \to 1-$.

Example 1. In the particular integral under discussion, we find from Eq. (6) of Article 9.9 that

$$\int_{-1}^{b} \sqrt{\frac{1+x}{1-x}}\, dx = \sin^{-1} x - \sqrt{1-x^2}\,\Big]_{-1}^{b}$$

$$= \sin^{-1} b - \sqrt{1-b^2} + \frac{\pi}{2}.$$

This is the number denoted above by $g(b)$. When b is slightly less than $+1$, $\sin^{-1} b$ is slightly less than $\pi/2$ and $\sqrt{1-b^2}$ is nearly zero. Hence

$$\lim_{b \to 1-} \int_{-1}^{b} \sqrt{\frac{1+x}{1-x}}\, dx = \lim_{b \to 1-}\left[\sin^{-1} b - \sqrt{1-b^2} + \frac{\pi}{2}\right]$$

$$= \frac{\pi}{2} - 0 + \frac{\pi}{2} = \pi.$$

The given integral therefore converges and its value is π.

The same result is obtained if, instead of finding the area by summing vertical elements (Fig. 9.4a), we sum horizontal elements (Fig. 9.4b). Then we find

$$A = \int_{y=0}^{\infty} (1-x)\, dy = \int_{0}^{\infty} \frac{2}{y^2+1}\, dy.$$

This time, the integral to be evaluated is an improper integral of the second type because the range of integration extends to infinity. In this case we investigate the integral from $y = 0$ to $y = c$ for large values of c:

$$\int_{0}^{c} \frac{2\, dy}{y^2+1} = 2 \tan^{-1} c.$$

We then *define* the integral from 0 to ∞ as the limit of this as $c \to \infty$ (if the limit exists); that is,

$$\int_{0}^{\infty} \frac{2\, dy}{y^2+1} = \lim_{c \to \infty} \int_{0}^{c} \frac{2\, dy}{y^2+1}$$

$$= \lim_{c \to \infty} (2 \tan^{-1} c) = \pi.$$

The limit does exist, since $\tan^{-1} c$ approaches $\pi/2$ as c increases indefinitely.

Example 2. As a second example, we consider

$$\int_{0}^{1} \frac{dx}{x}.$$

The function f in this case is defined by

$$f(x) = \frac{1}{x},$$

which becomes infinite at $x = 0$. We cut off the point $x = 0$ and start our integration at some positive number $b < 1$. (See Fig. 9.5.) That is, we consider the integral

$$\int_{b}^{1} \frac{dx}{x} = \ln x\,\Big]_{b}^{1} = \ln 1 - \ln b = \ln \frac{1}{b},$$

and investigate its behavior as b approaches zero from the right. Since

$$\lim_{b \to 0+} \int_{b}^{1} \frac{dx}{x} = \lim_{b \to 0+} \left(\ln \frac{1}{b}\right) = +\infty,$$

we say that the integral from $x = 0$ to $x = 1$ *diverges*.

$$f(x) = \frac{1}{x}$$

9.5

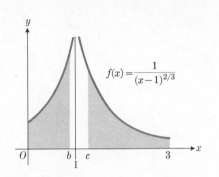

$$f(x) = \frac{1}{(x-1)^{2/3}}$$

9.6

The method to be used when the function f becomes infinite at an interior point of the range of integration is illustrated in the following example.

Example 3.
$$\int_0^3 \frac{dx}{(x-1)^{2/3}}.$$

The function

$$f(x) = \frac{1}{(x-1)^{2/3}}$$

becomes infinite at $x = 1$, which lies between the limits of integration 0 and 3. In such a case, we again cut out the point where $f(x)$ becomes infinite. This time we integrate from 0 to b, where b is slightly less than 1, and start again on the other side of 1 at c and integrate from c to 3 (Fig. 9.6). Then we get the two integrals

$$\int_0^b \frac{dx}{(x-1)^{2/3}} \quad \text{and} \quad \int_c^3 \frac{dx}{(x-1)^{2/3}}$$

to investigate. If the first of these has a definite limit as $b \to 1-$, and the second also has a definite limit as $c \to 1+$, then we say that the improper integral converges and that its value is given by

$$\int_0^3 \frac{dx}{(x-1)^{2/3}}$$

$$= \lim_{b \to 1-} \int_0^b \frac{dx}{(x-1)^{2/3}} + \lim_{c \to 1+} \int_c^3 \frac{dx}{(x-1)^{2/3}}.$$

If either limit fails to exist, we say that the given improper integral *diverges*. For this example, first,

$$\lim_{b \to 1-} \int_0^b (x-1)^{-2/3}\, dx$$

$$= \lim_{b \to 1-} [3(b-1)^{1/3} - 3(0-1)^{1/3}] = +3$$

and for the second limit,

$$\lim_{c \to 1+} \int_c^3 (x-1)^{-2/3}\, dx$$

$$= \lim_{c \to 1+} [3(3-1)^{1/3} - 3(c-1)^{1/3}] = 3\sqrt[3]{2}.$$

Since both limits exist and are finite, the original integral is said to converge and its value is $3 + 3\sqrt[3]{2}$.

Example 4. As further examples of the second type of improper integral, we consider

$$\int_1^\infty \frac{dx}{x} \quad \text{and} \quad \int_1^\infty \frac{dx}{x^2}.$$

The two curves

$$y_1 = \frac{1}{x} \quad \text{and} \quad y_2 = \frac{1}{x^2}$$

both approach the x-axis as $x \to \infty$ (Fig. 9.7). In the first case,

$$\int_1^b \frac{dx}{x} = \ln x \Big]_1^b = \ln b.$$

If we now let b take on larger and larger positive values, the logarithm of b increases indefinitely and

$$\lim_{b \to \infty} \int_1^b \frac{dx}{x} = \infty.$$

We therefore say that

$$\int_1^\infty \frac{dx}{x} = \infty$$

and that the integral *diverges*.

a|b

9.7

In the second case,

$$\int_1^b \frac{dx}{x^2} = -\frac{1}{x}\Big]_1^b = 1 - \frac{1}{b}.$$

This does have a definite limit, namely 1, as b increases indefinitely, and we say that the integral from 1 to ∞ converges and that its value is 1. That is,

$$\int_1^\infty \frac{dx}{x^2} = \lim_{b\to\infty} \int_1^b \frac{dx}{x^2} = \lim_{b\to\infty} \left(1 - \frac{1}{b}\right) = 1.$$

Sometimes we can determine whether a given integral converges or diverges by comparing it with a simpler integral.

Example 5. Even though we cannot find any simpler expression for

$$I(b) \equiv \int_1^b e^{-x^2}\, dx,$$

we can show that

$$\lim_{b\to\infty} I(b)$$

exists and is finite. For the function $I(b)$ represents the area between the x-axis and the curve

$$y = e^{-x^2}$$

between $x = 1$ and $x = b$. Clearly, this is an increasing function of b, so that there are two alternatives: Either

(a) $I(b)$ becomes infinite as $b \to \infty$, or

(b) $I(b)$ has a finite limit as $b \to \infty$.

We show that the first alternative cannot be the true one. We do this by comparing the area under the given

curve $y = e^{-x^2}$ with the area under the curve $y = e^{-x}$ (Fig. 9.8). The latter area, from $x = 1$ to $x = b$, is given by the integral

$$\int_1^b e^{-x}\, dx = -e^{-x}\Big]_1^b = e^{-1} - e^{-b},$$

which approaches the finite limit e^{-1} as $b \to \infty$. Since e^{-x^2} is less than e^{-x} for all x greater than one, the area under the given curve is certainly no greater than e^{-1} no matter how large b is.

9.8

The discussion above is summarized in the following inequalities:

$$I(b) = \int_1^b e^{-x^2}\, dx \leq \int_1^b e^{-x}\, dx = e^{-1} - e^{-b} \leq e^{-1},$$

that is,

$$I(b) \leq e^{-1} < 0.37.$$

Therefore $I(b)$ does not become infinite as $b \to \infty$, so alternative (a) is ruled out and alternative (b) must hold; that is,

$$\int_1^\infty e^{-x^2}\, dx = \lim_{b \to \infty} \int_1^b e^{-x^2}\, dx$$

converges to a definite finite value. We have not calculated what this limit is, but we know that it exists and is less than 0.37.

It should be pointed out that an improper integral may diverge without becoming infinite.

Example 6. The integral

$$\int_0^b \cos x\, dx = \sin b$$

takes all values between -1 and $+1$ as b varies between $2n\pi - \pi/2$ and $2n\pi + \pi/2$, where n is any integer. Hence,

$$\lim_{b \to \infty} \int_0^b \cos x\, dx$$

does not exist. We might say that this integral "diverges by oscillation."

EXERCISES

4/1   2-16 even

Show that the following improper integrals converge and evaluate them.

1. $\displaystyle\int_0^\infty \frac{dx}{x^2+1}$ 2. $\displaystyle\int_0^1 \frac{dx}{\sqrt{x}}$

3. $\displaystyle\int_{-1}^1 \frac{dx}{x^{2/3}}$ 4. $\displaystyle\int_1^\infty \frac{dx}{x^{1.001}}$

5. $\displaystyle\int_0^4 \frac{dx}{\sqrt{4-x}}$ 6. $\displaystyle\int_0^1 \frac{dx}{\sqrt{1-x^2}}$

7. $\displaystyle\int_0^\infty e^{-x} \cos x\, dx$ 8. $\displaystyle\int_0^1 \frac{dx}{x^{0.999}}$

Determine whether each of the following improper integrals converges or diverges.

9. $\displaystyle\int_1^\infty \frac{dx}{\sqrt{x}}$ 10. $\displaystyle\int_1^\infty \frac{dx}{x^3}$

11. $\displaystyle\int_1^\infty \frac{dx}{x^3+1}$ 12. $\displaystyle\int_0^\infty \frac{dx}{x^3}$

13. $\displaystyle\int_0^\infty \frac{dx}{x^3+1}$ 14. $\displaystyle\int_0^\infty \frac{dx}{1+e^x}$

15. $\displaystyle\int_0^{\pi/2} \tan x\, dx$ 16. $\displaystyle\int_{-1}^1 \frac{dx}{x^2}$

17. $\displaystyle\int_{-1}^1 \frac{dx}{x^{2/5}}$ 18. $\displaystyle\int_0^\infty \frac{dx}{\sqrt{x}}$

19. $\displaystyle\int_0^\infty \frac{dx}{\sqrt{x+x^4}}$

Hint. Compare the integral with $\int dx/\sqrt{x}$ for x near zero and with $\int dx/x^2$ for large x.

9.11 NUMERICAL METHODS FOR APPROXIMATING DEFINITE INTEGRALS

Certain important integrals that arise in physical and mathematical problems cannot be expressed in terms of the so-called elementary functions. For example, the length of one arch of the curve $y = \sin x$, Fig. 9.9, is given by

$$L = \int_0^\pi \sqrt{1 + \cos^2 x}\, dx.$$

The integral cannot be evaluated by any of the methods we have studied thus far. Nevertheless it can be evaluated numerically to any required number of decimal places by several methods. The trapezoidal rule is one. We indicate another below.

Any definite integral $\int_a^b f(x)\, dx$ can be interpreted as an area or as a combination of areas, some added and some subtracted. Such an integral can therefore be approximated by any method of approximating these areas. Instruments called *planimeters* are useful in this connection, but they have two drawbacks:

(a) the curve $y = f(x)$ must be drawn with some care, and

(b) the accuracy of the planimeter is limited to approximately the order of 1%.

Simpson's method, which we shall now study, avoids both of these drawbacks.

This method is based on the simple formula

$$A_p = \frac{h}{3}\,(y_0 + 4y_1 + y_2)$$

9.9

9.10

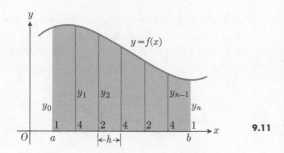

9.11

for the area under the arc of the parabola

$$y = Ax^2 + Bx + C$$

between $x = -h$ and $x = +h$. (See Fig. 9.10.*)

This formula is readily established as follows: In the first place, we have

$$A_p = \int_{-h}^{h} (Ax^2 + Bx + C)\, dx$$

$$= \frac{2Ah^3}{3} + 2Ch.$$

Since the curve passes through the three points

$$(-h, y_0), \quad (0, y_1), \quad \text{and} \quad (h, y_2),$$

———————

* We choose the interval $-h \le x \le h$ to simplify the algebra. There is no loss in generality in so doing, because the area does not depend on the location of the y-axis.

we also have

$$y_0 = Ah^2 - Bh + C, \qquad y_1 = C,$$
$$y_2 = Ah^2 + Bh + C,$$

from which there follows

$$C = y_1,$$
$$Ah^2 - Bh = y_0 - y_1,$$
$$Ah^2 + Bh = y_2 - y_1,$$
$$2Ah^2 = y_0 + y_2 - 2y_1.$$

Hence, expressing the area A_p in terms of the ordinates y_0, y_1, and y_2, we have

$$A_p = \frac{h}{3}(2Ah^2 + 6C) = \frac{h}{3}[(y_0 + y_2 - 2y_1) + 6y_1]$$

or

$$A_p = \frac{h}{3}(y_0 + 4y_1 + y_2). \tag{1}$$

Simpson's rule follows from applying this result to successive pieces of the curve $y = f(x)$ between $x = a$ and $x = b$. Each separate piece of the curve, covering an x-subinterval of width $2h$, is approximated by an arc of a parabola through its ends and its mid-point. The area under each parabolic arc is then given by an expression like Eq. (1) and the results are added to give

$$A_S = \frac{h}{3}[y_0 + 4y_1 + 2y_2 + 4y_3 + 2y_4 + \cdots$$
$$+ 2y_{n-2} + 4y_{n-1} + y_n], \tag{2}$$

which is taken as the approximate value of $\int_a^b f(x)\, dx$. In Eq. (2), $y_0, y_1, y_2, \ldots, y_n$ are the ordinates of the curve $y = f(x)$ at the points of abscissas

$$x_0 = a,$$
$$x_1 = a + h,$$
$$x_2 = a + 2h,$$
$$\vdots$$
$$x_n = a + nh = b$$

corresponding to a subdivision of the interval $a \le x \le b$ into n equal subintervals each of width $h = (b - a)/n$. (See Fig. 9.11.) The number n of subdivisions must be an _even_ integer if we are to apply the method. The application of the rule, Eq. (2), does not require a graph of the curve

$y = f(x)$ nor a determination of the approximating parabolic arcs. All the work is strictly arithmetical. For a continuous function f, the approximations generally get better as n increases and h gets smaller. By an extension of the Mean Value Theorem, it is possible to prove* that if f is continuous on $[a, b]$ and four times differentiable on (a, b), then there is a number c between a and b such that

$$\int_a^b f(x) \, dx = A_S - \frac{b-a}{180} f^{(4)}(c) \cdot h^4.$$

Problem 1. Use Simpson's rule with four subdivisions to find an approximate value of $\ln 2 = \int_1^2 (1/x) \, dx$.

Solution. We arrange the work in tabular form.

x	$y = 1/x$	Weighting factor	Product
1.00	1.00000	1	1.00000
1.25	0.80000	4	3.20000
1.50	0.66667	2	1.33333
1.75	0.57143	4	2.28572
2.00	0.50000	1	0.50000
		Sum =	8.31905

Since $h = \frac{1}{4}$, we must multiply the last sum by $h/3 = \frac{1}{12}$. Hence $A_S = \frac{1}{12}(8.31905) = 0.69325$. The approximation $\ln 2 \approx 0.69235$ is in error by 1 part in 6900 or about one-seventieth of one percent. Greater accuracy may be obtained by taking twice as many subdivisions.

EXERCISES

Find approximate numerical values for the following definite integrals by using Simpson's rule (a) with $n = 2$, and (b) with $n = 4$. Where possible, compare your answer with (c) the exact value.

1. $\int_0^2 x^2 \, dx$ 2. $\int_0^\pi \sin x \, dx$ 3. $\int_0^\pi \sqrt{\sin x} \, dx$

---

* See, for example, J. M. H. Olmsted, *Intermediate Analysis*, Appleton-Century-Crofts, p. 146.

4. $\int_0^\pi \dfrac{dx}{2 + \cos x}$ 5. $\int_0^\pi \dfrac{\sin x}{x} \, dx$ 6. $\int_0^1 \dfrac{dx}{x^2 + 1}$

7. Show that

$$\int_3^\infty e^{-3x} \, dx = \tfrac{1}{3} e^{-9} = 0.000041,$$

and hence that $\int_3^\infty e^{-x^2} \, dx < 0.000041$. Show further that $\int_0^\infty e^{-x^2} \, dx$ can be replaced by $\int_0^3 e^{-x^2} \, dx$ without introducing any errors in the first three decimal places of the answer. Evaluate this last integral by Simpson's rule with $n = 6$. (This illustrates one method by which a convergent improper integral may be approximated numerically.)

REVIEW QUESTIONS AND EXERCISES

1. What are some of the general methods presented in this chapter for finding an indefinite integral?

2. What substitution(s) would you consider trying if the integrand contained the following:

   (a) $\sqrt{x^2 + 9}$,   (b) $\sqrt{x^2 - 9}$,

   (c) $\sqrt{9 - x^2}$,   (d) $\sin^3 x \cos^2 x$,

   (e) $\sin^2 x \cos^2 x$,   (f) $\dfrac{1 + \sin \theta}{2 + \cos \theta}$?

3. What method(s) would you try if the integrand contained

   (a) $\sin^{-1} x$,   (b) $\ln x$,

   (c) $\sqrt{1 + 2x - x^2}$,   (d) $x \sin x$,

   (e) $\dfrac{2x + 3}{x^2 - 5x + 6}$,   (f) $\sin 5x \cos 3x$,

   (g) $\dfrac{1 - \sqrt{x}}{1 + \sqrt[4]{x}}$,   (h) $x\sqrt{2x + 3}$?

4. What numerical methods do you know for approximating a definite integral? How can an approximation usually be improved upon to give greater accuracy?

5. Discuss two types of improper integral. Define convergence and divergence of each type. Give examples of convergent and divergent integrals of each type.

MISCELLANEOUS EXERCISES

Evaluate the following integrals.

1. $\displaystyle\int \frac{\cos x\, dx}{\sqrt{1+\sin x}}$

2. $\displaystyle\int \frac{\sin^{-1} x\, dx}{\sqrt{1-x^2}}$

3. $\displaystyle\int \frac{\tan x\, dx}{\cos^2 x}$

4. $\displaystyle\int \frac{dx}{1-\sin x}$

5. $\displaystyle\int e^{\ln \sqrt{x}}\, dx$

6. $\displaystyle\int \frac{\cos \sqrt{x}}{\sqrt{x}}\, dx$

7. $\displaystyle\int \frac{dx}{\sqrt{x^2+2x+2}}$

8. $\displaystyle\int \frac{(3x-7)\, dx}{(x-1)(x-2)(x-3)}$

9. $\displaystyle\int x^2 e^x\, dx$

10. $\displaystyle\int \sqrt{x^2+1}\, dx$

11. $\displaystyle\int \frac{e^t\, dt}{1+e^{2t}}$

12. $\displaystyle\int \frac{dx}{e^x+e^{-x}}$

13. $\displaystyle\int \frac{dx}{1+\sqrt{x}}$

14. $\displaystyle\int \frac{dx}{\sqrt{1+\sqrt{x}}}$

15. $\displaystyle\int t^{2/3}(t^{5/3}+1)^{2/3}\, dt$

16. $\displaystyle\int \frac{\cot x\, dx}{\ln (\sin x)}$

17. $\displaystyle\int \frac{dt}{\sqrt{e^t+1}}$

18. $\displaystyle\int \frac{dt}{\sqrt{1-e^{-t}}}$

19. $\displaystyle\int \frac{\sin x\, e^{\sec x}}{\cos^2 x}\, dx$

20. $\displaystyle\int \frac{\cos x\, dx}{1+\sin^2 x}$

21. $\displaystyle\int \frac{dx}{\sqrt{2x-x^2}}$

22. $\displaystyle\int \frac{\sin x\, dx}{1+\cos^2 x}$

23. $\displaystyle\int \frac{\cos 2t}{1+\sin 2t}\, dt$

24. $\displaystyle\int \frac{dx}{\sin x \cos x}$

25. $\displaystyle\int \sqrt{1+\sin x}\, dx$

26. $\displaystyle\int \sqrt{1-\sin x}\, dx$

27. $\displaystyle\int \frac{dx}{\sqrt{(a^2-x^2)^3}}$

28. $\displaystyle\int \frac{dx}{\sqrt{(a^2+x^2)^3}}$

29. $\displaystyle\int \frac{\sin x\, dx}{\cos^2 x - 5\cos x + 4}$

30. $\displaystyle\int \frac{e^{2x}\, dx}{\sqrt[3]{1+e^x}}$

31. $\displaystyle\int \frac{dx}{x(x+1)(x+2)\cdots (x+m)}$

32. $\displaystyle\int \frac{dx}{x^6-1}$

33. $\displaystyle\int \frac{dy}{y(2y^3+1)^2}$

34. $\displaystyle\int \frac{x\, dx}{1+\sqrt{x}}$

35. $\displaystyle\int \frac{dx}{x(x^2+1)^2}$

36. $\displaystyle\int \ln\sqrt{x-1}\, dx$

37. $\displaystyle\int \frac{dx}{e^x-1}$

38. $\displaystyle\int \frac{d\theta}{1-\tan^2 \theta}$

39. $\displaystyle\int \frac{(x+1)\, dx}{x^2(x-1)}$

40. $\displaystyle\int \frac{x\, dx}{x^2+4x+3}$

41. $\displaystyle\int \frac{du}{(e^u-e^{-u})^2}$

42. $\displaystyle\int \frac{4\, dx}{x^3+4x}$

43. $\displaystyle\int \frac{dx}{5x^2+8x+5}$

44. $\displaystyle\int \frac{\sqrt{x^2-a^2}}{x}\, dx$

45. $\displaystyle\int e^x \cos 2x\, dx$

46. $\displaystyle\int \frac{dx}{x(3\sqrt{x}+1)}$

47. $\displaystyle\int \frac{dx}{x(1+\sqrt[3]{x})}$

48. $\displaystyle\int \frac{\cot \theta\, d\theta}{1+\sin^2 \theta}$

49. $\displaystyle\int \frac{z^5\, dz}{\sqrt{1+z^2}}$

50. $\displaystyle\int \frac{e^{4t}\, dt}{(1+e^{2t})^{2/3}}$

51. $\displaystyle\int \frac{dx}{x^{1/5}\sqrt{1+x^{4/5}}}$

52. $\displaystyle\int x \sec^2 x\, dx$

53. $\displaystyle\int x \sin^{-1} x\, dx$

54. $\displaystyle\int \frac{(x^3+x^2)\, dx}{x^2+x-2}$

55. $\displaystyle\int \frac{x^3+1}{x^3-x}\, dx$

56. $\displaystyle\int \frac{x\, dx}{(x-1)^2}$

57. $\displaystyle\int \frac{(2e^{2x}-e^x)\, dx}{\sqrt{3e^{2x}-6e^x-1}}$

58. $\displaystyle\int \frac{(x+1)\, dx}{(x^2+2x-3)^{2/3}}$

59. $\displaystyle\int \frac{dy}{(2y+1)\sqrt{y^2+y}}$

60. $\displaystyle\int \frac{dx}{x^2\sqrt{a^2-x^2}}$

61. $\displaystyle\int (1-x^2)^{3/2}\, dx$

62. $\displaystyle\int \ln (x+\sqrt{1+x^2})\, dx$

63. $\displaystyle\int x \tan^2 x\, dx$

64. $\displaystyle\int \frac{\tan^{-1} x}{x^2}\, dx$

65. $\displaystyle\int x \cos^2 x\, dx$

66. $\int x^2 \sin x \, dx$

67. $\int x \sin^2 x \, dx$

100. $\int \dfrac{dt}{t - \sqrt{1 - t^2}}$

101. $\int e^{-x} \tan^{-1}(e^x) \, dx$

68. $\int \dfrac{dt}{t^4 + 4t^2 + 3}$

69. $\int \dfrac{du}{e^{4u} + 4e^{2u} + 3}$

102. $\int \sin^{-1} \sqrt{x} \, dx$

103. $\int \ln(x + \sqrt{x}) \, dx$

70. $\int x \ln \sqrt{x + 2} \, dx$

71. $\int (x + 1)^2 e^x \, dx$

104. $\int \tan^{-1} \sqrt{x} \, dx$

105. $\int \ln(x^2 + x) \, dx$

72. $\int \sec^{-1} x \, dx$

73. $\int \dfrac{8 \, dx}{x^4 + 2x^3}$

106. $\int \ln(\sqrt{x} + \sqrt{1 + x}) \, dx$

74. $\int \dfrac{x \, dx}{x^4 - 16}$

75. $\int_0^{\pi/2} \dfrac{\cos x \, dx}{\sqrt{1 + \cos x}}$

107. $\int \cos \sqrt{x} \, dx$

108. $\int \sin \sqrt{x} \, dx$

76. $\int \dfrac{\cos x \, dx}{\sin^3 x - \sin x}$

77. $\int \dfrac{du}{(e^u + e^{-u})^2}$

109. $\int \tan^{-1} \sqrt{x + 1} \, dx$

110. $\int \sqrt{1 - x^2} \sin^{-1} x \, dx$

78. $\int \dfrac{x \, dx}{1 + \sqrt{x} + x}$

79. $\int \dfrac{\sec^2 t \, dt}{\sec^2 t - 3 \tan t + 1}$

111. $\int x \sin^2(2x) \, dx$

112. $\int \dfrac{\tan x \, dx}{\tan x + \sec x}$

80. $\int \dfrac{dt}{\sec^2 t + \tan^2 t}$

81. $\int \dfrac{dx}{1 + \cos^2 x}$

113. $\int \dfrac{dt}{\sqrt{e^{2t} + 1}}$

82. $\int e^{2t} \cos(e^t) \, dt$

83. $\int \ln \sqrt{x^2 + 1} \, dx$

114. $\int \dfrac{dx}{(\cos^2 x + 4 \sin x - 5) \cos x}$

84. $\int x \ln(x^3 + x) \, dx$

85. $\int x^3 e^{x^2} \, dx$

115. $\int \dfrac{dt}{a + be^{ct}}, \quad abc \neq 0$

86. $\int \dfrac{\cos x \, dx}{\sqrt{4 - \cos^2 x}}$

87. $\int \dfrac{\sec^2 x \, dx}{\sqrt{4 - \sec^2 x}}$

116. $\int \sqrt{\dfrac{1 - \cos x}{\cos \alpha - \cos x}} \, dx, \quad \begin{array}{l} \alpha \text{ constant,} \\ 0 < \alpha < x < \pi \end{array}$

88. $\int x^2 \sin(1 - x) \, dx$

89. $\int \dfrac{dx}{1 + \sin x}$

117. $\int \dfrac{dx}{\sin x - \cos x}$

118. $\int \ln \sqrt{1 + x^2} \, dx$

90. $\int \dfrac{dx}{1 + 2 \sin x}$

91. $\int \dfrac{dx}{\sin^3 x}$

119. $\int \ln(2x^2 + 4) \, dx$

120. $\int \dfrac{x^3}{\sqrt{1 - x^2}} \, dx$

92. $\int \dfrac{dx}{\cot^3 x}$

93. $\int (\sin^{-1} x)^2 \, dx$

121. $\int \dfrac{dx}{x(2 + \ln x)}$

122. $\int \dfrac{\cos 2x - 1}{\cos 2x + 1} \, dx$

94. $\int x \ln \sqrt[3]{3x + 1} \, dx$

95. $\int \dfrac{x^3 \, dx}{(x^2 + 1)^2}$

123. $\int \dfrac{dx}{x^3 + 1}$

124. $\int \dfrac{e^{2x} \, dx}{\sqrt[4]{e^x + 1}}$

96. $\int \dfrac{x \, dx}{\sqrt{1 - x}}$

97. $\int x \sqrt{2x + 1} \, dx$

125. $\int \dfrac{e^x \, dx}{1 + e^{2x}}$

126. $\int e^{\sqrt{t}} \, dt$

98. $\int \ln(x + \sqrt{x^2 - 1}) \, dx$

127. $\int \sin \sqrt{x + 1} \, dx$

128. $\int \cos \sqrt{1 - x} \, dx$

99. $\int \ln(x - \sqrt{x^2 - 1}) \, dx$

Evaluate the limits in Exercises 129 through 135 by identifying each one with an appropriate definite integral and evaluating the latter.

129. $\displaystyle\lim_{n\to\infty}\left(\frac{1}{n+1}+\frac{1}{n+2}+\cdots+\frac{1}{2n}\right)$

130. $\displaystyle\lim_{n\to\infty}\left(\frac{1}{\sqrt{n^2}}+\frac{1}{\sqrt{n^2+n}}+\frac{1}{\sqrt{n^2+2n}}+\cdots+\frac{1}{\sqrt{n^2+(n-1)n}}\right)$

131. $\displaystyle\lim_{n\to\infty}\left(\frac{\sin 0+\sin\dfrac{\pi}{n}+\sin\dfrac{2\pi}{n}+\cdots+\sin\dfrac{(n-1)\pi}{n}}{n}\right)$

132. $\displaystyle\lim_{n\to\infty}\left(\frac{1+\sqrt[n]{e}+\sqrt[n]{e^2}+\sqrt[n]{e^3}+\cdots+\sqrt[n]{e^{n-1}}}{n}\right)$

133. $\displaystyle\lim_{n\to\infty}\left(\frac{n}{n^2+0^2}+\frac{n}{n^2+1^2}+\frac{n}{n^2+2^2}+\cdots+\frac{n}{n^2+(n-1)^2}\right)$

134. $\displaystyle\lim_{n\to\infty}\sum_{k=1}^{n}\ln\sqrt[n]{1+\frac{k}{n}}$ 135. $\displaystyle\lim_{n\to\infty}\sum_{k=0}^{n-1}\frac{1}{\sqrt{n^2-k^2}}$

136. Show that $\int_0^\infty x^3 e^{-x^2}\,dx$ is a convergent integral, and evaluate it.

137. Show that $\int_0^1 \ln x\,dx$ is a convergent integral and find its value. Sketch the integrand $y=\ln x$ for $0 < x \le 1$.

138. Assuming that $|\alpha| \ne |\beta|$, prove that

$$\lim_{T\to\infty}\frac{1}{T}\int_0^T \sin\alpha x \sin\beta x\,dx = 0.$$

139. Evaluate $\displaystyle\lim_{h\to 0}\frac{1}{h}\int_2^{2+h} e^{-x^2}\,dx.$

140. At points of the curve $y^2 = 4px$, lines of length $h = y$ are drawn perpendicular to its plane. Find the area of the surface formed by these lines at points of the curve between $(0,0)$ and $(p, 2p)$.

141. A plane figure is bounded by a 90° arc of a circle of radius r and a straight line. Find its area and its centroid.

142. Find the coordinates of the center of gravity of the area bounded by the curves $y = e^x$, $x = 1$, and $y = 1$.

143. At points of a circle of radius r, perpendiculars to its plane are erected, the perpendicular at each point P being of length ks, where s is the arc of the circle from a fixed point A to P. Find the area of the surface formed by the perpendiculars along the arc beginning at A and extending once around the circle.

144. A plate in the first quadrant, bounded by the curves $y = e^x$, $y = 1$, and $x = 4$, is submerged vertically in water with its upper corner on the surface. The surface of the water is given by the line $y = e^4$. Find the total force on one side of the plate if the weight of water is 62.5 lb/ft³, and if the units of x and y are also measured in feet.

145. The area under the curve $xy = 1$, for $x \ge 1$, is rotated about the x-axis. If A is the area under the curve, V is the volume generated, and S is the surface area of this volume,

(a) is A finite?   (b) is V finite?   (c) is S finite?

Give reasons for your answers.

146. Answer the questions of Exercise 145 if the curve given there is replaced by the curve $y = e^{-x}$. Give reasons for your answers.

147. Find the centroid of the area bounded by $y = e^x$, $y = 0$, $x = 0$, $x = 1$.

148. Find the centroid of the area bounded by $y = \ln x$, $x = 1$, $y = 1$.

149. Find the length of arc of $y = \ln x$ from $x = 1$ to $x = e$.

150. The arc of Exercise 149 is rotated about the y-axis. Find the surface area generated. Check your answer by comparing it with the area of a frustum of a suitably related cone.

151. Find the length of arc of the curve $y = e^x$ from $x = 0$ to $x = 2$.

152. The arc of Exercise 151 is rotated about the x-axis. Find the surface area generated. Compare this area with the area of a suitably related frustum of a cone to check your answer.

153. One arch of the curve $y = \cos x$ is rotated about the x-axis. Find the surface area generated.

154. Use Simpson's rule to compute, approximately, the length of arc of $y = \cos x$ from $x = -\pi/2$ to $x = \pi/2$. Check your answer by consulting a table of elliptic integrals, if one is available.

155. A thin wire is bent into the shape of one arch of the curve $y = \cos x$. Find its center of mass (see Exercises 153, 154).

156. The area between the graph of $y = \ln (1/x)$, the x-axis, and the y-axis is revolved around the x-axis. Find the volume of the solid it generates.

157. Find the total perimeter of the curve
$$x^{2/3} + y^{2/3} = a^{2/3}.$$

158. Find the length of arc of the curve $y = \ln (\cos x)$ from $x = 0$ to $x = \pi/3$.

159. Find the area of the surface generated by rotating the curve
$$x^{2/3} + y^{2/3} = a^{2/3}$$
about the x-axis.

160. A thin homogeneous wire is bent into the shape of one arch of the curve $x^{2/3} + y^{2/3} = a^{2/3}$. Find its center of mass (see Exercises 157, 159).

161. Determine whether the integral
$$\int_1^\infty \ln x \, \frac{dx}{x^2}$$
converges or diverges.

162. Sketch the curves
   (a) $y = x - e^x$,   (b) $y = e^{(x - e^x)}$,

and show the behavior of each for large $|x|$.

Show that the following integrals converge and compute their values.

   (c) $\int_{-\infty}^b e^{(x - e^x)} \, dx$ (d) $\int_{-\infty}^\infty e^{(x - e^x)} \, dx$

163. The gamma function $\Gamma(x)$ is defined, for $x > 0$, by the definite integral
$$\Gamma(x) = \int_0^\infty t^{x-1} e^{-t} \, dt.$$

   (a) Sketch graphs of the integrand $y = t^{x-1} e^{-t}$ against t, $t > 0$, for the three typical cases $x = \frac{1}{2}$, 1, 3. Find maxima, minima, and points of inflection (if they exist).

   (b) Show that the integral converges if $x > 0$.

   (c) Show that the integral diverges if $x \leq 0$.

   (d) Using the integration by parts, demonstrate that $\Gamma(x + 1) = x\Gamma(x)$, for $x > 0$.

   (e) Using the result of part (d), show that, if n is a positive integer, $\Gamma(n) = (n - 1)!$ where $0! = 1$ (by definition) and if m is a positive integer, $m!$ is the product of the positive integers from 1 through m inclusive.

   (f) Discuss how one might compute a table of values of $\Gamma(x)$ for the domain $1 \leq x \leq 2$, say. Consult such a table, if available, and sketch the graph of $y = \Gamma(x)$ for $0 < x \leq 3$.

164. Determine whether the integral $\int_0^\infty t^{x-1} (\ln t) e^{-t} \, dt$ converges or diverges for fixed $x > 0$. Sketch the integrand $y = t^{x-1} \ln t \, e^{-t}$ vs. t, $t > 0$, for the two cases $x = \frac{1}{2}$ and $x = 3$.

165. Solve the differential equation $d^2x/dt^2 = -k^2x$, subject to the initial conditions $x = a$, $dx/dt = 0$ when $t = 0$.

   Hint. Let $dx/dt = v$,
$$d^2x/dt^2 = dv/dt = v \, dv/dx.$$

166. Find $\displaystyle\lim_{n \to \infty} \int_0^1 \frac{ny^{n-1}}{1+y} \, dy$.

167. Prove that if n is a positive integer, or zero, then
$$\int_{-1}^1 (1 - x^2)^n \, dx = \frac{2^{2n+1}(n!)^2}{(2n+1)!},$$
with $0! = 1$; $n! = 1 \cdot 2 \cdots n$ for $n \geq 1$.

PLANE ANALYTIC GEOMETRY

CHAPTER 10

10.1 CURVES AND EQUATIONS

We use analytic geometry, which combines algebra and calculus with geometry, in two types of problem:

(a) to study the geometric properties of a curve when its equation is given, and

(b) to find an equation of the curve when its geometric properties are known.

Locus

An equation of the form

$$F(x, y) = 0 \qquad (1)$$

describes a set which is the locus of all and only those points $P(x, y)$ whose coordinates satisfy the given equation. If the locus for example, is a curve, every point on the curve must satisfy the equation and every point that satisfies the equation lies on the curve. We have already had some experience in analyzing a given equation to find the turning points and points of inflection of the curve it represents. We shall now consider certain other important characteristics that we may find by investigating a given equation.

In this chapter we shall assume that the scales on the x- and y-axes are the same, unless we specifically note otherwise.

Symmetry

If the equation of the curve is unaltered when x is replaced by $-x$, that is, if

$$F(x, y) = F(-x, y),$$

then the points (x_1, y_1) and $(-x_1, y_1)$ are both on the curve when either of them is. Then the curve is symmetric with respect to the y-axis. (See Fig. 10.1a.) In particular, an equation which contains only even powers of x represents such a curve.

Other symmetries that are easily detected are:

Symmetry about the x-axis, if the equation is unaltered when y is replaced by $-y$; in particular, if only even powers of y occur. (See Fig. 10.1b.)

Symmetry about the origin, if the equation is unaltered when x and y are replaced by $-x$ and $-y$ respectively. (See Fig. 10.1c.)

a | b

c | d

10.1

Symmetry about the 45° line $y = x$ if the equation is unaltered when x and y are interchanged. (See Fig. 10.1d.)

Example 1. $\qquad x^2 + y^2 = 1.$

This curve is symmetric about both axes, about the origin, and about the line $y = x$.

Example 2. $\qquad x^2 - y^2 = 1.$

This curve is symmetric about both axes and the origin. Not symmetric about the line $y = x$.

Example 3. $\qquad xy = 1.$

This curve is not symmetric about either axis. Symmetric about the origin and about the line $y = x$.

Extent

Only real values of x and y are considered in determining the points (x, y) whose coordinates satisfy a given equation. When even powers of a variable appear in the equation, the solution for that variable may involve square roots (or other even roots). The *extent* of the curve may then be limited by the condition that negative numbers do not have real square roots.

Example 4. $\qquad x^2 + y^2 = 1.$

When this equation is solved for y, we get

$$y = \pm\sqrt{1 - x^2}.$$

The quantity under the radical is negative if $|x| > 1$. The extent of the curve in the x-direction is therefore limited to the interval $-1 \le x \le 1$. By symmetry about the line $y = x$, the curve is also limited in the y-direction to $-1 \le y \le 1$.

Example 5. $\qquad x^2 - y^2 = 1.$

Solving for y, we get

$$y = \pm\sqrt{x^2 - 1}.$$

In this case, y is imaginary unless $|x| \ge 1$. There is no curve between the two lines $x = -1$ and $x = +1$. Solving for x, we get

$$x = \pm\sqrt{1 + y^2}.$$

The quantity under the radical is positive (actually it is greater than or equal to one) for all real values of y, $-\infty < y < +\infty$. The extent of this curve is not limited in the y-direction.

Intercepts

The point or points where a given curve crosses the x-axis can be found by setting $y = 0$ in the equation and solving for x. These abscissas are called the *x-intercepts*. The y-intercepts are found in an analogous way, by setting $x = 0$. If the labor involved in finding the intercepts is not excessive, they may be determined and will give specific points on the curve.

Example 6. $\qquad x^2 + y^2 = 1$.

Setting $y = 0$, we have $x^2 = 1$. Therefore $(1, 0)$ and $(-1, 0)$ give the x-intercepts. By symmetry, $(0, 1)$ and $(0, -1)$ give the y-intercepts.

Example 7. $\qquad x^2 - y^2 = 1$.

Setting $y = 0$, we find the x-intercepts at $(1, 0)$ and at $(-1, 0)$. Setting $x = 0$, we obtain $y^2 = -1$, which has no real solutions. The curve does not have intercepts on the y-axis (see Example 5).

Example 8. $\qquad xy = 1$.

Setting either $x = 0$ or $y = 0$ leads to the equation $0 = 1$, which has no solutions. There are no x- or y-intercepts.

Asymptotes

As the point $P(x, y)$ on a given curve moves farther and farther away from the vicinity of the origin, it may happen that the distance between P and some fixed line tends to zero. In such a case the line is called an *asymptote* of the curve. For example, if the equation of the curve has the form

$$y = \frac{N(x)}{D(x)}, \qquad (2)$$

where $N(x)$ and $D(x)$ are polynomials without any factors in common, and if $x = c$ is a root of the equation

$$D(x) = 0, \qquad (3)$$

10.2

then as the x-coordinate of the tracing point $P(x, y)$ approaches c, two things will occur:

1. $y \to \infty$. Hence the distance $OP \to \infty$, and

2. $(x - c) \to 0$. That is, the horizontal distance $P'P$ between the vertical line $x = c$ and the curve tends to zero (see Fig. 10.2). In other words, *the line $x = c$ is an asymptote of the curve in Eq. (2) if $x = c$ makes the denominator, $D(x)$, vanish.* Such asymptotes are thus found by solving the equation explicitly for y in terms of x; then, if the result is a fraction, we set the denominator of the fraction equal to zero and solve for the numerical values of x. A similar procedure with the roles of x and y reversed shows that values of y which cause the denominator to vanish in the expression

$$x = \frac{f(y)}{g(y)} \qquad (4)$$

may give horizontal asymptotes of the curve. An alternate method for finding such asymptotes is to let $x \to \pm\infty$ (provided the extent of the curve does not prohibit this) in Eq. (2) and find the limiting values of y.

Example 9. $\qquad y^2(x^2 - x) = x^2 + 1$. $\qquad (5)$

Solving for y, we obtain

$$y = \pm\sqrt{\frac{x^2 + 1}{x(x - 1)}}. \qquad (6)$$

The expression under the radical must not be negative, so no portion of the curve lies between the lines $x = 0$ and $x = 1$ (see Fig. 10.3). But all values of $x > 1$ and all negative values of x, that is, $x < 0$, are permissible.

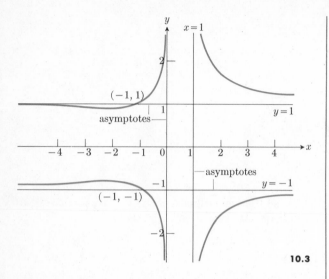

10.3

As x approaches zero *from the left*, $y \to \pm\infty$; and as x approaches one *from the right*, $y \to \pm\infty$. The lines $x = 0$ and $x = 1$ are asymptotes of the curve. Since arbitrarily large values of $|x|$ are permitted, we also investigate the behavior of the curve as $x \to -\infty$ and again as $x \to +\infty$. The expression

$$\frac{\infty^2 + 1}{\infty(\infty - 1)},$$

which appears if we substitute $x = \infty$ directly into (6), is meaningless, but if we write the equation of the curve in the equivalent form

$$y^2 = \frac{x^2 + 1}{x^2 - x} = \frac{1 + \dfrac{1}{x^2}}{1 - \dfrac{1}{x}}, \tag{7}$$

we readily see that $y^2 \to 1$ as $x \to \infty$ or as $x \to -\infty$. Thus the lines $y = 1$ and $y = -1$ are also asymptotes of the curve. We now scrutinize Eq. (7) more closely to see whether or not y^2 is necessarily always greater than one, or always less than one, or may be equal to one. Certainly when x tends to $+\infty$, the numerator in (7) is greater than one, while the denominator is less than one, and hence the fraction is larger than one. That is,

$$y^2 > 1 \quad \text{and} \quad y^2 \to 1 \quad \text{as } x \to +\infty. \tag{8}$$

On the other hand, when x tends to $-\infty$, both $1/x^2$ and $-1/x$ are positive, so that both the numerator and de-

nominator in (7) are greater than one. However, $1/x^2$ will be less than $-1/x$, so that the numerator is less than the denominator. That is,

$$y^2 < 1 \quad \text{and} \quad y^2 \to 1 \quad \text{as } x \to -\infty. \tag{9}$$

To determine whether or not we may ever have $y^2 = 1$, we try it, say in (5), and find

$$y^2 = 1 \quad \text{when} \quad x = -1. \tag{10}$$

We now have quite a bit of information about the curve represented by Eq. (5). It is immediately evident that the curve is symmetric about the x-axis, because y may be replaced by $-y$ without changing the equation. There is no curve between $x = 0$ and $x = 1$. The lines

$$x = 0, \quad x = 1, \quad y = 1, \quad y = -1$$

are asymptotes of the curve. It crosses $y = 1$ and $y = -1$ at $x = -1$. There is no x-intercept, because putting $y = 0$ in Eq. (5) requires $0 = x^2 + 1$, which has only imaginary roots. Using this information, we may sketch the curve with a fair degree of accuracy (see Fig. 10.3). In fact, it becomes apparent that the curve has a minimum (and a symmetrically located maximum) somewhat to the left of $x = -1$, and that there is also a point of inflection to the left of this turning point. To find these points accurately requires that we determine dy/dx and d^2y/dx^2. The turning points will be found to occur at

$$(-1 - \sqrt{2}, \pm\sqrt{2\sqrt{2} - 2}).$$

The algebra involved in finding the points of inflection is excessive.

Direction at a point

The three curves

(a) $\qquad y = x, \quad$ for which $\quad \dfrac{dy}{dx} = 1,$

(b) $\qquad y = x^2, \quad$ for which $\quad \dfrac{dy}{dx} = 2x,$

(c) $\qquad y = \sqrt{x}, \quad$ for which $\quad \dfrac{dy}{dx} = \dfrac{1}{2\sqrt{x}},$

all pass through the origin and the point $(1, 1)$. But their behavior for small values of x is radically different. The individual nature of any one of them in the vicinity of $(0, 0)$ is better indicated if the

10.4

direction of the curve at that point is also given. This, of course, means that it is desirable to find the slope of each of them at $(0, 0)$. We find the inclination angles are respectively $45°$, $0°$, and $90°$ (see Fig. 10.4).

Example 10. $\quad y^2 = x^2(1 - x^2)$.

This curve has symmetry with respect to both axes and the origin (see Fig. 10.5). Its extent in the x-direction is limited to $|x| \leq 1$. Differentiating implicitly, we find

$$y' = \frac{x - 2x^3}{y}.$$

At one x-intercept, $(1, 0)$, the slope is infinite. At the origin, which is another intercept, the expression we have for y' becomes $0/0$, which is meaningless. However, if we replace y in the denominator by its equivalent expression in terms of x, we obtain

$$y' = \frac{x(1 - 2x^2)}{\pm x\sqrt{1 - x^2}} = \pm \frac{1 - 2x^2}{\sqrt{1 - x^2}}.$$

As $x \to 0$, this gives $y' = \pm 1$. The same result can be obtained by considering the limit, as P approaches the origin O, of the slope of the secant line through O and

a second point $P(x, y)$ on the curve. Denoting this slope by m_{sec}, we have

$$m_{\text{sec}} = \frac{\text{rise}}{\text{run}} = \frac{y - 0}{x - 0} = \pm\sqrt{1 - x^2}.$$

When $P \to O$, $x \to 0$ and $m_{\text{sec}} \to \pm 1$. The double sign means, of course, that if P approaches O along the branch of the curve given by

$$y = x\sqrt{1 - x^2},$$

then the limit of the slope of the secant is $+1$, while the branch given by

$$y = -x\sqrt{1 - x^2}$$

has slope -1 at the origin (Fig. 10.5). We also find turning points at $x = \pm\sqrt{\frac{1}{2}}$, $y = \pm\frac{1}{2}$. Note that we may determine the extent of the curve in the y-direction by comparing the equation of the curve in the form

$$x^4 - x^2 + y^2 = 0$$

with the quadratic equation

$$az^2 + bz + c = 0,$$

whose solutions are

$$z = \frac{-b \pm \sqrt{b^2 - 4ac}}{2a}.$$

Taking $z = x^2$, $a = 1$, $b = -1$, and $c = y^2$, this leads to

$$x^2 = \frac{1 \pm \sqrt{1 - 4y^2}}{2},$$

and it is seen that there is no portion of the curve above the line $y = \frac{1}{2}$ or below the line $y = -\frac{1}{2}$.

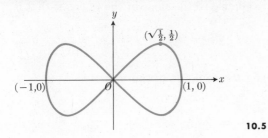

10.5

We observe in Example 10 that the equation is of the second degree in y and of the fourth degree in x. A line parallel to the y-axis has the equation $x =$ constant. Solving the equation of the curve and the equation of the line simultaneously will therefore produce at most two values of y; that is, such a line will cut the curve in at most two points. Similarly, because $y^2 = x^2(1 - x^2)$ is of the fourth degree in x, a line parallel to the x-axis will cut the curve in at most four points. The line $y = c$ and the curve will, in fact, have

(a) no intersections if $|c| > \frac{1}{2}$,

(b) two intersections if $|c| = \frac{1}{2}$,

(c) four intersections if $0 < |c| < \frac{1}{2}$,

(d) three intersections if $c = 0$.

In cases (b) and (d), the results may be interpreted as limiting cases of (c) with some of the intersections coinciding.

EXERCISES

Analyze each of the equations below to investigate the following properties of the curve:

(a) symmetry,   (b) extent,

(c) intercepts,   (d) asymptotes,

(e) slope at the intercepts.

Locate a few points and sketch the curve, taking into account the information discovered above.

1. $y^2 = x(x - 2)$ 2. $y^2 = \dfrac{x}{x - 2}$

3. $x^4 + y^4 = 1$ 4. $x^2 = \dfrac{1 + y^2}{1 - y^2}$

5. $x^2 = \dfrac{y^2 + 1}{y^2 - 1}$ 6. $y = x + \dfrac{1}{x}$

7. $y = x^2 + 1$ 8. $y = \dfrac{1}{x^2 + 1}$

9. $y = x^2 - 1$ 10. $y = \dfrac{1}{x^2 - 1}$

10.2 TANGENTS AND NORMALS

In Chapter 1, we learned that a straight line of slope m which passes through the point (x_1, y_1) is represented by an equation

$$y - y_1 = m(x - x_1). \tag{1}$$

The equation of a line *tangent* to a given curve $y = f(x)$ at a given point (x_1, y_1) on the curve can be found at once by taking

$$m = \left(\frac{dy}{dx}\right)_{(x_1, y_1)} = f'(x_1)$$

in Eq. (1), which then becomes

$$y - y_1 = f'(x_1)(x - x_1). \tag{2}$$

In this equation, x_1, y_1, and $f'(x_1)$ are all *constants*; the variables x and y appear only linearly.

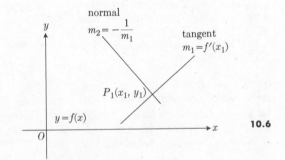

10.6

The line through $P_1(x_1, y_1)$ and perpendicular to the tangent line is called the *normal* to the curve at P_1 (see Fig. 10.6). Its slope is the negative reciprocal of the slope of the tangent, that is,

$$m_2 = -\frac{1}{m_1} = \frac{-1}{f'(x_1)},$$

and the equation of the *normal* is

$$y - y_1 = \frac{-1}{f'(x_1)}(x - x_1). \tag{3}$$

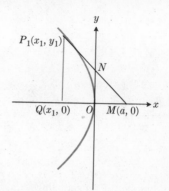

10.7

Problem 1. The tangent to the curve

$$y^2 = 4px \qquad (4)$$

at the point $P_1(x_1, y_1)$ intersects the x-axis at M and the y-axis at N. Show that N is the midpoint of the segment MP_1.

Solution. The curve is symmetric about the x-axis and lies entirely to the right of the y-axis if p is positive, or entirely to the left of the y-axis if p is negative (see Fig. 10.7).

Its slope at any point is found from

$$\frac{dy}{dx} = \frac{2p}{y}.$$

The tangent to the curve at the origin is vertical and for this point the problem becomes meaningless. But if P_1 is any point on the curve (4) other than the origin, then the equation of the line tangent to the curve at P_1 is

$$y - y_1 = \frac{2p}{y_1}(x - x_1).$$

The point $M(a, 0)$ where this line cuts the x-axis *lies on the line*, and hence

$$-y_1 = \frac{2p}{y_1}(a - x_1),$$

which gives

$$a = x_1 - \frac{y_1^2}{2p}. \qquad (5)$$

The point (x_1, y_1) is *on the curve*, and hence

$$y_1^2 = 4px_1,$$

so that

$$\frac{y_1^2}{2p} = 2x_1,$$

which reduces (5) to

$$a = -x_1. \qquad (6)$$

Equation (6) tells us that the origin bisects the line segment MQ joining $M(-x_1, 0)$ and $Q(x_1, 0)$. Hence, by similar triangles, point N bisects the segment MP_1.

Problem 2. Show that the normal to the curve

$$x^2 + y^2 = a^2 \qquad (7)$$

at any point (x_1, y_1) on it passes through the origin.

Solution. Differentiating (7) implicitly and solving for dy/dx, we find

$$\frac{dy}{dx} = -\frac{x}{y}$$

as the slope of the *tangent* at (x, y). The slope of the *normal* at (x_1, y_1) is therefore

$$m = \frac{y_1}{x_1},$$

and the equation of the normal is

$$y - y_1 = \frac{y_1}{x_1}(x - x_1). \qquad (8)$$

When we clear of fractions, (8) reduces to

$$x_1 y = y_1 x.$$

Clearly, the origin lies on this line, since the coordinates $x = 0$, $y = 0$ satisfy the equation.

10.8   a| $k < h^2$.   **b|** $k = h^2$.   **c|** $k > h^2$.

Problem 3. Show that the number of tangent lines that can be drawn from the point $Q(h, k)$ to the curve

$$y = x^2 \qquad (9)$$

is two, one, or zero accordingly as k is less than h^2, equal to h^2, or greater than h^2, respectively.

Solution. Figure 10.8 represents the curve and each of the three cases $k < h^2$, $k = h^2$, $k > h^2$. From the fact that $d^2y/dx^2 = 2$ is always positive, so that the curve is concave upward, we see that the results stated are equivalent to saying that two tangents can be drawn from a point on the convex side of the curve, no tangents can be drawn from a point on the concave side of the curve, and only one tangent can be drawn from a point on the curve. This is geometrically evident, but we shall adopt an analytical approach as follows.

Suppose that a tangent *can* be drawn to the curve from Q touching the curve at some point $P_1(x_1, y_1)$ which is at present not known. Then, using Eq. (2), we find the equation of this tangent line to be

$$y - y_1 = 2x_1(x - x_1).$$

Since $Q(h, k)$ is *on this line*, its coordinates must satisfy the equation

$$k - y_1 = 2x_1(h - x_1). \qquad (10a)$$

Also, since (x_1, y_1) is *on the curve*, its coordinates must satisfy the equation

$$y_1 = x_1^2. \qquad (10b)$$

Now in reality, h and k are known to us but x_1 and y_1 are not. We therefore have two equations, (10a) and (10b), for two unknowns, x_1 and y_1. We eliminate y_1 between them and obtain

$$k - x_1^2 = 2hx_1 - 2x_1^2,$$

or

$$x_1^2 - 2hx_1 + k = 0.$$

If we solve this for x_1 by means of the quadratic formula, we obtain

$$x_1 = h \pm \sqrt{h^2 - k}. \qquad (10c)$$

Only real values of x_1 correspond to points P_1 on the curve; hence no tangent may be drawn if $h^2 - k$ is negative, which is the same condition as saying k is greater than h^2. If $h^2 = k$, then the two roots in (10c) coincide and give only one point, namely $x_1 = h$, $y_1 = k = h^2$, to which the tangent can be drawn. But if $k < h^2$, the two roots in (10c) are distinct and each root gives a value of x_1 which with $y_1 = x_1^2$ determines a point P_1 such that the line QP_1 is tangent to the curve, so that two tangents may be drawn.

Angle between two curves

Let C_1 and C_2 be two curves which intersect at a point P. Then the angle between C_1 and C_2 at P is, by definition, the angle β between their tangents at P (Fig. 10.9). If these tangents are, respectively, L_1 and L_2, they have slopes

$$m_1 = \tan \phi_1, \quad m_2 = \tan \phi_2.$$

Then $\tan \beta$ can be found from m_1 and m_2 as follows. Since

$$\beta = \phi_2 - \phi_1,$$

we have

$$\tan \beta = \tan (\phi_2 - \phi_1) = \frac{\tan \phi_2 - \tan \phi_1}{1 + \tan \phi_2 \tan \phi_1}$$

$$= \frac{m_2 - m_1}{1 + m_2 m_1}. \qquad (11)$$

Here β is measured in the counterclockwise direction from L_1 to L_2.

10.9

10.10

We recall that the lines L_1 and L_2 are perpendicular if $m_2 = -1/m_1$. In this case we say that the curves C_1 and C_2 are *orthogonal*.

Problem 4. Show that every curve of the family

$$xy = a, \quad a \neq 0 \tag{12a}$$

is orthogonal to every curve of the family

$$x^2 - y^2 = b, \quad b \neq 0. \tag{12b}$$

Solution. The two families of curves are sketched in Fig. 10.10. At a point $P(x, y)$ on any curve of (12a), the slope is

$$\frac{dy}{dx} = -\frac{y}{x}, \tag{13a}$$

and on any curve of (12b) the slope is

$$\frac{dy}{dx} = \frac{x}{y}. \tag{13b}$$

At a point of intersection, the values of x and y in (13b) are the same as in (13a), and the two curves are orthogonal because these slopes are negative reciprocals of each other. The cases $x = 0$ or $y = 0$ cannot occur in Eqs. (13) if (x, y) is a point of intersection of any curve (12a) and a curve (12b), since a and b are restricted to be constants different from zero. That every curve in (12a) does in fact intersect every curve in (12b) follows from the fact that the equation

$$x^2 - \frac{a^2}{x^2} = b,$$

which results from eliminating y between (12a) and (12b), has real roots for every pair of nonzero real constants a and b.

The curves in (12b) are called *orthogonal trajectories* of the curves in (12a). Such mutually orthogonal systems of curves are of particular importance in physical problems related to electrical potential, where the curves in one family correspond to lines of flow and those in the other family correspond to lines of constant potential. They also occur in hydrodynamics and in heat flow problems.

EXERCISES

1. Find the equation of the line tangent to the curve
$$y^2 - 2x - 4y - 1 = 0$$
at $(-2, 1)$.

2. Find the equation of the line normal to the curve
$$xy + 2x - 5y - 2 = 0$$
at $(3, 2)$.

3. Find the equations of the lines tangent to the curve
$$y = x^3 - 6x + 2$$
and parallel to the line $y = 6x - 2$.

4. Find the equations of the lines normal to the curve
$$xy + 2x - y = 0$$
and parallel to the line $2x + y = 0$.

5. Show that the two lines that are drawn from $(\frac{3}{2}, 0)$ tangent to the curve

$$x^2 - 4y + 4 = 0$$

are perpendicular.

6. Show that the two lines that are drawn from any point on the line $x = -p$ tangent to the curve $y^2 = 4px$ are perpendicular (p = constant).

7. Does the line that is tangent to the curve $y = x^3$ at the point $(1, 1)$ intersect the curve at any other point? If so, find the point.

8. A tangent to the curve $y = x^3$ is drawn from $P_0(1, 5)$ to a point $P_1(x_1, y_1)$ on it. Find the coordinates of P_1. Is there more than one possibility for the point P_1? Why?

9. Find all lines that can be drawn normal to the curve $x^2 - y^2 = 5$ and parallel to the line $2x + 3y = 10$. Sketch the curve and the lines.

10. Find all lines that can be drawn tangent to the curve $4xy = 1$ from the point $P(-1, 2)$. Sketch the curve and the lines.

11. The line that is normal to the curve $y = x^2 + 2x - 3$ at $(1, 0)$ intersects the curve at what other point?

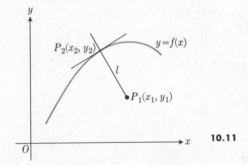

12. If l represents the distance from a fixed point $P_1(x_1, y_1)$ to a variable point $P(x, y)$ on a curve $y = f(x)$ (Fig. 10.11), then

$$l^2 = (x - x_1)^2 + [f(x) - y_1]^2.$$

Show that the derivative $d(l^2)/dx$ is equal to zero when $x = x_2$ if and only if the line P_1P_2 is normal to the curve at $P_2(x_2, f(x_2))$.

13. Show that the curve $2x^2 + 3y^2 = 5$ and the curve $y^2 = x^3$ intersect at right angles.

14. Let $P_1(x_1, y_1)$ and $P_2(x_2, y_2)$ be any two points on the curve $y = ax^2 + bx + c$, $a \neq 0$. If a line is drawn tangent to the curve at (x_0, y_0) and is parallel to the chord P_1P_2, show that $x_0 = (x_1 + x_2)/2$.

15. For what values of b is the line $y = 12x + b$ tangent to the curve $y = x^3$?

16. For what values of m is the line $y = mx$ tangent to the curve $y^2 + x^2 - 4x + 3 = 0$?

17. Find the interior angles of the triangle whose vertices are $A(1, 1)$, $B(3, -1)$, and $C(5, 2)$.

18. Find the slope of the line that bisects the angle ACB in the previous problem.

19. Let A, B, C be the interior angles of a triangle in which no angle is a right angle. By calculating $\tan(A + B + C)$ and observing that

$$A + B + C = 180°,$$

show that the equation

$$\tan A + \tan B + \tan C = \tan A \tan B \tan C$$

must be satisfied.

20. Calculate the interior angles of the triangle whose vertices are $A(1, 2)$, $B(2, -1)$, and $C(-1, 1)$, and check your results by showing that they satisfy the equation

$$\tan A + \tan B + \tan C = \tan A \tan B \tan C.$$

(See Exercise 19.)

21. Find the angles between the following pairs of curves.

(a) $3x + y = 5$, $2x - y = 4$
(b) $y = x^2$, $xy = 1$
(c) $x^2 + y^2 = 16$, $y^2 = 6x$
(d) $x^2 + xy + y^2 = 7$, $y = 2x$

10.3 NEWTON'S METHOD
FOR APPROXIMATING ROOTS OF EQUATIONS

Suppose we want to find a real root of the equation $f(x) = 0$. If the equation is linear or quadratic, we know simple rules to use. There are formulas for solving third and fourth degree equations, too, though they are less familiar. But there are no algebraic formulas for solving equations of the fifth degree or higher. Moreover, even the quadratic formula doesn't immediately give the answer in decimal form. Often we must look up the square root in a table or compute it. Newton's method, however, has these advantages:

(a) It applies to an equation of any degree. Indeed, it even applies to nonpolynomial equations such as $2 \sin x - x = 0$.

(b) It gives the answer in numerical form. We continue the computations until we have the degree of accuracy we want.

Its disadvantage is that the arithmetic becomes involved unless a calculating machine is used.

Newton's method proceeds as follows. If the equation we want to solve is $f(x) = 0$, we make a rough graph of $y = f(x)$. We estimate the root r, where the curve crosses the x-axis. This estimate is our first approximation; call it x_1. The next approximation, x_2, is the place where the *tangent* to the curve at $(x_1, f(x_1))$ crosses the x-axis (see Fig. 10.12). The equation of this tangent line is

$$y - f(x_1) = f'(x_1)(x - x_1). \qquad (1)$$

We assume that this line is not parallel to the x-axis, that is, $f'(x_1) \neq 0$. (If we started at a place where the slope is zero, we must start over again at a nearby place where the slope isn't zero.) Then the line crosses the x-axis at a point with coordinates $x = x_2$, $y = 0$ which satisfy (1). Hence

$$0 - f(x_1) = f'(x_1)(x_2 - x_1)$$
and

$$x_2 = x_1 - \frac{f(x_1)}{f'(x_1)}. \qquad (2)$$

Equation (2) provides the basis for an iterative process, since we may now replace x_1 by x_2 on the right-hand side and call the new result x_3 instead of x_2. In general, having arrived at an approximation x_n, we replace x_1 by x_n on the right-hand side of (2) and we replace x_2 by x_{n+1}, thus:

$$x_{n+1} = x_n - \frac{f(x_n)}{f'(x_n)}. \qquad (3)$$

A computing machine can be programmed with feedback to keep repeating the process of Eq. (3) automatically, as indicated in Fig. 10.13.

10.12

10.13 Feedback mechanism for iterating Newton's method.

10.14

Example 1. We may use Newton's method to solve $x^2 = 5$ to two decimals. We take $f(x) = x^2 - 5$, and sketch the curve

$$y = f(x) = x^2 - 5.$$

A root of the equation $x^2 = 5$ corresponds to a place where this curve crosses the x-axis. From Fig. 10.14, we see that one crossing is between 2 and 3, and is closer to 2 than to 3. We therefore take $x_1 = 2$ as our first approximation. Then we compute x_2 from Eq. (2).

10.15

Here we have the following information:

$$f(x) = x^2 - 5, \qquad f(2) = -1,$$
$$f'(x) = 2x, \qquad f'(2) = 4.$$

Hence

$$x_2 = 2 - (-\tfrac{1}{4}) = \tfrac{9}{4} = 2.25.$$

To get the next approximation, we use Eq. (3) with $n = 2$:

$$x_3 = x_2 - \frac{f(x_2)}{f'(x_2)}$$

with

$$f(x_2) = f(\tfrac{9}{4}) = (\tfrac{9}{4})^2 - 5 = \tfrac{1}{16}$$
$$f'(x_2) = f'(\tfrac{9}{4}) = 2(\tfrac{9}{4}) = \tfrac{9}{2}.$$

Hence

$$x_3 = \frac{9}{4} - \frac{\tfrac{1}{16}}{\tfrac{9}{2}} = \frac{161}{72} = 2.236^+.$$

Since

$$(2.236)^2 = 4.999696 \quad \text{and} \quad (2.237)^2 = 5.004169,$$

it is clear that the positive root is between 2.236 and 2.237, hence is 2.24 to two decimal places.

Example 2. Newton's method may be used to find cube roots, fourth roots, and so on. We shall illustrate the method for finding the cube root of 2. That is, we shall try to find a root of the equation $x = \sqrt[3]{2}$ or $x^3 = 2$. We first put $f(x) = x^3 - 2$ and sketch the graph of $y = f(x)$ (see Fig. 10.15). Since $f(1) = -1$ and $f(2) = 6$, we let our first approximation be $x_1 = 1$. Then Eq. (2) becomes

$$x_2 = x_1 - \frac{f(x_1)}{f'(x_1)}$$
$$= x_1 - \frac{(x_1^3 - 2)}{3x_1^2}$$
$$= \tfrac{2}{3}x_1 + \tfrac{1}{3}(2/x_1^2). \qquad (4)$$

We have written Eq. (4) in a form that shows x_2 is a "weighted average" of x_1 (with coefficient $\tfrac{2}{3}$) and of $2/x_1^2$ (with coefficient $\tfrac{1}{3}$). The sum of these coefficients is 1, but we "weight" x_1 in our average twice as heavily as we do $2/x_1^2$. This same procedure may of course be repeated with x_2 in place of x_1 on the right-hand side of (4) and x_3 on the left. In general, we have

$$x_{n+1} = \tfrac{2}{3}x_n + \tfrac{1}{3}(2/x_n^2). \qquad (5)$$

If at any stage the numbers x_n and $2/x_n^2$ are equal, then x_{n+1} is also equal to this common value, and it is $\sqrt[3]{2}$,

since
$$x_n = 2/x_n^2$$

implies
$$x_n^3 = 2.$$

Starting with $x_1 = 1$, we find the first three approximations are

$$x_1 = 1, \quad x_2 = \tfrac{4}{3} = 1.33^+, \quad x_3 = \tfrac{91}{72} = 1.264^-.$$

A table of cube roots gives $\sqrt[3]{2} = 1.259921$ to six decimal places. Our third approximation is too large by about 0.004, but 1.26 is correct to two decimal places.

Remark 1. The accuracy of Newton's method for functions f which possess continuous first and second derivatives can be estimated by applying the Mean Value Theorem. (See Exercise 13.) One estimate that we can obtain by this theorem is

$$|x_2 - r| \le (x_1 - r)^2 (M/m), \qquad (6)$$

where M is the maximum absolute value of the second derivative and m the minimum absolute value of the first derivative in an interval that contains the root r and the estimates x_1 and x_2. The error decreases if the first guess is accurate enough to make

$$\left| (x_1 - r) \frac{M}{m} \right| < 1. \tag{7}$$

In Example 1, for instance, we had

$$f(x) = x^2 - 5, \quad f'(x) = 2x, \quad f''(x) = 2,$$

with $r = \sqrt{5}$, and we had $x_1 = 2$ and all other approximations x_n between 2 and $\frac{9}{4}$. Hence in (6) we could take $M = 2$, $m = 4$ and have

$$|x_2 - \sqrt{5}| \le \tfrac{1}{2}(x_1 - \sqrt{5})^2.$$

The same inequality applies to any two successive approximations x_{n+1} and x_n:

$$|x_{n+1} - \sqrt{5}| \le \tfrac{1}{2}(x_n - \sqrt{5})^2.$$

This inequality shows that the number of decimal places of accuracy doubles with each successive iteration.

In Example 2, we had

$$f(x) = x^3 - 2, \quad f'(x) = 3x^2, \quad f''(x) = 6x,$$

with $r = \sqrt[3]{2} = 1.26^-$; and $x_1 = 1$, $x_2 = \frac{4}{3}$, and all other approximations lie between x_1 and x_2. Hence in (6) we may take $M = 6(\frac{4}{3}) = 8$, $m = 3$, and get

$$|x_2 - \sqrt[3]{2}| \le (\tfrac{8}{3})(x_1 - \sqrt[3]{2})^2.$$

The condition (7) is satisfied since the left side of the inequality (7) is actually less than 0.7.

Remark 2. We can get a good picture of how the Newton process converges in a favorable situation such as that shown in Fig. 10.16. Here x_1 is to the left of r. The tangent to the curve at $A(x_1, f(x_1))$ crosses the x-axis at x_2 to the right of r. The second tangent line, through $B(x_2, f(x_2))$ crosses at x_3, much nearer r. And the third tangent line, through $C(x_3, f(x_3))$, is practically indistinguishable from the curve itself in the vicinity of the root r.

10.16

10.17

Remark 3. In some cases, Newton's method may not converge. For instance, if the graph of $y = f(x)$ is like Fig. 10.17, we may have

$$x_1 = r - h, \qquad x_2 = r + h,$$

and successive approximations go back and forth between these two values alternately. A function such as

$$f(x) = \begin{cases} \sqrt{x - r} & \text{for } x \ge r \\ -\sqrt{r - x} & \text{for } x \le r \end{cases} \tag{8}$$

has this property. No amount of iteration of the process will bring us any closer to the root r than our initial guess. (Also see Exercise 12.)

EXERCISES

Sketch the graph of $y = f(x)$ in Exercises 1 through 6. Show that $f(a)$ and $f(b)$ have opposite signs, and use Newton's method to estimate the root of the equation $f(x) = 0$ between a and b. One might use $x_1 = (a + b)/2$ as first approximation.

1. $f(x) = x^2 + x - 1$, $a = 0$, $b = 1$
2. $f(x) = x^3 + x - 1$, $a = 0$, $b = 1$
3. $f(x) = x^4 + x - 3$, $a = 1$, $b = 2$
4. $f(x) = x^4 - 2$, $a = 1$, $b = 2$
5. $f(x) = 2 - x^4$, $a = -1$, $b = -2$
6. $f(x) = \sqrt{2x + 1} - \sqrt{x + 4}$, $a = 2$, $b = 4$

7. Suppose our first guess is lucky, in the sense that x_1 is a root of $f(x) = 0$. What happens to x_2 and later approximations?

8. In Example 2, take $x_3 = 1.26$ and compute x_4 to five decimal places. Compare with the six-place $\sqrt[3]{2}$ given in the text. How does your result check with the statement that "when one approximation is good to two decimal places, the next Newton's-method approximation will be good to about four decimals"?

9. To find $x = \sqrt[q]{a}$, we apply Newton's method to $f(x) = x^q - a$. Here we assume that a is a positive real number and q is a positive integer. Show that x_2 is a "weighted average" of x_1 and a/x_1^{q-1}, and find the coefficients m_1, m_2 such that

$$x_2 = m_1 x_1 + m_2 (a/x_1^{q-1})$$

for

$$m_1 > 0, \quad m_2 > 0 \quad m_1 + m_2 = 1.$$

What conclusion would you reach if x_1 and a/x_1^{q-1} were equal? What would be the value of x_2 in that case? (You may also wish to read the article by J. P. Ballantine, "An Averaging Method of Extracting Roots," *American Mathematical Monthly*, Vol. 63, 1956, pp. 249–252, where more efficient ways of averaging are discussed. Also see J. S. Frame, "The Solution of Equations by Continued Fractions," ibid., Vol. 60, 1953, pp. 293–305.)

10. In Example 2, let $e_1 = x_1 - r$ and $e_2 = x_2 - r$ be the errors in our first two approximations of $r = \sqrt[3]{2}$. Show algebraically that $e_2 = e_1^2 (2x_1 + r)/(3x_1^2)$. Similar equations relate the errors in any two successive approximations. All our approximations in

Example 2 lie between $x_1 = 1$ and $x_2 = \frac{4}{3}$, inclusive. Deduce that the factor $(2x_n + r)/(3x_n^2)$ is not greater than $(\frac{8}{3} + r)/3$, which in turn is less than the quantity $(2.67 + 1.26)/3 = 1.31$. Therefore, $e_{n+1} \leq 1.31 e_n^2$.

11. Show that Newton's method applied to $f(x)$ in Eq. (8) leads to $x_2 = r + h$ if $x_1 = r - h$, and to $x_2 = r - h$ if $x_1 = r + h$, $h > 0$. Interpret the result geometrically.

12. (See Remark 3.) Is it possible that successive approximations actually get "worse," in that x_{n+1} is farther away from the root r than x_n is? Can you find such a "pathological" example?
Hint. Try cube roots in place of square roots in Eq. (8).

13. Using the following hints, derive the inequality (6).

(1) By the Mean Value Theorem there is a number a between x_1 and r such that

$$f(x_1) - f(r) = f'(a)(x_1 - r).$$

If the minimum of the absolute value of $f'(x)$ in an interval containing x_1 and r is m, and $m \neq 0$, then $f'(a) \neq 0$. We assume that r is a root of $f(r) = 0$. Hence

$$x_1 - r = f(x_1)/f'(a). \qquad (a)$$

(2) By Eq. (2),

$$x_2 - x_1 = -f(x_1)/f'(x_1). \qquad (b)$$

(3) Add (a) and (b) to get

$$x_2 - r = \frac{f(x_1)}{f'(a)f'(x_1)} [f'(x_1) - f'(a)]$$
$$= \frac{x_1 - r}{f'(x_1)} [f'(x_1) - f'(a)]. \qquad (c)$$

(4) By the Mean Value Theorem, there is a number b between x_1 and a such that

$$f'(x_1) - f'(a) = f''(b)(x_1 - a). \qquad (d)$$

(5) From (c) and (d), deduce that

$$x_2 - r = (x_1 - r)(x_1 - a) \frac{f''(b)}{f'(x_1)}, \qquad (e)$$

where a and b are numbers between x_1 and r. In particular, therefore,

$$|x_1 - a| \leq |x_1 - r|. \qquad (f)$$

Now deduce (6) from (e) and (f).

10.4 DISTANCE BETWEEN TWO POINTS: EQUATIONS OF LOCI

It is at once apparent from Fig. 10.18 and the theorem of Pythagoras that the distance d between the two points $P_1(x_1, y_1)$ and $P_2(x_2, y_2)$ is given by

$$d = \sqrt{(x_2 - x_1)^2 + (y_2 - y_1)^2}. \qquad (1)$$

This formula is particularly useful in finding the equation of a curve when its geometric character depends on one or more distances.

Problem. Find the locus of $P(x, y)$ if the distance from P to the origin is equal to the distance from P to the line $L: x = 4$.

Solution. (See Fig. 10.19.) The distance from P to L is the perpendicular distance PQ from P to $Q(4, y)$, where

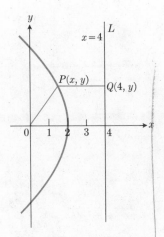

10.19 The locus of P when P is equidistant from the origin and from the line L.

Q has the same ordinate as P. Thus

$$PQ = \sqrt{(4 - x)^2 + (y - y)^2} = |4 - x|.$$

The distance OP is

$$OP = \sqrt{x^2 + y^2}.$$

The condition of the locus is $OP = PQ$, or

$$\sqrt{x^2 + y^2} = |4 - x|. \qquad (1)$$

If (1) holds, so does the equation we get by squaring:

$$x^2 + y^2 = 16 - 8x + x^2,$$

or

$$y^2 = 16 - 8x. \qquad (2)$$

That is, if a point belongs to the locus, then its coordinates must satisfy Eq. (2). The converse is also true, for if Eq. (2) holds, then

$$\sqrt{x^2 + y^2} = \sqrt{x^2 + (16 - 8x)} = \sqrt{(x - 4)^2}$$
$$= |x - 4| = |4 - x|,$$

and hence

$$OP = PQ.$$

Therefore Eq. (2) expresses both the necessary and the sufficient condition on the coordinates of $P(x, y)$ for P to belong to the locus.

EXERCISES

In Exercises 1 through 8, use the distance formula to derive the equation of the locus of points $P(x, y)$ that satisfy the specified conditions. Analyze the equation and sketch its graph.

1. P is equidistant from the two points $A(-2, 1)$ and $B(2, -3)$.

2. The distance from P to $F_1(-1, 0)$ is twice its distance to $F_2(2, 0)$.

3. The product of its distances from $F_1(-2, 0)$ and $F_2(2, 0)$ is 4.

4. The sum of the distances from P to $F_1(1, 0)$ and $F_2(0, 1)$ is constant and the curve passes through the origin.

5. The distance of P from the line $x = -2$ is 2 times its distance from the point $(2, 0)$.

6. The distance of P from the point $(-3, 0)$ is 4 more than its distance from the point $(3, 0)$.

7. The distance of P from the line $y = 1$ is 3 less than its distance from the origin.

8. P is 3 units from the point $(2, 3)$.

9. Find a point that is equidistant from the three points $A(0, 1)$, $B(1, 0)$, $C(4, 3)$. What is the radius of the circle through A, B, and C?

10. Find the distance from the point $P_1(x_1, y_1)$ to the straight line $Ax + By + C = 0$.

10.5 THE CIRCLE

Definition. *A circle is the locus of points in a plane that are at a given distance from a given point.*

The equation of a circle

Let $C(h, k)$ be the given point, the center of the circle. Let r be the given distance, the radius of the circle. Let $P(x, y)$ be a point on the circle. Then

$$CP = r, \qquad (1)$$

or

$$\sqrt{(x - h)^2 + (y - k)^2} = r,$$

or

$$(x - h)^2 + (y - k)^2 = r^2. \qquad (2)$$

If (1) is satisfied so is (2), and conversely if $r > 0$. Therefore (2) is the equation of the locus. (See Fig. 10.20.)

Problem 1. Find the equation of the circle with center at the origin and with radius r.

Solution. If $h = k = 0$, Eq. (2) becomes

$$x^2 + y^2 = r^2. \qquad (3)$$

Problem 2. Find the circle through the origin with center at $C(2, -1)$.

Solution. Its equation, (2), is of the form

$$(x - 2)^2 + (y + 1)^2 = r^2.$$

Since it goes through the origin, $x = y = 0$ must satisfy the equation. Hence $(0 - 2)^2 + (0 + 1)^2 = r^2$, or $r^2 = 5$. The equation is

$$(x - 2)^2 + (y + 1)^2 = 5.$$

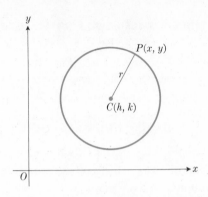

10.20   Circle: $(x - h)^2 + (y - k)^2 = r^2$.

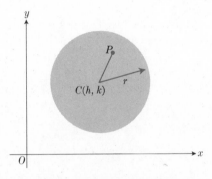

10.21   The region $(x - h)^2 + (y - k)^2 < r^2$, the interior of the circle with center $C(h, k)$ and radius r.

10.22

Problem 3. What is the locus of points $P(x, y)$ whose coordinates satisfy the inequality

$$(x - h)^2 + (y - k)^2 < r^2? \qquad (4)$$

Solution. The left side of (4) is the square of the distance CP from $C(h, k)$ to $P(x, y)$. The inequality is satisfied if and only if

$$CP < r,$$

that is, if and only if P lies inside the circle of radius r with center at $C(h, k)$. (See Fig. 10.21.)

Problem 4. Analyze the equation

$$x^2 + y^2 + 4x - 6y = 12.$$

Solution. We complete the squares in the x terms and y terms and get

$$(x^2 + 4x + 4) + (y^2 - 6y + 9) = 12 + 4 + 9,$$

or

$$(x + 2)^2 + (y - 3)^2 = 25.$$

This is of the same form as Eq. (2); therefore it represents a circle with center $C(-2, 3)$ and radius $r = 5$. Its graph is shown in Fig. 10.22.

Remark 1. An equation of the form

$$Ax^2 + Ay^2 + Dx + Ey + F = 0, \quad A \neq 0, \quad (5)$$

can often be reduced to the form of Eq. (2) by completing the squares as we did in Example 4. More specifically, we may divide (5) by A and write

$$\left(x^2 + \frac{D}{A}x\right) + \left(y^2 + \frac{E}{A}y\right) = -\frac{F}{A}. \qquad (6)$$

To complete the squares for x, we must add

$$(D/2A)^2 = D^2/(4A^2);$$

and for y we add

$$(E/2A)^2 = E^2/(4A^2).$$

Of course, we must add to both sides of Eq. (6), thus obtaining

$$\left(x + \frac{D}{2A}\right)^2 + \left(y + \frac{E}{2A}\right)^2 = -\frac{F}{A} + \frac{D^2 + E^2}{4A^2}$$

$$= \frac{D^2 + E^2 - 4AF}{4A^2}. \qquad (7)$$

Equation (7) is like Eq. (2), with

$$r^2 = \frac{D^2 + E^2 - 4AF}{4A^2}, \qquad (8)$$

provided this expression is positive. Then (5) represents a circle with center at $(-D/2A, -E/2A)$ and radius $r = \sqrt{(D^2 + E^2 - 4AF)/(4A^2)}$.

If Eq. (8) is equal to zero, the locus reduces to a single point, and if it is negative, there are no points (with real coordinates) that satisfy Eq. (7) or Eq. (5).

It is recommended that the reader apply the method of Problem 4, rather than using formulas, to handle problems of this type. The thing to remember is that an equation like (5), which is *quadratic in x and in y, with equal coefficients of x^2 and y^2, and with no xy-term, represents a circle* (or a single point, or no real locus).

Remark 2. Equation (5) can be divided by A and be replaced by an equation of the form

$$x^2 + y^2 + C_1 x + C_2 y + C_3 = 0, \qquad (9)$$

where C_1, C_2, C_3 are three constants. The three coefficients in (9) can often be determined so as to satisfy three prescribed conditions: for example, that the circle go through three given (noncollinear) points; or be tangent to three given nonconcurrent lines; or be tangent to two lines and pass through a given point not on either line.

Problem 5. Find the circle through the three points $A(1, 0)$, $B(0, 1)$, and $C(2, 2)$.

Solution. Let Eq. (9) be the equation of the circle. Then substitute for x and y the coordinates of A, B, and C, since these points are to be on the circle.

Point	$x^2 + y^2 +$	$C_1 x +$	$C_2 y +$	$C_3 = 0$	
$A(1, 0)$	1	$+ C_1$		$+ C_3 = 0$	
$B(0, 1)$	1		$+ C_2$	$+ C_3 = 0$	(10)
$C(2, 2)$	$4 + 4$	$+ 2C_1$	$+ 2C_2$	$+ C_3 = 0$	

Equations (10) are three equations for the three unknowns. Subtracting the second equation from the first, we get

$$C_2 = C_1.$$

Substitute C_1 for C_2 in the third equation:

$$8 + 4C_1 + C_3 = 0.$$

Subtract the first equation from this:

$$7 + 3C_1 = 0.$$

Hence

$$C_2 = C_1 = -\tfrac{7}{3}$$

and

$$C_3 = -1 - C_1 = \tfrac{4}{3}.$$

Therefore the equation is

$$x^2 + y^2 - \tfrac{7}{3}x - \tfrac{7}{3}y + \tfrac{4}{3} = 0,$$

or

$$3x^2 + 3y^2 - 7x - 7y + 4 = 0.$$

Of course this example could equally well have been solved starting with Eq. (2), which contains the three unknowns h, k, and r. Or we could have found the center Q of the circle by locating the point of intersection of the perpendicular bisectors of the segments AB and BC. The radius is the distance from the center Q to any one of the three points A, B, or C.

EXERCISES

In Exercises 1 through 6, find the equation of the circle having the given center $C(h, k)$ and radius r.

1. $C(0, 2)$, $r = 2$ 2. $C(-2, 0)$, $r = 3$
3. $C(3, -4)$, $r = 5$.   4. $C(1, 1)$, $r = \sqrt{2}$
5. $C(-2, -1)$, $r = \sqrt{6}$ 6. $C(-4, 2)$, $r = 4$

In Exercises 7 through 12, find the center and radius of the given circle.

7. $x^2 + y^2 - 2y = 3$ 8. $x^2 + y^2 + 2x = 8$
9. $3x^2 + 3y^2 + 6x = 1$ 10. $2x^2 + 2y^2 + x + y = 0$
11. $x^2 + y^2 + 2x - 4y + 5 = 0$
12. $x^2 + y^2 + 4x + 4y + 9 = 0$

13. The center of a circle is $C(2, 2)$. The circle goes through the point $A(4, 5)$. Find its equation.

14. The center of a circle is $C(-1, 1)$. The circle is tangent to the line $x + 2y = 4$. Find its equation.

15. A circle passes through the points $A(2, -2)$ and $B(3, 4)$. Its center is on the line $x + y = 2$. Find its equation.

16. Show geometrically that the lines that are drawn from the exterior point $P_1(x_1, y_1)$ tangent to the circle

$$(x - h)^2 + (y - k)^2 = r^2$$

have length l given by

$$l^2 = (x_1 - h)^2 + (y_1 - k)^2 - r^2.$$

17. Find an equation of the circle that passes through the three points $A(2, 3)$, $B(3, 2)$, and $C(-4, 3)$.

18. Find the locus of the point $P(x, y)$ if the sum of the squares of its distances from the two points $(-5, 2)$ and $(1, 4)$ is always 52. Identify and sketch the curve.

19. Is the point $(0.1, 3.1)$ inside, outside, or on the circle $x^2 + y^2 - 2x - 4y + 3 = 0$? Why?

20. If the distance from $P(x, y)$ to the point $(6, 0)$ is twice its distance from the point $(0, 3)$, show that the locus is a circle and find the center and radius.

21. Find the circle inscribed in the triangle whose sides are the lines

$$4x + 3y = 24,$$
$$3x - 4y = 18,$$
$$4x - 3y + 32 = 0.$$

Hint. The distance from the point (h, k) to the line $ax + by + c = 0$ is

$$\frac{|ah + bk + c|}{\sqrt{a^2 + b^2}},$$

by Eq. (10), Article 1.5.

22. Let P be a point outside a given circle C. Let PT be tangent to C at T. Let the line PN from P through the center of C intersect C at M and N. Prove that $PM \cdot PN = (PT)^2$.

23. It is known that any angle inscribed in a semicircle is a right angle. Prove the converse. If for every choice of the point $P(x, y)$ on a curve C joining O and A, the angle OPA is a right angle, then the curve is a circle or a semicircle having OA as diameter.

24. Suppose that Eqs. (2) and (9) represent the same circle.

(a) Express C_1, C_2, and C_3 in terms of h, k, and r.
(b) Express h, k, and r in terms of C_1, C_2, and C_3.

10.6 THE PARABOLA

Definition. *A parabola is the locus of points in a plane equidistant from a given point and a given line. The given point is called the focus of the parabola and the given line is called the directrix.*

The equation of a parabola

We choose the y-axis through the focus F and perpendicular to the directrix L, and take the origin halfway between F and L. If the distance between F and L is $2p$, we may assign F coordinates $(0, p)$ and the equation of L is $y = -p$, as in Fig. 10.23. Then $P(x, y)$ is on the parabola if and only if the distances PF and PQ are equal:

$$PF = PQ, \tag{1}$$

where $Q(x, -p)$ is the foot of the perpendicular from P to L. From the distance formula,

$$PF = \sqrt{x^2 + (y - p)^2} \quad \text{and} \quad PQ = \sqrt{(y + p)^2}.$$

We equate these two expressions, square, and simplify; then

$$x^2 = 4py. \tag{2}$$

This equation must be satisfied by any point on the locus. Conversely, if (2) is satisfied, then

$$\begin{aligned} PF &= \sqrt{x^2 + (y - p)^2} \\ &= \sqrt{4py + (y^2 - 2py + p^2)} \\ &= \sqrt{(y + p)^2} = PQ \end{aligned}$$

and $P(x, y)$ is on the locus. In other words, Eq. (2) is both a necessary and a sufficient condition on the coordinates x and y of points on the parabola.

Discussion. In Eq. (2), assume p is positive. Then y cannot be negative for real x, and the curve lies above the x-axis. It is symmetric about the y-axis, since x appears only to an even power.

The axis of symmetry of the parabola is also called the "axis of the parabola." The point on this axis midway between the focus and the directrix is on the parabola, since it is equidistant from the focus and the directrix. It is called the *vertex* of the parabola. The origin is the vertex of the parabola in Fig. 10.23. The tangent to a parabola at its vertex is parallel to the directrix. From Eq. (2) we find the slope

10.23 Parabola: $x^2 = 4py$.

10.24

of the tangent at any point is $dy/dx = x/2p$, and this is zero at the origin. The second derivative is $d^2y/dx^2 = 1/2p$, which is positive, so the curve is concave upward. A geometric method for constructing points on a parabola (in contrast to using its equation to locate points) is described in Exercise 24 below.

Problem 1. Find the focus and directrix of the parabola

$$x^2 = 8y. \tag{3}$$

Solution. Equation (3) matches (2) if we take $4p = 8$, $p = 2$. The focus is on the axis of symmetry (the y-axis), p units from the vertex, that is, at $F(0, 2)$. The directrix is the line $y = -2$. Every point on the graph of (3) is equidistant from $F(0, 2)$ and from the line $y = -2$. See Fig. 10.24.

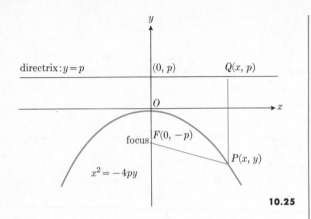

directix: $y = p$ $(0, p)$ $Q(x, p)$

O

focus $F(0, -p)$

$P(x, y)$

$x^2 = -4py$

10.25

Remark 1. Suppose the parabola opens downward, as in Fig. 10.25, with its focus $F(0, -p)$ and directrix the line $y = p$. The effect is to change the sign of p in Eq. (2), which now becomes

$$x^2 = -4py. \qquad (4)$$

We may also interchange the roles of x and y in Eqs. (2) and (4). The resulting equations

$$y^2 = 4px \qquad (5a)$$

and

$$y^2 = -4px \qquad (5b)$$

also represent parabolas, but now they are symmetric about the x-axis because y appears only to an even power. The *vertex* is still at the origin. The directrix is perpendicular to the axis of symmetry, and p units from the vertex. The focus is on the axis of symmetry, also p units from the vertex, and "inside" the curve. If we assume p is positive in Eqs. (5), then (5a) opens toward the right, because x must be greater than or equal to zero, while (5b) opens toward the left. Figure 10.26 shows graphs of parabolas of these two types.

Translation of axes

If the vertex of the parabola is at the point $V(h, k)$, Eqs. (2), (4), and (5) no longer apply in those forms. However, it is easy to determine what the appropriate equation is, by considering a new coordinate system, with its origin O' at V, and axes parallel to the original axes (see Fig. 10.27). Every point P in the plane then has two sets of coordinates, say x and y in the original system, and x', y' in the new. To go from O to P, we have a horizontal displacement x and a vertical displacement y. The abscissa may be resolved into two horizonal displacements: h from O to O', and x' from O' to P. Similarly, the ordinate is the resultant of two vertical displacements: k from O to O', and y' from O' to P. Thus

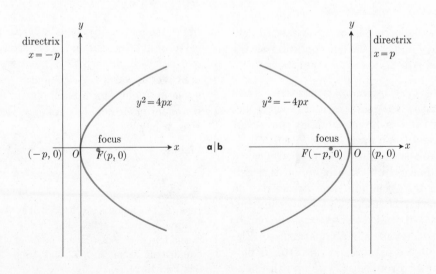

directrix $x = -p$

$y^2 = 4px$

focus

$(-p, 0)$ O $F(p, 0)$

a | **b**

directrix $x = p$

$y^2 = -4px$

focus

$F(-p, 0)$ O $(p, 0)$

10.26

10.27 Translation of axes.

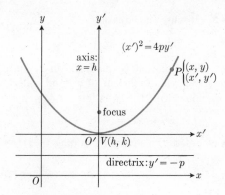

10.28 Parabola with vertex at $V(h, k)$.

the two sets of coordinates are related as follows:

$$(x = x' + h, \quad y = y' + k), \qquad (6a)$$

or

$$(x' = x - h, \quad y' = y - k). \qquad (6b)$$

Equations (6) are called the equations for *translation of axes*, because the new coordinate axes may be obtained by moving the old axes to the position of the new ones in a motion known as a pure translation without rotation.

Suppose we now consider a parabola with vertex $V(h, k)$ and opening upward, as in Fig. 10.28. In terms of $x'y'$-coordinates, Eq. (2) provides us with the equation of the parabola in the form

$$(x')^2 = 4py'. \qquad (7)$$

By using Eqs. (6), we may express this in xy-coordinates by the equation

$$(x - h)^2 = 4p(y - k). \qquad (8a)$$

The axis of symmetry of the parabola in (8a) is the line $x = h$. Observe that this corresponds to setting the quadratic term $(x - h)^2$ in (8a) equal to zero. When p is positive, $y - k$ must be greater than or equal to zero in (8a), for real $x - h$, and therefore the graph opens upward. The focus is on the axis of symmetry, p units above the vertex at $x = h$, $y = k + p$. The directrix is p units below the vertex and perpendicular to the axis of symmetry.

Other forms of equations of parabolas are

$$(x - h)^2 = -4p(y - k), \qquad (8b)$$

$$(y - k)^2 = 4p(x - h), \qquad (8c)$$

$$(y - k)^2 = -4p(x - h). \qquad (8d)$$

Equation (8b) has a graph symmetric about $x = h$, opening downward; (8c), symmetric about $y = k$ and opening to the right ($x \geq h$); (8d), symmetric about $y = k$ and opening to the left ($x \leq h$).

Problem 2. Discuss the parabola

$$y = x^2 + 4x. \qquad (9)$$

Solution. We complete the square in the x terms by adding 4 to both sides of Eq. (9):

$$y + 4 = x^2 + 4x + 4$$
$$= (x + 2)^2.$$

This is of the form

$$(x - h)^2 = 4p(y - k)$$

with

$$h = -2, \quad k = -4,$$

$$4p = 1, \quad p = \tfrac{1}{4}.$$

The vertex of the parabola is $V(-2, -4)$; its axis of symmetry $(x + 2)^2 = 0$; and it opens upward because $y \geq -4$ for real x. The graph is shown in Fig. 10.29. The focus is on the axis of symmetry, $\tfrac{1}{4}$-unit above the vertex, at $F(-2, -3\tfrac{3}{4})$. The directrix is parallel to the x-axis, $\tfrac{1}{4}$-unit below the vertex. Its equation is $y = -4\tfrac{1}{4}$.

$x = -2$

$y = x^2 + 4x$

F

$V(-2, -4)$

directix:
$y = -4\frac{1}{4}$

10.29

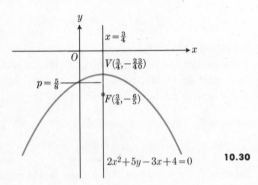

$x = \frac{3}{4}$

O

$V(\frac{3}{4}, -\frac{23}{40})$

$p = \frac{5}{8}$

$F(\frac{3}{4}, -\frac{6}{5})$

$2x^2 + 5y - 3x + 4 = 0$

10.30

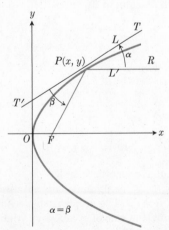

T

L

α

$P(x, y)$

R

L'

T'

β

O F

$\alpha = \beta$

10.31 In a parabolic reflector, the angles α and β are equal.

Remark 2. The clue to an equation of a parabola is that it is quadratic in one of the coordinates and linear in the other. Whenever we have such an equation we may reduce it to one of the standard forms (8a, b, c, d) by completing the square in the coordinate that appears quadratically. We then put the linear terms in the form

$$\pm 4p(x - h) \quad \text{or} \quad \pm 4p(y - k).$$

Then the information about vertex, distance from vertex to focus, axis of symmetry, and direction the curve opens can all be read from the equation in this standard form.

Problem 3. Discuss the equation

$$2x^2 + 5y - 3x + 4 = 0.$$

Solution. This equation is quadratic in x, linear in y. We divide by 2, the coefficient of x^2, and collect all the x terms on one side of the equation:

$$x^2 - \tfrac{3}{2}x = -\tfrac{5}{2}y - 2.$$

Now we complete the square by adding $(-\tfrac{3}{4})^2 = \tfrac{9}{16}$ to both sides:

$$(x - \tfrac{3}{4})^2 = -\tfrac{5}{2}y - 2 + \tfrac{9}{16} = -\tfrac{5}{2}y - \tfrac{23}{16}.$$

To get the y terms in the form $-4p(y - k)$, we factor out $-\tfrac{5}{2}$, and write

$$(x - \tfrac{3}{4})^2 = -\tfrac{5}{2}(y + \tfrac{23}{40}).$$

This has the form

$$(x - h)^2 = -4p(y - k)$$

with

$$h = \tfrac{3}{4}, \quad k = -\tfrac{23}{40}, \quad 4p = \tfrac{5}{2}.$$

Hence the vertex is $V(\tfrac{3}{4}, -\tfrac{23}{40})$. The axis of symmetry is $(x - \tfrac{3}{4})^2 = 0$, or $x = \tfrac{3}{4}$; and the distance from the vertex to the focus is

$$p = \tfrac{5}{8}.$$

Since $y - k$ must here be ≤ 0 for real x, the curve opens downward, and the focus is p units below the vertex at $F(\tfrac{3}{4}, -\tfrac{6}{5})$. The graph is shown in Fig. 10.30.

Remark 3. In Fig. 10.31 the line L through $P(x, y)$ is tangent to the parabola, F is the focus, and the line L' through $P(x, y)$ is parallel to the axis of the parabola. The angles $\alpha = \angle RPT$ and $\beta = \angle T'PF$ are equal (see Exercise 31). This accounts for the property of a parabolic reflector that rays originating from the focus are reflected parallel to the axis. Or, rays coming into the reflector parallel to the axis are reflected to the focus. These properties are used in parabolic mirrors of telescopes and in parabolic radar antennas.

EXERCISES

In Exercises 1 through 6, the vertex V and focus F of a parabola are given. Find the equation of the parabola and of its directrix. Sketch the graph showing the focus, vertex, and directrix.

1. $V(0, 0)$, $F(0, 2)$ 2. $V(0, 0)$, $F(-2, 0)$
3. $V(-2, 3)$, $F(-2, 4)$ 4. $V(0, 3)$, $F(-1, 3)$
5. $V(-3, 1)$, $F(0, 1)$ 6. $V(1, -3)$, $F(1, 0)$

In Exercises 7 through 12, the vertex V and directrix L of a parabola are given. Find the equation of the parabola and its focus. Sketch the graph showing the focus, vertex, and directrix.

7. $V(2, 0)$, L the y-axis
8. $V(1, -2)$, L the x-axis
9. $V(-3, 1)$, L the line $x = 1$
10. $V(-2, -2)$, L the line $y = -3$
11. $V(0, 1)$, L the line $x = -1$
12. $V(0, 1)$, L the line $y = 2$

In Exercises 13 through 22, find the vertex, axis of symmetry, focus, and directrix of the given parabola. Sketch the curve, showing these features.

13. $x^2 + 8y - 2x = 7$ 14. $x^2 - 2y + 8x + 10 = 0$
15. $y^2 + 4x = 8$ 16. $x^2 - 8y = 4$
17. $x^2 + 2x - 4y - 3 = 0$ 18. $y^2 + x + y = 0$
19. $4y^2 - 8y + 3x - 2 = 0$ 20. $y^2 + 6y + 2x + 5 = 0$
21. $3x^2 - 8y - 12x = 4$ 22. $3x - 2y^2 - 4y + 7 = 0$

23. What is the locus of points whose coordinates satisfy the inequality $x^2 < 8y$? Sketch.

24. Explain why the following method of locating points on the graph of a parabola is valid.

    (a) Construct a family of lines parallel to the directrix.

10.32 Construction of points on a parabola with focus F and directrix L.

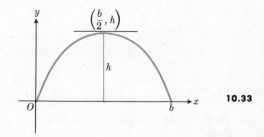

10.33

(b) Set a compass to measure the distance d from the directrix to one of these lines L'. With the focus as center, construct an arc of radius d intersecting L' in points A' and B', as in Fig. 10.32.

(c) Repeat the process with other lines L'', L''', and so on, constructing points A'', B'', A''', B''', and so on. The points so constructed lie on a parabola with focus F, directrix L.

25. Use the method of Exercise 24 to construct the graph of the parabola with focus $F(2, 2)$ and directrix the line $x + y = 0$.

26. Find the equation of the parabola of Exercise 25. *Hint.* The distance from a point (x, y) to the line $Ax + By + C = 0$ is

$$\frac{|Ax + By + C|}{\sqrt{A^2 + B^2}}.$$

27. Find the equation of the parabolic arch of base b and altitude h in Fig. 10.33.

28. Given the three points $(-1, 2)$, $(1, -1)$, and $(2, 1)$.
    (a) Find a parabola passing through the given points and having its axis parallel to the x-axis.
    (b) Find a parabola passing through the given points and having its axis parallel to the y-axis.

29. Suppose a and b are positive numbers. Sketch the parabolas

$$y^2 = 4a^2 - 4ax$$

and

$$y^2 = 4b^2 + 4bx$$

in the same diagram. Show that they have a common focus, the same for any a and b. Show that they intersect at $(a - b, \pm 2\sqrt{ab})$, and that each "a-parabola" is orthogonal to every "b-parabola." (Using different values of a and b, we obtain families of confocal parabolas. Each family is a set of orthogonal trajectories of the other family. See Article 10.2.)

30. What is the locus of the equation

$$(2x + y - 3)(x^2 + y^2 - 4)(x^2 - 8y) = 0?$$

Give a reason for your answer.

31. Prove that the angles α and β in Fig. 10.31 are equal.

32. Prove that the tangent to the parabola $y^2 = 4px$ at $P_1(x_1, y_1)$ intersects the axis of symmetry x_1 units to the left of the vertex. (This provides a simple method for constructing the tangent to a parabola at any point on it.)

33. Show that the area of a parabolic segment of altitude h and base b is $\frac{2}{3}bh$ (see Exercise 27).

34. Show that the volume generated by rotating the area bounded by the parabola $y = (4h/b^2)x^2$ and the line $y = h$ about the y-axis is equal to one and one-half times the volume of the corresponding inscribed cone.

35. The condition for equilibrium of the section OP of a cable that supports a weight of w pounds per foot measured along the horizontal (Fig. 10.34) is

$$\frac{dy}{dx} = \frac{wx}{H} \left(= \frac{T \sin \phi}{T \cos \phi} \right),$$

where the origin O is taken at the low point of the cable and H is the horizontal tension at O. Show that the curve in which the cable hangs is a parabola.

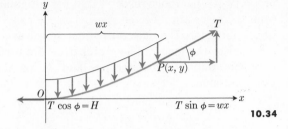

10.34

36. Assume, from optics, that when a ray of light is reflected by a mirror the angle of incidence is equal to the angle of reflection. If a mirror is formed by rotating a parabola about its axis and silvering the resulting surface, show that a ray of light emanating from the focus of the parabola is reflected parallel to the axis.

10.7 THE ELLIPSE

Definition. *An ellipse is the locus of points $P(x, y)$ the sum of whose distances from two fixed points is constant.*

The equation of an ellipse

If the two fixed points, called *foci*, are taken at $F_1(-c, 0)$ and $F_2(c, 0)$, and the sum of the distances $PF_1 + PF_2$ is denoted by $2a$ (see Fig. 10.35), then the coordinates of P must satisfy the equation

$$\sqrt{(x + c)^2 + y^2} + \sqrt{(x - c)^2 + y^2} = 2a.$$

10.35   Ellipse: $\dfrac{x^2}{a^2} + \dfrac{y^2}{b^2} = 1.$

To simplify this expression, we transpose the second radical to the right side of the equation, square, and simplify, to obtain

$$a - \frac{c}{a}x = \sqrt{(x-c)^2 + y^2}.$$

Again we square and simplify, and obtain

$$\frac{x^2}{a^2} + \frac{y^2}{a^2 - c^2} = 1. \tag{1}$$

Since the sum $PF_1 + PF_2 = 2a$ of two sides of the triangle F_1F_2P is greater than the third side $F_1F_2 = 2c$, the term $(a^2 - c^2)$ in (1) is positive and has a real positive square root, which we denote by b:

$$b = \sqrt{a^2 - c^2}. \tag{2}$$

Then (1) takes the more compact form

$$\frac{x^2}{a^2} + \frac{y^2}{b^2} = 1, \tag{3}$$

from which it is readily seen that the curve is symmetric about both axes and lies inside the rectangle bounded by the lines $x = a$, $x = -a$, $y = b$, $y = -b$. The intercepts of the curve are at $(\pm a, 0)$ and $(0, \pm b)$. The curve intersects each axis at an angle of $90°$, since

$$\frac{dy}{dx} = \frac{-b^2 x}{a^2 y}$$

is zero at $x = 0$, $y = \pm b$, and $dx/dy = 0$ at $y = 0$, $x = \pm a$.

We have shown that the coordinates of P must satisfy (1) if P satisfies the geometric condition $PF_1 + PF_2 = 2a$. Conversely, if x and y satisfy the algebraic equation (1) with $0 < c < a$, then

$$y^2 = (a^2 - c^2)\frac{a^2 - x^2}{a^2},$$

and substituting this in the radicals below, we find that

$$PF_1 = \sqrt{(x+c)^2 + y^2} = \left| a + \frac{c}{a}x \right| \tag{4a}$$

and

$$PF_2 = \sqrt{(x-c)^2 + y^2} = \left| a - \frac{c}{a}x \right|. \tag{4b}$$

Since x is restricted to the domain $-a \le x \le a$, the value of $(c/a)x$ lies between $-c$ and c, and thus both $a + (c/a)x$ and $a - (c/a)x$ are positive, both being between $a + c$ and $a - c$. Hence the absolute values in (4a) and (4b) yield

$$PF_1 = a + \frac{c}{a}x, \quad PF_2 = a - \frac{c}{a}x. \tag{5}$$

Adding these, we see that $PF_1 + PF_2$ has a value $2a$ independent of the position of P on the curve. Thus the *geometric property* and *algebraic equation* are equivalent.

In Eq. (3), $b^2 = a^2 - c^2$ is less than a^2. The *major axis* of the ellipse is the segment of length $2a$ between the x-intercepts $(\pm a, 0)$. The *minor axis* is the segment of length $2b$ between the y-intercepts $(0, \pm b)$. The numbers a and b are also referred to respectively as semimajor axis and semiminor axis. If these semiaxes are $a = 4$, $b = 3$, then Eq. (3) is

$$\frac{x^2}{16} + \frac{y^2}{9} = 1. \tag{6a}$$

On the other hand, if we interchange the roles of x and y in (6a), we get the equation

$$\frac{x^2}{9} + \frac{y^2}{16} = 1, \tag{6b}$$

which must also represent an ellipse, but one with its major axis vertical rather than horizontal. Graphs of Eqs. (6a) and (6b) are given in Figs. 10.36(a) and 10.36(b).

There is never any need for confusion in analyzing equations like (6a) and (6b). We simply find the intercepts on the axes of symmetry; then we know which way the major axis runs. The foci are always on the major axis. And if we use the letters a, b, and c to represent the lengths of semimajor axis, semiminor axis, and half-distance between foci, then Eq. (2) tells us that

$$b^2 = a^2 - c^2,$$

or

$$a^2 = b^2 + c^2. \tag{7}$$

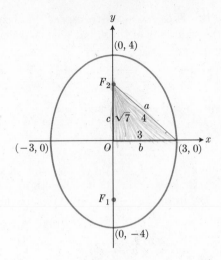

10.36 **a|** The major axis of $\dfrac{x^2}{16} + \dfrac{y^2}{9} = 1$ is horizontal.

b| The major axis of $\dfrac{x^2}{9} + \dfrac{y^2}{16} = 1$ is vertical.

Hence a is the hypotenuse of a right triangle of sides b and c, as in Fig. 10.36. When we start with an equation like (6a) or (6b), we can read off a^2 and b^2 from it at once. Then Eq. (7) determines c^2 as their difference. So in either of Eqs. (6a) and (6b), we have

$$c^2 = 16 - 9 = 7.$$

Therefore the foci are $\sqrt{7}$ units from the center of the ellipse, as shown.

Center not at the origin

The *center* of an ellipse is defined as the point of intersection of its axes of symmetry. If the center is at $C(h, k)$, and the axes of the ellipse are parallel to the x- and y-axes, then we may introduce new coordinates

$$x' = x - h, \quad y' = y - k, \tag{8}$$

using C as origin O' of $x'y'$-coordinates. The equation of the ellipse in the new coordinates is either

$$\frac{x'^2}{a^2} + \frac{y'^2}{b^2} = 1 \tag{9a}$$

or

$$\frac{x'^2}{b^2} + \frac{y'^2}{a^2} = 1, \tag{9b}$$

depending on which way the major axis runs.

Problem 1. Analyze the equation

$$9x^2 + 4y^2 + 36x - 8y + 4 = 0.$$

Solution. To complete the squares, we collect the x terms and the y terms separately:

$$9(x^2 + 4x) + 4(y^2 - 2y) = -4.$$

We then complete the square in each set of parentheses, obtaining

$$9(x^2 + 4x + 4) + 4(y^2 - 2y + 1) = -4 + 36 + 4.$$

We now divide both sides by 36 and write

$$\frac{(x+2)^2}{4} + \frac{(y-1)^2}{9} = 1.$$

Setting

$$x' = x + 2, \quad y' = y - 1,$$

we see that the new origin $x' = 0$, $y' = 0$ is the same as the point $x = -2$, $y = 1$. In terms of the new coordinates, the equation is

$$\frac{x'^2}{4} + \frac{y'^2}{9} = 1,$$

which represents an ellipse with intercepts at $(0, \pm 3)$ on the y'-axis and $(\pm 2, 0)$ on the x'-axis. To locate the foci, we use the relation

$$c = \sqrt{a^2 - b^2}.$$

Here $a^2 = 9, \quad b^2 = 4,$

so $c = \sqrt{5}.$

The foci are at the points $(0, \pm\sqrt{5})$ on the y'-axis or at $(-2, 1 \pm \sqrt{5})$ in terms of the original coordinates. (See Fig. 10.37.)

We recall (Fig. 10.35) that the essential *geometric* property of an ellipse is that the sum of the distances from any point on it to the two foci be a constant:

$$PF_1 + PF_2 = 2a.$$

The essential *algebraic* property of its equation when written in the form of a quadratic without a cross-product term is that the x^2- and y^2-terms have the same sign.

To discuss the properties of the ellipse in more detail, we shall assume that its equation has been reduced to the form

$$\frac{x^2}{a^2} + \frac{y^2}{b^2} = 1, \quad a > b > 0. \qquad (10)$$

Although the distance c from the center of the ellipse to a focus does not appear in its equation, we may still determine c as in the examples above from the equation

$$c^2 = a^2 - b^2, \qquad (11)$$

which is another way of writing Eq. (7).

A simple geometric method of finding c is shown in Fig. 10.38. (The figure also indicates $c = ae$ where $e = c/a$ is called the *eccentricity*.) This method for finding c is based on the following considerations. Since the sum of the distances

$$PF_1 + PF_2$$

is equal to $2a$ for *every point* P on the ellipse, then certainly this must hold when P is taken to be at the y-intercept B. But the y-axis is the perpendicular bisector of the line segment F_1F_2, and hence every point on it is equidistant from the foci F_1 and F_2. We therefore have

$$BF_1 + BF_2 = 2a \quad \text{and} \quad BF_1 = BF_2;$$

hence

$$BF_1 = BF_2 = a.$$

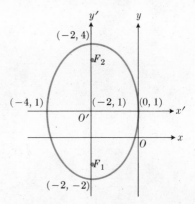

10.37 The ellipse $9x^2 + 4y^2 + 36x - 9y + 4 = 0$.

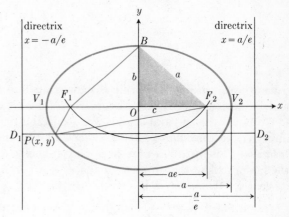

10.38

We may therefore use B as the center of a circular arc of radius a. It will cut the x-axis in the two foci F_1 and F_2. Equation (11) then follows at once from applying the Theorem of Pythagoras to the right triangle OBF_2 in the figure.

Eccentricity

If we keep a fixed and vary c over the range $0 \le c \le a$, the resulting ellipses will vary in shape, being circular when $c = 0$ and becoming flatter as c increases, until in the extreme case $c = a$, the "ellipse" reduces to the line segment F_1F_2 joining the two foci (Fig. 10.39). The ratio

$$e = \frac{c}{a}, \qquad (12)$$

$$c = 0$$
$$e = 0$$

$$F_1 = F_2$$

$$c = \frac{4a}{5} \quad e = \frac{4}{5}$$

$$F_1 \qquad\qquad F_2$$

10.39

$$F_1 \qquad \begin{array}{c} c = a \\ e = 1 \end{array} \qquad F_2$$

the center along the major axis, one finds successively

a *focus* at distance ae from the center,

a *vertex* at distance a from the center,

a *directrix* at distance a/e from the center.

An interesting feature of the "focus-and-directrix" property is that it furnishes a common bond uniting the parabola, ellipse, and hyperbola: If a point $P(x, y)$ is such that its distance PF from a fixed point (the focus) is proportional to its distance PD from a fixed line (the directrix), that is, if

$$PF = e \cdot PD, \qquad (15)$$

where e is a constant of proportionality, then the locus of P is

(a) a *parabola* if $e = 1$,

(b) an *ellipse* of eccentricity e if $e < 1$, and

(c) a *hyperbola* of eccentricity e if $e > 1$.

Constructions

There are several methods of constructing an ellipse. One of these simply uses the definition directly. The two ends of a string of length $2a$ are held fixed at the foci F_1 and F_2 and a pencil traces the curve as it is held taut against the string (see Fig. 10.40a).

A second method makes use of a straightedge AB of length $a + b$. Place point A on the y-axis and B on the x-axis, and on the graph paper, make a dot at $P(x, y)$ at distance a from A (see Fig. 10.40b). In terms of the angle θ that line AB makes with the (negative) x-axis, we have

$$x = a \cos \theta, \quad y = b \sin \theta, \qquad (16)$$

and hence

$$\frac{x^2}{a^2} + \frac{y^2}{b^2} = \cos^2 \theta + \sin^2 \theta = 1.$$

Therefore $P(x, y)$ is on the ellipse, Eq. (10).

A third method is to construct two concentric circles of radii a and b (see Fig. 10.40c). A line making an angle θ with the horizontal is drawn from the center cutting the two circles in points A and B respectively. The vertical line through A and the

called the *eccentricity* of the ellipse, varies from 0 to 1 and indicates the degree of departure from circularity.

We recall that a parabola has one focus and one directrix. Each ellipse has two foci and two directrices. The *directrices* are lines perpendicular to the major axis of the ellipse at distances $\pm a/e$ from its center. The *parabola* has the property that

$$PF = 1 \cdot PD \qquad (13)$$

for any point P on it, where F is the focus and D is the point nearest P on the directrix. For an *ellipse*, it is not difficult to show (see Exercise 21) that the equations that take the place of (13) are

$$PF_1 = e \cdot PD_1, \quad PF_2 = e \cdot PD_2. \qquad (14)$$

Here e is the eccentricity, P is any point on the ellipse, F_1 and F_2 are the foci, and D_1 and D_2 are the points nearest P on the two directrices. In Eq. (14), the corresponding directrix and focus must be used; that is, if one uses the distance from P to the focus F_1, one must also use the distance from P to the directrix at the same end of the ellipse (see Fig. 10.38). We thus associate the directrix $x = -a/e$ with the focus $F_1(-c, 0)$, and the directrix $x = a/e$ with the focus $F_2(c, 0)$. In terms of the semimajor axis a and eccentricity $e < 1$, as one goes away from horizontal line through B intersect in a point P whose coordinates also satisfy (16). By varying the angle θ from 0 to 360°, as many points as desired may be obtained on the ellipse.

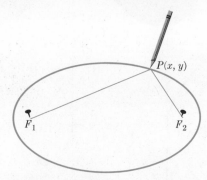

a| $PF_1 + PF_2 = 2a$.

b| $x = a \cos \theta$, $y = b \sin \theta$; $\dfrac{x^2}{a^2} + \dfrac{y^2}{b^2} = 1$.

|c| 10.40

EXERCISES

In Exercises 1 through 5, find the equation of an ellipse having the given center C, focus F, and semimajor axis a. Sketch the graph and give the eccentricity of each ellipse.

1. $C(0, 0)$, $F(0, 2)$, $a = 4$
2. $C(0, 0)$, $F(-3, 0)$, $a = 5$
3. $C(0, 2)$, $F(0, 0)$, $a = 3$
4. $C(-3, 0)$, $F(-3, -2)$, $a = 4$
5. $C(2, 2)$, $F(-1, 2)$, $a = \sqrt{10}$

6. The end points of the major and minor axes of an ellipse are $(1, 1)$, $(3, 4)$, $(1, 7)$, and $(-1, 4)$. Sketch the ellipse, give its equation, and find its foci.

7. Find the center, vertices, and foci of the ellipse $25x^2 + 9y^2 - 100x + 54y - 44 = 0$. Sketch the curve.

8. Sketch the following ellipses.

   (a) $9x^2 + 4y^2 = 36$ (b) $4x^2 + 9y^2 = 144$

   (c) $\dfrac{(x-1)^2}{16} + \dfrac{(y+2)^2}{4} = 1$

   (d) $4x^2 + y^2 = 1$
   (e) $16(x-2)^2 + 9(y+3)^2 = 144$

9. Find the equation of the ellipse that passes through the origin and has foci at $(-1, 1)$ and $(1, 1)$.

10. Find the eccentricity and the directrices of the ellipse $x^2/7 + y^2/16 = 1$.

11. Find the volume generated by rotating an ellipse of semiaxes a and b ($a > b$) about its major axis.

12. Set up the integrals that give

    (a) the area of a quadrant of the circle $x^2 + y^2 = a^2$,

    (b) the area of a quadrant of the ellipse

$$b^2x^2 + a^2y^2 = a^2b^2.$$

Show that the integral in (b) is b/a times the integral in (a) and deduce the area of the ellipse from the known area of the circle.

13. An ellipsoid is generated by rotating an ellipse about its major axis. The inside surface of the ellipsoid is silvered to produce a mirror. Show that a ray of light emanating from one focus will be reflected to the other focus. (Sound waves also follow such paths; it is this property of ellipsoids that accounts for phenomena in certain "whispering galleries.")

14. Find the length of the chord perpendicular to the major axis of the ellipse $b^2x^2 + a^2y^2 = a^2b^2$ and passing through a focus. (This chord is called the "latus rectum" of the ellipse.)

15. Find the equation of an ellipse of eccentricity $\frac{2}{3}$ if the line $x = 9$ is one directrix and the corresponding focus is at $(4, 0)$.

16. Find the values of the constants A, B, and C if the ellipse $4x^2 + y^2 + Ax + By + C = 0$ is to be tangent to the x-axis at the origin and to pass through the point $(-1, 2)$.

17. Show that the line tangent to the ellipse

$$(x^2/a^2) + (y^2/b^2) = 1$$

at the point $P_1(x_1, y_1)$ on it is

$$\frac{xx_1}{a^2} + \frac{yy_1}{b^2} = 1.$$

18. Graph the locus of $P(x, y)$ if $9x^2 + 16y^2 < 144$.

19. Graph the locus of $P(x, y)$ if

$$(x^2 + 4y)(2x - y - 3)(x^2 + y^2 - 25)$$
$$\times (x^2 + 4y^2 - 4) = 0.$$

20. Graph the locus of $P(x, y)$ if

$$(x^2 + y^2 - 1)(9x^2 + 4y^2 - 36) < 0.$$

10.8 THE HYPERBOLA

Definition. *A hyperbola is the locus of $P(x, y)$ if the difference of its distances from two fixed points is constant.*

The equation of a hyperbola

Taking the fixed points at $F_1(-c, 0)$ and $F_2(c, 0)$ and the constant equal to $2a$ (see Fig. 10.41), we

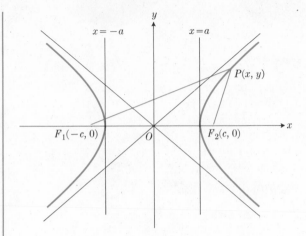

10.41   Hyperbola: $\dfrac{x^2}{a^2} - \dfrac{y^2}{b^2} = 1$.

have the condition

$$\sqrt{(x + c)^2 + y^2} - \sqrt{(x - c)^2 + y^2} = 2a$$

or

$$\sqrt{(x - c)^2 + y^2} - \sqrt{(x + c)^2 + y^2} = 2a.$$

The second equation is like the first, with $2a$ replaced by $-2a$. Hence we write the first one with $\pm 2a$, transpose one radical to the right-hand side of the equation, square, and simplify. One radical still remains. We isolate it and square again. We then obtain the equation

$$\frac{x^2}{a^2} + \frac{y^2}{a^2 - c^2} = 1. \tag{1}$$

So far, this is just like the equation for an ellipse. But now $a^2 - c^2$ is negative, because the *difference* in two sides of the triangle F_1F_2P is less than the third side:

$$2a < 2c.$$

So in this case $c^2 - a^2$ is positive and has a real positive square root which we call b:

$$b = \sqrt{c^2 - a^2}, \tag{2a}$$

or

$$a^2 - c^2 = -b^2. \tag{2b}$$

The equation of the hyperbola now becomes

$$\frac{x^2}{a^2} - \frac{y^2}{b^2} = 1, \tag{3}$$

which is analogous to the equation of an ellipse; the only differences are the minus sign in the equation of the hyperbola, and the new relation among a, b, and c given by Eq. (2b). The hyperbola, like the ellipse, is symmetric with respect to both axes and the origin, but it has no real y-intercepts and in fact no portion of the curve lies between the lines $x = a$ and $x = -a$.

If we start with a point $P(x, y)$ whose coordinates satisfy Eq. (3), the distances PF_1 and PF_2 will be given (see Exercise 14) by

$$PF_1 = \sqrt{(x + c)^2 + y^2} = \left| a + \frac{c}{a}x \right|, \quad (4a)$$

$$PF_2 = \sqrt{(x - c)^2 + y^2} = \left| a - \frac{c}{a}x \right|, \quad (4b)$$

as for the ellipse. But now c is greater than a, and P is either to the right of the line $x = a$, that is, either

$$x > a;$$

or else P is to the left of the line $x = -a$ and

$$x < -a.$$

The absolute values in Eqs. (4) work out to be

$$\left. \begin{array}{l} PF_1 = a + \dfrac{c}{a}x \\[2mm] PF_2 = \dfrac{c}{a}x - a \end{array} \right\} \quad \text{if } x > a \qquad (5a)$$

and

$$\left. \begin{array}{l} PF_1 = -\left(a + \dfrac{c}{a}x\right) \\[2mm] PF_2 = a - \dfrac{c}{a}x \end{array} \right\} \quad \text{if } x < -a. \qquad (5b)$$

Thus, when P is to the right of the line $x = a$, the condition $PF_1 - PF_2 = 2a$ is satisfied, while if P is to the left of $x = -a$, the condition

$$PF_2 - PF_1 = 2a$$

is fulfilled (Fig. 10.41). In either case, *any point P that satisfies the geometric conditions must satisfy the algebraic equation and, conversely, any point that satisfies the algebraic equation does also satisfy the geometric conditions.*

Asymptotes

The left-hand side of (3) can be factored and the equation written in the form

$$\left(\frac{x}{a} - \frac{y}{b}\right)\left(\frac{x}{a} + \frac{y}{b}\right) = 1,$$

or

$$\frac{x}{a} - \frac{y}{b} = \frac{ab}{bx + ay}. \tag{6a}$$

Analysis of (3) shows that one branch of the curve lies in the first quadrant and has infinite extent. If the point P moves along this branch so that x and y both become infinite, then the right-hand side of (6a) tends to zero; hence the left-hand side must do likewise. That is,

$$\lim_{\substack{x \to \infty \\ y \to \infty}} \left(\frac{x}{a} - \frac{y}{b}\right) = 0, \tag{6b}$$

which leads us to speculate that the straight line

$$\frac{x}{a} - \frac{y}{b} = 0 \tag{7a}$$

may be an asymptote of the curve. To see that this is definitely so, we investigate the vertical distance $(y_2 - y_1)$ between the curve and the line where we take

$$y_2 = \frac{b}{a}x$$

on the line, and

$$y_1 = \frac{b}{a}\sqrt{x^2 - a^2}$$

on the curve (Fig. 10.42). We then multiply both sides of Eq. (6b) by b, and see that

$$\lim_{x \to \infty} (y_2 - y_1) = 0.$$

Since this vertical distance tends to zero, certainly the perpendicular distance from the line to the curve

10.42

10.43

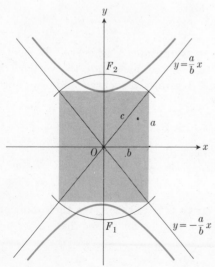

10.44 Hyperbola: $\dfrac{y^2}{a^2} - \dfrac{x^2}{b^2} = 1$.

also approaches zero, and the line in Eq. (7a) is an asymptote of the hyperbola.

By symmetry, the line

$$\frac{x}{a} + \frac{y}{b} = 0 \tag{7b}$$

is also an asymptote of the hyperbola. Both asymptotes may be obtained by simply replacing the "one" on the right side of (3) by a zero and then factoring. In sketching a hyperbola (Fig. 10.43), it is convenient to mark off distances a to the right and to the left of the origin along the x-axis and distances b above and below the origin along the y-axis, and to construct a rectangle with sides passing through these points, parallel to the coordinate axes. The diagonals of this rectangle, extended, are then the asymptotes of the hyperbola. The semidiagonal

$$c = \sqrt{a^2 + b^2}$$

can also be used as the radius of a circle that will cut the x-axis in two points, $F_1(-c, 0)$ and $F_2(c, 0)$, which are the foci of the hyperbola.

If we interchange x and y in Eq. (3), the new equation

$$\frac{y^2}{a^2} - \frac{x^2}{b^2} = 1 \tag{8}$$

represents a hyperbola with foci on the y-axis. Its graph is shown in Fig. 10.44.

Center not at the origin

The *center* of a hyperbola is the point of intersection of its axes of symmetry. If the center is $C(h, k)$, we may introduce a translation to new coordinates

$$x' = x - h, \quad y' = y - k \tag{9}$$

with origin O' at the center. In terms of the new coordinates, the equation of the hyperbola is either

$$\frac{x'^2}{a^2} - \frac{y'^2}{b^2} = 1, \tag{10a}$$

or

$$\frac{y'^2}{a^2} - \frac{x'^2}{b^2} = 1. \tag{10b}$$

Problem 1. Analyze the equation

$$x^2 - 4y^2 + 2x + 8y - 7 = 0.$$

Solution. We complete the squares in the x and y terms separately and reduce to standard form:

$$(x^2 + 2x) - 4(y^2 - 2y) = 7,$$

$$(x^2 + 2x + 1) - 4(y^2 - 2y + 1) = 7 + 1 - 4,$$

$$\frac{(x+1)^2}{4} - (y-1)^2 = 1.$$

The translation of axes

$$x' = x + 1, \quad y' = y - 1$$

reduces the equation to

$$\frac{x'^2}{4} - \frac{y'^2}{1} = 1,$$

which represents a hyperbola with center at $x' = 0$, $y' = 0$, or $x = -1$, $y = 1$, and having

$$a^2 = 4, \quad b^2 = 1, \quad c^2 = a^2 + b^2 = 5,$$

and asymptotes

$$\frac{x'}{2} - y' = 0, \quad \frac{x'}{2} + y' = 0.$$

The foci have coordinates $(\pm\sqrt{5}, 0)$ relative to the new axes or, since

$$x = x' - 1, \quad y = y' + 1,$$

the coordinates relative to the original axes are

$$(-1 \pm \sqrt{5}, 1).$$

The curve is sketched in Fig. 10.45.

Problem 2. Analyze the equation

$$x^2 - 4y^2 - 2x + 8y - 2 = 0.$$

Solution. Proceeding as before, we obtain

$$(x - 1)^2 - 4(y - 1)^2 = 2 + 1 - 4 = -1.$$

The standard form requires a plus one on the right side of the equation, so we change signs and have

$$4(y - 1)^2 - (x - 1)^2 = 1.$$

10.45

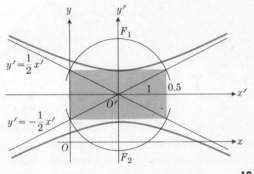

10.46

Comparison with (10) indicates that we should write the first term of this equation as $(y - 1)^2$ divided by 0.25:

$$\frac{(y-1)^2}{0.25} - \frac{(x-1)^2}{1} = 1.$$

The translation $x' = x - 1$, $y' = y - 1$ replaces this by

$$\frac{y'^2}{0.25} - \frac{x'^2}{1} = 1,$$

which represents a hyperbola with center at $x' = y' = 0$, or $x = y = 1$. The curve has intercepts at $(0, \pm 0.5)$ on the y'-axis but does not cross the x'-axis. Here (10b) applies, with

$$a^2 = 0.25, \quad b^2 = 1, \quad c^2 = a^2 + b^2 = 1.25.$$

The lines (Fig. 10.46)

$$\frac{y'}{0.5} - x' = 0, \quad \frac{y'}{0.5} + x' = 0$$

are the asymptotes, while the foci are at $(0, \pm\sqrt{1.25})$ on the y'-axis.

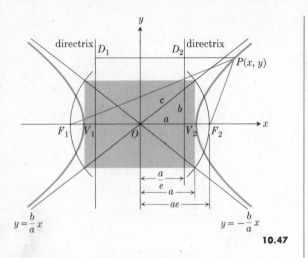

directrix D_1 D_2 directrix

$P(x, y)$

c
b
a

F_1 V_1 O V_2 F_2

$\dfrac{a}{e}$
a
ae

$y = \dfrac{b}{a} x$ $y = -\dfrac{b}{a} x$

10.47

It is worth noting that there is no restriction $a > b$ for the hyperbola as there is for the ellipse, and the direction in which the hyperbola opens is controlled by the *signs* rather than by the relative *sizes* of the coefficients of the quadratic terms.

In our further discussion of the hyperbola, we shall assume that it has been referred to axes through its center and that its equation has the form

$$\frac{x^2}{a^2} - \frac{y^2}{b^2} = 1. \tag{11}$$

Then

$$c^2 = a^2 + b^2. \tag{12}$$

As for the ellipse, we define the *eccentricity* e to be

$$e = \frac{c}{a},$$

and since $c \geq a$, the eccentricity of a hyperbola is never less than unity. The lines

$$x = \frac{a}{e}, \qquad x = -\frac{a}{e}$$

are the *directrices*.

We shall now verify that a point $P(x, y)$ whose coordinates satisfy Eq. (11) also has the property that

$$PF_1 = e \cdot PD_1 \tag{13a}$$

and

$$PF_2 = e \cdot PD_2, \tag{13b}$$

where $F_1(-c, 0)$ and $F_2(c, 0)$ are the foci while

$$D_1\left(-\frac{a}{e}, y\right) \quad \text{and} \quad D_2\left(\frac{a}{e}, y\right)$$

are the points nearest P on the directrices.

We shall content ourselves with establishing the results (13a, b) for any point P on the right branch of the hyperbola; the method is the same when P is on the left branch. Reference to Eqs. (5a) then shows that

$$PF_1 = \frac{c}{a} x + a = e\left(x + \frac{a}{e}\right)$$
$$PF_2 = \frac{c}{a} x - a = e\left(x - \frac{a}{e}\right), \tag{14a}$$

while we see from Fig. 10.47 that

$$PD_1 = x + \frac{a}{e},$$
$$PD_2 = x - \frac{a}{e}. \tag{14b}$$

These results combine to establish the "focus-and-directrix" properties of the hyperbola expressed in Eqs. (13a, b). Conversely, if Eqs. (14a) are satisfied, it is also true that

$$PF_1 - PF_2 = 2a.$$

That is, P satisfies the requirement that the difference of its distances from the two foci is constant.

It is possible to devise various schemes for sketching a hyperbola. In one method (see Fig. 10.48) we exploit the equation

$$PF_1 = 2a + PF_2$$

by constructing a circle of radius r with center at F_2 and another circle of radius $2a + r$ with center at F_1. The points P, P' where the two circles intersect are points on the hyperbola. By varying r, as many points on the hyperbola as desired may be obtained. Interchanging the roles of the two foci F_1 and F_2 allows us to obtain points on the other branch of the hyperbola.

10.48

EXERCISES

1. Sketch the following hyperbolas.

(a) $\dfrac{x^2}{9} - \dfrac{y^2}{16} = 1$ (b) $\dfrac{x^2}{16} - \dfrac{y^2}{9} = 1$

(c) $\dfrac{y^2}{9} - \dfrac{x^2}{16} = 1$ (d) $\dfrac{x^2}{9} - \dfrac{y^2}{16} = -1$

In Exercises 2 through 8, find the center, vertices, foci, and asymptotes of the given hyperbola. Sketch the curve.

2. $9(x-2)^2 - 4(y+3)^2 = 36$

3. $4(x-2)^2 - 9(y+3)^2 = 36$

4. $4(y+3)^2 - 9(x-2)^2 = 1$

5. $5x^2 - 4y^2 + 20x + 8y = 4$

6. $4x^2 = y^2 - 4y + 8$ 7. $4y^2 = x^2 - 4x$

8. $4x^2 - 5y^2 - 16x + 10y + 31 = 0$

9. Show that the line tangent to the hyperbola

$$b^2x^2 - a^2y^2 = a^2b^2$$

at a point $P(x_1, y_1)$ on it has an equation that may be written in the form $b^2xx_1 - a^2yy_1 = a^2b^2$.

10. Find the volume generated when the area bounded by the hyperbola $b^2x^2 - a^2y^2 = a^2b^2$ and the line $x = c$, through its focus $(c, 0)$, is rotated about the y-axis.

11. Show that the equation

$$\frac{x^2}{9-C} + \frac{y^2}{5-C} = 1$$

represents

(a) an ellipse if C is any constant less than 5,

(b) a hyperbola if C is any constant between 5 and 9,

(c) no real locus if C is greater than 9.

Show that each ellipse in (a) and each hyperbola in (b) has foci at the two points $(\pm 2, 0)$, independent of the value of C.

12. Find the equation of the hyperbola with foci at $(0, 0)$ and $(0, 4)$ if it is required to pass through the point $(12, 9)$.

13. One focus of a hyperbola is located at the point $(1, -3)$ and the corresponding directrix is the line $y = 2$. Find the equation of the hyperbola if its eccentricity is $\frac{3}{2}$.

14. Deduce Eqs. $(4a, b)$ from Eq. (1).

10.9 SECOND-DEGREE CURVES

The circle, parabola, ellipse, and hyperbola are curves whose equations are all special cases of the following general equation of the second degree:

$$Ax^2 + Bxy + Cy^2 + Dx + Ey + F = 0. \qquad (1)$$

For example, the circle

$$(x-h)^2 + (y-k)^2 = r^2$$

may be obtained from Eq. (1) by taking

$$A = C = 1, \quad B = 0, \quad D = -2h,$$
$$E = -2k, \quad F = h^2 + k^2 - r^2,$$

and the parabola

$$x^2 = 4py$$

is obtained by taking

$$A = 1, \quad E = -4p, \quad B = C = D = F = 0.$$

In fact, even the straight line is a special case of (1) with $A = B = C = 0$, but this reduces (1) to a *linear* equation instead of maintaining its status as a second-degree equation. The terms Ax^2, Bxy, and Cy^2 are the second degree, or quadratic terms, and we shall presently investigate the nature of the

10.49

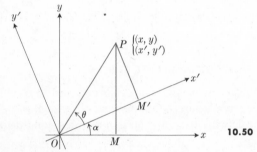

10.50

which is a special case of Eq. (1) in which the cross-product term is present. The asymptotes of the hyperbola in Eq. (2) are the x- and y-axes, and the transverse axis of the hyperbola (which is the axis of symmetry on which the foci lie) makes an angle of 45° with the coordinate axes. In fact, the cross-product term is present only in some similar circumstance, where the axes have been "tilted."

We shall now see how the equation of a curve is modified if it is referred to $x'y'$-axes by a rotation through an angle α in the counterclockwise direction. Referring to Fig. 10.50, we have

$$x = OM = OP \cos (\theta + \alpha),$$
$$y = MP = OP \sin (\theta + \alpha), \tag{3a}$$

while

$$x' = OM' = OP \cos \theta,$$
$$y' = M'P = OP \sin \theta. \tag{3b}$$

Using the relationships

$$\cos (\theta + \alpha) = \cos \theta \cos \alpha - \sin \theta \sin \alpha,$$
$$\sin (\theta + \alpha) = \sin \theta \cos \alpha + \cos \theta \sin \alpha,$$

in (3a) and taking account of (3b), we find

$$x = x' \cos \alpha - y' \sin \alpha,$$
$$y = x' \sin \alpha + y' \cos \alpha, \tag{4}$$

which are known as the equations for *rotation of axes*.

To illustrate their application, suppose that we take $\alpha = 45°$ and find the equation of the hyperbola of (2) in terms of the new coordinates. Since $\cos 45° = \sin 45° = \sqrt{\frac{1}{2}}$, we substitute

$$x = \frac{x' - y'}{\sqrt{2}}, \quad y = \frac{x' + y'}{\sqrt{2}}$$

into Eq. (2) and obtain

$$(x')^2 - (y')^2 = a^2,$$

which is like Eq. (3), Article 10.8, with $b = a$.

If we apply the general rotation of axes of equations (4) to the general quadratic equation (1), we

---

curve represented by Eq. (1) when at least one of these quadratic terms is present.

The so-called "cross-product" term Bxy has not appeared in the equations we found in Articles 10.5 through 10.8. This results from the way in which we chose coordinate axes, namely, such that at least one of them is parallel to an axis of symmetry of the curve in question. However, suppose we seek to find the equation of a hyperbola with foci at $F_1(-a, -a)$ and $F_2(a, a)$ for example, and with $|PF_1 - PF_2| = 2a$ (Fig. 10.49). Then

$$\sqrt{(x + a)^2 + (y + a)^2}$$
$$- \sqrt{(x - a)^2 + (y - a)^2} = \pm 2a,$$

and when we transpose one radical, square, solve for the radical that still appears, and square again, this reduces to

$$2xy = a^2, \tag{2}$$

obtain a new quadratic equation of the form

$$A'x'^2 + B'x'y' + C'y'^2 + D'x' + E'y' + F' = 0, \tag{5}$$

with new coefficients related to the old as follows:

$$\begin{aligned}
A' &= A \cos^2 \alpha + B \cos \alpha \sin \alpha + C \sin^2 \alpha, \\
B' &= B (\cos^2 \alpha - \sin^2 \alpha) + 2(C - A) \sin \alpha \cos \alpha, \\
C' &= A \sin^2 \alpha - B \sin \alpha \cos \alpha + C \cos^2 \alpha, \\
D' &= D \cos \alpha + E \sin \alpha, \\
E' &= -D \sin \alpha + E \cos \alpha, \\
F' &= F.
\end{aligned} \tag{6}$$

If we start with an equation in which the cross-product term is present ($B \neq 0$), then we can always find an angle of rotation α such that the new cross-product term is eliminated. To find the angle α that does this, we simply put $B' = 0$ in the second equation of (6) and solve for α. It is easier to do this if we note that

$$\cos^2 \alpha - \sin^2 \alpha = \cos 2\alpha$$

and

$$2 \sin \alpha \cos \alpha = \sin 2\alpha,$$

so that

$$B' = B \cos 2\alpha + (C - A) \sin 2\alpha.$$

Hence B' will vanish if we choose α so that

$$\cot 2\alpha = \frac{A - C}{B}. \tag{7}$$

Example. The curve whose equation is

$$x^2 + xy + y^2 = 3$$

has $A = B = C = 1$. Choosing α according to Eq. (7),

$$\cot 2\alpha = 0, \quad 2\alpha = 90°, \quad \alpha = 45°,$$

and substituting

$$x = \frac{x' - y'}{\sqrt{2}}, \quad y = \frac{x' + y'}{\sqrt{2}}$$

according to (4), we obtain

$$3(x')^2 + (y')^2 = 6.$$

This may be identified as an ellipse with its foci on the new y'-axis.

Since axes may be rotated to eliminate the cross-product term, there is no loss in generality in assuming that this has been done. Then the quadratic equation (5), with $B' = 0$, will look like Eq. (1), with $B = 0$:

$$Ax^2 + Cy^2 + Dx + Ey + F = 0. \tag{8}$$

Eq. (8) represents

(a) a straight line, if $A = C = 0$ and not both D and E vanish.

(b) a circle, if $A = C \neq 0$. In special cases the locus may reduce to a single point, or no real locus.

(c) a parabola, if (8) is quadratic in one variable, linear in the other.

(d) an ellipse, if A and C are both positive or both negative. In special cases the locus may reduce to a single point, or no real locus.

(e) a hyperbola, if A and C are of opposite signs, both different from zero. In special cases the locus may reduce to a pair of intersecting straight lines (for example, $x^2 - y^2 = 0$).

We have already seen how to reduce (8) to the standard form for the equation of a circle, parabola, ellipse, or hyperbola by completing the squares (as needed) and translating to new axes.

Summary

Any second-degree equation in x and y represents a circle, parabola, ellipse, or hyperbola (except for certain special cases in which the locus may reduce to a point, a line, a pair of lines, or fail to exist, as noted above). Conversely, any of these curves has an equation of the second degree. To find the curve, given its equation,

(1) rotate axes (if necessary) to eliminate the cross-product term, and

(2) translate axes (if desired) to reduce the equation to a recognizable standard form.

EXERCISES

1. Show that the equation $x^4 + 6x^2y^2 + y^4 = 32$ becomes $x'^4 + y'^4 = 16$ under a 45° rotation of axes. Sketch the curve and the two sets of axes.

2. Use the definition of an ellipse to find the equation of an ellipse with foci at $F_1(-1, 0)$ and $F_2(0, \sqrt{3})$ if it passes through the point $(1, 0)$. Through what angle α should the axes be rotated to eliminate the cross-product term from the equation found?

3. Show that the equation

$$x^2 + y^2 = r^2 \quad \text{becomes} \quad x'^2 + y'^2 = r^2$$

for every choice of the angle α in the equations for rotation of axes.

4. Show that $A' + C' = A + C$ for every choice of the angle α in Eqs. (6).

5. Show that $B'^2 - 4A'C' = B^2 - 4AC$ for every choice of the angle α in Eqs. (6).

6. Show that a rotation of the axes through 45° will eliminate the cross-product term from Eq. (1) whenever $A = C$.

7. Find the equation of the curve

$$x^2 + 2xy + y^2 = 1$$

after a rotation of axes that makes $A' = 0$ in Eq. (6).

By a rotation of axes, transform each equation into an equation that has no cross-product term.

8. $3x^2 + 2xy + 3y^2 = 19$ 9. $x^2 - 3xy + y^2 = 5$
10. $3x^2 + 4\sqrt{3}xy - y^2 = 7$

10.10 INVARIANTS AND THE DISCRIMINANT

It is sometimes useful to apply directly to the equation

$$Ax^2 + Bxy + Cy^2 + Dx + Ey + F = 0 \quad (1)$$

a criterion that will tell whether the curve is a parabola, an ellipse, or a hyperbola, without first performing a rotation of axes to eliminate the cross-product term. Our discussion has shown that a

rotation of axes through an angle α determined by

$$\cot 2\alpha = \frac{A - C}{B} \quad (2)$$

will transform the equation to the equivalent form

$$A'x'^2 + B'x'y' + C'y'^2 + D'x' + E'y' + F' = 0 \quad (3)$$

with new coefficients $A', \ldots, F'$ related to the old as in Eq. (6), Article 10.9, and with $B' = 0$ for the particular choice of α satisfying Eq. (2) above.

Now if a curve has an equation (3) except that it has no cross-product term, it is

(a) *a parabola* if A' or $C' = 0$ (but not both) and if both x' and y' appear in the equation;

(b) *an ellipse* (or in exceptional cases, a single point, or empty) if A' and C' have the same sign, that is, if $A'C' > 0$;

(c) *a hyperbola* (or in exceptional cases, a pair of intersecting lines) if A' and C' have opposite signs, that is, if $A'C' < 0$.

However, it has been discovered that the coefficients A, B, C and A', B', C' satisfy the condition

$$B^2 - 4AC = B'^2 - 4A'C' \quad (4)$$

for *any* rotation of axes. [This can easily be verified by use of Eq. (6), Article 10.9.] That is, the quantity $B^2 - 4AC$ is *invariant* under a rotation of axes. But when the particular rotation is performed that makes $B' = 0$, the right-hand side of (4) becomes simply $-4A'C'$. The criteria above, expressed in terms of A' and C', can now be expressed in terms of the *discriminant*:

$$\text{discriminant} = B^2 - 4AC. \quad (5)$$

Thus we can say that the curve is

(a) *a parabola* (or in certain special cases, a pair of parallel lines, or one line, or an empty locus), if $B^2 - 4AC = 0$;

(b) *an ellipse* (or in exceptional cases, a single point, or empty) if $B^2 - 4AC < 0$;

(c) *a hyperbola* (or in exceptional cases, a pair of intersecting lines) if $B^2 - 4AC > 0$.

The following problem illustrates some of the special cases of (a).

Problem 1. What is the locus represented by the equation $x^2 - 4xy + 4y^2 + F = 0$ if

(a) $F = 0$,   (b) $F = 1$,   (c) $F = -1$?

Solution. The discriminant is

$$B^2 - 4AC = (-4)^2 - 16 = 0.$$

However, the locus is not a parabola because it is the same as $(x - 2y)^2 = -F$. This is a single line $x = 2y$ if $F = 0$; it is empty if $F = 1$; and it is two parallel lines $x - 2y = \pm 1$ if $F = -1$.

Another invariant associated with Eqs. (1) and (3) is the sum of the coefficients of the squared terms. For it is evident from Eq. (6), Article 10.9, that

$$A' + C' = A (\cos^2 \alpha + \sin^2 \alpha) + C (\sin^2 \alpha + \cos^2 \alpha),$$

or

$$A' + C' = A + C, \tag{6}$$

since

$$\sin^2 \alpha + \cos^2 \alpha = 1$$

for any angle α.

The two invariants (4) and (6) may be used as a check against numerical errors in performing a rotation of axes of a quadratic equation. They may also be used to find the new coefficients of the quadratic terms

$$A'x'^2 + B'x'y' + C'y'^2,$$

with

$$B' = 0,$$

as in the following problem.

Problem 2. Determine the equation to which

$$x^2 + xy + y^2 = 1$$

reduces when the axes are rotated to eliminate the cross-product term.

Solution. From the original equation we find

$$B^2 - 4AC = -3, \quad A + C = 2.$$

Then, taking $B' = 0$, we have, from (4) and (6),

$$-4A'C' = -3, \quad A' + C' = 2.$$

Substituting $C' = 2 - A'$ from the second of these into the first, we obtain the quadratic equation

$$4A'^2 - 8A' + 3 = 0,$$

which factors into

$$(2A' - 3)(2A' - 1) = 0$$

and gives

$$A' = \tfrac{3}{2} \quad \text{or} \quad A' = \tfrac{1}{2}.$$

The corresponding values of C' are

$$C' = \tfrac{1}{2} \quad \text{or} \quad C' = \tfrac{3}{2}.$$

The equation therefore is

$$\tfrac{3}{2}x'^2 + \tfrac{1}{2}y'^2 = 1,$$

or

$$\tfrac{1}{2}x'^2 + \tfrac{3}{2}y'^2 = 1$$

in the new coordinates. Hence the curve is an ellipse.

It should be noted that when no first power terms are present in the original equation, they will also be absent in the new equation. This is due to the fact that a rotation of axes preserves the algebraic degree of each term of the equation; or we may refer to Eq. (6), Article 10.9, which shows that D' and E' are both zero if D and E are.

EXERCISES

Use the discriminant to classify each of the following second-degree equations as representing a circle, an ellipse, a parabola, or a hyperbola.

1. $x^2 + y^2 + xy + x - y = 3$
2. $2x^2 - y^2 + 4xy - 2x + 3y = 6$
3. $x^2 + 4xy + 4y^2 - 3x = 6$
4. $x^2 + y^2 + 3x - 2y = 10$
5. $xy + y^2 - 3x = 5$
6. $3x^2 + 6xy + 3y^2 - 4x + 5y = 12$
7. $x^2 - y^2 = 1$ 8. $2x^2 + 3y^2 - 4x = 7$
9. $x^2 - 3xy + 3y^2 + 6y = 7$

10. When $B^2 - 4AC$ is negative, the equation

$$Ax^2 + Bxy + Cy^2 = 1$$

represents an ellipse. If the semiaxes have lengths a and b, the area of the ellipse is πab. Show that the area of the ellipse given above is $2\pi/\sqrt{4AC - B^2}$.

11. Show, by reference to Eq. (6), Article 10.9 that

$$D'^2 + E'^2 = D^2 + E^2$$

for every angle of rotation α.

12. If $C = -A$ in Eq. (1), show that there is a rotation of axes for which $A' = C' = 0$ in the resulting Eq. (3). Find the angle α that makes $A' = C' = 0$ in this case.
Hint. Since $A' + C' = 0$, one need only make the further requirement that $A' = 0$ in Eq. (3).

10.11 SECTIONS OF A CONE

The circle, parabola, ellipse, and hyperbola are known as *conic* sections because each may be obtained by cutting a cone by a plane. If the cutting plane is perpendicular to the axis of the cone, the section is a circle.

In general, suppose the cutting plane makes an angle α with the axis of the cone and let the generating angle of the cone be β (see Fig. 10.51). Then the section is

   (i) a circle, if $\alpha = 90°$,

   (ii) an ellipse, if $\beta < \alpha < 90°$,

   (iii) a parabola, if $\alpha = \beta$,

   (iv) a hyperbola, if $0 \leq \alpha < \beta$.

The connection between these curves as we have defined them and the sections from a cone is readily made by reference to Fig. 10.52. The figure is drawn to illustrate the case of an ellipse, but the argument holds for the other cases as well.

A sphere is inscribed tangent to the cone along a circle C, and tangent to the cutting plane at a point F. Point P is any point on the conic section. We shall see that F is a focus, and that the line L, in which the cutting plane and the plane of the circle C intersect, is a directrix of the curve. To this end let Q be the point where the line through P parallel

10.51

10.52

to the axis of the cone intersects the plane of C, let A be the point where the line joining P to the vertex of the cone touches C, and let PD be perpendicular to line L at D. Then PA and PF are two lines tangent to the same sphere from a common point P and hence have the same length:

$$PA = PF.$$

Also, from the right triangle PQA, we have

$$PQ = PA \cos \beta;$$

and from the right triangle PQD, we find that

$$PQ = PD \cos \alpha.$$

Hence

$$PA \cos \beta = PD \cos \alpha,$$

or

$$\frac{PA}{PD} = \frac{\cos \alpha}{\cos \beta}.$$

But since $PA = PF$, this means that

$$\frac{PF}{PD} = \frac{\cos \alpha}{\cos \beta}. \qquad (1)$$

Since α and β are constant for a given cone and a given cutting plane, Eq. (1) has the form

$$PF = e \cdot PD.$$

This characterizes P as belonging to a parabola, an ellipse, or a hyperbola, with focus at F and directrix L, accordingly as $e = 1$, $e < 1$, or $e > 1$ respectively, where

$$e = \frac{\cos \alpha}{\cos \beta}$$

is thus identified with the eccentricity.

EXERCISES

1. Sketch a figure similar to Fig. 10.52 where the conic section is a parabola, and carry through the argument of Article 10.11 on the basis of such a figure.

2. Sketch a figure similar to Fig. 10.52 where the conic section is a hyperbola, and carry through the argument of Article 10.11 on the basis of such a figure.

3. Which parts of the construction described in Article 10.11 become impossible when the conic section is a circle?

4. Let one directrix be the line $x = -p$ and take the corresponding focus at the origin. Using Eq. (15) of Article 10.7, derive the equation of the general conic section of eccentricity e. If e is neither 0 nor 1, show that the center of the conic section has coordinates

$$\left(\frac{pe^2}{1 - e^2}, 0 \right).$$

REVIEW QUESTIONS AND EXERCISES

1. Discuss criteria for symmetry of a curve with respect to

   (a) the x-axis, (b) the y-axis,

   (c) the origin, (d) the line $y = x$.

2. Define *asymptote*. How do you find vertical and horizontal asymptotes of a curve if its equation is given in the form $y = f(x)/g(x)$?

3. How do you find the extent of a curve (or, alternatively, strips of the plane from which the curve is excluded)?

4. Name the conic sections.

5. What kind of equation characterizes the conic sections?

6. If the equation of a conic section is given, and it contains no xy-term, how can you tell by inspection whether it is a parabola, circle, ellipse, or hyperbola? How can you tell what the curve is if there is an xy-term in the equation?

7. What are the equations of transformation of co-ordinates

   (a) for a translation of axes?

   (b) for a rotation of axes?

   Illustrate with diagrams.

8. What two quantities that are associated with the equation of a conic section remain invariant under a rotation of axes?

9. Sketch a parabola and label its vertex, focus, axis, and directrix. What is the definition of a parabola? What is the equation of your parabola?

10. Sketch an ellipse and label its vertices, foci, axes, and directrices. What is the definition of an ellipse? What is the equation of your ellipse?

11. Sketch a hyperbola and label its vertices, foci, axes, asymptotes, and directrices. What is the definition of a hyperbola? What is the equation of your hyperbola?

12. A ripple tank is made by bending a strip of tin around the perimeter of an ellipse for the wall of the tank and soldering a flat bottom onto this. An inch or two of water is put in the tank and the experimenter pokes a finger into it, right at one focus of the ellipse. Ripples radiate outward through the water, reflect from the strip around the edge of the tank, and (in a short time) a drop of water spurts up at the second focus. Why?

MISCELLANEOUS EXERCISES

In Exercises 1 through 9, determine the following properties of the curves whose equations are given: (A) symmetry, (B) extent, (C) intercepts, (D) asymptotes, (E) slope at intercepts. Use this information in sketching the curves.

1. (a) $y^2 = x(4 - x)$; (b) $y^2 = x(x - 4)$;

   (c) $y^2 = \dfrac{x}{4 - x}$

2. (a) $y = x + \dfrac{1}{x^2}$; (b) $y^2 = x + \dfrac{1}{x^2}$; (c) $y = x^2 + \dfrac{1}{x}$

3. (a) $y = x(x + 1)(x - 2)$; (b) $y^2 = x(x + 1)(x - 2)$

4. (a) $y = \dfrac{8}{4 + x^2}$; (b) $y = \dfrac{8}{4 - x^2}$; (c) $y = \dfrac{8x}{4 + x^2}$

5. (a) $xy = x^2 + 1$; (b) $y = \dfrac{x^2}{x - 1}$

6. (a) $y^2 = x^4 - x^2$; (b) $y^2 = \dfrac{x - 1}{x - 2}$

7. $x^2 y - y = 4(x - 2)$

8. $y = \dfrac{x^2 + 1}{x^2 - 1}$ 9. $x^2 + xy + y^2 = 3$

10. Let C be the curve in Exercise 9. Let $P(x, y)$ be a point on C. Let $P'(kx, ky)$ be a point on the line OP from the origin to P. If k is held constant, what is the equation of the locus described by P' as P traces out the curve C?

11. Sketch the graph whose equation is

    $$(y - x + 2)(2y + x - 4) = 0.$$

12. A certain graph has an equation of the form

    $$ay^2 + by = \frac{cx + d}{ex^2 + fx + g},$$

where a, b, c, d, e, f, and g are constants whose value in each case is either 0 or 1. From the following information about the graph, determine the constants and give a reason for your choice in each case.

Extent. The curve does not exist for $x < -1$. All values of y are permissible.

Symmetry. The curve is symmetric about the x-axis.

Intercepts. No y-intercept; x-intercept at $(-1, 0)$.

Asymptotes. Both axes; no others.

Sketch the graph.

13. Each of the following inequalities describes one or more regions of the xy-plane. Sketch first the locus obtained by replacing the inequality sign by an equal sign; then indicate the region that contains the points whose coordinates satisfy the given inequality.

    (a) $x < 3$ (b) $x < y$

    (c) $x^2 < y$ (d) $x^2 + y^2 > 4$

    (e) $x^2 + xy + y^2 < 3$ (f) $x^2 + xy + y^2 > 3$

    (g) $y^2 < \dfrac{x}{4 - x}$

14. Write an equation of the tangent to the curve

    $$x^2 - 2xy + y^2 + 2x + y - 6 = 0.$$

    at the point $(2, 2)$.

15. Sketch the curves $xy = 2$ and $x^2 - y^2 = 3$ in one diagram, and show that they intersect orthogonally.

16. Find equations of the lines that are tangent to the curve $y = x^3 - 6x + 2$ and are parallel to the line $y = 6x - 2$.

17. Prove that if a line is drawn tangent to the curve $y^2 = kx$ at a point $P(x, y)$ not at the origin, then the portion of the tangent that lies between the x-axis and P is bisected by the y-axis.

18. Through the point $P(x, y)$ on the curve $y^2 = kx$, lines are drawn parallel to the axes. The rectangular area bounded by these two lines and the axes is divided into two portions by the given curve.

    (a) If these two areas are rotated about the y-axis, show that they generate two solids whose volumes are in the ratio of four to one.

    (b) What is the ratio of the volumes of the solids generated when these areas are rotated about the x-axis?

19. Show that the curves

    $$2x^2 + 3y^2 = a^2 \quad \text{and} \quad ky^2 = x^3$$

    are orthogonal for all values of the constants a and k ($a \neq 0$, $k \neq 0$). Sketch the four curves corresponding to $a = 2$, $a = 4$, $k = \frac{1}{2}$, $k = -2$ in one diagram.

20. Show, analytically, that an angle inscribed in a semicircle is a right angle.

21. Two points P, Q are called symmetric with respect to a circle if P and Q lie on the same ray through the center and if the product of their distances from the center is equal to the square of the radius. Given that Q describes the straight line $x + 2y - 5 = 0$, find the locus of the point P that is symmetric to Q with respect to the circle $x^2 + y^2 = 4$.

22. A point $P(x, y)$ moves so that the ratio of its distances from two fixed points is a constant k. Show that the locus is a circle if $k \neq 1$, and is a straight line if $k = 1$.

23. Show that the centers of all chords of the parabola $x^2 = 4py$ with slope m lie on a straight line and find its equation.

24. The line through the focus F and the point $P(x_1, y_1)$ on the parabola $y^2 = 4px$ intersects the parabola in a second point $Q(x_2, y_2)$. Find the coordinates of Q in terms of y_1 and p. If O is the vertex and PO cuts the directrix at R, prove that QR is parallel to the axis of the parabola.

25. Find the point (or points) on the curve $x^2 = y^3$ nearest the point $P(0, 4)$. Sketch the curve and the shortest line from P to the curve.

26. Prove that every line through the center of the circle $(x - h)^2 + (y - k)^2 = r^2$ is orthogonal to the circle.

27. Find all points on the curve $x^2 + 2xy + 3y^2 = 3$, where the tangent line is perpendicular to the line $x + y = 1$.

28. A line PT is drawn tangent to the curve $xy = x + y$ at the point $P(-2, \frac{2}{3})$. Find equations of two lines that are normal to the curve and perpendicular to PT.

29. Sketch the loci described by the following equations.

    (a) $(x + y)(x^2 + y^2 - 1) = 0$

    (b) $(x + y)(x^2 + y^2 - 1) = 1$

    Hint. In (b), consider intersections of the locus with the line $x + y = k$ for different values of the constant k.

30. Find the center and radius of the circle through the two points $A(2, 0)$ and $B(6, 0)$ and tangent to the curve $y = x^2$.

31. Find the center of the circle that passes through the point $(0, 1)$ and is tangent to the curve $y = x^2$ at $(2, 4)$.

32. Let L_1, L_2, L_3 be three straight lines, no two of which are parallel. Let $L_i = a_i x + b_i y + c_i = 0$, $i = 1, 2, 3$, be the equation of the line L_i.

    (a) Describe the locus whose equation is

    $$L_1 L_2 + h L_2 L_3 + k L_1 L_3 = 0,$$

    assuming h and k are constants.

    (b) Use the method of part (a) and determine h and k so that the equation represents a circle through the points of intersection of the lines

    $$x + y - 2 = 0, \quad x - y + 2 = 0, \quad y - 2x = 0.$$

    (c) Find a parabola, axis vertical, through the points of intersection of the lines in (b).

33. A comet moves in a parabolic orbit with the sun at the focus. When the comet is 4×10^7 miles from the sun, the line from the sun to it makes an angle of $60°$ with the axis of the orbit (drawn in the direction in which the orbit opens). Find how near the comet comes to the sun.

34. Sketch in one diagram the curves

    $$y^2 = 4x + 4, \quad y^2 = 64 - 16x,$$

    and find the angles at which they intersect.

35. Find an equation of the curve such that the distance from any point $P(x, y)$ on the curve to the line $x = 3$ is the same as its distance to the point $(4, 0)$. Sketch the curve.

36. Two radar stations lying along an east-west line are separated by 20 mi. Choose a coordinate system such that their positions are $(-10, 0)$ and $(10, 0)$. A low-flying plane traveling from west to east is known to have a speed of v_0 mi/sec. At $t = 0$ a signal is sent from the station at $(-10, 0)$, bounces off the plane, and is received at $(10, 0)$ $30/c$ sec later (c is the velocity of the signal). When $t = 10/v_0$, another signal is sent out from the station at $(-10, 0)$, reflects off the plane, and is once again received $30/c$ sec later by the other station. What is the position of the plane when it reflects the second signal, pro-

viding that one assumes $v_0 \ll c$ (that is, v_0 is much less than c)?

37. A line is drawn tangent to the parabola $y^2 = 4px$ at a point $P(x, y)$ on the curve. Let A be the point where this tangent line crosses the axis of the parabola, let F be the focus, and let PD be the line parallel to the axis of the parabola and intersecting the directrix at D. Prove that $AFPD$ is a rhombus.

38. Find the equation of the locus of a point $P(x, y)$ if the distance from P to the vertex is twice the distance from P to the focus of the parabola $x^2 = 8y$. Name the locus.

39. Prove that the tangent to a parabola at a point P cuts the axis of the parabola at a point whose distance from the vertex equals the distance from P to the tangent at the vertex.

40. Discuss the locus of the equation

    $$x^4 - (y^2 - 9)^2 = 0$$

    and sketch its graph.

41. Show that the curve $C: x^4 - (y^2 - 9)^2 = 1$ approaches part of the curve $x^4 - (y^2 - 9)^2 = 0$ as the point $P(x, y)$ moves farther and farther away from the origin. Sketch. Do any points of C lie inside the circle $x^2 + y^2 = 9$? Give a reason for your answer.

42. The ellipse $(x^2/a^2) + (y^2/b^2) = 1$ divides the plane into two regions; one inside the ellipse, the other outside. Show that points in one of these regions have coordinates that satisfy the inequality

    $$(x^2/a^2) + (y^2/b^2) < 1,$$

    while in the other, $(x^2/a^2) + (y^2/b^2) > 1$. (Consider the effect of replacing x, y in the given equation by $x' = kx$, $y' = ky$, with $k < 1$ in one case and $k > 1$ in the other.)

43. Find an equation of an ellipse with foci at $(1, 0)$ and $(5, 0)$, and one vertex at the origin.

44. Let $F_1 = (3, 0)$, $F_2 = (0, 5)$, $P = (-1, 3)$.

    (a) Find the distances $F_1 P$ and $F_2 P$.

    (b) Does the origin O lie inside or outside the ellipse that has F_1 and F_2 as its foci and that passes through the point P? Why?

45. Find the greatest area of a rectangle inscribed in the ellipse $(x^2/a^2) + (y^2/b^2) = 1$, with sides parallel to the coordinate axes.

46. Show that the line $y = mx + c$ is tangent to the conic section $Ax^2 + y^2 = 1$ if and only if the constants A, m, and c satisfy the condition

$$A(c^2 - 1) = m^2.$$

47. Starting from the general equation for the conic, find the equation of the conic with the following properties:

(a) It is symmetric with respect to the origin.

(b) It passes through the point $(1, 0)$.

(c) The tangent to it at the point $(-2, 1)$ on it is the line $y = 1$.

48. Find an ellipse with one vertex at the point $(3, 1)$, the nearer focus at the point $(1, 1)$, and eccentricity $\frac{2}{3}$.

49. By a suitable rotation of axes, show that the equation $xy - x - y = 1$ represents a hyperbola. Sketch.

50. Find an equation of a hyperbola with eccentricity equal to $\sqrt{2}$ and with vertices at the points $(2, 0)$ and $(-2, 0)$.

51. Sketch the conic $\sqrt{2}y - 2xy = 3$. Locate its center and find its eccentricity.

52. If c is a fixed positive constant, then

$$\frac{x^2}{t^2} + \frac{y^2}{t^2 - c^2} = 1 \quad (c^2 < t^2)$$

defines a family of ellipses, any member of which is characterized by a particular value of t. Show that every member of the family

$$\frac{x^2}{t^2} - \frac{y^2}{c^2 - t^2} = 1 \quad (t^2 < c^2)$$

intersects any member of the first family at right angles.

53. Sketch the locus $|x| + |y| = 1$ and find the area it encloses.

54. Show that if the tangent to a curve at a point $P(x, y)$ passes through the origin, then $dy/dx = y/x$ at the point. Hence show that no tangent can be drawn from the origin to the hyperbola $x^2 - y^2 = 1$.

55. (a) Find the coordinates of the center and the foci, the lengths of the axes, and the eccentricity of the ellipse

$$x^2 + 4y^2 - 4x + 8y - 1 = 0.$$

(b) Do likewise with the hyperbola

$$3x^2 - y^2 + 12x - 3y = 0,$$

and in addition find equations of its asymptotes.

56. If the ends of a line segment of constant length move along perpendicular lines, show that a point P on the segment, at distances a and b from the ends, describes an ellipse.

57. Sketch the loci

(a) $(9x^2 + 4y^2 - 36)(4x^2 + 9y^2 - 36) = 0$,

(b) $(9x^2 + 4y^2 - 36)(4x^2 + 9y^2 - 36) = 1$.

Is the curve in (b) bounded or does it extend to points arbitrarily far from the origin? Give a reason for your answer.

58. Let p, q be positive numbers such that $q < p$. If r is a third number, prove that the equation

$$\left(\frac{x^2}{p - r}\right) + \left(\frac{y^2}{q - r}\right) = 1$$

represents

(a) an ellipse if $r < q$,

(b) a hyperbola if $q < r < p$,

(c) nothing if $p < r$.

Prove that all these ellipses and hyperbolas have the same foci, and find these foci.

59. Find the eccentricity of the hyperbola $xy = 1$.

60. On a level plane the sound of a rifle and that of the bullet striking the target are heard at the same instant. What is the locus of the hearer?

61. Show that any tangent to the hyperbola $xy = a^2$ determines with its asymptotes a triangle of area $2a^2$.

62. Given the hyperbola

$$9x^2 - 4y^2 - 18x - 16y + 29 = 0.$$

Find the coordinates of the center and foci, and the equations of the asymptotes. Sketch.

63. By an appropriate rotation, eliminate the xy-term from the equation

$$7x^2 - 8xy + y^2 = 9.$$

64. Show that the tangent to the conic section

$$Ax^2 + Bxy + Cy^2 + Dx + Ey + F = 0$$

at a point (x_1, y_1) on it has an equation that may be written in the form

$$Axx_1 + B\left(\frac{x_1 y + xy_1}{2}\right) + Cyy_1$$

$$+ D\left(\frac{x + x_1}{2}\right) + E\left(\frac{y + y_1}{2}\right) + F = 0.$$

65. (a) Find the eccentricity and center of the conic

$$x^2 + 12y^2 - 6x - 48y + 9 = 0.$$

(b) Find the vertex of the conic

$$x^2 - 6x - 12y + 9 = 0.$$

(c) Sketch the conics in one diagram.

66. Find an equation of the circle passing through the three points common to the conics of Exercise 65.

67. Two vertices A, B of a triangle are fixed and the vertex $C(x, y)$ moves in such a way that

$$\angle A = 2(\angle B).$$

Find the locus of C.

68. Find the equation into which $x^{1/2} + y^{1/2} = a^{1/2}$ is transformed by a rotation of axes through $45°$, and elimination of radicals.

69. Show that $dx^2 + dy^2$ is invariant under any rotation of axes about the origin.

70. Show that $x\, dy - y\, dx$ is invariant under any rotation of axes about the origin.

71. Graph the locus $x^{2n} + y^{2n} = a^{2n}$ for the following values of n:

(a) 1,   (b) 2,   (c) 100.

In each instance find where the curve cuts the line $y = x$.

72. Let P be a point on the hyperbola

$$\frac{x^2}{a^2} - \frac{y^2}{b^2} = 1,$$

and let d_1 and d_2 be the distances from P to the asymptotes of the hyperbola. Prove that the product of these distances is a constant. Note: The distance from a point $P_1(x_1, y_1)$ to a line $Ax + By + C = 0$ is

$$\frac{|Ax_1 + By_1 + C|}{(A^2 + D^2)^{\frac{1}{2}}}.$$

73. If a and b are positive integers, the point (a, b) is called a positive lattice point. Let R be the region described by the inequalities $x > 0$, $y > 0$, $xy \leq 6$. (a) How many lattice points are there in R? (b) How many of the lattice points in R are on the hyperbola $xy = 6$? On $xy = 5$? On $xy = 4$? On $xy = 3$? On $xy = 2$? On $xy = 1$? (c) How many of the lattice points in R are on the line $x = 1$? On $x = 2$? On $x = 3$? On $x = 4$? On $x = 5$? On $x = 6$? On $x = 7$?

74. (Continuation.) For any positive integer k, let $d(k)$ denote the number of positive integers that divide k exactly. Thus, $d(1) = 1$, $d(2) = 2$, $d(6) = 4$. (The positive divisors of 6 are 1, 2, 3, and 6.) If n is a positive integer and R is the region described by $x > 0, y > 0, xy \leq n$, and $T(n)$ is the total number of positive lattice points in R, express $T(n)$ in terms of $d(1), d(2), \ldots, d(n)$.

75. (Continuation.) Let R, n, and $T(n)$ be as in exercise 74. (a) If k is any positive integer, how many of the lattice points in R are there on the line $x = k$? (b) Use the result of part (a) to express $T(n)$ as a sum from $k = 1$ to n of $g(k)$ where $g(k)$ is the number of lattice points in R on the line $x = k$.

Remark. The results of exercises 74 and 75 can be used to answer this question: If n is any positive integer, what (approximately) is the average number of positive divisors of the first n positive integers? You may enjoy working on this question. One possible answer is that the average number of positive divisors of $1, 2, \ldots, n$ is approximately $\ln n$. This approximation is based on estimating $T(n)$ by the area of R.

POLAR COORDINATES

CHAPTER 11

We know that a point can be located in a plane by giving its abscissa and ordinate relative to a given coordinate system. Such x- and y-coordinates are called *Cartesian* coordinates, in honor of the French mathematician-philosopher René Descartes* (1596–1650), who is credited with discovering this method of fixing the position of a point in a plane.

11.1

Another useful way to locate a point in a plane is by *polar coordinates* (see Fig. 11.1). First, we fix an *origin* O and an *initial ray*† from O. The point P has polar coordinates r, θ, with

$$r = \text{directed distance from } O \text{ to } P, \quad \text{(1a)}$$

and

$$\theta = \text{directed angle from initial ray to } OP. \quad \text{(1b)}$$

As in trigonometry, the angle θ is *positive* when measured counterclockwise and negative when measured clockwise (Fig. 11.1). But the angle associated with a given point is not unique (Fig. 11.2). For instance, the point 2 units from the origin, along the ray $\theta = 30°$, has polar coordinates $r = 2$, $\theta = 30°$. It also has coordinates $r = 2$, $\theta = -330°$, or $r = 2$, $\theta = 390°$.

There are occasions when we wish to allow r to be negative. That's why we say "directed distance"

---

* For an interesting biographical account together with an excerpt from Descartes' own writings, see *World of Mathematics*, Vol. 1, pp. 235–253.

† A *ray* is a half-line consisting of a vertex and points of a line on one side of the vertex. For example, the origin and positive x-axis is a ray. The points on the line $y = 2x + 3$ with $x \geq 1$ is another ray; its vertex is (1, 5).

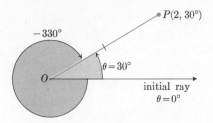

11.2 The ray $\theta = 30°$ is the same as the ray $\theta = -330°$.

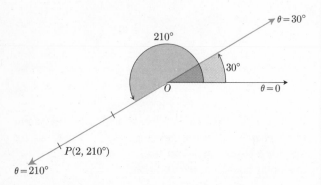

11.3 The rays $\theta = 30°$ and $\theta = 210°$ make a line.

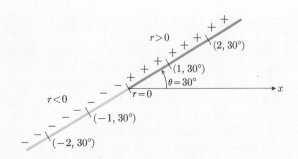

11.4 The terminal ray $\theta = \pi/6$ and its negative.

in Eq. (1a). The ray $\theta = 30°$ and the ray $\theta = 210°$ together make up a complete line through O (see Fig. 11.3). The point $P(2, 210°)$ 2 units from O on the ray $\theta = 210°$ has polar coordinates $r = 2$, $\theta = 210°$. It can be reached by a person standing at O and facing out along the initial ray, if he first turns 210° counterclockwise, and then goes forward

2 units. He would reach the same point by turning only 30° counterclockwise from the initial ray and then going *backward* 2 units. So we say that the point also has polar coordinates $r = -2$, $\theta = 30°$.

Whenever the angle between two rays is 180°, the rays actually make a straight line. We then say that either ray is the negative of the other. Points on the ray $\theta = \alpha$ have polar coordinates (r, α) with $r \geq 0$. Points on the negative ray, $\theta = \alpha + 180°$, have coordinates (r, α) with $r \leq 0$. The origin is $r = 0$. (See Fig. 11.4 for the ray $\theta = 30°$ and its negative. A word of caution: The "negative" of the ray $\theta = 30°$ is the ray $\theta = 30° + 180° = 210°$ and *not* the ray $\theta = -30°$. "Negative" refers to the directed distance r.)

There is a great advantage in being able to use both polar and Cartesian coordinates at once. To do this, we use a common origin and take the initial ray as the positive x-axis, and take the ray $\theta = 90°$ as the positive y-axis. The coordinates, shown in Fig. 11.5, are then related by the equations

$$x = r \cos \theta, \quad y = r \sin \theta. \qquad (2)$$

These are the equations that define $\sin \theta$ and $\cos \theta$ when r is positive. They are also valid if r is negative, because

$$\cos (\theta + 180°) = -\cos \theta,$$

$$\sin (\theta + 180°) = -\sin \theta,$$

so positive r's on the $(\theta + 180°)$-ray correspond to negative r's associated with the θ-ray. When $r = 0$, then $x = y = 0$, and P is the origin.

If we impose the condition

$$r = a \quad (a \text{ constant}), \qquad (3)$$

then the locus of P is a circle with center O and radius a, and P describes the circle once as θ varies from 0 to 360° (see Fig. 11.6). On the other hand, if we let r vary and hold θ fixed, say

$$\theta = 30°, \qquad (4)$$

the locus of P is the straight line shown in Fig. 11.4.

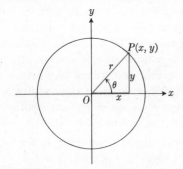

11.5 Polar and Cartesian coordinates.

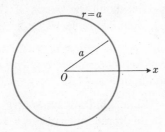

11.6 The circle $r = a$ is the locus of P.

We adopt the convention that r may be any real number, $-\infty < r < \infty$. Then $r = 0$ corresponds to $x = 0$, $y = 0$ in Eqs. (2), regardless of θ. That is,

$$r = 0, \quad \theta \text{ any value}, \qquad (5)$$

is the origin, $x = 0$, $y = 0$.

The same point may be represented in several different ways in polar coordinates. For example, the point $(2, 30°)$, or $(2, \pi/6)$, has the following representations: $(2, 30°)$, $(2, -330°)$, $(-2, 210°)$, $(-2, -150°)$. These and all others are summarized in the two formulas

$$\left.\begin{array}{l} (2, 30° + n\,360°), \\ (-2, 210° + n\,360°), \end{array}\right\} \quad n = 0, \pm 1, \pm 2, \ldots ;$$

or, if we represent the angles in radians, in the two formulas

$$\left.\begin{array}{l} (2, \tfrac{1}{6}\pi + 2n\pi), \\ (-2, \tfrac{7}{6}\pi + 2n\pi), \end{array}\right\} \quad n = 0, \pm 1, \pm 2, \ldots$$

The fact that the same point may be represented in several different ways in polar coordinates makes added care necessary in certain situations. For example, the point $(2a, \pi)$ is on the curve

$$r^2 = 4a^2 \cos \theta \qquad (6)$$

even though its coordinates as given do not satisfy the equation, because the same point is represented by $(-2a, 0)$ and these coordinates do satisfy the equation. The same point $(2a, \pi)$ is on the curve

$$r = a(1 - \cos \theta), \qquad (7)$$

and hence this point should be included among the points of intersection of the two curves represented by Eqs. (6) and (7). But if we solve the equations simultaneously by first substituting $\cos \theta = r^2/4a^2$ from (6) into (7) and then solving the resulting quadratic equation

$$\left(\frac{r}{a}\right)^2 + 4\left(\frac{r}{a}\right) - 4 = 0$$

for

$$\frac{r}{a} = -2 \pm 2\sqrt{2}, \qquad (8)$$

we do *not* obtain the point $(2a, \pi)$ as a point of intersection. The reason is simple enough: The point is not on the curves "simultaneously" in the sense of being reached at the "same time," since it is reached in the one case when $\theta = 0$ and in the other case when $\theta = \pi$. It is as though two ships describe paths that intersect at a point, but the ships do not collide because they reach the point of intersection at different times! The curves represented by Eqs. (6) and (7) are shown in Fig. 11.11(b). They are seen to intersect at the four points

$$(0, 0), \quad (2a, \pi), \quad (r_1, \theta_1), \quad (r_1, -\theta_1), \qquad (9a)$$

where

$$r_1 = (-2 + 2\sqrt{2})a,$$
$$\cos \theta_1 = 1 - \frac{r_1}{a} = 3 - 2\sqrt{2}. \qquad (9b)$$

Only the last two of the points (9a) are found from the simultaneous solution; the first two are disclosed only by the graphs of the curves.

EXERCISES

1-4 col I   5-7

1. Plot the following points, given in polar form, and find *all* polar coordinates of each point.

   (a) $(3, \pi/4)$ (b) $(-3, \pi/4)$
   (c) $(3, -\pi/4)$ (d) $(-3, -\pi/4)$

2. Graph the locus of points $P(r, \theta)$ whose polar coordinates satisfy the given equation, inequality, or inequalities.

   (a) $r = 2$ (b) $r < 2$
   (c) $r > 1$ (d) $1 < r < 2$
   (e) $0° \le \theta \le 30°$ $r \ge 0$ (f) $\theta = 120°$, $r \le -2$
   (g) $\theta = 60°$, $-1 \le r \le 3$ (h) $\theta = 495°$, $r \ge -1$

3. Find Cartesian coordinates of the points in Ex. 1.

4. Graph the loci.

   (a) $r \cos \theta = 2$ (b) $r \sin \theta = -1$
   (c) $r \cos (\theta - 60°) = 3$
   Hint. Rotate axes so that $\theta' = \theta - 60°$.
   (d) $r \sin (\theta + 45°) = 4$ (e) $r \cos (30° - \theta) = 0$

5. Show that $(2, \frac{3}{4}\pi)$ is on the curve $r = 2 \sin 2\theta$.

6. Show that $(\frac{1}{2}, \frac{3}{2}\pi)$ is on the curve $r = -\sin (\theta/3)$.

7. Show that these equations represent the same curve: $r = \cos \theta + 1$, $r = \cos \theta - 1$.

Find some intersections of the following pairs of curves (a = constant).

8. $r^2 = 2a^2 \sin 2\theta$, $r = a$

9. $r = a \sin \theta$, $r = a \cos \theta$

10. $r = a(1 + \cos \theta)$, $r = a(1 - \sin \theta)$

11. $r = a(1 + \sin \theta)$, $r = 2a \cos \theta$

12. $r = a \cos 2\theta$, $r = a(1 + \cos \theta)$

11.2 GRAPHS OF POLAR EQUATIONS

The graph of an equation $F(r, \theta) = 0$ consists of all those points whose coordinates (in some form) satisfy the equation. Frequently the equation gives r explicitly in terms of θ, as

$$r = f(\theta).$$

As many points as desired may then be obtained by substituting values of θ and calculating the corresponding values of r. In particular, it is desirable to plot the points where r is a maximum or a minimum and to find the values of θ when the curve passes through the origin, if that occurs.

Certain types of *symmetry* are readily detected. For example, the curve is:

(a) symmetric about the origin, if the equation is unchanged when r is replaced by $-r$;

(b) symmetric about the x-axis, if the equation is unchanged when θ is replaced by $-\theta$;

(c) symmetric about the y-axis, if the equation is unchanged when θ is replaced by $\pi - \theta$.

These and certain other tests for symmetry are readily verified by considering the symmetrically located points in Fig. 11.7.

[*Question.* What kind of symmetry occurs if the equation is unaltered when r and θ are replaced by $-r$ and $-\theta$, respectively?]

To illustrate how symmetries are used in analyzing equations, we shall discuss and sketch three curves.

Example 1. Consider

$$r = a(1 - \cos \theta),$$

where a is a positive constant. Since

$$\cos (-\theta) = \cos \theta,$$

the equation is unaltered when θ is replaced by $-\theta$; hence the curve is symmetric about the x-axis (Fig. 11.7b). Also, since

$$-1 \le \cos \theta \le 1,$$

the values of r vary between 0 and $2a$. The minimum value $r = 0$ occurs at $\theta = 0$, and the maximum value $r = 2a$ occurs at $\theta = \pi$. Moreover, as θ varies from 0 to π, $\cos \theta$ decreases from 1 to -1, hence $1 - \cos \theta$ increases from 0 to 2; that is, r increases from 0 to $2a$ as the radius vector OP swings from $\theta = 0$ to $\theta = \pi$. We mark the points from the following table.

θ	0	60°	90°	120°	180°
r	0	$\dfrac{a}{2}$	a	$\dfrac{3a}{2}$	$2a$

11.7 **a|** Symmetry about the origin. **b|** Symmetry about the x-axis. **c|** Symmetry about the y-axis.

We then sketch a smooth curve through these points (see Fig. 11.8) in such a way that r increases as θ increases. (Our reason for sketching it in this way is that

$$dr/d\theta = a\sin\theta$$

is positive for $0 < \theta < \pi$.) Then we exploit the symmetry of the curve and reflect this portion across the x-axis. The result is the curve shown in Fig. 11.9, which is called a *cardioid* because of its heart-shaped appearance. The behavior of this curve at the origin and the angles between its tangents and the coordinate axes at the other intercepts are more easily discussed at a later time. However, we may investigate the slope of the cardioid at the origin as follows: Let P be a point on the curve in the first quadrant, where P is destined to approach O along the curve (see Fig. 11.10a). Then, as $P \to O$, the slope of OP ($= \tan\theta$) approaches the slope of the tangent at O. But $P \to O$ as $\theta \to 0$, and hence

$$\lim_{\theta\to 0}(\text{slope of } OP) = \lim_{\theta\to 0}\tan\theta = 0.$$

That is, the slope of the tangent to the curve at the origin is zero.

In fact, for any curve that passes through the origin, say when $\theta = \theta_0$, the discussion above would be modified only to the extent of saying that $P \to O$ along the curve as $\theta \to \theta_0$, and hence that

$$\left(\frac{dy}{dx}\right)_{\theta=\theta_0} = \lim_{\theta\to\theta_0}(\tan\theta) = \tan\theta_0.$$

But $(dy/dx)_{\theta=\theta_0}$ is also the tangent of the angle between the x-axis and the curve at this point. Hence the line $\theta = \theta_0$ is tangent to the curve at the origin. In other words, whenever a curve passes through the origin for a value θ_0 of θ, it does so *tangent* to the line $\theta = \theta_0$. See Fig. 11.10(b).

11.8

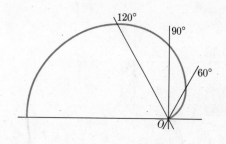

$r = a(1 - \cos\theta)$

11.9

a|b

11.10

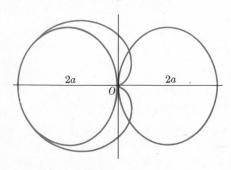

$r^2 = 4a^2 \cos \theta$

a | b

11.11

Example 2. Consider

$$r^2 = 4a^2 \cos \theta.$$

This curve is symmetric about the origin. Two values,

$$r = \pm 2a\sqrt{\cos \theta},$$

correspond to each value of θ for which $\cos \theta > 0$, namely,

$$-\frac{\pi}{2} < \theta < \frac{\pi}{2}.$$

Furthermore, the curve is symmetric about the x-axis, since θ may be replaced by $-\theta$ without altering the value of $\cos \theta$. The curve passes through the origin at $\theta = \pi/2$ and is tangent to the y-axis at this point. Since $\cos \theta$ never exceeds unity, the maximum value of r is $2a$, which occurs at $\theta = 0$. As θ increases from 0 to $\pi/2$, $|r|$ decreases from $2a$ to 0. The curve is sketched in Fig. 11.11(a) and again in Fig. 11.11(b) with the cardioid of Example 1.

Example 3. Consider $r\theta = a$, a a positive constant. When $\theta = 0$ the equation becomes $0 = a$, which is not

true. That is, there is no point on the curve for $\theta = 0$. However, suppose θ is a *small* positive angle. Then from $r = a/\theta$, we see that r is large and positive. Consider the situation in Fig. 11.12. No matter how small the positive angle θ may be, if r is sufficiently large the point P may be far above the x-axis. In fact, we need to see what happens to

$$y = r \sin \theta = \frac{a}{\theta} \sin \theta$$

for small positive values of θ. We know, of course, that

$$\lim_{\theta \to 0} \frac{\sin \theta}{\theta} = 1,$$

and hence that

$$\lim_{\theta \to 0} y = \lim_{\theta \to 0} a \frac{\sin \theta}{\theta} = a.$$

This shows that the line $y = a$ is an asymptote of this curve. So we think of the curve being traced by a point P that starts far out near the line $y = a$ for $\theta = 0 +$ and moves in the direction indicated by the arrows in Fig. 11.13(a) as θ increases and r decreases. As the radius vector OP continues to rotate about the origin, it shrinks in length, and P describes a spiral which coils around the origin with r tending to zero as the angle θ increases indefinitely.

11.12

When r and θ are replaced by $-r$ and $-\theta$ respectively, the equation is unaltered. Hence for every point $(r_1\ \theta_1)$ on the curve in Fig. 11.13(a), there is a point $(-r_1,\ -\theta_1)$ symmetrically located with respect to the y-axis also on the curve $r\theta = a$. We therefore reflect the curve in Fig. 11.13(a) in the y-axis, obtaining another spiral which coils around the origin in the clockwise sense as θ approaches minus infinity. The complete curve is indicated in Fig. 11.13(b). It is called a *hyperbolic spiral*, the adjective "hyperbolic" being used in this connection because the equation $r\theta = a$ is analogous to the equation $xy = a$, which represents a hyperbola in Cartesian coordinates.

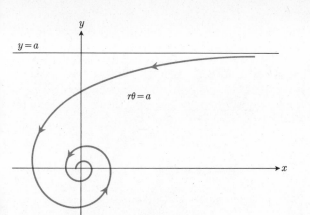

11.13 Hyperbolic spiral.

EXERCISES

1. Find the polar form of the equation of the line $3x + 4y = 5$.

2. If the polar coordinates (r, θ) of a point P satisfy the equation $r = 2a \cos \theta$, what equation is satisfied by the Cartesian coordinates (x, y) of P?

Discuss and sketch each of the following curves.

3. $r = a(1 + \cos \theta)$ 4. $r = a(1 - \sin \theta)$

5. $r = a \sin 2\theta$ 6. $r^2 = 2a^2 \cos 2\theta$

7. $r = a(2 + \sin \theta)$ 8. $r = a(1 + 2 \sin \theta)$

9. $r = \theta$ 10. $r = a \sin (\theta/2)$

11. Find the points on the curve $r = a(1 + \cos \theta)$ where the tangent is

   (a) parallel to the x-axis,

   (b) parallel to the y-axis.

   Hint. Express x and y in terms of θ. Then calculate dy/dx.

12. Sketch the curves

$$r = a(1 + \cos \theta), \qquad r = 3a \cos \theta$$

in one diagram and find the angle between their tangents at the point of intersection that lies in the first quadrant.

11.3 POLAR EQUATIONS OF THE CONIC SECTIONS AND OTHER CURVES

The relationships given in Article 11.1 between Cartesian and polar coordinates enable us to change any Cartesian equation into a polar equation for the same curve.

Example. The circle

$$x^2 + y^2 - 2ax = 0, \qquad (1)$$

with center at $(a, 0)$ and radius a, becomes

$$(r \cos \theta)^2 + (r \sin \theta)^2 - 2a(r \cos \theta) = 0,$$

which reduces to

$$r(r - 2a \cos \theta) = 0.$$

The locus obtained by putting the first factor equal to zero, $r = 0$, is just one point, the origin. The other factor vanishes when

$$r = 2a \cos \theta. \qquad (2)$$

This includes the origin among its points and hence represents the entire locus given by Eq. (1).

The example illustrates one method of finding the polar equation for a curve, namely, by transforming its Cartesian equation into polar form. An alternative method is to derive the polar equation directly from some geometric property. For example,

a|b

11.14

11.15

11.16

take the circle in Fig. 11.14 and let $P(r, \theta)$ be a representative point on the circle. Then angle OPA is a right angle (why?) and from the right triangle OPA, we read

$$\frac{r}{2a} = \cos \theta, \quad \text{or} \quad r = 2a \cos \theta,$$

which is the same equation obtained above.

We shall apply this second method to obtain equations of various curves in the following problems.

Problem 1. Find the polar equation of the circle of radius a with center at (b, β).

Solution. We let $P(r, \theta)$ be a representative point on the circle and apply the law of cosines to the triangle OCP (Fig. 11.15) to obtain

$$a^2 = b^2 + r^2 - 2br \cos (\theta - \beta). \qquad (3)$$

If the circle passes through the origin, then $b = a$ and the equation takes the simpler form

$$r[r - 2a \cos (\theta - \beta)] = 0,$$

or

$$r = 2a \cos (\theta - \beta). \qquad (4)$$

In particular, if $\beta = 0$, Eq. (4) reduces to the result we have obtained before, while if $\beta = 90°$, so that the center of the circle lies on the y-axis (Fig. 11.16), Eq. (4) reduces to

$$r = 2a \sin \theta. \qquad (5)$$

Problem 2. The normal from the origin to the line L intersects L at the point $N(p, \beta)$. Find the polar equation of L.

Solution. We let $P(r, \theta)$ be a representative point on the line L in Fig. 11.17, and from the right triangle ONP we read the result

$$r \cos (\theta - \beta) = p. \qquad (6)$$

This equation is simply a more general form of the equation

$$r \cos \theta = p, \qquad (7)$$

11.17

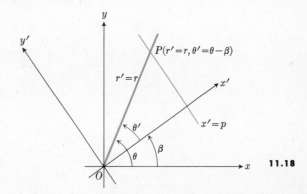

11.18

which is the polar form of the line

$$x = p.$$

In fact, if we perform a rotation of axes as in Fig. 11.18, the new polar coordinates (r', θ') are related to the old polar coordinates as follows:

$$r' = r, \quad \theta' = \theta - \beta. \tag{8}$$

If we apply this rotation to Eq. (6), we get

$$r' \cos \theta' = p.$$

But

$$r' \cos \theta' = x',$$

so the equation is the same as

$$x' = p,$$

which represents a straight line p units from and parallel to the y'-axis.

Problem 3. Find the polar locus of P if the product of its distances to the two points $F_1(a, \pi)$ and $F_2(a, 0)$ is a constant, say b^2.

Solution. We let $P(r, \theta)$ be a representative point on the locus and determine the equation satisfied by the co-ordinates r and θ in order to fulfill the requirement

$$d_1 d_2 = b^2, \tag{9}$$

where $d_1 = PF_1$ and $d_2 = PF_2$ (Fig. 11.19). We apply the law of cosines twice: once to the triangle OPF_2:

$$d_2^2 = r^2 + a^2 - 2ar \cos \theta,$$

and again to the triangle OPF_1:

$$d_1^2 = r^2 + a^2 - 2ar \cos (\pi - \theta).$$

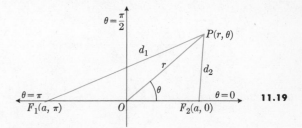

11.19

But

$$\cos (\pi - \theta) = -\cos \theta,$$

so that

$$d_1^2 = r^2 + a^2 + 2ar \cos \theta.$$

Hence

$$d_1^2 d_2^2 = (r^2 + a^2)^2 - (2ar \cos \theta)^2,$$

or

$$b^4 = a^4 + r^4 + 2a^2 r^2 (1 - 2 \cos^2 \theta).$$

The trigonometric identity

$$\cos 2\theta = 2 \cos^2 \theta - 1$$

enables us to put our equation in the form

$$b^4 = a^4 + r^4 - 2a^2 r^2 \cos 2\theta. \tag{10}$$

One special case allows the locus to pass through the origin, namely, if $b = a$. Then the equation simplifies still further to that of the *lemniscate*

$$r^2 = 2a^2 \cos 2\theta. \tag{11}$$

The graphs of the curves represented by (10) for different values of the ratio b/a are shown in Fig. 11.20(a) through (c). The curves in both (a) and (b) are called *lemniscates*, and the curve in (c) consists of two separate closed portions known as "ovals of Cassini."

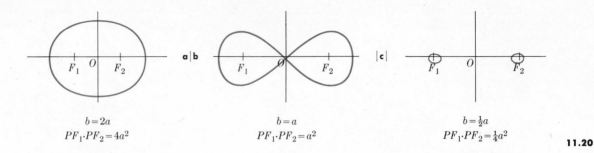

$$b = 2a$$
$$PF_1 \cdot PF_2 = 4a^2$$

$$b = a$$
$$PF_1 \cdot PF_2 = a^2$$

$$b = \tfrac{1}{2}a$$
$$PF_1 \cdot PF_2 = \tfrac{1}{4}a^2$$

11.20

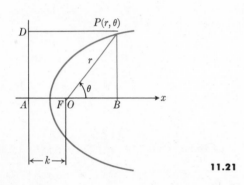

11.21

Problem 4. Find the polar equation of the conic section of eccentricity e if the focus is at the origin and the associated directrix is the line $x = -k$.

Solution. We adopt the notation of Fig. 11.21 and use the focus-and-directrix property

$$PF = e \cdot PD, \qquad (12)$$

which allows us to handle the parabola, ellipse, and hyperbola all at the same time.

By taking the origin at the focus F, we have

$$PF = r,$$

while

$$PD = AB$$

and

$$AB = AF + FB = k + r \cos \theta.$$

Then Eq. (12) is the same as

$$r = e(k + r \cos \theta).$$

If we solve this equation for r, we get

$$r = \frac{ke}{1 - e \cos \theta}. \qquad (13)$$

Typical special cases of (13) are obtained by taking

$$e = 1, \quad r = \frac{k}{1 - \cos \theta} = \frac{k}{2} \csc^2 \frac{\theta}{2}, \qquad (14a)$$

which represents a *parabola;*

$$e = \tfrac{1}{2}, \quad r = \frac{k}{2 - \cos \theta}, \qquad (14b)$$

which represents an *ellipse;* and

$$e = 2, \quad r = \frac{2k}{1 - 2 \cos \theta}, \qquad (14c)$$

which represents a *hyperbola.*

It is worth noting that the denominator in Eq. (14b) for the ellipse can never vanish, so that r remains finite for all values of θ. But r becomes infinite as θ approaches 0 in (14a) and as θ approaches $\pi/3$ in (14c).

By replacing the constant ke in Eq. (13) by its equivalent value

$$ke = a(1 - e^2)$$

when $e < 1$, we may let $e \to 0$ and $ke \to a$ and get

$$r = a$$

in the limit. That is, the circle of radius a and center at O is a limiting case of the curves represented by Eq. (13).

EXERCISES

1. A line segment of length $2a$ slides with its ends on the x- and y-axes. Find the polar equation of the locus described by the point $P(r, \theta)$ at which the perpendicular from the origin intersects the moving line. Sketch the curve.

2. OA is a diameter of a circle of radius a, AC is tangent to the circle, and OC intersects the circle at B. On OC the point $P(r, \theta)$ is found such that $OP = BC$. With O as origin, OA as x-axis, and angle AOP as θ, find the polar equation of the locus of P and sketch the curve. Show that $x = 2a$ is an asymptote. The curve is called a "cissoid," meaning "ivy-like."

In Exercises 3 through 7, determine the polar equation and sketch the given curve.

3. $x^2 + y^2 - 2ay = 0$
4. $(x^2 + y^2)^2 + 2ax(x^2 + y^2) - a^2 y^2 = 0$
5. $x \cos \alpha + y \sin \alpha = p$ (α, p constants)
6. $y^2 = 4ax + 4a^2$ 7. $(x^2 + y^2)^2 = x^2 - y^2$

In Exercises 8 through 13, determine the Cartesian equation and sketch the given curve.

8. $r = 4 \cos \theta$
9. $r = 6 \sin \theta$
10. $r = \sin 2\theta$
11. $r^2 = 2a^2 \cos 2\theta$
12. $r = 8/(1 - 2 \cos \theta)$
13. $r = a(1 + \sin \theta)$

14. Sketch the following loci.

(a) $r = 2 \cos (\theta + 45°)$ (b) $r = 4 \csc (\theta - 30°)$
(c) $r = 5 \sec (60° - \theta)$ (d) $r = 3 \sin (\theta + 30°)$
(e) $r = a + a \cos (\theta - 30°)$
(f) $0 \le r \le 2 - 2 \cos \theta$

15. (a) How can the angle β and the distance p (see Fig. 11.17 and Eq. 6) be determined from the Cartesian equation $ax + by = c$ for a straight line? (b) Specifically, find p, β, and the polar equation for the straight line $\sqrt{3}x + y = 6$.

16. The focus of a parabola is at the origin and its directrix is the line $4 = r \cos (\theta + \pi/3)$. Find the polar equation of the parabola.

17. One focus of a hyperbola of eccentricity $\frac{5}{4}$ is at the origin and the corresponding directrix is the line $r \cos \theta = 9$. Find the polar coordinates of the second focus. Also determine the polar equation of the hyperbola and sketch.

18. From the origin a line is drawn perpendicular to a tangent of the circle $r = 2a \cos \theta$. Find the locus of the point of intersection and sketch the curve.

19. Find the maximum and minimum values of r that satisfy Eq. (10), first in terms of a and b, and then specifically for the cases $b = 2a$, $b = a$, and $b = a/2$.

20. Determine the slopes of the lines that are tangent to the lemniscate $r^2 = 2a^2 \cos 2\theta$ at the origin.

21. Equation (14b), $r = k/(2 - \cos \theta)$, represents an ellipse with one focus at the origin. Sketch the curve and its directrices for the case $k = 2$ and locate the center of the ellipse.

22. In the case $e > 1$, Eq. (13) represents a hyperbola. From the polar form of the equation, determine the slopes of the asymptotes of the hyperbola of eccentricity e.

23. Show, by reference to a figure, that the distance from the line

$$r \cos (\theta - \beta) = p$$

to the point $P_1(r_1, \theta_1)$ is

$$|r_1 \cos (\theta_1 - \beta) - p|.$$

11.4 THE ANGLE ψ BETWEEN THE RADIUS VECTOR AND THE TANGENT LINE

In Cartesian coordinates, when we want to discuss the direction of a curve at a point, we use the angle ϕ from the positive x-axis to the tangent line. In polar coordinates, it is more convenient to make use of the angle ψ (psi) from the *radius vector* to the tangent line. Then the relationship

$$\phi = \theta + \psi, \tag{1}$$

which can be read from Fig. 11.22, makes it a simple matter to find ϕ if that angle is desired instead of ψ.

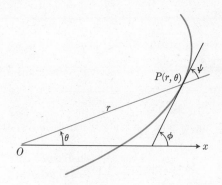

11.22 The angle ψ between the tangent vector and the radius vector.

Suppose the equation of the curve is given in the form $r = f(\theta)$, where $f(\theta)$ is a differentiable function of θ. Then from

$$x = r \cos \theta, \qquad y = r \sin \theta, \qquad (2)$$

we see that x and y are differentiable functions of θ with

$$\frac{dx}{d\theta} = -r \sin \theta + \cos \theta \frac{dr}{d\theta},$$

$$\frac{dy}{d\theta} = r \cos \theta + \sin \theta \frac{dr}{d\theta}. \qquad (3)$$

Since $\psi = \phi - \theta$ from (1),

$$\tan \psi = \tan (\phi - \theta) = \frac{\tan \phi - \tan \theta}{1 + \tan \phi \tan \theta},$$

while

$$\tan \phi = \frac{dy/d\theta}{dx/d\theta}, \qquad \tan \theta = \frac{y}{x}.$$

Hence

$$\tan \psi = \frac{\dfrac{dy/d\theta}{dx/d\theta} - \dfrac{y}{x}}{1 + \dfrac{y}{x} \dfrac{dy/d\theta}{dx/d\theta}} = \frac{x \dfrac{dy}{d\theta} - y \dfrac{dx}{d\theta}}{x \dfrac{dx}{d\theta} + y \dfrac{dy}{d\theta}}. \qquad (4)$$

The numerator in the last expression in Eq. (4) is found by substitution from Eqs. (2) and (3) to be

$$x \frac{dy}{d\theta} - y \frac{dx}{d\theta} = r^2.$$

Similarly, the denominator is

$$x \frac{dx}{d\theta} + y \frac{dy}{d\theta} = r \frac{dr}{d\theta}.$$

When we substitute these into Eq. (4), we obtain the very simple final result

$$\tan \psi = \frac{r}{dr/d\theta}. \qquad (5)$$

Note. This formula for $\tan \psi$ is much simpler than the formula

$$\tan \phi = \frac{r \cos \theta + (\sin \theta) \, dr/d\theta}{-r \sin \theta + (\cos \theta) \, dr/d\theta} \qquad (6)$$

that one obtains by calculating

$$\frac{dy}{dx} = \frac{dy/d\theta}{dx/d\theta}$$

from (3). This is why it is usually preferable to work with the angle ψ rather than with ϕ in the case of polar coordinates.

One may also obtain a simple expression for the differential element of arc length ds by squaring and adding the differentials

$$dx = -r \sin \theta \, d\theta + \cos \theta \, dr,$$

$$dy = r \cos \theta \, d\theta + \sin \theta \, dr.$$

We find that

$$ds^2 = dx^2 + dy^2 = r^2 \, d\theta^2 + dr^2.$$

11.23

This result and the result for $\tan \psi$ are both easily remembered in the form

$$\tan \psi = \frac{r \, d\theta}{dr}, \qquad (7a)$$

$$ds^2 = r^2 \, d\theta^2 + dr^2, \qquad (7b)$$

if we refer to the "differential triangle" shown in Fig. 11.23. We simply treat dr and $r \, d\theta$ as the two legs and ds as the hypotenuse of an ordinary right triangle with the angle ψ opposite the side $r \, d\theta$. If we realize that certain terms of higher order are being neglected, we may think of dr as the component of displacement along the radius vector and $r \, d\theta$ as the component at right angles to this produced by the displacement ds along the curve. The relationships (7a) and (7b) may be read at once from this triangle. We should realize, of course, that the *proof* of these equations did not depend on any such "differential triangle" and that the latter represents only a mnemonic device.

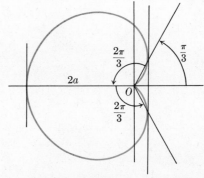

a| Cardioid: $r = a(1 - \cos\theta)$.   **b|** Vertical tangents to the cardioid.

11.24

To find the angle ψ, we use (7a); and to find the length of a polar curve, we find ds from (7b) and integrate between appropriate limits as illustrated in the following problems.

Problem 1. Find the angle ψ for the cardioid (Fig. 11.24a)

$$r = a(1 - \cos\theta). \tag{8a}$$

Solution. From the equation of the curve, we get

$$dr = a \sin\theta \, d\theta, \tag{8b}$$

so that

$$\tan\psi = \frac{r \, d\theta}{dr} = \frac{a(1 - \cos\theta) \, d\theta}{a \sin\theta \, d\theta} = \tan\frac{\theta}{2}.$$

As θ varies from 0 to 2π, the angle ψ varies from 0 to π according to the equation $\psi = \theta/2$. Thus at the y-intercepts the tangent line makes an angle of 45° with the vertical, at the origin the curve is tangent to the x-axis, and at $(2a, \pi)$ the tangent line makes an angle of 90° with the negative x-axis.

Suppose we ask for the points on the cardioid where the tangent line is vertical (see Fig. 11.24b). Denoting the inclination angle of the tangent line by ϕ and recalling that

$$\phi = \psi + \theta \quad \text{and} \quad \psi = \tfrac{1}{2}\theta,$$

we get $\phi = \tfrac{3}{2}\theta$. Since the tangent is vertical when

$$\phi = \frac{\pi}{2} + n\pi,$$

the values of θ satisfy

$$\theta = \frac{2}{3}\phi = \frac{\pi}{3} + \frac{2}{3}n\pi.$$

Taking $n = 0, -1, 1, -2, 2, \ldots$, we obtain

$$\theta = \frac{\pi}{3}, \quad \frac{-\pi}{3}, \quad \pi, \quad -\pi, \quad \frac{5}{3}\pi, \quad \ldots$$

These lead to three distinct points, namely,

$$\left(\frac{a}{2}, \pm\frac{\pi}{3}\right) \quad \text{and} \quad (2a, \pi),$$

whose radius vectors are evenly spaced 120° apart.

Problem 2. Find the length of the cardioid

$$r = a(1 - \cos\theta).$$

Solution. Substituting dr and r from (8b, a) into (7b), we have

$$ds^2 = a^2 \, d\theta^2 \, [\sin^2\theta + (1 - \cos\theta)^2]$$
$$= 2a^2 \, d\theta^2 (1 - \cos\theta)$$

and

$$ds = a\sqrt{2}\,\sqrt{1 - \cos\theta}\,d\theta.$$

To integrate the expression on the right, we recall the trigonometric identity

$$1 - \cos\theta = 2\sin^2\frac{\theta}{2},$$

and have

$$ds = 2a\left|\sin\frac{\theta}{2}\right|d\theta.$$

Since $\sin\theta/2$ is not negative when θ varies from 0 to 2π, we obtain

$$s = \int_0^{2\pi} 2a \sin\frac{\theta}{2}\,d\theta = -4a\cos\frac{\theta}{2}\Big]_0^{2\pi} = 8a.$$

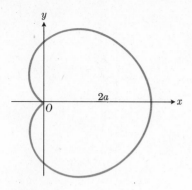

11.25   Cardioid: $r = a(1 + \cos \theta)$.

11.26   Lemniscate: $r^2 = 2a^2 \cos 2\theta$.

We observe in passing that in letting θ range from 0 to 2π, we start at the cusp at the origin, go once around the smooth portion of the cardioid and return to the cusp. In doing this we do not pass *across* the cusp (see Fig. 11.24a). If, on the other hand, we take the cardioid $r = a(1 + \cos \theta)$, the appropriate procedure for avoiding the cusp (Fig. 11.25) is to let θ increase from $-\pi$ to π, or we may use the symmetry of the curve and calculate half of the total length by letting θ vary from 0 to π.

Problem 3. The lemniscate

$$r^2 = 2a^2 \cos 2\theta$$

is revolved about the y-axis. Find the area of the surface generated.

Solution. An element of arc length ds (Fig. 11.26) generates a portion of surface area

$$dS = 2\pi x \, ds,$$

where

$$x = r \cos \theta, \quad ds = \sqrt{dr^2 + r^2 \, d\theta^2}.$$

That is,

$$dS = 2\pi r \cos \theta \sqrt{dr^2 + r^2 \, d\theta^2} = 2\pi \cos \theta \sqrt{r^2 \, dr^2 + r^4 \, d\theta^2}.$$

From the equation of the curve, we get

$$r \, dr = -2a^2 \sin 2\theta \, d\theta.$$

Then

$$(r^2 \, dr^2 + r^4 \, d\theta^2) = (2a^2 \, d\theta)^2 (\sin^2 2\theta + \cos^2 2\theta)$$

and

$$dS = 4\pi a^2 \cos \theta \, d\theta.$$

The total surface area is generated by the loop of the lemniscate to the right of the y-axis between $\theta = -\pi/4$ and $\theta = +\pi/4$, so that

$$S = \int_{-\pi/4}^{\pi/4} 4\pi a^2 \cos \theta \, d\theta = 4\pi a^2 \sqrt{2}.$$

EXERCISES

1. For the hyperbolic spiral $r\theta = a$, show that $\psi = 135°$ when $\theta = 1$ radian, and that $\psi \to 90°$ as the spiral winds around the origin. Sketch the curve and indicate ψ for $\theta = 1$ radian.

2. Show, by reference to a figure, that the angle β between the tangents to two curves at a point of intersection may be found from the formula

$$\tan \beta = \frac{\tan \psi_2 - \tan \psi_1}{1 + \tan \psi_2 \tan \psi_1}.$$

When will the two curves intersect orthogonally?

3. Find a point of intersection of the parabolas

$$r = \frac{1}{1 - \cos \theta}, \quad r = \frac{3}{1 + \cos \theta},$$

and find the angle between the tangents to these curves at this point.

4. Find points on the cardioid $r = a(1 + \cos \theta)$ where the tangent line is horizontal.

5. Find the length of the cardioid $r = a(1 + \cos \theta)$. *Hint.*

$$\int \sqrt{1 + \cos \theta} \, d\theta = \int \sqrt{2} \, |\cos \theta/2| \, d\theta.$$

6. A thin, uniform wire is bent into the shape of the cardioid $r = a(1 + \cos \theta)$. Find its center of gravity $(\bar{x}, \bar{y})$.

Hint. $\int \cos \theta \cos \theta/2 \, d\theta$ can be evaluated by substituting $\cos \theta = 1 - 2 \sin^2 \theta/2$ and then letting $u = \sin \theta/2$.

7. The lemniscate $r^2 = 2a^2 \cos 2\theta$ is rotated about the x-axis. Find the area of the surface generated.

8. Find the length of the curve $r = a \sin^2 \theta/2$ from $\theta = 0$ to $\theta = \pi$. Sketch the curve.

9. Find the length of the parabolic spiral $r = a\theta^2$ between $\theta = 0$ and $\theta = \pi$. Sketch the curve.

10. Find the length of the curve $r = a \sin^3 \theta/3$ between $\theta = 0$ and $\theta = \pi$. Sketch the curve.

11. Find the surface area generated by rotating the curve $r = 2a \cos \theta$ about the line $\theta = \pi/2$. Sketch.

11.5 PLANE AREAS IN POLAR COORDINATES

The area AOB in Fig. 11.27 is bounded by the rays $\theta = \alpha$, $\theta = \beta$, and the curve $r = f(\theta)$. We imagine the angle AOB as being divided into n parts

$$\Delta\theta = \frac{\beta - \alpha}{n},$$

and we approximate the area in a typical sector POQ by the area of a *circular* sector of radius r and central angle $\Delta\theta$, that is

$$\text{area of } POQ \approx \tfrac{1}{2}r^2\,\Delta\theta,$$

and hence the entire area AOB is approximately

$$\sum_{\theta=\alpha}^{\beta} \tfrac{1}{2}r^2\,\Delta\theta.$$

We might note that if in fact the function $r = f(\theta)$ which represents the polar curve is a continuous function of θ for $\alpha \le \theta \le \beta$, then there is a θ_k between θ and $\theta + \Delta\theta$ such that the circular sector of radius

$$r_k = f(\theta_k)$$

and central angle $\Delta\theta$ gives the *exact* area of POQ (Fig. 11.28). Then the entire area is given exactly by

$$A = \sum \tfrac{1}{2}r_k^2\,\Delta\theta = \sum \tfrac{1}{2}[f(\theta_k)]^2\,\Delta\theta.$$

If we let $\Delta\theta \to 0$, we may apply the Fundamental Theorem of the integral calculus and obtain

$$A = \lim_{\Delta\theta\to0} \sum \tfrac{1}{2}[f(\theta_k)]^2\,\Delta\theta$$
$$= \tfrac{1}{2}\int_\alpha^\beta [f(\theta)]^2\,d\theta.$$

11.27

11.28

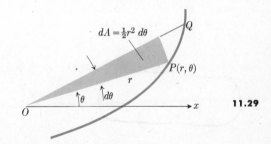

11.29

This is equivalent to the integral

$$A = \int_\alpha^\beta \tfrac{1}{2}r^2\,d\theta. \tag{1}$$

This result may also be remembered as the integral of the differential element of area (Fig. 11.29),

$$dA = \tfrac{1}{2}r^2\,d\theta,$$

taken between the appropriate limits on θ.

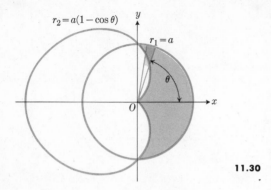

$r_2 = a(1 - \cos \theta)$

$r_1 = a$

11.30

Problem. Find the area that is inside the circle $r = a$ and outside the cardioid $r = a(1 - \cos \theta)$. (See Fig. 11.30.)

Solution. We take a representative element of area

$$dA = dA_1 - dA_2,$$

where

$$dA_1 = \tfrac{1}{2}r_1^2 \, d\theta, \quad dA_2 = \tfrac{1}{2}r_2^2 \, d\theta$$

with

$$r_1 = a, \quad r_2 = a(1 - \cos \theta).$$

Such elements of area belong to the region inside the circle and outside the cardioid, provided that θ lies between

$$-\frac{\pi}{2} \quad \text{and} \quad +\frac{\pi}{2},$$

where the curves intersect. Hence

$$A = \int_{-\pi/2}^{\pi/2} \tfrac{1}{2}(r_1^2 - r_2^2) \, d\theta$$

$$= \int_{-\pi/2}^{\pi/2} \frac{a^2}{2} (2 \cos \theta - \cos^2 \theta) \, d\theta$$

$$= a^2 \int_{-\pi/2}^{\pi/2} \cos \theta \, d\theta - \frac{a^2}{2} \int_{-\pi/2}^{\pi/2} \frac{1 + \cos 2\theta}{2} \, d\theta$$

$$= a^2 \left(2 - \frac{\pi}{4} \right).$$

As a check against gross errors, we observe that this is roughly 80% of the area of a semicircle of radius a, and this seems reasonable when we look at the tinted area in Fig. 11.30.

EXERCISES

Note. The trigonometric identities

$$\sin^2 \theta = \tfrac{1}{2}(1 - \cos 2\theta), \quad \cos^2 \theta = \tfrac{1}{2}(1 + \cos 2\theta)$$

should be used to evaluate $\int \sin^2 \theta \, d\theta$ and $\int \cos^2 \theta \, d\theta$ in certain of the problems that follow.

1. Find the total area inside the cardioid
$$r = a(1 + \cos \theta).$$

2. Find the total area inside the circle $r = 2a \sin \theta$.

3. Find the total area inside the lemniscate
$$r^2 = 2a^2 \cos 2\theta.$$

4. Find that portion of the area inside the lemniscate $r^2 = 2a^2 \cos 2\theta$ that is not included in the circle $r = a$. Sketch.

5. Find the area inside the curve $r = a(2 + \cos \theta)$.

6. Find the area common to the circles $r = 2a \cos \theta$ and $r = 2a \sin \theta$. Sketch.

7. Find the area inside the circle $r = 3a \cos \theta$ and outside the cardioid $r = a(1 + \cos \theta)$.

REVIEW QUESTIONS AND EXERCISES

1. Make a diagram to show the standard relations between Cartesian coordinates (x, y) and polar coordinates (r, θ). Express each set of coordinates in terms of the other kind.

2. If a point has polar coordinates (r_1, θ_1), what other polar coordinates represent the same point?

3. What is the expression for area between curves in polar coordinates?

4. What is the expression for length of arc of a curve in polar coordinates? For area of a surface of revolution?

5. What are some criteria for symmetry of a curve if its polar coordinates satisfy the equation $r = f(\theta)$? Illustrate your discussion with specific examples.

6. An artificial satellite is in an orbit that passes over the North and South Poles of the earth. When it is over the North Pole it is at the highest point of its orbit, 1000 miles above the earth's surface. Above the South Pole it is at the lowest point of its orbit, 300 miles above the earth's surface.

(a) Assuming that the orbit (with reference to the earth) is an ellipse with one focus at the center of the earth, find its eccentricity. (Take the diameter of the earth to be 8000 miles.)

(b) Using the north-south axis of the earth as polar axis, and the center of the earth as origin, find a polar equation of the orbit.

MISCELLANEOUS EXERCISES

Discuss and sketch each of the curves in Exercises 1 through 13 (where a is a positive constant).

1. $r = a\theta$ 2. $r = a(1 + \cos 2\theta)$

3. (a) $r = a \sec \theta$ (b) $r = a \csc \theta$

   (c) $r = a \sec \theta + a \csc \theta$

4. $r = a \sin\left(\theta + \dfrac{\pi}{3}\right)$

5. $r^2 + 2r(\cos \theta + \sin \theta) = 7$

6. $r = a \cos \theta - a \sin \theta$ 7. $r \cos \dfrac{\theta}{2} = a$

8. $r^2 = a^2 \sin \theta$ 9. $r^2 = 2a^2 \sin 2\theta$

10. $r = a(1 - 2 \sin 3\theta)$

11. (a) $r = \cos 2\theta$ (b) $r^2 = \cos 2\theta$

12. (a) $r = 1 + \cos \theta$ (b) $r = \dfrac{1}{1 + \cos \theta}$

13. (a) $r = \dfrac{2}{1 - \cos \theta}$ (b) $r = \dfrac{2}{1 + \sin \theta}$

14. Sketch and discuss the graph whose equation in polar coordinates is
$$r = 1 - \tan^2 \theta.$$
Show that it has no vertical asymptotes.

Sketch each of the pairs of curves in Exercises 15 through 20, and find all points of intersection and the angle between their tangents at each point of intersection.

15. $r = a$, $r = 2a \sin \theta$

16. $r = a$, $r = a(1 - \sin \theta)$

17. $r = a \sec \theta$, $r = 2a \sin \theta$

18. $r = a \cos \theta$, $r = a(1 + \cos \theta)$

19. $r = a(1 + \cos 2\theta)$, $r = a \cos 2\theta$

20. $r^2 = 4 \cos 2\theta$, $r^2 = \sec 2\theta$

21. Find the equation, in polar coordinates, of a parabola whose focus is at $r = 0$ and whose vertex is at $r = 1$, $\theta = 0$.

22. Find the polar equation of the straight line with intercepts a and b on the lines $\theta = 0$, $\theta = \pi/2$.

23. Find the equation of a circle with center on the ray $\theta = \pi$, of radius a, and passing through the origin.

24. Find the polar equation of a parabola with focus at the origin and vertex at $(a, \pi/4)$.

25. Find the polar equation of an ellipse with one focus at the origin, the other at $(2, 0)$, and a vertex at $(4, 0)$.

26. Find the polar equation of a hyperbola with one focus at the origin, center at $(2, \pi/2)$, and vertex at $(1, \pi/2)$.

27. Three loran stations are located (in polar coordinates) at $(a, 0)$, $(0, 0)$, and $(a, \pi/4)$. Radio signals are sent out from the three stations simultaneously. A plane receiving the signals notes that the signals from the second and third stations arrive $a/2\nu$ sec later than that from the first. If ν is the velocity of a radio signal, what is the location of the plane in polar coordinates?

28. Show that the parabolas
$$r = a/(1 + \cos \theta), \quad r = b/(1 - \cos \theta)$$
are orthogonal at each point of intersection ($ab \neq 0$).

29. Find the angle between the ray $\theta = \pi/2$ and the cardioid $r = a(1 - \cos \theta)$ at their intersection.

30. Find the angle between the line $r = 3 \sec \theta$ and the curve $r = 4(1 + \cos \theta)$ at one of their intersections.

31. Find the slope of the tangent line to the curve
$$r = a \tan (\theta/2)$$
at $\theta = \pi/2$.

32. Check that the two curves $r = 1/(1 - \cos \theta)$ and $r = 3/(1 + \cos \theta)$ intersect at the point $(2, \pi/3)$. Find the angle between the tangents to these curves at this point.

33. The equation $r^2 = 2 \csc 2\theta$ represents a curve in polar coordinates.

   (a) Sketch the curve.

   (b) Find the equation of the curve in rectangular coordinates.

   (c) Find the angle at which the curve intersects the line $\theta = \pi/4$.

34. A given curve cuts all rays $\theta = $ constant at the constant angle α.

   (a) Show that the area bounded by the curve and two rays $\theta = \theta_1$, $\theta = \theta_2$, is proportional to $r_2^2 - r_1^2$, where (r_1, θ_1) and (r_2, θ_2) are polar coordinates of the ends of the arc of the curve between these rays. Find the factor of proportionality.

   (b) Show that the length of the arc of the curve in (a) is proportional to $r_2 - r_1$ and find the proportionality constant.

35. The cardioid $r = a(1 - \cos \theta)$ is rotated about the initial line.

   (a) Find the area of the surface generated.
   Hint. You may use the facts

   $$\sin \theta = 2 \sin (\theta/2) \cos (\theta/2),$$

   $$1 - \cos \theta = 2 \sin^2 (\theta/2)$$

   to evaluate your integral.

   (b) Set up the definite integral (or integrals) that would be used to find the centroid of the area in (a).

   (c) Find the centroid of the area in (a).

36. Let P be a point on the hyperbola $r^2 \sin 2\theta = 2a^2$. Show that the triangle formed by OP, the tangent at P, and the initial line is isosceles.

37. Verify that the formula for finding the length of a curve in polar form gives the correct result for the circumference of the circles

   (a) $r = a$,   (b) $r = a \cos \theta$,
   (c) $r = a \sin \theta$.

38. If $r = a \cos^3 (\theta/3)$, show that $ds = a \cos^2 (\theta/3) \, d\theta$ and determine the perimeter of the curve.

39. Find the area that lies inside the curve

   $$r = 2a \cos 2\theta$$

   and outside the curve $r = a\sqrt{2}$.

40. Sketch the curves

   $$r = 2a \cos^2 (\theta/2), \quad r = 2a \sin^2 (\theta/2),$$

   and find the area they have in common.

Find the total area enclosed by each of the curves in Exercises 41 through 47.

41. $r^2 = a^2 \cos 2\theta$ 42. $r = a(2 - \cos \theta)$
43. $r = a(1 + \cos 2\theta)$ 44. $r = 2a \cos \theta$
45. $r = 2a \sin 3\theta$ 46. $r^2 = 2a^2 \sin 3\theta$
47. $r^2 = 2a^2 \cos^2 (\theta/2)$

48. Find the area that is inside the cardioid

   $$r = a(1 + \sin \theta)$$

   and outside the circle $r = a \sin \theta$.

49. Find the area that is inside the circle $r = 4 \cos \theta$ and outside $r = 2$.

50. Find the area that is inside $r^2 = 2a^2 \cos 2\theta$ and outside the circle $r = a$.

51. Find the area that is inside the circle $r = 5 \cos \theta$ and outside the curve $r = 2 + \cos \theta$.

52. Find the area of the region between the two loops of the limaçon $r = 2 + 4 \cos \theta$.

HYPERBOLIC FUNCTIONS

CHAPTER 12

12.1 INTRODUCTION*

In this chapter we shall consider certain combinations of the exponentials e^x and e^{-x} which are called "hyperbolic functions." There are two reasons why we study these functions. One reason is that they are used in solving certain engineering problems. For example, the tension at any point in a cable suspended by its ends and hanging under its own weight, such as an electric transmission line, may be computed in terms of hyperbolic functions. We shall investigate the hanging cable in some detail in Article 12.6. A second reason for studying the hyperbolic functions is that they are useful in connection with differential equations.

12.2 DEFINITIONS AND IDENTITIES

The combinations $\frac{1}{2}(e^u + e^{-u})$ and $\frac{1}{2}(e^u - e^{-u})$ occur with sufficient frequency that it has been found convenient to give special names to them. It may not be clear at this particular time why the names about to be introduced are especially appropriate. But it will become more apparent as we proceed that these functions have many properties analogous, respectively, to $\cos u$ and $\sin u$. And just as $\cos u$ and $\sin u$ are easily identified with the point (x, y) on the unit circle $x^2 + y^2 = 1$, where by properly defining u we may take $x = \cos u$ and $y = \sin u$, so it is also possible to identify

$$\cosh u = \tfrac{1}{2}(e^u + e^{-u}),$$
$$\sinh u = \tfrac{1}{2}(e^u - e^{-u}), \tag{1}$$

with the coordinates of the point (x, y) on the "unit hyperbola" $x^2 - y^2 = 1$.

Equations (1) are the *definitions* of the *hyperbolic cosine* of u ($\cosh u$, which is often pronounced to rhyme with "gosh you") and of the *hyperbolic sine* of u ($\sinh u$, which is pronounced as though it were spelled "cinch u").

Suppose we check the statement that the point (x, y) with $x = \cosh u$ and $y = \sinh u$ lies on the unit hyperbola. We simply substitute the defining

---

* This chapter can be omitted without loss of continuity.

relations (1) into the equation of the hyperbola, and see whether or not these coordinates do satisfy the equation:

$$x^2 - y^2 = 1,$$

$$\cosh^2 u - \sinh^2 u \overset{?}{=} 1,$$

$$\tfrac{1}{4}(e^{2u} + 2 + e^{-2u}) - \tfrac{1}{4}(e^{2u} - 2 + e^{-2u}) \overset{?}{=} 1,$$

$$\tfrac{1}{4}(e^{2u} + 2 + e^{-2u} - e^{2u} + 2 - e^{-2u}) \overset{?}{=} 1,$$

$$\tfrac{1}{4}(4) \overset{?}{=} 1. \quad \text{(Yes!)}$$

Actually, if we let

$$x = \cosh u = \tfrac{1}{2}(e^u + e^{-u}), \tag{2}$$
$$y = \sinh u = \tfrac{1}{2}(e^u - e^{-u}),$$

then when u varies from $-\infty$ to $+\infty$, the point $P(x, y)$ describes the right-hand branch of the hyperbola $x^2 - y^2 = 1$. The sense in which the curve is described is indicated by the arrows in Fig. 12.1. Since e^u is always positive and $e^{-u} = 1/e^u$ is also positive, it follows that $x = \cosh u = \tfrac{1}{2}(e^u + e^{-u})$ is positive for all real values of u, $-\infty < u < +\infty$. Hence the point (x, y) remains always to the right of the y-axis.

12.1

The bit of hyperbolic trigonometry that we have just established is the basic identity

$$\cosh^2 u - \sinh^2 u = 1. \tag{3}$$

This is analogous to, but not the same as, the ordinary trigonometric identity, $\cos^2 u + \sin^2 u = 1$. We shall now investigate additional points of analogy between these two types of functions.

The remaining hyperbolic functions are *defined* in terms of $\sinh u$ and $\cosh u$ as follows:

$$\tanh u = \frac{\sinh u}{\cosh u} = \frac{e^u - e^{-u}}{e^u + e^{-u}},$$

$$\coth u = \frac{\cosh u}{\sinh u} = \frac{e^u + e^{-u}}{e^u - e^{-u}},$$

$$\operatorname{sech} u = \frac{1}{\cosh u} = \frac{2}{e^u + e^{-u}},$$

$$\operatorname{csch} u = \frac{1}{\sinh u} = \frac{2}{e^u - e^{-u}}. \tag{4}$$

If we divide the identity (3) by $\cosh^2 u$, we get

$$1 - \tanh^2 u = \operatorname{sech}^2 u, \tag{5a}$$

and if we divide it by $\sinh^2 u$, we get

$$\coth^2 u - 1 = \operatorname{csch}^2 u. \tag{5b}$$

Since from (1) we find that

$$\cosh u + \sinh u = e^u, \tag{6a}$$

$$\cosh u - \sinh u = e^{-u}, \tag{6b}$$

it is apparent that *any* combination of the exponentials e^u and e^{-u} can be replaced by a combination of $\sinh u$ and $\cosh u$, and conversely. Also, since e^{-u} is positive, (6b) shows that $\cosh u$ is always greater than $\sinh u$. But for large values of u, e^{-u} is small, and $\cosh u \approx \sinh u$.

The graphs of the hyperbolic functions are shown in Fig. 12.2 (a–d).

At $x = 0$, $\cosh x = 1$ and $\sinh x = 0$, so the hyperbolic functions all have the same values at 0 that the corresponding trigonometric functions have. The hyperbolic cosine is an *even function*, that is,

$$\cosh (-x) = \cosh x, \tag{7}$$

and the hyperbolic sine is an *odd function*, that is,

$$\sinh (-x) = -\sinh x; \tag{8}$$

so one curve is symmetric about the y-axis and the other is symmetric with respect to the origin. Here again the hyperbolic functions behave like the ordinary trigonometric (or circular) functions.

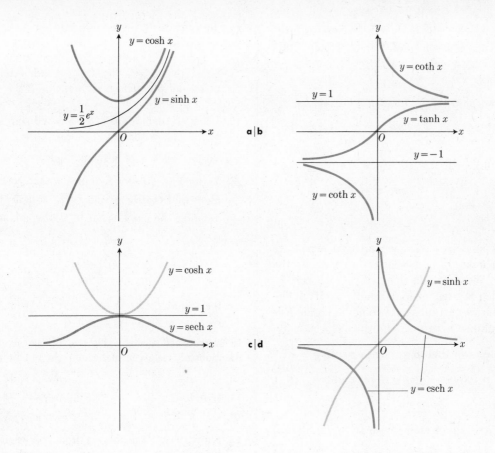

12.2

The hyperbolic functions are so important and useful that their numerical values have been calculated and tabulated just as have the circular functions, at least for sinh x, cosh x, and tanh x. The values of the other functions can be expressed in terms of these, so it is unnecessary to tabulate them too. Some slide rules also have sinh x and cosh x scales, and the values of these functions may be read directly in the same way that e^x may be read from the LL-scales.

Certain major differences between the hyperbolic and the circular functions should be noted. For example, the circular functions are periodic:

$$\sin(x + 2\pi) = \sin x, \quad \tan(x + \pi) = \tan x, \quad \text{etc.}$$

But the *hyperbolic functions are not periodic.* Again, they differ greatly in the range of values they assume:

sin x varies between -1 and $+1$, oscillates;
sinh x varies from $-\infty$ to $+\infty$, steadily increases;

cos x varies between -1 and $+1$, oscillates;
cosh x varies from $+\infty$ to $+1$ to $+\infty$;

$|\sec x|$ is never less than unity;
sech x is never greater than unity, is always positive;

tan x varies between $-\infty$ and $+\infty$;
tanh x varies between -1 and $+1$.

Another difference is exhibited in the behavior of the functions as $x \to \pm\infty$. In the case of the circular functions, sin x, cos x, tan x, and so on, we can say nothing very specific about their behavior for large values of x. On the other hand, the hyperbolic functions behave very much like $e^x/2$, $e^{-x}/2$, unity, or zero, as follows:

For x large and positive: *For x negative, $|x|$ large:*

$$\cosh x \approx \sinh x$$
$$\approx \tfrac{1}{2}e^x,$$

$$\cosh x \approx -\sinh x$$
$$\approx \tfrac{1}{2}e^{-x},$$

$$\tanh x \approx \coth x \approx 1,$$

$$\tanh x \approx \coth x \approx -1,$$

$$\operatorname{sech} x \approx \operatorname{csch} x$$
$$\approx 2e^{-x} \approx 0.$$

$$\operatorname{sech} x \approx -\operatorname{csch} x$$
$$\approx 2e^{x} \approx 0.$$

$$(9)$$

Additional analogies will be apparent when we study the calculus of hyperbolic functions in the next article. We conclude this article with certain formulas which the reader may readily verify. The following identities require only some algebraic calculations combined with the definitions (1), namely,

$$\sinh (x + y) = \sinh x \cosh y + \cosh x \sinh y,$$
$$\cosh (x + y) = \cosh x \cosh y + \sinh x \sinh y. \tag{10}$$

These in turn give

$$\sinh 2x = 2 \sinh x \cosh x, \tag{11a}$$

$$\cosh 2x = \cosh^2 x + \sinh^2 x, \tag{11b}$$

when we take $y = x$. The second of these leads to certain useful "half-angle" formulas when we combine it with the basic identity

$$1 = \cosh^2 x - \sinh^2 x. \tag{3}$$

For if we add (11b) and (3), we have

$$\cosh 2x + 1 = 2 \cosh^2 x, \tag{12a}$$

while if we subtract (3) from (11b), we get

$$\cosh 2x - 1 = 2 \sinh^2 x. \tag{12b}$$

Thus practically all the circular trigonometric identities have hyperbolic analogies. The formulas (3) and (10) are easily verified in terms of the definitions (1). The others follow from these by straightforward algebraic manipulations.

EXERCISES

1. Show that $x = -\cosh u$, $y = \sinh u$ represents a point on the left-hand branch of the hyperbola $x^2 - y^2 = 1$.

2. Using the definitions of $\cosh u$ and $\sinh u$ given by Eq. (1), show that

$$\cosh (-u) = \cosh u \quad \text{and} \quad \sinh (-u) = -\sinh u.$$

3. Verify Eqs. (10) for $\sinh (x + y)$ and $\cosh (x + y)$.

4. Show that $(\cosh x + \sinh x)^n = \cosh nx + \sinh nx$.

5. Let L be the line tangent to the hyperbola

$$x^2 - y^2 = 1$$

at the point $P_1(x_1, y_1)$, where

$$x_1 = \cosh u, \qquad y_1 = \sinh u.$$

Show that L cuts the x-axis at the point $(\operatorname{sech} u, 0)$ and the y-axis at $(0, -\operatorname{csch} u)$.

In Exercises 6 through 11, one of the six hyperbolic functions of u is given; determine the remaining five.

6. $\sinh u = -\tfrac{3}{4}$ 7. $\cosh u = \tfrac{17}{15}$

8. $\tanh u = -\tfrac{7}{25}$ 9. $\coth u = \tfrac{13}{12}$

10. $\operatorname{sech} u = \tfrac{3}{5}$ 11. $\operatorname{csch} u = \tfrac{5}{12}$

12. Show that the distance r from the origin O to the point $P(\cosh u, \sinh u)$ on the hyperbola $x^2 - y^2 = 1$ is $r = \sqrt{\cosh 2u}$.

13. Show that the line tangent to the hyperbola at its vertex A in Fig. 12.1 intersects the line OP in the point $(1, \tanh u)$. This gives a geometric representation of $\tanh u$.

14. If θ lies in the interval $-\pi/2 < \theta < \pi/2$ and $\sinh x = \tan \theta$, show that

$$\cosh x = \sec \theta, \quad \tanh x = \sin \theta, \quad \coth x = \csc \theta,$$

$$\operatorname{csch} x = \cot \theta, \quad \text{and} \quad \operatorname{sech} x = \cos \theta.$$

12.3 DERIVATIVES AND INTEGRALS

Let u be a differentiable function of x and differentiate

$$\sinh u = \tfrac{1}{2}(e^u - e^{-u}),$$
$$\cosh u = \tfrac{1}{2}(e^u + e^{-u}), \tag{1}$$

with respect to x. Applying the formulas

$$\frac{de^u}{dx} = e^u \frac{du}{dx},$$

$$\frac{de^{-u}}{dx} = e^{-u} \frac{d(-u)}{dx} = -e^{-u} \frac{du}{dx},$$

we get

$$\frac{d(\sinh u)}{dx} = \cosh u \frac{du}{dx}, \qquad \text{(XXI)}$$

$$\frac{d(\cosh u)}{dx} = \sinh u \frac{du}{dx}. \qquad \text{(XXII)}$$

Then, if we let

$$y = \tanh u = \frac{\sinh u}{\cosh u}$$

and differentiate as a fraction, we get

$$\frac{d(\tanh u)}{dx} = \frac{\cosh u \dfrac{d(\sinh u)}{dx} - \sinh u \dfrac{d(\cosh u)}{dx}}{\cosh^2 x}$$

$$= \frac{\cosh^2 u \dfrac{du}{dx} - \sinh^2 u \dfrac{du}{dx}}{\cosh^2 u}$$

$$= \frac{(\cosh^2 u - \sinh^2 u) \dfrac{du}{dx}}{\cosh^2 u}$$

$$= \frac{1}{\cosh^2 u} \frac{du}{dx}$$

$$= \text{sech}^2 u \frac{du}{dx}.$$

In a similar manner, we may establish the rest of the formulas in the following list.

$$\frac{d(\tanh u)}{dx} = \text{sech}^2 u \frac{du}{dx} \qquad \text{(XXIII)}$$

$$\frac{d(\coth u)}{dx} = -\text{csch}^2 u \frac{du}{dx} \qquad \text{(XXIV)}$$

$$\frac{d(\text{sech } u)}{dx} = -\text{sech } u \tanh u \frac{du}{dx} \qquad \text{(XXV)}$$

$$\frac{d(\text{csch } u)}{dx} = -\text{csch } u \coth u \frac{du}{dx} \qquad \text{(XXVI)}$$

Note that aside from the pattern of algebraic signs, these formulas are the exact analogs of the formulas for the corresponding circular functions. Again, exactly half of them have minus signs, but we no longer attach the minus signs to the derivatives of the cofunctions, but rather note that the first three, $\sinh u$, $\cosh u$, and $\tanh u$, have positive derivatives and the last three have negative derivatives.

Each of these derivative formulas has a matching differential formula. These in turn may be integrated at once to produce the following integration formulas.

$$(1) \int \sinh u \, du = \cosh u + C$$

$$(2) \int \cosh u \, du = \sinh u + C$$

$$(3) \int \text{sech}^2 u \, du = \tanh u + C$$

$$(4) \int \text{csch}^2 u \, du = -\coth u + C \qquad (2)$$

$$(5) \int \text{sech } u \tanh u \, du = -\text{sech } u + C$$

$$(6) \int \text{csch } u \coth u \, du = -\text{csch } u + C$$

Problem 1. Show that $y = a \cosh (x/a)$ satisfies the differential equation

$$\frac{d^2y}{dx^2} = \frac{w}{H} \sqrt{1 + \left(\frac{dy}{dx}\right)^2}, \qquad (3)$$

provided that $a = H/w$, where H and w are constants.

Solution. By differentiating $y = a \cosh (x/a)$, we find

$$\frac{dy}{dx} = a \sinh \frac{x}{a} \cdot \frac{1}{a} = \sinh \frac{x}{a}, \qquad \frac{d^2y}{dx^2} = \cosh \frac{x}{a} \cdot \frac{1}{a}.$$

We substitute these into (3) and obtain

$$\frac{1}{a} \cosh \frac{x}{a} \overset{?}{=} \frac{w}{H} \sqrt{1 + \sinh^2 \frac{x}{a}} \qquad (a)$$

$$= \frac{w}{H} \sqrt{\cosh^2 \frac{x}{a}} \qquad (b)$$

$$= \frac{w}{H} \cosh \frac{x}{a}, \qquad (c)$$

which is a true equation provided $a = H/w$.

Remark 1. In going from (a) to (b) above, we used the fundamental identity

$$\cosh^2 u - \sinh^2 u = 1$$

in the form

$$1 + \sinh^2 u = \cosh^2 u.$$

In going from (b) to (c), we used the fact that $\cosh u$ is always positive, and hence

$$\sqrt{\cosh^2 u} = |\cosh u| = \cosh u.$$

Remark 2. The differential equation (3) expresses the condition for equilibrium of forces acting on a section AP of a hanging cable (Fig. 12.3). We imagine the rest of the cable as having been removed and the section AP from the lowest point A to the representative point $P(x, y)$ as being in equilibrium under the forces

(1) H = horizontal tension pulling on the cable at A,

(2) T = tangential tension pulling on the cable at P,

(3) $W = ws$ = weight of s feet of the cable at w pounds per foot of length from A to P.

Then equilibrium of the cable requires that the horizontal and vertical components of T balance H and W respectively:

$$T \cos \phi = H, \qquad T \sin \phi = W = ws. \qquad (4)$$

By division, we get

$$\frac{T \sin \phi}{T \cos \phi} = \tan \phi = \frac{W}{H}$$

or

$$\frac{dy}{dx} = \frac{ws}{H}, \qquad (5)$$

since $\tan \phi = dy/dx$. The arc length s in Eq. (5) would be found by integrating

$$ds = \sqrt{1 + \left(\frac{dy}{dx}\right)^2}\, dx$$

from A to P. But instead of doing so, we may differentiate Eq. (5) with respect to x:

$$\frac{d^2 y}{dx^2} = \frac{w}{H} \frac{ds}{dx},$$

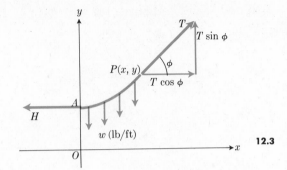

12.3

and then substitute $\sqrt{1 + (dy/dx)^2}$ in place of ds/dx to obtain Eq. (3) above.

Remark 3. In Problem 1, we pulled the equation $y = a \cosh (x/a)$ out of the hat, so to speak, and showed by substitution that it satisfies the differential equation (3). In Article 12.6, we shall adopt the more straightforward approach of simply solving Eq. (3) subject to the initial conditions

$$\frac{dy}{dx} = 0 \quad \text{and} \quad y = y_0$$

$$\text{when} \quad x = 0.$$

By choosing the origin so that

$$y_0 = a = \frac{H}{w},$$

we shall find that the solution is indeed the one given above, namely,

$$y = a \cosh \frac{x}{a} \quad \text{with } a = \frac{H}{w}. \qquad (6)$$

Problem 2. Show that the tension in the cable at $P(x, y)$ in Fig. 12.3 is

$$T = wy.$$

Solution. We make use of the fact that

$$\frac{dy}{dx} = \tan \phi,$$

since T acts along the tangent, and

$$T = \frac{H}{\cos \phi} = H \sec \phi,$$

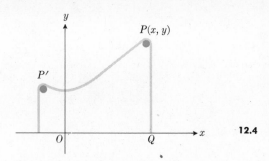

12.4

by Eq. (4a). Then, differentiating (6), we have

$$\tan \phi = \frac{dy}{dx} = \sinh \frac{x}{a}$$

and

$$\sec \phi = \sqrt{\sec^2 \phi} = \sqrt{1 + \tan^2 \phi} = \sqrt{1 + \left(\frac{dy}{dx}\right)^2}$$

$$= \sqrt{1 + \sinh^2 \frac{x}{a}} = \sqrt{\cosh^2 \frac{x}{a}} = \cosh \frac{x}{a}.$$

Therefore

$$T = H \sec \phi = H \cosh \frac{x}{a}, \qquad (7a)$$

where

$$a = \frac{H}{w}, \quad \text{or} \quad H = wa. \qquad (7b)$$

Combining (7a) and (7b), we have $T = wa \cosh (x/a)$, or, when we take account of Eq. (6),

$$T = wy.$$

This means that the tension at P is equal to the weight of y feet of the cable. Thus if the end of the cable to the right of P is allowed to hang down over a smooth peg while the cable is held at P so that it does not slip, and if the cable is then cut off at the point Q where it crosses the x-axis (Fig. 12.4), it may then be released at P and the weight wy of the section of cable PQ will be just sufficient to prevent the cable from slipping. If this is carried out at two different points P and P', the cable may be draped over two smooth pegs without slipping, provided the free ends reach just to the x-axis. The curve, $y = a \cosh (x/a)$, is called a *catenary* from the Latin word *catena*, meaning chain. The x-axis is called the directrix of the catenary.

EXERCISES

1. Establish the validity of the formulas XXIV through XXVI.

Find dy/dx in Exercises 2 through 9.

2. $y = \sinh 3x$

3. $y = \cosh^2 5x$

4. $y = \cosh^2 5x - \sinh^2 5x$

5. $y = \tanh 2x$

6. $y = \coth (\tan x)$

7. $y = \operatorname{sech}^3 x$

8. $y = 4 \operatorname{csch} (x/4)$

9. $\sinh y = \tan x$

Integrate each of the following.

10. $\displaystyle\int \cosh (2x + 1) \, dx$

11. $\displaystyle\int \tanh x \, dx$

12. $\displaystyle\int \frac{\sinh x}{\cosh^4 x} \, dx$

13. $\displaystyle\int \frac{4 \, dx}{(e^x + e^{-x})^2}$

14. $\displaystyle\int \frac{e^x - e^{-x}}{e^x + e^{-x}} \, dx$

15. $\displaystyle\int \tanh^2 x \, dx$

16. $\displaystyle\int \frac{\sinh \sqrt{x}}{\sqrt{x}} \, dx$

17. $\displaystyle\int \cosh^2 3x \, dx$

18. $\displaystyle\int \sqrt{\cosh x - 1} \, dx$

19. Find the area of the hyperbolic sector AOP bounded by the arc AP and the lines OA, OP through the origin, in Fig. 12.1.

20. Show that the straight line $y = x/2 + 1$ and the catenary $y = \cosh x$ intersect at the two points $(0, 1)$ and $(0.930, 1.465)$. (Consult tables for $\cosh x$.)

21. Two successive poles supporting an electric power line are 100 ft apart, the supporting members being at the same level. If the wire dips 25 ft at the center,

(a) find the length of the wire between supports, and

(b) find the tension in the wire at its lowest point if its weight is $w = 0.3$ lb/ft.

Hint. First find a from the equation

$$25/a + 1 = \cosh 50/a,$$

which can be related to Exercise 20 with $x = 50/a$.

22. The equation $\sinh x = \tan \theta$, $-\pi/2 < \theta < \pi/2$, defines θ as a function of x:

$$\theta = \tan^{-1} (\sinh x),$$

to which the name "gudermannian of x" has been attached, written

$$\theta = \mathrm{gd}\, x.$$

Show that

$$\frac{d\theta}{dx} = \frac{1}{\cosh x} = \frac{1}{\sec \theta},$$

so that $\sec \theta \, d\theta = dx$ and

$$\int \sec \theta \, d\theta = \mathrm{gd}^{-1} \theta + C = \sinh^{-1} (\tan \theta) + C.$$

23. Sketch the curve $\theta = \mathrm{gd}\, x$ (see Exercise 22) by the following procedure. First sketch the curves

$$y = \sinh x, \quad y = \tan \theta, \quad -\pi/2 < \theta < \pi/2,$$

on separate xy- and θy-planes. Starting in the xy-plane with any value of x, $-\infty < x < +\infty$, determine the corresponding value of y from the curve $y = \sinh x$. Transfer this y reading to the y-axis in the θy-plane and determine the corresponding value of θ from the curve $y = \tan \theta$. Use this value of θ as ordinate and the original value of x as abscissa to plot a point on the curve $\theta = \mathrm{gd}\, x$.

24. Show that the curve $\theta = \mathrm{gd}\, x$ (see Exercises 22 and 23) has the lines $\theta = \pm\pi/2$ as horizontal asymptotes, is always rising (from left to right), has a point of inflection at the origin, and is symmetric with respect to the origin.

12.4 GEOMETRIC MEANING OF THE HYPERBOLIC RADIAN

We are now in a position to illustrate the meaning of the variable u in the equations

$$x = \cosh u, \quad y = \sinh u \tag{1}$$

as they relate to the point $P(x, y)$ on the unit hyperbola

$$x^2 - y^2 = 1. \tag{2}$$

Before we do so, however, we shall find the analogous meaning of the variable θ in the equations

$$x = \cos \theta, \quad y = \sin \theta \tag{3}$$

as they relate to the point $P(x, y)$ on the unit circle

$$x^2 + y^2 = 1. \tag{4}$$

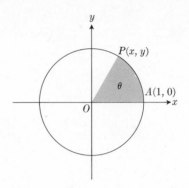

12.5

The most familiar interpretation of θ is, of course, that it is the radian measure of the angle AOP in Fig. 12.5, that is

$$\theta = \frac{\mathrm{arc}\ AP}{\mathrm{radius}\ OA}.$$

But we also recall that the area of a circular sector of radius r and central angle θ (radians) is given by $(\frac{1}{2})r^2\theta$. Since this is a unit circle,

$$\mathrm{area\ of\ sector}\ AOP = \tfrac{1}{2}\theta$$

or, if we solve this for θ,

$$\theta = \text{twice the area of sector } AOP. \tag{5}$$

Of course we must realize that θ is a pure (dimensionless) number and that Eq. (5) really says that the *value* of θ which Eqs. (3) associate with the point $P(x, y)$ on the unit circle is twice the *number* of square units of area that the radius vector OP sweeps out as P moves along the circle from A to its final position P. Thus when the area of the sector AOP is one-half the area of a square having OA as a side, then $\theta = 1$ and the coordinates of P represent $\cos 1$ and $\sin 1$. Negative values of θ would be interpreted as corresponding to areas swept over in a clockwise rotation of OA.

Now for the unit hyperbola

$$x^2 - y^2 = 1,$$

we shall find an analogous interpretation for the variable u in the equations

$$x = \cosh u, \quad y = \sinh u.$$

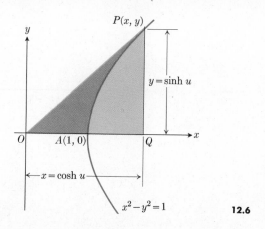

$y = \sinh u$

$P(x, y)$

$A(1, 0)$

Q

$x = \cosh u$

$x^2 - y^2 = 1$

12.6

To see that this is indeed the case, we shall calculate the area of the sector AOP in Fig. 12.6. This area is clearly equal to the area of the triangle QOP minus the area QAP bounded above by the curve, below by the x-axis, and on the right by the vertical line QP. But this area is simply

$$\text{area } AQP = \int_A^P y \, dx = \int_A^P \sinh u \, d(\cosh u)$$
$$= \int_A^P \sinh^2 u \, du.$$

By Eq. (12b), Article 12.2, we then have

$$\text{area } AQP = \tfrac{1}{2} \int_A^P (\cosh 2u - 1) \, du$$
$$= \tfrac{1}{2}[\tfrac{1}{2} \sinh 2u - u]_{A(u=0)}^{P(u=u)}$$
$$= \tfrac{1}{4} \sinh 2u - \tfrac{1}{2}u$$
$$= \tfrac{1}{2} \sinh u \cosh u - \tfrac{1}{2}u.$$

Hence the area of the sector AOP is equal to

$$\text{area of } OQP - \text{area of } AQP;$$

in terms of hyperbolic functions, this is

$$\tfrac{1}{2} \sinh u \cosh u - (\tfrac{1}{2} \sinh u \cosh u - \tfrac{1}{2}u) = \tfrac{1}{2}u.$$

Solving for u, we have

$$u = \text{twice the area of the sector } AOP. \qquad (6)$$

As for the circle, a positive value of u is associated with an area above the x-axis and a negative value with an area below the x-axis, and areas are to be measured in terms of the unit square having OA as side. The term *hyperbolic radian* is sometimes used in connection with the variable u in Eq. (6), but here again, u is just a dimensionless real number. For example, cosh 2 and sinh 2 may be interpreted as the coordinates of P when the area of the sector AOP is just equal to the area of a square having OA as side.

12.5 THE INVERSE HYPERBOLIC FUNCTIONS

If we start with

$$x = \sinh y, \qquad (1)$$

then as y varies continuously from $-\infty$ to $+\infty$, x does likewise. Graphically, this means that we may start with any real value on the y-axis in Fig. 12.7 and draw a horizontal line to the curve. Then a vertical line to the x-axis locates exactly one value of x such that the point (x, y) is on the curve. On the other hand, we could equally well reverse these steps and start with any real value x on the x-axis, go along a vertical line to the curve, then on a horizontal line to the y-axis. This latter procedure gives us y as a function of x, and the notation we use is

$$y = \sinh^{-1} x. \qquad (2)$$

Here we have no problem about principal values, as we did in the case of the inverses of the circular functions, since the correspondence between the real numbers x and the real numbers y in Eq. (1) is one-to-one. Equation (1) says exactly the same thing as Eq. (2):

$$y = \sinh^{-1} x \quad \text{means} \quad x = \sinh y.$$

The inverse hyperbolic cosine, however, is double-valued, and it is desirable to prescribe a principal branch. For if we start with the equation

$$x = \cosh y, \qquad (3)$$

then y and $-y$ both give the same value of x; that is, the correspondence between y-values and x-values is two-to-one, so that if x is considered the independent variable, there are *two* corresponding values of y. This is analogous to the situation surrounding

12.7

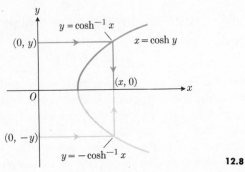

12.8

the equation $x = y^2$, which defines x as a single-valued function of y; but when x is given and we ask for y, the result is $y = \pm\sqrt{x}$. In the case of the inverse hyperbolic cosine, we take the positive values of y as the principal branch:

$$y = \cosh^{-1} x \quad \text{means} \quad x = \cosh y,$$

where

$$y \geq 0 \quad \text{and} \quad x \geq 1. \tag{4}$$

Thus in Fig. 12.8, the equation $x = \cosh y$ represents the entire curve, but $y = \cosh^{-1} x$ represents only that portion above the x-axis, while the portion below the x-axis is given by $y = -\cosh^{-1} x$.

Reference to Fig. 12.2 shows that the only other double-valued inverse is the inverse hyperbolic secant, and again we select the positive branch. That is,

$$y = \operatorname{sech}^{-1} x, \quad y > 0, \quad 0 < x \leq 1 \tag{5}$$

defines the principal branch and the numbers x and y satisfy

$$x = \operatorname{sech} y. \tag{6}$$

Since

$$\operatorname{sech} y = \frac{1}{\cosh y},$$

Eq. (6) is equivalent to

$$\cosh y = \frac{1}{x}$$

and the restriction $y > 0$ defines the same branch as in (5), so that

$$y = \cosh^{-1} \frac{1}{x}.$$

That is,

$$\operatorname{sech}^{-1} x = \cosh^{-1} \frac{1}{x}.$$

Similarly, we see that $y = \operatorname{csch}^{-1} x = \sinh^{-1}(1/x)$ means

$$\operatorname{csch} y = x. \tag{7}$$

Also,

$$y = \tanh^{-1} x \quad \text{means} \quad x = \tanh y, \tag{8a}$$

$$y = \coth^{-1} x \quad \text{means} \quad x = \coth y. \tag{8b}$$

The graphs of the various inverse hyperbolic functions are given in Figs. 12.7, 12.8, and 12.9. Numerical values of $\sinh^{-1} x$, $\cosh^{-1} x$ and $\tanh^{-1} x$ may be read from the tables of $\sinh x$, $\cosh x$, and $\tanh x$ respectively in the same way that antilogarithms are read from tables of logarithms.

Example 1. Suppose it is required to find $\tanh^{-1} 0.25$. If we let

$$x = \tanh^{-1} 0.25,$$

then

$$\tanh x = 0.25.$$

We consult a table of hyperbolic tangents and we find the following entries.

x	$\tanh x$	$\tanh x$ (rounded off)
0.25	0.24492	0.24
0.26	0.25430	0.25

Since we want the entry which corresponds to

$$\tanh x = 0.25,$$

we may simply round off the tabular entries to two significant figures and read $x = 0.26$. Or else we may

a|b

c|d

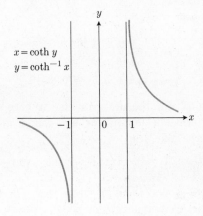

12.9

take $\tanh x = 0.25000$ and interpolate between the readings listed above. Using ordinary proportional parts, we have

$$x_1 = 0.25, \qquad \tanh x_1 = 0.24492,$$

$$x = (?), \qquad \tanh x = 0.25000,$$

$$x_2 = 0.26, \qquad \tanh x_2 = 0.25430;$$

$$\frac{x - x_1}{x_2 - x_1} = \frac{\tanh x - \tanh x_1}{\tanh x_2 - \tanh x_1},$$

$$\frac{x - x_1}{0.01} = \frac{508}{938} = 0.54,$$

$$x = 0.2554 = \tanh^{-1} 0.25000.$$

An alternative method for evaluating the inverse hyperbolic functions is to express each of them in terms of logarithms, as illustrated below for $\tanh^{-1} x$. Let

$$y = \tanh^{-1} x;$$

then

$$\tanh y = x,$$

or

$$x = \frac{\sinh y}{\cosh y} = \frac{\frac{1}{2}(e^y - e^{-y})}{\frac{1}{2}(e^y + e^{-y})}$$

$$= \frac{e^y - \dfrac{1}{e^y}}{e^y + \dfrac{1}{e^y}} = \frac{e^{2y} - 1}{e^{2y} + 1}.$$

We now solve this equation for e^{2y}:

$$xe^{2y} + x = e^{2y} - 1,$$

or

$$1 + x = e^{2y}(1 - x),$$

and

$$e^{2y} = \frac{1 + x}{1 - x}.$$

Hence

$$y = \tanh^{-1} x = \frac{1}{2} \ln \frac{1 + x}{1 - x}, \quad |x| < 1. \quad (9)$$

The variable x in Eq. (9) is restricted to the domain $|x| < 1$, since $x = \tanh y$ lies in this interval for all real values of y, $-\infty < y < +\infty$.

Example 2

$$\tanh^{-1} 0.25 = \frac{1}{2} \ln \frac{1.25}{0.75} = \frac{1}{2} \ln \frac{5}{3}$$

$$= \tfrac{1}{2}(\ln 5 = \ln 3) = 0.25542.$$

The expressions for the other inverse hyperbolic functions in terms of logarithms are found in a similar manner. They are:

$$\sinh^{-1} x = \ln (x + \sqrt{x^2 + 1}), \quad -\infty < x < \infty,$$

$$\cosh^{-1} x = \ln (x + \sqrt{x^2 - 1}), \quad x \geq 1,$$

$$\operatorname{sech}^{-1} x = \ln \left(\frac{1 + \sqrt{1 - x^2}}{x} \right)$$

$$= \cosh^{-1} \left(\frac{1}{x} \right), \quad 0 < x \leq 1,$$

$$\operatorname{csch}^{-1} x = \ln \left(\frac{1}{x} + \frac{\sqrt{1 + x^2}}{|x|} \right) \quad (10)$$

$$= \sinh^{-1} \left(\frac{1}{x} \right), \quad x \neq 0,$$

$$\coth^{-1} x = \frac{1}{2} \ln \frac{x + 1}{x - 1} = \tanh^{-1} \left(\frac{1}{x} \right), \quad |x| > 1.$$

It should be evident that the logarithmic expressions are, on the whole, rather cumbersome, and that the inverse hyperbolic functions do provide a useful shorthand wherever these expressions arise.

The chief merit of the inverse hyperbolic functions lies in their usefulness in integration. This will easily be understood after we have derived the following formulas for their derivatives.

$$\frac{d(\sinh^{-1} u)}{dx} = \frac{1}{\sqrt{1 + u^2}} \frac{du}{dx}, \quad \text{(XXVII)}$$

$$\frac{d(\cosh^{-1} u)}{dx} = \frac{1}{\sqrt{u^2 - 1}} \frac{du}{dx}, \quad \text{(XXVIII)}$$

$$\frac{d(\tanh^{-1} u)}{dx} = \frac{1}{1 - u^2} \frac{du}{dx}, \quad |u| < 1, \quad \text{(XXIX)}$$

$$\frac{d(\coth^{-1} u)}{dx} = \frac{1}{1 - u^2} \frac{du}{dx}, \quad |u| > 1, \quad \text{(XXX)}$$

$$\frac{d(\operatorname{sech}^{-1} u)}{dx} = \frac{-1}{u\sqrt{1 - u^2}} \frac{du}{dx}, \quad \text{(XXXI)}$$

$$\frac{d(\operatorname{csch}^{-1} u)}{dx} = \frac{-1}{|u|\sqrt{1 + u^2}} \frac{du}{dx}. \quad \text{(XXXII)}$$

The proofs of these all follow the same method. We illustrate for the case of $\cosh^{-1} u$.

Let

$$y = \cosh^{-1} u;$$

then

$$\cosh y = u, \qquad \sinh y \frac{dy}{dx} = \frac{du}{dx},$$

and

$$\frac{dy}{dx} = \frac{1}{\sinh y} \frac{du}{dx}.$$

But

$$\cosh^2 y - \sinh^2 y = 1,$$

$$\cosh y = u,$$

so that

$$\sinh y = \pm\sqrt{\cosh^2 y - 1}$$

$$= \pm\sqrt{u^2 - 1},$$

and

$$\frac{dy}{dx} = \frac{1}{\pm\sqrt{u^2 - 1}} \frac{du}{dx}.$$

The ambiguous sign will be $+$ if we restrict attention to the principal value, $y = \cosh^{-1} y$, $y \geq 0$, for then $\sinh y \geq 0$ and the ambiguous sign is the same as the sign of $\sinh y$. Thus XXVIII is established. The identities (5a) and (5b), Article 12.2, with y in place of u, will be found to be useful in proving formulas XXIX to XXXII. The reader should have no difficulty in deriving these results.

Remark. The restrictions $|u| < 1$ and $|u| > 1$ in XXIX and XXX respectively are due to the fact that

if $$y = \tanh^{-1} u,$$

then $$u = \tanh y,$$

and since $$-1 < \tanh y < 1,$$

this means $|u| < 1$. Similarly,

$$y = \coth^{-1} u, \qquad u = \coth y$$

requires $|u| > 1$. The distinction becomes important when we invert the formulas to get integration formulas, since otherwise we would be unable to tell whether we should write $\tanh^{-1} u$ or $\coth^{-1} u$ for

$$\int \frac{du}{1 - u^2}.$$

The following integration formulas follow at once from the differential formulas XXVII′ to XXXII′, that are obtained by multiplying both sides of XXVII to XXXII by dx:

(a) $\displaystyle\int \frac{du}{\sqrt{1 + u^2}} = \sinh^{-1} u + C,$

(b) $\displaystyle\int \frac{du}{\sqrt{u^2 - 1}} = \cosh^{-1} u + C,$

(c) $\displaystyle\int \frac{du}{1 - u^2} = \begin{cases} \tanh^{-1} u + C & \text{if } |u| < 1 \\ \coth^{-1} u + C & \text{if } |u| > 1 \end{cases}$

$$\qquad\qquad = \frac{1}{2} \ln \left| \frac{1 + u}{1 - u} \right| + C, \qquad (11)$$

(d) $\displaystyle\int \frac{du}{u\sqrt{1 - u^2}} = -\operatorname{sech}^{-1} |u| + C$

$$\qquad\qquad = -\cosh^{-1}\left(\frac{1}{|u|}\right) + C,$$

(e) $\displaystyle\int \frac{du}{u\sqrt{1 + u^2}} = -\operatorname{csch}^{-1} |u| + C$

$$\qquad\qquad = -\sinh^{-1}\left(\frac{1}{|u|}\right) + C.$$

EXERCISES

1. Solve the equation $x = \sinh y = \frac{1}{2}(e^y - e^{-y})$ for e^y in terms of x, and thus show that

$$y = \ln (x + \sqrt{1 + x^2}).$$

(This equation expresses $\sinh^{-1} x$ as a logarithm.)

2. Express $\cosh^{-1} x$ in terms of logarithms by using the method of Exercise 1.

3. Establish formula XXVII.

4. Establish formula XXIX.

5. Establish formula XXXI.

Find dy/dx in Exercises 6 through 10.

6. $y = \sinh^{-1} (2x)$

7. $y = \tanh^{-1} (\cos x)$

8. $y = \cosh^{-1} (\sec x)$

9. $y = \coth^{-1} (\sec x)$

10. $y = \operatorname{sech}^{-1} (\sin 2x)$

Evaluate the following integrals.

11. $\displaystyle\int \frac{dx}{\sqrt{1 + 4x^2}}$

12. $\displaystyle\int \frac{dx}{\sqrt{4 + x^2}}$

13. $\displaystyle\int_0^{0.5} \frac{dx}{1 - x^2}.$

14. $\displaystyle\int_{5/4}^2 \frac{dx}{1 - x^2}$

15. $\displaystyle\int \frac{dx}{x\sqrt{4 + x^2}}$

16. If a body of mass m falling from rest under the action of gravity encounters an air resistance proportional to the square of the velocity, then the velocity v at time t satisfies the differential equation

$$m(dv/dt) = mg - kv^2,$$

where k is a constant of proportionality and $v = 0$ when $t = 0$. Show that

$$v = \sqrt{\frac{mg}{k}} \tanh\left(\sqrt{\frac{gk}{m}}\, t\right),$$

and hence deduce that the body approaches a "limiting velocity" $= \sqrt{mg/k}$ as $t \to \infty$.

12.6 THE HANGING CABLE

We conclude this chapter by deriving the solution of the differential equation

$$\frac{d^2y}{dx^2} = \frac{w}{H} \sqrt{1 + \left(\frac{dy}{dx}\right)^2},$$ (1)

which is the equation of equilibrium of forces on a hanging cable discussed in Problem 1, Article 12.3. Since Eq. (1) involves the second derivative, we shall require two conditions to determine the constants of integration. By choosing the y-axis to be the vertical line through the lowest point of the cable, one condition becomes

$$\frac{dy}{dx} = 0 \quad \text{when } x = 0.$$ (2a)

Then we may still move the x-axis up or down to suit our convenience. That is, we let

$$y = y_0 \quad \text{when } x = 0,$$ (2b)

and we may choose y_0 so as to give us the simplest form in our final answer. (See Fig. 12.10.)

It is customary, when solving an equation such as (1), to introduce a single letter to represent dy/dx. The letter p is often used. Thus we let

$$\frac{dy}{dx} = p,$$ (3a)

and then we may write

$$\frac{d^2y}{dx^2} = \frac{dp}{dx},$$ (3b)

so that Eq. (1) takes the form

$$\frac{dp}{dx} = \frac{w}{H} \sqrt{1 + p^2}.$$

We may now separate the variables to get

$$\frac{dp}{\sqrt{1+p^2}} = \frac{w}{H} dx,$$

or

$$\int \frac{dp}{\sqrt{1+p^2}} = \frac{w}{H} x + C_1.$$ (4a)

12.10

The integral on the left is of the same form, with p in place of u, as (11a), Article 12.5. Hence (4a) becomes

$$\sinh^{-1} p = \frac{w}{H} x + C_1.$$ (4b)

Since $p = dy/dx = 0$ when $x = 0$, we determine the constant of integration $\sinh^{-1} 0 = C_1$, from which (see Fig. 12.7) we have $C_1 = 0$. Therefore Eq. (4) becomes

$$\sinh^{-1} p = \frac{w}{H} x,$$

or

$$p = \sinh\left(\frac{w}{H} x\right).$$ (5a)

We substitute $p = dy/dx$, multiply by dx, and have

$$dy = \sinh\left(\frac{w}{H} x\right) dx,$$

or

$$y = \int \sinh\left(\frac{w}{H} x\right) dx$$

$$= \frac{H}{w} \int \sinh\left(\frac{w}{H} x\right) d\left(\frac{w}{H} x\right)$$

$$= \frac{H}{w} \cosh\left(\frac{w}{H} x\right) + C_2.$$ (5b)

The condition $y = y_0$ when $x = 0$ determines C_2:

$$y_0 = \frac{H}{w} \cosh 0 + C_2,$$

$$C_2 = y_0 - \frac{H}{w},$$ (5c)

and hence

$$y = \frac{H}{w} \cosh\left(\frac{w}{H} x\right) + y_0 - \frac{H}{w}. \qquad \text{(5d)}$$

Clearly, this equation will have a simpler form if we choose y_0 so that

$$y_0 = \frac{H}{w}.$$

We do so. The answer then takes the form

$$y = \frac{H}{w} \cosh\left(\frac{w}{H} x\right),$$

or

$$y = a \cosh\frac{x}{a} \quad \text{with } a = \frac{H}{w}. \qquad \text{(6)}$$

EXERCISES

1. Find the length of arc of the catenary

$$y = a \cosh x/a$$

from $A(0, a)$ to $P_1(x_1, y_1)$, $x_1 > 0$.

2. Show that the area bounded by the x-axis, the catenary $y = a \cosh x/a$, the y-axis, and the vertical line through $P_1(x_1, y_1)$, $x_1 > 0$, is the same as the area of a rectangle of altitude a and base s, where s is the length of the arc from $A(0, a)$ to P_1. (See Exercise 1.)

3. The catenary $y = a \cosh x/a$ is revolved about the x-axis. Find the surface area generated by the portion of the curve between the points $A(0, a)$ and $P_1(x_1, y_1)$, $x_1 > 0$.

4. Find the center of gravity of the arc of the catenary $y = a \cosh x/a$ between two symmetrically located points $P_0(-x_1, y_1)$ and $P_1(x_1, y_1)$.

5. Find the volume generated when the area of Exercise 2 is revolved about the x-axis.

6. (a) The length of the arc AP (Fig. 12.10) is

$$s = a \sinh x/a.$$

(See Exercise 1.) Show that the coordinates of $P(x, y)$ may be expressed as functions of the arc length s as follows:

$$x = a \sinh^{-1}\frac{s}{a}, \qquad y = \sqrt{s^2 + a^2}.$$

(b) Calculate dx/ds and dy/ds from (a) and verify that $(dx/ds)^2 + (dy/ds)^2 = 1$.

7. A cable 32 feet long and weighing 2 pounds per foot has its ends fastened at the same level to two posts 30 feet apart.

(a) Show that the constant a in Eq. (6) must satisfy the equation

$$\sinh u = \frac{16}{15} u, \qquad u = \frac{15}{a}.$$

(See Exercise 6a.)

(b) Sketch graphs of the curves $y_1 = \sinh u$, $y_2 = \frac{16}{15}u$ and show (by consulting tables) that they intersect at $u = 0$ and $u = \pm 0.6$ (approximately).

(c) Using the results of (b), find the dip in the cable at its center.

(d) Using the results of (b), find the tension in the cable at its lowest point.

REVIEW QUESTIONS AND EXERCISES

1. Define each of the hyperbolic functions.

2. State three trigonometric identities [such as formulas for $\sin(A + B)$, $\cos(A - B)$, $\cos^2 A + \sin^2 A = 1$, and so forth]. What are the corresponding hyperbolic identities? Verify them.

3. Develop formulas for derivatives of the six hyperbolic functions.

4. What is the domain of the hyperbolic sine? What is its range?

5. What are the domain and range of the hyperbolic cosine? Of the hyperbolic tangent?

6. State some differences between the graphs of the trigonometric functions and their hyperbolic counterparts (for example, sine and sinh, cosine and cosh, tangent and tanh).

7. If $y = A \sin(at) + B \cos(at)$, then $y'' = -a^2 y$. What is the corresponding differential equation satisfied by $y = A \sinh(at) + B \cosh(at)$?

8. Define $\sinh^{-1}$ and $\cosh^{-1}$ functions. What are their domains? What are their ranges? What are their derivatives?

MISCELLANEOUS EXERCISES

1. Prove the hyperbolic identity

$$\cosh 2x = \cosh^2 x + \sinh^2 x.$$

2. Verify that $\tanh x = \sinh 2x/(1 + \cosh 2x)$.

3. Sketch the curves $y = \cosh x$ and $y = \sinh x$ in one diagram. To each positive value of x corresponds a point P on $y = \sinh x$ and a point Q on $y = \cosh x$. Calculate the limit of the distance PQ as x becomes infinitely large.

4. If $\cosh x = \frac{5}{4}$, find $\sinh x$ and $\tanh x$.

5. If $\operatorname{csch} x = -\frac{9}{40}$, find $\cosh x$ and $\tanh x$.

6. If $\tanh x > \frac{5}{13}$, show that

$$\sinh x > 0.4 \quad \text{and} \quad \operatorname{sech} x < 0.95.$$

7. Let $P(x, y)$ be a point on the curve $y = \tanh x$ (Fig. 12.2b). Let AB be the vertical line segment through P with A and B on the asymptotes of the curve. Let C be a semicircle with AB as diameter. Let L be a line through P perpendicular to AB and cutting C in a point Q. Show that $PQ = \operatorname{sech} x$.

8. Prove that $\sinh 3u = 3 \sinh u + 4 \sinh^3 u$.

9. Find equations of the asymptotes of the hyperbola represented by the equation $y = \tanh (\frac{1}{2} \ln x)$.

10. A particle moves along the x-axis according to one of the following laws:

   (a) $\qquad x = a \cos kt + b \sin kt,$
   (b) $\qquad x = a \cosh kt + b \sinh kt.$

   In both cases, show that the acceleration is proportional to x, but that in the first case it is always directed toward the origin while in the second case it is directed away from the origin.

11. Show that $y = \cosh x$, $\sinh x$, $\cos x$, and $\sin x$ all satisfy the relationship $d^4y/dx^4 = y$.

Find dy/dx in Exercises 12 through 21.

12. $y = \sinh^2 3x$

13. $\tan x = \tanh^2 y$

14. $\sin^{-1} x = \operatorname{sech} y$

15. $\sinh y = \sec x$

16. $\tan^{-1} y = \tanh^{-1} x$

17. $y = \tanh (\ln x)$

18. $x = \cosh (\ln y)$

19. $y = \sinh (\tan^{-1} e^{3x})$

20. $y = \sinh^{-1} (\tan x)$

21. $y^2 + x \cosh y + \sinh^2 x = 50$

Evaluate the integrals in Exercises 22 through 31.

22. $\displaystyle\int \frac{d\theta}{\sinh \theta + \cosh \theta}$

23. $\displaystyle\int \frac{\cosh \theta \, d\theta}{\sinh \theta + \cosh \theta}$

24. $\displaystyle\int \sinh^3 x \, dx$

25. $\displaystyle\int e^x \sinh 2x \, dx$

26. $\displaystyle\int \frac{e^{2x} - 1}{e^{2x} + 1} \, dx$

27. $\displaystyle\int_0^1 \frac{dx}{4 - x^2}$

28. $\displaystyle\int_3^5 \frac{dx}{4 - x^2}$

29. $\displaystyle\int \frac{e^t \, dt}{\sqrt{1 + e^{2t}}}$

30. $\displaystyle\int \frac{\sin x \, dx}{1 - \cos^2 x}$

31. $\displaystyle\int \frac{\sec^2 \theta \, d\theta}{\sqrt{\tan^2 \theta - 1}}$

Sketch the loci in Exercises 32 through 34.

32. $y = \dfrac{1}{2} \ln \dfrac{1 + \tanh x}{1 - \tanh x}$

33. $y = \tan \left(\dfrac{\pi}{2} \tanh x \right)$

34. $\cosh y = 1 + \dfrac{x^2}{2}$

35. If the arc s of the catenary $y = a \cosh (x/a)$ is measured from the lowest point, show that

$$dy/dx = s/a.$$

36. A body starting from rest falls under the attraction of gravity but encounters resistance proportional to the square of its velocity. Show that if the body could continue to fall indefinitely under these same conditions, its velocity would approach a limiting value. Find the distance it would fall in time t.

37. Evaluate the limit, as $x \to \infty$, of $\cosh^{-1} x - \ln x$.

38. Evaluate

$$\lim_{x \to \infty} \int_1^x \left(\frac{1}{\sqrt{1 + t^2}} - \frac{1}{t} \right) dt.$$

VECTORS AND PARAMETRIC EQUATIONS

CHAPTER 13

13.1 PARAMETRIC EQUATIONS IN KINEMATICS

In Newtonian mechanics, the motion of a particle in a plane is usually described by means of a pair of differential equations expressing Newton's second law of motion,*

$$\mathbf{F} = \frac{d(m\mathbf{v})}{dt}. \qquad (1)$$

Here $\mathbf{F}$ is the vector force acting on the particle of mass m at time t and $\mathbf{v}$ is its vector velocity at time t. When the x- and y-components of Eq. (1) are separated, the equivalent equations are

$$F_x = \frac{d(mv_x)}{dt}, \qquad F_y = \frac{d(mv_y)}{dt}. \qquad (2)$$

In addition to these laws of motion, we require a knowledge of the position and velocity of the particle at some given instant. Then the position of the particle at all later instants is determined by the prescribed forces. The result of integrating the second-order differential equations (2) subject to the given initial conditions usually yields equations that determine the x- and y-coordinates of the particle as functions of t:

$$x = f(t), \quad y = g(t). \qquad (3)$$

These equations are called *parametric equations* of the path of the particle and t is called the *parameter*. Equations (3) contain more information about the motion of the particle than does the *Cartesian equation*

$$y = F(x) \qquad (4)$$

that one obtains from (3) by eliminating t. The parametric equations tell *where* the particle goes and *when* it gets to any given place, whereas the Cartesian equation tells only the curve along which the particle travels.

---

* Vectors are indicated by bold-faced Roman letters. In handwritten work, it is customary to indicate them by a small arrow over each letter which represents a vector.

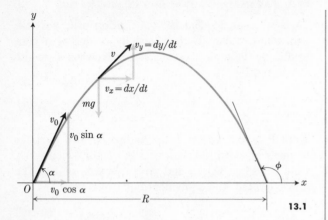

13.1

Example. We shall illustrate these ideas by determining the path of a projectile. Suppose the projectile is fired with an initial velocity v_0 at an angle of elevation α. Assuming that gravity is the only force acting on the projectile, we shall find its motion.

We introduce coordinate axes with origin at the point where the projectile begins its motion, as in Fig. 13.1. The initial conditions may then be taken to be

$$t = 0: \qquad x = 0, \qquad y = 0;$$

$$\frac{dx}{dt} = v_0 \cos \alpha, \qquad \frac{dy}{dt} = v_0 \sin \alpha. \tag{5}$$

The force components at time t, with appropriate sign, are

$$F_x = 0, \quad F_y = -mg,$$

so that the differential equations (2) become

$$0 = m \frac{d^2 x}{dt^2}, \tag{6a}$$

$$-mg = m \frac{d^2 y}{dt^2}. \tag{6b}$$

Each of Eqs. (6) requires two integrations. This introduces a total of four constants of integration. These may be evaluated by using the initial conditions (5). Thus by integration one obtains from (6a)

$$\frac{d^2 x}{dt^2} = 0, \quad \frac{dx}{dt} = c_1, \quad x = c_1 t + c_2, \tag{7a}$$

and from (6b)

$$\frac{d^2 y}{dt^2} = -g, \qquad \frac{dy}{dt} = -gt + c_3,$$

$$y = -\tfrac{1}{2}gt^2 + c_3 t + c_4. \tag{7b}$$

From the initial conditions, we find

$$c_1 = v_0 \cos \alpha, \quad c_2 = 0,$$

$$c_3 = v_0 \sin \alpha, \quad c_4 = 0. \tag{7c}$$

The position of the projectile at time t (seconds, say, after firing) is given by

$$x = (v_0 \cos \alpha) t, \tag{8a}$$

$$y = -\tfrac{1}{2}gt^2 + (v_0 \sin \alpha) t. \tag{8b}$$

For a given angle of elevation α and a given muzzle velocity v_0, the position of the projectile at any time may be determined from the parametric equations (8). The equations may be used to answer such questions as the following:

1. How high does the projectile rise vertically?

2. How far does the projectile travel horizontally?

3. What is the range of the projectile (horizontally) in terms of the angle of elevation? What angle produces the maximum range?

The projectile will attain maximum height when its y velocity component is zero; that is, when

$$\frac{dy}{dt} = -gt + v_0 \sin \alpha = 0$$

or when

$$t = t_m = \frac{v_0 \sin \alpha}{g}.$$

Then

$$y_{\max} = -\tfrac{1}{2}g(t_m)^2 + (v_0 \sin \alpha) t_m = \frac{(v_0 \sin \alpha)^2}{2g}.$$

To find the horizontal range of the projectile, we find the time when it strikes the ground, that is, when $y = 0$. From (8b), we have

$$y = t(-\tfrac{1}{2}gt + v_0 \sin \alpha) = 0$$

when

$$t = 0 \quad \text{or} \quad t = \frac{2v_0 \sin \alpha}{g} = 2t_m.$$

Clearly, $t = 0$ corresponds to the instant when the projectile is fired, so that $t = 2t_m$ gives the range $x = R$:

$$R = v_0 \cos \alpha \, \frac{2v_0 \sin \alpha}{g}$$

$$= \frac{v_0^2}{g} \sin 2\alpha.$$

For a given muzzle velocity, this shows that the maximum range is obtained when $\sin 2\alpha = 1$, that is, when $\alpha = 45°$.

The slope of the path of the projectile at any point may also be found directly from Eqs. (8):

$$\frac{dy}{dx} = \frac{dy/dt}{dx/dt} = \frac{-gt + v_0 \sin \alpha}{v_0 \cos \alpha}.$$

At $y = 0$, $x = R$, we found

$$t = \frac{2v_0 \sin \alpha}{g},$$

and hence

$$\frac{dy}{dx} = \frac{-2v_0 \sin \alpha + v_0 \sin \alpha}{v_0 \cos \alpha}$$

$$= -\tan \alpha.$$

This shows that the angle ϕ (Fig. 13.1) is $\pi - \alpha$, so that the projectile returns to the earth at the same angle as that at which it was fired.

Finally, the Cartesian equation of the path is readily obtained from Eqs. (8); for we need only substitute

$$t = \frac{x}{v_0 \cos \alpha}$$

from (8a) into (8b) to eliminate t and obtain

$$y = -\left(\frac{g}{2v_0^2 \cos^2 \alpha}\right) x^2 + (\tan \alpha)x. \qquad (9)$$

Since this equation is linear in y and quadratic in x, it represents a *parabola*. Thus the path of a projectile *in vacuo* (neglecting air resistance) is a parabola.

When air resistance is taken into account, the differential equations obtained are too complicated for an analytic solution, but they can be integrated numerically using high-speed computers. Against a moving target, in particular, the *time* is also of great importance, so that equations or tables which give x and y in terms of t are preferred over the Cartesian form.

EXERCISES

In Exercises 1 through 4, the projectile is assumed to obey the laws of motion discussed above, in which air resistance is neglected.

1. Find two values of the angle of elevation that will enable a projectile to reach a target on the same level as the gun and 25,000 feet distant from it if the initial velocity is 1000 ft/sec. Determine the times of flight corresponding to these two angles.

2. Show that doubling of the initial velocity of a projectile multiplies both the maximum height and the range by a factor of four.

3. Show that a projectile attains three-quarters of its maximum height in one-half the time required to reach that maximum.

4. Suppose a target moving at the constant rate of a ft/sec is level with and b ft away from a gun at the instant the gun is fired. If the target moves in a horizontal line directly away from the gun, show that the muzzle velocity v_0 and angle of elevation α must satisfy the equation

$$v_0^2 \sin 2\alpha - 2a \, v_0 \sin \alpha - bg = 0,$$

if the projectile is to strike the target.

In Exercises 5 through 7, find parametric equations and sketch the curve described by the point $P(x, y)$ for $t \geq 0$ if its coordinates satisfy the given differential equations and initial conditions.

5. $\dfrac{dx}{dt} = x$, $\quad \dfrac{dy}{dt} = -x^2$; $\quad t = 0$, $x = 1$, $y = -4$

6. $\dfrac{dx}{dt} = y$, $\quad \dfrac{dy}{dt} = y^2$; $\quad t = 0$, $x = 0$, $y = 1$

7. $\dfrac{dx}{dt} = \sqrt{1 - x^2}$, $\quad \dfrac{dy}{dt} = x^2$;

$\qquad t = 0$, $x = 0$, $y = 1$

13.2 PARAMETRIC EQUATIONS IN ANALYTIC GEOMETRY

The solutions of differential equations of motion are not the only ways in which parametric equations arise. For example, we have frequently had occasion to use equations such as

$$x = a \cos \theta, \quad y = a \sin \theta \qquad (1)$$

to represent a circle. Here θ is the parameter and Eqs. (1) are parametric equations of the circle (Fig. 13.2). Similarly

$$x = a \cos \phi, \quad y = b \sin \phi \qquad (2)$$

are parametric equations of an ellipse whose Cartesian equation is

$$\frac{x^2}{a^2} + \frac{y^2}{b^2} = 1.$$

Example 1. The parabola

$$y^2 = 4px \qquad (3)$$

can be parametrized in several ways. One method is to use as parameter the slope

$$t = dy/dx$$

of the tangent to the curve at (x, y) (see Fig. 13.3a). Since

$$2y \frac{dy}{dx} = 4p, \quad \text{or} \quad \frac{dy}{dx} = \frac{2p}{y},$$

the parametric equations in this case are

$$y = \frac{2p}{t}, \quad x = \frac{p}{t^2}. \qquad (4)$$

If we use the parameter defined (Fig. 12.3b) by $m = y/x$, we have

$$y^2 = m^2 x^2 \quad \text{and} \quad y^2 = 4px,$$

which lead to

$$x = \frac{4p}{m^2}, \quad y = \frac{4p}{m} \qquad (5)$$

as the parametric equations.

Sometimes the parametric equations of a locus and the Cartesian equation are not coextensive.

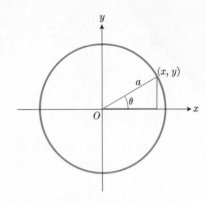

13.2

Example 2. Suppose the parametric equations of a curve are

$$x = \cosh \theta, \quad y = \sinh \theta. \qquad (6)$$

Then the hyperbolic identity

$$\cosh^2 \theta - \sinh^2 \theta = 1$$

enables us to eliminate θ and write

$$x^2 - y^2 = 1 \qquad (7)$$

as the Cartesian equation of the curve. Closer scrutiny, however, shows that Eq. (7) *includes too much.* For $x = \cosh \theta$ is never less than unity, so the parametric equations represent a curve lying wholly to the right of the y-axis, whereas the Cartesian equation (7) represents both the right- and left-hand branches of the hyperbola (Fig. 13.4). The left-hand branch could be excluded by taking only positive values of x. That is,

$$x = \sqrt{1 + y^2} \qquad (8)$$

does represent the same curve as (6).

Example 3. Consider the curve whose parametric equations are

$$x = \cos 2\theta, \quad y = \cos \theta. \qquad (9)$$

This curve is certainly restricted to lie within the square that is determined by the conditions

$$-1 \le x \le 1, \quad -1 \le y \le 1.$$

But we eliminate θ as follows:

$$x = \cos 2\theta = 2 \cos^2 \theta - 1 = 2y^2 - 1.$$

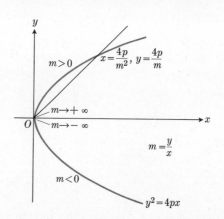

13.3

Thus every point on the locus described by Eqs. (9) also lies on the curve given by

$$x = 2y^2 - 1 \tag{10}$$

and, in addition, is restricted by

$$|x| \leq 1, \quad |y| \leq 1.$$

If we omit these restrictions, Eq. (10) represents the complete parabola

$$y^2 = \tfrac{1}{2}(x + 1)$$

with vertex at $(-1, 0)$ and opening to the right, as shown in Fig. 13.5. The parametric equations, on the other hand, represent only the arc ABC. Referring to Eqs. (9), we readily see that the point starts at $A(1, 1)$ when $\theta = 0$, moves along AB to $B(-1, 0)$ as θ varies from 0 to $\pi/2$, and continues to $C(1, -1)$ as θ increases to π. As θ varies from π to 2π, the point traverses the arc CBA back to A. Since both x and y are periodic functions of θ of period 2π, further variations in θ result in retracing the same portion of the parabola.

The following problem illustrates further how parametric equations may be derived from geometric properties of a curve. Suppose that a wheel of radius a rolls along a horizontal straight line without slipping: Find the locus described by a point on a spoke of the wheel at distance b from its center. Such a curve is called a *trochoid*. When $b = a$, the tracing point is on the circumference of the wheel, and the trochoid in this case is called a *cycloid*.

13.4

13.5

13.6

In Fig. 13.6, we take the x-axis as the line the wheel rolls along, with the y-axis through a low point of the trochoid. Point P describes the curve in question. It is customary to use the angle ϕ through which CP has rotated as the parameter. We introduce $x'y'$-axes parallel to the xy-axes but having their origin at the center of the circle C (Fig. 13.7). If (h, k) are the coordinates of C relative to the xy-axes, then the xy-coordinates of P are related to its $x'y'$-coordinates as follows:

$$x = h + x', \quad y = k + y'. \qquad (11)$$

From the fact that the circle rolls along the x-axis without slipping, we see that the distance OM that the wheel has moved horizontally is just equal to the arc $MN = a\phi$. (Roll the wheel back; then N will fall at the origin O.) The xy-coordinates of C are therefore

$$h = a\phi, \quad k = a. \qquad (12)$$

From Fig. 13.7, we may immediately read

$$x' = b \cos \theta, \quad y' = b \sin \theta,$$

or, since

$$\theta = \frac{3\pi}{2} - \phi,$$

$$x' = -b \sin \phi, \quad y' = -b \cos \phi. \qquad (13)$$

We substitute these results and Eqs. (12) into Eqs. (11) and obtain

$$x = a\phi - b \sin \phi, \quad y = a - b \cos \phi \qquad (14)$$

as parametric equations of the trochoid. The

cycloid (Fig. 13.8a)

$$x = a(\phi - \sin \phi), \quad y = a(1 - \cos \phi), \qquad (15)$$

obtained from (14) by taking $b = a$, is the most important special case of a trochoid.

13.7

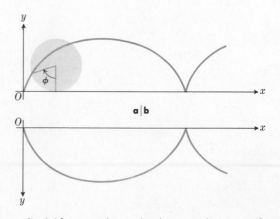

13.8   Cycloid: $x = a(\phi - \sin \phi)$, $y = a(1 - \cos \phi)$.

Note. If we reflect the cycloid and the y-axis across the x-axis, Eqs. (15) still apply and the resulting curve (Fig. 13.8b) has several interesting properties, one of which we shall now discuss without proof. The proofs belong to a branch of mathematics known as the calculus of variations. Much of the fundamental theory of this subject is attributable to the Bernoulli brothers, John and James, who were friendly rivals and stimulated each other with mathematical problems in the form of challenges. One of these, the brachistochrone problem, was: Among all smooth curves joining two given points, find that one along which a bead might slide, subject only to the force of gravity, *in the shortest time*. (*Brachistochrone* is derived from two Greek words that together mean "shortest time.")

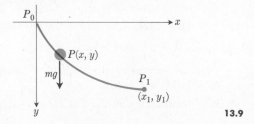

13.9

The two points, labeled P_0 and P_1 in Fig. 13.9, may be taken to lie at the origin and at (x_1, y_1) respectively in a vertical plane. We can formulate the problem in mathematical terms as follows. The kinetic energy of the bead at the start is zero, since its velocity is zero. The work done by gravity in moving the particle from $(0, 0)$ to any point (x, y) is mgy and this must be equal to the change in kinetic energy; that is,

$$mgy = \tfrac{1}{2}mv^2 - \tfrac{1}{2}m(0)^2.$$

Thus the velocity

$$v = ds/dt$$

that the particle has when it reaches $P(x, y)$ is

$$v = \sqrt{2gy}.$$

That is,

$$\frac{ds}{dt} = \sqrt{2gy},$$

or

$$dt = \frac{ds}{\sqrt{2gy}} = \frac{\sqrt{1 + \left(\dfrac{dy}{dx}\right)^2}\, dx}{\sqrt{2gy}}.$$

The time t_1 required for the bead to slide from P_0 to P_1 depends on the particular curve $y = f(x)$ along which it moves; it is given by

$$t_1 = \int_0^{x_1} \sqrt{\frac{1 + (f'(x))^2}{2gf(x)}}\, dx. \tag{16}$$

The problem is *to find the curve $y = f(x)$ that passes through the points $P_0(0, 0)$ and $P_1(x_1, y_1)$ and minimizes the value of the integral in Eq. (16).*

At first sight, one might guess that the straight line joining P_0 and P_1 would also yield the shortest time, but a moment's reflection will cast some doubt on this conjecture. For there may be some gain in time by having the particle start to fall vertically at first, thereby building up its velocity more quickly than if it were to slide along an inclined path. With this increased velocity, one may be able to afford to travel over a longer path and still reach P_1 in a shorter time. The solution of the problem is beyond the present book, but the brachistochrone curve is actually an arc of a cycloid through P_0 and P_1, having a cusp at the origin. [The interested reader is referred to the book *Calculus of Variations* by G. A. Bliss, The Mathematical Association of America (1925), for a discussion of this problem and others belonging to this branch of mathematics.]

If we write Eq. (16) in the equivalent form

$$t_1 = \int \sqrt{\frac{dx^2 + dy^2}{2gy}}$$

and then substitute Eqs. (15) into this, we obtain

$$t_1 = \int_{\phi=0}^{\phi_1} \sqrt{\frac{a^2(2 - 2\cos\phi)}{2ga(1 - \cos\phi)}}\, d\phi$$

$$= \phi_1 \sqrt{\frac{a}{g}}$$

as the time required for the particle to slide from P_0 to P_1. The time required to reach the bottom of the arc is obtained by taking $\phi_1 = \pi$. Now it is a remarkable fact, which we shall soon demonstrate, that the time required to slide along the cycloid from $(0, 0)$ to the lowest point $(a\pi, 2a)$ is the same as the time required for the particle, starting from rest, to slide from *any intermediate point* of the arc, say (x_0, y_0), to $(a\pi, 2a)$. For the latter case, one has

$$v = \sqrt{2g(y - y_0)}$$

13.10

as the velocity at $P(x, y)$, and the time required is

$$T = \int_{\phi_0}^{\pi} \sqrt{\frac{a^2(2 - 2\cos\phi)}{2ag(\cos\phi_0 - \cos\phi)}}\, d\phi$$

$$= \sqrt{\frac{a}{g}} \int_{\phi_0}^{\pi} \sqrt{\frac{1 - \cos\phi}{\cos\phi_0 - \cos\phi}}\, d\phi$$

$$= \sqrt{\frac{a}{g}} \int_{\phi_0}^{\pi} \sqrt{\frac{2\sin^2\frac{\phi}{2}}{\left(2\cos^2\frac{\phi_0}{2} - 1\right) - \left(2\cos^2\frac{\phi}{2} - 1\right)}}\, d\phi$$

$$= 2\sqrt{\frac{a}{g}} \left[-\sin^{-1}\frac{\cos\frac{\phi}{2}}{\cos\frac{\phi_0}{2}} \right]_{\phi_0}^{\pi}$$

$$= 2\sqrt{\frac{1}{g}}(-\sin^{-1} 0 + \sin^{-1} 1) = \pi\sqrt{\frac{a}{g}}.$$

Since this answer is independent of the value of ϕ_0, it follows that the same length of time is required to reach the lowest point on the cycloid no matter where on the arc the particle is released from rest. Thus, in Fig. 13.10, three particles that start at the same time from O, A, and B will reach C simultaneously. In this sense, the cycloid is also a *tautochrone* (meaning "the same time") as well as being a *brachistochrone*.

EXERCISES

In Exercises 1 through 10, sketch the graph of the curve described by the point $P(x, y)$ as the parameter t varies over the domain given. Also determine the Cartesian equation of the curve in each case.

1. $x = \cos t$, $y = \sin t$, $0 \le t \le 2\pi$
2. $x = \cos 2t$, $y = \sin t$, $0 \le t \le 2\pi$
3. $x = \sec t$, $y = \tan t$, $-\pi/2 < t < \pi/2$
4. $x = 2 + 4\sin t$, $y = 3 - 2\cos t$, $0 \le t \le 2\pi$
5. $x = 2t + 3$, $y = 4t^2 - 9$, $-\infty < t < \infty$
6. $x = \cosh t$, $y = \sinh t$, $0 \le t < \infty$
7. $x = 2 + 1/t$, $y = 2 - t$, $0 < t < \infty$
8. $x = t + 1$, $y = t^2 + 4$, $0 \le t < \infty$
9. $x = t^2 + t$, $y = t^2 - t$, $-\infty < t < \infty$
10. $x = 3 + 2\operatorname{sech} t$, $y = 4 - 3\tanh t$, $-\infty < t < \infty$

11. Find parametric equations of the semicircle
$$x^2 + y^2 = a^2, \quad y > 0,$$
using as parameter the slope $t = dy/dx$ of the tangent to the curve at (x, y).

12. Find parametric equations of the semicircle
$$x^2 + y^2 = a^2, \quad y > 0,$$
using as parameter the variable θ defined by the equation $x = a\tanh\theta$.

13. Find parametric equations of the circle
$$x^2 + y^2 = a^2,$$
using as parameter the arc length s measured counterclockwise from the point $(a, 0)$ to the point (x, y).

14. Find parametric equations of the catenary
$$y = a\cosh x/a,$$
using as parameter the length of arc s from the point $(0, a)$ to the point (x, y), with the sign of s taken to be the same as the sign of x.

15. If a string wound around a fixed circle is unwound while held taut in the plane of the circle, its end traces an *involute* of the circle. Let the fixed circle be located with its center at the origin O and have radius a. Let the initial position of the tracing point P be $A(a, 0)$ and let the unwound portion of the string PT be tangent to the circle at T. Derive parametric equations of the involute, using the angle AOT as the parameter ϕ.

16. When a circle rolls externally on the circumference of a second, fixed circle, any point P on the circumference of the rolling circle describes an *epicycloid*. Let the fixed circle have its center at the origin O and have radius a. Let the radius of the rolling circle be b and let the initial position of the tracing

point P be $A(a, 0)$. Determine parametric equations of the epicycloid, using as parameter the angle θ from the positive x-axis to the line of centers.

17. When a circle rolls on the inside of a fixed circle any point P on the circumference of the rolling circle describes a *hypocycloid*. Let the fixed circle be $x^2 + y^2 = a^2$, let the radius of the rolling circle be b, and let the initial position of the tracing point P be $A(a, 0)$. Use the angle θ from the positive x-axis to the line of centers as parameter and determine parametric equations of the hypocycloid. In particular, if $b = a/4$, show that

$$x = a \cos^3 \theta, \quad y = a \sin^3 \theta.$$

18. Find the length of one arch of the cycloid

$$x = a(\phi - \sin \phi), \quad y = a(1 - \cos \phi).$$

19. Show that the slope of the cycloid

$$z = a(\phi - \sin \phi), \quad y = a(1 - \cos \phi)$$

is $dy/dx = \cot \phi/2$. In particular, the tangent to the cycloid is vertical when ϕ is 0 or 2π.

20. Show that the slope of the trochoid

$$x = a\phi - b \sin \phi, \quad y = a - b \cos \phi$$

is always finite if $b < a$.

21. There exists a bell-shaped curve that can be constructed as follows: Let C be a circle of radius a having its center at $(0, a)$ on the y-axis. The variable line OA through the origin O intersects the line $y = 2a$ in the point A and intersects the circle in the point B. A point P on the curve is now located by taking the intersection of lines through A and B parallel to the y- and x-axes respectively. Find parametric equations of the curve, using as parameter the angle θ from the x-axis to the line OA. Also find the Cartesian equation.

13.3 VECTOR COMPONENTS AND THE UNIT VECTORS i AND j

Some physical quantities are completely determined when their magnitudes, in terms of specific units, are given. Such quantities are called *scalars*, and are exemplified by mass and length. Other quantities, like forces and velocities, in which the direc-

tion as well as the magnitude is important, are called *vectors*. It is customary to represent a vector by a directed line segment whose direction represents the direction of the vector and whose length (in terms of some chosen unit of length) represents the magnitude.

The most satisfactory algebra of vectors is based on a representation of each vector in terms of its components parallel to the axes of a Cartesian coordinate system. This is accomplished by using the same unit of length on both the x- and y-axes, with unit vectors along these axes used as basic components in terms of which every vector in the plane may be expressed. Thus, in Fig. 13.11, the vector from $(0, 0)$ to $(1, 0)$ is the unit vector $\mathbf{i}$, while $\mathbf{j}$ is the unit vector from $(0, 0)$ to $(0, 1)$. Then $a\mathbf{i}$, a being a scalar, represents a vector parallel to the x-axis, having magnitude $|a|$ and pointing to the right if a is positive, and to the left if a is negative. Similarly, $b\mathbf{j}$ is a vector parallel to the y-axis and having the same sense as $\mathbf{j}$ or the opposite sense, depending on the sign of b.

We shall ordinarily deal with "free vectors," meaning that a vector is free to move about under parallel displacements. We say that two vectors are *equal* provided they have the same direction and the same magnitude. The same condition may be expressed algebraically by saying that

$$a\mathbf{i} + b\mathbf{j} = a'\mathbf{i} + b'\mathbf{j} \quad \text{if and only if} \quad a = a', b = b'.$$

That is, two vectors are equal if and only if their corresponding components are equal. Thus, in Fig. 13.11, the vector $\overrightarrow{AB}$ is equal to $a\mathbf{i}$, and the vector $\overrightarrow{OP}$ from $(0, 0)$ to the point $(a, 0)$ on the x-axis is also equal to $a\mathbf{i}$.

13.11

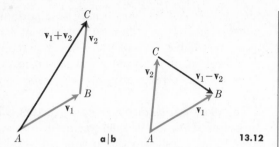

13.12

Addition

Two vectors $\mathbf{v}_1$ and $\mathbf{v}_2$ are *added* by drawing a vector $\mathbf{v}_1$, say from A to B in Fig. 13.12(a), and then a vector equal to $\mathbf{v}_2$ starting from the terminal point of $\mathbf{v}_1$; thus $\mathbf{v}_2 = \overrightarrow{BC}$ in Fig. 13.12(a). The sum $\mathbf{v}_1 + \mathbf{v}_2$ is then the vector from the starting point A of $\mathbf{v}_1$ to the terminal point C of $\mathbf{v}_2$:

$$\mathbf{v}_1 = \overrightarrow{AB}, \quad \mathbf{v}_2 = \overrightarrow{BC},$$

$$\therefore \mathbf{v}_1 + \mathbf{v}_2 = \overrightarrow{AB} + \overrightarrow{BC} = \overrightarrow{AC}.$$

If we apply this principle to the vectors $a\mathbf{i}$ and $b\mathbf{j}$ in Fig. 13.11, we see that $a\mathbf{i} + b\mathbf{j}$ is the vector hypotenuse of a right triangle whose vector sides are $a\mathbf{i}$ and $b\mathbf{j}$ respectively. If the vectors $\mathbf{v}_1$ and $\mathbf{v}_2$ are given in terms of components

$$\mathbf{v}_1 = a_1\mathbf{i} + b_1\mathbf{j},$$

$$\mathbf{v}_2 = a_2\mathbf{i} + b_2\mathbf{j},$$

then

$$\mathbf{v}_1 + \mathbf{v}_2 = (a_1 + a_2)\mathbf{i} + (b_1 + b_2)\mathbf{j} \qquad (1)$$

has x- and y-components obtained by adding the x- and y-components of $\mathbf{v}_1$ and $\mathbf{v}_2$.

Subtraction

To *subtract* one vector $\mathbf{v}_2$ from another vector $\mathbf{v}_1$ geometrically, we draw them both from a common initial point and then draw the vector from the tip of $\mathbf{v}_2$ to the tip of $\mathbf{v}_1$. Thus in Fig. 13.12(b), we have

$$\mathbf{v}_1 = \overrightarrow{AB}, \quad \mathbf{v}_2 = \overrightarrow{AC},$$

and

$$\mathbf{v}_1 - \mathbf{v}_2 = -\mathbf{v}_2 + \mathbf{v}_1 = \overrightarrow{CA} + \overrightarrow{AB} = \overrightarrow{CB}.$$

In terms of components, vector subtraction follows the simple algebraic law

$$\mathbf{v}_1 - \mathbf{v}_2 = (a_1 - a_2)\mathbf{i} + (b_1 - b_2)\mathbf{j},$$

which says that corresponding components are subtracted.

Multiplication by scalars

The algebraic operation of multiplying a vector $\mathbf{v} = a\mathbf{i} + b\mathbf{j}$ by a scalar c is also simple:

$$c(a\mathbf{i} + b\mathbf{j}) = (ca)\mathbf{i} + (cb)\mathbf{j}.$$

Geometrically, $c\mathbf{v}$ is a vector whose length is $|c|$ times the length of $\mathbf{v}$ and whose direction is the same as that of $\mathbf{v}$ if c is positive, and is opposite to that of $\mathbf{v}$ if c is negative. Thus $3\mathbf{v}$ has the same sense as $\mathbf{v}$ and is three times as long; while $-2\mathbf{v}$ is twice as long as $\mathbf{v}$ but is directed in the opposite sense (Fig. 13.13).

13.13

The unit vectors $\mathbf{i}$ and $\mathbf{j}$ serve the useful purpose of allowing us to keep the components separated from one another when we operate on the vectors algebraically.

The length of the vector $\mathbf{v}$ is usually denoted by $|\mathbf{v}|$, which is read "magnitude of v." Reference to Fig. 13.11 shows that $\mathbf{v} = a\mathbf{i} + b\mathbf{j}$ is the hypotenuse of a right triangle whose legs have lengths $|a|$ and $|b|$ respectively. Hence we may apply the theorem of Pythagoras to obtain

$$|a\mathbf{i} + b\mathbf{j}| = \sqrt{a^2 + b^2}. \qquad (2)$$

Zero vector

Any vector whose length is zero is called the *zero vector*, $\mathbf{0}$. The vector

$$a\mathbf{i} + b\mathbf{j} = \mathbf{0},$$

if and only if

$$a = b = 0.$$

Unit vector

Any vector **u** whose length is equal to the unit of length used along the coordinate axes is called a *unit vector*. If **u** is a unit vector obtained by rotating the unit vector **i** through an angle θ in the positive direction, then (see Fig. 13.14) **u** has a horizontal component

$$u_x = \cos \theta$$

and a vertical component

$$u_y = \sin \theta,$$

so that

$$\mathbf{u} = \mathbf{i} \cos \theta + \mathbf{j} \sin \theta. \qquad (3)$$

If we allow the angle θ in Eq. (3) to vary from 0 to 2π, say, then the point P traces out the unit circle $x^2 + y^2 = 1$ precisely once in the counterclockwise direction.

Example. As an illustration of how vector methods may be applied to problems in geometry, we shall derive parametric equations of the involute of a circle. This is the locus described by the endpoint P of a string that is held taut as it is unwound from the circle. In Fig. 12.15, the origin is taken at the center of the circle whose radius is a. The x-axis passes through the point A where P started when the string was all wound onto the circle. The figure illustrates the position of P after a length of string

$$TP = \text{arc } AT = a\theta$$

has been unwound. The line TP is drawn tangent to the circle, since the string is held taut as it is unwound. Now the vector from the origin O to the point P is simply

$$\overrightarrow{OP} = \mathbf{i}x + \mathbf{j}y. \qquad (4)$$

On the other hand, the same vector is also given by

$$\overrightarrow{OP} = \overrightarrow{OT} + \overrightarrow{TP}, \qquad (5)$$

and if we express the right-hand side in terms of the parameter θ, we may equate the two right-hand sides of (4) and (5) and separate the components to obtain x and y in terms of θ. Now

$$\overrightarrow{OT} = a\mathbf{u}_1 \quad \text{and} \quad \overrightarrow{TP} = (a\theta)\mathbf{u}_2,$$

where $\mathbf{u}_1$ and $\mathbf{u}_2$ are unit vectors making angles θ and $\theta + 3\pi/2$ respectively with the x-axis. (See Fig. 13.16.)

13.14

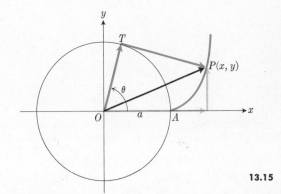

13.15

13.16

Then, applying (3), we have

$$\mathbf{u}_1 = \mathbf{i} \cos \theta + \mathbf{j} \sin \theta$$

and

$$\mathbf{u}_2 = \mathbf{i} \cos \left(\theta + \frac{3\pi}{2} \right) + \mathbf{j} \sin \left(\theta + \frac{3\pi}{2} \right)$$
$$= \mathbf{i} \sin \theta - \mathbf{j} \cos \theta.$$

Therefore

$$\overrightarrow{OP} = a\mathbf{u}_1 + (a\theta)\mathbf{u}_2$$
$$= a(\mathbf{i} \cos \theta + \mathbf{j} \sin \theta) + a\theta(\mathbf{i} \sin \theta - \mathbf{j} \cos \theta)$$
$$= a\,(\cos \theta + \theta \sin \theta)\mathbf{i} + a\,(\sin \theta - \theta \cos \theta)\mathbf{j}.$$

We equate this with $x\mathbf{i} + y\mathbf{j}$ and, since corresponding components must be equal, we obtain the parametric equations

$$\begin{aligned} x &= a\,(\cos \theta + \theta \sin \theta), \\ y &= a\,(\sin \theta - \theta \cos \theta). \end{aligned} \qquad (6)$$

EXERCISES

In Exercises 1 through 10, express each of the vectors in the form $a\mathbf{i} + b\mathbf{j}$. Indicate all quantities graphically.

1. $\overrightarrow{P_1P_2}$, if P_1 is the point $(1, 3)$ and P_2 is the point $(2, -1)$

2. $\overrightarrow{OP_3}$, if O is the origin and P_3 is the midpoint of the vector $\overrightarrow{P_1P_2}$ joining $P_1(2, -1)$ and $P_2(-4, 3)$

3. The vector from the point $A(2, 3)$ to the origin

4. The sum of the vectors $\overrightarrow{AB}$ and $\overrightarrow{CD}$, given the four points $A(1, -1)$, $B(2, 0)$, $C(-1, 3)$, and $D(-2, 2)$

5. A unit vector making an angle of 30° with the positive x-axis

6. The unit vector obtained by rotating $\mathbf{j}$ through 120° in the clockwise direction

7. A unit vector having the same direction as the vector $3\mathbf{i} - 4\mathbf{j}$

8. A unit vector tangent to the curve $y = x^2$ at the point $(2, 4)$

9. A unit vector normal to the curve $y = x^2$ at the point $P(2, 4)$ and pointing from P toward the concave side of the curve (that is, an "inner" normal)

10. A unit vector tangent to the involute of a circle whose parametric equations are given in Eq. (6)

Find the lengths of each of the following vectors and the angle that each makes with the positive x-axis.

11. $\mathbf{i} + \mathbf{j}$ 12. $2\mathbf{i} - 3\mathbf{j}$ 13. $\sqrt{3}\,\mathbf{i} + \mathbf{j}$
14. $-2\mathbf{i} + 3\mathbf{j}$ 15. $5\mathbf{i} + 12\mathbf{j}$ 16. $-5\mathbf{i} - 12\mathbf{j}$

17. Use vector methods to determine parametric equations for the trochoid of Fig. 13.6, by taking

$$\mathbf{R} = \overrightarrow{OP} = \overrightarrow{OM} + \overrightarrow{MC} + \overrightarrow{CP}.$$

18. Let A, B, C, D be the vertices, in order, of a quadrilateral. Let A', B', C', D' be the midpoints of the sides AB, BC, CD, and DA, in order. Prove that $A'B'C'D'$ is a parallelogram.

   Hint. First show that $\overrightarrow{A'B'} = \overrightarrow{D'C'} = \frac{1}{2}\overrightarrow{AC}$.

19. Using vectors, show that the diagonals of a parallelogram bisect each other.

   Method. Let A be one vertex and let M and N be the midpoints of the diagonals. Then show that $\overrightarrow{AM} = \overrightarrow{AN}$.

13.4 VELOCITY AND ACCELERATION

We shall be interested in applications of vectors to problems in physics. For applications to *statics*, we need only a knowledge of the *algebra* of vectors. But for applications to *dynamics*, we also require a knowledge of the *calculus* of vectors.

Position vector

Suppose the point P moves along a curve in the xy-plane, and suppose we know its position at any time t. This means that the motion of P is described by a pair of functions f and g:

$$x = f(t), \quad y = g(t). \qquad (1)$$

The vector from the origin to P is customarily called the *position vector* of P, although it might be appropriate to call it the "radar" vector. This vector is a function of t given by

$$\mathbf{R} = \mathbf{i}x + \mathbf{j}y, \qquad (2a)$$

or

$$\mathbf{R} = \mathbf{i}f(t) + \mathbf{j}g(t). \qquad (2b)$$

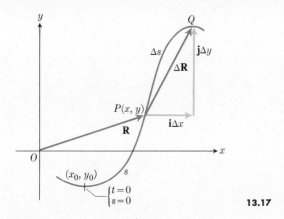

13.17

Velocity vector

We now raise the question as to what physical meaning we might attach to the *derivative* of **R** with respect to t. Mathematically, we have already *defined* the derivative as

$$\frac{d\mathbf{R}}{dt} = \lim_{\Delta t \to 0} \frac{\Delta \mathbf{R}}{\Delta t}, \qquad (3)$$

where **R** is given by (2a) and

$$\mathbf{R} + \Delta \mathbf{R} = \mathbf{i}(x + \Delta x) + \mathbf{j}(y + \Delta y). \qquad (4)$$

Here $P(x, y)$ represents the position of the particle at time t, while $Q(x + \Delta x, y + \Delta y)$ gives its position at time $t + \Delta t$. By subtracting (2a) from (4), we obtain

$$\Delta \mathbf{R} = \mathbf{i}\,\Delta x + \mathbf{j}\,\Delta y, \qquad (5)$$

which is the vector $\overrightarrow{PQ}$ in Fig. 13.17. The remaining calculations needed to give $d\mathbf{R}/dt$ proceed as follows:

$$\frac{\Delta \mathbf{R}}{\Delta t} = \mathbf{i}\frac{\Delta x}{\Delta t} + \mathbf{j}\frac{\Delta y}{\Delta t},$$

$$\lim_{\Delta t \to 0} \frac{\Delta \mathbf{R}}{\Delta t} = \lim_{\Delta t \to 0} \left(\mathbf{i}\frac{\Delta x}{\Delta t} + \mathbf{j}\frac{\Delta y}{\Delta t} \right)$$

$$= \mathbf{i} \lim_{\Delta t \to 0} \frac{\Delta x}{\Delta t} + \mathbf{j} \lim_{\Delta t \to 0} \frac{\Delta y}{\Delta t},$$

$$\frac{d\mathbf{R}}{dt} = \mathbf{i}\frac{dx}{dt} + \mathbf{j}\frac{dy}{dt}. \qquad (6)$$

The result (6) is equivalent to what would be obtained by differentiating both sides of (2a) with

respect to t, holding **i** and **j** constant. The geometric significance of (6) may be learned by calculating the direction and the magnitude of this vector:

$$\text{slope of } \frac{d\mathbf{R}}{dt} = \frac{\text{rise}}{\text{run}} = \frac{dy/dt}{dx/dt} = \frac{dy}{dx},$$

$$\text{magnitude of } \frac{d\mathbf{R}}{dt} = \left| \frac{d\mathbf{R}}{dt} \right| = \left| \mathbf{i}\frac{dx}{dt} + \mathbf{j}\frac{dy}{dt} \right| \qquad (7)$$

$$= \sqrt{\left(\frac{dx}{dt}\right)^2 + \left(\frac{dy}{dt}\right)^2} = \left| \frac{ds}{dt} \right|.$$

Here s represents arc length along the curve measured from some starting point (x_0, y_0).

If we draw a vector equal to $d\mathbf{R}/dt$, placing its initial point at P, the resulting vector will

(a) be tangent to the curve at P, since its slope equals dy/dx, which is the same as the slope of the curve at P, and

(b) have magnitude $= |ds/dt|$, which gives the instantaneous speed of the particle at P.

Thus, physically, the vector $d\mathbf{R}/dt$, when drawn from P, is a suitable representation of the *velocity vector*, which has the same two properties (a) and (b).

We may now summarize by saying that if we differentiate the position vector

$$\mathbf{R} = \mathbf{i}x + \mathbf{j}y$$

with respect to time, the result gives the *velocity vector*

$$\mathbf{v} = \frac{d\mathbf{R}}{dt} = \mathbf{i}\frac{dx}{dt} + \mathbf{j}\frac{dy}{dt}.$$

It is customary to think of the velocity vector as being drawn at the point P.

Acceleration

The acceleration vector **a** is obtained from **v** by a further differentiation:

$$\mathbf{a} = \frac{d\mathbf{v}}{dt} = \mathbf{i}\frac{d^2x}{dt^2} + \mathbf{j}\frac{d^2y}{dt^2}. \qquad (8)$$

For a particle of constant mass m moving under the action of an applied force **F**, Newton's second law of motion states that

$$\mathbf{F} = m\mathbf{a}. \qquad (9)$$

Since one ordinarily visualizes the force vector as being *applied at P*, it is customary to adopt the same viewpoint about the acceleration vector **a**.

Example. A particle $P(x, y)$ moves on the hyperbola

$$x = r \cosh \omega t, \quad y = r \sinh \omega t, \qquad (10)$$

where r and ω are positive constants. (See Fig. 13.18.) Then

$$\mathbf{R} = \mathbf{i}(r \cosh \omega t) + \mathbf{j}(r \sinh \omega t),$$

$$\mathbf{v} = \frac{d\mathbf{R}}{dt} = \mathbf{i}(\omega r \sinh \omega t) + \mathbf{j}(\omega r \cosh \omega t),$$

$$\mathbf{a} = \mathbf{i}(\omega^2 r \cosh \omega t) + \mathbf{j}(\omega^2 r \sinh \omega t)$$

$$= \omega^2 \mathbf{R}.$$

This means that the force $\mathbf{F} = m\mathbf{a} = m\omega^2\mathbf{R}$ has a magnitude

$$m\omega^2|\mathbf{R}| = m\omega^2|\overrightarrow{OP}|,$$

which is directly proportional to the distance OP, and that its direction is the same as the direction of **R**. Thus the force is directed away from O.

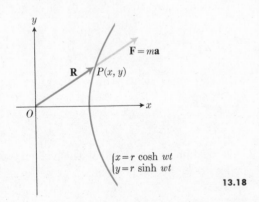

$$\begin{cases} x = r \cosh wt \\ y = r \sinh wt \end{cases}$$

13.18

The next example illustrates how we obtain the path of motion by integrating Eq. (9) when the force **F** is a given function of time, and the initial position and initial velocity of the particle are given. In general the force **F** may depend upon the position of P as well as on the time, and the problem of integrating the differential equations so obtained is usually discussed in textbooks on that subject. (For example, see Martin and Reissner, *Elementary Differential Equations*, Addison-Wesley, 1961.)

Problem. (See Fig. 13.19.) The force acting on a particle P of mass m is given as a function of t by

$$\mathbf{F} = \mathbf{i} \cos t + \mathbf{j} \sin t.$$

If the particle starts at the point $(c, 0)$ with initial velocity $v_0\mathbf{j}$ perpendicular to the x-axis, find the curve it describes.

Solution. If we denote the position vector by

$$\mathbf{R} = \mathbf{i}x + \mathbf{j}y,$$

we may restate the problem as follows. Find **R** if

$$\mathbf{F} = m \frac{d^2\mathbf{R}}{dt^2} = \mathbf{i} \cos t + \mathbf{j} \sin t \qquad (11)$$

and if, at $t = 0$,

$$\mathbf{R} = \mathbf{i}c, \quad \frac{d\mathbf{R}}{dt} = \mathbf{j}v_0. \qquad (12)$$

In (11) we let $\mathbf{v} = d\mathbf{R}/dt$, and separate the variables to obtain

$$m \, d\mathbf{v} = (\mathbf{i} \cos t + \mathbf{j} \sin t) \, dt.$$

Integrating this, we have

$$m\mathbf{v} = m \frac{d\mathbf{R}}{dt} = \mathbf{i} \sin t - \mathbf{j} \cos t + \mathbf{C}_1, \qquad (13)$$

where the constant of integration is a *vector* denoted by $\mathbf{C}_1$. The value of $\mathbf{C}_1$ may be found by using the initial velocity, the right-hand equation in (12), in Eq. (13), with $t = 0$:

$$m\mathbf{j}v_0 = -\mathbf{j} + \mathbf{C}_1,$$

$$\mathbf{C}_1 = (mv_0 + 1)\mathbf{j}.$$

Substituting this into (13), we have

$$m \frac{d\mathbf{R}}{dt} = \mathbf{i} \sin t + (mv_0 + 1 - \cos t)\mathbf{j}.$$

Another integration gives

$$m\mathbf{R} = -\mathbf{i} \cos t + \mathbf{j}(mv_0 t + t - \sin t) + \mathbf{C}_2.$$

The initial condition $\mathbf{R} = \mathbf{i}c$ (Eq. 12) enables us to evaluate $\mathbf{C}_2$:

$$mc\mathbf{i} = -\mathbf{i} + \mathbf{C}_2, \quad \mathbf{C}_2 = \mathbf{i}(mc + 1),$$

so that the position vector $\mathbf{R}$ is given by

$$\mathbf{R} = \frac{1}{m}\,[\mathbf{i}(mc + 1 - \cos t) + \mathbf{j}(mv_0t + t - \sin t)].$$

The parametric equations of the curve are found by equating components of this expression for $\mathbf{R}$ with

$$\mathbf{R} = \mathbf{i}x + \mathbf{j}y,$$

which gives

$$x = c + \frac{1 - \cos t}{m}, \quad y = v_0t + \frac{t - \sin t}{m}.$$

13.19

EXERCISES

In Exercises 1 through 8, $\mathbf{R} = \mathbf{i}x + \mathbf{j}y$ is the vector from the origin to the moving point $P(x, y)$ at time t. Find the velocity and acceleration vectors for any t. Also find these vectors and the speed at the particular instant given.

1. $\mathbf{R} = (a\cos\omega t)\mathbf{i} + (a\sin\omega t)\mathbf{j}$,
   a and ω being positive constants, $t = \pi/(3\omega)$

2. $\mathbf{R} = (2\cos t)\mathbf{i} + (3\sin t)\mathbf{j}$, $\quad t = \pi/4$

3. $\mathbf{R} = (t + 1)\mathbf{i} + (t^2 - 1)\mathbf{j}$, $\quad t = 2$

4. $\mathbf{R} = (\cos 2t)\mathbf{i} + (2\sin t)\mathbf{j}$, $\quad t = 0$

5. $\mathbf{R} = e^t\mathbf{i} + e^{-2t}\mathbf{j}$, $\quad t = \ln 3$

6. $\mathbf{R} = (\sec t)\mathbf{i} + (\tan t)\mathbf{j}$, $\quad t = \pi/6$

7. $\mathbf{R} = (\cosh 3t)\mathbf{i} + (2\sinh t)\mathbf{j}$, $\quad t = 0$

8. $\mathbf{R} = [\ln(t + 1)]\mathbf{i} + t^2\mathbf{j}$, $\quad t = 1$

9. If the force that acts on a particle P of mass m is $F = -mg\mathbf{j}$, where m and g are constants, and the particle starts from the origin with velocity

$$\mathbf{v}_0 = (v_0\cos\alpha)\mathbf{i} + (v_0\sin\alpha)\mathbf{j}$$

   at time $t = 0$, find the vector $\mathbf{R} = \mathbf{i}x + \mathbf{j}y$ from the origin to P at time t.

10. Exercise 9 describes the motion of a projectile *in vacuo*. If the projectile encounters a resistance pro-

portional to the velocity, the force is

$$\mathbf{F} = -mg\mathbf{j} - k\frac{d\mathbf{R}}{dt}.$$

Show that one integration of $\mathbf{F} = md^2\mathbf{R}/dt^2$ leads to the differential equation

$$\frac{d\mathbf{R}}{dt} + \frac{k}{m}\mathbf{R} = \mathbf{v}_0 - gt\mathbf{j}.$$

(This differential equation can in turn be integrated by means of the following device: Multiply both sides of the equation by $e^{(k/m)t}$. Then the left-hand side is the derivative of the product $\mathbf{R}e^{(k/m)t}$ and both sides can be integrated.)

13.5 TANGENTIAL VECTORS

As the point P moves along a given curve in the xy-plane, we may imagine its position as being specified by the length of arc s from some arbitrarily chosen reference point P_0 on the curve. The vector

$$\mathbf{R} = \mathbf{i}x + \mathbf{j}y$$

from O to $P(x, y)$ is therefore a function of s, and we shall now investigate the properties of $d\mathbf{R}/ds$. To this end, let P have coordinates (x, y) corresponding to the value s, while $Q(x + \Delta x, y + \Delta y)$ corresponds to $s + \Delta s$. Then

$$\frac{\Delta\mathbf{R}}{\Delta s} = \mathbf{i}\frac{\Delta x}{\Delta s} + \mathbf{j}\frac{\Delta y}{\Delta s} = \frac{PQ}{\Delta s} \tag{1}$$

is a *vector* whose magnitude is chord PQ divided by arc PQ, and this approaches unity as $\Delta s \to 0$. Hence

$$\frac{d\mathbf{R}}{ds} = \lim_{\Delta s \to 0}\frac{\Delta\mathbf{R}}{\Delta s} \tag{2}$$

is a *unit* vector. The *direction* of this unit vector is the limiting direction approached by the direction of $\Delta\mathbf{R}/\Delta s$ as $\Delta s \to 0$. Now

$$\frac{\Delta\mathbf{R}}{\Delta s} = \frac{\overrightarrow{PQ}}{\Delta s}$$

has the same direction as $\overrightarrow{PQ}$ when (a) Δs is positive, or else it has the same direction as $\overrightarrow{QP}$ when (b) Δs is negative. Figure 13.20(a, b) illustrates these two cases and shows that in *either* case, $\Delta\mathbf{R}/\Delta s$ is directed along the chord through P and Q and that it points in the direction of increasing s [that is, upward to the right, although ΔR points downward and to the left in Fig. 13.20(b).] As $\Delta s \to 0$ and $Q \to P$, the direction of the chord through P and Q approaches the direction of the *tangent* to the curve at P. Thus the limiting direction of $\Delta R/\Delta s$, in other words the *direction of* $d\mathbf{R}/ds$, is along the *tangent to the curve at* P, and its sense is that which points in the direction of increasing arc length s (that is, away from P_0 when s is positive, or toward P_0 when s is negative). Hence

$$\frac{d\mathbf{R}}{ds} = \mathbf{T} \qquad (3)$$

is a *unit vector* which is *tangent to the curve at* P. (See Fig. 13.21.)

If we let $\Delta s \to 0$ in Eq. (1), we find that

$$\frac{d\mathbf{R}}{ds} = \mathbf{i}\frac{dx}{ds} + \mathbf{j}\frac{dy}{ds}, \qquad (4)$$

and this may be used to find $\mathbf{T}$ at any point of a curve whose equation is given.

Problem 1. (See Fig. 13.22.) Find the unit vector $\mathbf{T}$ tangent to the circle

$$x = a\cos\theta, \quad y = a\sin\theta,$$

at any point $P(x, y)$.

Solution. From the equations of the curve, we have

$$dx = -a\sin\theta\, d\theta, \quad dy = a\cos\theta\, d\theta,$$

and

$$ds^2 = dx^2 + dy^2 = a^2(\sin^2\theta + \cos^2\theta)\, d\theta^2$$
$$= a^2\, d\theta^2,$$

so that $ds = \pm a\, d\theta$.

If we measure arc length in the counterclockwise direction, with $s = 0$ at $(a, 0)$, s will be an increasing function of θ, so the $+$-sign should be taken: $ds = a\, d\theta$. Then

$$\mathbf{T} = \frac{d\mathbf{R}}{ds} = \mathbf{i}\frac{dx}{ds} + \mathbf{j}\frac{dy}{ds}$$

$$= \mathbf{i}\left(\frac{-a\sin\theta\, d\theta}{a\, d\theta}\right) + \mathbf{j}\left(\frac{a\cos\theta\, d\theta}{a\, d\theta}\right)$$

$$= -\mathbf{i}\sin\theta + \mathbf{j}\cos\theta.$$

a|b

13.20

13.21

13.22

EXERCISES

In Exercises 1 through 5, $\mathbf{R} = \mathbf{i}x + \mathbf{j}y$ is the vector from the origin O to $P(x, y)$. For each of these motions, find the unit tangent vector $\mathbf{T} = d\mathbf{R}/ds$.

1. $\mathbf{R} = 2\mathbf{i}\cos t + 2\mathbf{j}\sin t$ 2. $\mathbf{R} = e^t\mathbf{i} + t^2\mathbf{j}$

3. $\mathbf{R} = (\cos^3 t)\mathbf{i} + (\sin^3 t)\mathbf{j}$

4. $\mathbf{R} = \mathbf{i}x + \mathbf{j}x^2$

5. $\mathbf{R} = (\cos 2t)\mathbf{i} + (2\cos t)\mathbf{j}$

13.6 CURVATURE AND NORMAL VECTORS

Our next step is to consider the rate of change of the unit tangent vector $\mathbf{T}$ as P moves along the curve. Of course the length of $\mathbf{T}$ is constant, always being equal to unity. But the direction of $\mathbf{T}$ changes, since it is tangent to the curve and this tangent changes direction from point to point unless the curve is a straight line.

Motion in a plane

We may specify the direction of $\mathbf{T}$ by means of the angle ϕ between the x-axis and $\mathbf{T}$ if the motion is in the xy-plane (see Fig. 13.23). The rate of change of this slope angle ϕ with respect to arc length s (measured in radians per unit of length) is taken as the mathematical *definition of the curvature* of the curve at P. The Greek letter κ (kappa) is used to denote curvature, and its definition is given by the equation

$$\kappa = \frac{d\phi}{ds}, \tag{1}$$

where

$$\tan \phi = \frac{dy}{dx}, \quad ds = \pm\sqrt{dx^2 + dy^2}.^*$$

---

*There is great merit in using as an alternate definition for (1): $\kappa = |d\phi/ds|$. Equation (2a) then contains no ambiguous sign in the numerator. Instead, the numerator is $|d^2y/dx^2|$. Such a definition renders the problems of deciding on the appropriate sign for κ immaterial. If such a definition is adopted, similar modification should be made in the definition for ρ, page 387.

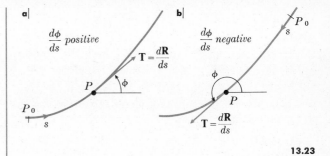

13.23

13.24

One may derive a formula for κ from the equations above in a straightforward manner:

$$\phi = \tan^{-1}\frac{dy}{dx}, \quad \frac{d\phi}{dx} = \frac{\dfrac{d^2y}{dx^2}}{1 + \left(\dfrac{dy}{dx}\right)^2},$$

and

$$\frac{ds}{dx} = \pm\sqrt{1 + \left(\frac{dy}{dx}\right)^2},$$

so that

$$\kappa = \frac{d\phi}{ds} = \frac{d\phi/dx}{ds/dx} = \frac{\pm\dfrac{d^2y}{dx^2}}{\left[1 + \left(\dfrac{dy}{dx}\right)^2\right]^{3/2}}. \tag{2a}$$

The ambiguous sign in (2a) is plus if ds/dx is positive, that is, if s increases as we move along the curve from left to right (as on the lower half of the circle in Fig. 13.22). But the ambiguous sign is minus if ds/dx is negative (as on the upper half of the circle in Fig. 13.22).

It is desirable for our purposes to have κ carry the same sign as $d\phi/ds$; hence we shall need to keep the ambiguous sign in Eq. (2a), subject to the discussion above. The sign of $d\phi/ds$ depends, of course, upon whether ϕ increases or decreases as s increases. Geometric considerations (Figs. 13.23 and 13.24) show that

κ is positive if the concave side of the curve lies on our left and

κ is negative if the concave side of the curve lies on our right,

as we "walk" along the curve in the direction of increasing s.

In Fig. 13.23(a), we indicate that s increases as we go from left to right along the curve. If we go from P to a nearby point P' to the right of P (corresponding to a positive Δs), we see that the tangent at P' is steeper than at P; hence $\Delta \phi$ is also positive, so that

$$ d\phi/ds = \lim_{\Delta s \to 0} (\Delta \phi / \Delta s) $$

is positive at P. We also see that the concave side of the curve is on our left as we travel along the curve in the direction indicated.

A similar analysis of the situation illustrated by Fig. 13.23(b) leads to the conclusion that $d\phi/ds$ is negative at P, since a small increase in s causes a decrease in ϕ. In this case, κ is negative and the concave side of the curve is on our right as we go along the curve in the direction of increasing s.

Finally, the two cases illustrated in Fig. 13.24(a) and (b) show that the geometric interpretation of the sign of κ which was given above holds valid in every case. It should be pointed out that some writers take the sign of κ to be the same as the sign of d^2y/dx^2, which corresponds to assuming that ds/dx is positive.

We may arrive at a formula for κ in terms of dx/dy and d^2x/dy^2 if we use

$$ \phi = \cot^{-1} \frac{dx}{dy} \quad \text{and} \quad \kappa = \frac{d\phi}{ds} = \frac{d\phi/dy}{ds/dy} . $$

The result, which corresponds to (2a), is

$$ \kappa = \frac{\pm \dfrac{d^2x}{dy^2}}{\left[1 + \left(\dfrac{dx}{dy}\right)^2\right]^{3/2}} . \tag{2b} $$

If the equation of the curve is given in parametric form:

$$ x = f(t), \quad y = g(t), $$

then

$$ \phi = \tan^{-1} \left(\frac{dy/dt}{dx/dt} \right), $$

and if we use

$$ \kappa = \frac{d\phi/dt}{ds/dt}, $$

the calculations are as follows:

$$ \frac{d\phi}{dt} = \frac{1}{1 + \left(\dfrac{dy/dt}{dx/dt}\right)^2} \; \frac{\dfrac{dx}{dt}\dfrac{d^2y}{dt^2} - \dfrac{dy}{dt}\dfrac{d^2x}{dt^2}}{\left(\dfrac{dx}{dt}\right)^2} $$

$$ = \frac{\dot{x}\ddot{y} - \dot{y}\ddot{x}}{\dot{x}^2 + \dot{y}^2} \quad \left[\dot{x} = \frac{dx}{dt}, \quad \ddot{x} = \frac{d^2x}{dt^2} \right] $$

and

$$ \frac{ds}{dt} = \pm\sqrt{\dot{x}^2 + \dot{y}^2}, $$

so that

$$ \kappa = \pm \frac{\dot{x}\ddot{y} - \dot{y}\ddot{x}}{[\dot{x}^2 + \dot{y}^2]^{3/2}} . \tag{2c} $$

On a straight line, ϕ is constant, so $d\phi/ds$ is zero and Eq. (2a) says that *the curvature of a straight line is zero.*

If we apply (2), or (1), to a circle of radius a, we find that the curvature of a circle is constant in magnitude. In fact, we see from Fig. 13.25 that both s and ϕ may be expressed in terms of the angle θ:

$$ s = a\theta, \quad \phi = \theta + \frac{\pi}{2}, \tag{3} $$

so that

$$ \kappa = \frac{d\phi}{ds} = \frac{d\theta}{a\,d\theta} = \frac{1}{a} . $$

That is, the curvature of a circle is equal to the *reciprocal of its radius.* The smaller the circle, the greater its curvature. "Turning around on a dime"

13.25

osculating circle

center of curvature

curve

radius of curvature

$P(x, y)$

13.26

$\mathbf{N} = \dfrac{d\mathbf{T}}{d\phi}$

$\mathbf{T}$

ϕ

P

s

P_0

a | b

P_0

s

ϕ

P

$\mathbf{T}$

$\mathbf{N} = \dfrac{d\mathbf{T}}{d\phi}$

13.27

indicates a more rapid change of direction per unit of arc length than does turning around on a silver dollar!

Circle and radius of curvature

The circle that is tangent to a given curve at P, whose center lies on the concave side of the curve and which has the same curvature as the curve has at P, is called the *circle of curvature*. Its radius is $1/\kappa$. We define the *radius of curvature* at P to be ρ, where

$$\rho = \frac{1}{\kappa} = \frac{\left[1 + \left(\dfrac{dy}{dx} \right)^2 \right]^{3/2}}{\pm \dfrac{d^2 y}{dx^2}}. \tag{4}$$

As we have defined it, ρ has the same sign as κ. The center of the circle of curvature is called the center of curvature. The circle of curvature has its first and second derivatives equal respectively to the first and second derivatives of the curve itself at this point. For this reason it has a higher degree of contact with the curve at P than has any other circle, and so it is also called the *osculating* circle! (See Fig. 13.26.) Since velocity and acceleration involve only the first and second time-derivatives of the coordinates of P, it is natural to expect that the instantaneous velocity and acceleration of a particle moving on any curve may be expressed in terms of instantaneous velocity and acceleration of an associated particle moving on the osculating circle. This will be investigated in the next article.

Unit normal vector

We return once more to the question of the rate of change of the unit vector $\mathbf{T}$ as P moves along the curve. In terms of the slope angle ϕ, Fig. 13.27, we may write

$$\mathbf{T} = \mathbf{i} \cos \phi + \mathbf{j} \sin \phi, \tag{5}$$

and then the derivative

$$\frac{d\mathbf{T}}{d\phi} = -\mathbf{i} \sin \phi + \mathbf{j} \cos \phi \tag{6}$$

has magnitude

$$\left|\frac{d\mathbf{T}}{d\phi}\right| = \sqrt{\sin^2 \phi + \cos^2 \phi} = 1.$$

Its slope is

$$\frac{\cos \phi}{-\sin \phi} = \frac{-1}{\tan \phi},$$

which is the negative reciprocal of the slope of $\mathbf{T}$. Therefore $d\mathbf{T}/d\phi$ is perpendicular to $\mathbf{T}$. In fact, we see from Eq. (6) that

$$\frac{d\mathbf{T}}{d\phi} = \mathbf{N}, \qquad (7)$$

where $\mathbf{N}$ is the *unit normal* vector

$$\mathbf{N} = \mathbf{i} \cos (\phi + 90°) + \mathbf{j} \sin (\phi + 90°)$$
$$= -\mathbf{i} \sin \phi + \mathbf{j} \cos \phi$$

obtained by rotating the unit tangent vector $\mathbf{T}$ through 90° in the counterclockwise direction.

If we combine Eqs. (7) and (1), we have

$$\frac{d\mathbf{T}}{ds} = \frac{d\mathbf{T}}{d\phi} \frac{d\phi}{ds} = \mathbf{N}\kappa. \qquad (8)$$

We observe in passing that whether κ is positive or negative, $\mathbf{N}\kappa$ is always directed toward the concave side of the curve. (See Figs. 13.23, 13.24, and 13.27.)

EXERCISES

Find the curvature of each of the curves in Exercises 1 through 9.

1. $y = a \cosh (x/a)$ 2. $y = \ln (\cos x)$

3. $y = e^{2x}$ 4. $x = a \cos^3 t,$
                            $y = a \sin^3 t$

5. $x = a (\cos \theta + \theta \sin \theta),$
    $y = a (\sin \theta - \theta \cos \theta)$

6. $x = a(\theta - \sin \theta),$
    $y = a(1 - \cos \theta)$

7. $x = \ln \sec y$

8. $x = \frac{1}{3}(y^2 + 2)^{3/2}$

9. $x = \dfrac{y^4}{4} + \dfrac{1}{8y^2}$

10. Find the equation of the osculating circle associated with the curve $y = e^x$ at the point $(0, 1)$. By calculating dy/dx and d^2y/dx^2 at the point $(0, 1)$ from the equation of this circle, verify that these derivatives have the same values there as do the corresponding derivatives for the curve $y = e^x$. Sketch the curve and the osculating circle.

11. Show that when x and y are considered as functions of arc length s, the unit vectors $\mathbf{T}$ and $\mathbf{N}$ may be expressed as follows:

$$\mathbf{T} = \mathbf{i}\frac{dx}{ds} + \mathbf{j}\frac{dy}{ds},$$

$$\mathbf{N} = -\mathbf{i}\frac{dy}{ds} + \mathbf{j}\frac{dx}{ds},$$

where $dx/ds = \cos \phi$, $dy/ds = \sin \phi$, and ϕ is the angle from the positive x-axis to the tangent line.

13.7 TANGENTIAL AND NORMAL COMPONENTS OF THE VELOCITY AND ACCELERATION VECTORS

In mechanics, it is useful to be able to discuss the motion of a particle P in terms of its instantaneous speed ds/dt, its acceleration along its path d^2s/dt^2, and the curvature of its path. This is easy if we refer the velocity and acceleration vectors to the unit vectors $\mathbf{T}$ and $\mathbf{N}$, rather than using horizontal and vertical components.

In Article 13.4, we found the velocity vector is given by

$$\mathbf{v} = \frac{d\mathbf{R}}{dt}, \qquad (1)$$

where $\mathbf{R} = \mathbf{i}x + \mathbf{j}y + \mathbf{k}z$ is the position vector $\overrightarrow{OP}$. We may also write this in the form

$$\mathbf{v} = \frac{d\mathbf{R}}{dt} = \frac{d\mathbf{R}}{ds}\frac{ds}{dt},$$

or

$$\mathbf{v} = \mathbf{T}\frac{ds}{dt}, \qquad (2)$$

if we use the result of Eq. (3), Article 13.5. This is in keeping with our earlier remark that the velocity vector is tangent to the curve and has magnitude $|ds/dt|$. (See Fig. 13.28.)

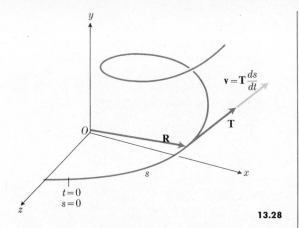

13.28

To obtain the acceleration vector, we differentiate Eq. (2) with respect to t:

$$\mathbf{a} = \frac{d\mathbf{v}}{dt} = \mathbf{T}\frac{d^2s}{dt^2} + \frac{ds}{dt}\frac{d\mathbf{T}}{dt}.$$

By Eq. (8), Article 13.6, we have

$$\frac{d\mathbf{T}}{dt} = \frac{d\mathbf{T}}{ds}\frac{ds}{dt} = \mathbf{N}\kappa\frac{ds}{dt},$$

so that

$$\mathbf{a} = \mathbf{T}\frac{d^2s}{dt^2} + \mathbf{N}\kappa\left(\frac{ds}{dt}\right)^2. \qquad (3)$$

Equation (3) expresses the acceleration vector in terms of its tangential and normal components. The *tangential component* d^2s/dt^2 is simply the derivative of the speed ds/dt of the particle in its path. The *normal component* is directed toward the concave side of the curve and has magnitude

$$\kappa\left(\frac{ds}{dt}\right)^2 = \frac{(ds/dt)^2}{\rho} = \frac{v^2}{\rho},$$

where v is the instantaneous speed of the particle and ρ is the radius of curvature of the path at the point in question. This explains why a large normal force, which must be supplied by friction between the tires and the roadway, is required to hold an automobile on a level road if it makes a sharp turn (small ρ) at a moderate speed or a moderate turn at high speed (large v^2). (See Sears, *Mechanics, Heat, and Sound*, p. 187, for a discussion of the banking of curves.)

If the particle is moving in a circle with *constant* speed $v = ds/dt$, then d^2s/dt^2 is zero, and the only acceleration is the normal acceleration v^2/p toward the center of the circle. If the speed is not constant, the acceleration vector $\mathbf{a}$ is the resultant of the tangential and normal components, as in Fig. 13.29.

13.29

The following example illustrates how the tangential and normal components of velocity and acceleration may be computed when the equations of motion are known. In particular, it should be noted that the equation

$$|\mathbf{a}|^2 = a_x^2 + a_y^2 = a_T^2 + a_N^2 \qquad (4)$$

is used to determine the normal component of acceleration

$$a_N = \sqrt{|\mathbf{a}|^2 - a_T^2}. \qquad (5)$$

Example. The coordinates of a moving particle at time t are given by

$$x = \cos t + t\sin t, \quad y = \sin t - t\cos t.$$

Thus

$$\mathbf{v} = \mathbf{i}\frac{dx}{dt} + \mathbf{j}\frac{dy}{dt}$$

$$= \mathbf{i}[-\sin t + t\cos t + \sin t]$$
$$\quad + \mathbf{j}[\cos t + t\sin t - \cos t]$$

$$= \mathbf{i}t\cos t + \mathbf{j}t\sin t$$

and

$$\mathbf{a} = \frac{d\mathbf{v}}{dt} = \mathbf{i}[-t \sin t + \cos t] + \mathbf{j}[t \cos t + \sin t].$$

Now the tangential component of velocity is

$$\frac{ds}{dt} = |\mathbf{v}| = \sqrt{(t \cos t)^2 + (t \sin t)^2} = t,$$

and the tangential component of acceleration is

$$a_T = \frac{d^2 s}{dt^2} = \frac{d}{dt}\left(\frac{ds}{dt}\right) = \frac{d}{dt}(t) = 1.$$

We use Eq. (5) to determine the normal component of acceleration:

$$\begin{aligned} a_N &= \sqrt{|\mathbf{a}|^2 - a_T^2} \\ &= \sqrt{(-t \sin t + \cos t)^2 + (t \cos t + \sin t)^2 - 1} \\ &= t. \end{aligned}$$

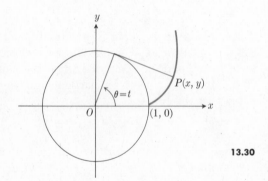

13.30

Here the tangential acceleration has constant magnitude and the normal acceleration starts with zero magnitude at $t = 0$ and increases with time. The equations of motion are the same as the parametric equations for the involute of a circle of unit radius with $\theta = t$ (see Fig. 13.30). We could also readily find the radius of curvature without any complicated calculations from the equation $a_N = v^2/\rho$, since $v^2 = |\mathbf{v}|^2 = t^2$ and $a_N = t$ and hence

$$\rho = \frac{v^2}{a_N} = \frac{t^2}{t} = t.$$

EXERCISES

1. With the book closed, derive vector expressions for the velocity and acceleration in terms of tangential and normal components. Check your derivations with those given in the text.

In Exercises 2 through 6, find the velocity and acceleration vectors, and then find the speed ds/dt and the tangential and normal components of acceleration.

2. $\mathbf{R} = \mathbf{i} \cosh 2t + \mathbf{j} \sinh 2t$

3. $\mathbf{R} = (2t + 3)\mathbf{i} + (t^2 - 1)\mathbf{j}$

4. $\mathbf{R} = a \cos \omega t \mathbf{i} + a \sin \omega t \mathbf{j}$,
   a and ω positive constants

5. $\mathbf{R} = \mathbf{i} \ln (t^2 + 1) + \mathbf{j}(t - 2 \tan^{-1} t)$

6. $\mathbf{R} = \mathbf{i}e^t \cos t + \mathbf{j}e^t \sin t$

7. Deduce from Eq. (3) that a particle will move in a straight line if the normal component of acceleration is identically zero.

8. Show that the radius of curvature of a plane curve is given by

$$\rho = \frac{(\dot{x}^2 + \dot{y}^2)}{\sqrt{\ddot{x}^2 + \ddot{y}^2 - \ddot{s}^2}},$$

where

$$\dot{x} = \frac{dx}{dt}, \quad \ddot{x} = \frac{d^2 x}{dt^2}, \quad \cdots \text{ and } \ddot{s} = \frac{d}{dt}(\sqrt{\dot{x}^2 + \dot{y}^2}).$$

9. If a particle moves in a curve with constant speed, show that the force is always directed along the normal.

10. If the force acting on a particle is at all times perpendicular to the direction of motion, show that the speed remains constant.

13.8 POLAR COORDINATES

If the particle P moves on a plane curve whose equation is given in polar coordinates, it is convenient to express the velocity and acceleration vectors in terms of still a third set of unit vectors. We introduce **unit vectors**

$$\mathbf{u}_r = \mathbf{i} \cos \theta + \mathbf{j} \sin \theta, \tag{1}$$
$$\mathbf{u}_\theta = -\mathbf{i} \sin \theta + \mathbf{j} \cos \theta,$$

which point respectively along the radius vector $\overrightarrow{OP}$, and at right angles to $\overrightarrow{OP}$ and in the direction of increasing θ, as shown in Fig. 13.31. Then we find from (1) that

$$\frac{d\mathbf{u}_r}{d\theta} = -\mathbf{i}\sin\theta + \mathbf{j}\cos\theta = \mathbf{u}_\theta, \tag{2}$$

$$\frac{d\mathbf{u}_\theta}{d\theta} = -\mathbf{i}\cos\theta - \mathbf{j}\sin\theta = -\mathbf{u}_r.$$

13.31

This says that the result of differentiating either one of the unit vectors $\mathbf{u}_r$ and $\mathbf{u}_\theta$ with respect to θ is equivalent to rotating that vector through 90° in the positive (counterclockwise) direction.

Since the vectors $\mathbf{R} = \overrightarrow{OP}$ and $r\mathbf{u}_r$ have the same direction, and the length of $\mathbf{R}$ is the absolute value of the polar coordinate r of $P(r, \theta)$, we have

$$\mathbf{R} = r\mathbf{u}_r. \tag{3}$$

To obtain the velocity, we must differentiate this with respect to t, remembering that both r and $\mathbf{u}_r$ may be variables. From (2) it is clear that

$$\frac{d\mathbf{u}_r}{dt} = \frac{d\mathbf{u}_r}{d\theta}\frac{d\theta}{dt} = \mathbf{u}_\theta\frac{d\theta}{dt}, \tag{4}$$

$$\frac{d\mathbf{u}_\theta}{dt} = \frac{d\mathbf{u}_\theta}{d\theta}\frac{d\theta}{dt} = -\mathbf{u}_r\frac{d\theta}{dt}.$$

Hence

$$\mathbf{v} = \frac{d\mathbf{R}}{dt} = \mathbf{u}_r\frac{dr}{dt} + r\frac{d\mathbf{u}_r}{dt}$$

becomes

$$\mathbf{v} = \mathbf{u}_r\frac{dr}{dt} + \mathbf{u}_\theta r\frac{d\theta}{dt}. \tag{5}$$

13.32

Of course this velocity vector is tangent to the curve at P and has magnitude

$$|\mathbf{v}| = \sqrt{(dr/dt)^2 + r^2(d\theta/dt)^2} = |ds/dt|.$$

In fact, if the three sides of the "differential triangle" of sides dr, $r\,d\theta$, and ds are all divided by dt, the result will be a similar triangle having sides dr/dt, $r\,d\theta/dt$, and ds/dt, which illustrates the vector equation

$$\mathbf{v} = \mathbf{T}\frac{ds}{dt}$$

$$= \mathbf{u}_r\frac{dr}{dt} + \mathbf{u}_\theta r\frac{d\theta}{dt}.$$

(See Fig. 13.32.)

The acceleration vector is found by differentiating the velocity vector in (5) as follows:

$$\mathbf{a} = \frac{d\mathbf{v}}{dt} = \left(\mathbf{u}_r\frac{d^2r}{dt^2} + \frac{dr}{dt}\frac{d\mathbf{u}_r}{dt}\right)$$

$$+ \left(\mathbf{u}_\theta r\frac{d^2\theta}{dt^2} + \mathbf{u}_\theta\frac{dr}{dt}\frac{d\theta}{dt} + \frac{d\mathbf{u}_\theta}{dt}r\frac{d\theta}{dt}\right).$$

When Eqs. (4) are used to evaluate the derivatives of $\mathbf{u}_r$ and $\mathbf{u}_\theta$ and the components are separated, the result becomes

$$\mathbf{a} = \mathbf{u}_r\left[\frac{d^2r}{dt^2} - r\left(\frac{d\theta}{dt}\right)^2\right]$$

$$+ \mathbf{u}_\theta\left[r\frac{d^2\theta}{dt^2} + 2\frac{dr}{dt}\frac{d\theta}{dt}\right]. \tag{6}$$

The polar form is particularly convenient in discussing the motion of a particle in what is called a "central force field." By this we mean that the force acting on the particle is always directed toward a single point, the center of force, which we choose as origin (Fig. 13.33). Then from $\mathbf{F} = m\mathbf{a}$, we see that the $\mathbf{u}_\theta$ component of acceleration must vanish. That is, in any central force field

$$r\frac{d^2\theta}{dt^2} + 2\frac{dr}{dt}\frac{d\theta}{dt} = 0 \qquad (7)$$

where the origin is at the center of force. (For instance, the sun would be chosen as the origin in discussing the gravitational attraction between the sun and a planet.) To integrate the differential equation (7), let

$$u = \frac{d\theta}{dt};$$

then

$$r\frac{du}{dt} + 2u\frac{dr}{dt} = 0$$

or

$$r\,du = -2u\,dr, \qquad \frac{du}{u} = -2\frac{dr}{r},$$

$$\ln|u| = -2\ln|r| + c_1,$$

$$\ln|ur^2| = c_1, \qquad |ur^2| = e^{c_1} = C,$$

or

$$r^2\frac{d\theta}{dt} = \pm C. \qquad (8)$$

We recognize the left side of this equation as $2\,dA/dt$, where $dA = \frac{1}{2}r^2\,d\theta$ is the area swept over as the radius vector $\overline{OP}$ rotates through a small angle $d\theta$. Hence, Eq. (8) says that the radius vector *sweeps over area at a constant rate* in a central force field. This is Kepler's second law of planetary motion, and it is thus seen to be a consequence of the fact that the field of gravitational attraction of the sun for the planets is a central force field.

13.33

EXERCISES

1. With the book closed, derive vector expressions for velocity and acceleration in terms of components along and at right angles to the radius vector. Check your derivations with those given in the text.

In Exercises 2 through 6, find the velocity and acceleration vectors in terms of the unit vectors $\mathbf{u}_r$ and $\mathbf{u}_\theta$.

2. $r = a(1 - \cos\theta)$, $\dfrac{d\theta}{dt} = 3$

3. $r = a\sin 2\theta$, $\dfrac{d\theta}{dt} = 2t$ 4. $r = e^{a\theta}$, $\dfrac{d\theta}{dt} = 2$

5. $r = a(1 + \sin t)$, $\theta = 1 - e^{-t}$

6. $r = 2\cos 4t$, $\theta = 2t$

7. If a particle moves in an ellipse whose polar equation is $r = c/(1 - e\cos\theta)$ and the force is directed toward the origin, show that the magnitude of the force is proportional to $1/r^2$.

REVIEW QUESTIONS AND EXERCISES

1. When are two vectors equal?

2. How are two vectors added? Subtracted?

3. If a vector is multiplied by a scalar, how is the result related to the original vector? In your discussion include all possible values of the scalar: positive, negative, and zero.

4. Define the derivative of a vector function.

5. Develop formulas for the derivatives, with respect to θ, of the unit vectors $\mathbf{u}_r$ and $\mathbf{u}_\theta$.

6. Develop vector formulas for velocity and acceleration of a particle moving in a plane curve:

   (a) in terms of Cartesian coordinates,

   (b) in terms of polar coordinates,

   (c) in terms of distance traveled along the curve and unit vectors tangent and normal to the curve.

7. (a) Define curvature of a plane curve.

   (b) Define radius of curvature.

   (c) Define center of curvature.

   (d) Define osculating circle.

8. Develop a formula for the curvature of a curve whose parametric equations are $x = f(t)$, $y = g(t)$.

9. In what way does the curvature of a curve affect the acceleration of a particle moving along the curve? In particular, discuss the case of constant-speed motion along a curve.

10. State and derive Kepler's second law concerning motion in a central force field.

11. Give examples of two ways in which parametric equations of a curve may arise.

12. What is the relation between a locus represented by parametric equations and the locus represented by the Cartesian equations that we may get when we eliminate the parameter? Illustrate with an example.

MISCELLANEOUS EXERCISES

In Exercises 1 through 10, find parametric equations of the locus of $P(x, y)$ for the data given.

1. $\dfrac{dx}{dt} = x^2, \quad \dfrac{dy}{dt} = x; \quad t = 0, \ x = 1, \ y = 1$

2. $\dfrac{dx}{dt} = \cos^2 x, \quad \dfrac{dy}{dt} = x; \quad t = 0, \ x = \dfrac{\pi}{4}, \ y = 0$

3. $\dfrac{dx}{dt} = e^t, \quad \dfrac{dy}{dt} = xe^x; \quad t = 0, \ x = 1, \ y = 0$

4. $\dfrac{dx}{dt} = 6 \sin 2t, \quad \dfrac{dy}{dt} = 4 \cos 2t; \quad t = 0, \ x = 0, \ y = 4$

5. $\dfrac{dx}{dt} = 1 - \cos t, \quad \dfrac{dy}{dt} = \sin t; \quad t = 0, \ x = 0, \ y = 0$

6. $\dfrac{dx}{dt} = \sqrt{1 + y}, \quad \dfrac{dy}{dt} = y; \quad t = 0, \ x = 0, \ y = 1$

7. $\dfrac{dx}{dt} = \operatorname{sech} x, \quad \dfrac{dy}{dt} = x; \quad t = 0, \ x = 0, \ y = 0$

8. $\dfrac{dx}{dt} = \cosh \dfrac{t}{2}, \quad \dfrac{dy}{dt} = x; \quad t = 0, \ x = 2, \ y = 0$

9. $\dfrac{dx}{dt} = y, \quad \dfrac{dy}{dt} = -x; \quad t = 0, \ x = 0, \ y = 4$

10. $\dfrac{d^2x}{dt^2} = -\dfrac{dx}{dt}, \quad \dfrac{dy}{dt} = x; \quad t = 0, \ x = 1, \ y = 1, \ \dfrac{dx}{dt} = 1$

11. A particle is projected with velocity v at an angle α to the horizontal from a point that is at the foot of a hill inclined at an angle ϕ to the horizontal, where
$$0 < \phi < \alpha < (\pi/2).$$
Show that it reaches the ground at a distance
$$\frac{2v^2 \cos \alpha}{g \cos^2 \phi} \sin (\alpha - \phi)$$

measured up the face of the hill. Hence show that the greatest range achieved for a given v is when $\alpha = (\phi/2) + (\pi/4)$.

12. A wheel of radius 4 in. rolls along the x-axis with angular velocity 2 rad/sec. Find the locus described by a point on a spoke and 2 in. from the center of the wheel if it starts from the point $(0, 2)$ at time $t = 0$.

13. OA is the diameter of a circle of radius a. AN is tangent to the circle at A. A line through O making angle θ with diameter OA intersects the circle at M and tangent line at N. On ON a point P is located so that $OP = MN$. Taking O as origin, OA along the y-axis, and angle θ as parameter, find parametric equations of the locus described by P.

14. Let a line AB be the x-axis of a system of rectangular coordinates. Let the point C be the point $(0, 1)$. Let the line DE through C intersect AB at F. Let P and P' be the points on DE such that $PF = P'F = a$. Find parametric equations of the loci of P and P' in terms of the angle $\theta = \angle CFB$.

15. For the curve
$$x = a(t - \sin t), \quad y = a(1 - \cos t),$$
find the following quantities.

   (a) The area bounded by the x-axis and one loop of the curve

   (b) The length of one loop

   (c) The radius of curvature

   (d) The area of the surface of revolution obtained by rotating one loop about the x-axis

   (e) The coordinates of the centroid of the area in (a)

16. In Fig. 13.34, D is the midpoint of side AB and E is one-third of the way between C and B. *Using vectors*, prove that F is the midpoint of the line CD.

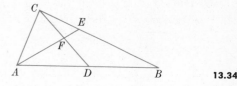

13.34

17. The vectors $2\mathbf{i} + 3\mathbf{j}$, $4\mathbf{i} + \mathbf{j}$, and $5\mathbf{i} + y\mathbf{j}$ have their initial points at the origin. Find the value of y so that the vectors terminate on one straight line.

18. **A** and **B** are vectors from the origin to the two points A and B. The point P is determined by the vector $\overrightarrow{OP} = x\mathbf{A} + y\mathbf{B}$, where x and y are positive quantities, neither of which is zero, and whose sum is equal to one. Prove that P lies on the line segment AB.

19. Using vector methods, prove that the segment joining the midpoints of two sides of a triangle is parallel to, and half the length of, the third side.

20. Let ABC be a triangle and let M be the midpoint of AB. Let P be the point on CM that is two-thirds of the way from C to M. Let O be any point in space.

    (a) Show that

$$\overrightarrow{OP} = \left(\frac{\overrightarrow{OA} + \overrightarrow{OB} + \overrightarrow{OC}}{3}\right).$$

    (b) Show how the result in (a) leads to the conclusion that the medians of a triangle meet in a point.

21. A, B, C are the vertices of a triangle and a, b, c are the midpoints of the opposite sides. Show that

$$\overrightarrow{Aa} + \overrightarrow{Bb} + \overrightarrow{Cc} = \mathbf{0}.$$

    Interpret the result geometrically.

22. Vectors are drawn from the center of a regular polygon to its vertices. Show that their sum is zero.

23. Let **A**, **B**, **C** be vectors from a common point O to points A, B, C.

    (a) If A, B, C are collinear, show that three constants x, y, z (not all zero) exist such that

$$x + y + z = 0 \quad \text{and} \quad x\mathbf{A} + y\mathbf{B} + z\mathbf{C} = \mathbf{0}.$$

    (b) Conversely, if three constants x, y, z (not all zero) exist such that

$$x + y + z = 0 \quad \text{and} \quad x\mathbf{A} + y\mathbf{B} + z\mathbf{C} = \mathbf{0},$$

    show that A, B, C are collinear.

24. A particle moves in the xy-plane according to the time law

$$x = 1/\sqrt{1 + t^2}, \quad y = t/\sqrt{1 + t^2}.$$

    (a) Compute the velocity vector and acceleration vector when $t = 1$.

    (b) At what time is the speed of the particle a maximum?

25. A circular wheel with unit radius rolls along the x-axis uniformly, rotating one half-turn per second (Fig. 13.35). The position of a point P on the circumference is given by the formula

$$\overrightarrow{OP} = \mathbf{R} = \mathbf{i}(\pi t - \sin \pi t) + \mathbf{j}(1 - \cos \pi t).$$

    (a) Determine the velocity (*vector*) **v** and the acceleration (*vector*) **a** at time t.

    (b) Determine the slopes (as functions of t) of the two straight lines PC and PQ joining P to the center C of the wheel and to the point Q that is topmost at the instant.

    (c) Show that the directions of the vectors **v** and **a** can be expressed in terms of the straight lines described in (b).

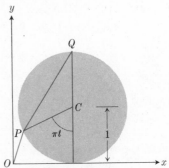

13.35

26. The motion of a particle in the xy-plane is given by

$$\mathbf{R} = \mathbf{i}at \cos t + \mathbf{j}at \sin t.$$

    Find the speed, and the tangential and normal components of the acceleration.

27. A particle moves in such a manner that the derivative of the position vector is always perpendicular to the position vector. Show that the particle moves on a circle with center at the origin.

28. The position of a point at time t is given by the formulas $x = e^t \cos t$, $y = e^t \sin t$.

    (a) Show that $\mathbf{a} = 2\mathbf{v} - 2\mathbf{r}$.

    (b) Show that the angle between the radius vector **r** and the acceleration vector **a** is constant, and find this angle.

29. Given the instantaneous velocity $\mathbf{v} = a\mathbf{i} + b\mathbf{j}$ and acceleration $\mathbf{a} = c\mathbf{i} + d\mathbf{j}$ of a particle at a point P on its path of motion, determine the curvature of the path at P.

30. Find the parametric equations, in terms of the parameter θ, of the locus of the center of curvature of the cycloid

$$x = a(\theta - \sin \theta), \quad y = a(1 - \cos \theta).$$

31. Find the point on the curve $y = e^x$ for which the radius of curvature is a minimum.

32. (a) Given a closed curve having the property that every line parallel to the x-axis or the y-axis has at most two points in common with the curve. Let

$$x = x(t), \quad y = y(t), \quad \alpha \le t \le \beta,$$

be equations of the curve. Prove that if dx/dt and dy/dt are continuous, then the area bounded by the curve is

$$\frac{1}{2} \left| \int_\alpha^\beta \left[x(t) \frac{dy}{dt} - y(t) \frac{dx}{dt} \right] dt \right|.$$

(b) Use the result of (a) to find the area inside the ellipse

$$x = a \cos \phi, \quad y = b \sin \phi, \quad 0 \le \phi \le 2\pi.$$

What does the answer become when $a = b$?

33. For the curve defined by the equations

$$x = \int_0^\theta \cos \left(\tfrac{1}{2} \pi t^2 \right) dt, \quad y = \int_0^\theta \sin \left(\tfrac{1}{2} \pi t^2 \right) dt,$$

calculate the curvature κ as a function of the length of arc s, where s is measured from $(0, 0)$.

34. The curve for which the length of the tangent intercepted between the point of contact and the y-axis is always equal to 1 is called the *tractrix*. Find its equation. Show that the radius of curvature at each point of the curve is inversely proportional to the length of the normal intercepted between the point on the curve and the y-axis. Calculate the length of arc of the tractrix, and find the parametric equations in terms of the length of arc.

35. Let $x = x(t)$, $y = y(t)$ be a closed curve. A constant length p is measured off along the normal to the curve. The extremity of this segment describes a curve which is called a *parallel curve* to the original curve. Find the length of arc, the radius of curvature, and the area enclosed by the parallel curve.

36. Given the curve represented by the parametric equations

$$x = 32t,$$
$$y = 16t^2 - 4.$$

(a) Calculate the radius of curvature of the curve at the point where $t = 3$.

(b) Find the length of the curve between the points where $t = 0$ and $t = 1$.

37. Find the velocity, acceleration, and speed of a particle whose position at time t is

$$x = 3 \sin t,$$
$$y = 2 \cos t.$$

Also find the tangential and normal components of the acceleration.

38. The position of a particle at time t is given by the equations

$$x = 1 + \cos 2t, \quad y = \sin 2t.$$

Find

(a) the normal and tangential components of acceleration at time t;

(b) the radius of curvature of the path;

(c) the equation of the path in polar coordinates, using the x-axis as the line $\theta = 0$ and the y-axis as the line $\theta = \pi/2$.

39. A particle moves so that its position at time t has the polar coordinates $r = t$, $\theta = t$. Find the velocity $\mathbf{v}$, the acceleration $\mathbf{a}$, and the curvature κ at any time t.

40. Find an expression for the curvature of the curve whose equation in polar coordinates is $r = f(\theta)$.

41. (a) Find the equation in *polar coordinates* of the curve

$$x = e^{2t} \cos t,$$
$$y = e^{2t} \sin t.$$

(b) Find the length of this curve from $t = 0$ to $t = 2\pi$.

42. Express the velocity vector in terms of $\mathbf{u}_r$ and $\mathbf{u}_\theta$ for a point moving in the xy-plane according to the law

$$\mathbf{r} = (t + 1)\mathbf{i} + (t - 1)\mathbf{j}.$$

43. The polar coordinates of a particle at time t are

$$r = e^{\omega t} + e^{-\omega t}, \quad \theta = t,$$

where ω is a constant. Find the acceleration vector when $t = 0$.

44. A slender rod, passing through the fixed point O, is rotating about O in a plane at the constant rate of 3 rad/min. An insect is crawling along the rod toward O at the constant rate of 1 in/min. Use polar coordinates in the plane, with point O as the origin, and assume that the insect starts at the point $r = 2$, $\theta = 0$.

   (a) Find, in polar form, the vector velocity and vector acceleration of the insect when it is halfway to the origin.

   (b) What will be the length of the path, in the plane, that the insect has traveled when it reaches the origin?

45. A smooth ball rolls inside a long hollow tube while the tube rotates with constant angular velocity ω about an axis perpendicular to the axis of the tube. Assuming no friction between the ball and the sides of the tube, show that the distance r from the axis of rotation to the ball satisfies the differential equation

$$d^2r/dt^2 - \omega^2 r = 0.$$

   If at time $t = 0$ the ball is at rest (relative to the tube) at $r = a > 0$, find r as a function of t.

46. Find the orbit of a planet relative to the sun, assuming the sun to be fixed at the origin and the force acting on the planet to be directed toward the sun with magnitude $\gamma m M / r^2$ where γ is the universal gravitational constant, M is the mass of the sun, m is the mass of the planet, and r is its distance from the sun. Choose the initial line to pass through the perihelion point of the orbit, and assume the velocity at perihelion is v_0. Show that the path is a circle, ellipse, parabola, or hyperbola according as $v_0^2 r_0 / \gamma M$ equals one, lies between one and two, equals two, or is greater than two.

INFINITE SERIES

CHAPTER 14

In Article 10.3, we became acquainted with Newton's method for finding a root of an equation $f(x) = 0$. The procedure was

(a) to guess a first approximation x_1, and

(b) to get a new approximation x_{n+1} from any current approximation x_n, by means of the formula

$$x_{n+1} = x_n - \frac{f(x_n)}{f'(x_n)}. \tag{1}$$

In theory, we might continue this procedure indefinitely, producing an infinite succession of approximations $x_1, x_2, x_3, \ldots$ Indeed, to each positive integer n there corresponds an nth approximation x_n. The set of all ordered pairs of the form (n, x_n), $n = 1, 2, \ldots$, is an example of a *sequence*.

There are many other ways of producing sequences. Consider, for example, a geometric progression like $1, \frac{1}{2}, \frac{1}{4}, \frac{1}{8}, \ldots$, where each term is one-half its predecessor. Suppose we number the terms $1, 2, 3, \ldots$ in order, as in the following table.

Number of term (index)	1	2	3	4	. . .	n	. . .
Value of term	1	$\frac{1}{2}$	$\frac{1}{4}$	$\frac{1}{8}$	. . .	$(\frac{1}{2})^{n-1}$	. . .

We now consider the set of all pairs of the form $(n, (\frac{1}{2})^{n-1})$, where the first element in each pair is the index that shows the ordinal number of that pair, and the second element is the value of the corresponding term of the geometric progression. This set is another example of a sequence, in agreement with the following general definition.

Definition. *A sequence is a function whose domain is the set of positive integers.*

We may denote the function by f. Then its value at n is $f(n)$. The sequence f is the set

$$\{(n, f(\text{n})) : n = 1, 2, 3, \ldots\};$$

that is, the set of all pairs $(n, f(n))$, with n a positive integer.

14.1   The graph of the sequence $\{(n, 1/n: n = 1, 2, \ldots\}$.

14.2   The graph of the sequence $\{1 + (-1)^n/2^n\}$, and the limit $L = 1$.

Example 1. The set $\{(n, 1/n): n = 1, 2, 3, \ldots\}$ is a sequence whose value at n is $1/n$. (See Fig. 14.1.)

Notation. Since the domain of a sequence is always the same (the set of positive integers), it is customary to shorten the notation and just write $\{f(n)\}$ instead of $\{(n, f(n))\}$. Thus the sequence

$$\{(n, 1/n): n = 1, 2, 3, \ldots\}$$

would be abbreviated simply $\{1/n\}$. Similarly $\{1/2^{n-1}\}$ would denote the sequence

$$\{(n, 1/2^{n-1}): n = 1, 2, 3, \ldots\}.$$

We also write $\{a_n\}$ to denote the sequence whose ordinate is $y = a_n$ at the abscissa $x = n$.

Limit of a sequence

A sequence $\{(n, a_n)\}$ may have a different value a_n for each different value of n. But it may also happen that as n increases, the different a_n's tend to cluster around some fixed number L. If there is such a number L, with the property that $|L - a_n|$ is arbitrarily small for all sufficiently large values of the index n, we say that a_n *converges to L as limit*, and write

$$\lim_{n \to \infty} a_n = L.$$

By the phrase "$|L - a_n|$ is arbitrarily small for all sufficiently large values of n," we mean that to any positive number ϵ there corresponds an index N such that

$$|L - a_n| < \epsilon \quad \text{for all } n > N. \tag{2}$$

That is, all terms after the Nth lie within the distance ϵ from L. If no such limit exists, then we say that the given sequence *diverges*.

Remark 1. The sequence $\{(n, a_n)\}$ has the limit L if and only if its graph has the line $y = L$ as horizontal asymptote. For example, the x-axis ($y = 0$) is an asymptote of the graph of $\{(n, 1/n)\}$, and also of the graph of $\{(n, (\frac{1}{2})^{n-1})\}$. Both sequences converge to zero as $n \to \infty$. Again, the sequence

$$\left\{ (n, a_n): a_n = 1 + \frac{(-1)^n}{2^n} \right\}$$

converges to 1 as $n \to \infty$. (See Fig. 14.2.)

Remark 2. As we recalled above, Newton's method for finding a solution of an equation $f(x) = 0$ is to guess a first approximation x_1 and then to use the formula

$$x_{n+1} = x_n - \frac{f(x_n)}{f'(x_n)}$$

to generate, by iteration, a sequence $\{x_n\}$. In favorable circumstances, the sequence converges to a number L that satisfies the equation $f(L) = 0$.

Remark 3. Iteration is used as a method for solving many different types of problems, particularly with high-speed computing machines. The technique is to start with a first approximation, use that to compute a second approximation, the second to get a third, then a fourth, and so on. The process generates a sequence which we hope will converge to a solution of the problem.*

Infinite series

One very important way of creating a sequence $\{s_n\}$ is by addition. Suppose the numbers to be added are $u_1, u_2, u_3, \ldots, u_n, \ldots$ We let

$$
\begin{aligned}
s_1 &= u_1, \\
s_2 &= u_1 + u_2, \\
s_3 &= u_1 + u_2 + u_3, \\
&\vdots \\
s_n &= u_1 + u_2 + \cdots + u_n = \sum_{k=1}^{n} u_k.
\end{aligned}
\tag{3}
$$

As n increases without bound, we are led to consider the symbol, or "set of marks,"

$$
u_1 + u_2 + u_n + \cdots + u_n + \cdots,
\tag{4a}
$$

which we shall also denote by

$$
\sum_{k=1}^{\infty} u_k.
\tag{4b}
$$

Such an expression is called an *infinite series*. One object in the present chapter is to see what meaning, if any, can be attached to an expression such as (4).

The sequence $\{s_n\}$, Eq. (3), is called the *sequence of partial sums* of the series (4a, b). The nth partial sum of the series is s_n. If s_n converges to a limit S as $n \to \infty$:

$$
\lim_{n \to \infty} s_n = S,
\tag{5}
$$

then we say that the series *converges* and that its *sum* is S. We indicate this by writing

$$
\sum_{k=1}^{\infty} u_k = \lim_{n \to \infty} \left(\sum_{k=1}^{n} u_k \right) = S.
\tag{6}
$$

On the other hand, if the sequence of partial sums diverges, we then say that the series *diverges*. In other words, the behavior of the series (convergence

---

* For a discussion of some specific examples, see the article "Feed it back," by Francis Scheid, in the *Mathematics Teacher*, Vol. LII, No. 4, April 1959, pp. 226–229.

or divergence) is the behavior of its sequence of partial sums. Later in this chapter we shall study several methods for testing a given series in order to determine whether it converges or diverges. For the present, we shall want to use the following theorem.

Theorem 1. *A necessary condition for the convergence of an infinite series*

$$
u_1 + u_2 + \cdots + u_n + \cdots
$$

is that

$$
\lim_{n \to \infty} u_n = 0.
\tag{7}
$$

Remark 4. The statement that the condition (7) is a "necessary condition for convergence" means that the condition must be satisfied if the series converges. Therefore it follows that when (7) is *not* satisfied, then the series *diverges*. This is frequently a useful test for divergence; namely, if the nth term of the series does not have a limit, or if it has a limit different from zero, as $n \to \infty$, then the series diverges. For example, the series

$$
\frac{1}{2} + \frac{2}{3} + \frac{3}{4} + \frac{4}{5} + \cdots + \frac{n}{n+1} + \cdots
$$

diverges, since

$$
u_n = \frac{n}{n+1}
$$

approaches 1 instead of 0 as $n \to \infty$. *Caution.* The theorem does *not* give a *sufficient* condition for convergence. That is, it does not follow that a series converges just because its nth term approaches zero as $n \to \infty$. The truth of this statement is illustrated by the series

$$
\tfrac{1}{2} + \underbrace{\tfrac{1}{4} + \tfrac{1}{4}}_{2\ \text{terms}} + \underbrace{\tfrac{1}{8} + \tfrac{1}{8} + \tfrac{1}{8} + \tfrac{1}{8}}_{4\ \text{terms}}
$$

$$
+ \underbrace{\tfrac{1}{16} + \tfrac{1}{16} + \cdots + \tfrac{1}{16}}_{8\ \text{terms}} + \cdots
$$

$$
+ \underbrace{\frac{1}{2^k} + \frac{1}{2^k} + \cdots + \frac{1}{2^k}}_{2^{k-1}\ \text{terms}} + \cdots
\tag{8}
$$

Proof. Let
$$s_n = u_1 + u_2 + \cdots + u_n$$
denote the nth partial sum of the series. Suppose the series converges to S; that is, suppose
$$\lim_{n \to \infty} s_n = S.$$

Then, corresponding to any preassigned positive number ϵ, there is an index N such that all terms of the sequence $\{s_n\}$ after the Nth one lie between $S - \epsilon/2$ and $S + \epsilon/2$. Hence no two of them may differ by as much as ϵ. That is, if m and n are both greater than N, then
$$|s_n - s_m| < \epsilon.$$

In particular, this inequality holds if
$$m = n - 1 \quad \text{and} \quad n > N + 1.$$
But
$$\begin{aligned}
s_n - s_{n-1} &= (u_1 + u_2 + \cdots + u_n) \\
&\quad - (u_1 + u_2 + \cdots + u_{n-1}) \\
&= u_n.
\end{aligned}$$
Therefore
$$|u_n| < \epsilon \quad \text{when } n > N + 1.$$

Since ϵ was any positive number whatever, this means that
$$\lim_{n \to \infty} u_n = 0. \quad \square$$

Remark 5. It is worth noting that the sum
$$u_1 + u_2 + \cdots + u_n$$
is always defined (if n is a positive integer and $u_1, u_2, \ldots, u_n$ are finite numbers). When the series
$$u_1 + u_2 + \cdots + u_n + \cdots$$
has a "sum," in the sense that its sequence of partial sums has a *limit*, the symbol "+" has acquired new meaning, as has the word "sum." We can now "add" infinitely many numbers, in certain cases, not by actual addition, but rather by the process of finding a *limit*. This is a typical illustration of the way in which mathematics generalizes familiar concepts to increase their usefulness.

Example 2. We shall illustrate the method of finding the "sum" of an infinite series for the case of the repeating decimal
$$0.3333\cdots = \frac{3}{10} + \frac{3}{100} + \frac{3}{1000} + \frac{3}{10,000} + \cdots.$$
Here
$$s_1 = \frac{3}{10},$$
$$s_2 = \frac{3}{10} + \frac{3}{10^2},$$
$$\vdots$$
$$s_n = \frac{3}{10} + \frac{3}{10^2} + \cdots + \frac{3}{10^n}.$$

We can obtain an explicit algebraic expression for s_n as follows. We multiply both sides of the equation for s_n by $\frac{1}{10}$ and obtain
$$\frac{1}{10} s_n = \frac{3}{10^2} + \frac{3}{10^3} + \cdots + \frac{3}{10^n} + \frac{3}{10^{n+1}}.$$

When we subtract this from s_n, we have
$$s_n - \frac{1}{10} s_n = \frac{3}{10} - \frac{3}{10^{n+1}} = \frac{3}{10}\left(1 - \frac{1}{10^n}\right).$$
Therefore
$$\frac{9}{10} s_n = \frac{3}{10}\left(1 - \frac{1}{10^n}\right),$$
or
$$s_n = \frac{3}{9}\left(1 - \frac{1}{10^n}\right).$$

Clearly, as n approaches ∞, $\left(\frac{1}{10}\right)^n$ approaches 0, and
$$\lim_{n \to \infty} s_n = \frac{3}{9} = \frac{1}{3}.$$

We can therefore write the sum of the infinite series:
$$\frac{3}{10} + \frac{3}{10^2} + \frac{3}{10^3} + \cdots + \frac{3}{10^n} + \cdots = \frac{1}{3}.$$

The repeating-decimal illustration is a special case of a *geometric series*.

Definition. *A series of the form*
$$a + ar + ar^2 + ar^3 + \cdots + ar^{n-1} + \cdots \quad (9)$$
is called a geometric series. The ratio of any term to the one before it is r, if $a \neq 0$.

The sum of the first n terms of (9) is

$$s_n = a + ar + ar^2 + \cdots + ar^{n-1}. \quad (10)$$

Multiplying both sides of (10) by r gives

$$rs_n = ar + ar^2 + \cdots + ar^{n-1} + ar^n. \quad (11)$$

When we subtract (11) from (10), many terms cancel on the right-hand side, leaving

$$(1 - r)s_n = a(1 - r^n). \quad (12)$$

If $r \neq 1$, we may divide (12) by $(1 - r)$:

$$s_n = \frac{a(1 - r^n)}{1 - r}, \quad r \neq 1. \quad (13a)$$

On the other hand, if $r = 1$ in (10), we get

$$s_n = na, \quad r = 1. \quad (13b)$$

We are interested in the limit as $n \to \infty$ in Eqs. (13a) and (13b).

Clearly (13b), with $r = 1$, has no finite limit if $a \neq 0$. If $a = 0$, the series (9) is just

$$0 + 0 + 0 + \cdots,$$

and it converges to the sum zero.

If $r \neq 1$, we use (13a). In the right-hand side of (13a), n appears only in the expression r^n. This approaches zero as $n \to \infty$, if $|r| < 1$. Therefore

$$\lim_{n \to \infty} s_n = \lim_{n \to \infty} \frac{a(1 - r^n)}{1 - r}$$
$$= \frac{a}{1 - r}, \quad \text{if } |r| < 1. \quad (14)$$

If $|r| > 1$, then $|r^n| \to \infty$, and (9) diverges if $a \neq 0$. The last case is the one in which $r = -1$. Then

$$s_1 = a, \quad s_2 = a - a = 0, \quad s_3 = a, \quad s_4 = 0, \quad \ldots$$

If $a \neq 0$, then this sequence of partial sums has no limit as $n \to \infty$, and the series (9) diverges.

We have thus proved the following theorem.

Theorem 2. *If $|r| < 1$, then the geometric series*

$$a + ar + ar^2 + \cdots + ar^{n-1} + \cdots$$

converges to the sum $a/(1 - r)$. If $|r| \geq 1$, the series diverges unless $a = 0$. If $a = 0$, the series converges to the sum 0.

14.3

Problem. A ball is dropped from a point a feet above a flat surface. Each time the ball hits the ground after falling a distance h it rebounds a distance rh, where r is a positive fraction less than one. Find the total distance the ball travels.

Solution. (See Fig. 14.3.) The distance is given by the series

$$s = a + 2ar + 2ar^2 + 2ar^3 + \cdots.$$

The terms following the first one form a geometric series of sum $2ar/(1 - r)$. Hence the distance is

$$s = a + \frac{2ar}{1 - r} = a\frac{1 + r}{1 - r}.$$

For instance, if $a = 6$ ft and $r = \frac{2}{3}$, the distance is

$$s = 6\frac{1 + \frac{2}{3}}{1 - \frac{2}{3}} = 30 \text{ ft}.$$

EXERCISES

Determine which of the following sequences $\{a_n\}$ converge and which of them diverge. Find the limit of each sequence that converges.

1. $a_n = \dfrac{2n + 1}{1 - 3n}$

2. $a_n = \dfrac{n^2 - n}{2n^2 + n}$

3. $a_n = 1 + \dfrac{(-1)^n}{n}$

4. $a_n = \dfrac{1 + (-1)^n}{n}$

5. $a_n = 1 + (-1)^n$

6. $a_n = \sin n$

7. $a_n = \tanh n$ 8. $a_n = \dfrac{\ln n}{n}$

9. $a_n = e^n$ 10. $a_n = e^{-n}$

11. Prove that a given sequence $\{a_n\}$ cannot converge to two different limits L and L'.
    Hint. Take $\epsilon = \frac{1}{2}|L - L'|$ in (2).

12. Suppose the sequence $\{a_n\}$ converges to the limit L and the sequence $\{b_n\}$ converges to L'. Show that
    (a) $\{a_n + b_n\}$ converges to $L + L'$,
    (b) $\{ca_n\}$ converges to cL,
    (c) $\{a_n \cdot b_n\}$ converges to $L \cdot L'$,
    (d) $\{a_n/b_n\}$ converges to L/L', if $L' \neq 0$.

13. (a) If each term of a given sequence $\{a_n\}$ is less than or equal to a constant M, that is,

    $$\text{if}\quad a_n \leq M \quad \text{for all } n = 1, 2, 3, \ldots,$$

    and if $\{a_n\}$ converges to L, show that L is also less than or equal to M.
    (b) Give an example of a sequence $\{a_n\}$ such that $a_n \leq 1$ for all $n = 1, 2, 3, \ldots,$ but such that the sequence has no limit.

Find an explicit algebraic expression for the sum of the first n terms of each of the following series. Then compute the sum of the series, if the series converges.

14. $\left(1 - \dfrac{1}{2}\right) + \left(\dfrac{1}{2} - \dfrac{1}{3}\right) + \left(\dfrac{1}{3} - \dfrac{1}{4}\right) + \cdots$

    $$+ \left(\dfrac{1}{n} - \dfrac{1}{n+1}\right) + \cdots$$

15. $\dfrac{1}{1 \cdot 2} + \dfrac{1}{2 \cdot 3} + \dfrac{1}{3 \cdot 4} + \cdots + \dfrac{1}{n(n+1)} + \cdots$

    Hint. Compare with Exercise 14.

16. $\ln \dfrac{1}{2} + \ln \dfrac{2}{3} + \ln \dfrac{3}{4} + \cdots + \ln \dfrac{n}{n+1} + \cdots$

17. $1 + \dfrac{1}{2} + \dfrac{1}{4} + \cdots + \dfrac{1}{2^{n-1}} + \cdots$

    Hint. Multiply s_n by $\frac{1}{2}$ and subtract the result from s_n.

18. $2 + \dfrac{2}{3} + \dfrac{2}{9} + \dfrac{2}{27} + \cdots + \dfrac{2}{3^{n-1}} + \cdots$

    Hint. Compute $s_n - \frac{1}{3}s_n$.

19. $5 - \dfrac{5}{2} + \dfrac{5}{4} - \dfrac{5}{8} + \cdots + \dfrac{(-1)^{n-1}5}{2^{n-1}} + \cdots$

    Hint. Compute $s_n + \frac{1}{2}s_n$.

20. $\dfrac{9}{100} + \dfrac{9}{(100)^2} + \dfrac{9}{(100)^3} + \cdots + \dfrac{9}{(100)^n} + \cdots$

21. A ball is dropped from a height of 4 ft. Each time it strikes the ground after falling from a height of h ft, it rebounds a distance $\frac{3}{4}h$ ft. Find the total distance traveled by the ball.

22. (a) Express the repeating decimal

    $$0.234\ 234\,\dot{\ }234 \ldots$$

    as a ratio p/q of integers p and q.
    (b) Is it true that *every* repeating decimal is a rational number p/q? Give a reason for your answer.

23. Express the decimal number

    $$1.24\ 123\ 123\ 123 \ldots$$

    (which is a repeating decimal after the first three figures) as a rational number p/q.

24. (a) Show by long division that

    $$\dfrac{1}{1+t} = 1 - t + t^2 - t^3 + \cdots$$
    $$+ (-1)^n t^n + \dfrac{(-1)^{n+1}t^{n+1}}{1+t}.$$

    (b) By integrating the equation of (a) with respect to t from 0 to x, show that

    $$\ln(1+x) = x - \dfrac{x^2}{2} + \dfrac{x^3}{3} - \dfrac{x^4}{4} + \cdots$$
    $$+ (-1)^n \dfrac{x^{n+1}}{n+1} + R,$$

    where

    $$R = (-1)^{n+1} \int_0^x \dfrac{t^{n+1}}{1+t}\, dt.$$

    (c) If $x > 0$, show that

    $$|R| \leq \int_0^x t^{n+1}\, dt = \dfrac{x^{n+2}}{n+2}.$$

    Hint. As t varies from 0 to x, $1 + t \geq 1$.

    (d) If $x = \frac{1}{2}$, how large should n be, in (c) above, to guarantee that $|R| < 0.001$?
    (e) If $x = 1$, how large should n be, in (c) above, to guarantee that $|R| < 0.001$?

14.2 TESTS FOR CONVERGENCE OF A SERIES OF CONSTANTS

It is sometimes hard to apply the definition of convergence given in Article 14.1. This is true when we can't find any simple expression for the sum of the first n terms of a series as a function of n. In the present article, we shall learn several tests for determining whether or not a given series converges, tests that depend on the individual terms of the series rather than on their sums.

Consider a series of numbers

$$\sum_{k=1}^{\infty} u_k = u_1 + u_2 + u_3 + \cdots + u_n + \cdots. \quad (1)$$

As in Article 14.1, we say that the series (1) converges if the sequence s_n of partial sums

$$
\begin{aligned}
s_1 &= u_1, \\
s_2 &= u_1 + u_2, \\
&\vdots \\
s_n &= u_1 + u_2 + \cdots + u_n
\end{aligned}
\quad (2)
$$

tends to a definite finite limit as n increases without bound. If the partial sums s_n do not have such a limit, then the series is said to diverge. Most of the series considered in this book belong to one or the other of the following two types:

1. *Positive series:* Those in which all terms of the series are positive numbers.

2. *Alternating series:* Those in which the terms are alternately positive and negative. For example,

$$a_1 - a_2 + a_3 - a_4 + \cdots, \quad (3)$$

when each of the a's is positive.

Positive series

Suppose all the numbers u_k in (1) are positive. Then when we calculate the partial sums s_1, s_2, s_3, and so on, we see that each one is greater than its predecessor, since $s_{n+1} = s_n + u_{n+1}$. That is,

$$s_1 \leq s_2 \leq s_3 \leq \cdots \leq s_n \leq s_{n+1}. \quad (4)$$

A sequence $\{s_n\}$ that has the property (4) is called an *increasing* sequence. Theorem 3 gives the cardinal principle governing increasing sequences.

Theorem 3. *Let s_1, s_2, s_3, ... be an increasing sequence of real numbers. Then one or the other of the following alternatives must hold.*

A. *There is a finite constant M such that all terms of the sequence are less than or equal to M. In this case the sequence possesses a definite finite limit L which is also less than or equal to M.*

B. *The sequence diverges to plus infinity; that is, the numbers in the sequence $\{s_n\}$ ultimately exceed any preassigned number, no matter how large.*

14.4

We shall not attempt to give a rigorous proof of this theorem, but we may gain an intuitive appreciation of the result by adopting the following graphical approach. Suppose we plot the points $(1, s_1), (2, s_2), \ldots, (n, s_n)$ in the xy-plane (Fig. 14.4). Then if there is a line $y = M$ such that *none* of the points (n, s_n) lies above this line, it is intuitively clear that there is a *lowest* such line. That is, there is a line

$$y = L$$

such that none of the points lies above it but such that there are points (n, s_n) that lie above any *lower* line

$$y = L - \epsilon,$$

where ϵ is any positive number. Analytically, this means that the number L has the properties that

(a) $s_n \leq L$ for *all* values of n, and

(b) given any $\epsilon > 0$, there exists at least one integer N such that

$$s_N > L - \epsilon.$$

Then the fact that $\{s_n\}$ is an increasing sequence tells us further that

$$s_n \geq s_N > L - \epsilon \quad \text{for all } n \geq N.$$

This means that *all* the numbers s_n beyond the Nth one in the sequence lie within ϵ distance of L. This is precisely the condition for L to be the limit of the sequence s_n:

$$L = \lim_{n \to \infty} s_n.$$

Alternative B of the theorem comes into play when there are points (n, s_n) above any given line $y = M$, no matter how large M may be.

The theorem does not tell us how to find the limit L when it exists; it simply tells us whether or not there is such a limit. Briefly, it says that a *positive series either converges or else it becomes infinite.* Divergence by oscillation is ruled out.

Example 1. The series

$$\sum_{k=0}^{\infty} \frac{1}{k!} = 1 + \frac{1}{1!} + \frac{1}{2!} + \frac{1}{3!} + \cdots$$

converges because its terms are all less than or equal to the corresponding terms in the series

$$1 + \sum_{k=0}^{\infty} \frac{1}{2^k} = 1 + 1 + \frac{1}{2} + \frac{1}{2^2} + \cdots.$$

After its first term, the latter series is a simple geometric series of ratio $\frac{1}{2}$. The sum of terms after the first is $1/(1 - \frac{1}{2}) = 2$, so the sum of the series is 3. The partial sums of the first series are all less than 3. Hence the first series converges by virtue of our theorem about positive series, and its sum is less than or equal to 3. In fact, it is the series for e.

Example 2. The terms of the "harmonic" series

$$\sum_{k=1}^{\infty} \frac{1}{k} = 1 + \frac{1}{2} + \frac{1}{3} + \cdots$$

may be interpreted as representing the areas of rectangles, each of base unity and having altitudes equal

14.5

to $1, \frac{1}{2}, \frac{1}{3}, \ldots$, respectively. If we consider the sum of the first n terms of the series,

$$s_n = 1 + \frac{1}{2} + \frac{1}{3} + \cdots + \frac{1}{n},$$

we see (Fig. 14.5) that this represents the sum of the areas of n rectangles each of which is somewhat greater than the area under the corresponding portion of the curve $y = 1/x$. Therefore s_n is greater than the area under this curve between $x = 1$ and $x = n + 1$:

$$s_n > \int_1^{n+1} \frac{dx}{x} = \ln(n + 1).$$

By taking n sufficiently large, we can make

$$\ln(n + 1)$$

as large as we please:

$$\lim_{n \to \infty} \ln(n + 1) = +\infty.$$

Since $s_n > \ln(n + 1)$, this also means

$$\lim_{n \to \infty} s_n = +\infty.$$

Therefore the series

$$1 + \frac{1}{2} + \frac{1}{3} + \cdots + \frac{1}{n} + \cdots$$

diverges to plus infinity.

In the two examples just discussed we made two *comparisons*: first, between the given series and another series (Example 1), and second, between the given series and an integral (Example 2). We now state a theorem which embodies the so-called *comparison test* for positive series.

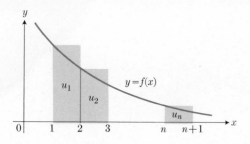

a|b

14.6

Theorem 4. *If each term of the positive series*

$$\sum_{k=1}^{\infty} u_k = u_1 + u_2 + u_3 + \cdots$$

is less *than the corresponding term of a known* convergent *series*

$$\sum_{k=1}^{\infty} c_k = c_1 + c_2 + c_3 + \cdots,$$

then $\sum u_k$ *converges. But if each term of the series* $\sum u_k$ *is* greater *than the corresponding term of a known* divergent *positive series*

$$\sum_{k=1}^{\infty} d_k = d_1 + d_2 + d_3 + \cdots,$$

then $\sum u_k$ *diverges.*

This theorem is an immediate consequence of Theorem 1.

When we compare a positive series with an integral, as we did above in Example 2, we are led to the *integral test*, which we now state as a theorem.

Theorem 5. *Suppose there is a decreasing continuous function* $f(x)$ *such that* $f(n) = u_n$ *is the nth term of the positive series*

$$u_1 + u_2 + \cdots + u_n + \cdots.$$

Then

the series $\sum_{n=1}^{\infty} u_n$ *and the integral* $\displaystyle\int_{1}^{\infty} f(x)\, dx$

both converge or both diverge.

Proof. See Fig. 14.6(a). The rectangles of areas $u_1, u_2, \ldots, u_n$ enclose more area than that under

the curve from $x = 1$ to $x = n + 1$; that is,

$$u_1 + u_2 + \cdots + u_n > \int_{1}^{n+1} f(x)\, dx.$$

In Fig. 14.6(b), the rectangles have been faced to the left instead of to the right. If we momentarily disregard the first rectangle, of area u_1, we see that

$$u_2 + u_3 + \cdots + u_n < \int_{1}^{n} f(x)\, dx.$$

If we include u_1, we have

$$u_1 + u_2 + \cdots + u_n < u_1 + \int_{1}^{n} f(x)\, dx.$$

Combining these results, we have

$$\int_{1}^{n+1} f(x)\, dx < u_1 + u_2 + \cdots + u_n < u_1 + \int_{1}^{n} f(x)\, dx.$$

If the integral $\int_{1}^{\infty} f(x)\, dx$ is finite, the right-hand inequality shows that the infinite series

$$\sum_{n=1}^{\infty} u_n$$

is also finite. But if $\int_{1}^{\infty} f(x)\, dx$ is infinite, then the left-hand inequality shows that the series is also infinite. Hence the series and the integral are both finite or both infinite. $\square$

Example 3. The *p*-series

$$\frac{1}{1^p} + \frac{1}{2^p} + \frac{1}{3^p} + \cdots + \frac{1}{n^p} + \cdots$$

converges if $p > 1$ and diverges if $p \le 1$. To prove this, let

$$f(x) = 1/x^p.$$

Then, if $p > 1$, we have

$$\int_1^\infty x^{-p}\, dx = \lim_{b\to\infty} \frac{x^{-p+1}}{-p+1}\Big]_1^b = \frac{1}{p-1},$$

which is finite. Hence the p-series converges if p is greater than one.

If $p = 1$, we have the *harmonic series*

$$1 + \frac{1}{2} + \frac{1}{3} + \cdots + \frac{1}{n} + \cdots,$$

which we already know diverges. Alternatively, by the integral test,

$$\int_1^\infty x^{-1}\, dx = \lim_{b\to\infty} \ln x\Big]_1^b = +\infty,$$

and since the integral diverges, the series does likewise.

Finally, if $p < 1$, then the terms of the p-series are greater than the corresponding terms of the divergent harmonic series. Hence the p-series diverges when $p < 1$, by the comparison test.

Remark 1. An integral may also be used to advantage to estimate the remainder R_n after n terms of a convergent series.

Example 4. Suppose we are interested in learning the numerical value of the series

$$\sum_{k=1}^\infty \frac{1}{k^2} = \frac{1}{1^2} + \frac{1}{2^2} + \frac{1}{3^2} + \cdots.$$

This is a p-series with $p = 2$, and hence we know that it converges. This means that the sequence of partial sums s_n,

$$s_n = \frac{1}{1^2} + \frac{1}{2^2} + \cdots + \frac{1}{n^2},$$

possesses a limit L. When n is "large enough," s_n is "close to" L. If we want to know L to a couple of decimal places, we might try to find an integer n such that the corresponding *finite* sum s_n differs from L by less, say, than 0.005. Then we would use this s_n in place of L, to two decimals. If we write

$$L = \sum_{k=1}^\infty \frac{1}{k^2} = \frac{1}{1^2} + \frac{1}{2^2} + \cdots + \frac{1}{n^2} + \frac{1}{(n+1)^2} + \cdots$$

and

$$s_n = \sum_{k=1}^n \frac{1}{k^2} = \frac{1}{1^2} + \frac{1}{2^2} + \cdots + \frac{1}{n^2},$$

14.7

we see that the error R_n is

$$R_n = L - s_n = \frac{1}{(n+1)^2} + \cdots.$$

We may estimate this error by thinking of the area under the curve

$$y = 1/x^2$$

from $x = n$ to ∞. From Fig. 14.7, we see that

$$R_n < \int_n^\infty \frac{1}{x^2}\, dx = \frac{1}{n},$$

which tells us that by taking 200 terms of the series, we can be sure that the difference between the sum L of the entire series and the sum s_{200} of these 200 terms will be less than 0.005.

A somewhat closer estimate of R_n results from using the trapezoidal rule to approximate the area under the curve in Fig. 14.7. Let us write u_k for $1/k^2$ and consider the trapezoidal approximation

$$\begin{aligned}
T_n &= \sum_{k=n}^\infty \tfrac{1}{2}(u_k + u_{k+1}) \\
&= \tfrac{1}{2}(u_n + u_{n+1}) + \tfrac{1}{2}(u_{n+1} + u_{n+2}) + \cdots \\
&= \tfrac{1}{2}u_n + u_{n+1} + u_{n+2} + \cdots = \tfrac{1}{2}u_n + R_n.
\end{aligned}$$

Now since the curve $y = 1/x^2$ is concave upward, it is clear that

$$T_n > \int_n^\infty \frac{1}{x^2}\, dx = \frac{1}{n},$$

and we have

$$R_n = T_n - \tfrac{1}{2}u_n > \frac{1}{n} - \frac{1}{2n^2}.$$

We now know that

$$\frac{1}{n} > R_n > \frac{1}{n} - \frac{1}{2n^2},$$

and $L = s_n + R_n$ may be estimated as follows:

$$s_n + \frac{1}{n} > L > s_n + \frac{1}{n} - \frac{1}{2n^2}.$$

Thus, by using $s_n + 1/n$ in place of s_n to estimate L, we shall be making an error which is numerically less than $1/(2n^2)$. By taking $n \geq 10$, this error is then made less than 0.005. The difference in time required to compute the sum of 10 terms versus 200 terms is sufficiently great to make this sharper analysis of practical importance.

What we have done in this specific example may be done in any case where the graph of the function $y = f(x)$ is concave upward, as in Fig. 14.7. We find that

$$u_1 + u_2 + \cdots + u_n + \int_n^\infty f(x)\,dx \qquad (5)$$

tends to overestimate the value of the series, but by an amount that is less than $u_n/2$.

Ratio test

The ratios

$$(u_2/u_1),\ (u_3/u_2),\ (u_4/u_3),\ \ldots,\ (u_{n+1}/u_n),\ \ldots$$

measure the rate of growth of the terms of a series. In a geometric series

$$1 + r + r^2 + r^3 + \cdots,$$

this rate of growth is a constant, r. We shall show that if the rate of growth in a positive series tends to a definite limit ρ as n becomes infinite:

$$\rho = \lim_{n\to\infty} \frac{u_{n+1}}{u_n},$$

then

(a) the series *converges* if $\rho < 1$,

(b) the series *diverges* if $\rho > 1$,

(c) the series may converge or it may diverge if $\rho = 1$.

(Remember that we are still speaking about *positive* series.)

To establish the validity of the ratio test, suppose we assume first that ρ is less than one. Let r be a number between ρ and one, for example,

$$r = (1 + \rho)/2.$$

Then the number ϵ defined by the equation

$$\epsilon = r - \rho$$

is positive. Since

$$\rho = \lim_{n\to\infty} \frac{u_{n+1}}{u_n},$$

we know that u_{n+1}/u_n must lie within a distance ϵ of ρ when n is large enough, say for all $n \geq N$. Then, in particular,

$$\frac{u_{n+1}}{u_n} < r = \rho + \epsilon \quad \text{when } n \geq N.$$

That is,

$$u_{N+1} < ru_N,$$
$$u_{N+2} < ru_{N+1} < r^2 u_N,$$
$$u_{N+3} < ru_{N+2} < r^3 u_N,$$
$$\vdots$$
$$u_{N+m} < ru_{N+m-1} < r^m u_N,$$

and

$$u_1 + u_2 + \cdots + u_N + u_{N+1} + u_{N+2} + \cdots$$
$$< u_1 + u_2 + \cdots + u_{N-1}$$
$$+ u_N(1 + r + r^2 + \cdots). \qquad (6)$$

Since $|r|$ is less than one, the geometric series $1 + r + r^2 + \cdots$ converges, and the right-hand side of the inequality (6) is finite. Therefore the series on the left converges, by the comparison test.

Next, suppose ρ is greater than one. Then, from some index m on, we have

$$\frac{u_{n+1}}{u_n} \geq 1 \qquad (n \geq m),$$

or

$$u_{m+1} \geq u_m,\ u_{m+2} \geq u_{m+1} \geq u_m,\ \ldots$$

Since u_m is positive, the sum of the terms

$$u_m + u_{m+1} + u_{m+2} + \cdots + u_{m+q}$$
$$\geq u_m(1 + 1 + \cdots + 1) = (q + 1)u_m$$

tends to infinity as q does. Hence in this case the series diverges.

Finally, the two series

$$\sum_{n=1}^{\infty} \frac{1}{n} \quad \text{and} \quad \sum_{n=1}^{\infty} \frac{1}{n^2}$$

both have rate-of-growth ratios that approach one as limit. Since one of these series converges while the other diverges, we have specific examples which show that the ratio test cannot be used to distinguish between convergence and divergence in case $\rho = 1$.

Remark 2. The ratio test is also useful in estimating the truncation error which results from using

$$s_N = u_1 + u_2 + \cdots + u_N$$

as an approximation to the sum of a convergent series

$$S = u_1 + u_2 + \cdots + u_N + (u_{N+1} + \cdots).$$

Suppose that $n \leq N$, and we know that the rate-of-growth ratio lies between two constants r_1 and r_2, both of which are positive and less than one:

$$r_1 \leq \frac{u_{n+1}}{u_n} \leq r_2 \quad \text{for} \quad n \geq N;$$

then the inequalities

$$r_1 u_n \leq u_{n+1} \leq r_2 u_n, \quad n = N, N+1, N+2, \ldots,$$

enable us to deduce that

$$u_N(r_1 + r_1^2 + r_1^3 + \cdots)$$
$$\leq u_{N+1} + u_{N+2} + u_{N+3} + \cdots$$
$$\leq u_N(r_2 + r_2^2 + r_2^3 + \cdots).$$

The two geometric series have sums

$$r_1 + r_1^2 + r_1^3 + \cdots = \frac{r_1}{1 - r_1},$$

$$r_2 + r_2^2 + r_2^3 + \cdots = \frac{r_2}{1 - r_2}.$$

Hence the error

$$R_N = u_{N+1} + u_{N+2} + u_{N+3} + \cdots$$

lies between

$$\frac{r_1 u_N}{1 - r_1} \quad \text{and} \quad \frac{r_2 u_N}{1 - r_2}.$$

That is,

$$\frac{r_1 u_N}{1 - r_1} \leq \sum_{k=1}^{\infty} u_k - \sum_{k=1}^{N} u_k \leq \frac{r_2 u_N}{1 - r_2} \quad \text{(7a)}$$

if

$$0 \leq r_1 \leq \frac{u_{n+1}}{u_n} \leq r_2 < 1, \quad \text{for } n \geq N. \quad \text{(7b)}$$

Problem 1. For what values of x does the series

$$x + \frac{x^3}{3} + \frac{x^5}{5} + \frac{x^7}{7} + \cdots \quad \text{(8)}$$

converge?

Solution. The nth term of the series (assuming the law of formation as indicated) is

$$u_n = \frac{x^{2n-1}}{2n - 1}.$$

We consider first the case where x is positive. Then the series is a positive series and the rate-of-growth ratio is

$$\frac{u_{n+1}}{u_n} = \frac{(2n - 1)}{(2n + 1)} x^2,$$

with limit

$$\rho = \lim_{n \to \infty} \frac{2n - 1}{2n + 1} x^2 = x^2.$$

The ratio test therefore tells us that the series converges if x is positive and less than one, and diverges if x is greater than one.

Since only odd powers of x occur in the series, we see that the series simply changes sign when x is replaced by $-x$. Therefore the series also converges for

$$-1 < x \leq 0,$$

and diverges for $x < -1$. The series converges to zero when $x = 0$.

We know, thus far, that the series

$$\text{converges for } |x| < 1,$$
$$\text{diverges for } |x| > 1,$$

but we don't know what happens when $|x| = 1$. To test at $x = 1$, we apply the integral test to the series

$$1 + \frac{1}{3} + \frac{1}{5} + \frac{1}{7} + \cdots + \frac{1}{2n - 1} + \cdots,$$

which we get by taking $x = 1$ in the series (8). The companion integral is

$$\int_1^\infty \frac{dx}{2x - 1} = \tfrac{1}{2} \ln (2x - 1) \Big]_1^\infty = \infty.$$

Hence the series diverges to $+\infty$ when $x = 1$, and it diverges to $-\infty$ when $x = -1$. We may therefore say that the only values of x for which the given series converges are $-1 < x < 1$.

EXERCISES

1. Prove that if $\sum u_k$ is a positive series and c is a positive constant, then $\sum u_k$ and $\sum (cu_k)$ both converge or both diverge.

2. What are the two alternatives, analogous to A and B of Theorem 1, for a sequence $\{s_n\}$ that is monotonically decreasing as n increases; that is, for which

$$s_1 \geq s_2 \geq s_3 \geq \cdots \geq s_n \geq s_{n+1} \geq \cdots?$$

Draw a graph to illustrate what happens when all terms of the sequence are greater than or equal to some constant m.

3. (a) Show that the sequence of numbers

$$s_n = \left(1 + \frac{1}{n}\right)^n$$

is an increasing sequence and that each s_n is less than 3.

Hint. Expand $(1 + 1/n)^n$ by the binomial theorem and show that

$$\left(1 + \frac{1}{n}\right)^n$$

$$= 1 + 1 + \frac{\left(1 - \dfrac{1}{n}\right)}{2!} + \frac{\left(1 - \dfrac{1}{n}\right)\left(1 - \dfrac{2}{n}\right)}{3!} + \cdots$$

$$+ \frac{\left(1 - \dfrac{1}{n}\right)\left(1 - \dfrac{2}{n}\right)\cdots\left(1 - \dfrac{n-1}{n}\right)}{n!}.$$

(b) From these two statements, what conclusion can we draw about the existence of the limit of s_n as n becomes infinite?

4. Consider the sequence of numbers

$$1, 0, 1, 0, 1, 0, \ldots$$

formed according to the rule

$$s_{2m-1} = 1, \quad s_{2m} = 0.$$

Does this sequence have a limit as n becomes infinite? Give a reason for your answer.

In Exercises 5 through 19, determine whether the given series converge or diverge. In each case, give a reason for your answer.

5. $\displaystyle\sum_{n=1}^{\infty} \frac{1}{10n}$

6. $\displaystyle\sum_{n=1}^{\infty} \frac{n.}{n+2}$

7. $\displaystyle\sum_{n=1}^{\infty} \frac{\sin^2 n}{2^n}$

8. $\displaystyle\sum_{n=1}^{\infty} \frac{n}{n^2 + 1}$

9. $\displaystyle\sum_{n=1}^{\infty} \frac{1}{1 + \ln n}$

10. $\displaystyle\sum_{n=3}^{\infty} \frac{1}{n \ln n}$

11. $\displaystyle\sum_{n=0}^{\infty} \frac{1}{(2n + 1)!}$

12. $\displaystyle\sum_{n=1}^{\infty} \frac{1}{n^2 + 1}$

13. $\displaystyle\sum_{n=1}^{\infty} \frac{\sqrt{n}}{n^2 + 1}$

14. $\displaystyle\sum_{n=1}^{\infty} \frac{n!}{n^n}$

15. $\displaystyle\sum_{n=1}^{\infty} \frac{(n + 1)(n + 2)}{n!}$

16. $\displaystyle\sum_{n=1}^{\infty} \frac{n^2}{2^n}$

17. $\displaystyle\sum_{n=0}^{\infty} \frac{(n + 3)!}{3! n! 3^n}$

18. $\displaystyle\sum_{n=1}^{\infty} \frac{2^n}{n^3 + 1}$

19. $\displaystyle\sum_{n=1}^{\infty} \frac{10^n}{n!}$

14.3 POWER SERIES EXPANSIONS OF FUNCTIONS

The rational operations of arithmetic are addition, subtraction, multiplication, and division. Using only these simple operations, we can evaluate any rational function of x. But other functions, such as $\ln x$, e^x, $\sin x$, and so on, cannot be evaluated so simply. Of course, these functions are so important that their values have been computed and the results printed in mathematical tables. But we may wonder how the tables were computed. The answer is: from power series.

Definition. *A power series is an expression of the form*

$$\sum_{k=0}^{\infty} a_k x^k = a_0 + a_1 x + a_2 x^2 + \cdots .$$

In this article we shall show how to use power series to represent a wide variety of functions.

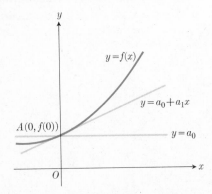

14.8 The tangent line $y = a_0 + a_1 x$ serves to approximate the function $y = f(x)$ for small values of x.

We shall concern ourselves with the problem of approximating a given function

$$y = f(x) \qquad (1)$$

by a sequence of polynomials $f_n(x)$ of the form

$$f_n(x) = a_0 + a_1 x + a_2 x^2 + \cdots + a_n x^n. \qquad (2)$$

In particular, since we expect to take larger and larger values of n, we shall be interested in making the approximation good for small values of x, since we want the terms that come far out in the series to be small. Hence we first focus our attention on a portion of the curve $y = f(x)$ in the neighborhood of the point $A(0, f(0))$ in Fig. 14.8. We then ask the following questions.

Question. What polynomial

$$y = f_0(x) = a_0,$$

of degree zero, gives the closest approximation to the given curve in the immediate neighborhood of the point A?

Answer. We want the horizontal line $y = a_0$ to pass through A. Hence we take $a_0 = f(0)$, which is the value of the given function at $x = 0$.

Question. What polynomial

$$y = a_0 + a_1 x,$$

of degree one, comes closest to fitting the given curve in the neighborhood of the point A?

Answer. The tangent line. That is, we want this approximating line to pass through A and to have the same slope there that the given curve has. This means that we should take

$$a_0 = f(0) \quad \text{and} \quad a_1 = f'(0).$$

Question. More generally, what polynomial

$$y = a_0 + a_1 x + a_2 x^2 + \cdots + a_n x^n,$$

of degree n, comes closest to fitting the given curve near A?

Answer. We take the approximating curve that passes through A and has the highest possible degree of contact with the given curve at A, in the sense that its derivatives of orders one, two, three, $\ldots$, n match the corresponding derivatives of the given function there. Thus, if we write

$$f_n(x) = a_0 + a_1 x + a_2 x^2 + a_3 x^3 + \cdots + a_n x^n$$

for the approximating polynomial, then its derivatives are

$$f_n'(x) = a_1 + 2a_2 x + 3a_3 x^2 + \cdots + na_n x^{n-1},$$
$$f_n''(x) = 2a_2 + 3 \cdot 2a_3 x + \cdots + n(n-1)a_n x^{n-2},$$
$$\vdots$$
$$f_n^{(n)}(x) = n!a_n.$$

We substitute $x = 0$ on the right-hand side of each of the above equations and set the results, respectively, equal to the values

$$f(0), f'(0), f''(0), \ldots, f^{(n)}(0)$$

of the given function and its first n derivatives at $x = 0$. We then determine the coefficients

$$a_0, a_1, a_2, \ldots, a_n$$

of the approximating polynomial $y = f_n(x)$ that has the highest degree of contact with the given curve at $A(0, f(0))$:

$$a_0 = f(0),$$
$$a_1 = f'(0),$$
$$a_2 = \frac{f''(0)}{2!},$$
$$\vdots$$
$$a_n = \frac{f^{(n)}(0)}{n!}.$$

That is, for our approximating polynomial of degree n, we take

$$f_n(x) = f(0) + f'(0)x + \frac{f''(0)}{2!}x^2$$
$$+ \frac{f'''(0)}{3!}x^3 + \cdots + \frac{f^{(n)}(0)}{n!}x^n. \quad (3)$$

Problem 1. Compute the polynomial $f_n(x)$ given by Eq. 3 that would be used to approximate the exponential function $f(x) = e^x$ near $x = 0$.

Solution. We require $f(0), f'(0), \ldots, f^{(n)}(0)$. For the given function,

$$f(x) = e^x; \qquad f(0) = e^0 = 1,$$

and

$$f'(x) = e^x; \qquad f'(0) = 1,$$
$$\vdots \qquad\qquad \vdots$$
$$f^{(n)}(x) = e^x; \qquad f^{(n)}(0) = 1.$$

Therefore we have

$$f_n(x) = 1 + x + \frac{x^2}{2!} + \frac{x^3}{3!} + \cdots + \frac{x^n}{n!}. \quad (4)$$

The question now naturally arises as to whether, for a fixed value of x, our approximating polynomials $f_n(x)$ converge to $f(x)$ as $n \to \infty$. Since $f_n(x)$ of Eq. (3) is the nth partial sum of the infinite series

$$f(0) + f'(0) \cdot x + \frac{f''(0)}{2!}x^2 + \cdots + \frac{f^{(n)}(0)}{n!}x^n + \cdots, \quad (5)$$

the question just posed is equivalent to inquiring whether the series (5) converges to $f(x)$ as sum. Of course, *every* one of our approximating polynomials has the correct value $f(0)$ at $x = 0$, but we are interested now in knowing also how far we may go away from $x = 0$ and still have convergence.

The series (5) is known as *Maclaurin's series* for the given function $f(x)$. If, instead of approximating to the function $f(x)$ for the values of x near zero, we are concerned with values of x near a, we write our approximating polynomials in powers of $x - a$:

$$f_n(x) = a_0 + a_1(x - a)$$
$$+ a_2(x - a)^2 + \cdots + a_n(x - a)^n.$$

When we now determine the coefficients

$$a_0, a_1, \ldots, a_n$$

so that the polynomial and its first n derivatives agree with the given function and its first n derivatives, at $x = a$, we are led to the series

$$f(a) + f'(a)(x - a) + \frac{f''(a)}{2!}(x - a)^2$$
$$+ \frac{f'''(a)}{3!}(x - a)^3 + \cdots$$
$$+ \frac{f^{(n)}(a)}{n!}(x - a)^n + \cdots, \quad (6)$$

where $f^{(n)}(a)$ denotes the value of the nth derivative of the function $f(x)$ at $x = a$. This is known as the *Taylor series* expansion of $f(x)$ about $x = a$. Since this includes the Maclaurin series, (5), as a special case, [namely, Eq. (6) with $a = 0$], we shall henceforth concern ourselves with the Taylor series. Since Eq. (6) calls for derivatives of *all* orders at $x = a$, it is clear that a function cannot possess a Taylor series expansion about $x = a$ unless the function possesses finite derivatives of all orders at $x = a$. For instance, $f(x) = \ln x$ does not possess a Maclaurin series expansion $(a = 0)$, since the function itself (to say nothing of its derivatives) does not have a finite value at $x = 0$. On the other hand, it does possess a Taylor series expansion in powers of $(x - 1)$, since $\ln x$ and all its derivatives are finite at $x = 1$.

Problem 2. Find the Maclaurin series expansion for the function $f(x) = (1 + x)^m$.

Solution. We need the derivatives

$$f'(x) = m(1 + x)^{m-1},$$
$$f''(x) = m(m - 1)(1 + x)^{m-2},$$
$$f'''(x) = m(m - 1)(m - 2)(1 + x)^{m-3},$$
$$\vdots$$
$$f^{(k)}(x) = m(m - 1)(m - 2) \cdots (m - k + 1)(1 + x)^{m-k}.$$

If we substitute the values of these derivatives at $x = 0$ into the basic Maclaurin series, (5):

$$f(0) + f'(0)x + \frac{f''(0)}{2!} x^2 + \cdots + \frac{f^{(k)}(0)}{k!} x^k + \cdots,$$

we then obtain

$$1 + mx + \frac{m(m - 1)}{2!} x^2 + \cdots$$
$$+ \frac{m(m - 1)(m - 2) \cdots (m - k + 1)}{k!} x^k + \cdots.$$

For a proof that this series converges to the given function $f(x) = (1 + x)^m$ when $|x| < 1$, see Olmsted, *Advanced Calculus*, pp. 423–425.

EXERCISES

In Exercises 1 through 6, use Eq. (3) to calculate the polynomial $f_n(x)$ that is associated with the given function $f(x)$.

1. e^{-x}

2. $\sin x$

3. $\cos x$

4. $\sin (x + \pi/4)$

5. $\sinh x$

6. $\cosh x$

In Exercises 7 through 13, use Eq. (6) to find the Taylor series expansion of the given function about the given value of a.

7. $f(x) = \ln x$ $a = 1$

8. $f(x) = \sqrt{x}$, $a = 4$

9. $f(x) = 1/x$, $a = -1$

10. $f(x) = \tan x$, $a = \pi/4$ (Find three terms of the series.)

11. $f(x) = \ln \cos x$, $a = \pi/3$ (Find three terms of the series.)

12. $f(x) = \sin x$, $a = \pi/6$

13. $f(x) = \cos x$, $a = -\pi/4$

14.4 TAYLOR'S THEOREM WITH REMAINDER

In the previous article, we raised some questions about convergence of the Taylor series. In this section, we give a theorem which answers some of these questions. Unfortunately, although several proofs of the theorem are known, none of them is easily motivated. The path we shall follow in arriving at the theorem starts with the simple formula

$$\int_a^b f'(t)\, dt = f(t) \Big]_a^b = f(b) - f(a). \qquad (1)$$

We integrate the left side of (1) by parts, with

$$u = f'(t), \qquad dv = dt,$$
$$du = f''(t)\, dt, \qquad v = t - b,$$

where we introduce the constant of integration $-b$ for future convenience. Thus we have

$$\int_a^b f'(t)\, dt = (t - b)f'(t) \Big]_a^b - \int_a^b (t - b)f''(t)\, dt$$
$$= (b - a)f'(a) + \int_a^b (b - t)f''(t)\, dt.$$

We perform a further integration by parts, this time with

$$u = f''(t), \qquad dv = (b - t)\, dt,$$
$$du = f'''(t)\, dt, \qquad v = -\frac{(b - t)^2}{2}.$$

Using this set of substitutions, we then arrive at the expression

$$\int_a^b (b-t)f''(t)\, dt = -\left.\frac{(b-t)^2}{2}f''(t)\right]_a^b + \int_a^b \frac{(b-t)^2}{2}f'''(t)\, dt = \frac{(b-a)^2}{2!}f''(a) + \int_a^b \frac{(b-t)^2}{2!}f'''(t)\, dt.$$

By continuing in this fashion, we find

$$\int_a^b f'(t)\, dt = (b-a)f'(a) + \frac{(b-a)^2}{2!}f''(a) + \frac{(b-a)^3}{3!}f'''(a) + \cdots + \frac{(b-a)^n}{n!}f^{(n)}(a) + \int_a^b \frac{(b-t)^n}{n!}f^{(n+1)}(t)\, dt.$$

Comparing this with Eq. (1), we have

$$f(b) = f(a) + (b-a)f'(a) + \frac{(b-a)^2}{2!}f''(a) + \cdots + \frac{(b-a)^n}{n!}f^{(n)}(a) + \int_a^b \frac{(b-t)^n}{n!}f^{(n+1)}(t)\, dt.$$

We may now replace b by x, and write

$$f(x) = f(a) + (x-a)f'(a) + \frac{(x-a)^2}{2!}f''(a) + \cdots + \frac{(x-a)^n}{n!}f^{(n)}(a) + R_n(x,a), \qquad (2)$$

where

$$R_n(x,a) = \int_a^x \frac{(x-t)^n}{n!}f^{(n+1)}(t)\, dt. \qquad (3)$$

The term $R_n(x,a)$ is called the *remainder* in the Taylor series expansion for $f(x)$. If the remainder is omitted in Eq. (2), the polynomial on the right-hand side of the equation gives only an approximation to the function on the left. The error in this approximation is what is measured by $R_n(x,a)$. Hence, to investigate convergence of the series, we need to investigate this remainder. First of all, the series converges to $f(x)$ if and only if

$$\lim_{n\to\infty} R_n(x,a) = 0. \qquad (4)$$

When (4) holds, however, we may also write

$$f(x) = \sum_{k=0}^{\infty} \frac{f^{(k)}(a)}{k!}(x-a)^k,$$

since the series on the right converges, at x, to the value $f(x)$. It is often possible to show that the remainder does approach zero without evaluating the integral in (3) explicitly. (See Exercises 1 and 3 and Example 1 below.)

The application of integration by parts n times in succession requires, of course, that the integral in Eq. (3) exist. This will indeed be the case if the derivative of order $(n+1)$ of the function exists and is continuous in some closed interval that includes the range of integration $[a, x]$ in (3).

Taylor's theorem. *Let f be a function that is continuous together with its first $n+1$ derivatives on an interval containing a and x. Then the value of the function at x is given by*

$$f(x) = f(a) + f'(a)(x-a)$$
$$+ \frac{f''(a)}{2!}(x-a)^2$$
$$+ \frac{f'''(a)}{3!}(x-a)^3 + \cdots$$
$$+ \frac{f^{(n)}(a)}{n!}(x-a)^n + R_n(x,a),$$

where

$$R_n(x,a) = \int_a^x \frac{(x-t)^n}{n!}f^{(n+1)}(t)\, dt.$$

Example 1. Let $f(x) = e^x$. This function and all its derivatives are everywhere continuous, so Taylor's theorem may be applied with any convenient value of a. We select $a = 0$, since the values of f and its derivatives are easy to compute there. Taylor's theorem leads to

$$e^x = 1 + x + \frac{x^2}{2!} + \frac{x^3}{3!} + \cdots + \frac{x^n}{n!} + R_n(x,0), \qquad (5)$$

which contains the remainder

$$R_n(x, 0) = \int_0^x \frac{(x - t)^n}{n!} e^t \, dt. \tag{6}$$

To avoid unnecessary complications, we temporarily assume that x is positive. Then we may *estimate* the remainder (6) by observing that the integrand is positive for $0 < t < x$, and that $e^t < e^x < 3^x$. Therefore

$$|R_n(x, 0)| \leq \int_0^x \frac{(x - t)^n}{n!} 3^x \, dt = 3^x \frac{x^{n+1}}{(n + 1)!}$$

for $x > 0$. When x is negative we must replace x by $|x|$ on the right-hand side of this inequality. But for all real values of x, $-\infty < x < +\infty$, we have

$$|R_n(x, 0)| \leq 3^{|x|} \frac{|x|^{n+1}}{(n + 1)!}. \tag{7}$$

Now that we have this estimate of the remainder term, we are ready to discuss the convergence of the Maclaurin series (Taylor series with $a = 0$) for e^x. There are two separate cases to be considered, according to whether or not $|x| \leq 1$.

Case 1. If $|x| \leq 1$, then $3^{|x|} \leq 3$, and (7) tells us that

$$|R_n(x, 0)| \leq \frac{3}{(n + 1)!} \quad \text{if} \quad |x| \leq 1. \tag{8}$$

Hence $R_n(x, 0)$ certainly approaches zero as n tends to infinity, and the following series converges to e^x for any number x whose absolute value is less than or equal to 1:

$$e^x = 1 + x + \frac{x^2}{2!} + \frac{x^3}{3!} + \cdots + \frac{x^n}{n!} + \cdots, \quad |x| \leq 1. \tag{9}$$

Using the estimate of the remainder given by (8), we may determine n (and thus the number of terms of the series to use) so as to guarantee a specified accuracy in computing the value of e^x. For example, we may calculate e by taking $x = 1$ in Eq. (9). If we do this, with $n = 3$, say, the error we make will be less than

$$3/4! = \tfrac{1}{8} = 0.125.$$

If we take $n = 7$, then the error is less than

$$3/8! < 0.75 \times 10^{-4},$$

and the approximation

$$e \approx 1 + 1 + \frac{1}{2!} + \frac{1}{3!} + \cdots + \frac{1}{7!}$$

is good to within one unit in the fourth decimal place. Since the remainder goes to zero as n tends to infinity, we also have the infinite series expansion for e:

$$e = 1 + 1 + \frac{1}{2!} + \frac{1}{3!} + \cdots. \tag{10}$$

The first two terms in the series (9) can be written as $1/0!$ and $x/1!$, provided that we adopt the definition

$$0! = 1.$$

This definition of $0!$ is commonly accepted, and with it the identity $n! = n(n - 1)!$ is satisfied for all positive integers n, including $n = 1$. The series for e^x, Eq. (9), now takes the compact form

$$e^x = \sum_{k=0}^{\infty} \frac{x^k}{k!}. \tag{11}$$

So far, we have only established Eq. (11) for $|x| \leq 1$, but we shall see that it is in fact valid for all real x.

Graphs of some of the approximating polynomials

$$f_n(x) = 1 + x + \frac{x^2}{2!} + \cdots + \frac{x^n}{n!} = \sum_{k=0}^{n} \frac{x^k}{k!},$$

for $-1 \leq x \leq 1$, are shown in Fig. 14.9 for $n = 1, 2$, and 3. All three approximations are tangent to the curve $y = e^x$ at $P_0(0, 1)$, and therefore lie close to that curve near P_0. But as $|x|$ increases, the parabola B is a better approximation than the straight line A; and the cubic curve C is better than either A or B. This is to be expected since the error (remainder term in the series) decreases as n increases.

Case 2. We now consider what happens to the remainder term, Eq. (6), as n increases, if $|x| > 1$. Then both $|x|^{n+1}$ and $(n + 1)!$ increase indefinitely as n does, but the factorial increases so much faster (for large n) that the ratio approaches zero:

$$\lim_{n \to \infty} \frac{|x|^{n+1}}{(n + 1)!} = 0. \tag{12}$$

(See Exercise 3 below.) For example, if $x = 5$, the ratio $5^{n+1}/(n + 1)!$ increases with n until we get to $n = 4$.

x	e^x	$1 + x$	$1 + x + \dfrac{x^2}{2!}$	$1 + x + \dfrac{x^2}{2!} + \dfrac{x^3}{3!}$
0	1	1	1	1
0.1	1.1052	1.1	1.105	1.10517−
0.2	1.2214	1.2	1.220	1.22133+
0.3	1.3499	1.3	1.345	1.34950
0.4	1.4918	1.4	1.480	1.49067−
0.5	1.6487	1.5	1.625	1.64583+
0.6	1.8221	1.6	1.780	1.81600
0.7	2.0138	1.7	1.945	2.00217−
0.8	2.2255	1.8	2.120	2.20533+
0.9	2.4596	1.9	2.305	2.42650
1.0	2.7183	2.0	2.500	2.66667−
−0.1	0.90484	0.9	0.905	0.904833+
−0.2	0.81873	0.8	0.820	0.818667−
−0.3	0.74082	0.7	0.745	0.740500
−0.4	0.67032	0.6	0.680	0.669333+
−0.5	0.60653	0.5	0.625	0.604167−
−0.6	0.54881	0.4	0.580	0.544000
−0.7	0.49659	0.3	0.545	0.487833+
−0.8	0.44933	0.2	0.520	0.434667−
−0.9	0.40657	0.1	0.505	0.383500
−1.0	0.36788	0.0	0.500	0.333333+

14.9 The graph of the function $y = e^x$, and graphs of three approximating polynomials, (A) a straight line, (B) a parabola, and (C) a cubic curve.

But as n continues to increase, one unit at a time, the numerator is multiplied each time by 5, but the denominator is multiplied by 6, or 7, or 8, and so on, and the ratio ultimately approaches zero. The additional factor $3^{|x|}$ doesn't change as $n \to \infty$, so we have

$$\lim_{n \to \infty} 3^{|x|} \frac{|x|^{n+1}}{(n+1)!} = 0$$

and, from (7),

$$\lim_{n \to \infty} R_n(x, 0) = 0$$

for any real x, $-\infty < x < +\infty$. Therefore

$$e^x = \sum_{k=0}^{\infty} \frac{x^k}{k!}, \qquad -\infty < x < +\infty. \tag{13}$$

The table of values accompanying Fig. 14.9 shows e^x, $1 + x$, $1 + x + x^2/2!$, and $1 + x + x^2/2! + x^3/3!$ for values of x from -1 to $+1$ at intervals of 0.1.

The remainder term (other forms)

In the formula

$$f(x) = f(a) + f'(a)(x - a) + \frac{f''(a)}{2!}(x - a)^2 + \cdots$$
$$+ \frac{f^{(n)}(a)}{n!}(x - a)^n + R_n(x, a), \tag{14}$$

we have expressed the remainder as an integral:

$$R_n(x, a) = \int_a^x \frac{(x - t)^n}{n!} f^{(n+1)}(t)\, dt. \tag{15}$$

Other expressions for the remainder may be obtained by applying the following theorem to this integral.

Theorem 6. *Let $g(t)$ and $h(t)$ be continuous for*

$$a \le t \le b,$$

and suppose that $h(t)$ *does not change sign in this interval. Then there exists a number c between a and b such that*

$$\int_a^b g(t)h(t)\,dt = g(c)\int_a^b h(t)\,dt. \qquad (16)$$

Proof. Let m and M be the least and greatest values of $g(t)$, respectively, for $t \in [a, b]$. Then

$$m \le g(t_i) \le M, \qquad (17)$$

for any t_i between a and b inclusive. We form a subdivision

$$a = t_0 < t_1 < t_2 < \cdots < t_n = b$$

of the interval $[a, b]$, with

$$t_i - t_{i-1} = \Delta t = \frac{b-a}{n}, \qquad i = 1, \dots, n,$$

and multiply each term in the inequalities (17) by $h(t_i)\,\Delta t$. Since the sign of $h(t)$ does not change over the interval, all the terms $h(t_1)\,\Delta t$ are of the same sign, say positive. [If they are all negative, replace $h(t)$ by $-h(t)$ in the argument that follows.] Then

$$mh(t_i)\,\Delta t \le g(t_i)\,h(t_i)\,\Delta t \le Mh(t_i)\,\Delta t,$$

and the order of inequality is preserved when we now sum on i from 1 to n; that is,

$$\sum_{i=1}^n mh(t_i)\,\Delta t \le \sum_{i=1}^n g(t_i)h(t_i)\,\Delta t \le \sum_{i=1}^n Mh(t_i)\,\Delta t. \qquad (18)$$

Finally, we let n increase indefinitely and recall that the sums then become definite integrals. Hence (18) leads to

$$m\int_a^b h(t)\,dt \le \int_a^b g(t)h(t)\,dt \le M\int_a^b h(t)\,dt,$$

or

$$m \le \frac{\int_a^b g(t)h(t)\,dt}{\int_a^b h(t)\,dt} \le M. \qquad (19)$$

Since

$$Q = \frac{\int_a^b g(t)h(t)\,dt}{\int_a^b h(t)\,dt} \qquad (20)$$

is a number between the least and greatest values taken on by $g(t)$ for $t \in [a, b]$, and since $g(t)$ is assumed to be continuous, there is a number c between a and b such that

$$Q = g(c).$$

This leads at once to the result in Eq. (16) and completes the proof of the theorem. $\square$

We now apply this theorem to the integral in Eq. (15), with

$$h(t) = \frac{(x-t)^n}{n!}, \qquad g(t) = f^{(n+1)}(t).$$

As t varies from a to x, $h(t)$ is continuous and does not change sign. Hence, if $f^{(n+1)}(t)$ is continuous, then Eq. (16) applies, and we have

$$R_n(x, a) = f^{(n+1)}(c)\int_a^x \frac{(x-t)^n}{n!}\,dt$$
$$= f^{(n+1)}(c)\frac{(x-a)^{n+1}}{(n+1)!}.$$

This is known as *Lagrange's* form of the remainder:

$$R_n(x, a) = f^{(n+1)}(c)\frac{(x-a)^{n+1}}{(n+1)!}, \qquad (21)$$

for c between a and x.*

In applying Eq. (21), we can ordinarily only estimate $f^{(n+1)}(c)$, since we do not know c itself exactly. But if we know that

$$m \le f^{(n+1)}(t) \le M$$

for

$$t \in [a, x] \quad \text{or} \quad t \in [x, a],$$

then we know from Eq. (21) that $R_n(x, a)$ *lies between*

$$m\frac{(x-a)^{n+1}}{(n+1)!} \quad \text{and} \quad M\frac{(x-a)^{n+1}}{(n+1)!}.$$

---

* Another proof of Taylor's theorem, leading directly to the Lagrange form of the remainder, is outlined in Exercise 74 (Extended Mean Value Theorem), in the Miscellaneous Exercises at the end of Chapter 5.

Note. There is another common form of remainder, known as *Cauchy's* form:

$$R_n(x, a) = \frac{(x - c')^n (x - a)}{n!} f^{(n+1)}(c'), \quad (22)$$

for c' between a and x. This form may be obtained by applying Eq. (16) to Eq. (15) with

$$h(t) = 1, \quad g(t) = \frac{(x - t)^n}{n!} f^{(n+1)}(t).$$

The Lagrange form, Eq. (21), is usually easier to apply, and in general gives satisfactory results. However, the Cauchy form is useful in proving convergence of certain series, such as the Maclaurin series for $\ln(1 + x)$ for $x \in [-1, 0]$.

Problem. Find the Maclaurin series expansion for $\sin x$, and show that the series converges to $\sin x$ for all finite x, $-\infty < x < +\infty$.

Solution. In Eq. (14), we take $f(x) = \sin x$, $a = 0$. Then

$$
\begin{aligned}
f(x) &= \sin x, & f(0) &= 0 \\
f'(x) &= \cos x = \sin(x + \pi/2), & f'(0) &= 1 \\
f''(x) &= -\sin x = \sin(x + \pi), & f''(0) &= 0 \\
f'''(x) &= -\cos x = \sin(x + 3\pi/2), & f'''(0) &= -1 \\
&\;\;\vdots & &\;\;\vdots \\
f^{(k)}(x) &= \sin(x + k\pi/2), & f^{(k)}(0) &= \sin(k\pi/2).
\end{aligned}
$$

The values of the function and its derivatives at $x = 0$ are given by the formula

$$f^{(k)}(0) = \sin(k\pi/2), \quad k = 0, 1, 2, \ldots, \quad (23)$$

where the notation $f^{(k)}(0)$ means the value of the kth derivative of $f(x)$ at $x = 0$ and the zeroth derivative of the function means the function itself. If k is an even integer $0, 2, 4, \ldots$, then $\sin(k\pi/2)$ is zero. If k is one of the integers $1, 5, 9, 13, \ldots$, of the form $4m + 1$, then $\sin(k\pi/2)$ is plus one, while if k is one of the integers $3, 7, \ldots$, of the form $4m + 3$, then $\sin(k\pi/2)$ is minus one. Thus when we substitute these values (23) into the Taylor series formula, Eq. (14), with $a = 0$, we obtain

$$\sin x = x - \frac{x^3}{3!} + \frac{x^5}{5!} - \frac{x^7}{7!} + \cdots$$
$$+ \frac{(-1)^{n-1} x^{2n-1}}{(2n-1)!} + 0 \cdot x^{2n} + R_{2n}(x, 0). \quad (24)$$

By Eq. (21), the remainder is

$$R_{2n}(x, 0) = \frac{x^{2n+1}}{(2n+1)!} \sin\left(c + \frac{(2n+1)\pi}{2}\right).$$

Even though the only thing we know about c is that it lies between 0 and x, we know that the sine never exceeds 1 in absolute value. Hence

$$|R_{2n}(x, 0)| \leq \frac{|x|^{2n+1}}{(2n+1)!}. \quad (25)$$

Now for any finite x whatever, no matter how large, the $(2n+1)!$ in the denominator of (25) goes to infinity more rapidly than the $|x|^{2n+1}$ in the numerator, and

$$\lim_{n \to \infty} \frac{|x|^{2n+1}}{(2n+1)!} = 0. \quad (26)$$

[See Exercise 3 for a discussion that establishes Eq. (26).] Therefore the sequence of partial sums $f_n(x)$ of the Maclaurin series

$$x - \frac{x^3}{3!} + \frac{x^5}{5!} - \frac{x^7}{7!} + \cdots$$

converges to $\sin x$ for any x, $-\infty < x < +\infty$, and we may write

$$\sin x = \sum_{k=1}^{\infty} \frac{(-1)^{k-1} x^{2k-1}}{(2k-1)!}, \quad -\infty < x < +\infty. \quad (27)$$

Figure 14.10 shows graphs of $y = \sin x$ and the first two approximating polynomials

$$A: y = x, \quad B: y = x - \frac{x^3}{3!}.$$

The cubic approximation is in error by less than $x^5/120$, so it is almost indistinguishable from the sine curve from $x = -1$ to $x = +1$. However, it crosses the x-axis at $\pm\sqrt{6} \approx \pm 2.45$, whereas the sine curve crosses at $\pm\pi \approx \pm 3.14$. The table of data for Fig. 18.10 also shows that the cubic approximation is in error by less than 0.01 from $x = 0$ to $x = 1$. The values of $\sin x$ were taken from a four-place table, x in radians.

Analogous methods may be used to show that

$$\cos x = \sum_{k=0}^{\infty} \frac{(-1)^k x^{2k}}{(2k)!}, \quad -\infty < x < \infty. \quad (28)$$

14.10 The graphs of $y = \sin x$ and of two approximating polynomials, (A) $y = x$ and (B) $y = x - x^3/6$. The three curves are symmetric with respect to the origin. (Note that the negative portions are not shown.)

x	$\sin x$	$x - \dfrac{x^3}{3!}$
0	0	0
0.1	0.0998	0.09983+
0.2	0.1987	0.19867−
0.3	0.2955	0.29550
0.4	0.3894	0.38933+
0.5	0.4794	0.47917−
0.6	0.5646	0.56400
0.7	0.6442	0.64283+
0.8	0.7174	0.71467−
0.9	0.7833	0.77850
1.0	0.8415	0.83333+
1.41	0.9871	0.94280−
1.5	0.9975	0.93750
1.57	1.0000−	0.92502
1.58	1.0000−	0.92261
1.6	0.9996	0.91733
2.45	0.63776	−0.00102

Euler's formula: $e^{i\theta} = \cos \theta + i \sin \theta.$

Although we deal almost entirely with real numbers in this book, the reader is probably familiar with the symbol i for $\sqrt{-1}$ and with the system of complex numbers $a + ib$ where a and b are any real numbers. We usually meet these numbers for the first time when we study quadratic equations. There is an extensive branch of mathematics, called *complex analysis*, or *theory of functions of complex variables*, that extends the concepts of differentiation and integration to functions $f(z)$ where $z = x + iy$ is a complex variable. One of the standard ways of extending the domain of any one of the functions like $\sin x$, or $\cos x$, or $\exp x$ to the complex domain is to use the Taylor series for that function, in powers of x, and just see what happens when we replace x by $x + iy$, x^2 by $(x + iy)^2 = x^2 - y^2 + i(2xy)$, and so on, and then separating the real and imaginary parts of the series we get. We shall not do exactly that, but something that is simpler. (For a more extensive development, see this author's *Calculus and Analytic Geometry*, 4th edition, Chapter 19, or books on Advanced Calculus or Theory of Functions.) It suffices for our purposes to look at the series for the cosine, sine, and exponential functions, as follows:

$$\cos \theta = 1 - \frac{\theta^2}{2!} + \frac{\theta^4}{4!} - \frac{\theta^6}{6!} + \cdots$$

$$\sin \theta = \theta - \frac{\theta^3}{3!} + \frac{\theta^5}{5!} - \frac{\theta^7}{7!} + \cdots$$

$$e^{i\theta} = 1 + \frac{(i\theta)}{1!} + \frac{(i\theta)^2}{2!} + \frac{(i\theta)^3}{3!} + \frac{(i\theta)^4}{4!} + \frac{(i\theta)^5}{5!}$$

$$+ \frac{(i\theta)^6}{6!} + \frac{(i\theta)^7}{7!} + \cdots$$

$$= 1 + i\theta - \frac{\theta^2}{2!} - i\frac{\theta^3}{3!} + \frac{\theta^4}{4!} + i\frac{\theta^5}{5!} - \frac{\theta^6}{6!}$$

$$- i\frac{\theta^7}{7!} + \cdots$$

$$= \left(1 - \frac{\theta^2}{2!} + \frac{\theta^4}{4!} - \frac{\theta^6}{6!} + \cdots\right)$$

$$+ i\left(\theta - \frac{\theta^3}{3!} + \frac{\theta^5}{5!} - \frac{\theta^7}{7!} + \cdots\right)$$

$$= \cos \theta + i \sin \theta.$$

The last result

$$e^{i\theta} = \cos \theta + i \sin \theta \qquad (29)$$

is known as *Euler's formula*. If we replace θ by $-\theta$ in it, or in the earlier series, we get a companion formula

$$e^{-i\theta} = \cos \theta - i \sin \theta \qquad (30)$$

because $\cos(-\theta) = \cos \theta$ and $\sin(-\theta) = -\sin \theta$. When we add and divide by 2, we find that we can write $\cos \theta$ in terms of the complex exponentials. Similarly, if we subtract and divide by $2i$, we can express $\sin \theta$ in terms of $e^{i\theta}$ and $e^{-i\theta}$. The results are as follows:

$$\cos \theta = \frac{e^{i\theta} + e^{-i\theta}}{2}, \qquad \sin \theta = \frac{e^{i\theta} - e^{-i\theta}}{2i}. \qquad (31)$$

EXERCISES

1. In connection with Eq. (15), show that the remainder term $R_n(x, a)$ in Taylor's theorem satisfies the inequality

$$|R_n(x, a)| \leq M \frac{|x - a|^{n+1}}{(n+1)!}$$

if there is a positive constant M such that

$$|f^{(n+1)}(t)| \leq M$$

for all t between a and x inclusive.

2. Using series, calculate e to five decimal places.

3. We encounter series where the nth term involves the fraction $x^n/n!$, and it is important to know how this function of the two variables x and n behaves for fixed values of x as n becomes larger and larger. The following analysis can be used to show that when $n \geq 2$, $n!$ is greater than $e(n/e)^n$, where $e = 2.718 \ldots$ is the base of natural logarithms.

   (a) $\qquad \ln n! = \ln 2 + \ln 3 + \cdots + \ln n$

   can be represented as the sum of the areas of $n - 1$ rectangles, as indicated in Fig. 14.11. Note that the first rectangle has its base on the x-axis from 1 to 2 and has altitude equal to $\ln 2$, etc. Since each base is of unit length, the area of the rectangle has the same magnitude as its altitude. Show that

$$\ln n! > \int_1^n \ln x \, dx$$
$$= n \ln n - n + 1, \quad n \geq 2.$$

(b) From the result of (a), show that

$$n! > e(n/e)^n, \quad n \geq 2.$$

(c) Assume that x is any finite real number. Use the result of (b) to show that

$$\lim_{n \to \infty} (x^n/n!) = 0.$$

In particular, show that $|x^n/n!| < 2^{-n}$ when n is greater than 2 and also greater than $2|ex|$.

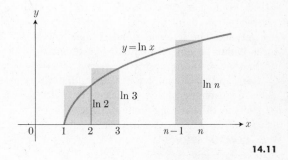

14.11

4. For what range of values of x can one replace $\sin x$ by $x - x^3/6$ with an error not greater than 5×10^{-4}?

5. If $\cos x$ is replaced by $1 - x^2/2$ and $|x| < 0.1$, what estimate can you give of the error?

6. For what range of values of x can one replace $\ln(1 + x)$ by x with an error not greater than one percent of the absolute value of x?

7. The approximation

$$\sqrt{1 + x} = 1 + x/2$$

is used when $|x|$ is small. Give an estimate of the error if $|x| < 0.01$.

8. A log-log slide rule gives readings of e^h for

$$0.01 \leq h \leq 10.$$

When $0 \leq h \leq 0.01$, show that e^h may be replaced simply by $1 + h$ with an error not greater than six-tenths of one percent of h.

9. The quantity $\sqrt{e} = e^{0.5}$ is to be computed from the series

$$e^x = 1 + x + \frac{x^2}{2!} + \cdots + \frac{x^n}{n!} + R_n(x, 0).$$

How large should one choose n to guarantee that

$$|R_n(x, 0)| < 0.0005?$$

10. Using Eq. (29) as the definition of $e^{i\theta}$, and trigonometric identities for $\cos(\theta_1 + \theta_2)$ and $\sin(\theta_1 + \theta_2)$, prove the law of addition of exponents:

$$e^{i\theta_1} \cdot e^{i\theta_2} = e^{i(\theta_1 + \theta_2)}.$$

11. In Eq. (31), let $\theta = ix$ and $i\theta = -x$ and deduce that

$$\cos(ix) = \cosh x \quad \text{and} \quad \sin(ix) = i\sinh x.$$

Remark: The (correct) identity $\cos^2(ix) + \sin^2(ix) = 1$ thus becomes the equally true identity $\cosh^2 x - \sinh^2 x = 1$. Analogies between the circular functions and the hyperbolic functions, like this one, are easily explained by the relation between the functions in the complex domain.

14.5 COMPUTATIONS

The Taylor series expansion

$$f(x) = f(a) + f'(a)(x - a) + \frac{f''(a)}{2!}(x - a)^2 + \cdots$$
$$+ \frac{f^{(n)}(a)}{n!}(x - a)^n + R_n(x, a) \qquad (1)$$

expresses the value of the function at x in terms of its value and the values of its derivatives at a, plus a remainder term which we hope is so small that it may safely be omitted. In applying series to numerical computations, it is therefore *necessary* that a be chosen so that $f(a), f'(a), f''(a), \ldots$ are known. In dealing with the trigonometric functions, for example, one might take

$$a = 0, \pm\pi/6, \pm\pi/4, \pm\pi/3, \pm\pi/2,$$

and so on. It is also clear that it is *desirable* to choose the value of a near the value of x for which the function is to be computed, to make $x - a$ small, and thereby to ensure that the terms of the series decrease rapidly as n increases.

Problem 1. What value of a might one choose in the Taylor series (1) to compute

(a) $\cos 5°$,   (b) $\sin 35°$?

Solution. (a) In the first case, one would probably choose $a = 0$. If we substitute

$$f(x) = \cos x \quad \text{and} \quad a = 0$$

in Eq. (1), we find that the series for $\cos x$ in powers of $x - 0$ is

$$\cos x = 1 - \frac{x^2}{2!} + \frac{x^4}{4!} - \cdots$$
$$+ (-1)^n \frac{x^{2n}}{(2n)!} + 0 \cdot x^{2n+1} + R_{2n+1}(x, 0). \qquad (2)$$

Since the derivatives of $\cos x$ are $\pm\sin x$ or $\pm\cos x$, which never exceed one in absolute value, the remainder with $|f^{(2n+1)}(c)| \leq 1$, leads to the estimate

$$|R_{2n+1}(x, 0)| \leq \frac{|x|^{2n+2}}{(2n+2)!};$$

this tends to zero as $n \to \infty$, for all $|x| < \infty$. In particular, to calculate $\cos 5°$, we take

$$x = \frac{5\pi}{180} = 0.08726\ 65 \quad \text{(radian measure!)}$$

and see that

$$\left| R_5\left(\frac{5\pi}{180}, 0\right) \right| \leq \frac{(0.088)^6}{6!} < \frac{(0.1)^6}{6!} < 10^{-8}.$$

Hence we may calculate $\cos 5°$ accurately to seven decimal places by using the approximation

$$\cos x \approx 1 - \frac{x^2}{2} + \frac{x^4}{24} \quad \left(x = \frac{5\pi}{180}\right).$$

(b) In calculating $\sin 35°$, we could again choose $a = 0$ and use the series

$$\sin x = x - \frac{x^3}{3!} + \frac{x^5}{5!} - \cdots$$
$$+ (-1)^n \frac{x^{2n+1}}{(2n+1)!} + 0 \cdot x^{2n+2}$$
$$+ R_{2n+2}(x, 0), \qquad (3)$$

or we could choose $a = \pi/6$ (which corresponds to 30°) and use the series

$$\sin x = \sin \frac{\pi}{6} + \cos \frac{\pi}{6} \left(x - \frac{\pi}{6} \right)$$

$$- \sin \frac{\pi}{6} \frac{(x - \pi/6)^2}{2!} - \cos \frac{\pi}{6} \frac{(x - \pi/6)^3}{3!} + \cdots$$

$$+ \sin \left(\frac{\pi}{6} + n \frac{\pi}{2} \right) \frac{(x - \pi/6)^n}{n!} + R_n \left(x, \frac{\pi}{6} \right).$$

The remainder in the series (3) satisfies the inequality

$$|R_{2n+2}(x, 0)| \le \frac{|x|^{2n+3}}{(2n+3)!}, \tag{4}$$

which tends to zero as n becomes infinite, no matter how large $|x|$ may be. We could therefore calculate $\sin 35°$ by placing

$$x = \frac{35\pi}{180} = 0.61086\ 53$$

in the approximation

$$\sin x \approx x - \frac{x^3}{6} + \frac{x^5}{120} - \frac{x^7}{5040},$$

with an error no greater than $(0.5)10^{-7}$, since

$$\left| R_8 \left(\frac{35\pi}{180}, 0 \right) \right| \le \frac{(0.62)^9}{9!} < \frac{0.016}{360,000} < (0.5)10^{-7}.$$

By using the series with $a = \pi/6$, we could obtain equal accuracy with a smaller exponent n, but at the expense of introducing $\cos(\pi/6) = \sqrt{3}/2$ as one of the coefficients. In this series, with $a = \pi/6$, we would take

$$x = 35\pi/180,$$

but the quantity that appears raised to the various powers is

$$x - \frac{\pi}{6} = \frac{5\pi}{180} = 0.08726\ 65,$$

which decreases rapidly when raised to high powers.

As a matter of fact, various trigonometric identities may be used, such as

$$\sin \left(\frac{\pi}{2} - x \right) = \cos x,$$

to enable one to calculate quite easily the sine or cosine of any number by means of the series in Eq. (2) or (3).

This method of finding the sine or cosine of a number is used in modern high-speed computers. It is more efficient for these large machines to calculate these trigonometric functions from series than it is for them to "read" tables.

Computation of logarithms

Tables of natural logarithms are computed from series. The starting point is the series for $\ln(1 + x)$ in powers of x:

$$\ln(1 + x) = x - \frac{x^2}{2} + \frac{x^3}{3} - \cdots + (-1)^{n-1} \frac{x^n}{n} + \cdots.$$

This series may be found directly from the Taylor series expansion, Eq. (1), with $a = 0$. It may also be obtained by integrating the geometric series for $1/(1 + t)$ from $t = 0$ to $t = x$:

$$\int_0^x \frac{dt}{1 + t} = \int_0^x (1 - t + t^2 - t^3 + \cdots)\, dt,$$

$$\ln(1 + t) \Big]_0^x = t - \frac{t^2}{2} + \frac{t^3}{3} - \frac{t^4}{4} + \cdots \Big]_0^x,$$

$$\ln(1 + x) = x - \frac{x^2}{2} + \frac{x^3}{3} - \frac{x^4}{4} + \cdots. \tag{5}$$

The expansion (5) is valid for $|x| < 1$, since then the remainder $R_n(x, 0)$ approaches zero as $n \to \infty$, as we shall now see.

The remainder is given by the integral of the remainder in the geometric series; that is,

$$R_n(x, 0) = \int_0^x \frac{(-1)^n t^n}{1 + t}\, dt. \tag{6}$$

We now suppose that $|x| < 1$. For every t between 0 and x inclusive, we have

$$|1 + t| \ge 1 - |x|$$

and

$$|(-1)^n t^n| = |t|^n,$$

so that

$$\left| \frac{(-1)^n t^n}{1 + t} \right| \le \frac{|t|^n}{1 - |x|}.$$

Therefore

$$|R_n(x, 0)| \leq \int_0^{|x|} \frac{t^n}{1 - |x|} \, dt$$

$$= \frac{1}{n + 1} \frac{|x|^{n+1}}{1 - |x|} \cdot \quad (7)$$

When $n \to \infty$, the right-hand side of the inequality in (7) approaches zero, and so must the left-hand side. Thus (5) holds for $|x| < 1$.

If we replace x by $-x$, we obtain

$$\ln(1 - x) = -x - \frac{x^2}{2} - \frac{x^3}{3} - \cdots - \frac{x^n}{n} - \cdots, \quad (8)$$

which is also valid for $|x| < 1$. When we subtract (8) from (5), we get

$$\ln \frac{1 + x}{1 - x} = 2 \left(x + \frac{x^3}{3} + \frac{x^5}{5} + \cdots + \frac{x^{2k-1}}{2k - 1} + \cdots \right) \quad (9)$$

for $|x| < 1$. Equation (9) may be used to compute the natural logarithm of any positive number y (see Fig. 14.12) by taking

$$y = \frac{1 + x}{1 - x} \quad \text{or} \quad x = \frac{y - 1}{y + 1} \cdot$$

But the series converges most rapidly for values of x near zero, or when $(1 + x)/(1 - x)$ is near one. For this reason, the logarithms of the numbers

$$\frac{2}{1}, \frac{3}{2}, \frac{4}{3}, \frac{5}{4}, \ldots, \frac{N + 1}{N}$$

are ordinarily computed first in forming a table of natural logarithms of the integers. Then it is a matter of simple arithmetic to compute

$$\ln 3 = \ln \tfrac{2}{1} + \ln \tfrac{3}{2},$$
$$\ln 4 = \ln 3 + \ln \tfrac{4}{3},$$
$$\ln 5 = \ln 4 + \ln \tfrac{5}{4},$$
$$\vdots$$
$$\ln(N + 1) = \ln N + \ln \frac{N + 1}{N} \cdot$$

14.12

For this purpose, one may solve the equation

$$\frac{1 + x}{1 - x} = \frac{N + 1}{N}$$

for

$$x = \frac{1}{2N + 1} \cdot$$

This may be substituted into Eq. (9), which becomes

$$\ln \frac{N + 1}{N}$$
$$= 2 \left(\frac{1}{2N + 1} + \frac{1}{3(2N + 1)^3} + \frac{1}{5(2N + 1)^5} + \cdots \right). \quad (10)$$

For example, to calculate $\ln 2$, we take $N = 1$, $x = \tfrac{1}{3}$, and calculate

$$
\begin{aligned}
x &= 0.33333 \ 33, \\
\tfrac{1}{3}x^3 &= 0.01234 \ 57, \\
\tfrac{1}{5}x^5 &= 0.00082 \ 30, \\
\tfrac{1}{7}x^7 &= 0.00006 \ 53, \\
\tfrac{1}{9}x^9 &= 0.00000 \ 56, \\
\tfrac{1}{11}x^{11} &= 0.00000 \ 05, \\
\hline
\text{Sum} \quad & \ \ 0.34657 \ 34; \\
\ln 2 &\approx 0.69314 \ 68.
\end{aligned}
$$

Computation of π

Archimedes (287–212 B.C.) gave the approximation

$$3\tfrac{1}{7} > \pi > 3\tfrac{10}{71}$$

in the third century B.C. A French mathematician, Vieta (1540–1603), gave the formula for $2/\pi$ as

$$\sqrt{\tfrac{1}{2}} \times \sqrt{\left(\tfrac{1}{2} + \tfrac{1}{2}\sqrt{\tfrac{1}{2}}\right)} \times \sqrt{\left(\tfrac{1}{2} + \tfrac{1}{2}\right)\sqrt{\tfrac{1}{2} + \tfrac{1}{2}\sqrt{\tfrac{1}{2}}}} \times \cdots,$$

which Turnbull* calls "the first actual formula for the time-honoured number 'π.'" Other interesting formulas for π include the following†:

$$\frac{\pi}{4} = \cfrac{1}{1 + \cfrac{1^2}{2 + \cfrac{3^2}{2 + \cfrac{5^2}{2 + \cdots}}}},$$

credited to Lord Brouncker, an Irish peer;

$$\frac{\pi}{4} = \frac{2 \times 4 \times 4 \times 6 \times 6 \times 8 \times \cdots}{3 \times 3 \times 5 \times 5 \times 7 \times 7 \times \cdots},$$

discovered by the English mathematician Wallis; and

$$\frac{\pi}{4} = 1 - \frac{1}{3} + \frac{1}{5} - \frac{1}{7} + \cdots,$$

known as Leibniz's formula. All these formulas involve limits. For example, Vieta's formula may be expressed in terms of the sequences $\{x_n\}$ and $\{s_n\}$ defined as follows:

$$x_1 = \sqrt{\tfrac{1}{2}},$$
$$x_2 = \sqrt{\tfrac{1}{2} + \tfrac{1}{2}x_1},$$
$$x_3 = \sqrt{\tfrac{1}{2} + \tfrac{1}{2}x_2},$$
$$\vdots$$
$$x_{n+1} = \sqrt{\tfrac{1}{2} + \tfrac{1}{2}x_n}$$

---

* *World of Mathematics*, Vol. 1, p. 121.
† *World of Mathematics*, Vol. 1, p. 138.

and $s_n = x_1 x_2 x_3 \ldots x_n$.

Vieta's formula says that

$$\lim_{n \to \infty} s_n = \frac{2}{\pi}.$$

Use $\sin 2A = 2 \sin A \cos A$ repeatedly to get

$$\sin x = 2^n \cos (x/2) \cos (x/4) \cos (x/8) \cdots \\ \cos (x/2^n) \sin (x/2^n)$$

Divide both sides of this equation by x, put $x = \pi/2$, and use half-angle formulas to evaluate $\cos (\pi/4)$, $\cos (\pi/8)$ and so on. Let $y = x/2^n$ and note that y tends to zero, and $(\sin y)/y$ approaches 1 as limit, as n increases.

Similarly, we could interpret the other formulas as expressing certain limits in terms of π. However, we now turn our attention to the series for $\tan^{-1} x$, since it leads to the Leibniz formula and others from which π has been computed to a great many decimal places.

Since

$$\tan^{-1} x = \int_0^x \frac{dt}{1 + t^2},$$

we integrate the geometric series (with remainder)

$$\frac{1}{1 + t^2} = 1 - t^2 + t^4 - t^6 + \cdots \\ + (-1)^n t^{2n} + \frac{(-1)^{n+1} t^{2n+2}}{1 + t^2}. \quad (11)$$

Thus

$$\tan^{-1} x = x - \frac{x^3}{3} + \frac{x^5}{5} - \frac{x^7}{7} + \cdots \\ + (-1)^n \frac{x^{2n+1}}{2n + 1} + R,$$

where

$$R = \int_0^x \frac{(-1)^{n+1} t^{2n+2}}{1 + t^2} \, dt.$$

The denominator of the integrand is greater than or equal to 1; hence

$$|R| \le \int_0^{|x|} t^{2n+2} \, dt = \frac{|x|^{2n+3}}{2n + 3}.$$

If $|x| \leq 1$, then the right-hand side of this inequality approaches zero as $n \to \infty$. Therefore R also approaches zero, and we have

$$\tan^{-1} x = \sum_{n=0}^{\infty} \frac{(-1)^n x^{2n+1}}{2n+1},$$

or

$$\tan^{-1} x = x - \frac{x^3}{3} + \frac{x^5}{5} - \frac{x^7}{7} + \cdots, \quad |x| \leq 1. \tag{12}$$

In 1961 this equation was used to compute π to more than 100,000 decimal places on an IBM 7090 computer.

Various trigonometric identities are useful if one wishes to use Eq. (12) to calculate π. For example, if

$$\alpha = \tan^{-1} \tfrac{1}{2} \quad \text{and} \quad \beta = \tan^{-1} \tfrac{1}{3},$$

then

$$\tan (\alpha + \beta) = \frac{\tan \alpha + \tan \beta}{1 - \tan \alpha \tan \beta}$$
$$= \frac{\tfrac{1}{2} + \tfrac{1}{3}}{1 - \tfrac{1}{6}} = 1 = \tan \frac{\pi}{4}$$

and

$$\frac{\pi}{4} = \alpha + \beta = \tan^{-1} \tfrac{1}{2} + \tan^{-1} \tfrac{1}{3}. \tag{13}$$

Now Eq. (12) may be used with $x = \tfrac{1}{2}$ to evaluate $\tan^{-1} \tfrac{1}{2}$, and with $x = \tfrac{1}{3}$ to evaluate $\tan^{-1} \tfrac{1}{3}$. The sum of these results, multiplied by 4, gives π. One identity that has been used in place of Eq. (13) for the calculation* of π is

$$\frac{\pi}{4} = 4 \tan^{-1} \frac{1}{5} - \tan^{-1} \frac{1}{239}. \tag{14}$$

Remark. We should mention the two types of numerical error that occur in computing with series. On the one hand, there is the so-called *truncation error*, which is the remainder $R_n(x, a)$ and consists of the sum of the infinite number of terms in the series that follow the term $(x - a)^n f^{(n)}(a)/n!$. This is the only error we have discussed so far. On the

---

* For details, see Wrench and Shanks, "Calculation of π to 100,000 Decimals," *Mathematics of Computation*, **16**, No. 77, Jan. 1962, pp. 76–99.

other hand, there is the so-called *round-off error* that enters in calculating the sum of the finite number of terms

$$f(a) + f'(a)(x - a) + \cdots + \frac{f^{(n)}(a)(x - a)^n}{n!}$$

when we approximate each of these terms by a decimal number with only a finite number of decimal places. For example, taking 0.3333 in place of $\tfrac{1}{3}$ introduces a round-off error equal to $10^{-4}/3$. There is likely to be a round-off error associated with each term in our computations, some of these being positive and some negative. In highly accurate computations, such as the fifteen-place tables of functions published by the Works Progress Administration, it is important to control both the truncation error and the round-off errors. *Truncation* errors can be reduced by taking more terms of the series; *round-off* errors can be reduced by taking more decimal places.

EXERCISES

In Exercises 1 through 8, use a suitable series to calculate the indicated quantity to three decimal places. In each case, show that the remainder term does not exceed 5×10^{-4}.

1. $\cos 31°$ 2. $\tan 46°$ 3. $\sqrt[3]{9}$

4. $(36)^{-1/5}$ 5. $\cosh 0.5$ 6. $\sinh 0.5$

7. $\ln 1.25$ 8. $\tan^{-1} 1.02$

9. Show that the ordinate of the catenary

$$y = a \cosh (x/a)$$

deviates from the ordinate of the parabola

$$x^2 = 2a(y - a)$$

by less than $0.003 |a|$ over the range $|x/a| \leq \tfrac{1}{3}$.

In Exercises 10 and 11, use series to evaluate the integrals to three decimal places.

10. $\displaystyle\int_0^{0.1} \frac{\sin x}{x} \, dx$

11. $\displaystyle\int_0^{0.1} e^{-x^2} \, dx$

12. Construct a table of natural logarithms $\ln N$ for $N = 1, 2, 3, \ldots, 10$ by the method discussed in connection with Eq. (10), but taking advantage of the relationships

$$\ln 4 = 2 \ln 2, \quad \ln 6 = \ln 2 + \ln 3,$$
$$\ln 8 = 3 \ln 2, \quad \ln 9 = 2 \ln 3,$$
$$\ln 10 = \ln 2 + \ln 5$$

to reduce the job to the calculation of relatively few logarithms by series. In fact, you may use $\ln 2$ as given in the text and calculate $\ln \frac{3}{2}$, $\ln \frac{5}{4}$, and $\ln \frac{7}{6}$ by series, and then combine these in suitable ways to get the logarithms of numbers N from 1 to 10.

13. Use Eqs. (12, 14) to calculate π to three decimals.

14. (a) Show that the integral

$$\int_0^x \frac{dt}{1 - t^2}$$

is equal to the integral

$$\int_0^x \left(1 + t^2 + t^4 + \cdots + t^{2n} + \frac{t^{2n+2}}{1 - t^2}\right) dt;$$

or, in other words, that

$$\tanh^{-1} x = x + \frac{x^3}{3} + \frac{x^5}{5} + \cdots + \frac{x^{2n+1}}{2n+1} + R,$$

where

$$R = \int_0^x \frac{t^{2n+2}}{1 - t^2} dt.$$

(b) Show that R in (a) is not greater than

$$\frac{1}{1 - x^2} \cdot \frac{|x|^{2n+3}}{2n+3}, \quad \text{if} \quad x^2 < 1.$$

15. (a) Differentiate the identity

$$\frac{1}{1 - x} = 1 + x + x^2 + \cdots + x^n + \frac{x^{n+1}}{1 - x}$$

to obtain the expansion

$$\frac{1}{(1 - x)^2} = 1 + 2x + 3x^2 + \cdots + nx^{n-1} + R.$$

(b) Prove that if $|x| < 1$, then $R \to 0$ as $n \to \infty$.

(c) In one throw of two dice, the probability of getting a score of 7 is $p = \frac{1}{6}$. If the dice are thrown

repeatedly, the probability that a 7 will appear for the first time at the nth throw is $q^{n-1}p$, where $q = 1 - p = \frac{5}{6}$. The expected number of throws until a 7 first appears is $\sum_{n=1}^{\infty} nq^{n-1}p$. Evaluate this series numerically.

(d) In applying statistical quality control to an industrial operation, an engineer inspects items taken at random from the assembly line. She classifies each item sampled as "good" or "bad." If the probability of a good item is p and of a bad item is $q = 1 - p$, the probability that the first bad item she finds is the nth inspected is $p^{n-1}q$. The average number inspected up to and including the first bad item found is $\sum_{k=1}^{\infty} np^{n-1}q$. Evaluate this series, assuming $0 < p < 1$.

16. In probability theory, a random variable X may assume the values $1, 2, 3, \ldots$, with probabilities $p_1, p_2, p_3, \ldots$, where p_k is the probability that X is equal to k, $(k = 1, 2, \ldots)$. It is customary to assume $p_k \geq 0$ and $\sum_{k=1}^{\infty} p_k = 1$. The *expected value* of X denoted by $E(X)$ is defined as $\sum_{k=1}^{\infty} kp_k$, provided that this series converges. In each of the following cases, show that $\sum p_k = 1$ and find $E(X)$ if it exists. [*Hint.* See Exercise 15.]

(a) $p_k = 2^{-k}$ (b) $p_k = \dfrac{5^{k-1}}{6^k}$

(c) $p_k = \dfrac{1}{k(k+1)} = \dfrac{1}{k} - \dfrac{1}{k+1}$

14.6 INDETERMINATE FORMS

The indeterminate form 0/0

In considering the ratio of two functions $f(x)$ and $g(x)$, we sometimes wish to know the value of

$$\lim_{x \to a} \frac{f(x)}{g(x)} \tag{1}$$

at a point a where both $f(x)$ and $g(x)$ vanish. In such a case we are led to the meaningless expression $0/0$ if we substitute $x = a$ in the numerator and denominator of the fraction.

Example 1. Both x and $\sin x$ are zero at $x = 0$. Therefore we cannot just put $x = 0$ in the numerator and denominator if we want to find the limit

$$\lim_{x \to 0} \frac{\sin x}{x},$$

which we know (from earlier investigations) is 1. This is also the derivative of $\sin x$ at $x = 0$. Indeed, the derivative

$$f'(a) = \lim_{x \to a} \frac{f(x) - f(a)}{x - a}$$

was our first example of the indeterminate form $0/0$, since both the numerator and the denominator of the fraction $[f(x) - f(a)]/(x - a)$ approach zero when x approaches a.

Suppose the functions f and g both possess Taylor series expansions in powers of $x - a$:

$$f(x) = f(a) + f'(a) \cdot (x - a) + \frac{f''(a)}{2!}(x - a)^2 + \cdots, \tag{2a}$$

$$g(x) = g(a) + g'(a) \cdot (x - a) + \frac{g''(a)}{2!}(x - a)^2 + \cdots, \tag{2b}$$

that converge to $f(x)$ and $g(x)$, respectively, in some interval $|x - a| < \delta$, where δ is a positive number. Then the series $(2a, b)$ may be used to calculate the limit (1), provided that the limit exists.

Problem 1

$$\lim_{x \to 1} \frac{\ln x}{x - 1}.$$

Solution. Let $f(x) = \ln x$, $g(x) = x - 1$. The Taylor series for $f(x)$, with $a = 1$, is found as follows:

$$f(x) = \ln x, \qquad f(1) = \ln 1 = 0,$$
$$f'(x) = 1/x, \qquad f'(1) = 1,$$
$$f''(x) = -1/x^2, \qquad f''(1) = -1,$$

so that

$$\ln x = 0 + (x - 1) - \tfrac{1}{2}(x - 1)^2 + \cdots.$$

Hence

$$\frac{\ln x}{x - 1} = 1 - \tfrac{1}{2}(x - 1) + \cdots$$

and

$$\lim_{x \to 1} \frac{\ln x}{x - 1} = \lim_{x \to 1} [1 - \tfrac{1}{2}(x - 1) + \cdots] = 1.$$

Problem 2

$$\lim_{x \to 0} \frac{\sin x - \tan x}{x^3}.$$

Solution. The Maclaurin series for $\sin x$ and $\tan x$, to terms in x^5, are

$$\sin x = x - \frac{x^3}{3!} + \frac{x^5}{5!} - \cdots,$$

$$\tan x = x + \frac{x^3}{3} + \frac{2x^5}{15} + \cdots$$

Hence

$$\sin x - \tan x = -\frac{x^3}{2} - \frac{x^5}{8} - \cdots,$$

and

$$\lim_{x \to 0} \frac{\sin x - \tan x}{x^3} = \lim_{x \to 0} \left(-\frac{1}{2} - \frac{x^2}{8} - \cdots \right) = -\frac{1}{2}.$$

It is sometimes more convenient to apply the following theorem instead of resorting to the use of series to evaluate the limit (1).

Theorem 7. l'Hôpital's rule. *If $f(a) = g(a) = 0$, and if the limit of the ratio $f'(t)/g'(t)$ as t approaches a exists, then*

$$\lim_{t \to a} \frac{f(t)}{g(t)} = \lim_{t \to a} \frac{f'(t)}{g'(t)}. \tag{3}$$

Remark 1. The primes denote derivatives with respect to t and it is tacitly assumed when we write $f'(t)/g'(t)$ that both $f'(t)$ and $g'(t)$ exist and that $g'(t)$ is not zero when t is different from, but sufficiently near to, $t = a$. Note particularly that $f'(t)/g'(t)$ is the derivative of the numerator divided by the derivative of the denominator, which is not the same as the derivative of the fraction $f(t)/g(t)$.

Proof. We shall establish Eq. (3) for the case where $t \to a+$. The method needs only minor modifications, such as reversing certain inequalities, to apply to $t \to a-$. The combination of these two cases then establishes the result.

Suppose, then, that $f(a) = g(a) = 0$ and that

(a) $f(t)$ and $g(t)$ are continuous functions of t for all t in the closed interval $[a, b]$,

14.13

(b) $f'(t)$ and $g'(t)$ exist for each t in the open interval (a, b), and

(c) $g'(t) \neq 0$ for all t in the open interval (a, b).

Now consider any t in the open interval (a, b). (See Fig. 14.13.) The fraction $F(t) = f(t)/g(t)$ can be interpreted as the slope of the chord OP joining the point $O(g(a), f(a))$ and the point $P(g(t), f(t))$ on the curve C represented by the parametric equations

$$x = g(t), \quad y = f(t), \quad a \leq t \leq b.$$

Our hypotheses are such that we may conclude that there is a point Q on the arc OP where the tangent to the curve is parallel to the chord. But the slope of the tangent at Q is

$$\left(\frac{dy}{dx}\right)_Q = \left(\frac{dy/dt}{dx/dt}\right)_Q = \frac{f'(t_1)}{g'(t_1)},$$

where t_1 is the value of t that corresponds to the point Q on the curve. We therefore have the result that if t is any number in the open interval (a, b), then there is at least one number t_1 between a and t such that

$$\frac{f(t)}{g(t)} = \frac{f'(t_1)}{g'(t_1)}. \tag{4}$$

[Note that the hypothesis $g'(t) \neq 0$ for $a < t < b$ assures us that the denominator on the right does not vanish.]

Now as $t \to a+$, t_1 does likewise, and

$$\lim_{t \to a+} \frac{f(t)}{g(t)} = \lim_{t_1 \to a+} \frac{f'(t_1)}{g'(t_1)} = \lim_{t \to a+} \frac{f'(t)}{g'(t)},$$

provided that the last limit above exists. This establishes the theorem for the case in which t

approaches a from above. The case in which t approaches a from below is proved in an analogous manner, and the two cases together give us the result stated as l'Hôpital's rule. □

From the geometric interpretation given in Fig. 14.13, it is clear that when the limit

$$\lim_{t \to a} \frac{f(t)}{g(t)} = \lim_{P \to O} (\text{slope of } OP)$$

exists, it is the same as the slope of the tangent to the curve at O. If $dx/dt = g'(t)$ did not vanish at $t = a$, we could simply write this slope as $f'(a)/g'(a)$ and have

$$\lim_{t \to a} \frac{f(t)}{g(t)} = \frac{f'(a)}{g'(a)}.$$

Equation (3) does better than this, however. Since it was established on the assumption that $g'(t)$ is different from zero in an *open* interval (a, b), it is valid whether or not $g'(a)$ is zero. Thus, if

$$f'(a) = g'(a) = 0,$$

then we are led to another indeterminate form $0/0$ and may again apply l'Hôpital's rule:

$$\lim_{t \to a} \frac{f'(t)}{g'(t)} = \lim_{t \to a} \frac{f''(t)}{g''(t)},$$

provided that the limit on the right exists.

In practice, the functions we deal with in this book are such as to satisfy the hypotheses laid down in deriving l'Hôpital's rule. We apply the method by proceeding to differentiate the numerator and denominator separately so long as we still get the form $0/0$ at $t = a$. As soon as one or the other of these derivatives is *different* from zero at $t = a$, we stop differentiating! It may happen that *one* of the derivatives is zero at $t = a$ and the other one not. Then the limit of the fraction is either zero or infinity, accordingly as the zero derivative occurs in the numerator or in the denominator. If we arrive at a limit that can be evaluated by some special method that we recognize, then we may use that method instead of continuing with l'Hôpital's.

Example 2

$$\lim_{t \to 0} \frac{\sqrt{1+t} - (1+t/2)}{t^2} \qquad [= \tfrac{0}{0}]$$

$$= \lim_{t \to 0} \frac{\tfrac{1}{2}(1+t)^{-1/2} - \tfrac{1}{2}}{2t} \qquad [\text{still} = \tfrac{0}{0}]$$

$$= \lim_{t \to 0} \frac{-\tfrac{1}{4}(1+t)^{-3/2}}{2} = -\frac{1}{8}.$$

Note that one obtains the same result by making use of the binomial series

$$(1+t)^{1/2} = 1 + \tfrac{1}{2}t - \tfrac{1}{8}t^2 + \cdots.$$

The indeterminate forms ∞/∞ and $\infty \cdot 0$

In more advanced textbooks it is proved that if $f(t) \to \infty$ and $g(t) \to \infty$ as $t \to a$, then

$$\lim_{t \to a} \frac{f(t)}{g(t)} = \lim_{t \to a} \frac{f'(t)}{g'(t)},$$

provided that the limit on the right exists.* This simply says that l'Hôpital's rule applies to the indeterminate form ∞/∞ as well as to the form $0/0$. The form $\infty \cdot 0$ must be reduced to one or the other of these two. In the notation $t \to a$, a may either be finite or infinite.

Problem 3

$$\lim_{t \to \infty} \frac{t^2 + t}{2t^2 + 1}.$$

Solution. This assumes the form ∞/∞ as $t \to \infty$.

(a) We apply l'Hôpital's rule and have

$$\lim_{t \to \infty} \frac{t^2 + t}{2t^2 + 1} = \lim_{t \to \infty} \frac{2t + 1}{4t} \qquad \left[\text{still} = \frac{\infty}{\infty}\right]$$

$$= \lim_{t \to \infty} \frac{2}{4} = \frac{1}{2}.$$

(b) Note that this could also have been evaluated by writing $t = 1/h$ and letting $h \to 0$:

---

*For more details, see "L'Hôpital's Rule," by A. E. Taylor, *American Mathematical Monthly*, **59**, 20–24, 1952.

$$\lim_{t \to \infty} \frac{t^2 + t}{2t^2 + 1} = \lim_{h \to 0} \frac{\dfrac{1}{h^2} + \dfrac{1}{h}}{\dfrac{2}{h^2} + 1} = \lim_{h \to 0} \frac{1 + h}{2 + h^2} = \frac{1}{2}.$$

(c) Another way is to divide both the numerator and denominator by t^2 (the highest power of t that occurs in either numerator or denominator) and observe that $1/t$ and $1/t^2$ approach zero as t increases without bound:

$$\lim_{t \to \infty} \frac{t^2 + t}{2t^2 + 1} = \lim_{t \to \infty} \frac{1 + \dfrac{1}{t}}{2 + \dfrac{1}{t^2}} = \frac{1 + 0}{2 + 0} = \frac{1}{2}.$$

This is actually the same as the method given in (b).

The indeterminate form $\infty - \infty$

The differences

$$n - n = 0, \qquad n - n^2 = n(1 - n),$$
$$n^2 - n = n(n - 1)$$

behave entirely differently as $n \to \infty$: But all become formally $\infty - \infty$, and illustrate why such an expression is called an indeterminate form.

It may be possible, by preliminary algebraic manipulations, to reduce an expression $F(t) - G(t)$ that becomes $\infty - \infty$ as t approaches a to a form $f(t)/g(t)$ that becomes $0/0$ or ∞/∞. Although l'Hôpital's rule is not to be applied to the original form, it may be applied to either of the forms ∞/∞ or $0/0$.

Problem 4

$$\lim_{x \to 0} \left(\frac{1}{\sin x} - \frac{1}{x} \right).$$

Solution. If $\qquad x \to 0+,$

then $\qquad \sin x \to 0+ \quad$ and $\quad 1/\sin x \to +\infty,$

while $\qquad 1/x \to +\infty.$

Thus the expression $(1/\sin x) - (1/x)$ formally becomes $+\infty - (+\infty)$, which is indeterminate. On the other hand, if $x \to 0-$, then

$$\frac{1}{\sin x} \to -\infty, \quad \text{and} \quad \frac{1}{x} \to -\infty,$$

so that $(1/\sin x) - (1/x)$ becomes $-\infty + \infty$, which is also indeterminate. But we may also write

$$\frac{1}{\sin x} - \frac{1}{x} = \frac{x - \sin x}{x \sin x} = \frac{x - \left[x - \dfrac{x^3}{3!} + \dfrac{x^5}{5!} - \cdots\right]}{x \cdot \left[x - \dfrac{x^3}{3!} + \dfrac{x^5}{5!} - \cdots\right]}$$

$$= \frac{x^3\left[\dfrac{1}{3!} - \dfrac{x^2}{5!} + \cdots\right]}{x^2\left[1 - \dfrac{x^2}{3!} + \cdots\right]} = x \frac{\dfrac{1}{3!} - \dfrac{x^2}{5!} + \cdots}{1 - \dfrac{x^2}{3!} + \cdots}.$$

Therefore

$$\lim_{x \to 0}\left(\frac{1}{\sin x} - \frac{1}{x}\right) = \lim_{x \to 0}\left[x \frac{\dfrac{1}{3!} - \dfrac{x^2}{5!} + \cdots}{1 - \dfrac{x^2}{3!} + \cdots}\right] = 0.$$

In fact, from the series expressions above we can see that if $|x|$ is small, then

$$\frac{1}{\sin x} - \frac{1}{x} \approx x \cdot \frac{1}{3!} = \frac{x}{6}, \quad \text{or} \quad \csc x \approx \frac{1}{x} + \frac{x}{6}.$$

The indeterminate forms 0^0, 1^∞, and ∞^0

The expressions 0^0, 1^∞, and ∞^0 symbolize the situations that arise when we consider the limit, as t approaches a, of a function of the form

$$y = f(t)^{g(t)},$$

where $\qquad f(a) = g(a) = 0;$ $\qquad\qquad$ (a)

or $\qquad f(a) = 1$ and $\lim_{t \to a} g(t) = \infty;$ $\qquad$ (b)

or $\qquad g(a) = 0$ and $\lim_{t \to a} f(t) = \infty.$ $\qquad$ (c)

In any such case, the natural logarithm of y becomes an indeterminate form of the type $0 \cdot (-\infty)$ or $\infty \cdot 0$. The method of dealing with such cases is illustrated by the following problem.

Problem 5. $\qquad \lim\limits_{h \to 0} (1 + h)^{1/h}.$

Solution. Let $\qquad y = (1 + h)^{1/h},$

so that

$$\ln y = \ln (1 + h)^{1/h} = \frac{1}{h}\ln (1 + h) = \frac{\ln (1 + h)}{h}.$$

This would assume the form

$$\frac{\ln (1 + 0)}{0} = \frac{0}{0},$$

if we were to substitute $h = 0$. By l'Hôpital's rule,

$$\lim_{h \to 0} \frac{\ln (1 + h)}{h} = \lim_{h \to 0} \frac{1/(1 + h)}{1} = 1;$$

that is,

$$\ln y \to 1 \quad \text{as} \quad h \to 0,$$

and, since $\ln y$ is a continuous function of y, which means that

$$\lim_{h \to 0} \ln y = \ln \left(\lim_{h \to 0} y\right) = 1,$$

we therefore have $\lim\limits_{h \to 0} y = e^1 = e.$

Remark 2. Many people feel that the expression 1^∞ cannot represent an indeterminate form. They say that one to any finite power is one, hence one to the power infinity is also one. But note, in the example above, that the base $1 + h$ is a variable which is not exactly equal to 1 except in the _limit_ as $h \to 0$. There is a difference, in other words, between

$$1^{1/h} \quad \text{and} \quad (1 + h)^{1/h},$$

even though both expressions formally become 1^∞ as $h \to 0$. If the reader is still skeptical, let him write out a few terms of the binomial expansion of $(1 + 1/n)^n$ for some large value of n, say $n = 10,000$. The result will be a fairly good approximation to $\lim_{h \to 0} (1 + h)^{1/h}$ (since $h = 1/n = 0.0001$ when $n = 10,000$).

EXERCISES

Evaluate the following limits by using series, or l'Hôpital's rule, or otherwise.

1. $\lim\limits_{t \to 0} \dfrac{1 - \cos t - \frac{1}{2}t^2}{t^4}$

2. $\lim\limits_{h \to 0} \dfrac{\sqrt{4 + h} - 2}{h}$

3. $\lim\limits_{x \to 0} \dfrac{\sqrt[3]{1 + x} - (1 + x/3)}{x^2}$

4. $\lim\limits_{x \to 0} \dfrac{\sinh x - \sin x}{x^3}$

5. $\lim\limits_{x \to 0} \dfrac{e^x - (1 + x)}{x^2}$

6. $\lim\limits_{h \to 0} \dfrac{(\sin h)/h - \cos h}{h^2}$

7. $\displaystyle\lim_{z\to 0}\frac{\sin(z^2)-\sin^2 z}{z^4}$

8. $\displaystyle\lim_{n\to\infty}\frac{n^3+3n^2}{2n^3-n}$

9. $\displaystyle\lim_{x\to\pi/2}\left(x-\frac{\pi}{2}\right)\tan 3x$

10. $\displaystyle\lim_{x\to 0+} x\ln x$

11. $\displaystyle\lim_{x\to+\infty}\frac{\ln x}{x}$

12. $\displaystyle\lim_{x\to+\infty}\frac{x^{100}}{e^x}$

13. $\displaystyle\lim_{x\to+\infty} x\sin\frac{1}{x}$

14. $\displaystyle\lim_{x\to+\infty}(x-\sqrt{x^2+x})$

15. $\displaystyle\lim_{x\to 1+}\left(\frac{1}{x-1}-\frac{1}{\sqrt{x-1}}\right)$

16. $\displaystyle\lim_{x\to 0}(1-2x)^{3/x}$

17. $\displaystyle\lim_{x\to+\infty}\left(1+\frac{2}{x}\right)^x$

18. $\displaystyle\lim_{x\to+\infty}(x+e^x)^{2/x}$

19. $\displaystyle\lim_{x\to 0+}(x+\sin x)^{\tan x}$

20. $\displaystyle\lim_{x\to 0+} x^x$

21. $\displaystyle\lim_{x\to 1-} x^{1/(1-x^2)}$

22. $\displaystyle\lim_{x\to 0+}(\cos\sqrt{x})^{1/x}$

23. $\displaystyle\lim_{x\to+\infty} x^{1/x}$

24. $\displaystyle\lim_{x\to+\infty}(\cosh x)^{1/x}$

25. (a) Prove that

$$\left(\int_0^x e^{t^2}\,dt\right)\to +\infty$$

as $x\to +\infty$.

(b) Find $\displaystyle\lim_{x\to\infty} x\int_0^x e^{t^2-x^2}\,dt$.

26. Find values of r and s such that

$$\lim_{x\to 0}(x^{-3}\sin 3x + rx^{-2}+s)=0.$$

14.7 CONVERGENCE OF POWER SERIES: ABSOLUTE CONVERGENCE

Problem 1, Article 14.2 showed how the ratio test may be applied to find the region of convergence of a power series. We must remember that the ratio test applies only to *positive* series. For a negative series, we simply factor out a minus sign from every term. This doesn't work, however, for a series such as

$$1+2x+3x^2+4x^3+\cdots+nx^{n-1}+\cdots, \qquad (1)$$

which becomes an *alternating* series when x is negative. To handle such series, we introduce the concept of *absolute* convergence.

Definition. *A series*

$$\sum_{k=1}^{\infty} u_k = u_1 + u_2 + \cdots$$

is said to be absolutely convergent if the corresponding series of absolute values

$$\sum_{k=1}^{\infty} |u_k| = |u_1| + |u_2| + \cdots$$

converges.

One reason that absolute convergence is important appears in the following theorem.

Theorem 8. *If a series converges absolutely, then it also converges when the absolute value signs are removed.*

Proof. Let the sum of the first n terms of $\sum u_k$ be denoted as usual by s_n, and let the sum of the first n terms of $\sum |u_k|$ be denoted by p_n. Suppose that

$$\lim_{n\to\infty} p_n = p$$

exists. We want to prove that $\lim s_n$ also exists. The following trick is effective: Consider the sum

$$q_n = (u_1+|u_1|) + (u_2+|u_2|) + \cdots$$
$$+ (u_n+|u_n|) = s_n + p_n. \qquad (2)$$

Each term of the series $\sum(u_k+|u_k|)$ is greater than or equal to zero, so the sequence of numbers $\{q_n\}$ is a monotone increasing sequence. On the other hand, q_n is less than or equal to

$$(|u_1|+|u_1|) + (|u_2|+|u_2|) + \cdots + (|u_n|+|u_n|);$$

in other words,

$$q_n \le 2p_n. \qquad (3)$$

Further, since $\{p_n\}$ is a monotone increasing sequence whose limit is p, we have

$$p_n \le p \quad \text{for all } n.$$

The inequality (3) therefore tells us that $q_n \le 2p$, and alternative (A) of Theorem 3, Article 14.2 holds with $M=2p$. Therefore

$$\lim_{n\to\infty} q_n = q$$

exists. Hence, from Eq. (2), $s_n = q_n - p_n$ also has a limit as n becomes infinite:

$$\lim_{n \to \infty} s_n = \lim_{n \to \infty} q_n - \lim_{n \to \infty} p_n = q - p. \ \square$$

We also repeat the following theorem from Article 14.1.

Theorem 9. *If a series $\sum u_k$ converges, then*

$$\lim_{n \to \infty} u_n = 0. \tag{4}$$

Remark. In determining the interval of convergence of a power series, we shall apply the ratio test to the series of *absolute values.* Thus, if

$$\rho = \lim_{n \to \infty} \left| \frac{u_{n+1}}{u_n} \right|,$$

the series

(a) converges absolutely if $\rho < 1$,

(b) diverges if $\rho > 1$, and

(c) may either converge or diverge if $\rho = 1$.

The only case for which the introduction of absolute value signs requires further discussion is case (b), $\rho > 1$. Here the terms do not get smaller in magnitude as n increases, since there is then an index N such that

$$|u_{n+1}/u_n| \geq 1 \quad \text{for all } n \geq N.$$

This, in turn, implies

$$|u_N| \leq |u_{N+1}| \leq |u_{N+2}| \leq |u_{N+3}| \leq \cdots,$$

so that the nth term does not approach zero as n becomes infinite. Hence the series diverges (with or without absolute value signs) whenever it happens that $\rho > 1$.

Theorem 10. *If a power series*

$$\sum_{k=0}^{\infty} a_k x^k = a_0 + a_1 x + a_2 x^2 + \cdots \tag{5}$$

converges for $x = c$ $(c \neq 0)$, then it converges absolutely for all $|x| < |c|$. If the series diverges for $x = d$, then it diverges for all $|x| > |d|$.

Proof. Suppose the series

$$\sum_{k=0}^{\infty} a_k c^k \tag{6}$$

converges. Then, by Theorem 9,

$$\lim_{n \to \infty} a_n c^n = 0.$$

Hence there is an index N such that

$$|a_n c^n| < 1 \quad \text{for all } n \geq N.$$

That is,

$$|a_n| < \frac{1}{|c|^n} \quad \text{for } n \geq N. \tag{7}$$

Now take any x such that $|x| < |c|$, and consider

$$|a_0| + |a_1 x| + \cdots$$
$$+ |a_{N-1} x^{N-1}| + |a_N x^N| + |a_{N+1} x^{N+1}| + \cdots.$$

There is only a finite number of terms prior to $|a_N x^N|$ and their sum is finite. Starting with $|a_N x^N|$ and beyond, the terms are less than

$$\left| \frac{x}{c} \right|^N + \left| \frac{x}{c} \right|^{N+1} + \left| \frac{x}{c} \right|^{N+2} + \cdots, \tag{8}$$

by virtue of the inequality (7). But the series in (8) is a geometric series with ratio $r = |x/c|$, which is less than 1 since $|x| < |c|$. Hence the series (8) converges, and thus the original series (5) converges absolutely. This argument establishes the first half of the theorem.

The second half of the theorem involves nothing new. For if the series diverges at $x = d$ and converges at a value x_0 with $|x_0| > |d|$, we may take $c = x_0$ in the first half of the theorem and conclude that the series converges absolutely at d. But the series cannot both converge absolutely and diverge at one and the same time. Hence if it diverges at d, it diverges for all $|x| > |d|$. $\square$

It is a consequence of Theorem 10 that a power series behaves in one or another of the following ways.

1. It converges only at $x = 0$.

2. It converges absolutely for all finite x,

$$-\infty < x < \infty.$$

3. There is a positive number c such that the series converges absolutely for $|x| < c$ and diverges for $|x| > c$. In this case, the series may converge or diverge at either or both of the points $x = c, x = -c$, the endpoints of the interval of convergence.

Problem. Find the interval of convergence for the series

$$\sum_{n=1}^{\infty} nx^{n-1}.$$

Solution. First we test for absolute convergence by calculating

$$\rho = \lim_{n \to \infty} \left| \frac{(n+1)x^n}{nx^{n-1}} \right| = |x|.$$

By the ratio test, the series converges absolutely if $|x| < 1$ and diverges if $|x| > 1$. When x is either $+1$ or -1, the nth term does not approach zero as n becomes infinite. Hence the series diverges at $x = \pm 1$. The interval of convergence is $-1 < x < 1$.

EXERCISES

In these exercises, find the interval in which the given power series converges absolutely.

1. $\displaystyle\sum_{n=0}^{\infty} x^n$

2. $\displaystyle\sum_{n=0}^{\infty} \frac{x^n}{n+1}$

3. $\displaystyle\sum_{n=1}^{\infty} n^2 x^n$

4. $\displaystyle\sum_{n=1}^{\infty} \frac{nx^n}{2}$

5. $\displaystyle\sum_{n=0}^{\infty} \frac{x^n}{n!}$

6. $\displaystyle\sum_{n=1}^{\infty} \frac{(-1)^{n-1} x^{2n-1}}{(2n-1)!}$

7. $\displaystyle\sum_{n=1}^{\infty} (-1)^{n-1} \frac{(x-1)^n}{n}$

8. $\displaystyle\sum_{n=1}^{\infty} \frac{n^2}{2^n} (x+2)^n$

9. $\displaystyle\sum_{n=1}^{\infty} \frac{2^n}{n(n+1)} (x-3)^{2n-1}$

10. $\displaystyle\sum_{n=0}^{\infty} \frac{(-1)^n x^{2n}}{2^{2n}(n!)^2}$

14.8 ALTERNATING SERIES: CONDITIONAL CONVERGENCE

When some of the terms of a series $\sum u_k$ are positive and some are negative, *the series converges if $\sum |u_k|$ converges.* Thus we may apply any of our tests for convergence of positive series, provided that we apply them to the series of absolute values. But we do not know, when the series of absolute values

diverges, whether the *original* series diverges or not. If it converges, but not absolutely, we say that it *converges conditionally*.

We discuss one simple case of series with mixed signs, that of an alternating series of the form

$$a_1 - a_2 + a_3 - a_4 + \cdots + (-1)^{n-1}a_n + \cdots, \quad (1)$$

where the a's are all positive.

Theorem 11. *If the following three conditions are all satisfied, then the series does converge.*

(a) *The series $\sum u_k$ is strictly alternating.*

(b) *The nth term tends to zero as n becomes infinite.*

(c) *Each term is numerically less than, or at most equal to, its predecessor.*

Proof. Suppose these three conditions are satisfied. Then we may write

$$u_k = (-1)^{k-1}a_k$$

and put the series in the form (1) with $a_{n+1} \leq a_n$. If n is an even integer, say $n = 2m$, then the sum of the first n terms is

$$\begin{aligned} s_{2m} &= (a_1 - a_2) + (a_3 - a_4) + \cdots \\ &\quad + (a_{2m-1} - a_{2m}) \\ &= a_1 - (a_2 - a_3) - (a_4 - a_5) - \cdots \\ &\quad - (a_{2m-2} - a_{2m-1}) - a_{2m}. \end{aligned}$$

The first way of writing s_{2m} exhibits it as the sum of m nonnegative terms, since each expression in parentheses is positive or zero. Hence $s_{2m+2} \geq s_{2m}$ and the sequence $\{s_{2m}\}$ is monotonically increasing. The second way of expressing s_{2m} shows, on the other hand, that

$$s_{2m} \leq a_1.$$

Hence we have a sequence $\{s_{2m}\}$ that is monotone increasing and is bounded above. Such a sequence has a limit, say

$$\lim_{m \to \infty} s_{2m} = L. \quad (2)$$

If we now form the sum of an odd number of terms, say

$$s_{2m+1} = a_1 - a_2 + a_3 - \cdots$$
$$+ a_{2m-1} - a_{2m} + a_{2m+1}$$
$$= s_{2m} + a_{2m+1},$$

the fact that the nth term approaches zero as n becomes infinite means that

$$\lim_{m \to \infty} a_{2m+1} = 0.$$

Hence, as $m \to \infty$,

$$\lim s_{m+1} = \lim s_{2m} + \lim a_{2m+1} = L. \quad (3)$$

Finally, we may combine Eqs. (2) and (3) and say simply

$$\lim_{n \to \infty} s_n = L,$$

where n may be either even or odd. □

The following graphical interpretation of the partial sums gives us added insight into the way in which an alternating series converges to its limit L when the three conditions of the theorem are satisfied. (See Fig. 14.14.) Starting from the origin O on a scale of real numbers, we lay off the positive distance

$$s_1 = a_1.$$

To find the point corresponding to

$$s_2 = a_1 - a_2$$

we must back up a distance equal to a_2. Since $a_2 \le a_1$, we do not back up any farther than O at most. Next we go forward a distance a_3 and mark the point corresponding to

$$s_3 = a_1 - a_2 + a_3.$$

Since $a_3 \le a_2$, we go forward by an amount which is no greater than the previous backward step; that is, s_3 is less than or equal to s_1. We continue in this seesaw fashion, backing up or going forward as the signs in the series demand. But each forward or backward step is shorter than (or at most the same size as) the preceding step, because $a_{n+1} \le a_n$. And since the nth term approaches zero as n increases, the size of step we take forward or backward gets smaller and smaller. We thus oscillate across the limit L, but the amplitude of oscillation con-

14.14

tinually decreases and approaches zero as its limit. The even-numbered partial sums $s_2, s_4, s_6, \ldots, s_{2m}$ continually increase toward L, while the odd-numbered sums $s_1, s_3, s_5, \ldots, s_{2m+1}$ continually decrease toward L. The limit L is between any two successive sums s_n and s_{n+1} and hence differs from either of them by an amount not greater than a_{n+1}.

Example 1. The series

$$1 - \frac{1}{2} + \frac{1}{3} - \frac{1}{4} + \cdots + \frac{(-1)^{n-1}}{n} + \cdots$$

satisfies the three conditions of the theorem.

(a) It is alternating.

(b) The nth term is

$$\frac{(-1)^{n-1}}{n},$$

which tends to zero as n increases.

(c) The terms decrease in absolute value, since

$$\frac{1}{n+1} < \frac{1}{n}.$$

Hence this series converges. But it converges conditionally and not absolutely, since the series of absolute values is

$$1 + \frac{1}{2} + \frac{1}{3} + \cdots + \frac{1}{n} + \cdots,$$

which we know diverges.

Remark. Suppose that when we compute the numerical value of an alternating series that satisfies the three conditions of the theorem and converges to a limit L, we stop after computing the sum s_n

of the first n terms. Then the error, which is represented by the remainder

$$R_n = L - s_n$$
$$= (-1)^n(a_{n+1} - a_{n+2} + a_{n+3} - \cdots),$$

has the same sign, $(-1)^n$, as the next term, and its absolute value is no greater than the absolute value of that term. That is, $L = s_n + R_n$, R_n has the same sign as $\pm a_{n+1}$, and $|R_n| \leq a_{n+1}$. This follows at once from the fact that

$$R_n = (-1)^n[a_{n+1} - (a_{n+2} - a_{n+3})$$
$$- (a_{n+4} - a_{n+5}) - \cdots]$$
$$= (-1)^n[(a_{n+1} - a_{n+2}) + (a_{n+3} - a_{n+4}) + \cdots];$$

note that the expression in brackets is positive (second form) but not greater than a_{n+1} (first form). Thus, in Example 1, if we stop with

$$s_{10} = 1 - \tfrac{1}{2} + \tfrac{1}{3} - \cdots - \tfrac{1}{10},$$

then we know that the exact value of the series is

$$L = s_{10} + R_{10},$$

where R_{10} is positive (because the next term is $+\tfrac{1}{11}$) and where $|R_{10}| < \tfrac{1}{11}$.

Example 2. We can now show that the series

$$\sum_{k=1}^{\infty} \frac{x^k}{k} = x + \frac{x^2}{2} + \frac{x^3}{3} + \frac{x^4}{4} + \cdots \quad (4)$$

converges for $-1 \leq x < 1$. To find this interval of convergence, we let $u_n = x_n/n$ and use the ratio test:

$$\rho = \lim_{n \to \infty} \left| \frac{u_{n+1}}{u_n} \right| = \lim_{n \to \infty} \left| \frac{x^{n+1}}{n+1} \frac{n}{x^n} \right| = |x|.$$

Hence the series converges absolutely if $|x| < 1$, and it diverges if $|x| > 1$. When $x = +1$, the series becomes

$$1 + \tfrac{1}{2} + \tfrac{1}{3} + \tfrac{1}{4} + \cdots,$$

which diverges to $+\infty$. When $x = -1$, the series becomes

$$-(1 - \tfrac{1}{2} + \tfrac{1}{3} - \tfrac{1}{4} + \cdots),$$

which is just the negative of the convergent alternating series considered in Example 1. Hence the series (4) converges for $-1 \leq x < 1$, and diverges for all other x.

EXERCISES

Find the interval of absolute convergence for each of the following series. If the interval is finite, determine whether the series converges or diverges at the endpoints.

1. $\sum_{n=0}^{\infty} \dfrac{x^{2n+1}}{2n+1}$

2. $\sum_{n=0}^{\infty} (-1)^n \dfrac{x^{2n+1}}{2n+1}$

3. $\sum_{n=1}^{\infty} \dfrac{(x-2)^n}{n^2}$

4. $\sum_{n=1}^{\infty} (-1)^{n-1} \dfrac{(x+1)^n}{n}$

5. $\sum_{n=1}^{\infty} \dfrac{(-1)^{n-1}(x-2)^n}{n \cdot 2^n}$

6. $\sum_{n=0}^{\infty} (-2)^n(n+1)(x-1)^n$

7. $\sum_{k=0}^{\infty} \dfrac{(3x+6)^k}{k!}$

8. $\sum_{n=0}^{\infty} n!x^n$

9. $\sum_{n=1}^{\infty} (-1)^n \dfrac{(2n-2)!}{2^{2n-2}(n-1)!(n-1)!} \dfrac{x^{2n-1}}{2n-1}$

10. $\sum_{n=1}^{\infty} \dfrac{(x+3)^{n-1}}{n}$

REVIEW QUESTIONS AND EXERCISES

1. Define "sequence," "series," "sequence of partial sums of a series."

2. Define convergence
   (a) of a sequence,
   (b) of an infinite series.

3. Which of the following statements are true, and which are false?
   (a) If a sequence does not converge, then it diverges.
   (b) If a sequence $\{n, f(n)\}$ does not converge, then $f(n)$ tends to infinity as n does.
   (c) If a series does not converge, then its nth term does not approach zero as n tends to infinity.
   (d) If the nth term of a series does not approach zero as n tends to infinity, then the series diverges.
   (e) If a sequence $\{n, f(n)\}$ converges, then there is a number L such that $f(n)$ lies within one unit of L
   (i) for all values of n,
   (ii) for all but a finite number of values of n.

(f) If all partial sums of a series are less than some constant L, then the series converges.

(g) If a series converges, then its partial sums s_n are bounded (that is, $m \le s_n \le M$ for some constants m and M).

4. List three tests for convergence (or divergence) of an infinite series.

5. Under what circumstances do you know that a bounded sequence converges?

6. Define absolute convergence and conditional convergence. Give examples of series that are

(a) absolutely convergent,

(b) conditionally convergent.

7. State Taylor's theorem with remainder, giving two different expressions for the remainder.

8. It can be shown (though not very simply) that the function f defined by

$$f(x) = \begin{cases} 0 & \text{when} \quad x = 0, \\ e^{-1/x^2} & \text{when} \quad x \ne 0 \end{cases}$$

is everywhere continuous, together with its derivatives of all orders. At zero, the derivatives are all equal to zero.

(a) Write the Taylor series expansion of f in powers of x.

(b) What is the remainder $R_n(x, 0)$ for this function? Does the Taylor series for f converge to $f(x)$ at some value of x different from zero? Give a reason for your answer.

9. If a Taylor series in powers of $x - a$ is to be used for the numerical evaluation of a function, what is necessary or desirable in the choice of a?

10. List two methods that may be useful in finding

$$\lim_{x \to a} \frac{f(x)}{g(x)} \quad \text{if} \quad f(a) = g(a) = 0.$$

Illustrate both methods with a single example.

11. What test is usually used to find the interval of convergence of a power series? Does this test also work at the end points of the interval? Illustrate with examples.

12. What test is usually used to decide whether or not a given alternating series converges? Give examples of convergent and divergent alternating series.

1. Find explicitly the nth partial sum of the series

$$\sum_{n=2}^{\infty} \ln\left(1 - \frac{1}{n^2}\right),$$

and thereby determine whether or not the series converges.

2. Evaluate

$$\sum_{k=2}^{\infty} \frac{1}{k^2 - 1}$$

by finding the nth partial sum and taking the limit as n becomes infinite.

3. Prove that the sequence $\{x_n\}$ and the series

$$\sum_{k=1}^{\infty} (x_{k+1} - x_k)$$

both converge or both diverge.

4. In an attempt to find a root of the equation $x = f(x)$, a first approximation x_1 is estimated from the graphs of $y = x$ and $y = f(x)$. Then $x_2, x_3, \ldots, x_n, \ldots$ are computed successively from the formula

$$x_n = f(x_{n-1}).$$

If the points $x_1, x_2, \ldots, x_n, \ldots$ all lie on an interval $[a, b]$ on which $f(x)$ has a derivative such that $|f'(x)| < M < 1$, show that the sequence $\{x_n\}$ converges to a root of the given equation.

5. Assuming $|x| > 1$, show that

$$\frac{1}{1 - x} = -\frac{1}{x} - \frac{1}{x^2} - \frac{1}{x^3} - \cdots.$$

6. (a) Find the expansion in powers of x of

$$\frac{x^2}{1 + x}.$$

(b) Does the series expansion of $x^2/(1 + x)$ in powers of x converge when $x = 2$? Give a brief reason.

7. Obtain the Maclaurin series expansion for $\sin^{-1} x$ by integrating the series for $(1 - t^2)^{-1/2}$ from 0 to x. Find the intervals of convergence of these series.

8. Obtain the Maclaurin series for

$$\ln(x + \sqrt{x^2 + 1}) = \sinh^{-1} x$$

by integrating the series for $(1 + t^2)^{-1/2}$ from 0 to x. Find the intervals of convergence of these two series.

9. Obtain the first four terms in the Maclaurin series for $e^{\sin x}$ by substituting the series for $y = \sin x$ in the series for e^y.

10. Assuming $|x| > 1$, obtain the expansions

$$\tan^{-1} x = \frac{\pi}{2} - \frac{1}{x} + \frac{1}{3x^3} - \frac{1}{5x^5} + \cdots, \quad x > 1,$$

$$\tan^{-1} x = -\frac{\pi}{2} - \frac{1}{x} + \frac{1}{3x^3} - \frac{1}{5x^5} + \cdots, \quad x < -1$$

by integrating the series

$$\frac{1}{1+t^2} = \frac{1}{t^2} \cdot \frac{1}{1 + (1/t^2)}$$

$$= \frac{1}{t^2} - \frac{1}{t^4} + \frac{1}{t^6} - \frac{1}{t^8} + \cdots$$

from $x(>1)$ to $+\infty$ or from $-\infty$ to $x(<-1)$.

11. (a) Obtain the Maclaurin series, through the term in x^6, for $\ln(\cos x)$ by substituting the series for $y = 1 - \cos x$ in the series for $\ln(1 - y)$.

(b) Use the result of (a) to estimate

$$\int_0^{0.1} \ln(\cos x)\,dx$$

to five decimal places.

12. Compute

$$\int_0^1 \frac{\sin x}{x}\,dx$$

to three decimal places.

13. Compute $\int_0^1 e^{-x^2}\,dx$ to three decimal places.

14. Expand the function $f(x) = \sqrt{1 + x^2}$ in powers of $(x - 1)$, obtaining three nonvanishing terms.

15. Expand the function $f(x) = 1/(1 - x)$ in powers of $(x - 2)$, and find the interval of convergence.

16. If $\tan x$ has the Maclaurin expansion

$$a_0 + a_1 x + a_2 x^2 + a_3 x^3 + \cdots,$$

find the first three nonvanishing terms.

17. Determine the Taylor series expansion of the function $f(x) = 1/(x + 1)$ in powers of $(x - 3)$.

18. Expand $\cos x$ in powers of $(x - \pi/3)$.

19. Find the first three terms of the Taylor series expansion of the function $1/x$ about the point π.

20. Let f and g be functions satisfying the following conditions:

(a) $f(0) = 1$,   (b) $g(0) = 0$,

(c) $f'(x) = g(x)$, $g'(x) = f(x)$.

Find $f(1)$, accurate to three decimal places.

21. Suppose

$$f(x) = \sum_{n=0}^{\infty} a_n x^n.$$

Prove that

(a) if $f(x)$ is an even function, then

$$a_1 = a_3 = a_5 = \cdots = 0;$$

(b) if $f(x)$ is an odd function, then

$$a_0 = a_2 = a_4 = \cdots = 0.$$

22. Show that the function $f(x) = e^{(e^x)}$ can be expanded into a power series in x, and find the first four terms (up to x^3).

23. Using a suitable series, complete the following four-place table of the function $f(x) = \arctan(x)$:

x	0.01	0.02	0.03	0.04	0.05	0.06	0.10
$f(x)$	0.0100	0.0200	0.0300	0.0400			

24. Give a quantitative estimate of the error involved in using $x - x^2/2$ as an approximation to $\ln(1 + x)$ for values of x between 0 and 0.2 inclusive.

25. If $(1 + x)^{1/3}$ is replaced by $1 + x/3$, and if $0 \le x \le \frac{1}{10}$, what estimate can be given for the error?

26. By considering the quotient of the power series for numerator and denominator, find

$$\lim_{x \to 0} \frac{\ln(1 - x) - \sin x}{1 - \cos^2 x}.$$

27. Find the limit of $[(\sin x)/x]^{1/x^2}$ as x approaches zero.

28. Without any lengthy calculations, show that $\lim 0^x \neq \lim x^0$ as $x \to 0+$.

29. Does the series $\sum_{n=1}^{\infty} \operatorname{sech} n$ converge or diverge? Why?

30. Does the series $\sum_{n=1}^{\infty} (-1)^n \tanh n$ converge or diverge? Why?

31. If $a_n > 0$ and $\sum_{n=1}^{\infty} a_n$ converges, prove that $\sum_{n=1}^{\infty} (1/a_n)$ diverges.

32. Establish the convergence or divergence of the series whose nth terms are as given.

(a) $\dfrac{1}{\ln (n+1)}$

(b) $\dfrac{n}{2(n+1)(n+2)}$

(c) $\dfrac{\sqrt{n+1}-\sqrt{n}}{\sqrt{n}}$

(d) $\dfrac{1}{n(\ln n)^2}$, $n \geq 2$

(e) $\dfrac{1+(-2)^{n-1}}{2^n}$

(f) $\dfrac{n}{1000n^2+1}$

(g) $\dfrac{e^n}{n!}$

(h) $\dfrac{1}{n\sqrt{n^2+1}}$

(i) $\dfrac{1}{n^{1+1/n}}$

(j) $\dfrac{1 \cdot 3 \cdot 5 \cdots (2n-1)}{2 \cdot 4 \cdot 6 \cdots (2n)}$

(k) $\dfrac{n^2}{n^3+1}$

(l) $\dfrac{n+1}{n!}$

33. Find the sum of the convergent series

$$\sum_{n=1}^{\infty} \frac{1}{(n+1)(n+2)}.$$

34. (a) Suppose $a_1, a_2, a_3, \ldots, a_n$ are positive numbers satisfying the following conditions:

(1) $a_1 \geq a_2 \geq a_3 \cdots$,

(2) the series $a_2 + a_4 + a_8 + a_{16} + \cdots$ diverges.

Show that the series

$$\frac{a_1}{1} + \frac{a_2}{2} + \frac{a_3}{3} + \cdots$$

is divergent.

(b) Use the result above to show that the series

$$\sum_{n=2}^{\infty} \frac{1}{n \ln n}$$

is divergent.

35. Let $a_n \neq 1$ and $a_n > 0$, and suppose that $\sum a_n$ converges.

(a) Show that $\sum a_n^2$ converges.

(b) Does

$$\sum \frac{a_n}{(1-a_n)}$$

converge?

(c) Does $\sum \ln (1+a_n)$ converge? Justify your conclusions.

36. Show that the series

$$\sum_{n=2}^{\infty} \frac{1}{n(\ln n)^k}$$

is convergent for $k > 1$.

37. Find the interval of convergence for the following series and test for convergence or divergence at the end points if the interval is finite.

(a) $1+\dfrac{x+2}{3 \cdot 1}+\dfrac{(x+2)^2}{3^2 \cdot 2}+\cdots+\dfrac{(x+2)^n}{3^n \cdot n}+\cdots$

(b) $1+\dfrac{(x-1)^2}{2!}+\dfrac{(x-1)^4}{4!}+\cdots+\dfrac{(x-1)^{2n-2}}{(2n-2)!}+\cdots$

(c) $\displaystyle\sum_{n=1}^{\infty} \frac{x^n}{n^n}$

(d) $\displaystyle\sum_{n=1}^{\infty} \frac{n!x^n}{n^n}$

(e) $\displaystyle\sum_{n=0}^{\infty} \frac{n+1}{2n+1} \frac{(x+3)^n}{2^n}$

(f) $\displaystyle\sum_{n=0}^{\infty} \frac{n+1}{2n+1} \frac{(x-2)^n}{3^n}$

(g) $\displaystyle\sum_{n=1}^{\infty} \frac{(-1)^{n-1}(x-1)^n}{n^2}$

(h) $\displaystyle\sum_{n=1}^{\infty} \frac{x^n}{n}$

38. Determine *all* the values of x for which the following series converge.

(a) $\displaystyle\sum_{n=1}^{\infty} \frac{(x-2)^{3n}}{n!}$

(b) $\displaystyle\sum_{n=1}^{\infty} \frac{2^n(\sin x)^n}{n^2}$

(c) $\displaystyle\sum_{n=1}^{\infty} \frac{1}{n}\left(\frac{x-1}{x}\right)^n$

39. A function is defined by the power series

$$y = 1 + \frac{1}{6}x^3 + \frac{1}{180}x^6 + \cdots$$

$$+ \frac{1 \cdot 4 \cdot 7 \cdots (3n-2)}{(3n)!}x^{3n} + \cdots.$$

(a) Find the interval of convergence of the series.

(b) Show that there exist two constants a and b such that the function so defined satisfies a differential equation of the form $y'' = x^a y + b$.

40. (a) Show that the series

$$1 - \int_1^2 \frac{dx}{x} + \frac{1}{2} - \int_2^3 \frac{dx}{x} + \frac{1}{3}$$
$$- \int_3^4 \frac{dx}{x} + \frac{1}{4} - \int_4^5 \frac{dx}{x} + \frac{1}{5} - \cdots$$

is convergent.

(b) If S is the sum of the series in (a), deduce that

$$\lim_{n \to \infty} \left(1 + \frac{1}{2} + \frac{1}{3} + \cdots + \frac{1}{n} - \ln n \right) = S.$$

41. (a) Does the series

$$\sum_{n=1}^{\infty} \frac{1}{[1 + (1/n)]^n}$$

converge or diverge? Why?

(b) Does the series

$$\sum_{n=1}^{\infty} [1 + (1/n)]^{-n^2}$$

converge or diverge? Why?

42. If $a_n > 0$ and the series

$$\sum_{n=1}^{\infty} a_n$$

converges, prove that

$$\sum_{n=1}^{\infty} \frac{a_n}{1 + a_n}$$

converges.

43. If $1 > a_n > 0$ and

$$\sum_{n=1}^{\infty} a_n$$

converges, prove that

$$\sum_{n=1}^{\infty} \ln (1 - a_n)$$

converges.

Hint. First show that

$$|\ln (1 - a_n)| \le \frac{a_n}{(1 - a_n)},$$

and then apply the answer to Exercise 35(b).

44. An infinite product, indicated by

$$\prod_{n=1}^{\infty} (1 + a_n),$$

is said to converge if the series $\sum_{n=1}^{\infty} \ln (1 + a_n)$ converges. (The series is the natural logarithm of the product.) Prove that the product converges if every $a_n > -1$ and if $\sum_{n=1}^{\infty} |a_n|$ converges.

Hint. Show that

$$|\ln (1 + a_n)| \le |a_n|/(1 - |a_n|) < 2|a_n|$$

when $|a_n| < \frac{1}{2}$.

If you have ready access to a computer, or calculator that can quickly produce sines, cosines, and square roots, you may enjoy investigating the convergence of sequences that satisfy the condition $x_{n+1} = f(x_n)$ for the following functions $f(x)$ and given values of x_1.

Remark. Note that, if $\lim x_n = L$, then also $\lim x_{n+1} = L$ and $x = L$ is a solution of the equation $x = f(x)$. The process can also be studied by using graphs of $y = x$ and $y = f(x)$.

45. $f(x) = \cos x$, $x_1 = 0$

46. $f(x) = 1 - \sin x$, $x_1 = 0$

47. $f(x) = \sqrt{1 - x}$, $x_1 = 0.5$

DIFFERENTIAL EQUATIONS

CHAPTER 15

15.1 INTRODUCTION

A differential equation is an equation that involves one or more derivatives, or differentials. Differential equations are classified by

(a) *type:* ordinary or partial,

(b) *order:* the order of the highest-order derivative that occurs in the equation,

(c) *degree:* the exponent of the highest power of the highest-order derivative, after the equation has been cleared of fractions and radicals in the dependent variable and its derivatives.

For example,

$$\left(\frac{d^3y}{dx^3}\right)^2 + \left(\frac{d^2y}{dx^2}\right)^5 + \frac{y}{x^2+1} = e^x \qquad (1)$$

is an ordinary differential equation, of order three and degree two.

Only "ordinary" derivatives occur when the dependent variable y is a function of a single independent variable x. On the other hand, if the dependent variable y is a function of two or more independent variables, say if

$$y = f(x, t)$$

where x and t are independent variables, then partial derivatives of y may occur.

A treatment of partial differential equations lies beyond the scope of this book.

Many physical problems lead to differential equations when formulated in mathematical terms. In Article 8.11, for example, we discussed two differential equations from the field of electrical engineering:

$$\frac{dQ}{dt} = -kQ \qquad (2)$$

and, for an RL-series circuit,

$$L\frac{di}{dt} + Ri = E. \qquad (3)$$

Again, in Article 13.1, we solved the system of differential equations

$$m\frac{d^2x}{dt^2} = 0, \qquad m\frac{d^2y}{dt^2} = -mg \qquad (4)$$

that arose from the formulation of the laws of motion of a projectile (neglecting air resistance). Indeed, one of the chief sources of differential equations in mechanics is Newton's second law:

$$\mathbf{F} = \frac{d}{dt}(m\mathbf{v}),\tag{5}$$

where $\mathbf{F}$ is the resultant of the forces acting on a body of mass m, and $\mathbf{v}$ is its velocity.

The following situation is a typical example of an application in the field of radiochemistry. Suppose that at time t, there are x, y, and z grams, respectively, of three radioactive substances A, B, and C which have the following properties. A, through radioactive decomposition, transforms into B at a rate proportional to the amount of A present. B, in turn, transforms into C at a rate which is proportional to the amount of B present. Finally, C transforms back into A at a rate which is proportional to the amount of C present. (See Fig. 15.1.) If we call the proportionality factors k_1, k_2, and k_3, respectively, we have the following system of differential equations:

$$\frac{dx}{dt} = -k_1 x + k_3 z,$$

$$\frac{dy}{dt} = k_1 x - k_2 y,\tag{6}$$

$$\frac{dz}{dt} = k_2 y - k_3 z.$$

The first of these simply says that the amount of A present at time t, namely x, is decreasing at a rate $k_1 x$ through transformation into substance B, but is gaining at a rate $k_3 z$ from substance C. The other two equations have similar meanings. It is an immediate consequence of Eqs. (6) that

$$\frac{dx}{dt} + \frac{dy}{dt} + \frac{dz}{dt} = 0.\tag{7}$$

From Eq. (7), in turn, we readily deduce that

$$x + y + z = \text{constant}.$$

In other words, in the hypothetical case under consideration, the total amount of substances A, B, and C remains constant.

15.1

15.2   SOLUTIONS

A function $y = f(x)$ is said to be a *solution* of a differential equation if the latter is identically satisfied when y and its derivatives are replaced throughout by $f(x)$ and its corresponding derivatives. For example, if c_1 and c_2 are any constants, then

$$y = c_1 \cos x + c_2 \sin x\tag{1a}$$

is a solution of the differential equation

$$\frac{d^2 y}{dx^2} + y = 0.\tag{1b}$$

A physical problem that translates into a differential equation usually involves additional conditions not expressed by the differential equation itself. In mechanics, for example, the initial position and velocity of the moving body are usually prescribed, as well as the forces. The differential equation, or equations, of motion will usually have solutions in which certain arbitrary constants occur. [Note the constants in Eq. (1a), for example.] However, it will be necessary to assign specific values to these arbitrary constants in order to meet the prescribed initial conditions. (See the problems and examples worked out in Articles 8.11 and 14.1.)

A differential equation of order n will in general possess a solution involving n arbitrary constants. (There is a more precise mathematical theorem, which we shall neither state nor prove.) This solution is called the *general* solution. Once this general solution is known, it is only a matter of algebra to determine specific values of the constants if initial conditions are also prescribed. Hence we shall devote our attention to the problem of finding the general solutions of certain types of differential equations.

The subject of differential equations is a complex one. The interested reader may consult textbooks on differential equations* or on advanced calculus† for more exhaustive treatments than we shall present here. The field is also the subject of current research by several eminent mathematicians, and nobody "knows all the answers."

Throughout this chapter, only *ordinary* differential equations will be considered. In outline, the next eight articles cover the following topics.

1. First-order equations
   - (a) variables separable
   - (b) homogeneous
   - (c) linear
   - (d) exact differentials

2. Special types of second-order equations

3. Linear equations with constant coefficients
   - (a) homogeneous
   - (b) nonhomogeneous

The reader will note that several new terms occur in this list; these will be defined in the appropriate places.

15.3 FIRST-ORDER EQUATIONS WITH VARIABLES SEPARABLE

A first-order differential equation can be solved by integration if it is possible to collect all y terms with dy and all x terms with dx. That is, if it is possible to write the equation in the form

$$f(y)\, dy + g(x)\, dx = 0,$$

then the general solution is

$$\int f(y)\, dy + \int g(x)\, dx = C,$$

where C is an arbitrary constant.

---

* See, for example, Martin and Reissner, *Elementary Differential Equations*, Addison-Wesley, 1961.
† See, for example, Kaplan, *Advanced Calculus*, Addison-Wesley, 1952.

Problem. Solve the equation

$$(x+1)\frac{dy}{dx} = x(y^2+1).$$

Solution. We change to differential form, separate the variables, and integrate:

$$(x+1)\, dy = x(y^2+1)\, dx,$$

$$\frac{dy}{y^2+1} = \frac{x\, dx}{x+1},$$

$$\tan^{-1} y = x - \ln|x+1| + C.$$

EXERCISES

Separate the variables and solve the following differential equations.

1. $x(2y-3)\, dx + (x^2+1)\, dy = 0$
2. $x^2(y^2+1)\, dx + y\sqrt{x^3+1}\, dy = 0$
3. $\dfrac{dy}{dx} = e^{x-y}$ 　　　　 4. $\sqrt{2xy}\,\dfrac{dy}{dx} = 1$
5. $\sin x\,\dfrac{dx}{dy} + \cosh 2y = 0$ 　 6. $\ln x\,\dfrac{dx}{dy} = \dfrac{x}{y}$
7. $xe^y\, dy + \dfrac{x^2+1}{y}\, dx = 0$
8. $y\sqrt{2x^2+3}\, dy + x\sqrt{4-y^2}\, dx = 0$
9. $\sqrt{1+x^2}\, dy + \sqrt{y^2-1}\, dx = 0$
10. $x^2 y\,\dfrac{dy}{dx} = (1+x)\csc y.$

15.4 FIRST-ORDER HOMOGENEOUS EQUATIONS

A differential equation that can be put into the form

$$\frac{dy}{dx} = F\left(\frac{y}{x}\right) \tag{1}$$

is said to be *homogeneous*. Such an equation can be solved by introducing a new dependent variable

$$v = \frac{y}{x}. \tag{2}$$

Then

$$y = vx, \qquad \frac{dy}{dx} = v + x\frac{dv}{dx},$$

and (1) becomes

$$v + x \frac{dv}{dx} = F(v). \tag{3}$$

Equation (3) can be solved by separation of variables:

$$\frac{dx}{x} + \frac{dv}{v - F(v)} = 0. \tag{4}$$

After (4) is solved, the solution of the original equation is obtained when we replace v by y/x.

Problem. Show that the equation

$$(x^2 + y^2)\, dx + 2xy\, dy = 0$$

is homogeneous, and solve it.

Solution. From the given equation, we have

$$\frac{dy}{dx} = -\frac{x^2 + y^2}{2xy} = -\frac{1 + (y/x)^2}{2(y/x)}.$$

This has the form of Eq. (1), with

$$F(v) = -\frac{1 + v^2}{2v}, \quad \text{where } v = \frac{y}{x}.$$

Then Eq. (4) becomes

$$\frac{dx}{x} + \frac{dv}{v + \frac{1 + v^2}{2v}} = 0, \quad \text{or} \quad \frac{dx}{x} + \frac{2v\, dv}{1 + 3v^2} = 0.$$

The solution of this is

$$\ln|x| + \tfrac{1}{3}\ln(1 + 3v^2) = \tfrac{1}{3}\ln C,$$

or

$$x^3(1 + 3v^2) = \pm C.$$

In terms of y and x, the solution is

$$x(x^2 + 3y^2) = C.$$

EXERCISES

Show that the following equations are homogeneous, and solve.

1. $(x + y)\, dy + (x - y)\, dx = 0$
2. $x^2\, dy + (y^2 - xy)\, dx = 0$
3. $(xe^{y/x} + y)\, dx - x\, dy = 0$

4. $(x^2 + y^2)\, dy - y^2\, dx = 0$
5. $\dfrac{dy}{dx} = \dfrac{-x + \sqrt{x^2 + y^2}}{y}$
6. If every member of a family of curves is a solution of the differential equation

$$M(x, y)\, dx + N(x, y)\, dy = 0,$$

while every member of a second family of curves is a solution of the related equation

$$N(x, y)\, dx - M(x, y)\, dy = 0,$$

then each curve of the one family is orthogonal to every curve of the other family. Each family is said to be a family of *orthogonal trajectories* of the other. Find the family of solutions of the differential equation

$$\frac{dy}{dx} = \frac{y^2 - x^2}{2xy}$$

and their orthogonal trajectories. Sketch both families of curves.

15.5 FIRST-ORDER LINEAR EQUATIONS

The complexity of a differential equation depends primarily on the way in which the *dependent* variable and its derivatives occur. Of particular importance are those equations that are linear. To find whether or not a differential equation is linear, we compute the degree of each of its terms, adding the exponents of the dependent variable, and of any of its derivatives that occur in the term. Thus, for example, the term (d^2y/dx^2) is of the first degree, while the term $y(dy/dx)$ is of the second degree because we must add 1 for the exponent of y, and 1 for the exponent of dy/dx. If every term of a differential equation is of degree zero or degree one, then the equation is linear.

A linear differential equation of first order can always be put into the standard form

$$\frac{dy}{dx} + Py = Q, \tag{1}$$

where P and Q are functions of x. One method for solving Eq. (1) is to find a function $\rho = \rho(x)$ such that if the equation is multiplied by ρ, the left-hand side becomes the derivative of the product ρy. That is, we multiply (1) by ρ:

$$\rho \frac{dy}{dx} + \rho P y = \rho Q, \qquad (1')$$

and then try to impose on ρ the condition that

$$\rho \frac{dy}{dx} + \rho P y = \frac{d}{dx}(\rho y). \qquad (2)$$

When we expand the right-hand side of (2) and cancel terms, we obtain

$$\frac{d\rho}{dx} = \rho P \qquad (3)$$

as the condition to be satisfied by ρ. In Eq. (3), $P = P(x)$ is a known function, so we can separate the variables and solve for ρ:

$$\frac{d\rho}{\rho} = P \, dx, \qquad \ln|\rho| = \int P \, dx + \ln C,$$

$$\rho = \pm C e^{\int P \, dx}. \qquad (4)$$

Since we do not require the most general function ρ, we may take $\pm C = 1$ in (4) and use

$$\rho = e^{\int P \, dx}. \qquad (5)$$

This function is called an *integrating factor* for Eq. (1). With its help, $(1')$ becomes

$$\frac{d}{dx}(\rho y) = \rho Q,$$

the solution of which is

$$\rho y = \int \rho Q \, dx + C. \qquad (6)$$

Since ρ is given by (5), and since P and Q are known from the given differential equation (1), we have in Eqs. (5) and (6) a summary of all that is required to solve (1).

Problem 1. $\qquad \dfrac{dy}{dx} + y = e^x.$

Solution. $\qquad P = 1, \qquad Q = e^x,$

$$\rho = e^{\int dx} = e^x,$$

$$e^x y = \int e^{2x} \, dx + C = \tfrac{1}{2} e^{2x} + C,$$

$$y = \tfrac{1}{2} e^x + C e^{-x}.$$

Problem 2. $\qquad x \dfrac{dy}{dx} - 3y = x^2.$

Solution. We put the equation in standard form:

$$\frac{dy}{dx} - \frac{3}{x} y = x,$$

and then read off

$$P = -\frac{3}{x}, \qquad Q = x.$$

Hence

$$\rho = e^{\int -(3/x) \, dx} = e^{-3 \ln x} = \frac{1}{e^{3 \ln x}} = \frac{1}{x^3},$$

and

$$\frac{1}{x^3} y = \int \frac{x}{x^3} \, dx + C = -\frac{1}{x} + C,$$

$$y = -x^2 + C x^3.$$

Remark 1. Note that whenever $\int P \, dx$ involves logarithms, as in the last example, it is profitable to simplify the expression for $e^{\int P \, dx}$ before substituting into Eq. (6). We make use of the properties of the logarithmic and exponential functions:

$$e^{\ln A} = A,$$
$$e^{m \ln A} = A^m,$$
$$e^{n + m \ln A} = A^m e^n.$$

Remark 2. A differential equation which is linear in y and dy/dx may also be separable, or homogeneous. In such cases, we have a choice of methods of solution. Observe also that an equation which is linear in x and dx/dy can be solved by the technique of this article; one need only interchange the roles of x and y in Eqs. (1), (5), and (6).

EXERCISES

1. $\dfrac{dy}{dx} + 2y = e^{-x}$

2. $2 \dfrac{dy}{dx} - y = e^{x/2}$

3. $x \dfrac{dy}{dx} + 3y = \dfrac{\sin x}{x^2}$

4. $x \, dy + y \, dx = \sin x \, dx$

5. $x \, dy + y \, dx = y \, dy$

6. $(x - 1)^3 \dfrac{dy}{dx} + 4(x - 1)^2 y = x + 1$

7. $\cosh x \, dy + (y \sinh x + e^x) \, dx = 0$

8. $e^{2y} \, dx + 2(xe^{2y} - y) \, dy = 0$

9. $(x - 2y) \, dy + y \, dx = 0$

10. $(y^2 + 1) \, dx + (2xy + 1) \, dy = 0$

15.6 FIRST-ORDER EQUATIONS WITH EXACT DIFFERENTIALS

An equation that can be written in the form

$$M(x, y) \, dx + N(x, y) \, dy = 0, \qquad (1)$$

is said to be *exact*, if there is a function $f(x, y)$ such that

$$df = M \, dx + N \, dy. \qquad (2)$$

Then (1) becomes

$$df = 0$$

and the solution is

$$f(x, y) = C,$$

where C is an arbitrary constant.

One can often recognize certain combinations of differentials that can be made exact by "ingenious devices."

Problem 1. $x \, dy - y \, dx = xy^2 \, dx.$

Solution. The combination $x \, dy - y \, dx$ may "ring a bell" in our memories and cause us to recall the formula

$$d\left(\frac{u}{v}\right) = \frac{v \, du - u \, dv}{v^2} = -\frac{u \, dv - v \, du}{v^2}.$$

Therefore we might divide the given equation by x^2, or change signs and divide by y^2. Clearly, the latter approach will be more profitable, so we proceed as follows:

$$x \, dy - y \, dx = xy^2 \, dx,$$

$$\frac{y \, dx - x \, dy}{y^2} = -x \, dx,$$

$$d\left(\frac{x}{y}\right) + x \, dx = 0, \qquad \frac{x}{y} + \frac{x^2}{2} = C.$$

Problem 2. $(x + y) \, dx + (x + \cos y) \, dy = 0.$

Solution. There are two kinds of terms:

(1) Those like $x \, dx$ and $\cos y \, dy$ in which the variables are separated, and

(2) terms like $y \, dx + x \, dy = d(xy)$ in which the variables can be combined in exact differentials but cannot be separated.

The original equation is the same as

$$d\left(\frac{x^2}{2} + \sin y + xy\right) = 0,$$

so the solution is

$$\frac{x^2}{2} + \sin y + xy = C.$$

EXERCISES

1. $(x + y) \, dx + (x + y^2) \, dy = 0$

2. $(2xe^y + e^x) \, dx + (x^2 + 1)e^y \, dy = 0$

3. $(2xy + y^2) \, dx + (x^2 + 2xy - y) \, dy = 0$

4. $(x + \sqrt{y^2 + 1}) \, dx - \left(y - \dfrac{xy}{\sqrt{y^2 + 1}}\right) dy = 0$

5. $x \, dy - y \, dx + x^3 \, dx = 0$

6. $x \, dy - y \, dx = (x^2 + y^2) \, dx$

7. $(x^2 + x - y) \, dx + x \, dy = 0$

8. $\left(e^x + \ln y + \dfrac{y}{x}\right) dx + \left(\dfrac{x}{y} + \ln x + \sin y\right) dy = 0$

9. $\left(\dfrac{y^2}{1 + x^2} - 2y\right) dx + (2y \tan^{-1} x - 2x + \sinh y) \, dy = 0$

10. $dy + \dfrac{y - \sin x}{x} \, dx = 0.$

15.7 SPECIAL TYPES OF SECOND-ORDER EQUATIONS

Certain types of second-order differential equations, of which the general form is

$$F\left(x, y, \frac{dy}{dx}, \frac{d^2y}{dx^2}\right) = 0, \qquad (1)$$

can be reduced to first-order equations by a suitable change of variables.

Type 1. Equations with dependent variable missing. If Eq. (1) has the special form

$$F\left(x, \frac{dy}{dx}, \frac{d^2y}{dx^2}\right) = 0, \qquad (2)$$

then we can reduce it to a first-order equation by substituting

$$p = \frac{dy}{dx}, \qquad \frac{d^2y}{dx^2} = \frac{dp}{dx}.$$

Then Eq. (2) takes the form

$$F\left(x, p, \frac{dp}{dx}\right) = 0,$$

which is of the first order in p. If this can be solved for p as a function of x, say

$$p = \phi(x, C_1),$$

then we can find y by an additional integration:

$$y = \int (dy/dx)\, dx = \int p\, dx = \int \phi(x, C_1)\, dx + C_2.$$

Note. For an example, see the solution of the differential equation

$$\frac{d^2y}{dx^2} = \frac{w}{H}\sqrt{1 + \left(\frac{dy}{dx}\right)^2}$$

in Article 12.6.

Type 2. Equations with independent variable missing. If Eq. (1) does not contain x explicitly but has the form

$$F\left(y, \frac{dy}{dx}, \frac{d^2y}{dx^2}\right) = 0, \qquad (3)$$

then the substitutions to use are

$$p = \frac{dy}{dx}, \qquad \frac{d^2y}{dx^2} = p\,\frac{dp}{dy}.$$

Then Eq. (3) takes the form

$$F\left(y, p, p\,\frac{dp}{dy}\right) = 0,$$

which is of order 1 in p. Its solution gives p in terms of y; a further integration gives the solution of Eq. (3).

Problem. $\qquad \dfrac{d^2y}{dx^2} + y = 0.$

Solution. Let

$$\frac{dy}{dx} = p, \qquad \frac{d^2y}{dx^2} = \frac{dp}{dx} = \frac{dp}{dy}\frac{dy}{dx} = \frac{dp}{dy}\, p,$$

and proceed as follows:

$$p\,\frac{dp}{dy} + y = 0, \quad \text{or} \quad p\, dp + y\, dy = 0;$$

hence

$$\frac{p^2}{2} + \frac{y^2}{2} = \frac{C_1^2}{2}, \quad \text{or} \quad p = \pm\sqrt{C_1^2 - y^2}.$$

But $p = dy/dx$, and therefore

$$\frac{dy}{dx} = \pm\sqrt{C_1^2 - y^2}, \quad \text{or} \quad \frac{dy}{\sqrt{C_1^2 - y^2}} = \pm dx.$$

Noting the trigonometric differential, we have

$$\sin^{-1}(y/C_1) = \pm(x + C_2),$$

or

$$y = C_1 \sin[\pm(x + C_2)] = \pm C_1 \sin(x + C_2).$$

Since C_1 is arbitrary, there is no need for the $\pm$-sign, and we have $y = C_1 \sin(x + C_2)$ as the general solution.

Remark. It was a matter of convenience, and no loss in generality, to call the first constant of integration $C_1^2/2$ instead of C_1. The sum $(p^2/2) + (y^2/2)$ is positive unless both p and y are zero. The possible alternative, $p = y = 0$, leads to the solution $y = 0$ which we could also get (in this example) by taking $C_1 = 0$ in the final (general) solution $y = C_1 \sin(x + C_2)$. But it sometimes happens that there is a special solution that does not come out of the "general" solution. Or, the first constant of integration might be positive, negative, or zero, and these alternatives may need to be considered separately (as in Exercise 2 that follows).

EXERCISES

1. $\dfrac{d^2y}{dx^2} + \dfrac{dy}{dx} = 0$ $\qquad$ 2. $\dfrac{d^2y}{dx^2} + y\,\dfrac{dy}{dx} = 0$

3. $\dfrac{d^2y}{dx^2} + x\,\dfrac{dy}{dx} = 0$ $\qquad$ 4. $x\,\dfrac{d^2y}{dx^2} + \dfrac{dy}{dx} = 0$

5. $\dfrac{d^2y}{dx^2} - y = 0$

6. $\dfrac{d^2y}{dx^2} + \omega^2 y = 0$, ω a constant $\neq 0$

7. A body of mass m is suspended from one end of a spring whose other end is attached to a rigid support. The body is allowed to come to rest, and is then pulled down an additional slight amount A and released. Find its motion.

   Hint. Assume Newton's second law of motion and Hooke's law, which says that the tension in the spring is proportional to the amount it is stretched. Let x denote the displacement of the body at time t, measured from the equilibrium position. Then

   $$m\frac{d^2x}{dt^2} = -kx,$$

   where k, the "spring constant," is the proportionality factor in Hooke's law.

8. A man suspended from a parachute falls through space under the pull of gravity. If air resistance produces a retarding force proportional to the man's velocity and he starts from rest at time $t = 0$, find the distance he falls in time t.

15.8 LINEAR EQUATIONS WITH CONSTANT COEFFICIENTS

An equation of the form

$$\frac{d^n}{dx^n}y + a_1\frac{d^{n-1}}{dx^{n-1}}y + a_2\frac{d^{n-2}}{dx^{n-2}}y + \cdots$$
$$+ a_{n-1}\frac{d}{dx}y + a_n y = F(x), \qquad (1)$$

which is linear in y and its derivatives, is called a *linear* equation of order n. If $F(x)$ is identically zero, the equation is said to be *homogeneous*, otherwise it is called nonhomogeneous. The equation is linear even though the coefficients $a_1, a_2, \ldots, a_n$ are functions of x. However, we shall consider only the case where these coefficients are *constants*.

It is convenient to introduce the symbol D to represent the operation of differentiation with respect to x. That is, we write $Df(x)$ to mean the same thing as $(d/dx)f(x)$. Furthermore, we define

powers of D to mean taking successive derivatives:

$$D^2f(x) = D\{Df(x)\} = \frac{d^2f(x)}{dx^2},$$

$$D^3f(x) = D\{D^2f(x)\} = \frac{d^3f(x)}{dx^3},$$

and so on. A polynomial in D is to be interpreted as an operator which, when applied to $f(x)$, produces a linear combination of f and its successive derivatives. For example,

$$(D^2 + D - 2)f(x) = D^2f(x) + Df(x) - 2f(x)$$
$$= \frac{d^2f(x)}{dx^2} + \frac{df(x)}{dx} - 2f(x).$$

Such a polynomial in D is called a "linear differential operator," and may be denoted by the single letter L. If L_1 and L_2 are two such linear operators, their sum and product are defined by the equations

$$(L_1 + L_2)f(x) = L_1f(x) + L_2f(x),$$
$$L_1L_2f(x) = L_1\{L_2f(x)\}.$$

Linear differential operators that are polynomials in D with constant coefficients satisfy basic algebraic laws. This makes it possible to treat them like ordinary polynomials so far as addition, multiplication, and factorization are concerned. Thus

$$(D^2 + D - 2)f(x) = (D + 2)(D - 1)f(x)$$
$$= (D - 1)(D + 2)f(x).$$

Since this is true for any twice-differentiable function f, we also write the equality between operators:

$$D^2 + D - 2 = (D + 2)(D - 1)$$
$$= (D - 1)(D + 2).$$

15.9 HOMOGENEOUS LINEAR SECOND-ORDER DIFFERENTIAL EQUATIONS WITH CONSTANT COEFFICIENTS

Now suppose we wish to solve a differential equation of order two, say

$$\frac{d^2y}{dx^2} + 2a\frac{dy}{dx} + by = 0, \qquad (1)$$

where a and b are constants. In operator notation, this becomes

$$(D^2 + 2aD + b)y = 0. \qquad (1')$$

In association with this differential equation, we consider the algebraic equation

$$r^2 + 2ar + b = 0, \qquad (1'')$$

which we get by replacing D by r and suppressing y. This is called the *characteristic equation* of the differential equation. Suppose the roots of $(1'')$ are r_1 and r_2. Then

$$r^2 + 2ar + b = (r - r_1)(r - r_2)$$

and

$$D^2 + 2aD + b = (D - r_1)(D - r_2).$$

Hence Eq. $(1')$ is equivalent to

$$(D - r_1)(D - r_2)y = 0. \qquad (2)$$

If we now let

$$(D - r_2)y = u, \qquad (3a)$$
$$(D - r_1)u = 0, \qquad (3b)$$

we can solve Eq. $(1')$ in two steps. From Eq. (3b), which is separable, we find

$$u = C_1 e^{r_1 x}.$$

We substitute this into (3a), which becomes

$$(D - r_2)y = C_1 e^{r_1 x},$$

or

$$\frac{dy}{dx} - r_2 y = C_1 e^{r_1 x}.$$

This equation is linear; its integrating factor is

$$\rho = e^{-r_2 x};$$

its solution (see Article 15.5) is

$$e^{-r_2 x} y = C_1 \int e^{(r_1 - r_2)x}\, dx + C_2. \qquad (4)$$

At this point we must consider two cases, $r_1 \neq r_2$ and $r_1 = r_2$.

Case 1. If $r_1 \neq r_2$, the evaluation of the integral in Eq. (4) leads to

$$e^{-r_2 x} y = \frac{C_1}{r_1 - r_2} e^{(r_1 - r_2)x} + C_2,$$

or

$$y = \frac{C_1}{r_1 - r_2} e^{r_1 x} + C_2 e^{r_2 x}.$$

Since C_1 is an arbitrary constant, so is $C_1/(r_1 - r_2)$, and the solution of Eq. (2) can be written simply as

$$y = C_1 e^{r_1 x} + C_2 e^{r_2 x}, \quad \text{if} \quad r_1 \neq r_2. \qquad (5)$$

Case 2. If $\qquad r_1 = r_2,$

then $\qquad e^{(r_1 - r_2)x} = e^0 = 1,$

and Eq. (4) reduces to

$$e^{-r_2 x} y = C_1 x + C_2,$$

or

$$y = (C_1 x + C_2)e^{r_2 x}, \quad \text{if} \quad r_1 = r_2. \qquad (6)$$

Problem 1. $\qquad \dfrac{d^2 y}{dx^2} + \dfrac{dy}{dx} - 2y = 0.$

Solution. The equation $r^2 + r - 2 = 0$ has roots

$$r_1 = 1, \qquad r_2 = -2.$$

Hence, by Eq. (5), the solution of the differential equation is

$$y = C_1 e^x + C_2 e^{-2x}.$$

Problem 2. $\qquad \dfrac{d^2 y}{dx^2} + 4\dfrac{dy}{dx} + 4y = 0.$

Solution. $\qquad r^2 + 4r + 4 = (r + 2)^2,$
$$r_1 = r_2 = -2,$$
$$y = (C_1 x + C_2)e^{-2x}.$$

Imaginary roots

If the coefficients a and b in Eq. (1) are real, the roots of the characteristic Eq. $(1'')$ will either be real, or will be a pair of complex conjugate numbers

$$r_1 = \alpha + i\beta, \qquad r_2 = \alpha - i\beta. \qquad (7)$$

If $\beta \neq 0$, then Eq. (5) applies, with the result

$$y = c_1 e^{(\alpha+i\beta)x} + c_2 e^{(\alpha-i\beta)x}$$
$$= e^{\alpha x}[c_1 e^{i\beta x} + c_2 e^{-i\beta x}]. \tag{8}$$

By Euler's formula (Eq. 29, Article 14.4),

$$e^{i\beta x} = \cos \beta x + i \sin \beta x,$$
$$e^{-i\beta x} = \cos \beta x - i \sin \beta x.$$

Hence Eq. (8) may be replaced by

$$y = e^{\alpha x}[(c_1 + c_2) \cos \beta x + i(c_1 - c_2) \sin \beta x]. \tag{9}$$

Finally, if we introduce new arbitrary constants

$$C_1 = c_1 + c_2 \quad \text{and} \quad C_2 = i(c_1 - c_2),$$

Eq. (9) takes the form

$$y = e^{\alpha x}[C_1 \cos \beta x + C_2 \sin \beta x]. \tag{9'}$$

The arbitrary constants C_1 and C_2 in (9') will be real, provided that the constants c_1 and c_2 in (9) are complex conjugates:

$$c_1 = \tfrac{1}{2}(C_1 - iC_2), \qquad c_2 = \tfrac{1}{2}(C_1 + iC_2).$$

To solve a problem in which the roots of the characteristic equation are complex conjugates, we simply write down the answer by Eq. (9').

Problem 3. $\dfrac{d^2y}{dx^2} + 2\dfrac{dy}{dx} + 2y = 0.$

Solution. The equation $r^2 + 2r + 2 = 0$ has roots

$$r_1 = -1 + i, \qquad r_2 = -1 - i.$$

Hence in Eq. (9'), we take

$$\alpha = -1, \qquad \beta = 1$$

and obtain

$$y = e^{-x}[C_1 \cos x + C_2 \sin x].$$

Problem 4. $\dfrac{d^2y}{dx^2} + \omega^2 y = 0, \quad \omega \neq 0.$

Solution. The equation $r^2 + \omega^2 = 0$ has roots

$$r_1 = i\omega, \qquad r_2 = -i\omega.$$

Hence we take $\alpha = 0$, $\beta = \omega$ in Eq. (9'), and obtain

$$y = C_1 \cos \omega x + C_2 \sin \omega x.$$

EXERCISES

1. $\dfrac{d^2y}{dx^2} + 2\dfrac{dy}{dx} = 0$ 2. $\dfrac{d^2y}{dx^2} + 5\dfrac{dy}{dx} + 6y = 0$

3. $\dfrac{d^2y}{dx^2} + 6\dfrac{dy}{dx} + 5y = 0$ 4. $\dfrac{d^2y}{dx^2} - 2\dfrac{dy}{dx} - 3y = 0$

5. $\dfrac{d^2y}{dx^2} + \dfrac{dy}{dx} + y = 0$ 6. $\dfrac{d^2y}{dx^2} - 4\dfrac{dy}{dx} + 4y = 0$

7. $\dfrac{d^2y}{dx^2} + 6\dfrac{dy}{dx} + 9y = 0$ 8. $\dfrac{d^2y}{dx^2} - 6\dfrac{dy}{dx} + 10y = 0$

9. $\dfrac{d^2y}{dx^2} - 2\dfrac{dy}{dx} + 4y = 0$ 10. $\dfrac{d^2y}{dx^2} - 10\dfrac{dy}{dx} + 16y = 0$

15.10 NONHOMOGENEOUS LINEAR SECOND-ORDER DIFFERENTIAL EQUATIONS WITH CONSTANT COEFFICIENTS

In Article 15.9, we learned how to solve the homogeneous equation

$$\dfrac{d^2y}{dx^2} + 2a\dfrac{dy}{dx} + by = 0. \tag{1}$$

We are now in a position to describe a method for solving the nonhomogeneous equation

$$\dfrac{d^2y}{dx^2} + 2a\dfrac{dy}{dx} + by = F(x). \tag{2}$$

To solve Eq. (2), we first obtain the general solution of the related homogeneous equation (1) that is obtained by replacing $F(x)$ by zero. Denote this solution by

$$y_h = C_1 u_1(x) + C_2 u_2(x), \tag{3}$$

where C_1 and C_2 are arbitrary constants and $u_1(x)$, $u_2(x)$ are functions of one or more of the following forms: e^{rx}, xe^{rx}, $e^{\alpha x} \cos \beta x$, $e^{\alpha x} \sin \beta x$.

Now we might, by inspection or by inspired guesswork, be able to discover *one* particular function $y = y_p(x)$ which satisfies Eq. (2). In this case, we would be able to solve Eq. (2) completely, as

$$y = y_h(x) + y_p(x).$$

Problem 1. $\dfrac{d^2y}{dx^2} + 2\dfrac{dy}{dx} - 3y = 6.$

Solution. The quantity y_h satisfies

$$\frac{d^2 y_h}{dx^2} + 2\frac{dy_h}{dx} - 3y_h = 0.$$

The characteristic equation is $r^2 + 2r - 3 = 0$, and its roots are $r_1 = -3$, $r_2 = 1$.

Hence

$$y_h = C_1 e^{-3x} + C_2 e^x.$$

Now to find a particular integral of the original equation, observe that y equal to a constant would do, provided that $-3y = 6$. Hence $y_p = -2$ is one particular solution. The complete solution is

$$y = y_p + y_h = -2 + C_1 e^{-3x} + C_2 e^x.$$

Variation of parameters

Fortunately, there is a general method for finding the solution of the nonhomogeneous Eq. (2) once the general solution of the corresponding homogeneous equation is known. The method is known as the method of *variation of parameters*. It consists in replacing the constants C_1 and C_2 in Eq. (3) by functions $v_1 = v_1(x)$ and $v_2 = v_2(x)$, and requiring (in a way to be explained) that the resulting expression satisfy Eq. (2). There are two functions to be determined, and requiring that Eq. (2) be satisfied is only one of the necessary conditions. As a second condition, we also require that

$$v_1' u_1 + v_2' u_2 = 0. \qquad (4)$$

Then we have

$$y = v_1 u_1 + v_2 u_2, \qquad \frac{dy}{dx} = v_1 u_1' + v_2 u_2',$$

$$\frac{d^2 y}{dx^2} = v_1 u_1'' + v_2 u_2'' + v_1' u_1' + v_2' u_2'.$$

If we substitute these expressions into the left-hand side of Eq. (2), we obtain

$$v_1 \left(\frac{d^2 u_1}{dx^2} + 2a\frac{du_1}{dx} + bu_1 \right)$$
$$+ v_2 \left(\frac{d^2 u_2}{dx^2} + 2a\frac{du_2}{dx} + bu_2 \right) + v_1' u_1' + v_2' u_2' = F(x).$$

The two terms in parentheses are zero, since u_1 and u_2 are solutions of the homogeneous equation (1). Hence Eq. (2) is satisfied if, in addition to Eq. (4), we require that

$$v_1' u_1' + v_2' u_2' = F(x). \qquad (5)$$

Equations (4) and (5) together may be solved for the unknown functions v_1' and v_2'. Then v_1 and v_2 can be found by integration. In applying the method, we can work directly from Eqs. (4) and (5); it is not necessary to rederive them.

Problem 1'. $\dfrac{d^2y}{dx^2} + 2\dfrac{dy}{dx} - 3y = 6.$

Solution. $u_1(x) = e^{-3x}, \qquad u_2(x) = e^x.$

$$v_1' e^{-3x} + v_2' e^x = 0, \qquad v_1'(-3e^{-3x}) + v_2' e^x = 6.$$

Solving these equations simultaneously, we have

$$v_1' = -\tfrac{3}{2}e^{3x}, \qquad v_2' = \tfrac{3}{2}e^{-x}.$$

Hence

$$v_1 = \int -\tfrac{3}{2}e^{3x}\, dx = -\tfrac{1}{2}e^{3x} + c_1,$$

$$v_2 = \int \tfrac{3}{2}e^{-x}\, dx = -\tfrac{3}{2}e^{-x} + c_2,$$

and

$$y = v_1 u_1 + v_2 u_2$$
$$= (-\tfrac{1}{2}e^{3x} + c_1)e^{-3x} + (-\tfrac{3}{2}e^{-x} + c_2)e^x$$
$$= -2 + c_1 e^{-3x} + c_2 e^x.$$

EXERCISES

1. $\dfrac{d^2y}{dx^2} + \dfrac{dy}{dx} = x$ 2. $\dfrac{d^2y}{dx^2} + y = \tan x$

3. $\dfrac{d^2y}{dx^2} + y = \sin x$ 4. $\dfrac{d^2y}{dx^2} + 2\dfrac{dy}{dx} + y = e^x$

5. $\dfrac{d^2y}{dx^2} + 2\dfrac{dy}{dx} + y = e^{-x}$ 6. $\dfrac{d^2y}{dx^2} - y = x$

7. $\dfrac{d^2y}{dx^2} - y = e^x$ 8. $\dfrac{d^2y}{dx^2} - y = \sin x$

9. $\dfrac{d^2y}{dx^2} + 4\dfrac{dy}{dx} + 5y = 10$ 10. $\dfrac{d^2y}{dx^2} + 4\dfrac{dy}{dx} + 5y = x + 2$

15.11 VIBRATIONS

Suppose that a spring of natural length L has its upper end fastened to a rigid support A (Fig. 15.2). A weight W of mass m is suspended from the spring. The weight stretches the spring to a length $L + s$ when the system is allowed to come to rest in a new equilibrium position. By Hooke's law, the tension in the spring is ks, where k is the so-called spring constant. The force of gravity pulling down on the weight is $W = mg$. Equilibrium requires that

$$ks = mg. \tag{1}$$

Suppose now that the weight is pulled down an additional amount a beyond the equilibrium position, and released. We shall discuss its motion.

Let x, with positive direction downward, denote the displacement of the weight away from equilibrium at any time t after the motion has started. Then the forces acting on the weight are

$$+mg \quad \text{(due to gravity)},$$

$$-k(s + x) \quad \text{(due to the spring tension)}.$$

By Newton's second law, the resultant of these forces is also equal to

$$m \frac{d^2x}{dt^2}.$$

Therefore

$$m \frac{d^2x}{dt^2} = mg - ks - kx. \tag{2}$$

By Eq. (1), $mg - ks = 0$, so that (2) becomes

$$m \frac{d^2x}{dt^2} + kx = 0. \tag{3}$$

In addition to the differential equation (3), the motion satisfies the initial conditions

$$\text{at} \quad t = 0, \quad x = a \quad \text{and} \quad \frac{dx}{dt} = 0. \tag{4}$$

Let $\omega = \sqrt{k/m}$. Then Eq. (3) becomes

$$\frac{d^2x}{dt^2} + \omega^2 x = 0,$$

15.2

and the general solution of the differential equation is

$$x = c_1 \cos \omega t + c_2 \sin \omega t. \tag{5}$$

To satisfy the initial conditions, we also compute

$$\frac{dx}{dt} = -c_1 \omega \sin \omega t + c_2 \omega \cos \omega t$$

and then substitute from (4). This yields

$$a = c_1, \qquad 0 = c_2 \omega.$$

Therefore

$$c_1 = a, \qquad c_2 = 0,$$

and

$$x = a \cos \omega t \tag{6}$$

describes the motion of the weight. Equation (6) represents simple harmonic motion of amplitude a and period $T = 2\pi/\omega$.

The two terms on the right-hand side of Eq. (5) can be combined into a single term by making use of the trigonometric identity

$$\sin (\omega t + \phi) = \cos \omega t \sin \phi + \sin \omega t \cos \phi.$$

This identity can be applied to Eq. (5) if and only if we take

$$c_1 = C \sin \phi, \qquad c_2 = C \cos \phi, \tag{7a}$$

where

$$C = \sqrt{c_1^2 + c_2^2} \quad \text{and} \quad \phi = \tan^{-1} \frac{c_1}{c_2}. \tag{7b}$$

(See Fig. 15.3.) Then Eq. (5) can be written in the alternative form

$$x = C \sin (\omega t + \phi). \qquad (8)$$

Here C and ϕ may be taken as two new arbitrary constants, replacing the two constants c_1 and c_2 of Eq. (5). Equation (8) represents simple harmonic motion of amplitude C and period $T = 2\pi/\omega$. The angle $\omega t + \phi$ is called the *phase angle*, and ϕ may be interpreted as the initial value of the phase angle. A graph of Eq. (8) is given in Fig. 15.4.

Equation (3) assumes that there is no friction in the system. Let's now consider the case where the motion of the weight is retarded by a friction force $c(dx/dt)$ proportional to the velocity, where c is a positive constant. Then the differential equation is

$$m \frac{d^2x}{dt^2} = -kx - c\frac{dx}{dt},$$

or

$$\frac{d^2x}{dt^2} + 2b\frac{dx}{dt} + \omega^2 x = 0, \qquad (9)$$

where

$$2b = \frac{c}{m} \quad \text{and} \quad \omega = \sqrt{\frac{k}{m}}.$$

It is possible to replace Eq. (9) by a simpler, related, equation if we introduce a new variable u by means of the substitution

$$x = e^{-bt} u. \qquad (10a)$$

Treating u as a twice-differentiable function of t, we compute the derivatives

$$\frac{dx}{dt} = e^{-bt}\frac{du}{dt} - be^{-bt} u$$

$$\frac{d^2x}{dt^2} = e^{-bt}\frac{d^2u}{dt^2} - 2be^{-bt}\frac{du}{dt} + b^2 e^{-bt} u.$$

When we substitute into the left side of Eq. (9) we get

$$e^{-bt}\left[\frac{d^2u}{dt^2} + (\omega^2 - b^2)u\right] = 0,$$

which means that Eq. (10a) will give us a solution

15.3

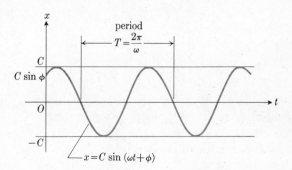

15.4 Representation of a vibration without damping.

of the original differential equation, Eq. (9), if u satisfies

$$\frac{d^2u}{dt^2} + (\omega^2 - b^2)u = 0. \qquad (10b)$$

There are three types of solutions of Eq. (9) that we get from Eqs. (10a, b), depending upon the relative sizes of b and ω.

Case 1. If $b = \omega$, then the solution of (9) is

$$x = (c_1 + c_2 t)e^{-\omega t}. \qquad (11)$$

As time goes on, x approaches zero. The motion is not oscillatory.

Case 2. If $b > \omega$, then the solution of (9) is

$$x = c_1 e^{r_1 t} + c_2 e^{r_2 t}, \qquad (12)$$

where

$$r_1 = -b + \sqrt{b^2 - \omega^2},$$

$$r_2 = -b - \sqrt{b^2 - \omega^2},$$

are the roots of the characteristic equation. Here again the motion is not oscillatory. Both r_1 and r_2 are negative, and x approaches zero as time goes on.

undercritical damping

critical damping
$x = (1+t)e^{-t}$

overcritical damping
$x = e^{-t} - 2e^{-2t}$

15.5

Case 3. If $b < \omega$, let

$$\omega^2 - b^2 = \alpha^2.$$

Then the solution of (9) is

$$x = e^{-bt}(c_1 \cos \alpha t + c_2 \sin \alpha t). \qquad (13a)$$

If we introduce the substitutions (7), we may also write Eq. (13a) in the equivalent form

$$x = Ce^{-bt} \sin (\alpha t + \phi). \qquad (13b)$$

This equation represents damped vibratory motion. It is analogous to simple harmonic motion, of period $T = 2\pi/\alpha$, except that the amplitude is not constant but is given by Ce^{-bt}. Since this tends to zero as t increases, the vibrations tend to die out as time goes on. Observe, however, that Eq. (13b) reduces to Eq. (8) in the absence of friction. The effect of friction is twofold:

1. The quantity

$$b = \frac{c}{2m}$$

appears as a coefficient in the exponential *damping factor* e^{-bt}. The larger b is, the more quickly do the vibrations tend to become unnoticeable.

2. The period $T = 2\pi/\alpha$ is greater than the period $T_0 = 2\pi/\omega$ in the friction-free system.

Curves representing solutions of Eq. (9) in typical cases are depicted in Figs. 15.4 and 15.5. The size of b, relative to ω, determines the kind of solution, and b also determines the rate of damping.

It is therefore customary to say that there is

(a) critical damping if $b = \omega$,

(b) overcritical damping if $b > \omega$,

(c) undercritical damping if $0 < b < \omega$,

(d) no damping if $b = 0$.

EXERCISES

1. Suppose the motion of the weight in Fig. 15.2 is governed by the differential equation (3). Find the motion if $x = x_0$ and $dx/dt = v_0$ at $t = 0$. Express the answer in two equivalent forms (Eqs. 5 and 8).

2. A 5-lb weight is suspended from the lower end of a spring whose upper end is attached to a rigid support. The weight extends the spring by 2 in. If, after the weight has come to rest in its new equilibrium position, it is struck a sharp blow which starts it downward with a velocity of 4 ft/sec, find its subsequent motion, assuming there is no friction.

3. A simple pendulum of length l makes an angle θ with the vertical. As it swings back and forth, its motion (neglecting friction) is governed by the differential equation

$$\frac{d^2\theta}{dt^2} = -\frac{g}{l} \sin \theta,$$

where g (the acceleration due to gravity, $g \approx 32$ ft/sec^2) is a constant. Solve the differential equation of motion, under the assumption that θ is sufficiently small that $\sin \theta$ may be replaced by θ without appreciable error. Assume that $\theta = \theta_0$ and $d\theta/dt = 0$ when $t = 0$.

4. A circular disc of mass m and radius r is suspended by a thin wire attached to the center of one of its flat faces. If the disc is twisted through an angle θ, torsion in the wire tends to turn the disc back in the opposite direction. The differential equation that governs the motion is

$$\frac{1}{2} mr^2 \frac{d^2\theta}{dt^2} = -k\theta,$$

where k is the coefficient of torsion of the wire. Find the motion if $\theta = \theta_0$ and $d\theta/dt = v_0$ at $t = 0$.

5. A cylindrical spar buoy, diameter 1 foot, weight 100 lb, floats partially submerged in an upright position. When it is depressed slightly from its equilibrium position and released, it bobs up and down, its motion being governed by the differential equation

$$\frac{100}{g} \frac{d^2x}{dt^2} = -16\pi x - c \frac{dx}{dt}.$$

Here $c\,(dx/dt)$ is the frictional resistance of the water. Find c if the period of oscilltion is observed to be 1.6 sec.

REVIEW QUESTIONS AND EXERCISES

1. Review methods for solving ordinary first-order and first-degree differential equations

   (a) when the variables are separable,

   (b) when the equation is homogeneous,

   (c) when the equation is linear in one variable,

   (d) when the equation is exact.

   Illustrate each with an example.

2. Review methods of solving second-order equations

   (a) with dependent variable missing,

   (b) with independent variable missing.

   Illustrate each with an example.

3. Review methods for solving linear differential equations with constant coefficients

   (a) in the homogeneous case,

   (b) in the nonhomogeneous case.

   Illustrate each with an example.

4. If an external force F acts on a system whose mass varies with time, Newton's law of motion is

$$\frac{d(mv)}{dt} = F + (v + u) \frac{dm}{dt}.$$

In this equation, m is the mass of the system at time t, v is its velocity, and $v + u$ is the velocity of the mass that is entering (or leaving) the system at the rate dm/dt. Suppose that a rocket of initial mass m_0 starts from rest, but is driven upward by firing some of its mass directly backward at the constant rate of

$$\frac{dm}{dt} = -b$$

units per second and at constant speed relative to the rocket $u = -c$. The only external force acting on the rocket is $F = -mg$, due to gravity. Under these assumptions, show that the height of the rocket above the ground at the end of t seconds (t small compared to m_0/b) is

$$y = c\left(t + \frac{m_0 - bt}{b} \ln \frac{m_0 - bt}{m_0} \right) - \frac{1}{2} gt^2.$$

(See Martin and Reissner, *Elementary Differential Equations*, 2nd edition, Addison-Wesley, 1961, pp. 26 ff.)

MISCELLANEOUS EXERCISES

Solve the following differential equations.

1. $y \ln y \, dx + (1 + x^2) \, dy = 0$

2. $\dfrac{dy}{dx} = \dfrac{y^2 - y - 2}{x^2 + x}$

3. $e^{x+2y} \, dy - e^{y-2x} \, dx = 0$

4. $\sqrt{1 + (dy/dx)^2} = ky$

5. $y \, dy = \sqrt{1 + y^4} \, dx$

6. $(2x + y) \, dx + (x - 2y) \, dy = 0$

7. $\dfrac{dy}{dx} = \dfrac{x^2 + y^2}{2xy}$

8. $x \dfrac{dy}{dx} = y + \sqrt{x^2 + y^2}$

9. $x \, dy = \left(y + x \cos^2 \dfrac{y}{x} \right) dx$

10. $x(\ln y - \ln x) \, dy = y(1 + \ln y - \ln x) \, dx$

11. $x \, dy + (2y - x^2 - 1) \, dx = 0$

12. $\cos y \, dx + (x \sin y - \cos^2 y) \, dy = 0$

13. $\cosh x \, dy - (y + \cosh x) \sinh x \, dx = 0$

14. $(x + 1) \, dy + (2y - x) \, dx = 0$

15. $(1 + y^2) \, dx + (2xy + y^2 + 1) \, dy = 0$

16. $(x^2 + y) \, dx + (e^y + x) \, dy = 0$

17. $(x^2 + y^2) \, dx + (2xy + \cosh y) \, dy = 0$

18. $(e^x + \ln y) \, dx + \dfrac{x + y}{y} \, dy = 0$

19. $x(1 + e^y) \, dx + \frac{1}{2}(x^2 + y^2)e^y \, dy = 0$

20. $\dfrac{d^2 y}{dx^2} - 2y \dfrac{dy}{dx} = 0$ 21. $\dfrac{d^2 x}{dy^2} + 4x = 0$

22. $\dfrac{d^2 y}{dx^2} = 1 + \left(\dfrac{dy}{dx}\right)^2$ 23. $\dfrac{d^2 x}{dy^2} = 1 - \left(\dfrac{dx}{dy}\right)^2$

24. $\dfrac{d^2 y}{dx^2} - 4\dfrac{dy}{dx} + 3y = 0$ 25. $x^2 \dfrac{d^2 y}{dx^2} + x \dfrac{dy}{dx} = 1$

26. $\dfrac{d^2 y}{dx^2} + 4y = \sec 2x$ 27. $\dfrac{d^2 y}{dx^2} - \dfrac{dy}{dx} - 2y = e^{2x}$

28. Find the *general solution* of the differential equation $4x^2 y'' + 4xy' - y = 0$, given that there is a particular solution of the form $y = x^c$ for some constant c.

29. Show that the only curves having constant curvature are circles and straight lines.

30. Find the orthogonal trajectories of the family of curves $x^2 = Cy^3$.

    Caution. The differential equation should not contain the arbitrary constant C.

31. Find the orthogonal trajectories of the family of circles $(x - C)^2 + y^2 = C^2$.

32. Find the orthogonal trajectories of the family of parabolas $y^2 = 4C(C - x)$.

33. The equation $d^2 y/dt^2 + 100y = 0$ represents a simple harmonic motion. Find the general solution of the equation and determine the constants of integration if $y = 10$, $dy/dt = 50$, when $t = 0$. Find the period and the amplitude of the motion.

In exercises 34–38, (a) find the general solution, and (b) find the solution that satisfies the given data.

34. (a) $\dfrac{d^2 y}{dx^2} + 16y = 0$

    (b) When $x = 0$: $y = 0$, $dy/dx = 5$.

35. (a) $\dfrac{d^2 y}{dx^2} - 16y = 0$

    (b) When $x = 0$: $y = 0$, $dy/dx = 5$.

36. (a) $\dfrac{d^2 x}{dt^2} - 2\dfrac{dx}{dt} - 3x = 0$

    (b) When $t = 0$: $x = 2$, $dx/dt = -2$.

37. (a) $\dfrac{d^2 y}{dt^2} + 2\dfrac{dy}{dt} + 5y = 0$

    (b) When $t = 0$: $y = 3$, $dy/dt = 5$.

38. (a) $\dfrac{d^2 y}{dx^2} - 4y = e^x$

    (b) When $x = 0$: $y = 0$, $dy/dx = 3$.

APPENDICES

A. Algebra

1. *Laws of exponents*

$$a^m a^n = a^{m+n},$$
$$(ab)^m = a^m b^m,$$
$$(a^m)^n = a^{mn},$$
$$a^{m/n} = \sqrt[n]{a^m}.$$

If $a \neq 0$,

$$\frac{a^m}{a^n} = a^{m-n},$$
$$a^0 = 1,$$
$$a^{-m} = \frac{1}{a^m}.$$

2. *Zero*

$a \cdot 0 = 0 \cdot a = 0$ for any finite number a.

If $a \neq 0$,

$$\frac{0}{a} = 0, \quad 0^a = 0, \quad a^0 = 1.$$

Division by zero is not defined.

3. *Fractions*

$$\frac{a}{b} + \frac{c}{d} = \frac{ad+bc}{bd}, \qquad \frac{a}{b} \cdot \frac{c}{d} = \frac{ac}{bd},$$

$$\frac{a/b}{c/d} = \frac{a}{b} \cdot \frac{d}{c}, \qquad \frac{-a}{b} = -\frac{a}{b} = \frac{a}{-b}.$$

$$\frac{(a/b) + (c/d)}{(e/f) + (g/h)} = \frac{(a/b) + (c/d)}{(e/f) + (g/h)} \cdot \frac{bdfh}{bdfh}$$
$$= \frac{(ad+bc)fh}{(eh+fg)bd}.$$

4. *Binomial Theorem, for n any positive integer*

$$(a+b)^n = a^n + na^{n-1}b + \frac{n(n-1)}{1 \cdot 2} a^{n-2}b^2$$
$$+ \frac{n(n-1)(n-2)}{1 \cdot 2 \cdot 3} a^{n-3}b^3 + \cdots$$
$$+ nab^{n-1} + b^n.$$

5. *Proportionality factor.* If y is proportional to x, or y varies directly as x, then $y = kx$ for some constant k, called the *proportionality factor.*

6. *Remainder Theorem and Factor Theorem.* If the polynomial $f(x)$ is divided by $x - r$ until a remainder is obtained that is independent of x, then this remainder R is equal to $f(r)$:

$$R = f(r).$$

In particular, $x - r$ is a *factor* of $f(x)$ if and only if r is a *root* of the equation $f(x) = 0$.

7. *Quadratic formula.* If $a \neq 0$, the roots of the equation $ax^2 + bx + c = 0$ are given by the formula

$$x = \frac{-b \pm \sqrt{b^2 - 4ac}}{2a}.$$

B. Geometry

Notation

$$A = \text{area}, \qquad B = \text{area of base},$$
$$C = \text{circumference},$$
$$S = \text{lateral or surface area},$$
$$V = \text{volume}.$$

1. *Triangle*　　　$A = \frac{1}{2}bh.$　　(Fig. 1)

2. *Similar triangles*

$$\frac{a'}{a} = \frac{b'}{b} = \frac{c'}{c}. \qquad \text{(Fig. 2)}$$

3. *Theorem of Pythagoras*

$$c^2 = a^2 + b^2. \qquad \text{(Fig. 3)}$$

4. *Parallelogram*

$$A = bh. \qquad \text{(Fig. 4)}$$

5. *Trapezoid*

$$A = \tfrac{1}{2}(a + b)h. \qquad \text{(Fig. 5)}$$

6. *Circle*

$$A = \pi r^2, \qquad C = 2\pi r. \qquad \text{(Fig. 6)}$$

7. *Any cylinder or prism with parallel bases*

$$V = Bh. \qquad \text{(Fig. 7)}$$

1

2

3

4

5

6

7a

7b

8. *Right circular cylinder*

$$V = \pi r^2 h, \qquad S = 2\pi r h. \qquad \text{(Fig. 8)}$$

9. *Any cone or pyramid*

$$V = \tfrac{1}{3}Bh. \qquad \text{(Fig. 9)}$$

10. *Right circular cone*

$$V = \tfrac{1}{3}\pi r^2 h, \qquad S = \pi r s. \qquad \text{(Fig.10)}$$

11. *Sphere*

$$V = \tfrac{4}{3}\pi r^3, \qquad A = 4\pi r^2. \qquad \text{(Fig. 11)}$$

C. Trigonometry

1. *Definitions and fundamental identities*   (Fig. 12)

$$\sin \theta = \frac{y}{r} = \frac{1}{\csc \theta},$$

$$\cos \theta = \frac{x}{r} = \frac{1}{\sec \theta},$$

$$\tan \theta = \frac{y}{x} = \frac{1}{\cot \theta},$$

$$\sin (-\theta) = -\sin \theta, \quad \cos (-\theta) = \cos \theta,$$

$$\sin^2 \theta + \cos^2 \theta = 1,$$

$$\sin 2\theta = 2 \sin \theta \cos \theta, \quad \cos 2\theta = \cos^2 \theta - \sin^2 \theta,$$

$$\sin (\alpha + \beta) = \sin \alpha \cos \beta + \cos \alpha \sin \beta,$$

$$\cos (\alpha + \beta) = \cos \alpha \cos \beta - \sin \alpha \sin \beta.$$

2. *Angles and sides of triangle*

Law of cosines:

$$a^2 = b^2 + c^2 - 2bc \cos A.$$

Law of sines:

$$\frac{\sin A}{a} = \frac{\sin B}{b} = \frac{\sin C}{c}.$$

$$\text{Area} = \tfrac{1}{2}bc \sin A = \tfrac{1}{2}ac \sin B = \tfrac{1}{2}ab \sin C.$$

D. Sets

The notation $A = \{x : \ldots\}$

is equivalent to the statement, "A is the set of all elements x such that ..."

The *union* of A and B contains every element that is in A, or in B, or in both A and B. It is denoted by

$$A \cup B.$$

The *intersection* of A and B contains every element that is in both A and B. It is denoted by $A \cap B$.

The *empty* set is denoted by $\emptyset$. If A and B have no elements in common, then

$$A \cap B = \emptyset.$$

8

9a   9b

10   11

12

APPENDIX II: TABLES OF FUNCTIONS

Table 1. Natural trigonometric functions

Degree	Radian	Sine	Cosine	Tangent	Degree	Radian	Sine	Cosine	Tangent
0°	0.000	0.000	1.000	0.000					
1°	0.017	0.017	1.000	0.017	46°	0.803	0.719	0.695	1.036
2°	0.035	0.035	0.999	0.035	47°	0.820	0.731	0.682	1.072
3°	0.052	0.052	0.999	0.052	48°	0.838	0.743	0.669	1.111
4°	0.070	0.070	0.998	0.070	49°	0.855	0.755	0.656	1.150
5°	0.087	0.087	0.996	0.087	50°	0.873	0.766	0.643	1.192
6°	0.105	0.105	0.995	0.105	51°	0.890	0.777	0.629	1.235
7°	0.122	0.122	0.993	0.123	52°	0.908	0.788	0.616	1.280
8°	0.140	0.139	0.990	0.141	53°	0.925	0.799	0.602	1.327
9°	0.157	0.156	0.988	0.158	54°	0.942	0.809	0.588	1.376
10°	0.175	0.174	0.985	0.176	55°	0.960	0.819	0.574	1.428
11°	0.192	0.191	0.982	0.194	56°	0.977	0.829	0.559	1.483
12°	0.209	0.208	0.978	0.213	57°	0.995	0.839	0.545	1.540
13°	0.227	0.225	0.974	0.231	58°	1.012	0.848	0.530	1.600
14°	0.244	0.242	0.970	0.249	59°	1.030	0.857	0.515	1.664
15°	0.262	0.259	0.966	0.268	60°	1.047	0.866	0.500	1.732
16°	0.279	0.276	0.961	0.287	61°	1.065	0.875	0.485	1.804
17°	0.297	0.292	0.956	0.306	62°	1.082	0.883	0.469	1.881
18°	0.314	0.309	0.951	0.325	63°	1.100	0.891	0.454	1.963
19°	0.332	0.326	0.946	0.344	64°	1.117	0.899	0.438	2.050
20°	0.349	0.342	0.940	0.364	65°	1.134	0.906	0.423	2.145
21°	0.367	0.358	0.934	0.384	66°	1.152	0.914	0.407	2.246
22°	0.384	0.375	0.927	0.404	67°	1.169	0.921	0.391	2.356
23°	0.401	0.391	0.921	0.424	68°	1.187	0.927	0.375	2.475
24°	0.419	0.407	0.914	0.445	69°	1.204	0.934	0.358	2.605
25°	0.436	0.423	0.906	0.466	70°	1.222	0.940	0.342	2.748
26°	0.454	0.438	0.899	0.488	71°	1.239	0.946	0.326	2.904
27°	0.471	0.454	0.891	0.510	72°	1.257	0.951	0.309	3.078
28°	0.489	0.469	0.883	0.532	73°	1.274	0.956	0.292	3.271
29°	0.506	0.485	0.875	0.554	74°	1.292	0.961	0.276	3.487
30°	0.524	0.500	0.866	0.577	75°	1.309	0.966	0.259	3.732
31°	0.541	0.515	0.857	0.601	76°	1.326	0.970	0.242	4.011
32°	0.559	0.530	0.848	0.625	77°	1.344	0.974	0.225	4.332
33°	0.576	0.545	0.839	0.649	78°	1.361	0.978	0.208	4.705
34°	0.593	0.559	0.829	0.675	79°	1.379	0.982	0.191	5.145
35°	0.611	0.574	0.819	0.700	80°	1.396	0.985	0.174	5.671
36°	0.628	0.588	0.809	0.727	81°	1.414	0.988	0.156	6.314
37°	0.646	0.602	0.799	0.754	82°	1.431	0.990	0.139	7.115
38°	0.663	0.616	0.788	0.781	83°	1.449	0.993	0.122	8.144
39°	0.681	0.629	0.777	0.810	84°	1.466	0.995	0.105	9.514
40°	0.698	0.643	0.766	0.839	85°	1.484	0.996	0.087	11.43
41°	0.716	0.656	0.755	0.869	86°	1.501	0.998	0.070	14.30
42°	0.733	0.669	0.743	0.900	87°	1.518	0.999	0.052	19.08
43°	0.750	0.682	0.731	0.933	88°	1.536	0.999	0.035	28.64
44°	0.768	0.695	0.719	0.966	89°	1.553	1.000	0.017	57.29
45°	0.785	0.707	0.707	1.000	90°	1.571	1.000	0.000	

Table 2. Exponential functions

x	e^x	e^{-x}	x	e^x	e^{-x}
0.00	1.0000	1.0000	2.5	12.182	0.0821
0.05	1.0513	0.9512	2.6	13.464	0.0743
0.10	1.1052	0.9048	2.7	14.880	0.0672
0.15	1.1618	0.8607	2.8	16.445	0.0608
0.20	1.2214	0.8187	2.9	18.174	0.0550
0.25	1.2840	0.7788	3.0	20.086	0.0498
0.30	1.3499	0.7408	3.1	22.198	0.0450
0.35	1.4191	0.7047	3.2	24.533	0.0408
0.40	1.4918	0.6703	3.3	27.113	0.0369
0.45	1.5683	0.6376	3.4	29.964	0.0334
0.50	1.6487	0.6065	3.5	33.115	0.0302
0.55	1.7333	0.5769	3.6	36.598	0.0273
0.60	1.8221	0.5488	3.7	40.447	0.0247
0.65	1.9155	0.5220	3.8	44.701	0.0224
0.70	2.0138	0.4966	3.9	49.402	0.0202
0.75	2.1170	0.4724	4.0	54.598	0.0183
0.80	2.2255	0.4493	4.1	60.340	0.0166
0.85	2.3396	0.4274	4.2	66.686	0.0150
0.90	2.4596	0.4066	4.3	73.700	0.0136
0.95	2.5857	0.3867	4.4	81.451	0.0123
1.0	2.7183	0.3679	4.5	90.017	0.0111
1.1	3.0042	0.3329	4.6	99.484	0.0101
1.2	3.3201	0.3012	4.7	109.95	0.0091
1.3	3.6693	0.2725	4.8	121.51	0.0082
1.4	4.0552	0.2466	4.9	134.29	0.0074
1.5	4.4817	0.2231	5	148.41	0.0067
1.6	4.9530	0.2019	6	403.43	0.0025
1.7	5.4739	0.1827	7	1096.6	0.0009
1.8	6.0496	0.1653	8	2981.0	0.0003
1.9	6.6859	0.1496	9	8103.1	0.0001
2.0	7.3891	0.1353	10	22026	0.00005
2.1	8.1662	0.1225			
2.2	9.0250	0.1108			
2.3	9.9742	0.1003			
2.4	11.023	0.0907			

Table 3. Natural logarithms of numbers

n	$\log_e n$	n	$\log_e n$	n	$\log_e n$
0.0	*	4.5	1.5041	9.0	2.1972
0.1	7.6974	4.6	1.5261	9.1	2.2083
0.2	8.3906	4.7	1.5476	9.2	2.2192
0.3	8.7960	4.8	1.5686	9.3	2.2300
0.4	9.0837	4.9	1.5892	9.4	2.2407
0.5	9.3069	5.0	1.6094	9.5	2.2513
0.6	9.4892	5.1	1.6292	9.6	2.2618
0.7	9.6433	5.2	1.6487	9.7	2.2721
0.8	9.7769	5.3	1.6677	9.8	2.2824
0.9	9.8946	5.4	1.6864	9.9	2.2925
1.0	0.0000	5.5	1.7047	10	2.3026
1.1	0.0953	5.6	1.7228	11	2.3979
1.2	0.1823	5.7	1.7405	12	2.4849
1.3	0.2624	5.8	1.7579	13	2.5649
1.4	0.3365	5.9	1.7750	14	2.6391
1.5	0.4055	6.0	1.7918	15	2.7081
1.6	0.4700	6.1	1.8083	16	2.7726
1.7	0.5306	6.2	1.8245	17	2.8332
1.8	0.5878	6.3	1.8405	18	2.8904
1.9	0.6419	6.4	1.8563	19	2.9444
2.0	0.6931	6.5	1.8718	20	2.9957
2.1	0.7419	6.6	1.8871	25	3.2189
2.2	0.7885	6.7	1.9021	30	3.4012
2.3	0.8329	6.8	1.9169	35	3.5553
2.4	0.8755	6.9	1.9315	40	3.6889
2.5	0.9163	7.0	1.9459	45	3.8067
2.6	0.9555	7.1	1.9601	50	3.9120
2.7	0.9933	7.2	1.9741	55	4.0073
2.8	1.0296	7.3	1.9879	60	4.0943
2.9	1.0647	7.4	2.0015	65	4.1744
3.0	1.0986	7.5	2.0149	70	4.2485
3.1	1.1314	7.6	2.0281	75	4.3175
3.2	1.1632	7.7	2.0142	80	4.3820
3.3	1.1939	7.8	2.0541	85	4.4427
3.4	1.2238	7.9	2.0669	90	4.4998
3.5	1.2528	8.0	2.0794	95	4.5539
3.6	1.2809	8.1	2.0919	100	4.6052
3.7	1.3083	8.2	2.1041		
3.8	1.3350	8.3	2.1163		
3.9	1.3610	8.4	2.1282		
4.0	1.3863	8.5	2.1401		
4.1	1.4110	8.6	2.1518		
4.2	1.4351	8.7	2.1633		
4.3	1.4586	8.8	2.1748		
4.4	1.4816	8.9	2.1861		

* Subtract 10 from $\log_e n$ entries for $n < 1.0$.

APPENDIX III:　TABLE OF INTEGRALS

1. $\int u\,dv = uv - \int v\,du$

2. $\int a^u\,du = \dfrac{a^u}{\ln a} + C, \qquad a \neq 1, \qquad a > 0$

3. $\int \cos u\,du = \sin u + C$

4. $\int \sin u\,du = -\cos u + C$

5. $\int (ax+b)^n\,dx = \dfrac{(ax+b)^{n+1}}{a(n+1)} + C, \qquad n \neq -1$

6. $\int (ax+b)^{-1}\,dx = \dfrac{1}{a}\ln|ax+b| + C$

7. $\int x(ax+b)^n\,dx = \dfrac{(ax+b)^{n+1}}{a^2}\left[\dfrac{ax+b}{n+2} - \dfrac{b}{n+1}\right] + C,$
$\qquad\qquad\qquad\qquad n \neq -1, -2$

8. $\int x(ax+b)^{-1}\,dx = \dfrac{x}{a} - \dfrac{b}{a^2}\ln|ax+b| + C$

9. $\int x(ax+b)^{-2}\,dx = \dfrac{1}{a^2}\left[\ln|ax+b| + \dfrac{b}{ax+b}\right] + C$

10. $\int \dfrac{dx}{x(ax+b)} = \dfrac{1}{b}\ln\left|\dfrac{x}{ax+b}\right| + C$

11. $\int (\sqrt{ax+b})^n\,dx = \dfrac{2}{a}\dfrac{(\sqrt{ax+b})^{n+2}}{n+2} + C, \qquad n \neq -2$

12. $\int \dfrac{\sqrt{ax+b}}{x}\,dx = 2\sqrt{ax+b} + b\int \dfrac{dx}{x\sqrt{ax+b}}$

13. (a) $\int \dfrac{dx}{x\sqrt{ax+b}} = \dfrac{2}{\sqrt{-b}}\tan^{-1}\sqrt{\dfrac{ax+b}{-b}} + C, \qquad$ if $\;b < 0$

 (b) $\int \dfrac{dx}{x\sqrt{ax+b}} = \dfrac{1}{\sqrt{b}}\ln\left|\dfrac{\sqrt{ax+b}-\sqrt{b}}{\sqrt{ax+b}+\sqrt{b}}\right| + C,$
$\qquad\qquad\qquad\qquad\qquad\qquad\quad$ if $\;b > 0$

14. $\int \dfrac{\sqrt{ax+b}}{x^2}\,dx = -\dfrac{\sqrt{ax+b}}{x} + \dfrac{a}{2}\int \dfrac{dx}{x\sqrt{ax+b}} + C$

15. $\int \dfrac{dx}{x^2\sqrt{ax+b}} = -\dfrac{\sqrt{ax+b}}{bx} - \dfrac{a}{2b}\int \dfrac{dx}{x\sqrt{ax+b}} + C$

16. $\int \dfrac{dx}{a^2+x^2} = \dfrac{1}{a}\tan^{-1}\dfrac{x}{a} + C$

17. $\int \dfrac{dx}{(a^2+x^2)^2} = \dfrac{x}{2a^2(a^2+x^2)} + \dfrac{1}{2a^3}\tan^{-1}\dfrac{x}{a} + C$

18. $\int \dfrac{dx}{a^2-x^2} = \dfrac{1}{2a}\ln\left|\dfrac{x+a}{x-a}\right| + C$

19. $\int \dfrac{dx}{(a^2-x^2)^2} = \dfrac{x}{2a^2(a^2-x^2)} + \dfrac{1}{2a^2}\int \dfrac{dx}{a^2-x^2}$

20. $\int \dfrac{dx}{\sqrt{a^2+x^2}} = \sinh^{-1}\dfrac{x}{a} + C = \ln|x + \sqrt{a^2+x^2}| + C$

21. $\int \sqrt{a^2+x^2}\,dx = \dfrac{x}{2}\sqrt{a^2+x^2} + \dfrac{a^2}{2}\sinh^{-1}\dfrac{x}{a} + C$

22. $\int x^2\sqrt{a^2+x^2}\,dx = \dfrac{x(a^2+2x^2)\sqrt{a^2+x^2}}{8} - \dfrac{a^4}{8}\sinh^{-1}\dfrac{x}{a} + C$

23. $\int \dfrac{\sqrt{a^2+x^2}}{x}\,dx = \sqrt{a^2+x^2} - a\sinh^{-1}\left|\dfrac{a}{x}\right| + C$

24. $\int \dfrac{\sqrt{a^2+x^2}}{x^2}\,dx = \sinh^{-1}\dfrac{x}{a} - \dfrac{\sqrt{a^2+x^2}}{x} + C$

25. $\int \dfrac{x^2}{\sqrt{a^2+x^2}}\,dx = -\dfrac{a^2}{2}\sinh^{-1}\dfrac{x}{a} + \dfrac{x\sqrt{a^2+x^2}}{2} + C$

26. $\int \dfrac{dx}{x\sqrt{a^2+x^2}} = -\dfrac{1}{a}\ln\left|\dfrac{a+\sqrt{a^2+x^2}}{x}\right| + C$

27. $\int \dfrac{dx}{x^2\sqrt{a^2+x^2}} = -\dfrac{\sqrt{a^2+x^2}}{a^2 x} + C$

28. $\int \dfrac{dx}{\sqrt{a^2-x^2}} = \sin^{-1}\dfrac{x}{a} + C$

29. $\int \sqrt{a^2-x^2}\,dx = \dfrac{x}{2}\sqrt{a^2-x^2} + \dfrac{a^2}{2}\sin^{-1}\dfrac{x}{a} + C$

30. $\int x^2\sqrt{a^2-x^2}\,dx$
$\qquad = \dfrac{a^4}{8}\sin^{-1}\dfrac{x}{a} - \dfrac{1}{8}x\sqrt{a^2-x^2}\,(a^2-2x^2) + C$

31. $\int \dfrac{\sqrt{a^2-x^2}}{x}\,dx = \sqrt{a^2-x^2} - a\ln\left|\dfrac{a+\sqrt{a^2-x^2}}{x}\right| + C$

32. $\int \dfrac{\sqrt{a^2-x^2}}{x^2}\,dx = -\sin^{-1}\dfrac{x}{a} - \dfrac{\sqrt{a^2-x^2}}{x} + C$

33. $\int \dfrac{x^2}{\sqrt{a^2-x^2}}\,dx = \dfrac{a^2}{2}\sin^{-1}\dfrac{x}{a} - \dfrac{1}{2}x\sqrt{a^2-x^2} + C$

34. $\int \dfrac{dx}{x\sqrt{a^2-x^2}} = -\dfrac{1}{a}\ln\left|\dfrac{a+\sqrt{a^2-x^2}}{x}\right| + C$

35. $\int \dfrac{dx}{x^2\sqrt{a^2-x^2}} = -\dfrac{\sqrt{a^2-x^2}}{a^2 x} + C$

36. $\int \dfrac{dx}{\sqrt{x^2-a^2}} = \cosh^{-1}\dfrac{x}{a} + C = \ln|x + \sqrt{x^2-a^2}| + C$

37. $\displaystyle\int \sqrt{x^2 - a^2}\, dx = \frac{x}{2}\sqrt{x^2 - a^2} - \frac{a^2}{2}\cosh^{-1}\frac{x}{a} + C$

38. $\displaystyle\int (\sqrt{x^2 - a^2})^n\, dx = \frac{x(\sqrt{x^2 - a^2})^n}{n+1}$
$$-\frac{na^2}{n+1}\int (\sqrt{x^2 - a^2})^{n-2}\, dx, \qquad n \neq -1$$

39. $\displaystyle\int \frac{dx}{(\sqrt{x^2 - a^2})^n} = \frac{x(\sqrt{x^2 - a^2})^{2-n}}{(2-n)a^2}$
$$-\frac{n-3}{(n-2)a^2}\int \frac{dx}{(\sqrt{x^2 - a^2})^{n-2}}, \qquad n \neq 2$$

40. $\displaystyle\int x(\sqrt{x^2 - a^2})^n\, dx = \frac{(\sqrt{x^2 - a^2})^{n+2}}{n+2} + C, \qquad n \neq -2$

41. $\displaystyle\int x^2\sqrt{x^2 - a^2}\, dx = \frac{x}{8}(2x^2 - a^2)\sqrt{x^2 - a^2}$
$$-\frac{a^4}{8}\cosh^{-1}\frac{x}{a} + C$$

42. $\displaystyle\int \frac{\sqrt{x^2 - a^2}}{x}\, dx = \sqrt{x^2 - a^2} - a\sec^{-1}\left|\frac{x}{a}\right| + C$

43. $\displaystyle\int \frac{\sqrt{x^2 - a^2}}{x^2}\, dx = \cosh^{-1}\frac{x}{a} - \frac{\sqrt{x^2 - a^2}}{x} + C$

44. $\displaystyle\int \frac{x^2}{\sqrt{x^2 - a^2}}\, dx = \frac{a^2}{2}\cosh^{-1}\frac{x}{a} + \frac{x}{2}\sqrt{x^2 - a^2} + C$

45. $\displaystyle\int \frac{dx}{x\sqrt{x^2 - a^2}} = \frac{1}{a}\sec^{-1}\left|\frac{x}{a}\right| + C = \frac{1}{a}\cos^{-1}\left|\frac{a}{x}\right| + C$

46. $\displaystyle\int \frac{dx}{x^2\sqrt{x^2 - a^2}} = \frac{\sqrt{x^2 - a^2}}{a^2 x} + C$

47. $\displaystyle\int \frac{dx}{\sqrt{2ax - x^2}} = \sin^{-1}\left(\frac{x-a}{a}\right) + C$

48. $\displaystyle\int \sqrt{2ax - x^2}\, dx = \frac{x-a}{2}\sqrt{2ax - x^2}$
$$+\frac{a^2}{2}\sin^{-1}\left(\frac{x-a}{a}\right) + C$$

49. $\displaystyle\int (\sqrt{2ax - x^2})^n\, dx = \frac{(x-a)(\sqrt{2ax - x^2})^n}{n+1}$
$$+\frac{na^2}{n+1}\int (\sqrt{2ax - x^2})^{n-2}\, dx$$

50. $\displaystyle\int \frac{dx}{(\sqrt{2ax - x^2})^n} = \frac{(x-a)(\sqrt{2ax - x^2})^{2-n}}{(n-2)a^2}$
$$+\frac{(n-3)}{(n-2)a^2}\int \frac{dx}{(\sqrt{2ax - x^2})^{n-2}}$$

51. $\displaystyle\int x\sqrt{2ax - x^2}\, dx = \frac{(x+a)(2x-3a)\sqrt{2ax - x^2}}{6}$
$$+\frac{a^3}{2}\sin^{-1}\frac{x-a}{a} + C$$

52. $\displaystyle\int \frac{\sqrt{2ax - x^2}}{x}\, dx = \sqrt{2ax - x^2} + a\sin^{-1}\frac{x-a}{a} + C$

53. $\displaystyle\int \frac{\sqrt{2ax - x^2}}{x^2}\, dx = -2\sqrt{\frac{2a-x}{x}} - \sin^{-1}\left(\frac{x-a}{a}\right) + C$

54. $\displaystyle\int \frac{x\, dx}{\sqrt{2ax - x^2}} = a\sin^{-1}\frac{x-a}{a} - \sqrt{2ax - x^2} + C$

55. $\displaystyle\int \frac{dx}{x\sqrt{2ax - x^2}} = -\frac{1}{a}\sqrt{\frac{2a-x}{x}} + C$

56. $\displaystyle\int \sin ax\, dx = -\frac{1}{a}\cos ax + C$

57. $\displaystyle\int \cos ax\, dx = \frac{1}{a}\sin ax + C$

58. $\displaystyle\int \sin^2 ax\, dx = \frac{x}{2} - \frac{\sin 2ax}{4a} + C$

59. $\displaystyle\int \cos^2 ax\, dx = \frac{x}{2} + \frac{\sin 2ax}{4a} + C$

60. $\displaystyle\int \sin^n ax\, dx = \frac{-\sin^{n-1} ax \cos ax}{na} + \frac{n-1}{n}\int \sin^{n-2} ax\, dx$

61. $\displaystyle\int \cos^n ax\, dx = \frac{\cos^{n-1} ax \sin ax}{na} + \frac{n-1}{n}\int \cos^{n-2} ax\, dx$

62. (a) $\displaystyle\int \sin ax \cos bx\, dx = -\frac{\cos(a+b)x}{2(a+b)} - \frac{\cos(a-b)x}{2(a-b)} + C,$
$$a^2 \neq b^2$$

(b) $\displaystyle\int \sin ax \sin bx\, dx = \frac{\sin(a-b)x}{2(a-b)} - \frac{\sin(a+b)x}{2(a+b)},$
$$a^2 \neq b^2$$

(c) $\displaystyle\int \cos ax \cos bx\, dx = \frac{\sin(a-b)x}{2(a-b)} + \frac{\sin(a+b)x}{2(a+b)},$
$$a^2 \neq b^2$$

63. $\displaystyle\int \sin ax \cos ax\, dx = -\frac{\cos 2ax}{4a} + C$

64. $\displaystyle\int \sin^n ax \cos ax\, dx = \frac{\sin^{n+1} ax}{(n+1)a} + C, \qquad n \neq -1$

65. $\displaystyle\int \frac{\cos ax}{\sin ax}\, dx = \frac{1}{a}\ln|\sin ax| + C$

66. $\displaystyle\int \cos^n ax \sin ax\, dx = -\frac{\cos^{n+1} ax}{(n+1)a} + C, \qquad n \neq -1$

67. $\displaystyle\int \frac{\sin ax}{\cos ax}\,dx = -\frac{1}{a}\ln|\cos ax| + C$

68. $\displaystyle\int \sin^n ax \cos^m ax\,dx = -\frac{\sin^{n-1} ax \cos^{m+1} ax}{a(m+n)}$

$$+ \frac{n-1}{m+n}\int \sin^{n-2} ax \cos^m ax\,dx,$$

$$n \neq -m \qquad \text{(If } n = -m, \text{ use No. 86.)}$$

69. $\displaystyle\int \sin^n ax \cos^m ax\,dx = \frac{\sin^{n+1} ax \cos^{m-1} ax}{a(m+n)}$

$$+ \frac{m-1}{m+n}\int \sin^n ax \cos^{m-2} ax\,dx,$$

$$m \neq -n \qquad \text{(If } m = -n, \text{ use No. 87.)}$$

70. $\displaystyle\int \frac{dx}{b + c \sin ax}$

$$= \frac{-2}{a\sqrt{b^2-c^2}}\tan^{-1}\left[\sqrt{\frac{b-c}{b+c}}\tan\left(\frac{\pi}{4}-\frac{ax}{2}\right)\right] + C, \qquad b^2 > c^2$$

71. $\displaystyle\int \frac{dx}{b + c \sin ax}$

$$= \frac{-1}{a\sqrt{c^2-b^2}}\ln\left|\frac{c + b\sin ax + \sqrt{c^2-b^2}\cos ax}{b + c\sin ax}\right| + C,$$

$$b^2 < c^2$$

72. $\displaystyle\int \frac{dx}{1 + \sin ax} = -\frac{1}{a}\tan\left(\frac{\pi}{4}-\frac{ax}{2}\right) + C$

73. $\displaystyle\int \frac{dx}{1 - \sin ax} = \frac{1}{a}\tan\left(\frac{\pi}{4}+\frac{ax}{2}\right) + C$

74. $\displaystyle\int \frac{dx}{b + c \cos ax}$

$$= \frac{2}{a\sqrt{b^2-c^2}}\tan^{-1}\left[\sqrt{\frac{b-c}{b+c}}\tan\frac{ax}{2}\right] + C, \qquad b^2 > c^2$$

75. $\displaystyle\int \frac{dx}{b + c \cos ax}$

$$= \frac{1}{a\sqrt{c^2-b^2}}\ln\left|\frac{c + b\cos ax + \sqrt{c^2-b^2}\sin ax}{b + c\cos ax}\right| + C,$$

$$b^2 < c^2$$

76. $\displaystyle\int \frac{dx}{1 + \cos ax} = \frac{1}{a}\tan\frac{ax}{2} + C$

77. $\displaystyle\int \frac{dx}{1 - \cos ax} = -\frac{1}{a}\cot\frac{ax}{2} + C$

78. $\displaystyle\int x \sin ax\,dx = \frac{1}{a^2}\sin ax - \frac{x}{a}\cos ax + C$

79. $\displaystyle\int x \cos ax\,dx = \frac{1}{a^2}\cos ax + \frac{x}{a}\sin ax + C$

80. $\displaystyle\int x^n \sin ax\,dx = -\frac{x^n}{a}\cos ax + \frac{n}{a}\int x^{n-1}\cos ax\,dx$

81. $\displaystyle\int x^n \cos ax\,dx = \frac{x^n}{a}\sin ax - \frac{n}{a}\int x^{n-1}\sin ax\,dx$

82. $\displaystyle\int \tan ax\,dx = -\frac{1}{a}\ln|\cos ax| + C$

83. $\displaystyle\int \cot ax\,dx = \frac{1}{a}\ln|\sin ax| + C$

84. $\displaystyle\int \tan^2 ax\,dx = \frac{1}{a}\tan ax - x + C$

85. $\displaystyle\int \cot^2 ax\,dx = -\frac{1}{a}\cot ax - x + C$

86. $\displaystyle\int \tan^n ax\,dx = \frac{\tan^{n-1} ax}{a(n-1)} - \int \tan^{n-2} ax\,dx, \qquad n \neq 1$

87. $\displaystyle\int \cot^n ax\,dx = -\frac{\cot^{n-1} ax}{a(n-1)} - \int \cot^{n-2} ax\,dx, \qquad n \neq 1$

88. $\displaystyle\int \sec ax\,dx = \frac{1}{a}\ln|\sec ax + \tan ax| + C$

89. $\displaystyle\int \csc ax\,dx = -\frac{1}{a}\ln|\csc ax + \cot ax| + C$

90. $\displaystyle\int \sec^2 ax\,dx = \frac{1}{a}\tan ax + C$

91. $\displaystyle\int \csc^2 ax\,dx = -\frac{1}{a}\cot ax + C$

92. $\displaystyle\int \sec^n ax\,dx = \frac{\sec^{n-2} ax \tan ax}{a(n-1)} + \frac{n-2}{n-1}\int \sec^{n-2} ax\,dx,$

$$n \neq 1$$

93. $\displaystyle\int \csc^n ax\,dx = -\frac{\csc^{n-2} ax \cot ax}{a(n-1)} + \frac{n-2}{n-1}\int \csc^{n-2} ax\,dx,$

$$n \neq 1$$

94. $\displaystyle\int \sec^n ax \tan ax\,dx = \frac{\sec^n ax}{na} + C, \qquad n \neq 0$

95. $\displaystyle\int \csc^n ax \cot ax\,dx = -\frac{\csc^n ax}{na} + C, \qquad n \neq 0$

96. $\displaystyle\int \sin^{-1} ax\,dx = x \sin^{-1} ax + \frac{1}{a}\sqrt{1 - a^2x^2} + C$

97. $\displaystyle\int \cos^{-1} ax\,dx = x \cos^{-1} ax - \frac{1}{a}\sqrt{1 - a^2x^2} + C$

98. $\displaystyle\int \tan^{-1} ax\,dx = x \tan^{-1} ax - \frac{1}{2a}\ln(1 + a^2x^2) + C$

99. $\int x^n \sin^{-1} ax\, dx = \dfrac{x^{n+1}}{n+1}\sin^{-1} ax - \dfrac{a}{n+1}\int \dfrac{x^{n+1}\, dx}{\sqrt{1-a^2x^2}}$,
$$n \neq -1$$

100. $\int x^n \cos^{-1} ax\, dx = \dfrac{x^{n+1}}{n+1}\cos^{-1} ax + \dfrac{a}{n+1}\int \dfrac{x^{n+1}\, dx}{\sqrt{1-a^2x^2}}$,
$$n \neq -1$$

101. $\int x^n \tan^{-1} ax\, dx = \dfrac{x^{n+1}}{n+1}\tan^{-1} ax - \dfrac{a}{n+1}\int \dfrac{x^{n+1}\, dx}{1+a^2x^2}$,
$$n \neq -1$$

102. $\int e^{ax}\, dx = \dfrac{1}{a}e^{ax} + C$

103. $\int b^{ax}\, dx = \dfrac{1}{a}\dfrac{b^{ax}}{\ln b} + C, \qquad b > 0, \quad b \neq 1$

104. $\int xe^{ax}\, dx = \dfrac{e^{ax}}{a^2}(ax - 1) + C$

105. $\int x^n e^{ax}\, dx = \dfrac{1}{a}x^n e^{ax} - \dfrac{n}{a}\int x^{n-1} e^{ax}\, dx$

106. $\int x^n b^{ax}\, dx = \dfrac{x^n b^{ax}}{a\ln b} - \dfrac{n}{a\ln b}\int x^{n-1} b^{ax}\, dx, \qquad b > 0, \quad b \neq 1$

107. $\int e^{ax}\sin bx\, dx = \dfrac{e^{ax}}{a^2+b^2}(a\sin bx - b\cos bx) + C$

108. $\int e^{ax}\cos bx\, dx = \dfrac{e^{ax}}{a^2+b^2}(a\cos bx + b\sin bx) + C$

109. $\int \ln ax\, dx = x\ln ax - x + C$

110. $\int x^n \ln ax\, dx = \dfrac{x^{n+1}}{n+1}\ln ax - \dfrac{x^{n+1}}{(n+1)^2} + C, \qquad n \neq -1$

111. $\int x^{-1}\ln ax\, dx = \dfrac{1}{2}(\ln ax)^2 + C$

112. $\int \dfrac{dx}{x\ln ax} = \ln|\ln ax| + C$

113. $\int \sinh ax\, dx = \dfrac{1}{a}\cosh ax + C$

114. $\int \cosh ax\, dx = \dfrac{1}{a}\sinh ax + C$

115. $\int \sinh^2 ax\, dx = \dfrac{\sinh 2ax}{4a} - \dfrac{x}{2} + C$

116. $\int \cosh^2 ax\, dx = \dfrac{\sinh 2ax}{4a} + \dfrac{x}{2} + C$

117. $\int \sinh^n ax\, dx = \dfrac{\sinh^{n-1} ax \cosh ax}{na} - \dfrac{n-1}{n}\int \sinh^{n-2} ax\, dx, \qquad n \neq 0$

118. $\int \cosh^n ax\, dx = \dfrac{\cosh^{n-1} ax \sinh ax}{na} + \dfrac{n-1}{n}\int \cosh^{n-2} ax\, dx, \qquad n \neq 0$

119. $\int x\sinh ax\, dx = \dfrac{x}{a}\cosh ax - \dfrac{1}{a^2}\sinh ax + C$

120. $\int x\cosh ax\, dx = \dfrac{x}{a}\sinh ax - \dfrac{1}{a^2}\cosh ax + C$

121. $\int x^n \sinh ax\, dx = \dfrac{x^n}{a}\cosh ax - \dfrac{n}{a}\int x^{n-1}\cosh ax\, dx$

122. $\int x^n \cosh ax\, dx = \dfrac{x^n}{a}\sinh ax - \dfrac{n}{a}\int x^{n-1}\sinh ax\, dx$

123. $\int \tanh ax\, dx = \dfrac{1}{a}\ln(\cosh ax) + C$

124. $\int \coth ax\, dx = \dfrac{1}{a}\ln|\sinh ax| + C$

125. $\int \tanh^2 ax\, dx = x - \dfrac{1}{a}\tanh ax + C$

126. $\int \coth^2 ax\, dx = x - \dfrac{1}{a}\coth ax + C$

127. $\int \tanh^n ax\, dx = -\dfrac{\tanh^{n-1} ax}{(n-1)a} + \int \tanh^{n-2} ax\, dx, \qquad n \neq 1$

128. $\int \coth^n ax\, dx = -\dfrac{\coth^{n-1} ax}{(n-1)a} + \int \coth^{n-2} ax\, dx, \qquad n \neq 1$

129. $\int \operatorname{sech} ax\, dx = \dfrac{1}{a}\sin^{-1}(\tanh ax) + C$

130. $\int \operatorname{csch} ax\, dx = \dfrac{1}{a}\ln\left|\tanh \dfrac{ax}{2}\right| + C$

131. $\int \operatorname{sech}^2 ax\, dx = \dfrac{1}{a}\tanh ax + C$

132. $\int \operatorname{csch}^2 ax\, dx = -\dfrac{1}{a}\coth ax + C$

133. $\int \operatorname{sech}^n ax\, dx = \dfrac{\operatorname{sech}^{n-2} ax \tanh ax}{(n-1)a} + \dfrac{n-2}{n-1}\int \operatorname{sech}^{n-2} ax\, dx,$
$$n \neq 1$$

134. $\int \operatorname{csch}^n ax\, dx$
$$= -\dfrac{\operatorname{csch}^{n-2} ax \coth ax}{(n-1)a} - \dfrac{n-2}{n-1}\int \operatorname{csch}^{n-2} ax\, dx, \qquad n \neq 1$$

135. $\displaystyle\int \operatorname{sech}^n ax \tanh ax \, dx = -\frac{\operatorname{sech}^n ax}{na} + C, \qquad n \neq 0$

136. $\displaystyle\int \operatorname{csch}^n ax \coth ax \, dx = -\frac{\operatorname{csch}^n ax}{na} + C, \qquad n \neq 0$

137. $\displaystyle\int e^{az} \sinh bx \, dx = \frac{e^{ax}}{2}\left[\frac{e^{bx}}{a+b} - \frac{e^{-bx}}{a-b}\right] + C, \qquad a^2 \neq b^2$

138. $\displaystyle\int e^{ax} \cosh bx \, dx = \frac{e^{ax}}{2}\left[\frac{e^{bx}}{a+b} + \frac{e^{-bx}}{a-b}\right] + C, \qquad a^2 \neq b^2$

139. $\displaystyle\int_0^\infty x^{n-1} e^{-x} \, dx = \Gamma(n) = (n-1)!, \qquad n > 0.$

140. $\displaystyle\int_0^\infty e^{-ax^2} \, dx = \frac{1}{2}\sqrt{\frac{\pi}{a}}, \qquad a > 0$

141. $\displaystyle\int_0^{\pi/2} \sin^n x \, dx = \int_0^{\pi/2} \cos^n x \, dx$

$\displaystyle\qquad = \frac{1 \cdot 3 \cdot 5 \cdots (n-1)}{2 \cdot 4 \cdot 6 \cdots n} \cdot \frac{\pi}{2}, \qquad$ if n is an even integer ≥ 2,

$\displaystyle\qquad = \frac{2 \cdot 4 \cdot 6 \cdots (n-1)}{3 \cdot 5 \cdot 7 \cdots n}, \qquad$ if n is an odd integer ≥ 3

ANSWERS TO EXERCISES

Article 1.1

1 through 15. If P is the point (x, y), the other points are $Q(x, -y)$, $R(-x, y)$, $S(-x, -y)$, $T(y, x)$.

16. 45°   17. 2   19. −1

20. No, because the line joining the given points crosses the y-axis at $(0, \frac{1}{2})$

Article 1.2

1. $(3, 1)$, 2, 3, $\sqrt{13}$
2. $(1, 4)$, −2, −3, $\sqrt{13}$
3. $(2, 2)$, 3, −3, $\sqrt{18}$
4. $(-1, -1)$, −3, 3, $\sqrt{18}$
5. $(1, -1)$, 2, 3, $\sqrt{13}$
6. $(-1, 2)$, −2, −3, $\sqrt{13}$
7. $(-1, 2)$, 2, −4, $\sqrt{20}$
8. $(-3, -2)$, −2, 4, $\sqrt{20}$
9. $(-1, -2)$, 2, 1, $\sqrt{5}$
10. $(-3, -1)$, −2, −1, $\sqrt{5}$
11. (a) $x^2 + y^2 = 25$
    (b) $x^2 + y^2 - 10x = 0$
    (c) $x^2 + y^2 - 6x - 8y = 0$
    (d) $(x - h)^2 + (y - k)^2 = 25$
12. $B(3, -3)$ 13. $A(u - h, v - k)$ 14. $B(0, 11)$

Article 1.3

1. −3, $\frac{1}{3}$ 2. 3, $-\frac{1}{3}$ 3. $-\frac{1}{3}$, 3
4. $-\frac{1}{2}$, 2   5. −1, 1   6. 0, ∞
7. 0, ∞ 8. −3, $\frac{1}{3}$ 9. −1, 1
10. ∞, 0   11. $\frac{2}{3}$, $-\frac{3}{2}$ 12. y/x, $-x/y$
13. 0, ∞ 14. ∞, 0   15. $-b/a$, a/b
16. Rectangle   17. Parallelogram   18. Rectangle
19. Parallelogram   20. No   21. $(1, 2)$

23. Yes, they lie on a line because the slope of BA is equal to the slope of AC.

24. No, because the slope of AC is 1 but the slope of CB is 3.

25. Yes, because $m_{AB} = m_{BC} = m_{CD} = 2$

26. No   27. Yes   28. $\left(\dfrac{x_1 + x_2}{2}, \dfrac{y_1 + y_2}{2}\right)$

29. Center $(\frac{3}{2}, \frac{3}{2})$, radius $\sqrt{8.5}$

Article 1.4

1. $2y = 3x$
2. $y = 1$
3. $x = 1$
4. $3x + 4y + 2 = 0$
5. $x = -2$
6. $x + y = 4$
7. $x/a + y/b = 1$
8. $y = 0$
9. $x = 0$
10. $x + y = 1$
11. 3
12. $\frac{3}{2}$
13. -1
14. 2
15. $\frac{1}{2}$
16. $-\frac{3}{4}$
17. $\frac{4}{3}$
18. $\frac{1}{2}$
19. $-b/a$
20. $-x_1/y_1$
21. $x + 2y = 5$
22. (a) $x - 2y + 6 = 0$ (b) $(\frac{2}{5}, \frac{16}{5})$ (c) $6/\sqrt{5}$
23. $y - 4 = \sqrt{3}(x - 1)$ 24. $180° - \tan^{-1} 2$
26. (a) $F = 1.8C + 32$ (b) $F = C$ at $-40°$
28. (a) Let $D = Ax_1 + By_1 + C$. If D and B agree in sign, then $BD > 0$, so that

$$\frac{DB}{B^2} = y_1 + \frac{Ax_1 + C}{B} > 0, \qquad y_1 > \frac{-(Ax_1 + B)}{C}.$$

Hence P_1 is above L.

(b) The inequalities are reversed, and P_1 is below L, if D and B have opposite signs.

(c) If $B = 0$, then we may assume $A \neq 0$. It then follows that P_1 is to the right of L when D and A agree in sign, but P_1 is to the left of L when D and A have opposite signs, because

$$AD/A^2 = x_1 + (C/A)$$

has the same sign as AD.

29. (a) 1 (b) $\frac{7}{5}$ (c) $\frac{9}{5}$ (d) 0

Article 1.5

9. $\{x \mid -4 < x < 4\}$
10. $\{x \mid -2 < x < 2\}$
11. $\{x \mid -3 \le x \le 7\}$
12. $\{x \mid -7 < x < 3\}$
13. $\{x \mid x \ge \frac{9}{2} \text{ or } x \le -\frac{1}{2}\}$
14. $\{x \mid -5 < x < 1\}$
15. $\{x \mid x < -1 \text{ or } x > 5\}$
16. $\{x \mid x < -5 \text{ or } x > -1\}$
17. $\{x \mid -\frac{7}{2} \le x \le \frac{1}{2}\}$
18. $\{x \mid x = 2 \text{ and } -1\}$
19. $\{x \mid 0 \le x \le 3\}$
20. $\emptyset$
21. $\{(x, y) \mid -1 < x < 1, y \in R\}$
22. $\{(x, y) \mid x \in R, -1 < y < 1\}$
23. I and III: $y = x$,   II and IV: $y = -x$
24. I: $y < x$,   II: $y < -x$,   III: $y > x$,   IV: $y > -x$

25. I: $y > x$,   II: $y > -x$,   III: $y < x$,   IV: $y < -x$
26. $x + y = 2$ or $x + y = -2$
27. $\{(x, y) \mid -2 < x + y < 2\}$
28. $\{(x, y) \mid x + y > 2 \text{ or } x + y < -2\}$
29. I: $x + y = 1$,   II: $-x + y = 1$,
III: $-(x + y) = 1$,   IV: $x - y = 1$
30. I: $x + y < 1$,   II: $-x + y < 1$,
III: $x + y > -1$,   IV: $-x + y > -1$
31. $\{(x, y) \mid 2 < x < 4 \text{ and } -3 < y < 7\}$
32. $\{(x, y) \mid -2 \le x \le 0 \text{ and } -2 < y < 3\}$

Article 1.6

3. True
4. False, e.g., if $|a| = 1$ and $|b| = \frac{1}{2}$
5. False, e.g., see Exercise 4
6. True
7. False, e.g., see Exercise 4
8. False, $a = 2$, $b = \frac{1}{4}$

Article 1.7

1. $\{t \mid -3 < t < 7, t \neq 2\}$; this deleted neighborhood is 10 units in length
2. $\{t \mid 3 - h < t < 3 + h\}$ 3. $t + 2$; 4
4. $t + x$; $2x$ 5. $-1/tx$; $-1/x^2$
6. $1/(\sqrt{t} + \sqrt{x})$; $\frac{1}{4}$

Miscellaneous exercises

1. (b) $-\frac{3}{2}$, $\frac{2}{3}$, $-\frac{3}{2}$, $\frac{2}{3}$, 0, ∞
(c) Yes, $ABCD$ (d) Yes, AEB (e) Yes, CD
(f) $2y + 3x = 26$, $2y + 3x = 0$,
$3y - 2x + 13 = 0$, $y = 6$, $x = 2$

(g)

L	AB	CD	AD	CE	BD
y-intercept	13	0	$-\frac{13}{3}$	6	none
x-intercept	$\frac{26}{3}$	0	$\frac{13}{2}$	none	2

2. (a) $3y + 2x = -7$ (b) $\sqrt{13}$
3. (a) No   (b) No
(c) Outside   (d) $(-2, -\frac{9}{7})$
4. $4y + 3x = 0$, $x = 0$
5. $((x_1 + x_2)/2, (y_1 + y_2)/2)$

7. (a) $-a/b$ (b) $(0, -c/b)$

    (c) $(-c/a, 0)$ (d) $ay - bx = 0$

8. Min $= 6$, max $= 23$. S is the triangle with vertices at $(0, 2)$, $(2, 0)$, and $(1, 5)$, plus its interior. The lines $3x + 4y = k$, $k \geq 0$, first meet S at the vertex $(2, 0)$, if we start with $k = 0$ and let k increase, and they leave at the vertex $(1, 5)$ when k increases through 23.

9. Four. Centers: $(0, \sqrt{5} - 2)$, $(0, -\sqrt{5} - 2)$, $(-\sqrt{5} - 1, 1)$, $(\sqrt{5} - 1, 1)$
Radii (in same order): $(3\sqrt{2} - \sqrt{10})/2$, $(3\sqrt{2} + \sqrt{10})/2$, $(\sqrt{10} + \sqrt{2})/2$, $(\sqrt{10} - \sqrt{2})/2$

10. $|b' - b|/\sqrt{1 + m^2}$

11. Straight line through point of intersection of the two given lines

12. $(\frac{17}{18}, \frac{23}{6})$ 13. $x + 5y = \pm 5\sqrt{2}$

17. $|t + 3| < |t - b|$ 18. $|t - b| < |t|$

19. $|t - 2| < |t - b|$ 20. $x > 2$ or $x < -1$

21. $x > 1$ or $x - 1$ 22. $\emptyset$

23. $-4 \leq x \leq -3$

Chapter 2

Article 2.1

1. (a) Increasing
   (b) Above: 9,   below: -1
   (c) $f(-\frac{3}{2}) = 0$
   (d) $-1 \leq f(x) \leq 9$

2. (a) Decreasing
   (b) Above: 7,   below: -3
   (c) $f(\frac{3}{2}) = 0$
   (d) $-3 \leq f(x) \leq 7$

3. (a) Increasing
   (b) Above: 1,   below: 0
   (c) None
   (d) $0 < f(x) < 1$

4. (a) Neither
   (b) Above: 1,   below: 0
   (c) $f(0) = 0$
   (d) $0 \leq f(x) \leq 1$

5. (a) Neither   (b) Above: 1, below: -1
   (c) $f(0) = f(\pi) = f(-\pi) = 0$ (d) $-1 \leq f(x) \leq 1$

Article 2.2

1. Range: $\{2\} \cup \{f(x) \mid 0 \leq f(x) \leq 1\}$;
$f(0) = f(2) = 0$; $f(1) = 1$;
$f(x) = 2$,   for $-3 \leq x < 0$

2. (b) $f(x) = x^3 + 3x^2 + 4x - 7$

3. $f(x) = \begin{cases} 2x, & 0 \leq x \leq 3 \\ -2x, & -3 \leq x < 0 \end{cases}$

4. $f(x) = \begin{cases} 2x, & 0 \leq x \leq 2 \\ 0, & -2 \leq x < 0 \end{cases}$

5. $f(x) = \begin{cases} \sin x, & 0 \leq x \leq \pi \\ -\sin x, & -\pi \leq x < 0 \end{cases}$

6. $f(x) = \begin{cases} 2\sin x, & 0 \leq x \leq \pi \\ 0, & -\pi \leq x < 0 \end{cases}$

7. $f(x) = \begin{cases} x - 2, & 2 \leq x \leq 5 \\ 2 - x, & 0 \leq x < 2 \end{cases}$

8. $f(x) = \begin{cases} 2x - 1, & \frac{1}{2} \leq x \leq 3 \\ 1 - 2x, & 0 \leq x < \frac{1}{2} \end{cases}$

9. $f(x) = \begin{cases} x - 1, & 1 \leq x \leq 3 \\ 1 - x, & -1 \leq x < 1 \end{cases}$

10. $f(x) = \begin{cases} 3x - 1, & \frac{1}{2} \leq x \leq 2 \\ 1 - x, & 0 \leq x < \frac{1}{2} \end{cases}$

11. $\{x \mid x > 1\}$ 12. $\{x \mid x \geq 1\}$

13. $\{x \mid x \leq 1, x \neq 0\}$ 14. $\{x \mid x \geq -2\}$

15. $\{x \mid -1 \leq x \leq 3\}$ 16. $\{x \mid |x| \geq 1\}$

17. $\{x \mid x \geq 1$ or $-1 \leq x \leq 0\}$ 18. $x = 0$

19. $\{x \mid x \in R\}$

20. $\{x \mid x \geq 0$ or $x < -1\}$

21. $\{x \mid x \in R, x \neq 0\}$

22. (a) $-2 \leq x \leq 2$
   (b) $x \leq -2$ or $x \geq 2$
   (c) $-2 \leq x \leq 4$
   (d) $0 \leq x \leq 2$

23. $|1 - x| = 1 - x$ if $x \leq 1$;
$|1 - x| = x - 1$ if $x > 1$.

Article 2.3

2. $f(x) = k(x) = m(x)$

3. $r(x) = s(x) = v(x)$

4. $\phi(x) = f(x) = h(x) = j(x)$

5. $f(2) = \frac{9}{2}$, $f(-1) = 0$, $f(1/x) = (1/x^2) - x$;
$f(x + \Delta x) = (x + \Delta x)^2 + 1/(x + \Delta x)$

$\sqrt{\dfrac{1}{x^2} + x} = \dfrac{1 + x^3}{x^2}$

6. See Fig. 2.3.6   7. See Fig. 2.3.7

8. See Fig. 2.3.8 a, b, c   9. See Fig. 2.3.9

10. $y = \dfrac{-x \pm \sqrt{12 - 3x^2}}{2}$, $\begin{cases} -2 \leq x \leq 2, \\ -2 \leq y \leq 2 \end{cases}$

11. (a) $h = 0$

  (b) $\Delta f(0, 0) = 0$, $\Delta f(-2, 4) = 0$,
      $\Delta f(0.0001, -0.0001) = -10^{-8}$

$h(x) = \dfrac{[x]}{x}$, $\begin{cases} x \neq 0, \\ -3 \leq x \leq 3 \end{cases}$

b | c

$y = \begin{cases} x, & 0 \leq x \leq 1, \\ 2 - x, & 1 < x \leq 2 \end{cases}$

(1, 1)

2.3.6

$g(x) = [x] + [-x]$, $-3 \leq x \leq 3$

2.3.8

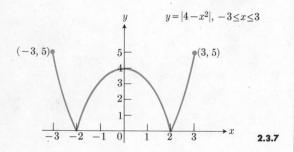

$y = |4 - x^2|$, $-3 \leq x \leq 3$

$(-3, 5)$ $(3, 5)$

2.3.7

$y = \operatorname{sgn} x$

2.3.9

Article 2.4

1. $D_f = \{x : -\infty < x < \infty\}$, $D_g = \{x : x \geq 1\}$,
   $D_{f+g} = D_{f \cdot g} = D_{g/f} = D_g$, $D_{f/g} = \{x : x > 1\}$

2. $D_f = \{x : x \neq 2\}$, $D_g = \{x : x > 1\}$,
   $D_{f+g} = D_{f \cdot g} = D_{f/g} = D_{g/f} = D_f \cap D_g$
   $= \{x : x > 1, x \neq 2\}$

3. $D_f = \{x : x \geq 0\}$, $D_g = \{x : x \geq -1\}$,
   $D_{f+g} = D_{f \cdot g} = D_{f/g} = D_f$, $D_{g/f} = \{x : x > 0\}$

4. The graph of g is the graph of f moved three units to the right.

5. $D_g = [a - c, b - c]$. Move the graph of f to the left by c units to get the graph of g. When the sine curve over $[-\pi, \pi]$ is moved $\pi/2$ units to the left, the result is the cosine curve over $[-3\pi/2, \pi/2]$. This agrees with the identity $\sin(x + \pi/2) = \cos x$.

$y = x - [x]$, $-3 \leq x \leq 3$

a

2.3.8

6. (a) $D_p = [-2\pi, 2\pi]$, $R_p = [-1, 1]$

   (b) $D_r = [-\pi/3, \pi/3]$, $R_r = [-1, 1]$

   (c) $D_q = [-\pi, \pi]$, $R_q = [-1, 1]$

7. See Fig. 2.4.7, and parts (a), (b), (c).

   (a) $D_g = (-8, 8)$, $R_g = [0, 6)$
     See Fig. 2.4.7(a).

   (b) $D_h = (-\frac{4}{3}, \frac{4}{3})$, $R_h = [0, 6)$
     See Fig. 2.4.7(b).

   (c) $D_k = (-1, 1)$, $R_k = [0, 6)$
     See Fig. 2.4.7(c).

$h(x) = f(3x/2)$,
$-\frac{4}{3} < x < \frac{4}{3}$

2.4.7b

$f(x) = 2x^2 - 2[|x|]^2, \; -2 < x < 2$
$= \begin{cases} 2x^2 & \text{for } |x| < 1, \\ 2x^2 - 2 & \text{for } 1 \le |x| < 2 \end{cases}$

2.4.7

$k(x) = f(-2x), \; |x| < 1$

2.4.7c

$g(x) = f(x/4), \; -8 < x < 8$

2.4.7a

8. (a) $D_f = [-\pi, \pi]$, $R_f = [-1, 2]$
   (b) $D_g = [-4\pi, 4\pi]$, $R_g = [-2, 4]$
   (c) $D_h = [-3\pi/2, \pi/2]$, $R_h = [-2, 4]$
   (d) $D_H = [-\pi, \pi]$, $R_H = [-4, 2]$
   See Fig. 2.4.8 for graph of $F(x)$ and the functions of parts (a) and (b).

9. $R_f = \{0, \frac{1}{3}, \frac{2}{3}\}$
   See Fig. 2.4.9.

10. (a) $D_g = [-1, 1]$, $R_g = [0, \frac{3}{2}]$
    (b) $D_h = [-\frac{3}{2}, \frac{3}{2}]$, $R_h = [0, 1]$
    (c) $D_F = [-\frac{1}{2}, \frac{1}{2}]$, $R_F = [0, 3]$
    (d) $D_H = [-1, 1]$, $R_H = [-1, 0]$

11. See Fig. 2.4.11 on page 473.

Article 2.5

1. $m(h) = 2$, $m(4) = 2$

3. $m(h) = \dfrac{-1}{x_1(x_1 + h)}$, $m(\frac{1}{4}) = -\frac{4}{5}$

5. $m(h) = \dfrac{|x_1 + h| - |x_1|}{h}$, $m(\frac{1}{2}) = -1$

7. True   9. False   11. True

13. $L = 4$, $\epsilon = 0.6$ 15. $L = 6$, $\epsilon \geq \frac{3}{4}$

Article 2.6

15.

Article 2.7

1. $2x$ 2. $3x^2$
3. 2 4. $2x - 1$
5. $-1/x^2$ 6. $-2/x^3$
7. $-2/(2x + 1)^2$ 8. $1/(x + 1)^2$
9. $4x - 1$ 10. $3x^2 - 12$
11. $4x^3$ 12. $2ax + b$

$F(x) = 1 + 3\cos 2x$, $-\pi \leq x \leq \pi$

$f(x) = \frac{1}{2}F(x)$, $|x| \leq \pi$

a|b

$g(x) = F(x/4)$, $|x| \leq 4\pi$

2.4.8

2.4.9

$|a|b|$

$|e|$

$|c|$

$|f|$

$|d|$

$|g|$

2.4.11

13. $1 + 1/x^2$

14. $a - b/x^2$

15. $1/\sqrt{2x}$

16. $1/(2\sqrt{x+1})$

17. $1/\sqrt{2x+3}$

18. $-1/(2x\sqrt{x})$

19. $-1/(2x+3)^{3/2}$

20. $x/\sqrt{x^2+1}$

21. $R_{f'} = \{-1, 1\}$,   same graphs

22. Domain $\{x \mid x \neq 0\}$. For $x \neq 0$ sgn$'$ $(x) = 0$ because slope of the graph is zero for $x \neq 0$.

Article 2.8

2. $4t + 5$

3. $gt + v_0$

4. 4

5. $2t - 3$

6. $-2 - 2t$

7. $8t + 12$

8. $2t - 4$

9. $-4t$

10. $64 - 32t$

12. 8,000 gal/min,   10,000 gal/min

13. (a) $2\pi r + \pi \, \Delta r$ (b) $2\pi r$

14. $4\pi r^2$

15. πh^2

Miscellaneous exercises

1. $x = \sqrt{(y+2)/(y-1)}$, $y \leq -2$, $y > 1$

2. $A = \pi r^2$, $C = 2\pi r$, $A = C^2/4\pi$

3. (a) $x < -1$, $x > -1$, $y < 0$, $y > 0$

   (b) All x, $0 < y \leq 1$

   (c) $x \geq 0$, $0 < y \leq 1$

4. $-5 < x < 3$

5. For $y \leq 4$, $x = y - 2$. For $y \geq 4$, $x = (y+2)/3$.

6. $y > 2$, $x = (y+2)/2$

7. $x = \dfrac{y \pm \sqrt{y^2 - 4}}{2}$, $|y| \geq 2$

9. (a) -3, -4, $x_1^2 + 2x_1 - 3$,

   $x_1^2 + 2x_1 \, \Delta x + (\Delta x)^2 + 2x_1 + 2 \, \Delta x - 3$

10. (c) $(\frac{1}{2}, -\frac{3}{4})$

12. $m(a, b) = (a + b - |a - b|)/2$

17. Take $\phi_k(x) = g_k(x)/g_k(x_k)$ where $g_k(x)$ is the product

   $$(x - x_1)(x - x_2) \cdots (x - x_n)$$

   with the factor $(x - x_k)$ deleted.

18. (a) $1/(1 - x)$ (b) $x/(x + 1)$

19. $2/(x + 1)^2$

20. $3\sqrt{x}/2$

21. $\frac{1}{3}x^{-2/3}$

22. $2x - 3$

23. $-1/(3x^2) + 2$

24. $1/(2\sqrt{t - 4})$

25. (a) 6 (b) $(0, 2)$

26. (a) $f(0) = 0$, $f(-1) = 1$, $f(1/x) = 2/(1 - x)$

   (b) $\dfrac{-2}{(x - 1)(x + \Delta x - 1)}$ (c) $\dfrac{-2}{(x - 1)^2}$

27. $P(\frac{45}{8}, \frac{2025}{4})$

28. $v = 180 - 32t$, $t = \frac{45}{8}$

29. (a) $-\dfrac{1}{V(V + \Delta V)}$ (b) $-\frac{1}{4}$

31. (a) Monotone increasing and monotone decreasing

   (b) Not monotone, strongly monotone if domain divided

   (c) Monotone increasing

   (d) Not monotone, strongly monotone if domain divided

   (e) Strong monotone

   (f) Not monotone, strongly monotone if domain divided

   (g) Not monotone, strongly monotone if domain divided

   (h) Strong monotone

Chapter 3

Article 3.1

1. $L = -1$, $0 < |x - 2| < \epsilon/3$

2. $L = 7$, N any deleted neighborhood of -1

3. $L = 2$, $0 < |x - 2| < 2\epsilon/(2 + \epsilon)$

4. $L = 4$, $0 < |x - 2| < \epsilon$

5. $L = 6$, $0 < |x - 5| < \epsilon$

6. $L = -5$, $0 < |x + 3| < 2\epsilon/3$

7. $L = -1/9$, $0 < |x - 3| < 27\epsilon/(1 + 9\epsilon)$

8. $h_3 = \max \{h_1, h_2\}$, $k_3 = \min \{k_1, k_2\}$

9. $|t^2 + t - 12| = |(t - 3)(t + 4)| < \epsilon$

   if $|t + 4| < 8$ and $|t - 3| < \epsilon/8$,

   thus if $0 < |t - 3| < \delta$ and $\delta \leq \min \{1, \epsilon/8\}$. Take $\epsilon = 0.1$ or 0.01 for parts (a) and (b).

10. Yes, because $|\sin (1/x)| \leq 1$, so $|f(x)| \leq |x| < \epsilon$ if $0 < |x| < \delta$ and $\delta \leq \epsilon$.

11. No, because sgn $x \to -1$, or $+1$, if $x \to 0$ through negative, or through positive, values. There is no number L that sgn x stays close to when x is near zero.

Article 3.2

1. 4   2. 0   3. 4   4. 4   5. 2

6. 0   7. 5   8. -1 9. 4

10. Apply Theorem 3 twice, first with

$$f(x) = p(x) + r(x) \quad \text{and} \quad g(x) = s(x),$$

second with

$$f(x) = p(x) \quad \text{and} \quad g(x) = r(x).$$

11. 1

12. (a)
$$\left| \frac{1}{x} - \frac{1}{3} \right| = \frac{|3 - x|}{3|x|} < \epsilon$$

if $\qquad |3x| \geq 3 \quad \text{and} \quad |x - 3| < 3\epsilon.$

Both are satisfied when x is in

$$N = \{x : 0 < |x - 3| < 3\epsilon \quad \text{and} \quad x \geq 1\}.$$

(b) When x is near c, $|cx|$ is near c^2 and is $> c^2/2$. Then

$$\left| \frac{1}{x} - \frac{1}{c} \right| = \frac{|c - x|}{|cx|} < \frac{2}{c^2} |c - x| < \epsilon$$

if both

$$|cx| > \frac{c^2}{2} \quad \text{and} \quad |x - c| < c^2 \frac{\epsilon}{2},$$

or if x is in

$$N = \left\{ x : 0 < |x - c| < c^2 \frac{\epsilon}{2} \quad \text{and} \quad cx > \frac{c^2}{2} \right\}.$$

13. 25   14. 0   15. 1   16. -8 17. 1

18. 2, because

$$|\sqrt{x} - 2| = \frac{|x - 4|}{\sqrt{x} + 2} \leq \frac{1}{2} |x - 4| < \epsilon$$

if $|x - 4| < 2\epsilon$

19. Let $f(x) = -g(x) = \sin (1/x)$.

20. Let $f(x) = g(x) = \operatorname{sgn} x$.

Article 3.3

1. (a) -10 (b) -20

2. 1   3. 18   4. 27   5. 36

6. 81   7. 2   8. 4   9. 4

10. 1   11. -1 12. -15

13. (a) $\frac{2}{5}$ (b) $\frac{2}{15}$ 14. $\frac{5}{4}$ 15. 10

16. 0   17. $\frac{1}{10}$ 18. No limit

19. No limit   20. $-\frac{1}{2}$

21. Let $f(x) = g(x) = 2 + \operatorname{sgn} x.$

22. $1/x^2$ most rapidly, $1/\sqrt{x}$ least rapidly

24. $(1 - \cos \theta) < \theta^2/2$ for all $\theta \neq 0$. Not true for $\theta = 0$.

25. $\frac{1}{2}$ 26. $\frac{3}{5}$ 27. $\frac{2}{7}$ 28. 1

29. 2   30. $\cos x$

Article 3.4

1. $\frac{2}{5}$ 2. $\frac{3}{10}$ 3. ∞ 4. 0   5. 0

6. 5   7. ∞ 8. 5   9. $\frac{1}{2}$ 10. 0

11. $\pm \infty$, the sign being the same as that of the quotient of the coefficients of the highest powers in f and g

17. (a, b) Yes, because

$$g(x) \geq \frac{7}{4} \quad \text{for all } x$$

(c) No

19. 2

20. Because the degree of $g(x)$ is greater than the degree of $f(x)$, $g(x)$ is not the zero polynomial and $g(x) \neq 0$ for sufficiently large values of x. Hence

$$f(x) + g(x) = g(x)[1 + f(x)/g(x)].$$

By Exercise 10, $f(x)/g(x) \to 0$ as $x \to \infty$. For some real numbers b and M_1, $g(x) > b$ for $x > M_1$; and for some real number M_2, $-\frac{1}{2} < f(x)/g(x) < \frac{1}{2}$ when $x > M_2$. Let $M = \max \{M_1, M_2\}$ and get $f(x) + g(x)$ between $\frac{1}{2}g(x)$ and $\frac{3}{2}g(x)$ for $x > M$. Therefore $f(x) + g(x) > -\frac{3}{2}|b|$ for $x > M$.

Miscellaneous exercises

1. $\frac{1}{2}$ 2. 0   3. $\frac{3}{7}$

4. $\frac{1}{3}$ 5. No limit   6. $2a$

7. 0   8. $2x$ 9. $1/(2\sqrt{x}), \quad x > 0$

10. $-1/x^2$ 11. ∞ 12. $\frac{1}{2}$

13. $-\frac{1}{10}$ 14. No limit   20. $\frac{3}{4}$

21. 0   22. $\frac{1}{2}$ 23. (a) 0   (b) 1

24. 1   25. -1 26. -1 27. 0

28. 0   29. ∞ 30. 4   31. 4

32. (a) 0   (b) $\frac{1}{3}$

(c) $\quad f(-1/x) = -(x^2 + x)/(5x^2 + 7x + 2),$
$$x \neq 0, -1, -\tfrac{2}{5},$$

$$f(0) = -\tfrac{1}{5},$$

$$1/f(x) = (2x^2 - 7x + 5)/(x - 1),$$
$$x \neq 1, \tfrac{5}{2}.$$

33. Only one line if $c = 1$; two parallel lines if $c = -\frac{2}{3}$. If $c \neq 1$ or $-\frac{2}{3}$, the intersection point is

$$\left(\frac{c+1}{3c+2}, \frac{-1}{15c+10} \right),$$

and the limit is $(\frac{2}{5}, -\frac{1}{25})$.

34. (a) 0   (b) $\frac{1}{2}$

35. δ less than or equal to the smaller of 1 and $\epsilon^2/3$

36. $M = 1 + 1/\epsilon$

Chapter 4

Article 4.1

1. $v = 2t - 4$, $a = 2$ 2. $v = 6t^2 - 10t + 4$, $a = 12t - 10$

3. $v = gt + v_0$, $a = g$ 4. $v = 4 - 2t$, $a = -2$

5. $v = 8t + 12$, $a = 8$ 6. $y' = 4x^3 - 21x^2 + 4x$, $y'' = 12x^2 - 42x + 4$

7. $y' = 15(x^2 - x^4)$, $y'' = 30(x - 2x^3)$ 8. $y' = 8(x-1)$, $y'' = 8$

9. $y' = x^3 - x^2 + x - 1$, $y'' = 3x^2 - 2x + 1$ 10. $y' = 8(x^3 - x)$, $y'' = 8(3x^2 - 1)$

11. $y' = 2x^3 - 3x - 1$, $y'' = 6x^2 - 3$ 12. $y' = 21(x^6 - x^2 + 2x)$, $y'' = 42(3x^5 - x + 1)$

13. $y' = 5x^4 - 2x$, $y'' = 20x^3 - 2$ 14. $y' = 2x + 1$, $y'' = 2$

15. $y' = 12x + 13$, $y'' = 12$ 16. (a) 400 ft   (b) 96 ft/sec

17. $y = 8x - 5$

18. $y = 4x \pm 2$. Least slope is $+1$, at $(0, 0)$.

19. $(-1, 27)$, $(2, 0)$ 20. $a = b = 1$, $c = 0$

21. $a = -3$, $b = 2$, $c = 1$ 22. $c = \frac{1}{4}$

Article 4.2

1. $x^2 - x + 1$

2. $(x-1)^2(x+2)^3(7x+2)$

3. $10x(x^2 + 1)^4$ 4. $12(x^2 - 1)(x^3 - 3x)^3$

5. $-2(2x^2 + 3x - 1)(x+1)(x^2+1)^{-4}$

6. $-2(x^2 + x + 1)/(x^2 - 1)^2$

7. $-19/(3x - 2)^2$ 8. $-4(x+1)(x-1)^{-3}$

9. $(1 - t^2)/(t^2 + 1)^2$ 10. $6(2t+3)^2$

11. $-2(2t - 1)(t^2 - t)^{-3}$ 12. $(t^2 + 2t)(t+1)^{-2}$

13. $(2 - 6t^2)/(3t^2 + 1)^2$ 14. $2(t - t^{-3})$

15. $3(2t + 3)(t^2 + 3t)^2$

Article 4.3

1. $-x/y$ 2. $\dfrac{1}{y(x+1)^2}$

3. $-(2x + y)/x$

4. $-(2xy + y^2)/(x^2 + 2xy)$

5. $3x^2/(2y)$ 6. $-(y/x)^{1/3}$ 7. $-(y/x)^{1/2}$

8. $\dfrac{y - 3x^2}{3y^2 - x}$ 9. $\dfrac{y}{x} - (x+y)^2$

10. $(x^2 + 1)^{-3/2}$ 11. $(2x^2 + 1)(x^2 + 1)^{-1/2}$

12. $\dfrac{x^4 - 1}{x^3 y}$ 13. $\dfrac{1 - 2y}{2x + 2y - 1}$

14. $\frac{1}{2}x^{-1/2} + \frac{1}{3}x^{-2/3} + \frac{1}{4}x^{-3/4}$

15. $\dfrac{2x}{y(x^2 + 1)^2}$ 16. $\dfrac{2x^3 - 3x^2 - 3y^2}{6xy - 2y^3}$

17. $5(3x + 7)^4/(2y^2)$

18. $(10x^2 + 30x - 8)(x + 5)^3(x^2 - 2)^2$

19. $-y^2/x^2$

20. $(6x + 15)(x^2 + 5x)^2$

21. $(2x - 1)/(2y)$ 22. $\dfrac{x(y^2 - 1)}{y(1 - x^2)}$

23. $-\dfrac{x^2 + 9}{3x^2(x^2 + 3)^{2/3}}$ 25. (a) $-x/y$ (b) $-1/y^3$

26. (a) $-x^2/y^2$ (b) $-2x/y^5$ 27. (a) $-x^{-1/3}y^{1/3}$ (b) $\frac{1}{3}x^{-4/3}y^{-1/3}$

28. (a) $-y(x + 2y)^{-1}$ (b) $2(x + 2y)^{-3}$ 30. (a) $7x - 4y = 2$ (b) $4x + 7y = 29$

31. (a) $3x - 4y = 25$ (b) $4x + 3y = 0$ 32. (a) $y = 3x + 6$ (b) $x + 3y = 8$

33. (a) $x = 3y$ (b) $3x + y = 10$ 34. (a) $3x - 4y = 10$ (b) $4x + 3y = 30$

35. (b) The function $y = x^{1/3}$ has no derivative at $x = 0$, but the y-axis is tangent to its graph there. The slope of $y = x^3$ is zero, and the x-axis is tangent to its graph at $(0, 0)$.

37. For $0 \leq x < 1$, $x^n \to 0$ as $n \to \infty$. The functions $f_n(1)$ for all n, so the limit is 1. Yes, there is a limit for each $x \in [0, 1]$, with $g(x) = 0$ for $x \in [0, 1)$ and $g(1) = 1$. The graph of g is the semiclosed interval $[0, 1)$, and the single point $(1, 1)$.

38. All five are differentiable on $(0, 1)$. The defining equation makes sense for $(-\infty, \infty)$, $n = 1, 3, 10, \frac{1}{3}$, and for $x \in [0, \infty)$, $n = \frac{1}{10}$. Those with fractional exponents fail to have derivatives at $x = 0$.

39. For $n = 1$, f_1 is its own inverse. For $n = 3$ and $n = \frac{1}{3}$, f and $f_{1/3}$ are inverses. The inverse of $f_{1/10}$ is a function with domain $[0, \infty)$, but it is not f_{10}. The inverse of f_{10} on $(-\infty, \infty)$ is not a function because $(-x)^{10} = x^{10}$.

Article 4.4

1. (a) $(2x + 2)\,\Delta x + (\Delta x)^2$
   (b) $(2x + 2)\,\Delta x$
   (c) $(\Delta x)^2$

2. (a) $(4x + 4)\,\Delta x + 2\,(\Delta x)^2$
   (b) $(4x + 4)\,\Delta x$
   (c) $2\,(\Delta x)^2$

3. (a) $(3x^2 - 1)\,\Delta x + 3x\,(\Delta x)^2 + (\Delta x)^3$
   (b) $(3x^2 - 1)\,\Delta x$
   (c) $3x\,(\Delta x)^2 + (\Delta x)^3$

4. (a) $4x^3\,\Delta x + 6x^2\,(\Delta x)^2 + 4x\,(\Delta x)^3 + (\Delta x)^4$
   (b) $4x^3\,\Delta x$
   (c) $6x^2\,(\Delta x)^2 + 4x\,(\Delta x)^3 + (\Delta x)^4$

5. (a) $-\dfrac{\Delta x}{x(x + \Delta x)}$ (b) $-\dfrac{\Delta x}{x^2}$
   (c) $\dfrac{(\Delta x)^2}{x^2(x + \Delta x)}$

6. 2.13   7. 0.51   8. 1.96
9. 0.494   10. 0.58   12. See Fig. 4.4.12

Article 4.5

1. $f_1(x) = 2\sqrt{x} + 1$, $x \geq 0$,
   $f_2(x) = \sqrt{2x + 1}$, $x \geq -\frac{1}{2}$

2. $f_1(x) = 1/(1 + x)$, $x \neq 0$, $x \neq -1$,
   $f_2(x) = 1 + (1/x)$, $x \neq 0$, $x \neq -1$

3. $f_1(x) = \sqrt{(1/x) - 1}$, $0 < x \leq 1$,
   $f_2(x) = 1/\sqrt{x - 1}$, $x > 1$

4. $f_1(x) = \sin(1/x)$, $x \neq 0$,
   $f_2(x) = \csc x$, $x \neq n\pi$, $n = 0, \pm 1, \pm 2, \ldots$

5. $f_1(x) = \cos(1/\sqrt{x})$, $x \geq 1/(4\pi^2)$,
   $f_2(x) = 1/\sqrt{\cos x}$, $|x| < \pi/2$ or $3\pi/2 < |x| \leq 2\pi$

6. $f_1(x) = |\sin x|$, $f_2(x) = \sin |x|$, $x \in (-\infty, \infty)$

4.4.12

7. $f_1(x) = 2|x| + 4$, $f_2(x) = |2x + 4|$, $x \in (-\infty, \infty)$

8. $f_1(x) = \frac{1}{2}(\tan x + |\tan x|)$, $x \in (-\pi/2, \pi/2)$,
   $f_2(x) = \tan[(x + |x|)/2]$, $x \in (-\infty, \pi/2)$

9. $f_1(x) = f_2(x) = x$; $x \in (-\infty, \infty)$

10. $f_1(x) = x$, $x \in [0, \infty)$,
    $f_2(x) = |x|$, $x \in (-\infty, \infty)$

12.

$z = (\sin x)^2 = \tfrac{1}{2} - \tfrac{1}{2}\cos 2x, \ |x| \le 2\pi$

Article 4.6

1. $9y = (x-1)^2$

2. $y^2 = x^3$

3. $y = \left(\dfrac{x}{1+x}\right)^2$

4. $y = \dfrac{x^2}{1-x}$

5. -3

6. $8x + 10$

7. $\dfrac{1}{2(x+1)^2}$

8. $\dfrac{4x}{3(x^2+1)^{1/3}}$

9. $18x + \dfrac{1}{3x^2}$

10. $\dfrac{4(3x+2)^4 - 2}{(3x+2)^3}$

Article 4.8

1. $(3x^2 - 6x + 5)\, dx$

2. $\dfrac{9x}{2y}(3x^2 + 1)^{1/2}\, dx$

3. $-\dfrac{2xy + y^2}{2xy + x^2}\, dx$

4. $2(1 - x^2)(1 + x^2)^{-2}\, dx$

5. $\dfrac{1 - 2x^2}{\sqrt{1 - x^2}}\, dx$

6. $(6 - 2x - x^2)(x^2 - 2x + 4)^{-2}\, dx$

7. $3(1 - x)^2(2x - 1)(2 - 3x)^{-2}\, dx$

8. $(2 - 2x + x^2)(1 - x)^{-2}\, dx$

9. 12.04

10. 9.2

11. 2.03

12. 0.5013

13. 79.69

14. (c) $5x - 3y = 8$

15. (c) $15x - y = 20$

16. (c) $11y = x + 16$

17. (c) $9x + y = 6$

18. (c) $4x + 2y = 9$

19. $-4t^3(t^2 - 1)^{-3}$

20. $2(t+1)^3(t-1)^{-3}$

Article 4.9

1. (a) $x = -1$

   (b) $x = 1$ or 3

2. Continuous

3. Take $\delta \le \epsilon$

4. Max $= 1$,   min $= 0$

---

5. Neither a maximum nor a minimum since

$$f(x_2) > f(x_1) \quad \text{if} \quad 0 < x_1 < x_2 < 1.$$

Hence we can always find x_2 such that

$$f(x_2) > f(x_1),$$

so $f(x_1)$ is *not* the maximum. This is true for any x_1 in the given domain. The same argument shows that no x_2 in the domain can give a minimum.

6. Take $a = 0$, $b = 1$, and $N = 0$ in Theorem 15 (ii).

7. Continuous but not differentiable

9. 7

10. $$|\sin x - \sin a| \le 2\left|\sin\frac{x-a}{2}\right| \le |x - a|$$

Miscellaneous exercises

1. $-4(x^2 - 4)^{-3/2}$

2. $(5 - 2x - y)/(x + 2y)$

3. $-y/(x + 2y)$

4. $(3x^2 + 4y)/(9y^2 - 4x)$

5. $-\dfrac{2xy}{x^2 + 2y}$

6. $\dfrac{-2(x+1)(x^2 + 2x + 2)}{x^3(x+2)^3}$

7. $(1 - x^2)^{-3/2}$

8. $\dfrac{-(2x + 3y^2)}{3y(2x + y)}$

9. $(x + 1)^{-2}$

10. $(2x + 1)^{-1/2}$

11. $(3x^3 - 2a^2x)/\sqrt{x^2 - a^2}$

12. $-4(2x - 1)^{-2}$

13. $2x(1 - x^2)^{-2}$

14. $3(x^2 + x + 1)^2(2x + 1)$

15. $-\dfrac{2x + 1}{2}(x^2 + x - 1)^{-3/2}$

16. $2x + 1$

17. $\dfrac{4x + 5}{2}\sqrt{2x^2 + 5x}$

18. $-(9/2)(4x + 5)(2x^2 + 5x)^{-5/2}$

19. $-\dfrac{y}{x}\left(\dfrac{2y\sqrt{xy} + 1}{4y\sqrt{xy} + 1}\right)$

20. $\dfrac{y - 2x}{2y - x}$

21. $-(y/x)^{1/3}$

22. $-\sqrt{y/x}$

23. $-y/x$

24. $-y/x$

25. $-\dfrac{1}{2}\left(\dfrac{x + 2y + y^2}{x + 2y + xy}\right)$

26. $\dfrac{x^2 - 2x - 1}{2(1 - x)^{1/2}(1 + x^2)^{3/2}}$

27. $\dfrac{1}{2y(x + 1)^2}$

28. $\dfrac{12x - 2xy - y^2}{x^2 + 2xy - 12y}$

29. $-\dfrac{y + 2}{x + 3}$

30. 1

31. $\dfrac{4x + 8}{\sqrt{4x^2 + 16x + 15}}$ 32. $\dfrac{2t(1 + t^2)^2}{(1 - t^2)}$

33. $2x\left[1 + \dfrac{(1 - x^2)}{(1 + x^2)^3}\right]$ 34. $m = 1,\ y = x$

35. $y + 2x = 6$ 36. $c = 4$

37. $m = 2,\ y - 2x = -5$ 38. $(2, 0)$ and $(-1, 27)$

39. (a) $10(x^2 + 2x)^4(x + 1)$ (b) $(3t - 1)/\sqrt{3t^2 - 2t}$

     (c) $r[(r^2 + 5)^{-1/2} + (r^2 - 5)^{-1/2}]$

     (d) $\dfrac{4x}{(x^2 + 1)^2}$

40. $27y + x = 28$ 41. $y + x = 3$

42. $(2x + 3)^{-1/2}$ 43. $-6(2 - 3x)$,

44. $-\frac{8}{5}$ $f(x) = (2 - 3x)^2$

45. $6\pi\,(\Delta r)^2$. It is the volume of a shell around the can with thickness Δr.

46. $\pi x(20 - x)$ 47. $x_1 = 40,\ p = 4\,(= 20\!\not\!c)$

49. $(x - 1)(2x - 1)$ 50. $(2x + 1)/9$

51. 56 ft/sec   52. $-\frac{12}{5}$

53. (a) $h + 2k = 5$

     (b) $h = -4,\ k = \frac{9}{2},\ r = 5\sqrt{5}/2$

54. $2\sqrt{x^2 + 1}$

55. $\dfrac{2}{3(2y + 1)(2x + 1)\sqrt{x^2 + x}}$

56. $2x\sqrt{3x^4 - 1}$

57. $\dfrac{3}{(x + 1)^2}\sin\left[\left(\dfrac{2x - 1}{x + 1}\right)^2\right]$

58. $y' = 2x - 3,\ y'' = 2$

59. $a = -32$ 60. $\dfrac{3(x - 2)}{(2x - 3)^{3/2}}$

61. $-\frac{3}{32}$ 62. $y' = 2,\ y'' = -2$

64. (a) $3(2x - 1)^{-5/2}$ (b) $-162(3x + 2)^{-4}$ (c) $6a$

66. $\Delta y = 0.92$, principal part $= 0.9$

67. $\sqrt{26} \approx 5.1$,

     $\sqrt[3]{26} \approx 2.963,\ y = x^{1/3},\ x = 27,\ \Delta x = -1$

68. 0.9999 69. 14 ± 0.044 ft

70. (a) $\dfrac{x(x + 2)}{(x + 1)^2}\,dx$ (b) $\dfrac{x}{y}\,dx$ (c) $\dfrac{-y}{x + 2y}\,dx$

72. $\delta = \epsilon/4$. The function is uniformly continuous for $-2 \le x \le 2$.

75. $m = \frac{1}{2},\ C = \sqrt{2}$

Chapter 5

Article 5.1

1. Falling, $x < \frac{1}{2}$; rising, $x > \frac{1}{2}$. Low point, $(\frac{1}{2}, \frac{3}{4})$.

2. Rising, $x < -1$; falling, $-1 < x < 2$; rising, $x > 2$. High point at $(-1, \frac{3}{2})$, low at $(2, -3)$.

3. Rising, $x < 0$; falling, $0 < x < 1$; rising $x > 1$. High point at $(0, 3)$, low at $(1, 2)$.

4. Rising, $x < -3$; falling, $-3 < x < 3$; rising, $x > 3$. High point at $(-3, 90)$, low at $(3, -18)$.

5. Falling, $x < -2$; rising, $-2 < x < 0$; falling, $0 < x < 2$; rising, $x > 2$. Low points at $(\pm 2, 0)$, high at $(0, 16)$.

6. Rising, $x < 0$; falling, $0 < x < 2$; rising, $x > 2$. High point at $(0, 4)$, low at $(2, 0)$.

7. Rising, $x < -4$; falling, $-4 < x < -1$, $-1 < x < 2$; rising, $x > 2$. High point at $(-4, -12)$, low at $(2, 0)$.

8. Falling, $x < -4$; rising, $-4 < x < 2$; falling, $x > 2$. Low point at $(-4, -\frac{1}{12})$. As $x \to 2,\ y \to \infty$.

9. Rising, $-2 < x < 0$; falling, $0 < x < 2$. High point at $(0, 2)$, low points at $(\pm 2, 0)$.

10. Falling, $x < -2$; rising, $x > 2$. Low points at $(\pm 2, 0)$. No curve for $|x| < 2$.

11. Rising for all x. Zero slope at $(0, 0)$.

Article 5.2

1. $\dfrac{dA}{dt} = 2\pi r\,\dfrac{dr}{dt}$ 2. $\dfrac{dV}{dt} = 4\pi r^2\,\dfrac{dr}{dt}$

3. $\dfrac{8}{5\pi}$ ft/min   5. $\dfrac{ax + by}{\sqrt{x^2 + y^2}}$ ft/sec

6. $\dfrac{25}{9\pi}$ ft/min   7. $\dfrac{10}{\sqrt{21}} = 2.2$ ft/sec

8. Increasing 33.7 ft/sec   9. $\dfrac{125}{144\pi}$ ft/min

10. $\dfrac{dy}{dt} = -x$. Clockwise

11. 8 ft/sec toward the lamppost. Decreasing 3 ft/sec

12. Increasing 8.75 psi/sec

13. 1500 ft/sec   14. 20 ft/sec

15. Thickness decreasing at the rate of $5/(72\pi)$ in/min. Area decreasing at the rate of $\frac{10}{3}$ in^2/min

16. $260/\sqrt{37}$ mi/hr

POINTS ARE ABSOLUTE Max. → Local Max &
Absolut Min + Local Min
except when f(x)=0

Article 5.4

M = high turning point
m = low turning point
I = inflection point

1. (a) $x > 2$ (b) $x < 2$ (c) Always
   (d) Never $m(2, -1)$

2. (a) Always   (b) Never   (c) $x < -1$
   (d) $x > -1$. Asymptote $x = -1$. (There is also a horizontal asymptote $y = 1$.)

3. (a) $-1 < x < 1$ (b) $x < -1$, $x > 1$
   (c) $x < 0$
   (d) $x > 0$, $M(1, 6)$, $m(-1, 2)$, $I(0, 4)$

4. (a) $x < -2$, $x > 3$ (b) $-2 < x < 3$
   (c) $x > \frac{1}{2}$
   (d) $x < \frac{1}{2}$, $M(-2, \frac{22}{3})$, $m(3, -\frac{27}{2})$, $I(\frac{1}{2}, -\frac{37}{12})$

5. (a) $x < -2$, $x > 2$ (b) $-2 < x < 2$, $x \neq 0$
   (c) $x > 0$ (d) $x < 0$, $M(-2, -4)$, $m(2, 4)$
   Asymptote $x = 0$ (also $y = x$).

6. (a) $x < -1$, $-1 < x < 0$
   (b) $0 < x < 1$, $x > 1$ (c) $|x| > 1$
   (d) $|x| < 1$, $M(0, 0)$.   Asymptotes $x = \pm 1$.
   (There is also a horizontal asymptote $y = 1$.)

9. $M(-1, 7)$

10. $M(-2, 28)$, $m(2, -4)$, $I(0, 12)$

11. $m(2, 0)$

12. $M(0, 2)$, $m(2, -2)$, $I(1, 0)$

13. $(1, -1)$ 14. $(16, -3)$, $(-16, 1)$

15. $(2, 0)$, $(1, \pm 1)$ 16. $(3, 1)$

19. Concave downward, because $f''(x) = -1/x^2$ is negative

21. (a) Three times: near $x = -1.2, -0.4, +0.8$
    (b) Once: near $x = -1.8$
    (c) Once: near $x = 1.2$

Article 5.5

M = local maximum, m = local minimum

1. $M(\frac{1}{2}, \frac{1}{4})$, $m_1(0, 0)$, $m_2(1, 0)$

2. $M(1/\sqrt{3}, 2/3\sqrt{3})$, $m_1(0, 0)$, $m_2(1, 0)$

3. $M_1(-2, 6)$, $M_2(\frac{1}{2}, \frac{1}{4})$, $M_3(2, 2)$, $m_1(0, 0)$, $m_2(1, 0)$

4. $m(-1, -\frac{1}{2})$, $M(1, \frac{1}{2})$

5. $f'(x) = (1 + |x|)^{-2}$. There are no critical points.

6. $m(0, 0)$

7. No maxima; minima at $(n, 0)$ for $n = 0, \pm 1, \pm 2, \ldots$

8. Each point in $[-2\pi, 2\pi]$ is a critical point. Local maxima at $(x, 1)$ for $x \in \{(-2\pi, -\pi) \cup (0, \pi)\}$, and local minima at $(x, -1)$ for $x \in \{(-\pi, 0) \cup (\pi, 2\pi)\}$

9. $m(\frac{1}{2}, 4)$

10. On $[-2, 3]$, $M_1(-2, 8)$, $M_2(3, 27)$ (the absolute maximum), and $m(0, 0)$. There is no absolute maximum on $[-2, 3)$.

Article 5.6

2. $(r\sqrt{2}) \times (r/\sqrt{2})$ 3. 32

4. $\frac{5}{3} \times \frac{14}{3} \times \frac{35}{3}$ (in.)

5. Use one-half of the fence parallel to the river.

6. $\sqrt{A/3} \times \sqrt{A/3} \times \frac{1}{2}\sqrt{A/3}$, where A is the given amount of material

7. $4 \times 4 \times 2$ (in.)   8. 4

9. 9 in. wide and 18 in. high

10. $V_{\max} = \dfrac{2\pi h^3}{9\sqrt{3}}$, h the given hypotenuse

11. $(100 + c)/2$ 12. $0.58L$

13. (a) 16   (b) -54 (c) -1
    The derivative $f'(x)$ is equal to zero when $2x^3 = a$, and then $f''(x) = +6$ if $a = 0$, or $f''(x) = +2$ if $a \neq 0$.

14. (a) $a = -3$, $b = -9$ (b) $a = -3$, $b = -24$

15. (a) Square, $\dfrac{4L}{4 + 3\sqrt{3}}$; triangle, $\dfrac{3\sqrt{3}L}{4 + 3\sqrt{3}}$
    (b) Use it all for the square.

16. $(\frac{1}{2}, -\frac{1}{2})$ and $(-\frac{1}{2}, \frac{1}{2})$

17. (a) $(c - \frac{1}{2}, \sqrt{c - \frac{1}{2}})$ (b) $(0, 0)$

18. $\frac{32}{81}\pi r^3$ 19. $\frac{4}{9}\pi r^3\sqrt{3}$

21. Width, $\dfrac{2r}{\sqrt{3}}$;   depth, $2r\sqrt{\frac{2}{3}}$

22. Width of beam = radius of log.

23. $\dfrac{x}{c - x} = \sqrt[3]{\dfrac{a}{b}}$, where x is the distance from the source of strength a.

24. Height of rectangle is $(4 + \pi)/8$ times diameter of semicircle.

25. $4/\pi$

26. Diameter = alt. of cylinder = $\sqrt[3]{\dfrac{3V}{\pi}}$,

    V = total volume

27. (a) Unity   (b) Zero

31. Before tax: Production = 7,500; price = $1.25, profit = $5,425. After tax: Production = 7,000; price = $1.30, profit = $4,700. To maximize his profit he should absorb 5¢ of the tax and add 5¢ to the price.

Article 5.7

4. If three of the roots of $f(x) = 0$, $x \in (a, b)$, are $x_1 < x_2 < x_3$, then, by Rolle's Theorem,

$$f'(c_1) = 0 \quad \text{and} \quad f'(c_2) = 0$$

for some

$$c_1 \in (x_1, x_2) \quad \text{and} \quad c_2 \in (x_2, x_3).$$

Now apply Rolle's Theorem to f' on $[c_1, c_2]$. *Generalization.* If $f(x) = 0$ has n roots in $[a, b]$, then $f'(x) = 0$ has $n - 1$ roots, $f''(x) = 0$ has $n - 2$ roots, $\ldots$, and $f^{(n-1)}(x) = 0$ has at least one root in (a, b).

5. The maximum of $\sin x$ is at $x = \pi/2$, so $c = \pi/2$.

Article 5.8

1. $\frac{1}{2}$ 2. $\sqrt{3}$ 3. $\frac{8}{27}$ 4. 1 5. $\frac{3}{2}$

10. (b) For $1 < c < .2$, we have $2 < c^2 + 1 < 5$, so $\frac{1}{2} > f'(c) > \frac{1}{5}$. Therefore $(\pi/4) + 0.2 < f(2) < (\pi/4) + 0.5$.

Article 5.9

1. $4.9 - \epsilon$, with $1/1000 < \epsilon < \sqrt{6}/2304$

3. (a) 2.1, 2.0975   (b) 1.5, 1.4375
    (c) 1.9, 1.8975   (d) 2.325, 2.2986

5. (a) 0 (b) $f'(a)$ (c) 0 (d) $\frac{1}{2}f''(a)$

Miscellaneous exercises

1. (a) $x < \frac{9}{2}$ 2. (a) $x > 3$, $x < \frac{1}{3}$
    (b) $x > \frac{9}{2}$ (b) $\frac{1}{3} < x < 3$
    (c) No values   (c) $x > \frac{5}{3}$
    (d) All values   (d) $x < \frac{5}{3}$

3. (a) $x < 3$ 4. (a) $|x| > \frac{1}{2}$
    (b) $x > 3$ (b) $|x| < \frac{1}{2}$
    (c) $0 < x < 2$ (c) $x > 0$
    (d) $x < 0$, $x > 2$ (d) $x < 0$

5. (a) $x > \sqrt[3]{2}$ 6. (a) $x < 0$, $x > 2$
    (b) $x < \sqrt[3]{2}$ (b) $0 < x < 2$
    (c) $x > 0$, $x < -\sqrt[3]{4}$ (c) $x \neq 0$
    (d) $-\sqrt[3]{4} < x < 0$ (d) Never

7. (a) $x < 0$ 8. (a) $x \neq -1$
    (b) $x > 0$ (b) Never
    (c) $x \neq 0$ (c) $x < -1$
    (d) Never   (d) $x > -1$

9. (a) $x \neq 0$ (b) Never
    (c) $x < 0$ (d) $x > 0$

10. (a) $-1 < x < 0$, $x > 1$
    (b) $x < -1$, $0 < x < 1$
    (c) $x < -1/\sqrt{3}$, $x > 1/\sqrt{3}$
    (d) $|x| < 1/\sqrt{3}$

11. (a) $x < -2b/a$, $x > 0$ 12. (a) $a < 1$, $x > 2$
    (b) $-2b/a < x < 0$ (b) $1 < x < 2$
    (c) $x > -b/a$ (c) $x > \frac{3}{2}$
    (d) $x < -b/a$ (d) $x < \frac{3}{2}$

13. (a) $x < -1$, $x > \frac{1}{3}$ 14. (a) $0 < x < 4$
    (b) $-1 < x < \frac{1}{3}$ (b) $x < 0$, $x > 4$
    (c) $x > -\frac{1}{3}$ (c) $x < 2$
    (d) $x < -\frac{1}{3}$ (d) $x > 2$

15. (a) At $x = 1$; because y' goes from $+$ to $-$
    (b) At $x = 3$; because y' goes from $-$ to $+$

17. If $v = k/\sqrt{s}$, then $dv/dt = -k/2s^2$.

18. $k^2/2$ 19. $\frac{1}{4}$ in/min   20. $(3/400\pi)$ ft/min

21. $dr/dt = -(3/400)$ ft/min
    $dA/dt = -\frac{6}{5}\pi$ ft^2/min
    $\Delta r \approx -(3/4000)$ ft; $\Delta A \approx -(3\pi/25)$ ft^2

22. (a) Approx. 606 mi/hr   (b) Approx. 0.83 mi

23. $\frac{1}{2}\sqrt{3}$ 24. $-480\sqrt{2}/7$

25. Yes, it will fill, because $dy/dt > 0.007$ for $y \leq 10$.

26. $a = -gR^2/s^2$ 28. $(\sqrt{3}/30)r$, increasing

29. Approx. 18 mi/hr   30. $(8/9\pi)$ ft/min

31. $\frac{20}{3}$ and $\frac{40}{3}$ 32. 10

33. 18 and 18, no

34. $a = 1$, $b = -3$, $c = -9$, $d = 5$

35. $\frac{1}{2}$ 36. $r = 25$ ft

37. $t = 1$, $s = 16$ 38. $r = 4$, $h = 4$

39. Diameter = height = 4 in.

40. $4\sqrt{3}$ 41. 276 (approx.)

42. (a) $(2, \pm\sqrt{3})$,   (b, c) $(1, 0)$

43. (a) $2\frac{1}{12}$ mi from A (b) $2\frac{1}{12}$ mi from A (c) at B

44. (a) True   (b) False   (c) True   (d) False

45. Each $= (P - b)/2$

46. Each $= \tan^{-1}(4k/b^2)$ 48. $m = \frac{1}{4}$

50. Sides are 110 yd, radii of semicircular ends are 110/π yd.

57. 6×18 ft   58. Approx. 16.4 in.

59. $(h^{2/3} + w^{2/3})^{3/2}$ ft

60. $v = \sqrt[n]{\dfrac{a}{(n-1)b}}$ 61. $r = \sqrt{A}$, $\theta = 2$ rad

62. Approx. 1.94 gal

63. (a) A decreasing 0.04π in^2/sec

   (b) $t = (5b - 3a)/(a^2 - b^2)$

64. $t = (R - cr)/(ca - b)$, where $c = \sqrt{a/b}$

66. (a) True

   (b) Not necessarily true:

   $f(x) = g(x) = 5 + x + x^3$ for $|x| \leq 1$, $a = 0$.

67. $x = \dfrac{1}{n}\sum_{i=1}^{n} c_i$ 68. $m = \frac{5}{7}$

70. Doesn't apply; derivative doesn't exist at $x = 0$.

72. $c = \pm\left(\dfrac{b^{2/3} + a^{1/3}b^{1/3} + a^{2/3}}{3}\right)^{3/2}$

73. Root -0.67

75. (a) $x = (c - b)/(2e)$ (b) $P = \frac{1}{2}(b + c)$

   (c) $-a + (c - b)^2/(4e)$

   (d) $P = \frac{1}{2}(b + t + c)$; that is, he adds $\frac{1}{2}t$ to his previous price.

Chapter 6

Article 6.2

1. $y = \dfrac{x^3}{3} + x + C$ 2. $y = -\dfrac{1}{x} + \dfrac{x^2}{2} + C$

3. $y^2 = x^2 + C$ 4. $3y^{1/2} = x^{3/2} + C$

5. $y^{2/3} = x^{2/3} + C$ 6. $-1/y = x^2 + C$

7. $y = x^3 - x^2 + 5x + C$ 8. $s = t^3 + 2t^2 - 6t + C$

9. $r = (2z + 1)^4/8 + C$

10. $-u^{-1} = 2v^4 - 4v^{-2} + C$

11. $x^{1/2} = 4t + C$

12. $y = 4t^3/3 + 4t - t^{-1} + C$

13. $y = z^3/3 - z^{-1} + C$ 14. $x^2 + 3x + C$

15. $\dfrac{x^3}{3} - \dfrac{2x^{3/2}}{3} + C$ 16. $\dfrac{(3x - 1)^{235}}{705} + C$

17. $\dfrac{-3(2 - 7t)^{5/3}}{35} + C$ 18. $\dfrac{2(2 + 5y)^{3/2}}{15} + C$

19. $\dfrac{-1}{9x + 6} + C$ 20. $-3\sqrt{1 - r^2} + C$

21. $\dfrac{(2x^2 + 1)^{3/2}}{6} + C$ 22. $\frac{1}{2}(1 + 2t^3)^{1/3} + C$

23. $\frac{1}{2}\sqrt{2y^2 + 1} + C$ 24. $\frac{2}{3}x^{3/2} + 2x^{1/2} + C$

25. $\frac{3}{4}(z^2 + 2z + 2)^{2/3} + C$

Article 6.3

1. $s = t^3 + s_0$ 2. $s = t^2 + t + s_0$

3. $s = \frac{1}{3}(t + 1)^3 - \frac{1}{3} + s_0$

4. $s = \frac{1}{5}t^5 + \frac{2}{3}t^3 + t + s_0$

5. $s = -(t + 1)^{-1} + 1 + s_0$

6. $s = s_0 + t\sqrt{2gs_0} + \frac{1}{2}gt^2$

7. $v = gt + v_0$,   8. $v = \frac{1}{2}t^2 + v_0$,

   $s = \frac{1}{2}gt^2 + v_0t + s_0$ $s = \frac{1}{6}t^3 + v_0t + s_0$

9. $v = \frac{3}{8}(2t + 1)^{4/3} + v_0 - \frac{3}{8}$,

   $s = \frac{9}{112}(2t + 1)^{7/3} + (v_0 - \frac{3}{8})t + s_0 - \frac{9}{112}$

10. $v = -\frac{1}{4}(2t + 1)^{-2} + v_0 + \frac{1}{4}$,

   $s = \frac{1}{8}(2t + 1)^{-1} + (v_0 + \frac{1}{4})t + s_0 - \frac{1}{8}$

11. $v = \frac{1}{5}t^5 + \frac{2}{3}t^3 + t + v_0$,

   $s = \frac{1}{30}t^6 + \frac{1}{6}t^4 + \frac{1}{2}t^2 + v_0t + s_0$

13. $4\sqrt{y} = x^2 + 4$ 14. $-y^{-1} = x^2 - 2$

15. $(3y + 10)^2 = (1 + x^2)^3$

16. $(1 + y^2)^{-1/2} = \dfrac{1}{\sqrt{2}} - 4x$

Article 6.4

9. $\cos^2 A + \sin^2 A = \cos 0 = 1$ 10. $\sin 0 = 0$

11. $\tan(A - B) = \dfrac{\tan A - \tan B}{1 + \tan A \tan B}$

12. $\tan(A + B) = \dfrac{\tan A + \tan B}{1 - \tan A \tan B}$

14. Cosine and secant are even. Sine, tangent, cotangent, cosecant are odd.

15. $\cos 2A = \cos^2 A - \sin^2 A,$
$\sin 2A = 2 \sin A \cos A$

Article 6.5

1. 1   2. 1   3. 2   4. $\frac{1}{3}$ 5. $\frac{5}{3}$
6. $\frac{1}{2}$ 7. 0   8. 0   9. $\frac{1}{2}$ 10. $\frac{2}{3}$
11. $\frac{3}{5}$ 12. 1   13. 2π 14. -2 15. $\frac{1}{2}$
16. 1   17. 2   18. $\cos a$ 19. $-\sin a$
20. $\pi/4$ 21. $3 \cos (3x + 4)$
22. $x \cos x + \sin x$ 23. $(x \cos x - \sin x)/x^2$
24. $-5 \sin 5x$ 25. $3x^2 \cos 3x + 2x \sin 3x$
26. $-\sin 2x/(2 + \cos 2x)^{1/2}$
27. 0   28. $6 \sin 3x/\cos^2 3x$
29. $6 \cos 2x + 8 \sin 2x$
30. $-24 \sin 2x \cos 2x$ or $-12 \sin 4x$
31. $2(\cos^2 x - \sin^2 x)$ or $2 \cos 2x$
32. $-\cos x/\sin^2 x$ 33. $-3 \sin 6x$
34. $\dfrac{-1}{\sin^2 x}$ 35. $\dfrac{\sin 2y + 2y \sin 2x}{\cos 2x - 2x \cos 2y}$
36. $(-\sin 8x)/y$ 40. $-\frac{1}{3} \cos 3x + C$
41. $\frac{1}{2} \sin (2x + 4) + C$ 42. $-\frac{1}{4} \cos (2x^2) + C$
43. $2 \sin \sqrt{x} + C$ 44. $-\frac{1}{2} \cos 2t + C$
45. $\frac{1}{3} \sin (3\theta - 1) + C$ 46. $\frac{4}{3} \sin 3y + C$
47. $\sin^2 z + C$ 48. $\frac{1}{3} \sin^3 x + C$
49. $-\frac{1}{6} \cos^3 2y + C$ 50. $\frac{1}{3} \sin 3t - \frac{1}{9} \sin^3 3t + C$
51. $1/\cos x + C$ 52. $-1/\sin x + C$
53. $\frac{2}{9}(2 + \sin 3t)^{3/2} + C$ 54. $\sqrt{2 - \cos 2t} + C$
55. $\frac{1}{2} \sin^4 \dfrac{y}{2} + C$ 56. $3 \sec \dfrac{z - 1}{3} + C$
57. $-\frac{1}{2} \cos^3 (2x/3) + C$ 58. $\frac{1}{5}(1 + \sin 2t)^{5/2} + C$
59. $-\frac{3}{2} \cos 2x + \frac{4}{3} \sin 3x + C$
60. $\frac{1}{3}(\sin^3 t - \cos^3 t) + C$

Article 6.6

1. 1.75,   2.25   2. 0.25,   1.25
3. $\pi/(2\sqrt{2}) \approx 1.12$, $(\pi/2)(1 + 1/\sqrt{2}) \approx 2.68$
4. 0.6345,   0.7595   5. 4.146,   6.146

Article 6.7

3. $\lim\limits_{n \to \infty} S_n = (ma + mb)/2 \cdot (b - a)$

4. $\lim\limits_{n \to \infty} S_n = b^3/3$ 5. $\lim\limits_{n \to \infty} S_n = b^4/4$

Article 6.8

1. 12   2. 4   3. $8\frac{2}{3}$
4. 2   5. $\frac{1}{15}$ 6. $57\frac{1}{3}$
7. 10   8. $4\frac{1}{3}$ 9. 1
10. $\frac{2}{9}$ 11. $\frac{1}{2}$ 12. $10\frac{2}{3}$
13. 2   14. $\frac{2}{3}$ 15. $\frac{4}{3}$
16. $\frac{2}{3}$ 17. $\pi/6$ 18. (b) $\pi a^2/4$

Article 6.9

1. (a) $c_k = \frac{1}{2}(x_k + x_{k-1})$

   (b) $c_k = \pm \sqrt[3]{\dfrac{x_{k-1}^2 + x_{k-1}x_k + x_k^2}{3}}$,
the sign being determined by the interval x_{k-1}, x_k.

   (c) $c_k = \sqrt[3]{\dfrac{x_{k-1}^3 + x_{k-1}^2 x_k + x_{k-1}x_k^2 + x_k^3}{4}}$

   (d) $c_k = \left(\dfrac{\sqrt{x_{k-1}} + \sqrt{x_k}}{2}\right)^2$

4. $S_n = b^4/4$ 5. $S_n = 2(\sqrt{b} - 1)$
6. 8   7. $\frac{7}{3}$ 8. $\frac{8}{3}$
9. $\frac{13}{3}$ 10. 2   11. 0
12. $\sqrt{2} - 1$ 13. $\frac{1}{2}$ 14. $\pi/2$
15. π/ω 16. $\frac{2}{9}$

17. (a) $A = \lim\limits_{n \to \infty} \sum\limits_{k=1}^{n} (18 - 2x_k^2) \Delta x_k$
            $(x_1 = -3, x_{n+1} = 3)$

   (b) $A = \displaystyle\int_{-3}^{3} (18 - 2x^2)\, dx = 72$

18. 0.692   19. $\sqrt{1 + x^2}$
20. $1/x$ 21. $-\sqrt{1 - x^2}$
22. $1/(1 + x^2)$ 23. $2 \cos (4x^2)$
24. $2x/(1 + \sqrt{1 - x^2})$ 25. $-\cos x/(2 + \sin x)$

Article 6.10 (I = integral, A = approximation)

2. $I = 2$, $A = 2$
3. $I = 4$, $A = 4.25$
4. $I = 4\sqrt{2}/3$, $A \approx 1.82$
5. $I = \frac{1}{2}$, $A \approx 0.53$

Article 6.12

1. $\int_a^b f(t)\,dt = -\int_b^a f(t)\,dt,$

$\int_a^c f(t)\,dt = \int_a^b f(t)\,dt + \int_b^c f(t)\,dt,$

$\dfrac{d}{dx}\int_a^x f(t)\,dt = f(x),$

$\int_a^b f(t)\,dt = f(c)\cdot(b-a),$

$\int_a^b f(t)\,dt = F(b) - F(a)$

2. (a) $\int_0^1 x\,dx + \int_1^2 \sin(\pi x)\,dx = \dfrac{1}{2} - \dfrac{2}{\pi}$

(b) $\int_0^1 (1-x)^{1/2}\,dx + \int_1^2 (7x-6)^{-1/3}\,dx = \dfrac{55}{42}$

3. (a) $F'(\frac{1}{2}) = \frac{1}{2},\quad F'(\frac{3}{2}) = -1$
(b) $F'(\frac{1}{2}) = \sqrt{\frac{1}{2}},\quad F'(\frac{3}{2}) = (\frac{9}{2})^{-1/3}$
(c) $F'(\frac{1}{2}) = \frac{2}{3},\quad F'(\frac{3}{2}) = -\frac{2}{5}$

Miscellaneous exercises

1. $x^2 y + 2 = cy$
2. $3\sqrt{y+1} = (1+x)^{3/2} + c$
3. $y^3 + 3y = x^3 - 3x + c$
4. $3(x^2 - y^2) + 4(x^{3/2} + y^{3/2}) = c$
5. $(2+x)^{-1} = -(3-y)^{-1} + c$
6. (a) $y = \frac{1}{3}(x^2 - 4)^{3/2} + 3$ (b) $y^2(1-x^2) = 1$
7. Yes, $y = x$ is such a curve.
8. $y = x^3 + 2x - 4$ 9. $(2\sqrt{2}/3)b^{3/4}$
10. (a) $v = \frac{2}{3}t^{3/2} - 2\sqrt{t} + 2$
(b) $s = \frac{4}{15}t^{5/2} - \frac{4}{3}t^{3/2} + 2t + 5$
11. $v = t^2 + 3t + 4,\quad \Delta s = 61\frac{1}{3}$
12. -8 ft/sec
    [*Note.* $d^2 x/dt^2 = v\,(dv/dx)$, where $v = dx/dt$.]
13. $h(10) = h(0) = 5$
14. $(1+y')(1+y'^2) + y''(y-x) = 0$
15. (a) $k = 38.72$ ft/sec^2 (b) 25 ft
16. $3y = (1+x^2)^{3/2} - 7$ 17. $h = 96t - 16t^2, 144$ ft
19. (a) ≈ 1.76 (b) ≈ 1.73

20. (a) 4 ft/sec   (b) $\frac{64}{3}$ ft
21. $(x^2/2) - x^{-1} + c$ 22. $\frac{1}{3}(y^2+1)^{3/2} + c$
23. $-\frac{1}{8}(1 + t^{4/3})^{-6} + c$ 24. $\frac{4}{3}(1+\sqrt{u})^{3/2} + c$
25. $-\frac{3}{5}(7-5r)^{1/3} + c$ 26. $\frac{1}{4}\sin 4x + c$
27. $\frac{1}{9}\sin^3 3x + c$ 28. $2\sqrt{\sin x} + c$
29. $\frac{1}{2}\sin(2x-1) + c$ 30. $-\frac{1}{4}\sqrt{25 - 4y^2} + c$
31. $-\sqrt{2/t} + c$ 32. $\frac{1}{3}(x^3 - 2x^{3/2}) + c$
33. $\frac{1}{3}(2-3x)^{-1} + c$ 34. $2\sin(1-2x)$
35. $-\csc^2 x$ 36. $10\sec^2 5x \tan 5x$
37. $20\sin^3 5x \cos 5x$
38. $\dfrac{\sin x \cos x (\sin x - \cos x)}{(\sin^3 x + \cos^3 x)^{2/3}}$
39. 0 42. $r\sqrt{2}/2$ ft   44. $|a|$
45. Yes; no; applies to identities, but not to equations
46. 480π mi/hr   47. $|3a\omega \sin\theta \cos\theta|$
48. $f(x) = x/\sqrt{x^2+1}$
49. (a) $\frac{10}{3}$ (b) $\frac{5}{3}$ (c) $\frac{1}{2}$
50. $dy/dx = -2x,\quad d^2y/dx^2 = -2$
51. $\int_0^1 f(x)\,dx$
52. (a) $\frac{1}{16}$ (b) $\frac{2}{3}$ (c) $2/\pi$
53. (a) $\sqrt{1+x^2} - x$ (b) $x_1 f(x_1)$
54. $d^2y/dx^2 = 4y$

Chapter 7

Article 7.2

1. (a) $\lim\limits_{\Delta y \to 0} \sum\limits_a^b (f(y) - g(y))\,\Delta y$
(b) $\int_a^b (f(y) - g(y))\,dy$

2. (a) $\frac{4}{3}$ (b) $\frac{1}{12}$ (c) $\frac{32}{3}$ (d) $\frac{32}{3}$ (e) $\frac{1}{6}$
(f) $\frac{4}{3}$ (g) $\frac{128}{15}$
3. $\sqrt{2} - 1$ 4. $\sqrt[3]{16} \approx 2.52$ 5. $\frac{1}{6}$

Article 7.3

1. 6 ft   2. $5\frac{1}{6}$ ft   3. $3\frac{2}{3}$ ft
4. 1 ft   5. 6 ft   6. 8 ft
7. $2\sqrt{2}$ ft   8. $2\frac{2}{3}$ ft
9. $6 - \sin 2 \approx 5.09$ (ft)
10. $1 + \cos 2 \approx 0.58$ (ft)

11. $2g$ 12. $4\frac{29}{30}$ ft   13. $3\frac{1}{6}$ ft

15. 6.45 ft,   3.22 ft/sec

Article 7.4

1. $\dfrac{8\pi}{3}$ 2. $\dfrac{\pi^2}{2}$ 3. $\dfrac{\pi}{30}$

4. $\dfrac{56\pi}{15}$ 5. $\dfrac{8\pi}{3}$ 6. $\dfrac{2\pi}{3}$

7. $\dfrac{256\pi}{5}$ 8. $\dfrac{48\pi}{5}$

9. (a) $\frac{1}{3}\pi r^2 h$ (b) $\frac{2}{3}\pi h^2 r$

10. (a) $\pi/6$ (b) $2\pi/15$

11. (a) 8π (b) $\frac{512}{15}\pi$ (c) $\frac{256}{5}\pi$ (d) $\frac{1088}{15}\pi$
    (e) $\frac{128}{3}\pi$

12. (a) $\pi h^2(a - \frac{1}{3}h)$
    (b) $0.1/12\pi$ (ft/sec) $= 6/\pi$ (in/min)

13. $\frac{4}{3}\pi a b^2$ 14. $\frac{512}{15}\pi$ 15. $\frac{16}{3}a^3$

16. $\frac{8}{3}a^3$ 17. $\frac{8}{3}a^3$ 18. $\frac{1}{16}\pi\sqrt{3}$

19. $15{,}990$ ft^3 20. $2\pi^2 a^2 b$

Article 7.6

1. 12   2. $\frac{8}{27}(10\sqrt{10} - 1)$

3. $\frac{14}{3}$ 4. $\frac{53}{6}$

5. $\frac{123}{32}$ 6. $\frac{4}{27}(10\sqrt{10} - 1)$

7. $\frac{1}{8}a\pi^2$ 8. 12   9. $\frac{21}{2}$

Article 7.7

1. $\frac{12}{5}\pi a^2$ 2. $\frac{99}{2}\pi$

3. $\frac{1}{27}\pi(10\sqrt{10} - 1)$ 4. $\frac{1}{6}\pi(17\sqrt{17} - 1)$

5. $\frac{1823}{18}\pi$ 6. $\frac{253}{20}\pi$

7. $\frac{2}{3}\pi(26\sqrt{26} - 2\sqrt{2})$ 8. $56\pi\sqrt{3}/5$

Article 7.8

1. (a) $2/\pi$ (b) 0   2. (a) $\frac{1}{2}$ (b) $\frac{1}{2}$

3. $\frac{49}{12}$ 4, $\frac{1}{2}$

5. $\alpha\dfrac{a+b}{2} + \beta$ 6. $\pi a/2$

7. $4a/\pi$ 8. $8a^2/3$ 9. $2a^2$

Article 7.9

1. $(4a/3\pi, 4a/3\pi)$ 2. $(0, \frac{2}{5}h^2)$

3. $\left(\dfrac{2a}{3(4-\pi)}, \dfrac{2a}{3(4-\pi)}\right)$ 4. $\left(\dfrac{\pi}{2}, \dfrac{\pi}{8}\right)$

5. $(\frac{2}{5}, 1)$ 6. $\frac{3}{7}h$ 7. $\frac{3}{5}h$

8. On the axis, $\frac{3}{4}h$ from vertex

9. On the axis, $\frac{3}{5}h$ from vertex

10. On the axis, $\frac{1}{2}h$ from vertex

11. $(0, \frac{1}{4}\pi r)$

Article 7.10

1. $(0, \frac{2}{5}c^2)$ 2. $(\frac{16}{105}, \frac{8}{15})$

3. $(0, \frac{12}{5})$ 4. $(1, -\frac{3}{5})$

5. $(\frac{3}{5}, 1)$

6. On the axis, $\frac{3}{4}h$ from the vertex

7. $(0, \frac{8}{3})$ $\left(0, \frac{8}{3}, 0\right)$ 8. $(\frac{4}{5}, 0)$

9. On the axis, $\frac{2}{3}h$ from the vertex

10. $\left(-r, \dfrac{3}{\pi + 2}r\right)$ 11. $\dfrac{17\sqrt{17} - 1}{12}$

12. $\left(\dfrac{2r}{\pi}, \dfrac{2r}{\pi}\right)$

Article 7.11

1. $c = 5$ lb/in,   80 inch-lb

2. $c = \dfrac{10}{\sin 10°}$ lb,   78.5 inch-lb

3. $\frac{1}{2}k$, where k is the proportionality factor

4. $\frac{1}{3}k$, k as in Exercise 3   5. $\frac{1}{2}mg\,R$

6. 1944 ft-lb

8. (Work done *on* the gas) $= -$(Work done *by* the gas) $= 3164\frac{1}{16}$ ft-lb

9. $6400\pi w/3$ 10. $276.7\,\pi w$

Miscellaneous exercises

1. $\frac{9}{2}$ 2. $6\frac{3}{4}$ 3. 1

4. $(7 - 4\sqrt{2})/2$ 5. $\frac{9}{2}$ 6. $\frac{32}{3}$

7. 18   8. $3^5/2^3$ 9. $a^2/6$

10. 14.95 correct value   11. 8

12. $\pi/4$ 13. $\frac{13}{3}$ 14. $\frac{9}{8}$

15. $\frac{64}{3}$

16. (a) $0 \le t < 2$ (b) $2 < t < 3$ (c) $\frac{29}{2}$ ft

17. (a) $\frac{3}{7}$ (b) $\frac{3}{8}$ (c) $y = 3/(2\sqrt{1 + 3x})$ (d) $\frac{3}{7}$

18. $f(x) = \sqrt{(2x - a)/\pi}$

19. (a) $3^5\pi/5$ (b) $189\pi/2$ (c) $81\pi/2$
    (d) $2^9\pi/15$ (e) $2^7\pi/3$

20. $f(x) = \pm\sqrt{(2x + 1)/\pi}$ 21. $32\pi/3$

22. (a) $2\pi a^3$ (b) $(\frac{16}{15})\pi a^3$ (c) $(\frac{8}{5})\pi a^3$

23. $V = 2\pi \int_0^2 x^2/\sqrt{x^3 + 8}\, dx = (8\pi/3)(2 - \sqrt{2})$

24. $(\pi/15)(88\sqrt{2} + 107)$ 25. $112\pi a^3/15$

26. $(\frac{8}{3})r^3$ 27. $\pi^2/4$

28. $28\pi/3$ 29. $2\sqrt{3}a^3$

30. $\frac{27}{20}$ 31. $153\pi/40$

32. $\frac{19}{3}$ 33. $(a/3)(3\sqrt{3} - 1)$

34. (a) $(\frac{2}{3})b^2$ (b) $(\frac{2}{3})b$

35. (a) $f(x) = a \pm x\sqrt{A^2 - 1},\ \ |A| \geq 1$ (b) No

36. (a) $\bar{v} = 72$ (b) $82\frac{2}{3}$

37. Vol. 401π,   average area 40.1π

38. $(\frac{9}{10}, \frac{9}{5})$ 39. $(\frac{3}{2}, \frac{12}{5})$

40. $(1, \frac{12}{5})$ 41. $(\frac{3}{4}, \frac{3}{10})$

43. (a) $(5a/7, 0)$ (b) $(2a/3, 0)$

44. $Mah + (h^2/a)$

45. $wr[1 - r/2R]$ ft-lb, R = radius of earth in feet

46. $(320w/3)(15\pi + 8)$ ft-lb

Chapter 8

Article 8.1

13. $6x \sec^2 (3x^2)$

14. $-2 \sin x \tan (\cos x) \sec^2 (\cos x)$

15. $-3 \csc^2 (3x + 5)$ 16. $-\frac{1}{2}(\cot x)^{-1/2} \csc^2 x$

17. 0 18. $\sec^3 x \tan x$

19. $3(1 + \sec^2 3x)$ 20. $6 \sec^2 2x$

21. $-\tan^2 x$ 22. $4 \sec^2 x \tan x$

23. $-2 \csc x (\csc x + \cot x)^2$

24. $12 \sin 3x \cos 3x$, or $6 \sin 6x$

25. $\frac{1}{2}(1 - \cos 2x)$, or $\sin^2 x$

26. $\frac{1}{2}(1 + \cos 2x)$, or $\cos^2 x$

27. $-\cos^3 (x/3)$

28. $-3 \cos \dfrac{x}{2} \sin \dfrac{x}{2}$, or $-\dfrac{3}{2} \sin x$

29. $\frac{1}{2}x \sin \dfrac{x}{2}$ 30. $\dfrac{2x}{\cos y + 2 \cos 2y}$

31. $3(\sin^2 x \cos x - \cos 3x)$ 32. $-5 \cos^3 5x$

33. $-\dfrac{\cos^2 (xy) + y}{x}$ 34. 10 when $x = -\sin^{-1} \frac{4}{5}$

35. max $y = 3/2$ when $x = \pi/6$,
    min $y = 1$ when $x = 0$ or $\pi/2$

38. 1.6π mi/sec   39. $120°$

40. $-\frac{1}{3} \cos 3t + C$ 41. $\frac{1}{2} \tan 2\theta + C$

42. $\frac{1}{4} \tan^4 x + C$ 43. $\frac{1}{3} \sec^3 x + C$

44. $2 \sec (x/2) + C$ 45. $\frac{1}{2}y + \frac{1}{4} \sin 2y + C$

46. $\tan \theta + C$ 47. $-3 \cot (\theta/3) + C$

48. $\frac{3}{2}$ 49. $(\pi/4)(4 - \pi)$

Article 8.2

1. $\dfrac{\sqrt{3}}{2}, \dfrac{\sqrt{3}}{3}, \dfrac{2\sqrt{3}}{3}, 2$ 2. $\dfrac{\sqrt{3}}{2}, -\sqrt{3}, -2, \dfrac{2\sqrt{3}}{3}$

3. π 4. $\pi/2$ 5. $-\pi/3$

8. (a) 0.735 (b) 0.6 (c) 0.96 (d) $\pi/3$
   (e) $2\pi/3$ (f) $\pi/6$

Article 8.3

5. $\dfrac{1}{\sqrt{4 - x^2}}$ 6. $\dfrac{1}{9 + x^2}$

7. $\dfrac{1}{|x|\sqrt{25x^2 - 1}}$ 8. $\dfrac{-2}{\sqrt{1 - 4x^2}}$

9. $\dfrac{4}{4 + x^2}$ 10. $\dfrac{1}{(x + 1)\sqrt{x}}$

11. $\dfrac{1}{x^2 + 1}$ 12. $\sin^{-1} x$

13. $(\sin^{-1} x)^2$ 14. $\cos^{-1} 2x$

15. $\sqrt{b(a + b)}$ ft   16. $\pi/6$

17. $\pi/2$ 18. $-\pi/12$

19. $-\pi/6$ 20. $\frac{1}{2} \sin^{-1} 2x + C$

21. $\pi/6$

Article 8.4

1. 0.1826 2. 0.3369

3. 0.6938 4. -0.6956

5. (a) Circumscribed   (b) Inscribed

6. (a) 0.0392 (b) -0.0408

7. $\ln 2 \approx \frac{2}{3}$ 8. $0.18226 < \ln 1.2 < 0.18267$

Article 8.5

1. $\dfrac{2x + 2}{x^2 + 2x}$ 2. $\dfrac{3}{x} (\ln x)^2$

3. $-\tan x$ 4. $\sec x$

5. $\dfrac{1}{x} + \dfrac{x}{x^2+1}$

6. $\dfrac{1}{x} + \dfrac{1}{2(x+2)}$

7. $\ln x$

8. $3x^2 \ln (2x) + x^2$

9. $\dfrac{1}{1-x^2}$

10. $\dfrac{1}{x(1+x^3)}$

11. $\dfrac{2}{x(2+3x)}$

12. $-\tan^{-1}\dfrac{x}{2}$

13. $\dfrac{\tan^{-1} x}{x^2}$

14. $3 (\ln x)^2 + (\ln x)^3$

15. $2 \cos (\ln x)$

16. $\sec^{-1} x$

17. $\ln (a^2 + x^2)$

18. $\dfrac{1}{x \ln x}$

19. $\frac{1}{2} \ln |2x+3| + C$

20. $-\frac{1}{3} \ln |2-3x| + C$

21. $\frac{1}{8} \ln (4x^2+1) + C$

22. $\ln (2-\cos x) + C$

23. $\ln |\sin x| + C$

24. $2x - 5 \ln |x| + C$

25. $x - \ln |x+1| + C$

26. $-\frac{1}{3} \ln |4-x^3| + C$

27. $-\frac{1}{2} \ln |1-x^2| + C$

28. $2 \ln (1 + \sqrt{x}) + C$

29. $\frac{1}{3} (\ln x)^3 + C$

30. $\dfrac{-1}{4x+6} + C$

Article 8.6

1. $4a$

2. $2b/3$

3. $3a/2$

4. $-2a$

5. $2a - 2b$

6. $2a + b$

7. $2b - 3a$

8. $2a + 2b$

9. $2b - a$

10. $(3b - a)/2$

Article 8.7

2. No inflection point because $y'' = 1/x$ is positive when x is positive.

3. Slope at $(x, y) = y$. Concave up because $y'' = y' = y$ is positive.

7. $\log_{10} N = \dfrac{\ln N}{\ln 10}$

Article 8.8

1. (a) x (b) x (c) x^{-2}
   (d) $-x^2$ (e) $1/x$ (f) $-x$
   (g) $1/x$ (h) x (i) $2x$
   (j) x^2 (k) $x - x^2$ (l) $-2x + 2 \ln x$
   (m) xe^x (n) x/y^2

2. $(x^2 + 2x)e^x$

3. $13e^{2x} \cos 3x$

4. $1/(1 + e^x)$

5. $\frac{1}{2}(e^x + e^{-x})$

6. $\frac{1}{2}(e^x - e^{-x})$

7. $4/(e^x + e^{-x})^2$

8. $e^{\sin^{-1} x}/\sqrt{1 - x^2}$

9. $-4xe^{-2x}$

10. $27x^2 e^{3x}$

11. xe^{ax}

12. $-2xe^{-x^2}$

13. $2e^{-x^2}(x - x^3)$

14. $e^x \left(\ln x + \dfrac{1}{x} \right)$

15. $\dfrac{e^x}{1 + e^{2x}}$

16. $2/\sqrt{e^{4x} - 1}$

17. $\frac{2}{3}e^{2x} \sec (x + 3y) - \frac{1}{3}$

18. $-e^{1/x}/x^2$

19. $(\cos^2 y) (e^x + 1/x)$

20. Start adding the terms: $(h) + (h/2) + (h/4) + \cdots$. The sum is always in $[h, 2h]$, and we can make it as close as we wish to either h or $2h$ by taking only one term, or by taking a very large number of terms. (The geometric series has the property that the sum of all the terms following any term is equal to that single term.) Because $h < 1 < 2h$, we can get sums that are less than 1 or greater than 1. Our aim is to come very close to 1, by judicious choice of summands. We let $f(n)$ be the cumulated sum after n steps, with $f(1) = h$. If, at any step,

$$1 - \epsilon < f(n) < 1 + \epsilon,$$

then we stop. Also keep $f(n) < 1 + \epsilon$ at all times. If $f(n) \le 1 - \epsilon$, and the last summand used in $f(n)$ is $h/2^m$, then the next candidate is $h/2^{m+1}$, and we test $f(n) + h/2^{m+1}$. If this number is less than $1 + \epsilon$, then we call it $f(n+1)$. If it is too large, we discard $h/2^{m+1}$ and try $f(n) + h/2^{m+2}$, and so on until we reach the first new summand $h/2^{m+k}$ for which $f(n+1) = f(n) + h/2^{m+k} < 1 + \epsilon$. We continue, with $n+1$ in place of n. These operations can be programmed.

22. (b) $y = 3e^{-2t}$

24. $\frac{1}{2}e^{2x} + C$

25. $\frac{1}{2}e^{x^2} + C$

26. $e^{\sin x} + C$

27. $3e^{x/3} + C$

28. $-\frac{4}{3}e^{-3x} + C$

29. $\frac{1}{2} \ln |1 + 2e^x| + C$

30. $\ln 2$

31. $\ln |e^x + e^{-x}| + C$

33. $p \ge 90$

34. $b \ge 40$

Article 8.9

1. $\dfrac{y(2x+1)}{2x(x+1)}$

2. $\dfrac{-2y}{3(x^2-1)}$

3. $\dfrac{y(4x^3 + 6x^2 + x + 3)}{3x(x+1)(x^2+1)}$

4. $\dfrac{y}{3}\left[\dfrac{1}{x}+\dfrac{1}{x+1}+\dfrac{1}{x-2}-\dfrac{2x}{x^2+1}-\dfrac{2}{2x+3}\right]$

5. $y\left[\dfrac{\sin x}{x}+\cos x\cdot\ln x\right]$ 6. $y[1+\sec^2 x\cdot\ln(\sin x)]$

7. $y(\sec x\tan x)\ln 2$ 8. $(2y\ln x)/x$

11. $\frac{3}{8}$ 12. $(3^{1.2}-1)/\ln 3\approx 2.49$

13. $(4\ln 4)^{-1}\approx 0.180$ 14. $24/(50\ln 5)\approx 0.298$

15. $(2\ln 4)^{-1}\approx 0.360$

Article 8.10

1. (a) 2   (b) $\frac{5}{3}$ 2. (a) 2   (b) $\frac{1}{2}$
   (c) -2 (d) -2 (c) $\frac{4}{3}$ (d) $\frac{2}{5}$

3. $\log_{1.5} 2 = \dfrac{\ln 2}{\ln 1.5}$ 4. 12

6. (a) 1.30103,   2.30103,
      $9.30103-10$, $8.30103-10$
   (b) 2.99574,   5.29833,
      $8.39056-10$, $6.08797-10$

7. (a) 1.46   (b) 0.68   (c) 2.47

8. (a) 2.02   (b) -1.36

9. (a) $3^{\tan x}\sec^2 x\ln 3$
   (b) $y\left[\dfrac{1}{x}\ln(x^2+1)+\dfrac{2x}{x^2+1}\ln x\right]$
   (c) $-2t(\ln 2)2^{-t^2}$ (d) $e^{-2\theta}(1-2\theta)$

Article 8.11

1. $\dfrac{mv_0}{k}[1-e^{-kt/m}]$,
   where k is a constant of proportionality.

2. $Q_0 e^{-kt}$ 3. $N_0 e^{kt}$

4. 1, 3   5. $-1, 2$

6. $-5, -1$ 7. $\pm 3, \pm 2$

Miscellaneous exercises

1. $2\cos 2x$ 2. $-8\sin(2x+\pi/4)$

3. $2\cos x+2\cos 2x$ 4. $(1+\cos x)^{-1}$

5. $-\csc y$ 6. $\cos^2 y$

7. $-2\cos(x/2)$ 8. $-\cos x$

9. $1-\cos x$

10. $\dfrac{x\cos x-\sin x}{x^2}$, $\begin{cases} y\to 1 \text{ as } x\to 0, \\ y\to 0 \text{ as } x\to\infty \end{cases}$

11. $\dfrac{x\cos x-2\sin x}{x^3}$, $\begin{cases} y\to\infty \text{ as } x\to 0, \\ y\to 0 \text{ as } x\to\infty \end{cases}$

12. $\sin\dfrac{1}{x}-\dfrac{1}{x}\cos\dfrac{1}{x}$, $\begin{cases} y\to 0 \text{ as } x\to 0, \\ y\to 1 \text{ as } x\to\infty \end{cases}$

13. $2x\sin\dfrac{1}{x}-\cos\dfrac{1}{x}$, $\begin{cases} y\to 0 \text{ as } x\to 0, \\ y\to\infty \text{ as } x\to\infty \end{cases}$

14. $(2/\pi)\cos^2(\pi y/2)$

15. (a) $\frac{1}{2}(e^x-e^{-x})$
    (b) $\frac{1}{2}(e^x+e^{-x})$
    (c) $4(e^x+e^{-x})^{-2}$

16. $e^{-x}(1-x)$

17. (a) $1+\ln x$ (b) $\frac{1}{2}x^{-1/2}(2+\ln x)$

18. (a) $x^{-2}(1-\ln x)$ (b) $\frac{1}{2}x^{-3/2}(2-\ln x)$
    (c) $x^{-3}(1-2\ln x)$

19. $e^{-x}(2\cos 2x-\sin 2x)$

20. (a) $2-e^{2x}$ (b) $(2-e^{2x})e^{(2x-\frac{1}{2}e^{2x})}$

21. (a) $1-e^x$ (b) $(1-e^x)e^{(x-e^x)}$

22. $(1+x^2)^{-1/2}$ 23. $(1-x^2)^{-1}$

24. $2x/(x^2+4)$

25. $\tan^{-1}(x/2)+2x/(x^2+4)$

26. $8(e^{2x}+e^{-2x})^{-2}$ 27. $2\sec x$

28. $xe^{2x}(3x\cos 3x+2x\sin 3x+2\sin 3x)$

29. $2x(1-x^4)^{-1/2}-(2x^2+1)e^{x^2}$

30. $\dfrac{4+x^3}{x(1+x^3)}+\left(\dfrac{2}{3}x^{-1/3}-x^{2/3}\right)\ln 7$

31. $2x(2-x)(x^2+2)^{1-x}-(x^2+2)^{2-x}\ln(x^2+2)$

32. $x^{-1}e^{-x}(1-x\ln x)$ 33. $1/x(x^2+1)$

34. $3/(3x-4)$ 35. $(6x+4)/(3x^2+4x)$

36. $(\ln x)^2(\ln x+3)$ 37. $3(1+\ln x)$

38. $x^2(1+3\ln x)$ 39. 1

40. $(x^2+2x)e^x$ 41. e^x

42. $1/x\ln x$

43. (a) $(1-x^2)/(1+x^2)^2$
    (b) $\frac{2}{3}(x^2+x-1)x^{-2/3}(x-2)^{-2/3}(x^2+1)^{-4/3}$

44. $f(0)=1$,   45. (a) $a^{x^2-x}(2x-1)\ln a$
    $f'(0)=5$,   (b) $(1+e^x)^{-1}$
    $f(0.01)\approx 1.05$ (c) $x^x(1+\ln x)$
                              (d) $x^{(1-2x)/x}(1-\ln x)$

48. $x = 1 + \sqrt{2}$ 49. $\dfrac{d^2y}{dx^2} = 4(e^x + e^{-x})^{-2}$

50. $y = \ln|2x - 9|$ 52. 0.88

53. $E = E_0 e^{-t/40}$, $t = 92.1$ sec

54. (b) $L = (e^{x_1} - e^{-x_1})/2$

55. $\pi^2/2$ 56. $\dfrac{y}{y_1} = \left(\dfrac{x}{x_1}\right)^2$

57. $y = 1 - \frac{1}{2}(e^x + e^{-x})$

58. $t(1/4) = 1/\pi$; it will not reach $x = 1/2$, because $t = (1/\pi)\tan(\pi x)$.

59. $1 + 4\ln\frac{3}{2} \approx 2.62$ 60. $2\sqrt{2}$

61. $y = 2e^x/(2 - e^x)$

62. $N = N_0 e^{0.02t}$, $t = 34.7$ yr

64. $(\pm a/\sqrt{2}, \; e^{-1/2})$ 65. $3\pi/8$ 66. $\pi\sqrt{3}$

67. (a) $\sec x$ (b) $\ln(1 + \sqrt{2})$

68. $(64a^2 + b^2\ln 3)/8a$ 69. $\pi(e^4 - 1)/2 \approx 84.2$

70. $(e - e^{-1})a^2 \approx 2.35a^2$ 71. $y^2 = 4x$

72. (a) $\ln 0.5 = -0.693$
    (b) $\ln 3 = 1.099$ (from tables)

73. (a) $y' = \ln x$ (b) 1.3

74. (a) $-\frac{1}{3}\ln|4 - 3x| + C$ (b) $5\ln|x - 3| + C$

75. (a) $\frac{1}{2}\ln 3 = 0.550$ (b) $\frac{1}{6}$

76. (a) $x + \ln x + C$ (b) $-\frac{1}{4}\ln|2x + 1| + x/2 + C$

77. $\ln 0.1 = -2.3026$, $\ln 0.25 = -1.3864$,
    $\ln 10 = 2.3026$, $\ln 20 = 2.9958$

78. $\pi\ln 4 \approx 4.35$ 79. $28\pi/3 \approx 29.4$

80. (a) $\frac{1}{3}\ln 2 \approx 0.23$ (b) $\frac{1}{2}(e^8 - e^{-1}) \approx 1490$
    (c) $\ln 3 \approx 1.10$ (d) $\frac{1}{2}\ln 26 \approx 1.63$ (e) e

81. 585 lb   82. $2000\pi\left(\frac{9}{10}\right)^t$ ft^3

84. (a) No, x could equal 4.
    (b) Yes, consider the graph of $y = (\ln x)/x$ for $x > 0$.

90. $e - 1$ 91. $\frac{1}{3}$ 92. $\frac{3}{2}$

93. $\frac{1}{7}$ 94. $-\frac{1}{24}$ 95. ∞

96. 0   97. 0   98. 2

99. $\frac{1}{6}$ 100. $\ln 5 - 1$

Chapter 9

Article 9.1

1. $\frac{1}{3}(2x + 3)^{3/2} + C$ 2. $\frac{1}{3}\ln|3x + 5| + C$

3. $-1/(4x + 14) + C$ 4. $\frac{1}{2}\ln|x^2 + 2x + 3| + C$

5. $-\ln|2 + \cos x| + C$ 6. $\frac{1}{8}\tan^4 2x + C$

7. $-\frac{1}{4}\sqrt{1 - 4x^2} + C$ 8. $\frac{1}{2}(x^{4/3} - 1)^{3/2} + C$

9. $\dfrac{-1}{12(3x^2 + 4)^2} + C$ 10. $\frac{2}{9}(x^3 + 5)^{3/2} + C$

11. $\frac{2}{3}(x^3 + 5)^{1/2} + C$ 12. $\frac{1}{8}\ln(4x^2 + 1) + C$

13. $\frac{1}{2}e^{2x} + C$ 14. $-e^{\cos x} + C$

15. $-\frac{1}{3}e^{-3x} + C$ 16. $2e^{\sqrt{x+1}} + C$

17. $-\frac{1}{3}\cos^3 x + C$ 18. $-\frac{1}{2}\csc^2 x + C$

19. $-\frac{1}{4}\cot^4 x + C$ 20. $\frac{1}{6}\tan^2 3x + C$

21. $\frac{1}{2}\ln|e^{2x} - e^{-2x}| + C$ 22. $-\frac{1}{6}\cos^3 2x + C$

23. $-\frac{1}{4}(1 + \cos\theta)^4 + C$ 24. $-\frac{1}{2}e^{-t^2} + C$

25. $\ln|\sin x| + C$ 26. $\ln|1 + \sin x| + C$

27. $\frac{1}{3}\sec^3 x + C$ 28. $-2\sqrt{1 + \cos\theta} + C$

29. $\frac{1}{3}e^{\tan 3x} + C$ 30. $-\frac{1}{3}(4 - \sin 2t)^{3/2} + C$

31. $-\frac{1}{2}(\csc 2x + \cot 2x) + C$

32. $x - \frac{1}{2}\sin 2x + C$ 33. $-\sqrt{1 + \cot 2t} + C$

34. $\frac{1}{3}e^{3x} + C$ 35. $\frac{1}{2}e^{\tan^{-1} 2t} + C$

36. $-\frac{1}{2}e^{-x^2} + C$ 37. $3^x/(\ln 3) + C$

38. $10^{2x}/(2\ln 10) + C$

39. (a) -1, $\frac{1}{2}(\ln x)^2 + C$ (b) 2, $\frac{1}{3}e^{x^3} + C$
    (c) $-\frac{1}{2}$, $-2\cos\sqrt{x} + C$

Article 9.2

1. $-\frac{2}{3}(1 + \cos t)^{3/2} + C$ 2. $\ln|2 - \cos\theta| + C$

3. $\frac{1}{2}\ln|1 + \tan 2x| + C$ 4. $-\frac{1}{3}\ln|\cos 3x| + C$

5. $\sin x - \frac{1}{3}\sin^3 x + C$ 6. $\frac{1}{4}\tan 4\theta - \theta + C$

7. (a) $\frac{1}{5}\cos^5 x - \frac{1}{3}\cos^3 x + C$
    (b) $\cos x + \sec x + C$

8. $\dfrac{\sec^n x}{n} + C$ if $n \neq 0$,
    $\ln|\sec x| + C$ if $n = 0$

9. $\dfrac{\tan^{n+1} x}{n + 1} + C$ if $n \neq -1$,
    $\ln|\tan x| + C$ if $n = -1$

10. $\dfrac{\sin^{n+1} x}{n + 1} + C$ if $n \neq -1$,
    $\ln|\sin x| + C$ if $n = -1$

11. $\dfrac{-\cos^{n+1} x}{n + 1} + C$ if $n \neq -1$,
    $-\ln|\cos x| + C$ if $n = -1$

12. $\frac{1}{9}\sin^3 3x + C$ 13. $-\frac{1}{8}\cos^4 2x + C$

14. $\frac{1}{12}\sec^4 3x + C$

15. $\frac{1}{9}\tan^3 3x + \frac{1}{3}\tan 3x + C$

16. $\frac{1}{2}\sin 2x - \frac{1}{6}\sin^3 2x + C$

17. $\frac{1}{4}\tan^2 2x + \frac{1}{2}\ln|\cos 2x| + C$

18. $\frac{1}{3}\sec^3 x - \sec x + C$ 19. $\frac{1}{3}\cos^3 x - \cos x + C$

20. $-1/(1+\sin x) + C$ 21. $\ln|2+\tan x| + C$

22. $-\sin t - \csc t + C$ 23. $\ln|1+e^x| + C$

24. $\dfrac{(\ln ax)^{n+1}}{n+1} + C$ if $n \neq -1$, $\ln|\ln ax| + C$ if $n = -1$

25. $\ln|\ln 3x| + C$

26. $-\ln|\sin x| - \frac{1}{2}\cot^2 x + C$

27. $-\frac{1}{6}\csc^3 2t + C$ 28. $-\cot x - \frac{1}{3}\cot^3 x + C$

29. $\tan x + \tan^3 x/3 + C$ 30. $1/(1+\cos x) + C$

31. $1/(3\sin 3x) - 1/(9\sin^3 3x) + C$

32. $-1/(4\sin^4 u) + 1/(2\sin^2 u) + C$

33. $e^{\tan x} + C$

34. $\cot 2x - 1/\sin 2x - x + C$

35. $\tan 2x + 1/\cos 2x - x + C$

36. $-\dfrac{\cot^{n-1} ax}{(n-1)a} - \displaystyle\int \cot^{n-2} ax\, dx,$

     $-\dfrac{\cot^3 3x}{9} + \dfrac{\cot 3x}{3} + x + C$

Article 9.3

1. $\frac{1}{3}\sin^3 x - \frac{1}{5}\sin^5 x + C$ 2. $\cos x + \sec x + C$

3. $\frac{1}{2}t - \frac{1}{8}\sin 4t + C$ 4. $\frac{1}{2}\theta + \frac{1}{12}\sin 6\theta + C$

5. $\dfrac{3}{8}x - \dfrac{1}{4a}\sin 2ax + \dfrac{1}{32a}\sin 4ax + C$

6. $\frac{1}{8}y - \frac{1}{32}\sin 4y + C$ 7. $\tan x + C$

8. $-\frac{1}{3}\cot^3 x - \cot x + C$ 9. $-\frac{1}{6}\csc^3 2t + C$

10. $\frac{5}{16}x - \frac{1}{4}\sin 2x + \frac{3}{64}\sin 4x + \frac{1}{48}\sin^3 2x + C$

11. $-\cos^3 3x/9 + \cos^5 3x/15 + C$

12. $-\frac{1}{2}[\sin 2t + (1/\sin 2t)] + C$

13. $\frac{1}{3}\tan^3 x + C$ 14. $\frac{3}{5}\tan^{5/3}\theta + C$

15. $\frac{1}{10}\sin 10x + C$ 16. $\frac{1}{2}\sin 2t + \frac{1}{6}\sin^3 2t + C$

17. 2   18. -2

Article 9.4

1. $0.2a$ 2. $\frac{1}{2}\sin^{-1} 2x + C$

3. $\dfrac{\pi a^2}{4}$ 4. $\sin^{-1}\dfrac{x-1}{2} + C$

5. $\frac{1}{2}\ln|\sec 2t + \tan 2t| + C$

6. $\ln(1+\sqrt{2}) \approx 0.88$ 7. $\pi/6$

8. $\sqrt{4+x^2} + C$ 9. $\frac{1}{2}\ln 2$

10. $\pi/8$ 11. $\frac{1}{4}\ln 3 = 0.2747$

12. $-\ln|\csc u + \cot u| + C$

13. $\dfrac{1}{a}\ln\left|\dfrac{x}{a+\sqrt{a^2+x^2}}\right| + C$

14. $-\sqrt{4-x^2} + \sin^{-1}\dfrac{x}{2} + C$

15. $\dfrac{1}{\sqrt{5}}\sin^{-1}(x\sqrt{5}/2) + C$

16. $\cos^{-1}\left(\dfrac{\cos\theta}{\sqrt{2}}\right) + C$ 17. $\dfrac{1}{|a|}\sec^{-1}\left|\dfrac{x}{a}\right| + C$

18. $\dfrac{1}{a}\ln\left|\dfrac{x}{a+\sqrt{a^2-x^2}}\right| + C$

19. $\dfrac{1}{a^2}\left(\dfrac{x}{\sqrt{a^2-x^2}}\right) + C$

20. $\dfrac{1}{2a^3}\left(\tan^{-1}\dfrac{x}{a} + \dfrac{ax}{a^2+x^2}\right) + C$

Article 9.5

1. $\pi/8$

2. $\sqrt{x^2-2x+5} + \ln|x-1+\sqrt{x^2-2x+5}| + C$

3. $2\sin^{-1}(x-1) - \sqrt{2x-x^2} + C$

4. $\sqrt{x^2-4x+3} + \ln|x-2+\sqrt{x^2-4x+3}| + C$

5. $2\sin^{-1}\dfrac{x-2}{3} - \sqrt{5+4x-x^2} + C$

6. $\ln|x-1+\sqrt{x^2-2x-8}| + C$

7. $\sqrt{8+2x-x^2} + C$

8. $\sqrt{x^2+4x+5} - 2\ln|x+2+\sqrt{x^2+4x+5}| + C$

9. $\frac{1}{2}\ln(x^2+4x+5) - 2\tan^{-1}(x+2) + C$

10. $\frac{1}{4}\ln(4x^2+4x+5) + \frac{1}{2}\tan^{-1}(x+\frac{1}{2}) + C$

Article 9.6

1. $\frac{1}{6}\ln|(x+5)^5(x-1)| + C$

2. $\frac{3}{4}\ln|x-3| + \frac{1}{4}\ln|x+1| + C$

3. $\frac{2}{3}\ln|x+5| + \frac{1}{3}\ln|x-1| + C$

4. $x - 2 \ln |x + 1| - \dfrac{1}{x+1} + C$

5. $\ln \left| \dfrac{x}{x+1} \right| + \dfrac{1}{x+1} + C$

6. $\dfrac{1}{4} \ln \dfrac{(x+1)^2}{x^2+1} + \dfrac{1}{2} \tan^{-1} x + C$

7. $\dfrac{1}{2} \ln \dfrac{x^2}{x^2+x+1} - \dfrac{1}{\sqrt{3}} \tan^{-1} \dfrac{2x+1}{\sqrt{3}} + C$

8. $\dfrac{1}{3} \ln \dfrac{2 + \cos \theta}{1 - \cos \theta} + C$ 9. $\ln \dfrac{1 + e^t}{2 + e^t} + C$

10. $\dfrac{1}{2} \left(\tan^{-1} x + \dfrac{x}{1 + x^2} \right) + C$

11. $x - \dfrac{3}{2} \tan^{-1} x + \dfrac{1}{2} \dfrac{x}{(1 + x^2)} + C$

Article 9.7

1. $\dfrac{x^2}{2} \ln x - \dfrac{x^2}{4} + C$

2. $\dfrac{x^{n+1}}{n+1} \ln ax - \dfrac{x^{n+1}}{(n+1)^2} + C$

3. $\dfrac{x^2 + 1}{2} \tan^{-1} x - \dfrac{1}{2} x + C$

4. $x \sin^{-1} ax + \dfrac{1}{a} \sqrt{1 - a^2 x^2} + C$

5. $\dfrac{1}{a^2} \sin ax - \dfrac{1}{a} x \cos ax + C$

6. $\dfrac{2x}{a^2} \cos ax - \dfrac{2}{a^3} \sin ax + \dfrac{x^2}{a} \sin ax + C$

7. $\dfrac{x}{a} \tan ax - \dfrac{1}{a^2} \ln |\sec ax| + C$

8. $\dfrac{e^{ax}}{a^2 + b^2} (a \sin bx - b \cos bx) + C$

9. $(x/2)[\sin (\ln x) - \cos (\ln x)] + C$

10. $(x/2)[\sin (\ln x) + \cos (\ln x)] + C$

11. $x \ln (a^2 + x^2) - 2x + 2a \tan^{-1} (x/a) + C$

12. $(x/2) \sin (2x + 1) + \frac{1}{4} \cos (2x + 1) + C$

13. $\left(\dfrac{x^2}{2} - \dfrac{1}{4} \right) \sin^{-1} x + \dfrac{x}{4} \sqrt{1 - x^2} + C$

14. $\dfrac{4\pi - 3\sqrt{3}}{6}$

15. $\dfrac{4\pi - 3\sqrt{3}}{3}$

16. $\dfrac{x^3}{3} \tan^{-1} x - \dfrac{x^2}{6} + \dfrac{1}{6} \ln (x^2 + 1) + C$

17. (b) $\frac{1}{32} x^4 [8 (\ln x)^2 - 4 \ln x + 1] + C$

18. (b) $\pi/16$

19. (b) $(x^3 - 3x^2 + 6x - 6)e^x + C$

20. (b) $\frac{1}{2} (\sec x \tan x + \ln |\sec x + \tan x|) + C$

   (c) $\frac{1}{2} (x\sqrt{x^2 + a^2} + a^2 \ln |x + \sqrt{x^2 + a^2}|) + C$

21. $P(x) = 1 - 3x^2$

Article 9.8

1. 2 2. 1

3. $\tan x + \sec x + C$ 4. $\pi/3\sqrt{3}$

5. $\dfrac{4}{\sqrt{3}} \tan^{-1} \left(\sqrt{3} \tan \dfrac{x}{2} \right) - x + C$

6. $-\frac{2}{5}$ 7. 0 8. π

Article 9.9

1. $-x + 4\sqrt{x} - 4 \ln |1 + \sqrt{x}| + C$

2. $\dfrac{2\sqrt{x}}{b} - \dfrac{2a}{b^2} \ln |a + b\sqrt{x}| + C$

3. $\dfrac{2(x + a)^{3/2}}{105} (15x^2 - 12ax + 8a^2) + C$

4. $2\sqrt{x + a} - 2\sqrt{b - a} \tan^{-1} \sqrt{\dfrac{x + a}{b - a}} + C$

5. $\dfrac{b - a}{2} \left(\ln \left| \dfrac{u - 1}{u + 1} \right| - \dfrac{2u}{u^2 - 1} \right) + C$,

   where $u = \sqrt{\dfrac{a + x}{b + x}}$

6. $\dfrac{1}{2} \ln |x + \sqrt{x^2 + a^2}| + \dfrac{x\sqrt{a^2 + x^2} - x^2}{2a^2} + C$

7. $(3\sqrt{2} - 4)/2$ 8. $\dfrac{1}{nc} \ln \left| \dfrac{x^n}{ax^n + c} \right| + C$

9. $2 + 2 \ln \left(\frac{3}{2} \right)$ 10. $3 \ln |\sqrt[3]{x} - 1| + C$

11. $-1 + 4 \ln \left(\frac{3}{2} \right)$ 12. $4 \ln \left| \dfrac{\sqrt[4]{x}}{1 - \sqrt[4]{x}} \right| + C$

13. $\frac{3}{2} y^{2/3} + \ln |1 + y^{1/3}| - \frac{1}{2} \ln |y^{2/3} - y^{1/3} + 1|$

   $- \sqrt{3} \tan^{-1} \dfrac{2y^{1/3} - 1}{\sqrt{3}} + C$

14. $\frac{2}{9}(z^3 - 2)\sqrt{z^3 + 1} + C$

15. $\frac{2}{3}(\sqrt{t^3 - 1} - \tan^{-1}\sqrt{t^3 - 1}) + C$

16. $\ln\left(\frac{4}{3}\right)$ 17. $2 + 4\ln\left(\frac{2}{3}\right)$

18. $-\frac{1}{2}\ln|\sin x + \cos^2 x|$

$$-\frac{1}{2\sqrt{5}}\ln\left|\frac{2\sin x - 1 - \sqrt{5}}{2\sin x - 1 + \sqrt{5}}\right| + C$$

19. $\frac{1}{3}\ln|x + 1| - \frac{1}{6}\ln|x^2 - x + 1|$

$$+ \frac{1}{\sqrt{3}}\tan^{-1}\frac{2x - 1}{\sqrt{3}} + C$$

20. $-2y^{1/2} - 3y^{1/3} - 6y^{1/6} - 6\ln|y^{1/6} - 1| + C$

Article 9.10

1. $\pi/2$ 2. 2   3. 6
4. 1000   5. 4   6. $\pi/2$
7. $\frac{1}{2}$ 8. 1000   9. Diverges
10. Converges   11. Converges   12. Diverges
13. Converges   14. Converges   15. Diverges
16. Diverges   17. Converges   18. Diverges
19. Converges

Article 9.11

1. $\frac{8}{3}$, $\frac{8}{3}$, $\frac{8}{3}$ 2. $2\pi/3$, $(1 + 2\sqrt{2})\pi/6$, 2
3. $2\pi/3$, 2.28   4. $5\pi/9$, 1.8, $\pi/\sqrt{3}$
5. 1.86, 1.85   6. 0.78, 0.785

Miscellaneous exercises

1. $2\sqrt{1 + \sin x} + C$ 2. $(\sin^{-1} x)^2/2 + C$
3. $(\tan^2 x)/2 + C$ 4. $\tan x + \sec x + C$
5. $(2x^{3/2})/3 + C$ 6. $2\sin\sqrt{x} + C$
7. $\ln|x + 1 + \sqrt{x^2 + 2x + 2}| + C$
8. $\ln|(x - 2)(x - 3)/(x - 1)^2| + C$
9. $(x^2 - 2x + 2)e^x + C$
10. $\frac{1}{2}(\ln|x + \sqrt{x^2 + 1}| + x\sqrt{1 + x^2}) + C$
11. $\tan^{-1}(e^t) + C$ 12. $\tan^{-1}(e^x) + C$
13. $2\sqrt{x} - 2\ln(1 + \sqrt{x}) + C$
14. $\frac{4}{3}(\sqrt{x} - 2)\sqrt{1 + \sqrt{x}} + C$
15. $\frac{9}{25}(t^{5/3} + 1)^{5/3} + C$ 16. $\ln|\ln\sin x| + C$
17. $\ln\dfrac{\sqrt{1 + e^t} - 1}{\sqrt{1 + e^t} + 1} + C$

18. $t + 2\ln(1 + \sqrt{1 - e^{-t}}) + C$

19. $e^{\sec x} + C$ 20. $\tan^{-1}(\sin x) + C$
21. $\sin^{-1}(x - 1) + C$ 22. $\cot^{-1}(\cos x) + C$
23. $\frac{1}{2}\ln|1 + \sin 2t| + C$ 24. $\ln|\tan x| + C$
25. $(-2\cos x)/\sqrt{1 + \sin x} + C$
26. $(2\cos x)/\sqrt{1 - \sin x} + C$
27. $x/(a^2\sqrt{a^2 - x^2}) + C$ 28. $x/(a^2\sqrt{a^2 + x^2}) + C$
29. $\frac{1}{3}\ln\dfrac{1 - \cos x}{4 - \cos x} + C$
30. $\frac{3}{10}(2e^x - 3)(1 + e^x)^{2/3} + C$
31. $\displaystyle\sum_{k=0}^{m}\frac{(-1)^k}{k!(m - k)!}\ln|x + k| + C$
32. $\dfrac{1}{12}\ln\dfrac{(x - 1)^2(x^2 - x + 1)}{(x + 1)^2(x^2 + x + 1)}$

$$-\frac{\sqrt{3}}{6}\tan^{-1}\left(\frac{x\sqrt{3}}{1 - x^2}\right) + C$$

33. $\frac{1}{3}[(2y^3 + 1)^{-1} + \ln|2y^3/(2y^3 + 1)|] + C$
34. $\frac{2}{3}x^{3/2} - x + 2x^{1/2} - 2\ln(1 + x^{1/2}) + C$
35. $\frac{1}{2}[\ln x^2 - \ln(1 + x^2) - x^2(1 + x^2)^{-1}] + C$
36. $(x - 1)\ln\sqrt{x - 1} - (x/2) + C$
37. $\ln|e^x - 1| - x + C$
38. $\dfrac{1}{4}\ln\left|\dfrac{1 + \tan\theta}{1 - \tan\theta}\right| + \dfrac{1}{2}\theta + C$
39. $x^{-1} + 2\ln|1 - x^{-1}| + C$
40. $\frac{1}{2}\ln|(x + 3)^3(x + 1)^{-1}| + C$
41. $-\dfrac{1}{2}\dfrac{1}{e^{2u} - 1} + C$
42. $\ln|x/\sqrt{x^2 + 4}| + C$
43. $\frac{1}{3}\tan^{-1}[(5x + 4)/3] + C$
44. $\sqrt{x^2 - a^2} - a\tan^{-1}(\sqrt{x^2 - a^2}/a) + C$
45. $e^x(\cos 2x + 2\sin 2x)/5 + C$
46. $\ln x - 2\ln(1 + 3\sqrt{x}) + C$
47. $\ln|x| - 3\ln|1 + \sqrt[3]{x}| + C$
48. $\ln|\sin\theta| - \frac{1}{2}\ln(1 + \sin^2\theta) + C$
49. $\frac{1}{15}(8 - 4z^2 + 3z^4)(1 + z^2)^{1/2} + C$
50. $\frac{3}{8}(e^{2t} - 3)(1 + e^{2t})^{1/3} + C$
51. $\frac{5}{2}(1 + x^{4/5})^{1/2} + C$ 52. $x\tan x + \ln|\cos x| + C$
53. $\frac{1}{4}[(2x^2 - 1)\sin^{-1} x + x\sqrt{1 - x^2}] + C$

54. $\dfrac{x^2}{2}+\dfrac{4}{3}\ln|x+2|+\dfrac{2}{3}\ln|x-1|+C$

55. $x+\ln|(x-1)/x|+C$

56. $\ln|x-1|-(x-1)^{-1}+C$

57. $\dfrac{2}{3}(3e^{2x}-6e^x-1)^{1/2}$
$+\dfrac{1}{\sqrt{3}}\ln|e^x-1+\sqrt{e^{2x}-2e^x-\tfrac{1}{3}}|+C$

58. $\dfrac{3}{2}(x^2+2x-3)^{1/3}+C$ 59. $\tan^{-1}(2\sqrt{y^2+y})+C$

60. $-\sqrt{a^2-x^2}/a^2x+C$

61. $\dfrac{3}{8}\sin^{-1}x+\dfrac{1}{8}(5x-2x^3)\sqrt{1-x^2}+C$

62. $x\ln(x+\sqrt{1+x^2})-\sqrt{1+x^2}+C$

63. $x\tan x-(x^2/2)+\ln|\cos x|+C$

64. $-(\tan^{-1}x)/x+\ln|x|-\ln\sqrt{1+x^2}+C$

65. $\dfrac{x^2}{4}+\dfrac{x\sin 2x}{4}+\dfrac{\cos 2x}{8}+C$

66. $-x^2\cos x+2x\sin x+2\cos x+C$

67. $\dfrac{x^2}{4}-\dfrac{x\sin 2x}{4}-\dfrac{\cos 2x}{8}+C$

68. $\dfrac{1}{2}\tan^{-1}t-\dfrac{1}{2\sqrt{3}}\tan^{-1}\left(\dfrac{t}{\sqrt{3}}\right)+C$

69. $\dfrac{1}{12}[4u-3\ln(1+e^{2u})+\ln(3+e^{2u})]+C$

70. $\dfrac{1}{4}(x^2-4)\ln(x+2)-x^2/8+x/2+C$

71. $(x^2+1)e^x+C$

72. $x\sec^{-1}x-\ln(|x|+\sqrt{x^2-1})+C$

73. $-2x^{-2}+2x^{-1}+\ln|x/(x+2)|+C$

74. $\dfrac{1}{16}\ln|(x^2-4)/(x^2+4)|+C$

75. $2-\sqrt{2}\ln(1+\sqrt{2})$ 76. $\ln|\cot x|+C$

77. $-\dfrac{1}{2}\dfrac{1}{e^{2u}+1}+C$

78. $x-2\sqrt{x}+\dfrac{4}{\sqrt{3}}\tan^{-1}\left(\dfrac{1+2\sqrt{x}}{\sqrt{3}}\right)+C$

79. $\ln|\tan t-2|-\ln|\tan t-1|+C$

80. $-t+\sqrt{2}\tan^{-1}(\sqrt{2}\tan t)+C$

81. $\dfrac{1}{\sqrt{2}}\tan^{-1}\left(\dfrac{\tan x}{\sqrt{2}}\right)+C$

82. $e^t\sin(e^t)+\cos(e^t)+C$

83. $x\ln\sqrt{x^2+1}-x+\tan^{-1}x+C$

84. $\dfrac{1}{2}x^2\ln(x^3+x)-\dfrac{3}{4}x^2+\dfrac{1}{2}\ln(x^2+1)+C$

85. $\dfrac{1}{2}(x^2-1)e^{x^2}+C$

86. $\ln|\sin x+\sqrt{3+\sin^2 x}|+C$

87. $\sin^{-1}(3^{-1/2}\tan x)+C$

88. $(x^2-2)\cos(1-x)+2x\sin(1-x)+C$

89. $\tan x-\sec x+C$

90. $3^{-1/2}[\ln|1+2\sin x|$
$-\ln|2+\sin x+\sqrt{3}\cos x|]+C$

91. $-\dfrac{1}{2}\cot x\csc x+\dfrac{1}{4}\ln\dfrac{1-\cos x}{1+\cos x}+C$

92. $\dfrac{1}{2}\tan^2 x+\ln|\cos x|+C$

93. $x(\sin^{-1}x)^2-2x+2\sqrt{1-x^2}\sin^{-1}x+C$

94. $\dfrac{1}{54}(9x^2-1)\ln|3x+1|-x^2/12+x/18+C$

95. $\dfrac{1}{2}\ln(x^2+1)+\dfrac{1}{2}(x^2+1)^{-1}+C$

96. $-\dfrac{2}{3}(x+2)\sqrt{1-x}+C$

97. $\dfrac{1}{15}(3x-1)(2x+1)^{3/2}+C$

98. $x\ln(x+\sqrt{x^2-1})-\sqrt{x^2-1}+C$

99. $x\ln(x-\sqrt{x^2-1})+\sqrt{x^2-1}+C$

100. $\dfrac{1}{2}\ln|t-\sqrt{1-t^2}|-\dfrac{1}{2}\sin^{-1}t+C$

101. $x-e^{-x}\tan^{-1}(e^x)-\dfrac{1}{2}\ln(1+e^{2x})+C$

102. $\dfrac{1}{2}(x-x^2)^{1/2}-\dfrac{1}{2}(1-2x)\sin^{-1}\sqrt{x}+C$

103. $x\ln(x+\sqrt{x})-x+\sqrt{x}-\ln(1+\sqrt{x})+C$

104. $(x+1)\tan^{-1}\sqrt{x}-\sqrt{x}+C$

105. $x\ln(x^2+x)+\ln(x+1)-2x+C$

106. $(x+\dfrac{1}{2})\ln(\sqrt{x}+\sqrt{1+x})-\dfrac{1}{2}\sqrt{x^2+x}+C$

107. $2\sqrt{x}\sin\sqrt{x}+2\cos\sqrt{x}+C$

108. $-2\sqrt{x}\cos\sqrt{x}+2\sin\sqrt{x}+C$

109. $(x+2)\tan^{-1}\sqrt{x+1}-\sqrt{x+1}+C$

110. $\dfrac{1}{4}(\sin^{-1}x)^2+\dfrac{1}{2}x\sqrt{1-x^2}\sin^{-1}x-x^2/4+C$

111. $\dfrac{1}{4}x^2-\dfrac{1}{8}x\sin 4x-\dfrac{1}{32}\cos 4x+C$

112. $\sec x-\tan x+x+C$

113. $\ln(\sqrt{e^{2t}+1}-1)-t+C$

114. $\ln[(1-\sin x)^{1/2}(1+\sin x)^{-1/18}(2-\sin x)^{-4/9}]$
$+1/(6-3\sin x)+C$

115. $\dfrac{1}{ac}\ln\left|\dfrac{e^{ct}}{a+be^{ct}}\right|+C$

116. $-2\sin^{-1}\left[\dfrac{\cos(x/2)}{\cos(\alpha/2)}\right]+C$

117. $\frac{1}{\sqrt{2}} \ln \left| \csc \left(x - \frac{\pi}{4} \right) - \cot \left(x - \frac{\pi}{4} \right) \right| + C$

118. $x \ln \sqrt{1 + x^2} - x + \tan^{-1} x + C$

119. $x \ln (2x^2 + 4) + 2\sqrt{2} \tan^{-1} (x/\sqrt{2}) - 2x + C$

120. $-\frac{1}{3}(1 - x^2)^{1/2}(2 + x^2) + C$

121. $\ln |2 + \ln x| + C$

122. $x - \tan x + C$

123. $\frac{1}{3} \ln |x + 1| - \frac{1}{6} \ln (x^2 - x + 1)$
$$+ \frac{1}{\sqrt{3}} \tan^{-1} \frac{2x - 1}{\sqrt{3}} + C$$

124. $\frac{4}{21}(e^x + 1)^{3/4}(3e^x - 4) + C$

125. $\tan^{-1} (e^x) + C$

126. $2e^{\sqrt{t}}(\sqrt{t} - 1) + C$

127. $-2\sqrt{x+1} \cos \sqrt{x+1} + 2 \sin \sqrt{x+1} + C$

128. $-2\sqrt{1-x} \sin \sqrt{1-x} - 2 \cos \sqrt{1-x} + C$

129. $\ln 2$ 130. $2\sqrt{2} - 2$ 131. $2/\pi$

132. $e - 1$ 133. $\pi/4$ 134. $2 \ln 2 - 1$

135. $\pi/2$ 136. $1/2$ 137. -1

139. e^{-4}

140. $4p^2(2\sqrt{2} - 1)/3$

141. Area $(\pi - 2)r^2/4$, centroid $2r\sqrt{2}/(3\pi - 6)$ from center.

142. $[1/(2e - 4), (e^2 - 3)/(4e - 8)] \approx (0.7, 1.5)$

143. $2\pi^2 k r^2$

144. $w(3e^8 - 20e^4 + 9)/4 \approx 123{,}000$ lb

145. Only V is finite; integrals for A and for S diverge.

146. $A = e^{-1}$, $V = \pi/(2e^2)$,
$$S = \pi[e^{-1}\sqrt{1 + e^{-2}} + \ln (e^{-1} + \sqrt{e^{-2} + 1})]$$

147. $(0.58, 0.93)$ 148. $(1.53, 0.696)$

149. About 2   150. About 23

151. About 6.8   152. About 175

153. $2\pi[\sqrt{2} + \ln (1 + \sqrt{2})] \approx 14.4$

154. About 3.82

155. $(0, 0.6)$ for arch $|x| \leq \pi/2$

156. 2π 157. $6a$

158. $\ln (2 + \sqrt{3}) \approx 1.32$ 159. $12\pi a^2/5$

160. $(2a/5, 2a/5)$ for first-quadrant arch

161. Converges, compare with $\displaystyle\int_1^{\infty} x^{-3/2} \, dx$.

162. (c) $1 - e^{-e^b}$ 164. Converges
    (d) 1

165. $x = a \cos kt$ 166. $\frac{1}{2}$

Chapter 10

Article 10.1

Note. The answer for each exercise in this article is accompanied by an appropriately numbered figure.

1. (a) About the x-axis
   (b) No curve for $0 < x < 2$
   (c) $(0, 0)$, $(2, 0)$ (e) ∞

2. (a) About the x-axis
   (b) No curve for $0 < x \leq 2$
   (c) $(0, 0)$ (d) $y = \pm 1$, $x = 2$ (e) ∞

3. (a) About both axes, the origin, and the line $y = x$
   (b) Curve is inside the square $|x| \leq 1$, $|y| \leq 1$
   (c) $(0, \pm 1)$, $(\pm 1, 0)$
   (e) Slope is 0 at $(0, \pm 1)$, ∞ at $(\pm 1, 0)$

4. (a) About both axes, and the origin
   (b) No curve for $|y| \geq 1$. No curve for $|x| < 1$
   (c) $(\pm 1, 0)$ (d) $y = \pm 1$ (e) ∞

5. (a) About both axes, the origin, and $y = x$
   (b) No curve for $|y| \leq 1$. No curve for $|x| \leq 1$
   (c) No intercepts   (d) $x = \pm 1$, $y = \pm 1$

6. (a) About the origin   (b) No curve for $|y| < 2$
   (c) No intercepts
   (d) $x = 0$; $y = x$ is also an asymptote.
   (e) Low point at $(1, 2)$, high point at $(-1, -2)$

7. (a) About the y-axis
   (b) Curve is confined to $y \geq 1$
   (c) $(0, 1)$ (e) 0

8. (a) About the y-axis   (b) $0 < y \leq 1$
   (c) $(0, 1)$ (d) $y = 0$ (e) 0

9. (a) About the y-axis   (b) $y \geq -1$
   (c) $(0, -1)$, $(\pm 1, 0)$ (e) 0, ± 2

10. (a) About the y-axis
    (b) No curve for $-1 < y \leq 0$
    (c) $(0, -1)$ (d) $x = \pm 1$, $y = 0$ (e) 0

$y^2 = x(x-2)$

$(0, 0)$ $(2, 0)$

10.1.1

$y^2 = \dfrac{x}{x-2}$

10.1.2

$x^4 + y^4 = 1$

$(0, 1)$

O $(1, 0)$

10.1.3

$x^2 = \dfrac{1+y^2}{1-y^2}$

10.1.4

$x^2 = \dfrac{y^2+1}{y^2-1}$

10.1.5

$y = x + \dfrac{1}{x}$

$(1, 2)$

$(-1, -2)$

10.1.6

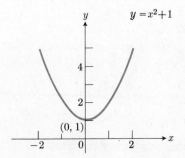

$y = x^2 + 1$

$(0, 1)$

10.1.7

$y = \dfrac{1}{x^2+1}$

$(0, 1)$

10.1.8

$y = x^2 - 1$

$(2, 3)$

$(-1, 0)$ $(1, 0)$

$(0, -1)$

10.1.9

$y = \dfrac{1}{x^2-1}$

$(0, -1)$

10.1.10

Article 10.2

1. $x + y + 1 = 0$ 2. $x + 2y = 7$

3. $6x - y = 14$, $y - 6x = 18$

4. $2x + y = \pm 3$ 7. Yes; $(-2, -8)$

8. $(-1, -1)$. No, because

$$2x_1^3 - 3x_1^2 + 5 = 0,$$

and this equation has only one real root.

9. $2x + 3y = \pm 12$

10. $x + y = 1$, $4x + y = -2$

11. $(-\frac{13}{4}, \frac{17}{16})$ 15. ± 16 16. $\pm 1/\sqrt{3}$

17. $A = \tan^{-1} \frac{5}{3}$, $B = \tan^{-1} 5$, $C = \tan^{-1} \frac{10}{11}$

21. (a) $45°$ (b) $\tan^{-1} 3$
    (c) $\tan^{-1} (5/\sqrt{3})$ (d) $\tan^{-1} (\frac{14}{3})$

Article 10.3

1. 0.618   2. 0.682   3. 1.165

4. 1.189   5. -1.189 6. 3

7. $x_1 = x_2 = x_3$, etc.

9. $m_1 = (q - 1)/q$, $m_2 = 1/q$

12. Yes, they may get worse.

Article 10.4

1. $x - y = 1$ 2. $x^2 + y^2 - 6x + 5 = 0$

3. $(x^2 + y^2)^2 + 8(y^2 - x^2) = 0$

4. $3x^2 + 3y^2 + 2xy - 4x - 4y = 0$

5. $3x^2 + 4y^2 - 20x + 12 = 0$

6. $5x^2 - 4y^2 = 20$ (right half only)

7. $x^2 = 10 - 2y + 6|y - 1|$

8. $x^2 + y^2 - 4x - 6y + 4 = 0$,

or $\begin{cases} x^2 = 4y + 4 & \text{when } y \geq 1, \\ x^2 = 16 - 8y & \text{when } y < 1 \end{cases}$

9. $(2, 2)$, $\sqrt{5}$ 10. $\dfrac{|Ax_1 + By_1 + C|}{\sqrt{A^2 + B^2}}$

Article 10.5

1. $x^2 + y^2 - 4y = 0$ 2. $x^2 + y^2 + 4x = 5$

3. $x^2 + y^2 - 6x + 8y = 0$

4. $x^2 + y^2 - 2x - 2y = 0$

5. $x^2 + y^2 + 4x + 2y = 1$

6. $x^2 + y^2 + 8x - 4y + 4 = 0$

7. $(0, 1)$, 2   8. $(-1, 0)$, 3

9. $(-1, 0)$, $2/\sqrt{3}$ 10. $(-\frac{1}{4}, -\frac{1}{4})$, $1/(2\sqrt{2})$

11. $(-1, 2)$, 0

12. No real locus, radius becomes imaginary.

13. $x^2 + y^2 - 4x - 4y = 5$

14. $5x^2 + 5y^2 + 10x - 10y + 1 = 0$

15. $(x - 0.7)^2 + (y - 1.3)^2 = 12.58$

17. $x^2 + y^2 + 2x + 2y - 23 = 0$

18. Circle, center $(-2, 3)$, radius 4

19. Center $(1, 2)$, radius $\sqrt{2}$
    Distance of $(0.1, 3.1)$ from center is $\sqrt{2.02}$.
    Point is outside the circle.

20. Center $(-2, 4)$, radius $2\sqrt{5}$

21. Center $(-1, 1)$, radius 5

24. (a) $C_1 = -2h$, $C_2 = -2k$, $C_3 = h^2 + k^2 - r^2$

(b) $h = -\dfrac{C_1}{2}$, $k = -\dfrac{C_2}{2}$, $r = \sqrt{\dfrac{C_1^2 + C_2^2 - 4C_3}{4}}$

Article 10.6

1. $x^2 = 8y$, $y = -2$ 2. $y^2 = -8x$, $x = 2$

3. $(x + 2)^2 = 4(y - 3)$, $y = 2$

4. $(y - 3)^2 = -4x$, $x = 1$

5. $(y - 1)^2 = 12(x + 3)$, $x = -6$

6. $(x - 1)^2 = 12(y + 3)$, $y = -6$

7. $y^2 = 8(x - 2)$, $F(4, 0)$

8. $(x - 1)^2 = -8(y + 2)$, $F(1, -4)$

9. $(y - 1)^2 = -16(x + 3)$, $F(-7, 1)$

10. $(x + 2)^2 = 4(y + 2)$, $F(-2, -1)$

11. $(y - 1)^2 = 4x$, $F(1, 1)$

12. $x^2 = -4(y - 1)$, $F(0, 0)$

13. $V(1, 1)$, $x = 1$, $F(1, -1)$, $y = 3$

14. $V(-4, -3)$, $x = -4$, $F(-4, -\frac{5}{2})$, $y = -\frac{7}{2}$

15. $V(2, 0)$, $y = 0$, $F(1, 0)$, $x = 3$

16. $V(0, -\frac{1}{2})$, $x = 0$, $F(0, \frac{3}{2})$, $y = -\frac{5}{2}$

17. $V(-1, -1)$, $x = -1$, $F(-1, 0)$, $y = -2$

18. $V(\frac{1}{4}, -\frac{1}{2})$, $y = -\frac{1}{2}$, $F(0, -\frac{1}{2})$, $x = \frac{1}{2}$

19. $V(2, 1)$, $y = 1$, $F(\frac{29}{16}, 1)$, $x = \frac{35}{16}$

20. $V(2, -3)$, $y = -3$, $F(\frac{3}{2}, -3)$, $x = \frac{5}{2}$

21. $V(2, -2)$, $x = 2$, $F(2, -\frac{4}{3})$, $y = -\frac{8}{3}$

22. $V(-3, -1)$, $y = -1$, $F(-\frac{21}{8}, -1)$, $x = -\frac{27}{8}$

23. Points above parabola $x^2 = 8y$

26. $(x - y)^2 - 8(x + y) + 16 = 0$

27. $b^2 y = 4hx(b - x)$

28. (a) $7y^2 - 3y + 6x - 16 = 0$
    (b) $7x^2 - 9x - 6y - 4 = 0$

30. The product is zero if and only if at least one factor is zero. Locus is the line $2x + y - 3 = 0$, the circle $x^2 + y^2 - 4 = 0$, and the parabola $x^2 - 8y = 0$.

Article 10.7

1. $x^2/12 + y^2/16 = 1$, $e = \frac{1}{2}$

2. $x^2/25 + y^2/16 = 1$, $e = \frac{3}{5}$

3. $9x^2 + 5(y - 2)^2 = 45$, $e = \frac{2}{3}$

4. $(x + 3)^2/12 + y^2/16 = 1$, $e = \frac{1}{2}$

5. $(x - 2)^2 + 10(y - 2)^2 = 10$, $e = 3/\sqrt{10}$

6. $9(x - 1)^2 + 4(y - 4)^2 = 36$, $F(1, 4 \pm \sqrt{5})$

7. $(2, -3)$, $(2, 2)$ and $(2, -8)$, $(2, 1)$ and $(2, -7)$

9. $x^2 + 2y^2 - 4y = 0$ 10. $e = \frac{3}{4}$, $y = \pm\frac{16}{3}$

11. $\frac{4}{3}\pi ab^2$

12. (a) $\displaystyle\int_0^a \sqrt{a^2 - x^2}\, dx\ (= \tfrac{1}{4}\pi a^2$ for $\frac{1}{4}$ of a circle)

    (b) $\displaystyle\frac{b}{a}\int_0^a \sqrt{a^2 - x^2}\, dx$. Area of ellipse $= \pi ab$.

14. $2b^2/a$ 15. $5x^2 + 9y^2 = 180$

16. $A = C = 0$, $B = -4$

18. Interior of ellipse $9x^2 + 16y^2 = 144$

19. Graph consists of parabola $x^2 + 4y = 0$, straight line $2x - y - 3 = 0$, circle $x^2 + y^2 - 25 = 0$, ellipse $x^2 + 4y^2 - 4 = 0$.

20. One factor must be positive, the other negative. Graph consists of region between circle $x^2 + y^2 = 1$ and ellipse $9x^2 + 4y^2 = 36$.

Article 10.8

2. $C(2, -3)$, $V(2 \pm 2, -3)$, $F(2 \pm \sqrt{13}, -3)$
   $A: 3(x - 2) = \pm 2(y + 3)$

3. $C(2, -3)$, $V(2 \pm 3, -3)$, $F(2 \pm \sqrt{13}, -3)$
   $A: 2(x - 2) = \pm 3(y + 3)$

4. $C(2, -3)$, $V(2, -3 \pm \frac{1}{2})$, $F(2, -3 \pm \sqrt{13}/6)$
   $A: 2(y + 3) = \pm 3(x - 2)$

5. $C(-2, 1)$, $V(-2 \pm 2, 1)$, $F(-2 \pm 3, 1)$
   $A: \sqrt{5}(x + 2) = \pm 2(y - 1)$

6. $C(0, 2)$, $V(\pm 1, 2)$, $F(\pm\sqrt{5}, 2)$
   $A: 2x = \pm(y - 2)$

7. $C(2, 0)$, $V(2 \pm 2, 0)$, $F(2 \pm \sqrt{5}, 0)$
   $A: x - 2 = \pm 2y$

8. $C(2, 1)$, $V(2, 1 \pm 2)$, $F(2, 1 \pm 3)$
   $A: 2(x - 2) = \pm\sqrt{5}(y - 1)$

10. $\frac{4}{3}\pi(b^4/a)$ 12. $x^2 - 3y^2 + 12y = 9$

13. $4x^2 - 5y^2 - 8x + 60y + 4 = 0$

Article 10.9

2. $15x^2 + 13y^2 - 2\sqrt{3}xy - 14\sqrt{3}y + 18x = 33$, $60°$

7. $2y'^2 = 1$ 8. $4x'^2 + 2y'^2 = 19$

9. $5y'^2 - x'^2 = 10$ 10. $5x'^2 - 3y'^2 = 7$

Article 10.10

1. Ellipse   2. Hyperbola   3. Parabola

4. Circle   5. Hyperbola   6. Parabola

7. Hyperbola   8. Ellipse   9. Ellipse

10. After rotation of axes to a form with $B' = 0$, we have $A' = 1/a^2$, $C' = 1/b^2$. Then $B'^2 - 4A'C' = -4/(a^2 b^2)$; hence

$$\pi ab = 2\pi/\sqrt{4A'C' - B'^2} = 2\pi/\sqrt{4AC - B^2}.$$

12. If $C = -A$, then $A + C = A' + C' = 0$ and $C' = -A'$. Hence $A' = C' = 0$ if $\tan 2\alpha = -2A/B$, by Eqs. (6), Article 10.9.

Article 10.11

3. Line L and the point D do not exist.

4. $(1 - e^2)x^2 + y^2 - 2pe^2 x - p^2 e^2 = 0$

Miscellaneous exercises

1. (a) A. Symmetric about the x-axis
      B. $0 \le x \le 4$, $-2 \le y \le 2$
      C. $(0, 0)$, $(4, 0)$
      D. None
      E. ∞ at both intercepts

   (b) A. Symmetric about the x-axis
      B. $x \le 0$, $x \ge 4$, all y
      C. $(0, 0)$, $(4, 0)$
      D. Asymptotic to $y = \pm(x - 2)$
      E. ∞ at both intercepts

   (c) A. Symmetric about the x-axis
      B. $0 \le x < 4$, all y
      C. $(0, 0)$
      D. Asymptotic to $x = 4$
      E. ∞ at $(0, 0)$

2. (a) A. None
   B. All y, $|x| > 0$
   C. $(-1, 0)$
   D. $y = x$, $x = 0$
   E. 3

   (b) A. Symmetric about the x-axis
   B. All y, $-1 \leq x < 0$, $x > 0$
   C. $(-1, 0)$
   D. $x = 0$
   E. ∞

   (c) A. None
   B. All y, $|x| > 0$
   C. $(-1, 0)$
   D. $x = 0$
   E. -3

3. (a) A. None
   B. All y, all x
   C. $(0, 0)$, $(-1, 0)$, $(2, 0)$
   D. None
   E. -2 at $(0, 0)$, 3 at $(-1, 0)$, 6 at $(2, 0)$

   (b) A. Symmetric about the x-axis
   B. All y, $-1 \leq x \leq 0$, $x \geq 2$
   C. $(0, 0)$, $(-1, 0)$, $(2, 0)$
   D. None
   E. ∞ at all intercepts

4. (a) A. Symmetric about the y-axis
   B. All x, $0 < y \leq 2$
   C. $(0, 2)$
   D. $y = 0$
   E. 0

   (b) A. Symmetric about the y-axis
   B. $y < 0$, $y \geq 2$, $x^2 \neq 4$
   C. $(0, 2)$
   D. $y = 0$, $x = \pm 2$
   E. 0

   (c) A. Symmetric about the origin
   B. $|y| \leq 2$, all x
   C. $(0, 0)$
   D. $y = 0$
   E. 2

5. (a) A. Symmetric about the origin
   B. $|y| \geq 2$, $|x| > 0$
   C. None
   D. $y = x$, $x = 0$
   E. ———

   (b) A. About $(1, 2)$
   B. $y \leq 0$, $y \geq 4$, $x \neq 1$

   C. $(0, 0)$
   D. $x = 1$, $y = x + 1$
   E. 0
   Remark: Translate axes to new origin at $(1, 2)$; becomes same as 5(a).

6. (a) A. Symmetric about both axes and the origin
   B. All y, $|x| \geq 1$ and $x = 0$
   C. $(0, 0)$, $(-1, 0)$, $(1, 0)$
   D. None
   E. ∞ at $(\pm 1, 0)$. No derivative exists at the isolated point $(0, 0)$.

   (b) A. Symmetric about the x-axis
   B. $x \leq 1$, $x > 2$, $y^2 \neq 1$
   C. $(0, \pm\sqrt{2}/2)$, $(1, 0)$
   D. $y = \pm 1$, $x = 2$
   E. $\mp\sqrt{2}/8$ at $(0, \pm\sqrt{2}/2)$, ∞ at $(1, 0)$

7. A. None
   B. $y \leq 4 - 2\sqrt{3}$, $y \geq 4 + 2\sqrt{3}$, $x^2 \neq 1$
   C. $(0, 8)$, $(2, 0)$
   D. $x = \pm 1$, $y = 0$
   E. -4 at $(0, 8)$, $\frac{4}{3}$ at $(2, 0)$

8. A. Symmetric about the y-axis
   B. $y \leq -1$, $y > 1$, $x^2 \neq 1$
   C. $(0, -1)$
   D. $x = \pm 1$, $y = 1$
   E. 0

9. A. Symmetric about the origin
   B. $|x| \leq 2$, $|y| \leq 2$
   C. $(0, \pm\sqrt{3})$, $(\pm\sqrt{3}, 0)$
   D. None
   E. $-\frac{1}{2}$ at $(0, \pm\sqrt{3})$, -2 at $(\pm\sqrt{3}, 0)$

10. $x^2 + xy + y^2 = 3k^2$

12. $a = c = d = e = 1$, $b = f = g = 0$

14. $y + 2x = 6$

16. $y = 6x - 14$, $y = 6x + 18$

18. (b) $1:1$

21. $5x^2 + 5y^2 = 4x + 8y$ 23. $x = 2pm$

24. $Q(4p^3/y_1^2, -4p^2/y_1)$ 25. $(\pm\frac{8}{9}\sqrt{3}, \frac{4}{3})$

27. $(-2, 1)$, $(2, -1)$

28. $27x - 3y + 56 = 0$, $27x - 3y - 104 = 0$

30. $r = 2.56$, center $(4, 1.61)$. Results are approximate and are based on 1.55 as positive root of
$$x^4 + 4x - 12 = 0.$$

31. $(-\frac{16}{5}, \frac{53}{10})$

32. (a) A conic passing through the points of intersection of the three lines, and tangent to the lines $L_1 + hL_3 = 0$, $L_2 + kL_3 = 0$, $hL_2 + kL_1 = 0$

  (b) $3x^2 + 3y^2 - 8x - 16y + 20 = 0$

  (c) $2y = 3x^2 - 4x + 4$

33. 10^7 mi   34. $\pi/2$

35. $y^2 = 2x - 7$ 36. $(5, 10\sqrt{10}/3)$

38. $3x^2 + 3y^2 - 16y + 16 = 0$,   circle

40. Locus consists of circle $x^2 + y^2 = 9$ and hyperbola $y^2 - x^2 = 9$.

41. No. For points inside the circle, $x^2 + (y^2 - 9)$ is negative while $x^2 - (y^2 - 9)$ is positive, so their product cannot equal 1.

43. $5x^2 + 9y^2 - 30x = 0$

44. (a) $F_1P = 5$, $F_2P = \sqrt{5}$

  (b) Outside, since

$$OF_1 + OF_2 = 8 > F_1P + F_2P = 5 + \sqrt{5}$$

45. $2ab$ 47. $x^2 + 4xy + 5y^2 = 1$

48. $(x + 3)^2/36 + (y - 1)^2/20 = 1$

50. $x^2 - y^2 = 4$

51. Center at $(\frac{1}{2}\sqrt{2}, 0)$, $e = \sqrt{2}$

52. *Hint.* Eliminate λ^2 and obtain the differential equation

$$xy(y')^2 + (x^2 - y^2 - c^2)y' - xy = 0$$

for both families. The product of the roots $y' = m_1$ and $y' = m_2$ is $m_1 m_2 = -1$.

53. Square, area $= 2$

55. (a) Center $(2, -1)$, foci $((4 \pm 3\sqrt{3})/2, -1)$, major axis 6, minor axis 3, $e = \sqrt{3}/2$

  (b) Center $(-2, -\frac{3}{2})$, foci $(-2 \pm \sqrt{13}, -\frac{3}{2})$, major axis $= \sqrt{13}$, conjugate axis $= \sqrt{39}$, $e = 2$, asymptotes: $2y \pm 2\sqrt{3}x + (3 \pm 4\sqrt{3}) = 0$

57. (b) Bounded. Both $9x^2 + 4y^2 - 36$ and $4x^2 + 9y^2 - 36$ exceed one when $4(x^2 + y^2) > 37$

58. Foci $(\pm\sqrt{p - q}, 0)$ 59. $\sqrt{2}$

60. On a branch of a hyperbola with the rifle and target at its foci

62. Center $(1, -2)$,   foci $(1, -2 \pm \sqrt{13})$, asymptotes $2(y + 2) = \pm 3(x - 1)$

63. $9x^2 - y^2 = 9$, or $9y^2 - x^2 = 9$

65. (a) Center $(3, 2)$, $e = \sqrt{\frac{11}{12}}$ (b) $(3, 0)$

66. $x^2 + y^2 - 6x - 15y + 9 = 0$

67. With $A(0, 0)$ and $B(c, 0)$, locus is left branch of hyperbola

$$3x^2 - y^2 - 4cx + c^2 = 0.$$

68. $2y'^2 - 2a\sqrt{2}x' + a^2 = 0$

Chapter 11

Article 11.1

1. (a) $(3, \frac{1}{4}\pi + 2n\pi)$, $(-3, -\frac{3}{4}\pi + 2n\pi)$,

  (b) $(-3, \frac{1}{4}\pi + 2n\pi)$, $(3, -\frac{3}{4}\pi + 2n\pi)$,

  (c) $(3, -\frac{1}{4}\pi + 2n\pi)$, $(-3, \frac{3}{4}\pi + 2n\pi)$,

  (d) $(-3, -\frac{1}{4}\pi + 2n\pi)$, $(3, \frac{3}{4}\pi + 2n\pi)$,

$$n = 0, \pm 1, \pm 2, \ldots$$

3. (a) $(3/\sqrt{2}, 3/\sqrt{2})$ (b) $(-3/\sqrt{2}, -3/\sqrt{2})$

  (c) $(3/\sqrt{2}, -3/\sqrt{2})$ (d) $(-3/\sqrt{2}, 3/\sqrt{2})$

5. $(2, \frac{3}{4}\pi)$ is the same as $(-2, -\frac{1}{4}\pi)$, and $2\sin(-\frac{1}{2}\pi) = -2$.

6. $(\frac{1}{2}, \frac{3}{2}\pi) = (-\frac{1}{2}, \frac{1}{2}\pi)$ and $-\sin\frac{1}{6}\pi = -\frac{1}{2}$

7. If (r_1, θ_1) satisfies $r_1 = \cos\theta_1 + 1$, then the same point has coordinates $(-r_1, \theta_1 + \pi)$ which satisfy the second equation. Also, if (r_2, θ_2) satisfies the second equation, then the coordinates $(-r_2, \theta_2 + \pi)$ of the same point satisfy the first equation.

8. $(\pm a, 15°)$, $(\pm a, 75°)$

9. The origin and $(a/\sqrt{2}, 45°)$

10. The origin and $(a + a/\sqrt{2}, -\frac{1}{4}\pi)$, $(a - a/\sqrt{2}, \frac{3}{4}\pi)$

11. The origin and $(\frac{8}{5}a, \sin^{-1}\frac{3}{5})$

12. The origin, $(a, \pm\frac{1}{2}\pi)$, $(\frac{1}{2}a, \pm\frac{2}{3}\pi)$, $(0.22a, \pm141.3°)$

Article 11.2

1. $r(3\cos\theta + 4\sin\theta) = 5$ 2. $x^2 + y^2 = 2ax$

11. (a) $(\frac{3}{2}a, \pm60°)$, $(0, 180°)$

  (b) $(2a, 0°)$, $(\frac{1}{2}a, \pm120°)$

12. $30°$

Article 11.3

1. $r = a\sin 2\theta$; a rose of 4 leaves

2. $r = 2a\sin\theta\tan\theta$; $x = r\cos\theta = 2a\sin^2\theta \to 2a$ as $\theta \to \pi/2$

3. $r = 2a\sin\theta$

4. $r = a(1 - \cos\theta)$, $r = -a(1 + \cos\theta)$. (Both equations represent the same curve.)

5. $r \cos(\theta - \alpha) = p$

6. $r(1 - \cos\theta) = 2a$, $r(1 + \cos\theta) = -2a$.   (Both equations represent the same curve.)

7. $r^2 = \cos 2\theta$ 8. $x^2 + y^2 = 4x$

9. $x^2 + y^2 = 6y$ 10. $(x^2 + y^2)^3 = 4x^2 y^2$

11. $(x^2 + y^2)^2 = 2a^2(x^2 - y^2)$

12. $3x^2 - y^2 + 32x + 64 = 0$

13. $x^2 + y^2 - ay = a\sqrt{x^2 + y^2}$

15. (a) $p = |c|/\sqrt{a^2 + b^2}$, $\cos\beta = a/\sqrt{a^2 + b^2}$,
     $\sin\beta = b/\sqrt{a^2 + b^2}$
     (b) $p = 3$, $\beta = 30°$

16. $r = 4/[1 - \sin(\theta - \frac{1}{6}\pi)]$

17. $(50, 0°)$, $r = 45/(4 + 5\cos\theta)$

18. $r = a(1 + \cos\theta)$

19. (a) $\max = \sqrt{a^2 + b^2}$, $\min = \sqrt{|a^2 - b^2|}$
     (b) $\max = a\sqrt{5}$, $\min = a\sqrt{3}$
        $\max = a\sqrt{2}$, $\min = 0$
        $\max = a\sqrt{5}/2$, $\min = a\sqrt{3}/2$

20. ± 1 21. $(\frac{2}{3}, 0°)$ 22. $\pm\sqrt{e^2 - 1}$

Article 11.4

2. When $\tan\psi_2 = -1/\tan\psi_1$

3. $(2, \pm 60°)$, $90°$

4. $(\frac{3}{2}a, \pm 60°)$, $(0, 180°)$ 5. $8a$

6. $(\frac{4}{5}a, 0)$ 7. $4\pi a^2 (2 - \sqrt{2})$

8. $2a$. The curve is the cardioid $r = \frac{1}{2}a(1 - \cos\theta)$.

9. $\frac{1}{3}a[(4 + \pi^2)^{3/2} - 8]$ 10. $\frac{1}{8}a(4\pi - 3\sqrt{3})$

11. $4\pi^2 a^2$

Article 11.5

1. $\frac{3}{2}\pi a^2$ 2. πa^2 3. $2a^2$

4. $\frac{1}{3}a^2(3\sqrt{3} - \pi)$ 5. $\frac{9}{2}\pi a^2$

6. $\frac{1}{2}a^2(\pi - 2)$ 7. πa^2

Review questions and exercises

6. (a) $e = \frac{7}{93} \approx 0.0754$
   (b) $r = ke/(1 - e\cos\theta) \approx 4623/(1 - 0.0754\cos\theta)$

Miscellaneous exercises

15. $\pi/3$ at $(a, \pi/6)$ and $(a, 5\pi/6)$

16. $\pi/4$ at $(a, 0)$ and (a, π)

17. 0 at $(a\sqrt{2}, \pi/4)$ 18. $\pi/2$ at $r = 0$

19. $\pi/4$ at $r = 0$, and $2\tan^{-1}(\sqrt{3}/6)$ at $(a/2, \theta_i)$,
    $\theta_i = \pm\pi/3$, $\pm 2\pi/3$

20. $\pi/3$ at $(\sqrt{2}, \pm\pi/6)$ and $(\sqrt{2}, \pm 5\pi/6)$

21. $\dot{r} = 2/(1 + \cos\theta)$

22. $r(b\cos\theta + a\sin\theta) = ab$

23. $r = -2a\cos\theta$

24. $r[1 + \cos(\theta - \frac{1}{4}\pi)] = 2a$

25. $r = 8/(3 - \cos\theta)$ 26. $r = 3/(1 + 2\sin\theta)$

27. $(0.75a, -3.44°)$, approximately

29. $\pi/4$ 30. $\pi/2$ 31. -1 32. $\pi/2$

33. (b) $xy = 1$ 34. (a) $(1/4)\tan\alpha$
    (c) $\pi/2$ (b) $\sec\alpha$

35. (a) $32\pi a^2/5$

    (b) $\bar{y} = 0$, $\bar{x} = 5a\int_0^\pi \sin^6\frac{\theta}{2}\cos\frac{\theta}{2}\cos\theta\,d\theta$
    (c) $\bar{x} = -50a/63$

38. $P = 3\pi a/2$ 39. $2a^2$ 40. $(3\pi - 8)a^2/2$

41. a^2 42. $9a^2\pi/2$ 43. $3\pi a^2/2$

44. πa^2 45. πa^2 46. $4a^2$

47. $a^2(\pi + 2)$ 48. $5\pi a^2/4$

Chapter 12

Article 12.2

6–11. Values of $\sinh u$, $\cosh u$, $\tanh u$, $\coth u$, $\operatorname{sech} u$, $\operatorname{csch} u$ are listed in the order given.

6. $-\frac{3}{4}, \frac{5}{4}, -\frac{3}{5}, -\frac{5}{3}, \frac{4}{5}, -\frac{4}{3}$

7. $\pm\frac{8}{15}, \frac{17}{15}, \pm\frac{8}{17}, \pm\frac{17}{8}, \frac{15}{17}, \pm\frac{15}{8}$

8. $-\frac{7}{24}, \frac{25}{24}, -\frac{7}{25}, -\frac{25}{7}, \frac{24}{25}, -\frac{24}{7}$

9. $\frac{12}{5}, \frac{13}{5}, \frac{12}{13}, \frac{13}{12}, \frac{5}{13}, \frac{5}{12}$

10. $\pm\frac{4}{3}, \frac{5}{3}, \pm\frac{4}{5}, \pm\frac{5}{4}, \frac{3}{5}, \pm\frac{3}{4}$

11. Same as 9.

Article 12.3

2. $3\cosh 3x$

3. $10\cosh 5x \sinh 5x = 5\sinh 10x$

4. 0 5. $2\operatorname{sech}^2 2x$

6. $-\sec^2 x \operatorname{csch}^2(\tan x)$ 7. $-3\operatorname{sech}^3 x \tanh x$

8. $-\operatorname{csch}(x/4)\coth(x/4)$ 9. $\sec^2 x \operatorname{sech} y$

10. $\frac{1}{2}\sinh(2x + 1) + C$ 11. $\ln\cosh x + C$

12. $-\frac{1}{3}\operatorname{sech}^3 x + C$ 13. $\tanh x + C$

14. $\ln \cosh x + C$

15. $x - \tanh x + C$

16. $2 \cosh \sqrt{x} + C$

17. $\frac{1}{2}x + \frac{1}{12} \sinh 6x + C$

18. $2\sqrt{2} \cosh (x/2) + C$

19. $u/2$

21. (a) 115 ft   (b) 16 lb

Article 12.5

2. $\cosh^{-1} x = \ln (x + \sqrt{x^2 - 1})$

6. $\dfrac{2}{\sqrt{1 + 4x^2}}$

7. $-\csc x$

8. $\sec x$ if $\tan x > 0$, $-\sec x$ if $\tan x < 0$

9. $-\csc x$

10. $-2 \csc 2x$ if $\cos 2x > 0$, $2 \csc 2x$ if $\cos 2x < 0$

11. $\frac{1}{2} \sinh^{-1} 2x + C$

12. $\sinh^{-1} \dfrac{x}{2} + C$

13. 0.5493

14. -0.5493

15. $-\frac{1}{2} \operatorname{csch}^{-1} \dfrac{|x|}{2} + C = -\frac{1}{2} \sinh^{-1} \dfrac{2}{|x|} + C$

Article 12.6

1. $a \sinh \dfrac{x_1}{a}$

3. $\dfrac{\pi a}{2} \left(2x_1 + a \sinh \dfrac{2x_1}{a} \right)$.

4. $\bar{x} = 0,$ $\bar{y} = \frac{1}{2}y_1 + \dfrac{x_1}{2} \operatorname{csch} \dfrac{x_1}{a}$

5. $\dfrac{\pi a^2}{4} \left(2x_1 + a \sinh \dfrac{2x_1}{a} \right)$

6. (b) $\dfrac{dx}{ds} = \dfrac{a}{\sqrt{s^2 + a^2}},$ $\dfrac{dy}{ds} = \dfrac{s}{\sqrt{a^2 + s^2}}$

7. (c) $a = 25$ ft,   dip ≈ 4.6 ft   (d) $H = 50$ lb

Miscellaneous exercises

3. $\lim PQ = 0$

4. $\sinh x = \pm\frac{3}{4},$ $\tanh x = \pm\frac{3}{5}$

5. $\cosh x = \frac{41}{9},$ $\tanh x = -\frac{40}{41}$

9. $y = 1$ 12. $3 \sinh 6x$

13. $\sec^2 x/(2 \tanh y \operatorname{sech}^2 y)$

14. $-(\cosh y \coth y)/\sqrt{1 - x^2}$

15. $\tanh y \tan x$ 16. $(1 + y^2)/(1 - x^2)$

17. $x^{-1} \operatorname{sech}^2 (\ln x) = 4x(x^2 + 1)^{-2}$

18. $y \operatorname{csch} (\ln y)$

19. $3e^{3x} \cosh (\tan^{-1} e^{3x})/(1 + e^{6x})$

20. $|\sec x|$

21. $-(\cosh y + \sinh 2x)/(2y + x \sinh y)$

22. $-e^{-\theta} + C$ 23. $(2\theta - e^{-2\theta})/4$

24. $(\cosh^3 x - 3 \cosh x)/3 + C$

25. $(e^{3x} + 3e^{-x})/6 + C$ 25. $\ln (\cosh x) + C$

27. $\frac{1}{2} \tanh^{-1} (\frac{1}{2})$

28. $\frac{1}{2}(\coth^{-1} \frac{5}{2} - \coth^{-1} \frac{3}{2})$

29. $\sinh^{-1} (e^t) + C$ 30. $-\tanh^{-1} (\cos x) + C$

31. $\cosh^{-1} (\tan \theta) + C$

36. (a) $\lim v = \sqrt{mg/k}$, where k = resistance proportionality factor; m = mass of body; g = acceleration due to gravity

(b) $s = (m/k) \ln \cosh (t\sqrt{gk/m})$

37. $\ln 2$ 38. $\ln [2/(1 + \sqrt{2})]$

Chapter 13

Article 13.1

1. $\alpha_1 = \frac{1}{2} \sin^{-1} 0.8 = 26°34'$
   $\alpha_2 = 90° - \alpha_1 = 63°26'$

5. $x = e^t,$ $y = -(7 + e^{2t})/2$

6. $y = (1 - t)^{-1},$ $x = -\ln |1 - t|$

7. $x = \sin t,$ $y = 1 + (t - \sin t \cos t)/2,$ $t \in [0, \pi/2]$
   $x = 1,$ $y = t + 1 - \pi/4,$ $t > \pi/2$

Article 13.2

1. $x^2 + y^2 = 1$

2. $x = 1 - 2y^2,$ $|y| \le 1$

3. $x^2 - y^2 = 1,$ $x > 0$

4. $\dfrac{(x - 2)^2}{16} + \dfrac{(y - 3)^2}{4} = 1$

5. $y = x^2 - 6x$

6. $4x^2 - y^2 = 4,$ $x \ge 1,$ $y \ge 0$

7. $(x - 2)(y - 2) + 1 = 0,$ $x > 2,$ $y < 2$

8. $y = x^2 - 2x + 5,$ $x \ge 1$

9. $2(x + y) = (x - y)^2$

10. $\dfrac{(x - 3)^2}{4} + \dfrac{(y - 4)^2}{9} = 1,$ $x > 3$

11. $x = \dfrac{-at}{\sqrt{t^2 + 1}},$ $y = \dfrac{a}{\sqrt{t^2 + 1}}$

12. $x = a \tanh \theta,$ $y = a \operatorname{sech} \theta$

13. $x = a \cos \dfrac{s}{a}$, $\quad y = a \sin \dfrac{s}{a}$

14. $x = a \sinh^{-1} \dfrac{s}{a}$, $\quad y = \sqrt{a^2 + s^2}$

15. $x = a \cos \phi + a\phi \sin \phi$, $\quad y = a \sin \phi - a\phi \cos \phi$

16. $x = (a + b) \cos \theta - b \cos \left(\dfrac{a+b}{b} \theta \right)$, ·

$\quad y = (a + b) \sin \theta - b \sin \left(\dfrac{a+b}{b} \theta \right)$

17. $x = (a - b) \cos \theta + b \cos \left(\dfrac{a-b}{b} \theta \right)$,

$\quad y = (a - b) \sin \theta - b \sin \left(\dfrac{a-b}{b} \theta \right)$

18. $8a$

21. (a) $x = 2a \cot \theta$, $\quad y = 2a \sin^2 \theta$

(b) $y = \dfrac{8a^3}{x^2 + 4a^2}$

Article 13.3

1. $\mathbf{i} - 4\mathbf{j}$ 2. $-\mathbf{i} + \mathbf{j}$

3. $-2\mathbf{i} - 3\mathbf{j}$ 4. $\mathbf{0}$

5. $\frac{1}{2}\sqrt{3}\mathbf{i} + \frac{1}{2}\mathbf{j}$ 6. $\frac{1}{2}\sqrt{3}\mathbf{i} - \frac{1}{2}\mathbf{j}$

7. $\frac{3}{5}\mathbf{i} - \frac{4}{5}\mathbf{j}$ 8. $\dfrac{\mathbf{i} + 4\mathbf{j}}{\sqrt{17}}$

9. $(-4\mathbf{i} + \mathbf{j})/\sqrt{17}$ 10. $\mathbf{i} \cos \theta + \mathbf{j} \sin \theta$

11. $\sqrt{2}$, $45°$

12. $\sqrt{13}$, $\tan^{-1}(-1.5) = -56.3°$

13. 2, $30°$

14. $\sqrt{13}$, $180° - \tan^{-1}(1.5) = 123.7°$

15. 13, $\tan^{-1}\frac{12}{5} = 67.4°$

16. 13, $180° + \tan^{-1}\frac{12}{5} = 247.4°$

Article 13.4

1. $\mathbf{v} = -a\omega \sin \omega t\mathbf{i} + a\omega \cos \omega t\mathbf{j}$,
$\mathbf{a} = -a\omega^2 \cos \omega t\mathbf{i} - a\omega^2 \sin \omega t\mathbf{j} = -\omega^2\mathbf{R}$;
when $\omega t = \pi/3$,

$\quad \mathbf{v} = a\omega(-\frac{1}{2}\sqrt{3}\mathbf{i} + \frac{1}{2}\mathbf{j})$, speed $= a\omega$,
$\quad \mathbf{a} = -a\omega^2(\frac{1}{2}\mathbf{i} + \frac{1}{2}\sqrt{3}\mathbf{j})$

2. $\mathbf{v} = -2 \sin t\mathbf{i} + 3 \cos t\mathbf{j}$, $\quad \mathbf{a} = -2 \cos t\mathbf{i} - 3 \sin t\mathbf{j}$;
at $t = \pi/4$,

$\quad \mathbf{v} = -\sqrt{2}\mathbf{i} + \frac{3}{2}\sqrt{2}\mathbf{j}$, speed $= \sqrt{6.5}$,
$\quad \mathbf{a} = -\sqrt{2}\mathbf{i} - \frac{3}{2}\sqrt{2}\mathbf{j}$

3. $\mathbf{v} = \mathbf{i} + 2t\mathbf{j}$, $\quad \mathbf{a} = 2\mathbf{j}$; at $t = 2$,

$\quad \mathbf{v} = \mathbf{i} + 4\mathbf{j}$, $\quad \mathbf{a} = 2\mathbf{j}$, speed $= \sqrt{17}$

4. $\mathbf{v} = -2 \sin 2t\mathbf{i} + 2 \cos t\mathbf{j}$,
$\mathbf{a} = -4 \cos 2t\mathbf{i} - 2 \sin t\mathbf{j}$; at $t = 0$,

$\quad \mathbf{v} = 2\mathbf{j}$, $\quad \mathbf{a} = -4\mathbf{i}$, speed $= 2$

5. $\mathbf{v} = e^t\mathbf{i} - 2e^{-2t}\mathbf{j}$, $\quad \mathbf{a} = e^t\mathbf{i} + 4e^{-2t}\mathbf{j}$; at $t = \ln 3$,

$\quad \mathbf{v} = 3\mathbf{i} - \frac{2}{9}\mathbf{j}$, $\quad \mathbf{a} = 3\mathbf{i} + \frac{4}{9}\mathbf{j}$, speed $= \frac{1}{9}\sqrt{733}$

6. $\mathbf{v} = \sec t \tan t\mathbf{i} + \sec^2 t\mathbf{j}$,
$\mathbf{a} = (\sec^3 t + \sec t \tan^2 t)\mathbf{i} + 2 \sec^2 t \tan t\mathbf{j}$;
at $t = \pi/6$,

$\quad \mathbf{v} = \frac{2}{3}\mathbf{i} + \frac{4}{3}\mathbf{j}$, $\mathbf{a} = (10\mathbf{i} + 8\mathbf{j})/3\sqrt{3}$, speed $= \frac{1}{3}\sqrt{20}$

7. $\mathbf{v} = 3 \sinh 3t\mathbf{i} + 2 \cosh t\mathbf{j}$,
$\mathbf{a} = 9 \cosh 3t\mathbf{i} + 2 \sinh t\mathbf{j}$; at $t = 0$,

$\quad \mathbf{v} = 2\mathbf{j}$, $\quad \mathbf{a} = 9\mathbf{i}$, speed $= 2$

8. $\mathbf{v} = \dfrac{\mathbf{i}}{t + 1} + 2t\mathbf{j}$, $\quad \mathbf{a} = \dfrac{-\mathbf{i}}{(t + 1)^2} + 2\mathbf{j}$;
at $t = 1$,

$\quad \mathbf{v} = \frac{1}{2}\mathbf{i} + 2\mathbf{j}$, $\quad \mathbf{a} = -\frac{1}{4}\mathbf{i} + 2\mathbf{j}$, speed $= \frac{1}{2}\sqrt{17}$

9. $\mathbf{R} = -\frac{1}{2}gt^2\mathbf{j} + \mathbf{v}_0 t = tv_0 \cos \alpha\mathbf{i} + (tv_0 \sin \alpha - \frac{1}{2}gt^2)\mathbf{j}$

Article 13.5

1. $-\mathbf{i} \sin t + \mathbf{j} \cos t$ 2. $\dfrac{e^t\mathbf{i} + 2t\mathbf{j}}{\sqrt{e^2 + 4t^2}}$

3. $-\cos t\mathbf{i} + \sin t\mathbf{j}$ 4. $\dfrac{\mathbf{i} + 2x\mathbf{j}}{\sqrt{1 + 4x^2}}$

5. $-\dfrac{2 \cos t\mathbf{i} + \mathbf{j}}{\sqrt{1 + 4 \cos^2 t}}$

Article 13.6

1. $\dfrac{1}{a} \text{sech}^2 \dfrac{x}{a}$ 2. $|\cos x|$

3. $\dfrac{4e^{2x}}{(1 + 4e^{4x})^{3/2}}$ 4. $\dfrac{1}{3a |\sin t \cos t|}$

5. $\dfrac{1}{|a\theta|}$ 6. $\dfrac{1}{4a} \left| \csc \dfrac{\theta}{2} \right|$

7. $|\cos y|$ 8. $\dfrac{2}{\sqrt{y^2 + 2}(y^2 + 1)^2}$

9. $\dfrac{|48y^5|}{(4y^6 + 1)^2}$

10. $(x+2)^2 + (y-3)^2 = 8$.

For the circle

$$y' = -\frac{x+2}{y-3}, \quad y'' = \frac{-8}{(y-3)^3}.$$

Both of these are equal to $+1$ at $(0, 1)$.

Article 13.7

2. $\mathbf{v} = 2\mathbf{i}\sinh 2t + 2\mathbf{j}\cosh 2t$,
$\mathbf{a} = 4\mathbf{i}\cosh 2t + 4\mathbf{j}\sinh 2t$,

$$\frac{ds}{dt} = |\mathbf{v}| = 2\sqrt{\sinh^2 2t + \cosh^2 2t} = 2\sqrt{\cosh 4t}.$$

$$a_T = \frac{d^2s}{dt^2} = \frac{4\sinh 4t}{\sqrt{\cosh 4t}},$$

$$a_N = \sqrt{|\mathbf{a}|^2 - a_T^2} = 4\sqrt{\operatorname{sech} 4t}$$

3. $a_T = \dfrac{2t}{\sqrt{1+t^2}}, \quad a_N = \dfrac{2}{\sqrt{1+t^2}}$

4. $a_T = 0, \quad a_N = \omega^2 a$

5. $a_T = 0, \quad a_N = \dfrac{2}{t^2+1}$

6. $a_T = \sqrt{2}e^t, \quad a_N = \sqrt{2}e^t$

Article 13.8

2. $\mathbf{v} = 3a\sin\theta\mathbf{u}_r + 3a(1-\cos\theta)\mathbf{u}_\theta$,
$\mathbf{a} = 9a(2\cos\theta - 1)\mathbf{u}_r + 18a\sin\theta\mathbf{u}_\theta$

3. $\mathbf{v} = 4at\cos 2\theta\mathbf{u}_r + 2at\sin 2\theta\mathbf{u}_\theta$,
$\mathbf{a} = (4a\cos 2\theta - 20at^2\sin 2\theta)\mathbf{u}_r$
$\quad + (2a\sin 2\theta + 16at^2\cos 2\theta)\mathbf{u}_\theta$

4. $\mathbf{v} = 2ae^{a\theta}\mathbf{u}_r + 2e^{a\theta}\mathbf{u}_\theta$,
$\mathbf{a} = 4e^{a\theta}(a^2 - 1)\mathbf{u}_r + 8ae^{a\theta}\mathbf{u}_\theta$

5. $\mathbf{v} = a\cos t\mathbf{u}_r + ae^{-t}(1+\sin t)\mathbf{u}_\theta$,
$\mathbf{a} = -a[\sin t + e^{-2t}(1+\sin t)]\mathbf{u}_r$
$\quad + ae^{-t}[2\cos t - 1 - \sin t]\mathbf{u}_\theta$

6. $\mathbf{v} = -8\sin 4t\mathbf{u}_r + 4\cos 4t\mathbf{u}_\theta$,
$\mathbf{a} = -40\cos 4t\mathbf{u}_r - 32\sin 4t\mathbf{u}_\theta$

Miscellaneous exercises

1. $x = (1-t)^{-1}, \quad y = 1 - \ln(1-t), \quad t < 1$

2. $x = \tan^{-1}(t+1)$,
$y = (t+1)\tan^{-1}(t+1)$
$\qquad\qquad -\frac{1}{4}\pi - \frac{1}{2}\ln(1+t+\frac{1}{2}t^2)$

3. $x = e^t, \quad y = e^{e^t} - e$

4. $x = 3 - 3\cos 2t, \quad y = 4 + 2\sin 2t$

5. $x = t - \sin t, \quad y = 1 - \cos t$

6. $y = e^t, \quad x = 2\sqrt{1+e^t} - 2\sqrt{2}$
$\qquad\qquad - 2\coth^{-1}\sqrt{1+e^t} + 2\coth^{-1}\sqrt{2}$

7. $x = \sinh^{-1} t, \quad y = t\sinh^{-1} t - \sqrt{1+t^2} + 1$

8. $x = 2 + 2\sinh(t/2), \quad y = 2t - 4 + 4\cosh(t/2)$

9. $x = 4\sin t, \quad y = 4\cos t$

10. $x = 2 - e^{-t}, \quad y = 2t + e^{-t}$

12. $x = 8t - 2\sin 2t, \quad y = 4 - 2\cos 2t$

13. $x = 2a\sin^2\theta\tan\theta, \quad y = 2a\sin^2\theta$

14. $x = \cot\theta \pm a\cos\theta, \quad y = \pm a\sin\theta$

15. (a) $3\pi a^2$ (b) $8a$ (c) $-4a\sin(t/2)$
(d) $64\pi a^2/3$ (e) $\pi a, (5a/6)$

17. 0

24. (a) $\mathbf{v} = 2^{-3/2}(-\mathbf{i} + \mathbf{j}), \quad \mathbf{a} = 2^{-5/2}(\mathbf{i} - 3\mathbf{j})$
(b) $t = 0$

25. (a) $\mathbf{v} = \pi(\mathbf{i}(1 - \cos\pi t) + \mathbf{j}\sin\pi t)$,
$\mathbf{a} = \pi^2(\mathbf{i}\sin\pi t + \mathbf{j}\cos\pi t)$
(b) Slope of $PC = \cot\pi t$,
slope of $PQ = \csc\pi t + \cot\pi t$
(c) Slope of $\mathbf{v}$ = slope of PQ,
slope of $\mathbf{a}$ = slope of PC

26. Speed $= a\sqrt{1+t^2}$,
$\qquad a_T = at/\sqrt{1+t^2}$,
$\qquad a_N = a(t^2+2)/\sqrt{1+t^2}$

28. (b) $\pi/2$

29. $|ad - bc|\,(a^2 + b^2)^{-3/2}$, provided $a^2 + b^2 \neq 0$

30. $x = a\theta + a\sin\theta, \quad y = -a(1 - \cos\theta)$

31. $(-\frac{1}{2}\ln 2, 1/\sqrt{2})$ 32. (b) $\pi ab, \pi a^2$

33. $\kappa = \pi s$

34. $y = \pm\sqrt{1-x^2} \pm \ln\dfrac{1 - \sqrt{1-x^2}}{x} + C.$

Set $C = 0$. Then

$x = e^{-s}$ [$s = -\ln x$, measured from $(1, 0)$],

$y = \pm\sqrt{1 - e^{-2s}} \pm \ln(e^s - \sqrt{e^{2s} - 1}).$

35. $\qquad\qquad s = s_0 + 2\pi p,$

$\qquad A = A_0 + s_0 p + \pi p^2, \quad R = R_0 + p,$

where s_0, A_0, R_0 are the length of arc, area, and radius of curvature of the original curve.

36. (a) $320\sqrt{10}$ (b) $16[\sqrt{2} + \ln(\sqrt{2} + 1)]$

37. $\mathbf{v} = 3\cos t\,\mathbf{i} - 2\sin t\,\mathbf{j}$,
    $\mathbf{a} = -3\sin t\,\mathbf{i} - 2\cos t\,\mathbf{j}$,
    speed $= (4 + 5\cos^2 t)^{1/2}$,
    $a_T = -5\sin t\cos t\,(4 + 5\cos^2 t)^{-1/2}$,
    $a_N = 6(4 + 5\cos^2 t)^{-1/2}$

38. (a) $a_T = 0$, $a_N = 4$ (b) 1   (c) $r = 2\cos\theta$

39. $\mathbf{v} = (\cos t - t\sin t)\mathbf{i} + (\sin t + t\cos t)\mathbf{j}$,
    $\mathbf{a} = -(t\cos t + 2\sin t)\mathbf{i} - (t\sin t - 2\cos t)\mathbf{j}$,
    $\kappa = (t^2 + 2)/(t^2 + 1)^{3/2}$

40. $\kappa = |f^2 + 2f'^2 - ff''|/(f^2 + f'^2)^{3/2}$

41. (a) $r = e^{2\theta}$ (b) $\frac{1}{2}\sqrt{5}(e^{4\pi} - 1)$

42. $\sqrt{2}\mathbf{u}_r$ 43. $2(\omega^2 - 1)\mathbf{i}$

44. (a) $\mathbf{v} = -\mathbf{u}_r + 3\mathbf{u}_\theta$, $\mathbf{a} = -9\mathbf{u}_r - 6\mathbf{u}_\theta$
    (b) $\sqrt{37} + \frac{1}{6}\ln(6 + \sqrt{37})$

45. $r = a\cosh\omega t$

46. $1/r - k = (1/k)(1 + e\cos\theta)$

Chapter 14

Article 14.1

1. Converges to $-\frac{2}{3}$ 2. Converges to $\frac{1}{2}$

3. Converges to 1   4. Converges to 0

5. Diverges   6. Diverges

7. Converges to 1   8. Converges to 0

9. Diverges   10. Converges to 0

13. (b) $a_n = \sin n$ is an example,
    $a_n = -n$ is another example.

14. $s_n = 1 - \dfrac{1}{n+1}$, sum $= 1$

15. Same as Exercise 14. Note that

$$\frac{1}{n \cdot (n+1)} = \frac{1}{n} - \frac{1}{n+1}.$$

16. $s_n = \ln\dfrac{1}{n+1}$, diverges

17. $s_n = 2 - \dfrac{1}{2^{n-1}}$, sum $= 2$

18. $s_n = 3 - \dfrac{1}{3^{n-1}}$, sum $= 3$

19. $s_n = \dfrac{10}{3}\left[1 + \dfrac{(-1)^{n+1}}{2^n}\right]$, sum $= \dfrac{10}{3}$

20. $s_n = \dfrac{1}{11}\left(1 - \dfrac{1}{100^n}\right)$, sum $= \dfrac{1}{11}$

21. 28 ft

22. (a) $\frac{234}{999}$
    (b) Yes, because it is of the form

$$p \cdot 10^{-k} + p \cdot 10^{-2k} + \cdots = p/(10^k - 1),$$

    where p and $10^k - 1 = q$ are integers.

23. $\dfrac{124}{100} + \dfrac{123}{99,900} = \dfrac{123,999}{99,900}$

24. (d) $n = 6$ (e) $n = 998$

Article 14.2

2. If the sequence is bounded below, then it has a definite finite limit. Otherwise, it diverges to minus infinity.

3. The limit exists and is less than or equal to three.

4. No, diverges, by oscillation

5. Diverges, by the integral test

6. The nth term approaches 1. Series diverges to plus infinity, by comparison with $\sum 1/n$.

7. Converges, by comparison with $\sum 1/2^n$

8. Diverges, by integral test

9. Diverges, by comparison with $\sum 1/n$

10. Diverges, by integral test

11. Converges, by ratio test

12. Converges, by comparison with $\sum 1/n^2$

13. Converges, by comparison with $\sum 1/n^{3/2}$

14–17. Converge, by ratio test

18. Diverges, by ratio test

19. Converges, by ratio test

Article 14.3

1. $1 - x + \dfrac{x^2}{2!} - \dfrac{x^3}{3!} + \cdots + \dfrac{(-1)^n x^n}{n!}$

2. $x - \dfrac{x^3}{3!} + \dfrac{x^5}{5!} - \dfrac{x^7}{7!} + \cdots + \dfrac{(-1)^m x^{2m+1}}{(2m+1)!}$

3. $1 - \dfrac{x^2}{2!} + \dfrac{x^4}{4!} - \dfrac{x^6}{6!} + \cdots + \dfrac{(-1)^m x^{2m}}{(2m)!}$

4. $\dfrac{\sqrt{2}}{2}\left(1 + x - \dfrac{x^2}{2!} - \dfrac{x^3}{3!} + \dfrac{x^4}{4!} + \dfrac{x^5}{5!} - \dfrac{x^6}{6!} - \cdots \right.$
   $\left. + \dfrac{x^{4m}}{(4m)!} + \dfrac{x^{4m+1}}{(4m+1)!} - \dfrac{x^{4m+2}}{(4m+2)!} - \dfrac{x^{4m+3}}{(4m+3)!}\right)$

5. $x + \dfrac{x^3}{3!} + \dfrac{x^5}{5!} + \dfrac{x^7}{7!} + \cdots + \dfrac{x^{2m+1}}{(2m+1)!}$

6. $1 + \dfrac{x^2}{2!} + \dfrac{x^4}{4!} + \cdots + \dfrac{x^{2m}}{(2m)!}$

7. $(x-1) - \dfrac{(x-1)^2}{2} + \dfrac{(x-1)^3}{3} - \dfrac{(x-1)^4}{4} + \cdots$

8. $2 + \dfrac{1}{2}\dfrac{(x-4)}{2} - \dfrac{1}{2 \cdot 4}\dfrac{(x-4)^2}{2^3}$

$\quad + \dfrac{1 \cdot 3}{2 \cdot 4 \cdot 6}\dfrac{(x-4)^3}{2^5} - \dfrac{1 \cdot 3 \cdot 5}{2 \cdot 4 \cdot 6 \cdot 8}\dfrac{(x-4)^4}{2^7} + \cdots$

9. $-1 - (x+1) - (x+1)^2 - (x+1)^3 - \cdots$

10. $1 + 2(x - \pi/4) + 2(x - \pi/4)^2 + \cdots$

11. $-\ln 2 - \sqrt{3}(x - \pi/3) - 2(x - \pi/3)^2 - \cdots$

12. $\dfrac{1}{2} + \dfrac{\sqrt{3}}{2}\left(x - \dfrac{\pi}{6}\right)$

$\quad - \dfrac{1}{2}\dfrac{(x-\pi/6)^2}{2!} - \dfrac{\sqrt{3}}{2}\dfrac{(x-\pi/6)^3}{3!} + \cdots$

13. $\dfrac{\sqrt{2}}{2}\left[1 + \left(x + \dfrac{\pi}{4}\right) - \dfrac{(x+\pi/4)^2}{2!} - \dfrac{(x+\pi/4)^3}{3!} + \cdots\right]$

Article 14.4

4. $|x| < \sqrt[5]{0.06} \approx 0.57$ 5. $|R_3(x, 0)| < 10^{-4}/24$

6. $-26 + \sqrt{675} \le x \le 0.02$

7. $|R_1(x, 0)| < \dfrac{x^2}{8(0.99)^{3/2}} < 1.3 \times 10^{-5}$

9. $n \ge 4$

Article 14.5

1. 0.85717   2. 1.0355   3. 2.08008

4. 0.48836   5. 1.1276   6. 0.5211

7. 0.22314   8. $\pi/4 + 0.01 = 0.795$

10. 0.09994   11. 0.09967

15. (c) 6   (d) $1/q$

16. (a) $E(X) = 2$ (b) $E(X) = 6$

(c) The series for $E(X)$ diverges.

Article 14.6

1. $-\frac{1}{24}$ 2. $\frac{1}{4}$ 3. $-\frac{1}{9}$ 4. $\frac{1}{3}$

5. $\frac{1}{2}$ 6. $\frac{1}{3}$ 7. $\frac{1}{3}$ 8. $\frac{1}{2}$

9. $-\frac{1}{3}$ 10. 0   11. 0   12. 0

13. 1   14. $-\frac{1}{2}$ 15. $+\infty$ 16. e^{-6}

17. e^2 18. e^2 19. 1   20. 1

21. $e^{-1/2}$ 22. $e^{-1/2}$ 23. 1   24. e

25. (b) $\frac{1}{2}$ 26. $r = -3$, $s = \frac{9}{2}$

Article 14.7

1. $-1 < x < 1$ 2. $-1 < x < 1$

3. $-1 < x < 1$ 4. $-2 < x < 2$

5. $-\infty < x < \infty$ 6. $-\infty < x < \infty$

7. $0 < x < 2$ 8. $-4 < x < 0$

9. $|x - 3| < 1/\sqrt{2}$ 10. $-\infty < x < \infty$

Article 14.8

1. $|x| < 1$, diverges at both $x = \pm 1$

2. $|x| < 1$, converges at both $x = \pm 1$

3. $|x - 2| \le 1$

4. $|x + 1| < 1$, converges at $x = 0$, diverges at -2

5. $|x - 2| < 2$, diverges at $x = 0$, converges at $x = 4$

6. $|x - 1| < \frac{1}{2}$, diverges at both $x = \frac{1}{2}$, $x = \frac{3}{2}$

7. $-\infty < x < \infty$

8. Converges only at $x = 0$

9. $|x| < 1$, converges at both $x = \pm 1$

10. $|x + 3| < 1$, converges at $x = -4$, diverges at -2

Miscellaneous exercises

1. $s_n = \ln[(n+1)/(2n)]$, series converges to $-\ln 2$.

2. $s_n = \frac{1}{2}[\frac{3}{2} - 1/n - 1/(n+1)]$,   limit $= \frac{3}{4}$

6. (a) $\displaystyle\sum_{n=2}^{\infty} (-1)^n x^n$

(b) No, for otherwise it would converge for $|x| < 2$, and it cannot converge when $x = -1$.

7. $(1 - t^2)^{-1/2} = \displaystyle\sum_{k=0}^{\infty} 2^{-2k}(k!)^{-2}(2k)!\, t^{2k}$,

$$-1 < t < 1;$$

$\sin^{-1} x = \displaystyle\sum_{k=0}^{\infty} 2^{-2k}(k!)^{-2}(2k)!\, x^{2k+1}/(2k+1)$,

$$-1 \le x \le 1$$

8. $(1 + t^2)^{-1/2} = \displaystyle\sum_{k=0}^{\infty} (-1)^k 2^{-2k}(k!)^{-2}(2k)!\, t^{2k}$,

$$-1 \le t \le 1;$$

$\sinh^{-1} x = \displaystyle\sum_{k=0}^{\infty} \dfrac{(-1)^k 2^{-2k}(k!)^{-2}(2k)!\, x^{2k+1}}{2k+1}$,

$$-1 \le x \le 1$$

9. $e^{\sin x} = 1 + x + \dfrac{x^2}{2!} - \dfrac{3x^4}{4!} - \cdots$

11. (a) $\ln \cos x = -\dfrac{x^2}{2} - \dfrac{x^4}{12} - \dfrac{x^6}{45} - \cdots$

    (b) -0.00017

12. 0.946 13. 0.747

14. $\sqrt{2}[1 + (x-1)/2 + (x-1)^2/8 + \cdots]$

15. $\displaystyle\sum_{n=0}^{\infty} (-1)^{n+1}(x-2)^n, \quad 1 < x < 3$

16. $\tan x = x + \dfrac{x^3}{3} + \dfrac{2x^5}{15} + \cdots$

17. $\displaystyle\sum_{n=0}^{\infty} \dfrac{(-1)^n (x-3)^n}{4^{n+1}}$

18. $\cos x = \dfrac{1}{2}\displaystyle\sum_{n=0}^{\infty} (-1)^n (x-\pi/3)^{2n}/(2n)!$

    $+ \dfrac{\sqrt{3}}{2}\displaystyle\sum_{n=0}^{\infty} (-1)^n (x-\pi/3)^{2n+1}/(2n+1)!$

19. $\displaystyle\sum_{n=0}^{\infty} \dfrac{(-1)^n (x-\pi)^n}{\pi^{n+1}}$

20. 1.543

22. $e^{e^x} = e\left(1 + x + \dfrac{2x^2}{2!} + \dfrac{5x^3}{3!} + \dfrac{15x^4}{4!} + \dfrac{52x^5}{5!} + \cdots\right)$

23. $\tan^{-1} 0.05 = 0.0500, \quad \tan^{-1} 0.06 = 0.0599,$
    $\tan^{-1} 0.1 = 0.0997$

24. 0.0027 25. -0.0011 26. $-\infty$ 27. $e^{-1/6}$

29. Converges, by the integral test

30. Diverges, since nth term doesn't approach zero

32. (a) Diverges   (b) Diverges
    (c) Diverges   (d) Converges
    (e) Diverges   (f) Diverges
    (g) Converges   (h) Converges
    (i) Diverges   (j) Diverges
    (k) Diverges   (l) Converges

33. $\frac{1}{2}$

35. (b) Converges   (c) Converges, by comparison test

37. (a) $-5 \le x < 1$ (b) $-\infty < x < \infty$
    (c) $-\infty < x < \infty$ (d) $-e < x < e$
    (e) $-5 < x < -1$ (f) $-1 < x < 5$
    (g) $0 \le x \le 2$ (h) $-1 \le x < 1$

38. (a) $-\infty < x < \infty$

    (b) $(6n-1)\pi/6 \le x \le (6n+1)\pi/6,$
    where $n = 0, \pm1, \pm2, \ldots$

    (c) $x \ge \frac{1}{2}$

39. (a) $-\infty < x < \infty$

    (b) $y'' = xy \quad (a = 1, b = 0)$

41. (a) Diverges, because the nth term approaches e^{-1},
    and not zero, as $n \to \infty$

    (b) Converges, by comparison with $\sum e^{-n}$

Chapter 15

Article 15.3

1. $(x^2 + 1)(2y - 3) = C$

2. $\frac{2}{3}\sqrt{x^3 + 1} + \frac{1}{2}\ln(y^2 + 1) = C$

3. $e^y = e^x + C$ 4. $y^{3/2} = 3\sqrt{x/2} + C$

5. $\sinh 2y - 2\cos x = C$

6. $\frac{1}{2}(\ln|x|)^2 = \ln|y| + C$

7. $(y-1)e^y + \dfrac{x^2}{2} + \ln|x| = C$

8. $\sqrt{2x^2 + 3} - 2\sqrt{4 - y^2} = C$

9. $\cosh^{-1} y + \sinh^{-1} x = C$

10. $-y\cos y + \sin y = -x^{-1} + \ln|x| + C$

Article 15.4

1. $2\tan^{-1}\dfrac{y}{x} + \ln(x^2 + y^2) = C$

2. $\dfrac{x}{y} = \ln|x| + C; \quad$ or $y = 0$

3. $\ln|x| + e^{-y/x} = C$ 4. $\ln|y| + \dfrac{2}{\sqrt{3}}\tan^{-1}\dfrac{2y-x}{x\sqrt{3}} = C$

5. $y^2 = 2Cx + C^2$

6. (a) $x^2 + y^2 = Cx$ (b) $x^2 + y^2 = Cy$

Article 15.5

1. $y = e^{-x} + Ce^{-2x}$ 2. $y = \frac{1}{2}(x + C)e^{x/2}$

3. $x^3 y = C - \cos x$ 4. $xy = C - \cos x$

5. $x = \dfrac{y}{2} + \dfrac{C}{y}$

6. $(x-1)^4 y = \dfrac{x^3}{3} - x + C$

7. $y\cosh x = C - e^x$ 8. $xe^{2y} = y^2 + C$

9. $xy = y^2 + C$ 10. $x = (C - y)/(1 + y^2)$

Article 15.6

1. $\dfrac{x^2}{2} + xy + \dfrac{y^3}{3} = C$ 2. $e^x + e^y(x^2 + 1) = C$

3. $x^2 y + xy^2 - \dfrac{y^2}{2} = C$

4. $x^2 + 2x\sqrt{y^2 + 1} - y^2 = C$

5. $2y + x^3 = Cx$ 6. $y = x \tan (x + C)$

7. $y = x(C - x - \ln |x|)$

8. $e^x + x \ln y + y \ln x - \cos y = C$

9. $y^2 \tan^{-1} x - 2xy + \cosh y = C$

10. $xy + \cos x = C$

Article 15.7

1. $y = C_1 e^{-x} + C_2$

2. $y = C$, or $y = -2a \tan (ax + C)$,
    or $y = 2a \tanh (ax + C)$,
    or $y = 2/(x + C)$

3. $y = C_1 \int e^{-x^2/2}\, dx + C_2$. Note that the integral appearing here could be evaluated as an infinite series, giving
$$y = C_1 \left[x - \frac{x^3}{2 \cdot 3} + \frac{x^5}{2 \cdot 4 \cdot 5} - \frac{x^7}{2 \cdot 4 \cdot 6 \cdot 7} + \cdots \right] + C_2.$$

4. $y = C_1 \ln |x| + C_2$ 5. $y = C_1 \sinh (x + C_2)$

6. $y = C_1 \sin (\omega x + C_2)$

7. $x = A \sin (\sqrt{k/m}\, t + \pi/2) = A \cos (\sqrt{k/m}\, t)$

8. $s = \dfrac{m^2 g}{k^2} \left[\dfrac{kt}{m} + e^{-kt/m} - 1 \right]$,
    where m is man's mass, g is the acceleration due to gravity, and k is the factor of proportionality in the air resistance $-kv$ (v being velocity)

Article 15.9

1. $y = C_1 + C_2 e^{-2x}$

2. $y = C_1 e^{-2x} + C_2 e^{-3x}$

3. $y = C_1 e^{-x} + C_2 e^{-5x}$

4. $y = C_1 e^{3x} + C_2 e^{-x}$

5. $y = e^{-x/2}[C_1 \cos (x\sqrt{3}/2) + C_2 \sin (x\sqrt{3}/2)]$

6. $y = (C_1 + C_2 x)e^{2x}$

7. $y = (C_1 + C_2 x)e^{-3x}$

8. $y = e^{3x}(C_1 \cos x + C_2 \sin x)$

9. $y = e^x(C_1 \cos \sqrt{3}x + C_2 \sin \sqrt{3}x)$

10. $y = C_1 e^{2x} + C_2 e^{8x}$

Article 15.10

1. $y = \dfrac{x^2}{2} - x + C_1 + C_2 e^{-x}$

2. $y = -\cos x \sinh^{-1} (\tan x) + C_1 \cos x + C_2 \sin x$

3. $y = -\tfrac{1}{2}x \cos x + C_1 \cos x + C_2 \sin x$

4. $y = \tfrac{1}{4}e^x + e^{-x}(C_1 + C_2 x)$

5. $y = e^{-x}(C_1 + C_2 x + \tfrac{1}{2}x^2)$

6. $y = C_1 e^x + C_2 e^{-x} - x$

7. $y = C_1 e^x + C_2 e^{-x} + \tfrac{1}{2}xe^x$

8. $y = C_1 e^x + C_2 e^{-x} - \tfrac{1}{2} \sin x$

9. $y = e^{-2x}(C_1 \cos x + C_2 \sin x) + 2$

10. $y = e^{-2x}(C_1 \cos x + C_2 \sin x) + \tfrac{1}{5}x + \tfrac{6}{25}$

Article 15.11

1. $x = x_0 \cos \omega t + \dfrac{v_0}{\omega} \sin \omega t = \sqrt{x_0^2 + \dfrac{v_0^2}{\omega^2}} \sin (\omega t + \phi)$,
    where $\omega = \sqrt{k/m}$, $\phi = \tan^{-1} (\omega x_0/v_0)$

2. $x = 0.288 \sin (13.9t)$; x in ft, t in sec.

3. $\theta = \theta_0 \cos (\sqrt{g/l}\, t)$

4. $\theta = \theta_0 \cos \omega t + (v_0/\omega) \sin \omega t$, where $\omega = \sqrt{2k/mr^2}$

5. $c = 5.1$ (lb sec/ft)

Miscellaneous exercises

1. $\ln (c \ln y) = -\tan^{-1} x$

2. $y = [cx^3 + 2(x + 1)^3][(x + 1)^3 - cx^3]^{-1}$

3. $y = \ln (c - \tfrac{1}{3}e^{-3x})$

4. $ky + \sqrt{k^2 y^2 - 1} = ce^{kx}$

5. $y^2 + \sqrt{y^4 + 1} = ce^{2x}$ 6. $x^2 + xy - y^2 = c$

7. $y^2 = x^2 + cx$ 8. $y + \sqrt{x^2 + y^2} = cx^2$

9. $y = x \tan^{-1} (\ln cx)$ 10. $y = xe^{\sqrt{2 \ln cx}}$

11. $y = (x^2 + 2)/4 + cx^{-2}$

12. $y - x \sec y = c$

13. $y = \cosh x \ln (c \cosh x)$

14. $y = \tfrac{1}{6}(2x^3 + 3x^2 + c)(x + 1)^{-2}$

15. $y^3 + 3xy^2 + 3(x + y) = c$

16. $x^3 + 3xy + 3e^y = c$

17. $x^3 + 3xy^2 + 3 \sinh y = c$

18. $e^x + x \ln y + y = c$

19. $x^2 + e^y(x^2 + y^2 - 2y + 2) = c$

20. $y = C,$ or $y = a \tan (ax + C),$
    or $y = -a \tanh (ax + C),$
    or $y = -1/(x + C)$

21. $x = C_1 \cos 2y + C_2 \sin 2y$

22. $y = -\ln |\cos (x + c)| + d$

23. $x = \pm(y + C),$ or $x + C_2 = \ln \cosh (y + C_1),$ or
    $x + C_2 = \ln \sinh (y + C_1)$

24. $y = c_1 e^x + c_2 e^{3x}$

25. $y = \frac{1}{2} (\ln cx)^2 + d$

26. $y = c_1 \sin 2x + c_2 \cos 2x$
    $\qquad + (x/2) \sin 2x + \frac{1}{4} \cos 2x \ln \cos 2x$

27. $y = c_1 e^{-x} + (c_2 + x/3)e^{2x}$

28. $y = e^x(c_1 \cos 2x + c_2 \sin 2x) + \frac{1}{8}e^{-x}$

29. $y = c_1 \sqrt{x} + c_2/\sqrt{x}$ 30. $\frac{3}{2}x^2 + y^2 = d$

31. $x^2 + (y - d)^2 = d^2$ 32. $y^2 = d^2 + 2\,dx$

33. $y = 10 \cos 10t + 5 \sin 10t$

INDEX